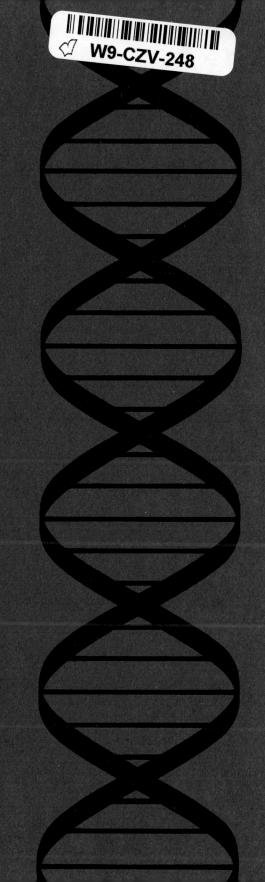

THE SCIENCE OF BIOLOGY

THE SCIENCE OF BIOLOGY

2d *Edition*

PAUL B. WEISZ

Professor of Biology

Brown University

McGRAW-HILL BOOK COMPANY, INC.

NEW YORK   TORONTO   LONDON

THE SCIENCE OF BIOLOGY

Library of Congress Catalog Card Number 62–21122

69119

III

This book is set in Caledonia, a type face designed for Linotype by the American graphic designer W. A. Dwiggins. The chapter titles and headings are Copperplate Gothic

PREFACE

In this second edition, the presentation of two subject areas, namely, morphological biology and plant biology, has been expanded and strengthened greatly. Moreover, all other parts of the subject matter have been brought up to date and reorganized in considerable measure. The result is a thoroughly revised text, in which comparatively few sections are the same as in the first edition.

The pedagogic aim has remained unchanged, however. Designed, like the first edition, to serve both the terminal student and the prospective major in biology, this edition again attempts to provide understanding of basic biological processes and principles. The approach is analytical and searches for the common foundations on which all living events are ultimately based. Inasmuch as such foundations are revealed by modern research the approach is also experimental; and to the extent that the foundations can be shown to have a biochemical basis, the approach is oriented as before toward what has come to be called "molecular" biology. All recent trends in teaching beginning biology, both on the college and secondary school levels, now are characterized similarly by such an orientation.

The broad conceptual format of the previous edition likewise has been retained, but the detailed organization and scope of the contents have been altered substantially. Part 1 now consists of two introductory chapters. To the first, on the nature of science, a section on scientific philosophy has been added. The second chapter, dealing with chemical processes, has been newly written to serve as a miniature chemistry course; it should provide the student with most of the basic chemical knowledge required for an appreciation of the biology to follow.

Part 2, The Living World, opens with a revised chapter on the origin of life and proceeds in sequence with chapter-length discussions of the nature of cells, organisms, species, and communities. In this examination of successively higher levels of living organization, the groundwork is also laid for detailed studies of various later topics. For example, an expanded section on chemical components in the chapter on cells includes accounts of the molecular structure of nucleic acids and adenosine phosphates, in preparation for the later analysis of gene functions and cellular energetics. Similarly, the chapter on organisms contains separate, newly written sections on plant and animal histology, in preparation for the later examination of organismic structure. The principal aim of Part 2, however, is to introduce the student to the entire living domain, from the level of the molecule to the level of the biogeographic supercommunity and from the primeval methane-ammonia atmosphere to the unforeseeable evolutionary future.

Part 3, The Living Organisms, is largely newly designed and without exact equivalent in the first edition. The chapter sequence represents an expansion, in morphological, evolutionary, and taxonomic directions, of the organismic theme introduced earlier. An opening section on systematics includes a discussion of the limitations of the traditional "two kingdoms" taxonomy and outlines a more realistic four-part classification of organisms into Monera, Protista, Metaphyta, and Metazoa. Each of these four major categories is then examined in a separate account. Emphasis here is on adult morphology, but organisms and their parts are considered not merely as entities which just happen to exist and therefore need to be inventoried. Instead, living entities are shown to have evolutionary, adaptive, and functional significance; the attempt is made to discuss organisms in a dynamic, interest-sustaining, and biologically meaningful way. Moreover, *all* groups of organisms, major as well as minor, receive appropriately detailed attention, and the characterization of the Protista and the Metaphyta is as complete as that of the Metazoa. The presentation also serves to show, incidentally, that "plant" and "animal" characteristics are relatively late evolutionary products, developed out of preexisting ancestral protistan characteristics. In general, notwithstanding the overall "molecular" orientation of the text, the subsidiary but very considerable stress on "nonmolecular" biology forms an important part of the basic design of this edition.

Part 4, Metabolism, begins with a newly prepared introductory chapter which analyzes the interrelations of the environment with metabolism as a whole, and which also examines the various fundamental patterns and processes of nutrition. Separate chapters on plant and animal nutrition, and on gas exchange, respiration, and energy utilization, then follow. The specific contents have been reorganized and revised substantially and have been brought to a level of biochemical and biophysical completeness consistent with present knowledge. For example, processes of ATP formation and electron transfers are discussed thoroughly not only in the context of respiration but also in that of photosynthesis. The background data presented in Chaps. 2, 3, and 4 suffice to prepare a student quite adequately for such a comparatively mature exposure to metabolic topics; experience shows clearly that even students without prior knowledge of chemistry and physics can follow along well and eventually understand.

Part 5, The Steady State, contains a newly organized opening chapter on DNA functions and general patterns of steady-state control. This is followed by a new, chapter-length presentation of control and behavioral biology in plants and by three revised chapters on control processes in animals. Part 6, Reproduction, begins with a comprehensive outline of basic principles of reproduction, an account which also includes sections on mitosis, sexuality, meiosis, and life cycle patterns. Specific reproductive processes of all major groups of organisms are then described in three largely newly written chapters. The part concludes with a reor-

ganized and expanded chapter on development, which deals both with principles of morphogenesis and differentiation and with specific developmental events on the cell, tissue, and organism levels of organization. Part 7, Adaptation, concludes the book. To the discussion of heredity in this part has been added a section on cistron analysis, and the revised chapters on evolution now include a critique of recapitulatory views as well as separate, newly organized sections on plant and animal paleontology.

Auxiliary teaching aids are even more extensive than in the previous edition. Many diagrams have been improved and redrawn, and many others, as well as numerous photographs, have been added. The lists of suggested collateral readings have been brought up to date and the glossary at the end of the book has been expanded. An expanded and revised second edition of the Laboratory Manual is now available in conjunction with the text, as is a revised Instructor's Manual. Furthermore, a Study Guide, written by Dr. Robert Brenner, of Brown University, and designed especially for use with this book, is offered for the first time.

In conclusion, it is perhaps not out of place to reiterate this author's conviction that a course of study, in biology as in any other field, ideally should be based on three principles of good teaching. The course should probe the *depth* of the subject matter, not merely or even necessarily its total breadth; it should strive to provide a conceptual *synthesis* of diverse data, not simply a disconnected catalog of so-called facts; and, above all, it should point the way toward a real *comprehension* of significant ideas and should not just require meaningless memorization. Whatever measure of success may or may not have been achieved in actually adhering to these principles, the preparation of this edition has in any event been guided by them.

I wish to thank my colleague Dr. Melvin S. Fuller, of Brown University, who has contributed in many different and important ways to the improvement of both the textual and the photographic content of this book. My gratitude for essential help in procuring and assembling photographs is herewith also extended to Miss Gabrielle Wunderlich, to many commercial organizations, and to numerous colleagues and friends both at Brown and elsewhere. Lastly, a special tribute is offered to Mr. Russell Peterson, whose artistry in executing line drawings unquestionably has added greatly not only to the appearance but also to the usefulness of this volume.

Paul B. Weisz

CONTENTS

PART 4 METABOLISM

PART 5   SELF-PERPETUATION: THE STEADY STATE

CELLULAR DEVELOPMENT
Nucleus and Cytoplasm
Cell–Cell Interactions

ORGANISMIC DEVELOPMENT
The Pattern   The Embryo

PART 7 SELF-PERPETUATION: ADAPTATION

PART 1
INTRODUCTION

Biology is a science, and it is closely interrelated with all other natural sciences, physics and chemistry in particular. Therefore, before a serious study of biology can properly be begun, the underlying foundations of this science should be examined. Two questions are clearly pertinent: what is a science, and what areas of physics and chemistry must be understood if biology is to be understood?

Answers to these prebiological questions are outlined in the two chapters of this introductory part.

THE NATURE OF SCIENCE

1

Our current civilization is so thoroughly permeated with science that, for many, the label "scientific" has become the highest badge of merit, the hallmark of progress, the dominant theme of the age of atoms and space. No human endeavor, so it is often claimed, can really be worthwhile or of basic significance unless it has a scientific foundation. Moreover, advertisements loudly proclaim the "scientific" nature of consumer goods, and their "scientifically proved" high quality is attested to by "scientific" experts. Human relations too are supposed to be "scientific" nowadays. Conversation and debate have become "scientific" discussions, and in a field such as sports, if one is a good athlete, he is a "scientific" athlete.

There are even those who claim to take their religion "scientifically" and those who stoutly maintain that literature, painting, and other artistic pursuits are reducible to "science," really. And then there are those who believe that science will eventually solve "everything" and that, if only the world were run more "scientifically," it would be a much better place.

Yet in contrast to this widespread confidence in things and activities which claim to be, and in a few cases actually are, scientific, large segments of society doubt and mistrust scientists as persons. To many, the scientist is somehow queer and "different." He is held to be naïve and more or less uninformed outside his specialty. He is pictured as a cold, godless calculating machine living in a strange, illusory world of his own.

Many circumstances in our civilization conspire to foster such false, stereotyped notions about science and scientists. However, no one who wishes to consider himself properly educated can afford to know about the meaning of science only what popular misconceptions, and "common knowledge," may have taught him. Especially is this true for one who is about to pursue studies in a modern science such as biology.

What then *is* the actual meaning of science? How did truly scientific undertakings develop, and how does science "work"? What can it do and, more especially, what can it not do? How does science differ from other forms of activity, and what place does it have in the scheme of modern culture?

THE ORIGIN OF SCIENCE

Science began in the distant past, long before human history was being recorded. Its mother was tribal *magic*.

The same mother also gave birth to religion and, probably even earlier, to art. Thus science, religion, and art have always been blood brothers. Their methods differ, but their aim is the same: to understand and interpret the universe and its workings and, from this, to promote the material and spiritual welfare of man where possible.

This was also the function of tribal magic. For long ages, magic was the rallying point of society, the central institution in which were concentrated the accumulated wisdom and experience of the day. The execution of magical procedures was in the hands of specially trained individuals, the medicine men and their equivalents. These were the forerunners of the scientists and the clergymen of today. How did science and religion grow out of magic? We may illustrate by means of an example.

Several thousand years ago, it was generally believed that magical rites were necessary to make wheat grow from planted seeds. In this particular instance, the rites took one of two forms. Either man intensified his sexual activity, in a solemn spring festival celebrated communally in the fields, or he abstained completely from sexual activity during the planting period.

The first procedure was an instance of *imitative* magic. The reasoning was that, since sowing seeds is like producing pregnancy in a woman, man could demonstrate to the soil what was wanted and so induce it to imitate man and be fertile. The second procedure, an instance of *contagious* magic, grew out of the assumption that only a limited amount of reproductive potency was available to living things. Consequently, if man did not use up his potency, that much more would become available for the soil. Depending on the tribe, the time, and the locality, either imitative or contagious magic might have been used to attain the same end, namely, to make the earth fruitful.

The fundamental weakness of magic was, of course, that it was unreliable. Sometimes it worked, and sometimes it did not work. Bad soil, bad grain, bad weather, and insect pests often must have defeated the best magic. In time, man must have realized that magical rites actually played no role in wheat growth, whereas soil conditions, grain quality, and good weather played very important roles. This was a momentous discovery—and a scientific one.

Magic became science when man accidentally found, or began to look for, situations which could be predictably controlled without magical rituals. In many situations where magic seemed to work successfully most of the time, man discovered an underlying scientific principle.

Yet there remained very many situations where magic did not work and where scientific principles could not be found. For example, in spite of good soil and good weather, wheat might not have grown because of virus or fungus infections. Such contingencies remained completely beyond understanding up to very modern times, and early man could only conclude that unseeable, uncontrollable "somethings" occasionally defeated his efforts. These somethings became spirits and gods. And unless prayers and sacrificial offerings maintained the good will of the gods, their wrath would undo human enterprise. Thus magical rituals evolved into primitively religious ones.

At this stage, medicine men ceased to be magicians and instead assumed the dual role of priest and scientist. Every personal or communal undertaking required both scientific and religious action: science, to put to use what was known; religion, to protect against possible failure by inducing the unknown to work on man's side.

In time, the "two-way" medicine man disappeared and made way for the specialized scientist and priest. In both religion and science, shades of the old magic lingered on for long periods. The religions still retain a high magical content today, and the sciences only recently dissociated from magic-derived pseudosciences such as alchemy, astrology, and the occult arts.

Throughout the early development of science and religion, emphasis was largely on practical matters. Science was primitively technological, and religion too was largely "applied," designed to deal with the concrete practical issues of the day. Man was preoccupied mainly with procuring food, shelter, and clothing, and science and religion served these necessities. Later, as a result of technological successes, more time became available for contemplation and cultural development, and this is when researchers and theorists appeared alongside the technologists, and theologians alongside the clergymen.

THE FORMS OF SCIENCE

Today there are three types of scientists carrying on two kinds of science.

One kind of scientist may be symbolized as a man who sits by the river on nice afternoons and who whittles away at a stick and wonders about things. Strange as it may seem to some, the most powerful science stems from such whittlers. Whereas most people who just sit manage merely to be lazy, a few quietly boil with rare powers and make the wheels of the world go round. Thinker-scientists of this sort usually are not too well known by the general public, unless their thoughts prove to be of outstanding importance. Newton, Einstein, Darwin, and Freud are among the best known.

A second kind of scientist is the serious young man in the white coat, reading the dials of monster machines while lights flash and buzzers purr softly. This picture symbolizes the technician, the lab man, the trained expert who tests, experiments, and works out the implications of what the whittler has been thinking.

The third kind of scientist is a relatively new phenomenon. He goes to an office, dictates to secretaries, and spends a good part of his time in conferences or in handling contracts, budgets, and personnel. This symbolizes the businessman-scientist, who gets and allocates the funds which buy time and privacy for the whittler and machines for the lab man.

Note, however, that every scientist worthy of the name actually is a complex mixture of philosopher, technician, and businessman all rolled into one, and none is a "pure" type. But the relative emphasis varies greatly in different scientists.

Whatever type mixture he may be, a scientist works either in basic research, often called **pure science,** or in technology, often called **applied science.**

Basic research is done primarily to further man's understanding of nature. Possible practical applications of the findings are here completely disregarded. Scientists in this field are more frequently of the philosopher–lab-man type than in technology. They may be found principally in university laboratories and research institutes and, in lesser numbers, in industry and government. They have little to show for their efforts beyond the written accounts of their work; hence it is comparatively hard for them to convince nonscientists that they are doing anything essential. However, government and every enlightened industry today either support independent research or conduct such research. And the public is beginning to realize that pure science is the soil from which applied science must develop.

Technology is concerned primarily with applying the results of pure science to practical uses. No lesser inventiveness and genius are required in this field than in basic research, though here the genius is more of a commercial and less of a philosophical nature. Physicians, engineers, crime detectives, drug manufacturers, agricultural scientists, all are technologists. They have services and tangible products to sell; hence the public recognizes their worth rather readily.

Here again, note that no scientist is pure researcher or pure technologist. Mixtures are in evidence once more, with emphasis one way or the other. Moreover, technology is as much the fertilizer of basic research as the other way round. As new theories suggest new ways of applying them, so new ideas for doing things suggest further advances in research. Thus, in most research today, pure and applied science work hand in hand. Many conclusions of pure science cannot be tested before the technologist thinks up the means of testing. Conversely, before the technologist can produce desirable new products, years of basic research may first be required. Insofar as every basic researcher must use equipment, however modest, he is also a technologist; and insofar as every technologist must understand how and why his products work, he is also a basic researcher.

It follows that any science shrivels whenever either of its two branches ceases to be effective. If for every dollar spent on science an immediate, tangible return is expected, and if the budding scientist is prevented from being a whittler by the necessity of producing something salable, then basic research will be in danger of drying up. And when that happens, technology too will become obsolete before long.

THE PROCEDURE OF SCIENCE

Everything that is science ultimately has its basis in the **scientific method.** Both the powers and the limitations of science are defined by this method. And wherever the scientific method cannot be applied, there cannot be science.

Taken singly, most of the steps of the scientific method involve commonplace procedures carried out daily by every person. Taken together, they amount to the most powerful tool man has devised to know and to control nature.

OBSERVATION

All science begins with *observation*, the first step of the scientific method.

At once this delimits the scientific domain; something that cannot be observed cannot be investigated by science. However, observation need not be direct. Atomic nuclei and magnetism, for example, cannot be perceived directly through our sense organs, but their effects can be observed with instruments. Similarly, mind cannot be observed directly, but its effects can be, as expressed, for example, in behavior.

For reasons which will become clear presently, it is necessary, furthermore, that an observation be *repeatable*, actually or potentially. Anyone who doubts that objects fall back to the ground after being thrown into the air can convince himself of it by repeating the observation. One-time events on earth are outside science.

Correct observation is a most difficult art acquired only after long experience and many errors. Everybody observes, with eyes, ears, touch, and all other senses, but few observe correctly. Lawyers experienced with witnesses, artists who teach students to draw objects in plain view, and scientists who try to see nature all can testify to this.

This difficulty of observation lies largely in unsuspected bias. People forever see what they *want* to see or what they think they *ought* to see. It is extremely hard to rid oneself of such unconscious prejudice and to see just what is actually there, no more and no less. Past experience, "common knowledge," and often teachers can be subtle obstacles to correct observation, and even experienced scientists may not always avoid them. That is why a scientific observation is not taken at face value until several scientists have repeated the observation independently and have reported the same thing. That is also a major reason why one-time, unrepeatable events normally cannot be science.

A scientific piece of work is only as good as the original observation. Observational errors persist into everything that follows, and the effort may be defeated before it has properly begun.

PROBLEM

After an observation has been made, the second step of the scientific method is to define a *problem*. In other words, one asks a question about the observation. How does so and so come about? What is it that makes such and such happen in this or that fashion? Question asking additionally distinguishes the scientist from the layman; everybody makes observations, but not everybody shows further curiosity.

More significantly, not everyone sees that there may actually be a problem connected with an observation. During thousands of years, even curious people simply took it for granted that a detached, unsupported object falls to the ground. It took genius to ask, "How come?" and few problems, indeed, have ever turned out to be more profound.

Thus scientists take nothing for granted, and they ask questions, even at the risk of irritating others. Question askers are notorious for getting themselves into trouble, and so it has always been with scientists. But they have to continue to ask questions if they are to remain scientists. And society has to expect annoying questions if it wishes to have science.

Anyone can ask questions. However, good questioning, like good observing, is a high art. To be valuable scientifically, a question must be *relevant*, and it must be *testable*. The difficulty is that it is often very hard or impossible to tell in advance whether a question is relevant or irrelevant, testable or untestable. If a man collapses on the street and passers-by want to help him, it may or may not be irrelevant to ask when he had his last meal. Without experience one cannot decide on the relevance of this question, and a wrong procedure might be followed.

As to the testability of questions, it is clear that proper testing techniques must be available, actually or potentially. This cannot always be guaranteed. For example, Einstein's fame rests, in part, on showing that it is impossible to test whether or not the earth moves through an "ether," an assumption held for many decades. All questions about an ether therefore become nonscientific, and we must reformulate associated problems until they become testable. Einstein did this, and he came up with relativity.

In general, science does best with "How?" or

"What?" questions. "Why?" questions are more trouble-some. Some of them can be rephrased to ask "How?" or "What?" But others such as "Why does the universe exist?" fall into the untestable category. These are out-side the domain of science.

HYPOTHESIS

Having asked a proper question, the scientist pro-ceeds to the third step of the scientific method. This involves the seemingly quite unscientific procedure of guessing. One guesses what the answer to the question might conceivably be. Scientists call this postulating a *hypothesis.*

Hypothesizing distinguishes the scientist still fur-ther from the layman. For while many people observe and ask questions, most stop·there. Some do wonder about likely answers, and scientists are among these.

Of course, a given question may have thousands of *possible* answers but only one *right* answer. Chances are therefore excellent that a random guess will be wrong. The scientist will not know whether his guess was or was not correct until he has completed the fourth step of the scientific method, *experimentation.* It is the function of every experiment to test the validity of a scientific guess.

If experimentation shows that the first guess was wrong, the scientist then must formulate a new hypoth-esis and once more test for validity by performing new experiments. Clearly, the guessing and guess testing might go on for years, and a right answer might never be found. This happens.

But here again, artistry, genius, and experience usually provide shortcuts. There are good guesses and bad ones, and the skilled scientist is generally able to decide at the outset that, of a multitude of possible answers, so and so many are unlikely answers. His knowledge of the field, his past experience, and the experience of others working on related problems nor-mally allow him to reduce the many possibilities to a few likelihoods.

This is also the place where hunches, intuitions, and lucky accidents aid science enormously. In one famous case, so the story has it, the German chemist Kekule went to bed one night after a fairly alcoholic party and dreamed of six monkeys chasing one another in a circle, the tail of one held in the teeth of the other. Practically our whole chemical industry is based on that dream, for it told the sleeping scientist what the long-sought structure of benzene was—as we now know, six carbon atoms "chasing" one another in a circle. And benzene is the fundamental parent substance for thou-sands of chemical products.

The ideal situation for which the scientist generally strives is to reduce his problem to just two distinct alternative possibilities, one of which, when tested by experiment, may then be answered with a clear "yes," the other with a clear "no." It is exceedingly difficult to streamline problems in this way, and with many it cannot be done. Very often the answer obtained is "maybe." However, if a clear yes or no does emerge, scientists speak of an elegant piece of work, and such performances often are milestones in science.

EXPERIMENT

Experimentation is the fourth step in the scientific method. At this point, science and nonscience finally and completely part company.

Most people observe, ask questions, and also guess at answers. But the layman stops here: "My answer is so logical, so reasonable, and it sounds so 'right' that it must be correct." The listener considers the argument, finds that it is indeed logical and reasonable, and is convinced. He then goes out and in his turn converts others. Before long, the whole world rejoices that it has the answer.

Now the small, kill-joy voice of the scientist is heard in the background: "Where is the evidence?" Under such conditions in history, it has often been easier and more convenient to eradicate the scientist than to eradicate an emotionally fixed public opinion. But doing away with the scientist does not alter the fact that answers without evidence are at best un-supported opinions, at worst wishful thinking and fanatical illusions. Experimentation can provide the necessary evidence, and whosoever then experiments after guessing at answers becomes truly "scientific" in his approach, be he a professional scientist or not.

On the other hand, experiments do not guarantee a scientific conclusion. For there is ample room within experimentation and in succeeding steps to become un-scientific again.

Experimentation is by far the hardest part of scientific procedure. There are no rules to follow; each experiment is a case unto itself. Knowledge and experi-ence usually help technically, but to design the experi-ment, to decide on the means by which a hypothesis might best be tested, that separates the genius from the dilettante. The following example will illustrate the point:

Suppose you observe that a chemical substance X, which has accidentally spilled into a culture dish full of certain disease-causing bacteria, kills all the bacteria in that dish. Problem: Can drug X be used to protect human beings against these disease-causing bacteria? Hypothesis: yes. Experiment: You go to a hospital and find a patient with the particular bacterial disease and inject some of the drug into the patient.

Possible result 1: Two days later the patient is well. Conclusion: hypothesis confirmed. You proceed to market the drug at high prices. Shortly afterward, users of the drug die by the dozens, and you are tried and convicted for homicide.

Possible result 2: Two days later the patient is dead. Conclusion: The drug is worthless, and you abandon your project. A year later a colleague of yours is awarded the Nobel prize for having discovered a drug X which cures a certain bacterial disease in man—the same drug and the same disease in which you had been interested.

In this example, the so-called experiment was not an experiment at all.

First, no allowance was made for the possibility that people of different age, sex, eating habits, prior medical history, hereditary background, etc., might react differently to the same drug. Obviously, one would have to test the drug on many categories of carefully preselected patients, and there would have to be many patients in each such category. Besides, one would make the tests first on mice, or guinea pigs, or monkeys.

Second, the quantity of drug to be used was not determined. Clearly, a full range of dosages would have to be tested for each different category of patient. We tacitly assume, moreover, that the drug is a pure substance, i.e., that it does not contain traces of other chemicals which might obscure, or interfere with, the results. If impurities are suspected, whole sets of separate experiments would have to be made.

Third, and most importantly, no account was taken of the possibility that your patient might have become well, or have died, in any case, even without your injecting the drug. What is needed here is **experimental control**; for every group of patients injected *with* drug solution, a precisely equal group must be injected with plain solution, *without* the drug. Then, by comparing results in the control and the experimental groups, one

can determine whether or not the recovery or death of patients is really attributable to the drug.

Note that every experiment requires at least two parallel tests or sets of tests identical in all respects except one. Of these parallel tests, one is the control series, and it provides a standard of reference for assessing the results of the experimental series. In drug experiments on people, not fewer than about 100,000 to 200,000 test cases, half of them controls, half of them experimentals, would be considered adequate. It should be easy to see why a single test on a single test case may give completely erroneous conclusions. Many repetitions of the same test, under as nearly identical conditions as possible, and at least one control test for each of the experimental tests—these are always prerequisite for any good experiment.

While an actual drug-testing program would be laborious, expensive, and time-consuming, the design of the experiment is nevertheless extremely simple. There are few steps to be gone through, and it is fairly clear what these steps must be. But there are many experiments in which the tests themselves may not take more than an hour or two, whereas thinking up appropriate, foolproof plans for the tests may have taken several years.

And despite a most ingenious design and a most careful execution, the result may still not be a clear yes or no. In a drug-testing experiment, for example, it is virtually certain that not 100 per cent of the experimental, drug-injected group will recover or that 100 per cent of the untreated control group will remain sick.

The actual results might be something like 70 per cent recovery in the experimentals and something like 20 per cent recovery in the controls. The experimentals here show that 30 per cent of the patients with that particular disease do not recover despite treatment, and the controls show that 20 per cent of the patients get well even without treatment. Moreover, if 70 out of every 100 experimental patients recover, then 20 out of these 70 were not actually helped by the drug, since, from the control data, they would have recovered even without treatment. Hence the drug is effective in only 70 per cent minus 20 per cent, or 50 per cent, of the cases.

Medically, this may be a major accomplishment, for having the drug is obviously better than not having it. But scientifically, one is confronted with an equivocal "maybe" result. It will probably lead to new research based on the new observation that some people respond to the drug and some do not and to the new problem of why and what can be done about it.

The result of any experiment represents **evidence.** That is, the original guess in answer to a problem is confirmed as correct or is invalidated. If invalidated, a new hypothesis, with new experiments, must be thought up. This is repeated until a hypothesis may be hit upon which can be supported with confirmatory experimental evidence.

As with legal evidence, scientific evidence can be strong and convincing, or merely suggestive, or poor. In any case, nothing has been proved. Depending on the strength of the evidence, one merely has a basis for regarding the original hypothesis with a certain degree of confidence.

Our new drug, for example, may be just what we claim it to be when we use it in this country. In another part of the world it might not work at all or it might work better. All we can confidently say is that our evidence is based on so and so many experiments with American patients, American bacteria, and American drugs and that under specified hospital conditions, with proper allowance for unspotted errors, the drug has an effectiveness of 50 per cent. Experimental results are never better or broader than the experiments themselves.

This is where many who have been properly scientific up to this point become unscientific. Their claims exceed the evidence; they mistake their partial answer for the whole answer; they contend to have proof for a fact, while all they actually have is some evidence for a hypothesis. There is always room for more and better evidence, or for new contradictory evidence, or indeed for better hypotheses.

THEORY

Experimental evidence is the basis for the fifth and final step in the scientific method, the formulation of a *theory*.

When a hypothesis has been supported by really convincing evidence, best obtained in many different laboratories and by many independent researchers, and when the total accumulated evidence is unquestionably reliable within carefully specified limits, then a theory may be proposed.

In our drug example, after substantial corroborating evidence has also been obtained from many other test localities, an acceptable theory would be the state-ment that "in such and such a bacterial disease, drug X is effective in 50 per cent of the cases."

This statement is considerably broader than the experiments on which it is based. Theories always are. The statement implies, for example, that drug X, regardless of who manufactures it, will be 50 per cent effective anywhere in the world, under any conditions, and can be used also for animals other than man.

Direct evidence for these extended implications does not exist. But inasmuch as drug X is already known to work within certain limits, the theory expresses the belief, the *probability*, that it may also work within certain wider limits.

To that extent every good theory has *predictive* value. It prophesies certain results. In contrast to nonscientific prophecies, scientific ones always have a substantial body of evidence to back them up. Moreover, the scientific prophecy does not say that something will certainly happen, but says only that something is *likely* to happen with a stated degree of probability.

A few theories have proved to be so universally valid and to have such a high degree of probability that they are spoken of as **natural laws.** For example, no exception has ever been found to the observation that an apple, if disconnected from a tree and not otherwise supported, will fall to the ground. A law of gravitation is based on such observations.

Yet even laws do not pronounce certainties. For all practical purposes, it may well be irrational to assume that some day an apple will rise from a tree, yet there simply is no evidence that can absolutely guarantee the future. Evidence can be used only to estimate probabilities.

Most theories actually have rather brief life spans. For example, if, in chickens, our drug X should be found to perform not with 50 per cent but with 80 per cent efficiency, then our original theory becomes untenable and obsolete. And the exception to the theory becomes a new observation, beginning a new cycle of scientific procedure.

Thus new research might show that chickens contain a natural booster substance in their blood which materially bolsters the action of the drug. This might lead to isolation, identification, and mass production of the booster substance, hence to worldwide improvement in curing the bacterial disease. And we would also have a new theory of drug action, based on the new evidence.

Thus science is never finished. One theory predicts,

holds up well for a time, exceptions are found, and a new, more inclusive theory takes over—for a while. We may note in passing that old theories do not become incorrect but merely become obsolete. Development of a new airplane does not mean that earlier planes can no longer fly. New theories, like new airplanes, merely range farther and serve more efficiently than earlier ones, but the latter still serve for their original purposes. Science is steady progression, not sudden revolution.

Clearly, knowledge of the scientific method does not by itself make a good scientist, any more than knowledge of English grammar alone makes a Shakespeare. At the same time, the demands of the scientific method should make it evident that scientists cannot be the cold, inhuman precision machines they are so often, and so erroneously, pictured to be. Scientists are essentially artists, and they require a sensitivity of eye and of mind as great as that of any master painter, and an imagination and keen inventiveness as powerful as that of any master poet.

THE LIMITATIONS OF SCIENCE

Observing, problem posing, hypothesizing, experimenting, and theorizing—this sequence of procedural steps is both the beginning and the end of science. To determine what science means in wider contexts, we must examine what scientific method implies and, more especially, what it does not imply.

THE SCIENTIFIC DOMAIN

First, scientific method defines the domain of science: *Anything to which the scientific method can be applied, now or in the future, is or will be science; anything to which the method cannot be applied is not science.*

This helps to clarify many a controversial issue. For example, does science have something to say about the concept of God? To determine this, we must find out if we can apply the scientific method.

Inasmuch as the whole universe and everything in it may be argued to be God's work, one may also argue that He is observable. It is possible, furthermore, to pose any number of problems, such as "Does He exist; is the universe indeed His doing?" and "Is He present everywhere and in everything?" One can also hypothesize; some might say "yes," some might say "no."

Can we design an experiment about God? To be reliable, we would need experimental control, i.e., two otherwise identical situations, one with God and one without. Now, what we wish to test is the hypothesis that God exists and is universal, i.e., that He is everywhere. Being a hypothesis thus far, this could be right or wrong.

If right, He would exist and exist everywhere; hence He would be present in *every* test we could possibly make. Thus we would never be able to devise a situation in which God is not present. But we need such a situation in order to have a controlled experiment.

But if the hypothesis is wrong, He would not exist, hence would be absent from *every* test we could possibly make. Therefore, we would never be able to devise a situation in which God *is* present. Yet we would need such a situation for a controlled experiment.

Right or wrong, our hypothesis is untestable either way, since we cannot run a controlled experiment. Hence we cannot apply the scientific method. The point is that the concept of God is outside the domain of science, and science cannot legitimately say anything about Him. He cannot be tested by science, because its method is inapplicable.

It should be carefully noted that this is a far cry from saying "Science disproves God," or "scientists must be godless; their method demands it." Nothing of the sort. Science specifically leaves anyone perfectly free to believe in any god whatsoever or in none. Many first-rate scientists are priests; many others are agnostics.

Science commits you to nothing more, and to nothing less, than adherence to scientific method.

Such adherence, it may be noted, is a matter of faith, just as belief in God or confidence in the telephone directory is a matter of faith. Whatever other faiths they may or may not hold, all scientists certainly have strong faith in the scientific method. So do those laymen who feel that having electric lights and not having bubonic plague are good things.

THE SCIENTIFIC AIM

A second consequence of the scientific method is that it defines the aim and purpose of science: *The objective of science is to make and to use theories.*

Many would say that the objective of science is to discover truth, to find out facts. We must be very careful here about the meaning of words. "Truth" is popularly used in two senses. It may indicate a temporary correctness, as in saying "It is true that my hair is brown." Or it may indicate an absolute, eternal correctness, as in saying "In plane geometry, the sum of the angles in a triangle is 180°."

From the earlier discussion on the nature of scientific method, it should be clear that science cannot deal with truth of the absolute variety. Something absolute is finished, known completely, once and for all. But science is never finished. Its method is unable to determine the absolute. Besides, once something is already known absolutely, there is no further requirement for science, since nothing further needs to be found out. Science can only adduce evidence for temporary truths, and another term for "temporary truth" is "theory." Because the word "truth," if not laboriously qualified, is ambiguous, scientists try not to use it at all.

The words "fact" and "proof" have a similar drawback. Both may indicate either something absolute or something temporary. If absolute, they are not science; if temporary, we have the less ambiguous word "evidence." Thus, science is content to find evidence for theories, and it leaves truths, proofs, and facts to others.

Speaking of words, "theorizing" is often popularly taken to mean "just talk and speculation." Consider, however, how successfully theorizing builds bridges!

SCIENCE AND VALUES

A third important implication of the scientific method is that *it does not make value judgments or moral decisions.*

It is the user of scientific results who may place valuations on them. But the results by themselves do not carry built-in values. And nowhere in the scientific method is there a value-revealing step.

The consequences of this are vast. For example, the science which produced the atomic bomb and penicillin cannot, of itself, tell whether these products are good things or bad things. Every man must determine that for himself as best he can. The scientist who discusses the moral aspects of nuclear weapons can make weightier statements than a layman only insofar as he may know more about what damage such weapons may or may not do. This will certainly influence his opinions. But whatever opinion he gives, it will be a purely personal evaluation made as a citizen, and any other scientist—or layman—who is equally well informed about the capacities of the weapons may conceivably disagree completely. Human values are involved here; science is not.

In all other types of evaluations as well, science is silent and noncommittal. Beauty, love, evil, happiness, virtue, justice, liberty, property, financial worth, all these are human values which science cannot peg. To be sure, love, for example, might well be a subject of scientific research, and research might show much about what love is and how it works. But such research could never discover that love is wonderful, an evaluation clear to anyone who has done a certain amount of nonscientific research.

It also follows that it would be folly to strive for a strictly "scientific" way of life or to expect strictly "scientific" government. Certainly the role of science might profitably be enlarged in areas of personal and public life where science can make a legitimate contribution. But a completely scientific civilization, adhering strictly to the rules of the scientific method, could never tell, for example, whether it is right or wrong to commit murder, or whether it is good or bad to love one's neighbor. Science cannot and does not give such answers. To be sure, this does not imply that science does away with morals. It merely implies that science cannot determine whether or not one ought to have moral standards, or what particular set of moral standards one ought to live by.

THE SCIENTIFIC PHILOSOPHY

A fourth and most important consequence of the scientific method is that it determines the philosophical foundation on which scientific pursuits must be based.

Inasmuch as the domain of science is the whole material universe, science must inquire into the nature of the forces which govern the universe and all happenings in it. What makes given events in the universe take place? What determines which event out of several possible ones will occur? And what controls or guides the course of any event to a particular conclusion?

Questions of this kind seek to discover the "prime mover" of the universe. As such they are actually philosophic questions of concern not only in science but in all other areas of human thought as well. Depending on how man answers such questions, he will adopt a particular philosophy of nature and this philosophy will then guide him in his various undertakings. Scientific man too must try to find answers, and we already know the framework within which the scientific answers must be given: to be useful in science, any statement about the universe or its parts must be consistent with the procedure of the scientific method. Therefore, if a given philosophy of nature can be verified wholly or even partly through experimental analysis, it will be valuable scientifically. But a philosophy which cannot be so verified will be without value in science, even though it may well be valuable in other areas of human thought.

Vitalism versus Mechanism

In the course of history, two major answers have been proposed regarding the governing forces of the universe. These answers are incorporated in two systems of philosophy called *vitalism* and *mechanism*.

Vitalism is the doctrine of the supernatural. It holds, essentially, that the universe and all happenings in it are controlled by supernatural powers. Such powers have been variously called gods, spirits, or simply "vital forces." Their influence is held to determine the nature and guide the behavior of atoms, planets, stars, living things, and indeed all components of the universe. Clearly, most religious philosophies are vitalistic ones.

Whatever value a vitalistic philosophy might have elsewhere, it cannot have value in science. This is because the supernatural is by definition beyond reach of the natural. Inasmuch as the scientific method is a wholly natural procedure, it cannot be used for an investigation of the supernatural. We have already noted earlier, for example, that science cannot prove or disprove anything about God. Any other vitalistic conception is similarly untestable by experiment and is therefore unusable as a *scientific* philosophy of nature.

A philosophy which *is* usable in science is that of mechanism. In the mechanistic view, the prime mover of the universe is a set of natural laws, i.e., the laws of physics and chemistry. Experiments carried out in the course of several centuries have shown what some of these laws are, and any happening in the universe is held to be governed by the laws. The foundation of mechanism is therefore natural rather than supernatural and is amenable to experimental analysis.

On the basis of the total experimental experience, the mechanistic philosophy holds that if all physical and chemical phenomena in the universe can be accounted for, no other phenomena will remain. Therefore, the controlling agent of the material in the universe must reside within the material itself. Moreover, it must consist of physical and chemical events *only*. As a further consequence, the particular course of any happening must be guided automatically, by the way in which the natural laws permit physical and chemical events to occur within given materials. Note that biological materials are included here; life too must be a result of physical and chemical events *only*. The course of life must be automatically self-determined by the physical and chemical events occurring within living matter.

Clearly, these differences between vitalism and mechanism point up a conceptual conflict between religion and science. But note that the conflict is not necessarily irreconcilable. To bridge the conceptual gap between the two philosophies, one might ask how the natural laws of the universe came into being to begin with. A possible answer is that they were created by God. In this view, the universe ran vitalistically up to the time that natural laws were created and ran mechanistically thereafter. The mechanist must then admit the existence of a supernatural Creator at the beginning of time (even though he has no *scientific* basis for either affirming or denying this; mechanism cannot, by definition, tell anything about a time at which natural laws might not have been in operation). Correspondingly, the vitalist must admit that any direct influence of God over the universe must have ceased once His natural laws were in operation. These laws would run the universe adequately, and further supernatural control would therefore not be necessary (or demonstrable, so long as the natural laws continued to operate without change).

Thus it is not necessarily illogical to hold both scientific and religious philosophies at the same time. However, it is decidedly illogical to try to use vitalistic ideas as explanations of scientific problems. Correct science does demand that supernatural concepts be kept out of natural events, i.e., those which can be investigated by means of the scientific method. However much a vitalist he might be in his nonscientific thinking, man in his scientific thinking must be a mechanist. And if he is not, he ceases to be scientific.

Many people, some scientists included, actually find it exceedingly difficult to keep vitalism out of science. Biological events, undoubtedly the most complex of all known events in the universe, have in the past been particularly subject to attempts at vitalistic interpretation. How, it has been asked, can the beauty of a flower ever be understood simply as a series of physical and chemical events? How can an egg, transforming itself into a baby, be nothing more than a "mechanism" like a clock? And how can a man, who thinks and experiences visions of God, be conceivably regarded as nothing more than a piece of "machinery"?

Mechanism *must* be inadequate as an explanation of life, it has been argued, and only something supernatural superimposed on the machine, some vital force, is likely to account for the fire of life.

In such replacements of mechanistic with mystical thought, the connotations of words often play a supporting role. For example, the words "mechanism" and "machine" usually bring to mind images of crude iron engines or clockworks. Such analogies tend to reinforce the suspicion of vitalists that those who regard living things as mere machinery must be simple-minded indeed. Consider, however, that the machines of today also include electronic computers which can learn, translate languages, compose music, play chess, make decisions, and improve their performance of such activities as they gather experience. In addition, theoretical knowledge now available would permit us to build a machine which could heal itself when injured and which could feed, sense, reproduce, and even evolve. Clearly, the term "mechanism" is not at all limited to crude, stupidly "mechanical" engines. And there is certainly nothing inherently simple-minded or reprehensible in the idea that living things are exquisitely complicated chemical mechanisms, some of which even have the capacity to think and to have visions of God.

On the contrary, if it could be shown that such a mechanistic view is at all justified, it would represent an enormous advance in our understanding of nature. In all the centuries of recorded history, vitalism in its various forms has hardly progressed beyond the mere initial assertion that living things are animated by supernatural forces. Just how such forces are presumed to do the animating has not been explained, nor have programs of inquiry been offered to find explanations. Actually, such inquiries are ruled out by definition, since natural man can never hope to fathom the supernatural. In the face of this closed door, mechanism provides the only way out for the curious. But is it justifiable to regard living things as pure mechanisms, even complicated chemical ones?

Notwithstanding the doubts expressed by some, a mechanistic interpretation of life is entirely justifiable and interjection of touches of vitalism is entirely unjustifiable. Science today *can* account for living properties in purely mechanistic terms. Moreover, biologists are well on their way to being able to create a truly living entity "in the test tube," solely by means of physical and chemical procedures obeying known natural laws. We shall discuss some of the requirements for such laboratory creation in the course of this book.

Evidently, vitalistic "aids" to explain the mechanistic universe are not only unjustifiable but also unnecessary.

It may be noted in this connection that, historically, vitalism has tended to fill the gaps left by incomplete scientific knowledge. Early man was a complete vitalist, who for want of better knowledge regarded even inanimate objects as "animated" by supernatural spirits. As scientific insight later increased, progressively more of the universe ceased to be in the domain of the supernatural. Thus it happened repeatedly that phenomena originally thought to be supernatural were later shown to be explainable naturally. So it has been with living phenomena as well. And those today who may still be prompted to fill gaps in scientific knowledge with vitalism must be prepared to have red faces tomorrow. Incidentally, it might also be pointed out in passing that even confirmed vitalists find it prudent on occasion to become ardent believers in mechanism, whether they realize it or not. For example, few vitalists hesitate to accept the mechanistic administrations of a physician at the first signs of disorder in their "machinery."

We conclude that a mechanistic view of nature is one component of the philosophic attitude required in science. A second component may now be considered.

Teleology versus Causalism

Even a casual observer must be impressed by the apparent nonrandomness of natural events. Every part of nature seems to follow a plan, and there is a distinct directedness to any given process. Living processes provide excellent instances of this. For example, developing eggs behave as if they knew exactly what the plan of the adult is to be. A chicken egg soon develops into an embryo with two wings and two legs, *as if* there existed a blueprint which specified that adult chickens should have two wings and two legs each. Moreover, since virtually all chicken eggs undergo the same course of growth, the impression of plan in development becomes reinforced strongly; one is led to conclude that the various parts of a chicken are there not just by random coincidence. Similarly, an earthworm which has been decapitated grows a new head, *as if* there were a plan which specified that every earthworm should have a head—not another tail and not two heads either, but one head.

All known natural processes, biological or otherwise, thus start at given beginnings and proceed to particular endpoints. This observation poses a philosophical problem: how is a starting condition directed toward a given terminal condition; how does a starting point appear to "know" what the endpoint is to be?

It will be noted that such questions have to do with a specific aspect of the more general problem of the controlling agents of the universe. We should expect, therefore, that two sets of answers would be available, one vitalistic and the other mechanistic. This is the case. In view of the discussion in the preceding section, a book on science such as this could properly disregard the vitalistic answers as inadmissible from the outset and proceed at once with an outline of the mechanistic position. It is nevertheless advisable to examine both positions, partly because such a procedure adds to an understanding of the nature and limitations of science, partly because it is important to be able to recognize vitalistic answers if and when they occur (as they occasionally still do) in what is supposed to be scientific thought.

According to vitalistic doctrines, natural events *appear* to be planned because they *are* planned. A supernatural "divine plan" is held to fix the fate of every part of the universe, and all events in nature, past, present, and future, are programmed in this plan. All nature is therefore directed toward a preordained goal, namely, the fulfillment of the divine plan. As a consequence, nothing happens by chance, but everything happens on purpose.

Being a vitalistic, experimentally untestable conception, the notion of purpose in natural events has no place in science. Does the universe exist for a purpose? Does man live for a purpose? You cannot hope for an answer from science, for science is not designed to tackle such questions. Moreover, if you already hold certain beliefs in these areas, you cannot expect science either to prove or to disprove them for you.

Yet many arguments have been attempted to show purpose from science. For example, it has been maintained by some that the whole purpose of the evolution of living things was to produce man. Here the evidence supporting the theory of evolution is invoked to prove that man was the predetermined goal from the very beginning.

This implies several things besides the conceit that man is the finest product of creation. It implies, for example, that nothing could ever come after man, for he is supposed to be the last word in living magnificence. As a matter of record, man is sorely plagued by an army of parasites which cannot live anywhere except inside people. And it is clear that you cannot have a man-requiring parasite before you have a man.

Many human parasites did evolve after man. Thus, the purpose argument would at best show that the whole purpose of evolution was to produce those living organisms which cause influenza, diphtheria, gonorrhea, and syphilis. This even the most ardent purpose arguer would probably not care to maintain.

If one is so inclined, he is of course perfectly free to believe that man is the pinnacle of it all. Then the rest of the universe with its billions of suns, including the living worlds which probably circle some of them, presumably are merely immense and fancy scenery for the microscopic stage on which man struts about. One may believe this, to be sure, but one cannot maintain that such beliefs are justified by evidence from science.

The essential point is that any purpose-implying argument, in this or in any other issue, stands on quicksand the moment science is invoked as a witness; for to say such and such is the goal, the ultimate purpose, is to state a belief and not a body of evidence adduced through the scientific method. Nowhere does this method include any purpose-revealing step.

The form of argumentation which takes recourse to purposes and supernatural planning is generally called *teleology*. In one system of teleology, the preordained plan exists outside natural objects, in an external Deity, for example. In another system, the plan resides within objects themselves. According to this view, a starting condition of an event proceeds toward a specific end condition because the starting object has built into it actual foreknowledge of what the end condition is to be. For example, the egg develops toward the goal of the adult because the egg *knows* what the adult state is to be. Similarly, evolution has occurred as it has because the participating starting chemicals had foreknowledge that the end should be man. Clearly, this and all other forms of teleology "explain" an end state by simply asserting it given at the beginning. And in thereby putting the future into the past, the effect before the cause, teleology negates time.

The scientifically useful alternative to teleology is called *causalism*. It has its foundations in mechanistic philosophy. Causalism denies foreknowledge of terminal states, preordination, purposes, goals, and fixed fates. It holds that natural events take place *sequentially*. Events occur only as other events *permit* them to occur, not as preordained goals or purposes make them occur. End states are consequences, not foregone conclusions, of beginning states. A headless earthworm regenerates a new head because conditions within the headless worm are such that only a head—*one* head—

can develop. It becomes the task of the biologist to find out what these conditions are and to see if, by changing the conditions, two heads or another tail could not be produced. Because scientists *can* obtain different end states after changing the conditions of initial states, the idea of predetermined goals loses all validity in scientific thought.

(Care must therefore be taken in scientific endeavors not to fall unwittingly into the teleological trap. Consider often-heard statements such as: "the *purpose* of the heart is to pump blood"; "the ancestors of birds evolved wings *so that* they could fly"; "eggs have yolk *in order to* provide food for development." The last statement, for example, implies that eggs can "foresee" the nutritional problem in development and that food will be required; therefore, they proceed to store up some. In effect, eggs are given human mentality. The teleologist is always anthropocentric; i.e., he implies that the natural events he discusses have minds like his. Substitute "and" for every "so that" or "in order to" and "function" for every "purpose" in biological statements and they become properly non-teleological.)

Clearly then, science in its present state of development must operate within carefully specified, self-imposed limits. The basic philosophic attitude must be mechanistic and causalistic, and we note that the results obtained through science are inherently without truth, without value, and without purpose.

But it is precisely because science is limited in this fashion that it advances. After centuries of earnest deliberation, mankind still does not agree on what truth is, values still change with the times and with places, and purposes remain as unfathomed as ever. On such shifting sands it has proved difficult to build a knowledge of nature. What little of nature we really know and are likely to know in the foreseeable future stands on the bedrock of science and its powerful tool, the scientific method.

THE LANGUAGE OF SCIENCE

SCIENCE AS A WHOLE

Fundamentally, science is a *language*, a system of communication. Religion, art, politics, English, and French are among other such languages. Like them, science enables man to travel into new countries of the mind and to understand and be understood in such countries. Like other languages, science too has its grammar—the scientific method, its authors and its literature—the scientists and their written work, and its various dialects or forms of expression—physics, chemistry, biology, etc.

Indeed, science is one of the few truly universal languages, understood all over the globe. Art, religion, and politics are also universal. But each of these languages has several forms, so that Baptists and Hindus, for example, have little in common either religiously, artistically, or politically. Science, however, has the same single form everywhere, and Baptists and Hindus do speak the same scientific language.

It should be clear that no one language is "truer" or "righter" than any other. There are only *different* languages, each serving its function in its own domain. Many an idea is an idiom of a specific language and is best expressed in that language. For example, the German "Kindergarten" has been imported as is into English and the American "baseball" has gone into the world without change. Likewise, one cannot discuss morality in the language of science, or thermodynamics in the language of religion, or artistic beauty in the language of politics; to the extent that each system of communication has specific idioms, there is no overlap or interchangeability among the systems.

On the other hand, many ideas can be expressed equally well in several languages. The English "water," the Latin "aqua," and the scientific "H_2O" are entirely equivalent, and no one of these is truer or righter than the others. They are merely different. Similarly, in one language man was created by God; in another man is a result of chance reactions among chemicals and of evolution. Again, neither the scientific nor the religious interpretation is the truer. If the theologian argues that everything was made by God, including scientists who think that man is the result of chance chemical reactions, then the scientist will argue back that chance chemical reactions created men with brains, including those theological brains which can conceive of a God who made everything. The impasse is permanent, and within their own systems of communication the scientist and the theologian are equally right. Many, of course, assume without warrant that it is the compelling duty of science to prove or disprove religious matters, and of religion, to prove or to disprove scientific matters.

The point is that there is no single "correct" formulation of any idea which spans various languages. There are only *different* formulations, and in given circumstances one or the other may be more useful, more satisfying, or more effective. Clearly, he who is adept in more than one language will be able to travel that much more widely and will be able to feel at ease in the company of more than one set of ideas.

We are, it appears, forever committed to multiple standards, according to the different systems of communication we use. But we have been in such a state all along, in many different ways. Thus, the color red means one thing politically, something else in a fall landscape, and is judged by a third standard in the fashion world. Or consider the different worth of the same dime to a child, to you, and to the United States Treasury. To be multilingual in his interpretation of the world has been the unique heritage of man from the beginning. Different proportions of the various languages may be mixed into the outlook of different individuals, but science, religion, art, politics, spoken language, all these and many more besides are always needed to make a full life.

BIOLOGY

Within the language of science, biology is an important dialect, permitting travel in the domain of *living things*. Man probably was a biologist before he was anything else. His own body in health and disease; the phenomena of birth, growth, and death; and the plants and other animals which gave him food, shelter, and clothing undoubtedly were matters of serious concern to even the first of his kind. The motives were sheer necessity and the requirements of survival. These same motives still prompt the same biological studies today; agriculture, medicine, and fields allied to them are the most important branches of modern applied biology. In addition, biology today is strongly experi-

mental, and pure research is done extensively all over the world. Some of this research promotes biological technology; all of it increases our understanding of how living things are constructed and how they operate.

Over the decades, the frontiers of biological investigations have been pushed into smaller and smaller realms. Some 100 to 150 years ago, when modern biology began, the chief interest was the whole plant or the whole animal, how it lived, where it could be found, and how it was related to other whole living things. Such studies have been carried on ever since, but, in addition, techniques gradually became available for the investigation of progressively smaller parts of the whole, their structures, their functions, and their relationships to one another. Thus it happened that, during the past few decades, the frontiers of biology were pushed down to the chemical level. And while research with larger biological units continues as before, the newest biology attempts to interpret living operations in terms of the chemicals which compose living creatures.

Biology here merges with chemistry. Today there are already many signs that the next frontier will be the atoms which in their turn compose the chemicals, and biology tomorrow will undoubtedly merge with atomic physics. Such a trend is quite natural; for ultimately, living things are atomic things. Penultimately, they are chemical things, and only on a large scale are they plants and animals. In the last analysis, therefore, biology must attempt to show how atoms, and chemicals made out of atoms, are put together to form, on the one hand, something like a rock or a piece of metal and, on the other, something like a flower or a human baby.

This book is an outline of how successful the attempt has been thus far.

REVIEW QUESTIONS

1. What are the aims and the limitations of science? Review fully. In what sense is science a language, and how does it differ from other, similar languages?

2. What characterizes the different present-day forms of science and the different specializations of scientists?

3. Review the steps of the scientific method and discuss the nature of each of these steps. Define "controlled experiment."

4. How would you show by controlled experiment:
   a. Whether or not temperature affects the rate of growth of living things?
   b. Whether or not houseflies can perceive differently colored objects?
   c. Whether or not plants use up some of the soil they grow in?

5. Suppose that it were found in question 4a that,

at an environmental temperature of 28°C, the growth of fertilized frog eggs into tadpoles occurs roughly twice as fast as at 18°C. What kinds of theories could such evidence suggest?

6. What are the historical and the modern relations of science and religion? Which of the ideas you have previously held about science should you now, after studying this chapter, regard as popular misconceptions?

7. Can you think of observations or problems which so far have not been investigated scientifically? Try to determine in each case whether or not such investigation is inherently possible. Why is mathematics not considered to be a science?

8. Describe the philosophic foundations of science. Define mechanism and causalism and contrast these systems of thought with those of vitalism and teleology. Can conceptual conflicts between science and religion be reconciled?

9. Consider the legal phrases "Do you swear to tell the truth and nothing but the truth?" and "Is it not a fact that on the night of . . . ?" If phrases of this sort were to be used in a strictly scientific context, how should they properly be formulated?

10. Biology is called one of the *natural sciences,* all of which deal with the composition, properties, and behavior of matter in the universe. Which other sciences are customarily regarded as belonging to this category, and what distinguishes them from one another and from biology? What are *social sciences?* Do they too operate by the scientific method?

SUGGESTED COLLATERAL READINGS

Those who wish to read more on the general nature of science may find any of the following books particularly instructive:

Arber, A.: "The Mind and the Eye," Cambridge University Press, Cambridge, England, 1954.

Baker, J. R.: "The Scientific Life," Macmillan, New York, 1943.

Beveridge, W. I. B.: "The Art of Scientific Investigation," Norton, New York, 1957.

Conant, J. B.: "Modern Science and Modern Man," Columbia University Press, New York, 1952.

————: "Science and Common Sense," Yale University Press, New Haven, Conn., 1951.

————: "On Understanding Science," Yale University Press, New Haven, Conn., 1947.

Russell, B.: "The Scientific Outlook," Norton, New York, 1931.

Sullivan, J.: "The Limitations of Science," Mentor 35, or Viking, New York, 1933.

Excellent accounts of various historical aspects of science may be found in the following:

Dampier, W. C.: "A History of Science," 3d ed., Macmillan, New York, 1942.

Singer, C.: "A History of Biology," rev. ed., Schuman, New York, 1950.

CHEMICAL PROCESSES

2

As noted in the preceding chapter, one of the most fruitful and significant advances in biology during the last century has been the firm recognition that *all living creatures consist entirely of chemicals.* Moreover, it is now also clear (see Chap. 3) that before there were living creatures on earth, there were only chemicals; living things originated out of chemicals. Chemicals in turn are composed of atoms. Thus, the story of life is largely a story of atoms and of chemicals, and it should not be surprising that physics and chemistry today are among the important background sciences to biology. Indeed, much of modern biology simply *is* physics or chemistry or both, and very many professional biologists are good physicists or chemists. You too will have to understand certain fundamentals of these background sciences before you can hope to understand the fundamentals of biology. Accordingly, this chapter introduces some of the physical and chemical information required for an appreciation of modern biology.

CHEMICAL SUBSTANCES

The universe is made up of 92 different basic kinds of materials called chemical **elements.** Iron, silver, gold, copper, and aluminum are some familiar examples of elements. Some others, most of them present also in living matter, are listed in Table 1. Man has learned to create artificially several other elements in addition to the 92 kinds found in nature. Plutonium is an example of these man-made elements. Each element consists of unimaginably tiny particles called **atoms.** An atom may be said to be the very smallest complete unit of an element. For example, a gold atom is the basic unit of the element gold.

Each element is given a chemical symbol, often the first letter or the first two letters of its English or Latin name. For example, the symbol for hydrogen is H, that for carbon is C, and that for silicon is Si (see also Table 1).

TABLE 1

Some common chemical elements

element	symbol	common valences
hydrogen	H	+1, 1
sodium	Na	+1
potassium	K	+1
chlorine	Cl	−1, 1
iodine	I	−1, 1
calcium	Ca	+2
magnesium	Mg	+2
sulfur	S	2
oxygen	O	2
copper	Cu	+1, +2
iron	Fe	+2, +3
carbon	C	2, 4
silicon	Si	4
aluminum	Al	3
nitrogen	N	3, 5
phosphorus	P	3, 5

To represent one atom of an element, one simply writes the appropriate symbol. For example, the letter H stands for one atom of hydrogen. If more than one atom is to be indicated, the appropriate number is put before the atomic symbol. For example, 5 H stands for five separate hydrogen atoms.

Under specific conditions of temperature, pressure, and concentration, most atoms are able to attach to and to remain linked to certain other atoms. Such combinations of two or more atoms are called **compounds**. As we shall see below, the atoms of a compound are held together by specific bonding forces referred to as chemical *bonds*.

Each compound has a particular chemical name and a particular formula, both name and formula reflecting the kinds and numbers of atoms in the compound. For example, table salt is technically the compound "sodium chloride," which indicates the presence of sodium and chlorine. The formula NaCl also shows the quantitative ratio of these components: one sodium atom is bonded to one chlorine atom. Water is technically the compound "hydrogen oxide" with the formula H_2O, which indicates the presence of two hydrogen atoms for every one of oxygen. Note generally that the number of like atoms in a compound is indicated as a subscript. For example, iron oxide (Fe_2O_3) contains two iron atoms for every three oxygen atoms. A more complex compound is calcium phosphate, with the formula $Ca_3(PO_4)_2$. This is a shorthand notation for the following combination of atoms: three calcium atoms are bonded to two subcombinations, each of the latter consisting of one phosphorus and four oxygen atoms. Evidently, 13 atoms altogether form one unit of the compound calcium phosphate.

If more than one unit of a compound is to be written in symbols, the appropriate number is put before the formula. For example, H_2O stands for a single unit of the compound water and 5 H_2O stands for five such units.

How do atoms form chemical bonds between them? In other words, how are compounds produced? To answer this, we must consider the internal structure of atoms.

ATOMS

The atoms of all elements are constructed out of components collectively known as *elementary particles*. Three types of elementary particles will concern us most: **protons, neutrons,** and **electrons**. Protons and neutrons occur in the center of an atom, where they form an *atomic nucleus*. Electrons are on the outside of such a nucleus.

A proton has mass, or "weight." This mass is the same for all protons, and it is given the arbitrary unit value 1. A mass of 1 also characterizes a neutron, which is consequently just as heavy as a proton. By contrast, the mass of an electron is very much less than 1, so much less, indeed, that its weight is practically negligible. Therefore, the total mass of a whole atom is concentrated almost entirely in its nucleus.

The mass of an atomic nucleus, i.e., the number of protons and neutrons present, determines the **atomic weight**. For example, the simplest type of atom is that of hydrogen. Its nucleus consists of a single proton, and there is a single electron on the outside; neutrons are absent. Since the nucleus therefore has a mass of 1, the atomic weight of hydrogen is said to be 1. By contrast, the most complex of the naturally occurring types of atoms is the atom of uranium. Its nucleus contains 92 protons as well as 146 neutrons. Therefore, the atomic weight of uranium is 238 (Fig. 2.1). The atomic weights of all other elements range between 1 and 238, according to the specific number of protons and neutrons in the atomic nuclei.

In addition to their mass, the elementary particles also have certain electrical properties. As suggested by

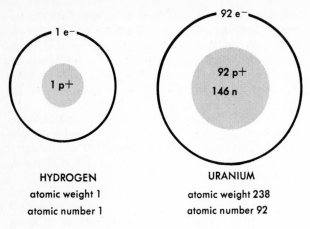

HYDROGEN
atomic weight 1
atomic number 1

URANIUM
atomic weight 238
atomic number 92

FIG. 2.1 The atomic structure of hydrogen and uranium. The atomic nucleus of hydrogen contains a single proton; that of uranium, 92 protons and 146 neutrons.

their name, neutrons are electrically neutral. Protons are electrically positive; more specifically, each proton carries one unit of positive electric charge. Electrons are electronegative, each carrying one unit of negative charge.

In each normal atom, the number of protons is exactly equal to the number of electrons. As noted, for example, a hydrogen atom consists of one proton (positively charged) and one electron (negatively charged). In a uranium atom there are 92 protons in the nucleus (see above), and there are also 92 electrons on the outside. All other atoms similarly display such numerical equality of the positive-charge carriers in the nucleus and the negative-charge carriers on the outside. Hence each atom considered as a whole is electrically neutral.

Note, incidentally, that the number of electrons (or protons) in an atom defines an **atomic number.** Hydrogen has atomic number 1; uranium, atomic number 92. It should be clear that if both the atomic number and the atomic weight of an atom are known, the composition of that atom is also known. For example, if the atomic number is 26 and the atomic weight is 56, then the atom contains 26 electrons on the outside and there must be 26 protons plus 30 neutrons in the nucleus. This happens to be the actual composition of an atom of iron. In certain contexts, rapid reference to either or both the atomic weight and atomic number of an element may be desirable. The appropriate figures are then indicated as a superscript and a subscript to the chemical symbol. For example, iron (Fe) may be symbolized as Fe^{56} or as $_{26}Fe^{56}$.

The electrons of an atom move in exceedingly rapid orbits around the atomic nucleus. An atom in effect resembles a miniature solar system. The nucleus is comparable to the central sun, and the electrons are comparable to the planets. Just as gravitational forces maintain the planets in orbit around the sun, so also do forces of electric attraction keep the negatively charged electrons in atomic orbits around the positively charged nucleus. Moreover, just as planetary orbits are located at various distances from the sun, so also are electron orbits spaced out from the atomic nucleus. Indeed, electrons can travel *only* at a number of fixed distances from the nucleus. The paths of the electrons at these distances may be said to mark out specific "shells," one outside the other.

Each such shell can hold only a fixed maximum number of electrons. The first shell, closest to the atomic nucleus, can hold a maximum of two electrons; the second shell, a maximum of eight electrons. Known maximums also characterize all other shells. In the case of a hydrogen atom, the single electron normally orbits in the first shell. Inasmuch as this shell *could* hold two electrons, hydrogen is said to have an *incomplete* or *open* shell. An atom of helium ($_2He^4$) possesses two electrons, both orbiting in the first shell. In this instance the shell holds the maximum possible number of electrons, and it is said to be *complete* or *closed.* In an atom of oxygen ($_8O^{16}$) eight orbital electrons are present. Two of these fill the first shell and the remaining six occupy the second. Since the second shell *could* hold eight electrons, this shell of oxygen is open. In atoms generally, electrons fill the orbital shells from the innermost outward. Thus, depending on the particular number of electrons present in a given atom, the outermost shell is either complete or to greater or lesser extent incomplete (Fig. 2.2).

It can be shown that an atom is electronically and chemically stable only when all of its electron shells are complete. A helium atom, possessing just the two electrons necessary to complete the first shell, is electronically entirely stable. It is also quite inert chemically; i.e., it is unable to react with other atoms. This holds similarly for the atoms of a few other elements, among them neon, argon, krypton, xenon, and radon. All of these contain just enough electrons to complete all orbital shells present. For example, neon possesses ten electrons, of which two fill the first shell and eight the second. Argon, analogously, possesses three closed shells; krypton, four; xenon, five; and radon, six. Elements of this kind are known as *inert gases.*

In the atoms of all other elements, the outermost shells of electrons are incomplete, and such atoms are electronically unstable. They reveal this instability by being reactive chemically. In other words, if appropriate kinds and appropriate numbers of such atoms are brought into mutual contact, their incomplete outer electron shells may make them undergo a *chemical reaction*. The result of such a reaction is the formation of chemical bonds between the atoms; i.e., a chemical compound is produced. Note that *the chemical properties of atoms are determined by their outermost electron shells*.

Different kinds of atoms form bonds and compounds in different ways. The following sections outline the principal alternatives.

IONS

Every atom has a tendency to complete its outer electron shell and so to become electronically stable. This tendency to acquire complete outer shells is exhibited more or less forcefully by different kinds of atoms, and it constitutes the underlying cause for chemical interactions among atoms.

How can an originally incomplete electron shell become complete? Consider an atom of chlorine ($_{17}Cl^{35}$). Of the 17 orbital electrons, 2 form a complete first shell, 8 a complete second shell, and the remaining 7 an incomplete third shell (see Fig. 2.2). Like the second shell, the third similarly can hold a maximum of 8 electrons. Evidently, the chlorine atom is just one electron short of having a complete outer shell. If the atom could in some way *gain* one more electron, it would satisfy its very strong tendency for electronic completeness and stability.

Consider now an atom of sodium ($_{11}Na^{23}$). Of the 11 electrons here present, 2 form a complete first shell, 8 a complete second shell, and the remaining 1 a highly incomplete third shell (see Fig. 2.2). If this atom were to *lose* the single electron in the third shell, its second shell would then in effect become the outermost shell. Inasmuch as this second shell is complete, the atom would have satisfied its tendency for completeness and would be stable.

It appears therefore that chlorine is unstable because it has one electron too few and that sodium is unstable because it has one electron too many. In view of this, could not *both* atoms become stable simultaneously if they transferred one electron from one atom to the other—if chlorine were to gain the one electron

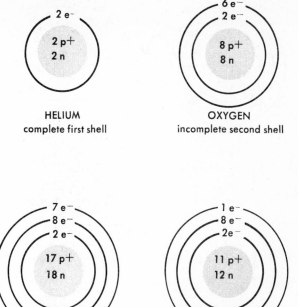

FIG. 2.2 The electron shells of various atoms. Helium, $_2He^4$, has a complete first shell of two electrons. In oxygen, $_8O^{16}$, the second shell is incomplete by two electrons. Chlorine, $_{17}Cl^{35}$, possesses a nearly complete third shell, and sodium, $_{11}Na^{23}$, a nearly empty third shell.

that sodium were to lose? This can indeed happen under appropriate conditions. When it does, it represents an example of one major class of chemical reactions: an **electron-transfer reaction** (Fig. 2.3).

More than two atoms may participate in such a reaction and more than one electron may be transferred. For example, consider the interaction of magnesium and fluorine. Magnesium possesses two electrons in its incomplete third shell; if it were to lose these two, it would become stable. Fluorine possesses seven electrons in its nearly complete second shell; if it were to gain one more electron, its second shell would contain a full set of eight. Magnesium and fluorine may now interact by electron transfer. However, magnesium must lose *two* electrons, yet fluorine need gain only *one*. To make the transaction balance, therefore, each mag-

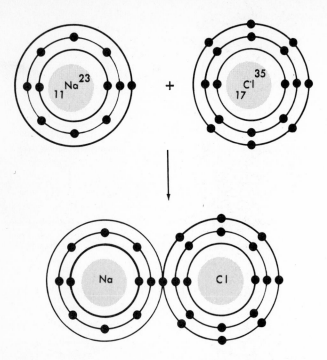

FIG. 2.3 Electron-transfer reactions. In a reaction between one atom of sodium and one of chlorine, the single electron in the third shell of sodium becomes transferred to the third shell of chlorine. As a result, sodium now has a complete outer (second) shell of eight electrons and chlorine has a complete outer (third) shell of eight electrons. In this joined form, the sodium and chlorine atoms constitute the compound sodium chloride.

nesium atom would have to interact with *two* fluorine atoms. This is how the reaction actually occurs (Fig. 2.4). In other words, if a magnesium-fluorine reaction is to achieve electronic stability for all participating atoms, then three atoms must interact and two electrons must be transferred. This reaction illustrates the general principle that a reaction can occur only if all participants achieve electronic stability. Different reactions therefore require the interaction of different numbers of given atoms and the transfer of different numbers of electrons.

In electron transfer among two or more atoms, those atoms which lose electrons may be called *electron donors* and those which gain them, *electron acceptors*. What determines whether an atom is an electron donor or an electron acceptor? For example, could not fluorine become stable by losing its seven outer electrons in-

stead of gaining an additional one? The answer is no, since it is exceedingly difficult to dislodge as many as seven electrons from an atom. Recall that electrons are negatively charged and are attracted to the positively charged protons in the atomic nucleus. Seven electrons are actually attracted very strongly, and they cannot be removed readily in one batch. Indeed, the nucleus exerts a sufficiently strong attracting force to capture and hold on to an additional electron from another atom. The situation is quite similar for chlorine and in general for all atoms in which the outermost shell is almost complete to begin with. Such atoms normally act as electron acceptors in transfer reactions.

Conversely, could not magnesium become stable by gaining six more electrons instead of losing the two in its outer shell? Here again the answer is no. In a shell capable of holding eight electrons, as few as two electrons are not attracted very strongly to the electropositive nucleus. Moreover, the attracting force of such a nucleus is not great enough to capture six additional electrons. Thus, magnesium normally acts as an electron donor. This holds also for sodium, for example,

FIG. 2.4 Electron-transfer reactions. A magnesium atom, with two electrons in its third shell, may lose these two electrons by reacting with two fluorine atoms, each of which requires one more electron for a complete second shell. The result of such an electron transfer is the compound magnesium fluoride, in which each of the three participating atoms now possesses a complete outer shell.

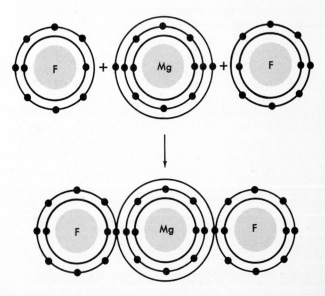

and generally for all atoms in which the outer shell is nearly empty to begin with.

The presence of few outer electrons therefore tends to identify an electron donor; and the presence of many outer electrons, an electron acceptor. We may note that electron donors are commonly known as *metals,* electron acceptors as *nonmetals.* Sodium and magnesium are metals; fluorine and chlorine are nonmetals. Electron transfer reactions commonly occur between metals and nonmetals.

Because of the negative charges of electrons, electron transfers have important electrical consequences. Consider again the transfer reaction between sodium and chlorine. Before the reaction, the sodium atom is electrically neutral, i.e., its total of 11 electrons is counterbalanced exactly by the 11 positively charged protons in the nucleus. During the reaction, one unit of negative charge, in the form of an electron, is lost from sodium. After the reaction, therefore, the sodium atom must be positively charged, for now there are only 10 electrons but the 11 protons are still present. Hence through the loss of one electron, sodium exhibits one unit of positive charge:

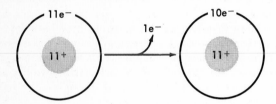

If we indicate a unit of positive charge by a superscript plus sign, we may also write

$$Na \longrightarrow e^- + Na^+$$

Analogously, chlorine is electrically neutral at the outset. During the reaction, it acquires one additional unit of negative charge in the form of an electron. After the reaction it must therefore be negatively charged:

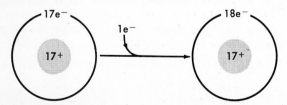

If we indicate a unit of negative charge by a superscript minus sign, we may write

$$Cl + e^- \longrightarrow Cl^-$$

We may now symbolize the sodium-chlorine reaction as a whole by writing

$$Na + Cl \longrightarrow Na^+ + Cl^-$$

or

$$Na + Cl \longrightarrow Na^+Cl^-$$

The equation implies that one electron has been transferred from sodium to chlorine, and it shows that the two atoms have acquired opposite unit charges as a result.

Similarly, in the reaction of magnesium and fluorine, the magnesium atom loses two electrons and then exhibits *two* units of positive charge. The two fluorine atoms accept the two electrons and so acquire negative charges. Symbolically,

$$Mg + 2\,F \longrightarrow Mg^{++} + 2\,F^-$$

or

$$Mg + 2\,F \longrightarrow Mg^{++}F_2^=$$

Atoms or groups of atoms carrying electric charges are known as *ions.* The symbols Na^+ and Mg^{++} stand for sodium ion and magnesium ion, respectively; the symbols F^- and Cl^- similarly stand for fluoride ion and chloride ion, respectively. Electron-transfer reactions may also be referred to as **ionic reactions.**

In such reactions, note that the total number of positive charges carried by one group of ions equals the total number of negative charges carried by the other group. Substances with opposite electric charges are attracted to each other, and we should therefore expect that positive and negative ions exert mutual electric attraction. This is the case; the force of attraction actually binds oppositely charged ions together. Any two ions so coupled are in effect united by a chemical bond, and the bonded group of ions represents a compound, an **ionic compound.** For example, in the reaction

$$Na + Cl \longrightarrow Na^+Cl^-$$

the endproduct is the ionic compound sodium chloride. It contains one bond between the sodium ion and the chloride ion, produced by the electric attraction these two ions have for each other.

The chemical bonds formed in electron transfer reactions are called **ionic bonds.** Note that every electron transferred establishes one ionic bond. Thus the magnesium ion Mg^{++}, resulting from the transfer of two electrons, forms two ionic bonds with other ions.

The number of bonds an ion forms with others indicates the *valence* or, more specifically, the **electrovalence** of the ion. The sodium ion is said to have a *positive* electrovalence of 1, since it is positively charged and has formed one ionic bond by the transfer of one electron. Analogously, the magnesium ion has a positive electrovalence of 2, having formed two ionic bonds by the transfer of two electrons. The fluoride ion, and similarly the chloride ion, each has a *negative* electrovalence of 1; it is negatively charged and has formed one bond by acquiring one electron. Generally, metal ions have positive valences and nonmetal ions negative valences (see Table 1). Note that, since valence numbers indicate the number of bonds formed, whole atoms have valences of zero; actual bonds are not yet in existence. However, whole atoms clearly have potential valences which become actual through electron transfers in ionic reactions.

In writing ionic compounds symbolically, it is not always necessary to indicate the electric charges of the ions. For example, instead of writing Na^+Cl^-, one may also write Na—Cl, the dash here representing the ionic bond. Or one may write, even more simply, NaCl. Similarly, the ionic compound magnesium fluoride, $Mg^{++}F^=_2$, may also be depicted simply as MgF_2. Even though such shorthand notations do not indicate the ionic nature of the components, ions are nevertheless present and ionic bonds unite them.

MOLECULES

Atoms may become electronically stable not only by transferring electrons but also by *sharing* electrons. For example, consider again a chlorine atom. As noted, it possesses seven outer electrons but it requires eight for a complete shell. If appropriate electron donors such as sodium atoms are in the vicinity, the eighth electron may be gained by ionic reaction, as we have seen. However, suppose that appropriate electron donors are not available and that only chlorine atoms are present. Under such circumstances, a chlorine atom may complete its outer shell by reacting with another chlorine atom. We know that a chlorine atom can attract one additional electron rather strongly. Therefore, if two chlorine atoms come into contact, each will attempt to capture an electron from the other atom. But since each atom holds on strongly to its own electrons, an actual transfer cannot take place. Instead, a mutual "tug of war" will continue, each atom holding its own electrons and at the same time trying to pull

one electron away from the other. The net result is a mutual attraction which will keep the two atoms in contact. Moreover, the atoms will *share* one pair of electrons: the sphere of influence of each atom will include seven outer electrons of its own plus one which is attracted from the other atom. Both atoms then behave as if they actually possessed eight outer electrons each, and this suffices to establish their electronic stability (Fig. 2.5).

Electron sharing may also occur among hydrogen atoms, for example. Hydrogen possesses one orbital electron, and it may act as an electron donor if appropriate electron acceptors are available. If chlorine is present, for example, an ionic reaction may occur:

$$H + Cl \longrightarrow H^+Cl^-$$

In the absence of electron acceptors, however, pairs of hydrogen atoms may share their electrons:

$$H\cdot + H\cdot \longrightarrow H:H$$

Through such pooling of the two electrons, the electrons no longer "belong" to either atom but belong equally to both. In effect, therefore, each of the two atoms attracts the two electrons necessary to complete its orbital shell.

More than one pair of electrons may be involved in a sharing process. For example, oxygen possesses six outer electrons and requires *two* more for a complete shell. Completion may be achieved if two oxygen atoms share *two* pairs of electrons. If we indicate only the outer electrons, we may write

$$\ddot{O}: + :\ddot{O} \longrightarrow \ddot{O}::\ddot{O}$$

The two pairs of electrons shown between the two O's in the endproduct are the shared pairs. Each O atom now attracts eight electrons, the required number for a complete shell.

Electron sharing may also occur among more than two atoms, and the atoms may be of different kinds. For example, one oxygen atom may share two of its six outer electrons with two hydrogen atoms. All three atoms may so acquire complete outer shells, i.e., oxygen a shell of eight electrons and each hydrogen a shell of two electrons:

$$\cdot\ddot{O}\cdot + H\cdot + H\cdot \longrightarrow H:\ddot{O}:H$$

We may conclude generally that electron sharing characterizes a second major class of chemical reactions. In some instances, as in the case of chlorine or hydrogen, a given atom may participate either in electron-

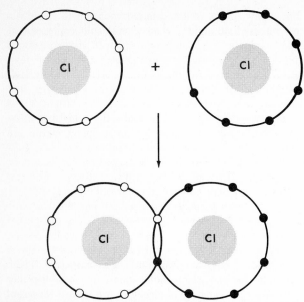

FIG. 2.5   Electron sharing. Two chlorine atoms are shown, only their seven outer electrons being indicated. These two atoms may share one pair of electrons, and so each atom may acquire a complete outer shell of eight electrons. The resulting compound is a molecule of chlorine, Cl_2.

sharing or in electron-transfer processes, depending on what other kinds of atoms are available for reaction. In other cases, an atom participates almost exclusively in one kind of reaction only. Thus, sodium or magnesium almost always transfer electrons. On the contrary, atoms such as oxygen, nitrogen, or carbon almost always share electrons. Carbon, for example, possesses four outer electrons and needs eight for a complete shell. Here it is just as easy (or difficult) to gain four as to lose four, and the carbon atom instead shares all four of its outer electrons. In reacting with four hydrogen atoms, for example:

$$\cdot\overset{}{\underset{}{C}}\cdot + 4\,H\cdot \longrightarrow H\!:\!\overset{\cdot\cdot}{\underset{\cdot\cdot}{C}}\!:\!H$$

Or, carbon may also react with two oxygen atoms:

$$:C + 2\,:\!\overset{\cdot\cdot}{O}\!: \longrightarrow :\!\overset{\cdot\cdot}{O}\!:\!:C:\!:\!\overset{\cdot\cdot}{O}\!:$$

As the electron distributions here indicate, each of the participating atoms again acquires a complete outer shell.

Through electron sharing, two or more atoms

become united into compounds. Compounds of this type are called **molecules,** and the reactions which produce them are called *molecular reactions.* In a molecule, the shared electrons represent the chemical bonds which hold the atoms together. Each shared electron pair represents one chemical bond, and we may note that bonds of this type are known as **covalent bonds.**

Since the formation of covalent bonds does not involve actual transfers of electrons, the participating atoms remain whole, electrically neutral atoms. The number of electrons an atom shares indicates its valence, more specifically, its **covalence.** Hydrogen exhibits a covalence of 1 when it shares its electron. As noted, it may also exhibit a positive electrovalence of 1 when it transfers its electron. Oxygen has a covalence of 2, nitrogen of 3, and carbon of 4. Put another way, oxygen can form two covalent bonds, nitrogen three, and carbon four (see Table 1).

In shorthand symbolizations of molecules, bonds may be indicated either by pairs of dots representing electron pairs or by dashes. Alternatively, bonds need not be indicated at all. For example:

Cl:Cl	or	Cl—Cl	or	Cl_2	*chlorine molecule*
H:H		H—H		H_2	*hydrogen molecule*
O::O		O=O		O_2	*oxygen molecule*
:N:::N:		N≡N		N_2	*nitrogen molecule*
H:O:H		H—O—H		H_2O	*water molecule*

$$H\!:\!\overset{H}{\underset{\cdot\cdot}{C}}\!:\!H \qquad H\!-\!\overset{\overset{\textstyle H}{|}}{\underset{\underset{\textstyle H}{|}}{C}}\!-\!H \qquad CH_4 \quad \textit{methane molecule}$$

$$O\!:\!:\!C\!:\!:\!O \qquad O\!=\!C\!=\!O \qquad CO_2 \quad \textit{carbon dioxide molecule}$$

A condensed shorthand formula obviously does not show whether a given compound is ionic or molecular. Only prior knowledge makes clear that a compound such as MgF_2 is ionic and a compound such as CO_2 is molecular. Where the distinction is important, ionic charges must be shown in one case and dot pairs or dashes in the other.

There are a great many compounds which are ionic but in which some or all of the ions consist of several atoms united by covalent bonds. For example, consider sulfuric acid:

$$H_2SO_4 = H_2{}^{++}SO_4{}^{=} = H^+ + H^+ + \left[\,:\!\overset{\displaystyle :\overset{\cdot\cdot}{O}:}{\underset{\displaystyle :\overset{\cdot\cdot}{O}:}{\overset{\cdot\cdot}{O}:\!\overset{\cdot\cdot}{S}\!:\!\overset{\cdot\cdot}{O}:}}\,\right]^{=}$$

sulfuric acid   *hydrogen ions*   *sulfate ion*

The sulfate ion is a moleculelike complex in which one sulfur atom and four oxygen atoms share their outer electrons. Both sulfur and oxygen possess six outer electrons each and require eight for complete shells. One sulfur and four oxygen atoms together therefore possess 5 times 6, or a total of 30, outer electrons. However, 32 are needed in the arrangement shown above to give each of the five atoms a complete outer shell. The two missing electrons are provided by hydrogen atoms, which serve as electron donors. The result is the formation of a compound consisting of two hydrogen ions and one sulfate ion, the latter carrying two negative charges.

CHEMICAL CHANGE

With certain exceptions unimportant in the present context, free atoms today do not exist naturally on the surface of the earth. As we shall see in the next chapter, atoms probably were free at one time, just after the origin of the earth. Later, atoms which could form compounds did so. Ever since, the earth has been very largely a collection of ionic and molecular compounds.

COMPOUNDS AND REACTIONS

The chemical properties of a compound are determined by the *arrangement*, the *numbers*, and the *types* of atoms present. Two molecules, for example, may contain the same set of atoms; but if these are arranged differently, the molecules will have different properties. Thus the molecules

contain identical atoms, and both molecules may be written as C_4H_{10}. But since their atoms are bonded in different patterns, they are in fact different kinds of molecules with different properties. As we shall see, differences in the bonding patterns of otherwise similar molecules are particularly significant in the chemistry of living matter.

The numbers and types of atoms in a compound determine its size and mass. A molecule composed of but a few atoms of low atomic weight will obviously be smaller and lighter than a molecule composed of many atoms of high atomic weight. Of the compounds present in living matter, most consist of atoms of relatively low atomic weights. Compounds containing low-weight atoms, such as hydrogen, carbon, nitrogen, and oxygen, are particularly abundant. But although the atomic weights are low, the **molecular weights** can be exceedingly high; given molecules in living matter are of very large size and contain hundreds and thousands of atoms each. Here it is the huge number of atoms, not their individual weights, which endows such compounds with high molecular weights.

As a direct consequence of its particular atomic composition and pattern of structure, every compound has a greater or lesser *energy content.* As we have seen, forces of mutual electric attraction between atoms or ions produce the chemical bonds of a compound. These bonding forces, which hold atoms or ions together with a certain tenacity or strength, are said to represent *chemical energy* or **bond energy.** The greater the attracting force between two atoms or ions, the greater is the bond energy. The general concept of energy is roughly equivalent in meaning to work potential, or the capacity to do work. Bond energy therefore implies work, i.e., the electrical work done by atoms which keeps them bonded together. Also, bond energy may be defined as the amount of work necessary to break a chemical bond. Two bonded atoms or ions will become disunited only if some external force pushes them apart and so breaks the bond. Such forcible separation requires work, or energy, and the amount of energy needed clearly must be at least great enough to overcome the attraction between the two atoms or ions. In other words, the energy required to break a bond equals the bond energy. Correspondingly, the total chemical energy of a compound may be defined as the energy required to break all the bonds in the compound.

Once a given bond is broken, two atoms or ions will no longer be joined and will then be free to form new bonds. For example, depending on conditions, the two atoms or ions might rejoin each other and re-form the same bond which united them originally. Or they might be attracted independently to other appropriate atoms or ions and form new bonds with them. In either event, the *potential* for bond formation now exists. Evidently, when a bond is broken, the original bond energy does not disappear. Rather, it continues to exist in potential form, namely, as the potential of separated atoms or ions to make new bonds. We may conclude therefore that, by virtue of its bond energies, every compound represents a "package" of stored chemical energy. If a given amount of work is performed on the compound, the energy package can be opened. Some or all of the chemical energy can thereby be brought "out of storage" and can become available for the formation of new packages, i.e., new compounds.

The clear implication is that compounds are not absolutely stable or permanent structures. On the contrary, if they are subjected to the impact of appropriate amounts of external energy, they may undergo chemical reactions and become different compounds as a result. In the course of such a reaction, changes occur in the numbers or the types or the arrangements of the atoms of the participating compounds. Depending on the manner in which the structure of compounds become changed, four general categories of reactions may be distinguished.

First, two or more compounds may add together and form a single larger compound. This is a **synthesis** reaction. For example,

$$CO_2 + H_2O \longrightarrow H_2CO_3$$
carbon dioxide   *water*   *carbonic acid*

Or, generally,

$$A + B \longrightarrow AB$$

Second, a given compound may break up into two or more smaller ones. This is a **decomposition** reaction, the reverse of synthesis. For example,

$$H_2CO_3 \longrightarrow H_2O + CO_2$$

Or, generally,

$$AB \longrightarrow A + B$$

Third, one or more of the atoms or ions of one compound may trade places with one or more of the atoms or ions of another compound. This is an **exchange** reaction. For example,

$$H^+Cl^- + Na^+OH^- \longrightarrow H^+OH^- (= H_2O) + Na^+Cl^-$$

Or, generally,

$$AB + CD \longrightarrow AD + BC$$

Lastly, the numbers and types of atoms in a compound may remain the same, but the bonding pattern of the atoms changes. This is a **rearrangement** reaction. For example,

Or, generally,

$$A \longrightarrow B$$

Note that in every equation illustrating a reaction, as above, the *total* numbers and types of atoms to the left of the arrow equal exactly the totals to the right of the arrow; in the reaction as a whole, atoms are neither gained nor lost. It is important to make sure that, whenever reactions are written out symbolically, the equations balance in this fashion.

IONIC DISSOCIATION

Virtually all chemical reactions of biological interest take place in a water medium, i.e., in *aqueous solution*. When put into water, molecular compounds may dissolve. If they do, they then exist as whole molecules. Ionic compounds may dissolve similarly, but in addition they also **dissociate** to greater or lesser extent. That is, many of the ionic bonds of such compounds are broken in the presence of water and the aqueous solution therefore contains free individual ions. For example,

$$NaCl \xrightarrow{H_2O} Na^+ + Cl^-$$
sodium chloride   *sodium ion*   *chloride ion*

$$CH_3COOH \xrightarrow{H_2O} CH_3COO^- + H^+$$
acetic acid   *acetate ion*   *hydrogen ion*

$$NH_4OH \xrightarrow{H_2O} NH_4^+ + OH^-$$
ammonium hydroxide   *ammonium ion*   *hydroxyl ion*

Inasmuch as dissociation produces equal amounts of positive and negative electric charges, solutions containing dissociated ionic compounds remain electrically neutral. However, the presence of free ions permits passage of electric currents through such solutions. Ionic compounds are therefore also called **electrolytes,** and molecular compounds are called **nonelectrolytes.**

Note that, in the second equation above, acetic acid dissociates in such a way that hydrogen ions are formed. This is what actually makes acetic acid an acid; any compound which dissociates to yield *hydrogen ions* is called an **acid**.

Analogously, any compound which dissociates to yield *hydroxyl ions,* OH⁻, as in the third equation above, is a **base** or an **alkali**.

A compound resulting from the chemical interaction of an acid and a base is a **salt**. Sodium chloride (NaCl) is a salt because it is formed by the interaction of hydrochloric acid (HCl) and sodium hydroxide (NaOH):

$$HCl + NaOH \longrightarrow NaCl + H_2O$$
$$\text{\textit{acid} \quad \textit{base} \qquad \textit{salt}}$$

Every ionic compound is either an acid or a base or a salt. We may distinguish between "strong" acids and "weak" acids, strong bases and weak bases, and strong salts and weak salts. The basis for such distinctions is the *extent* to which an ionic compound is dissociated. In a strong acid such as HCl, for example, all or virtually all of the ions are dissociated from one another. By contrast, in a weak acid such as CH_3COOH, only a few of the ions are dissociated; the others remain in the form of intact ionic compounds. The situation is analogous for bases and salts. In other words, water breaks the ionic bonds of different ionic compounds to different degrees. In the case of HCl, virtually all ionic bonds are broken; in the case of CH_3COOH, only some are broken. Consequently, a solution of acetic acid, for example, will contain partly the whole compound CH_3COOH and partly the free acetate and hydrogen ions (Fig. 2.6).

FIG. 2.6   In a strong acid, many ionic compounds are dissociated into ions (many single white and black particles); in a weak acid, very few of the ionic compounds are dissociated (many joined pairs of white and black particles).

weak acid:
many ionic compounds,
few ions

strong acid:
few ionic compounds,
many ions

It is often important to determine the acid or alkaline "strength" of a solution of ionic compounds, i.e., the degree to which the compounds are dissociated. This can be done with appropriate electrical apparatus by measuring the relative number of free H⁺ and OH⁻ ions present in the solution; for the more of these ions are found, the more the acids and bases present are dissociated. The result is expressed as a number called the **pH** of the solution. Mathematically, pH has been defined arbitrarily by the equation

$$pH = \log \frac{1}{[H^+]}$$

where [H⁺] indicates how many grams of H⁺ ions are present in 1 litre (l) of solution. For example, pure water dissociates to a very slight degree:

$$H_2O \longrightarrow H^+ + OH^-$$

Measurement shows that, in a liter of pure water, 0.0000001 gram (g) of H⁺ ions is present. The pH of pure water therefore is

$$pH_{water} = \log \frac{1}{0.0000001} = 7$$

Since water contains as many H⁺ ions as OH⁻ ions, it is neither acid nor basic but *chemically neutral*. We may note that any solution will be chemically neutral and will have a pH of 7 if its net H⁺ ion concentration is as in pure water.

Suppose that a given mixture of dissolved ionic compounds contains so much acid that, in a liter of the mixture, there is 0.1 g of H⁺ ions present, i.e., 1 million times as many as in pure water. Then the pH of that mixture would be

$$pH = \log \frac{1}{0.1} = 1$$

We may note in general that the *lower* than 7 the pH of a solution, the *more acid* it is, i.e., the more H⁺ ions are present relative to OH⁻ ions. Analogously, the *higher* than 7 the pH, the *more alkaline* is a solution, i.e., the fewer H⁺ ions are present relative to OH⁻ ions. The maximum possible acidity is indicated by pH 0; the maximum possible alkalinity, by pH 14 (Fig. 2.7).

Living matter, containing a mixture of variously dissociated acids, bases, and salts, usually has a pH very near neutrality. For example, the pH of human blood is generally 7.3. Distinctly higher or lower pH levels do occur, however (e.g., in lemons and stomach cavities, both of which contain characteristically quite

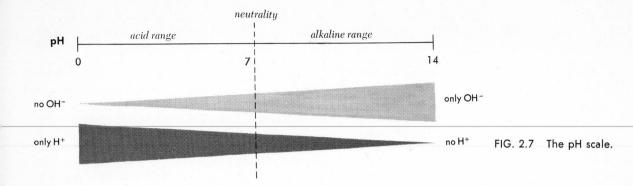

FIG. 2.7 The pH scale.

acid regions). Living matter does not tolerate significant variations of its normal acid-base balance, and its pH must remain within fairly narrow limits. If these limits should be exceeded, major chemical and physical disturbances which would be lethal would result.

We shall find later that many normal processes within living matter yield small amounts of excess acids or bases. But such small additions produce only negligible alterations of the pH. This is largely because living matter is **buffered**; i.e., it is protected to some extent against pH change.

For example, suppose we consider a solution of sodium bicarbonate ($NaHCO_3$), a salt normally present in living matter. This salt is more or less completely dissociated into sodium ions (Na^+) and bicarbonate ions (HCO_3^-). If now a little hydrochloric acid (HCl) is added, we should expect the solution to become more acid. Actually, however, the pH change will be rather slight. This is because the hydrogen ions of hydrochloric acid (H^+) have a chance to react with the bicarbonate ions (HCO_3^-). The result is the formation of carbonic acid (H_2CO_3):

$$NaHCO_3 \longrightarrow Na^+ + HCO_3^-$$
$$HCl \longrightarrow H^+ + Cl^-$$
$$H^+ + HCO_3^- \longrightarrow H_2CO_3$$

Carbonic acid is a *weak* acid; i.e., the compound does not dissociate to any great extent. But the solution above at first contains very many H^+ and HCO_3^- ions, far more than a carbonic acid solution can actually hold. Therefore, H^+ and HCO_3^- will bond together into the whole compound H_2CO_3, as above, until the amounts of the free ions are reduced appropriately. In effect, the free H^+ ions of the added HCl are being "taken out of circulation," and the HCl consequently will not be able to change the pH appreciably.

We say that the presence of HCO_3^- ions *buffers* the solution, i.e., protects it from major pH change if a little acid is added. Analogous buffering effects against added bases are produced by a number of positively charged ions. Inasmuch as living matter contains complex mixtures of various ionic compounds, it is buffered by virtue of its composition. The bicarbonate ion and also carbonate ions ($CO_3^=$) and phosphate ions ($PO_4^=$) are among the most important biological buffers. To be sure, if a living system or any buffered solution is flooded with large quantities of additional acids or bases, then buffer protection will become insufficient and pH will change.

ENERGY CHANGES

Regardless of whether compounds are ionic or molecular, a chemical reaction will be possible only if the compounds are sufficiently *activated*; i.e., they must be *ready* to react. Put differently, given amounts of starting energy, or **activation energy**, must have been supplied from an external source. The basic reason for such a requirement has already been outlined. In every reaction, at least one existing chemical bond is broken and at least one new bond is created. And as we have seen, it takes energy to break chemical bonds. Therefore, a certain amount of external energy, or activation energy, must be supplied to get the bond-breaking process started. Various kinds of external energy may serve to activate reactions. Heat is the most common kind, and, as is well known, many reactions can be started simply by applying heat to given compounds. Other types of energies suitable in particular cases include, for example, light, electricity, X rays, or mechanical energy in the form of pressure.

How do such energies produce their effect? The action of heat provides the general answer. Heat is a consequence of motion. All atoms, ions, and molecules, regardless of whether they are in a gas, a liquid, or a solid, vibrate uninterruptedly in random back-and-forth movements. We feel these movements as heat, and we measure them as temperature. A high temperature, for example, means that chemical units are in violent motion. Conversely, at − 273°C, the theoretical absolute zero of temperature, heat is by definition entirely absent and all chemical units are stationary. However, every known natural or experimentally produced material always contains at least some heat; and a given temperature is always proportional to the amount of heat motion, or *thermal agitation,* of the chemical units present.

Applying heat to a substance is therefore equivalent to intensifying the thermal agitation of its chemical units. One consequence of such an intensification is that the units will collide with one another more frequently. Molecules, for example, will jostle about so rapidly that the number of collisions per unit time will be greater. Collision means contact, and we already know that contact is necessary if two or more molecules are to react. Therefore, as heat increases the collision rate, it also increases the *opportunity* for reaction. A second consequence of increased thermal agitation is that existing chemical bonds may be broken. The atoms or ions within a compound may become agitated so violently that the force of their heat motion equals or exceeds the bonding force which holds them together. And once bonds within compounds are ready to break, the compounds are sufficiently activated to enter chemical reactions.

We may conclude generally that any form of energy may serve as activation energy if, directly or indirectly, it has one or both types of effects: if it increases the collision rate of two or more reactants and so improves the opportunity for reaction and if it agitates the internal structure of a reactant sufficiently to permit disruption of chemical bonds.

If heat activates the compounds taking part in a reaction, it should follow that the more heat is supplied, the faster the reaction will occur. This is so. The higher the temperature, the greater are reaction speeds. It can be shown that every temperature increase of 10°C approximately doubles to triples the speed of reactions. A **temperature coefficient,** conventionally designated by the letter Q, expresses how many times a reaction is speeded up by any stated increase of temperature. It can be shown that $Q_{10} = 2$ to 3 for chemical reactions generally. This statement reads: a 10° rise of temperature speeds reactions two to three times. The implica-

tions for reactions in living systems are important. For example, the chemical reactions in a housefly or a green plant will occur two or three times as fast on a day which is 10°C warmer than another.

Different kinds of reactions require different amounts of activation energy. In some cases, the activation produced by ordinary room temperature may suffice to allow a reaction to start. For example, water and metallic sodium react "spontaneously," i.e., at room temperature. But mix water and fat at room temperature and nothing happens. In this case, an appreciable reaction will occur only if more activation energy is supplied than is provided by the heat of the ordinary environment.

Once proper activation has taken place, continuation of a reaction similarly depends on energy: existing bonds must continue to be disrupted before formation of new bonds is possible. A reaction-maintaining energy source is therefore required. Depending on the nature of the reactants, this source is either the external environment or the reaction itself. These alternatives arise because different compounds contain different total amounts of chemical energy. For example, it often happens that the total bond energy of the compounds entering a reaction is *less* than the total bond energy of the compounds resulting from a reaction. To illustrate, suppose that in the generalized reaction

$$A + B \longrightarrow C + D$$

the total energy of all the bonds in A and B together is less than the total energy of all the bonds in C and D together. In such a case, evidently, less potential bond energy is available in the starting materials than is needed to form the actual bonds of the endproducts. An energy deficit exists in the starting materials, and under such circumstances the reaction cannot proceed unless the deficit is made up. It can be made up if the needed energy is supplied from an external source. The amount of external energy so required is called **reaction energy.** If we indicate it by the customary symbol ΔH, we may write

$$A + B + \Delta H \longrightarrow C + D$$

In other words, the reaction can be maintained only as long as ΔH continues to be available, along with A and B. All reactions which require a continued supply of external energy as above are referred to as **endergonic** or **endothermic** reactions. The sources of energy supply may be the same as those which provide activation energy. For example, heat may first be used as activation energy to start an endergonic process and continued heating may then provide the reaction energy necessary to maintain the process.

Alternatively, it may happen that in a reaction

$$A + B \longrightarrow C + D$$

the total bond energy in A and B together is *greater* than the total in C and D together. In such a case, more potential bond energy is available in the starting materials than is needed to form the actual bonds of the endproducts. The starting materials thus contain an energy excess and the reaction will take the form

$$A + B \longrightarrow C + D + \Delta H$$

In other words, the reaction yields energy. All such reactions are said to be **exergonic** or **exothermic**. Once reactions of this type are properly activated, further external energy supplies are not required. On the contrary, exergonic reactions produce enough energy of their own to become self-sustaining; the energy produced may suffice for continued self-activation of such reactions (Fig. 2.8). Self-maintaining reactions of this type operate like many familiar mechanical devices. A motor, for example, must first be started up and warmed up to a required temperature; i.e., activation energy must be supplied from the outside. But once the motor is running, its fuel-burning reactions usually generate enough energy to sustain their own operating temperature.

Moreover, a greater or lesser quantity of the

FIG. 2.8 External energy activates a reaction (left), and if the reaction is exergonic, it may generate so much heat that it becomes self-sustaining (right). External energy need then no longer be applied.

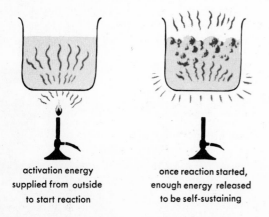

activation energy
supplied from outside
to start reaction

once reaction started,
enough energy released
to be self-sustaining

reaction energy produced by exergonic reactions also dissipates into the surroundings, most often in the form of heat. The heat produced by burning fuel is an example, burning being a series of exergonic chemical reactions. Certain reactions yield so much energy so rapidly that the reaction mixture explodes. An example is the explosive synthesis of water from gaseous hydrogen and oxygen. Under suitable conditions, some of the energy produced by an exergonic reaction may be made to perform useful work; for example, it may provide heat, drive an engine, or, indeed, activate other chemical reactions. In living systems, as we shall see, exergonic processes provide both activation energy and reaction energy for the maintenance of endergonic processes.

It will have become clear that, of the three aspects of energy here discussed, bond energy is the most fundamental. Because compounds contain bond energy, activation energy is needed to start a reaction. And because different compounds contain different amounts of bond energy, a chemical process either will require the environment to provide reaction energy or will be self-sustaining and will release reaction energy to the environment.

CATALYSIS

Most chemical reactions of biological interest require fairly high activation energies—so high, indeed, that most living processes should require environments far hotter than room temperature. This is evidently not the case; if living matter were heated substantially above room temperature it would quickly be killed. It remains true, nevertheless, that at the comparatively low temperatures at which living matter normally exists, the thermal agitation produced by the environment is insufficient to activate many reactions. How then are living processes possible? How are sufficient molecular collisions brought about without additional heat? The answer lies in *catalysis:* the acceleration of reactions by means of *catalysts* rather than heat.

Catalysts of various kinds are well known and widely used in the nonliving world. The special catalysts which occur in the living world are called **enzymes.** These substances are *proteins,* complex compounds about which much will be said later. For the present, we need note only that virtually every one of the thousands of chemical reactions in living matter is speeded up enormously by a particular enzyme protein. Without enzymes the reactions could not occur fast

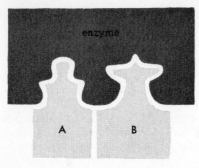

FIG. 2.9 The surfaces of molecules A and B fit into the surface of the enzyme. Reaction between A and B is thus speeded up, for contact between A and B does not depend on chance collision.

enough at ordinary temperatures to sustain life. Enzymes therefore represent a supplement to thermal agitation, a device through which reactions requiring high temperatures in test tubes can occur at low temperatures in living matter.

How does an enzyme work? Best available evidence indicates that, like catalysts of all kinds, an enzyme combines temporarily with the reacting compounds. Mutual contact of these compounds is then no longer a matter of chance collision but a matter of certainty; hence reactions are faster.

The protein nature of enzymes is essential to this reaction-accelerating effect. Protein molecules are huge, and an almost unlimited number of different kinds of proteins exists. Accordingly, proteins have distinct molecular surfaces and the geometries of these surfaces differ as the internal structure of the proteins differs. The nature of the surface appears to be the key to enzyme action. Consider the reaction

glucose + fructose ⟶ sucrose

Glucose has a given unique surface geometry, and so does fructose. Enzymatic acceleration of this reaction may now occur if the surfaces of both glucose and fructose happen to fit closely into the surface of a particular protein molecule. In other words, if the reacting molecules can become attached to a suitably shaped surface of an enzyme, then these molecules will be so close to each other that they may react chemically (Fig. 2.9). The enzyme itself remains almost passive here. It may provide a uniquely structured "platform" on which particular molecules may become trapped. Such trapping brings reacting molecules into contact far faster than chance collisions at that temperature;

hence reactions are accelerated. When they are held by the enzyme, glucose and fructose react and become sucrose, and sucrose then disengages from the enzyme surface.

In enzyme-accelerated reactions, it is customary to speak of reacting molecules such as glucose and fructose as the *substrates*. When substrate molecules are attached to an enzyme, the whole is referred to as an *enzyme-substrate complex*. Formation of such complexes may be thought of as a "lock-and-key" process. Only particularly shaped keys fit into particularly shaped locks. Just so, only certain types of molecules will establish a close fit with a given type of enzyme protein. For example, the enzyme in Fig. 2.10 may be effective in reactions involving substrates *a* or *b*, but not in those involving *c*.

Differences in the surface configuration of different types of proteins undoubtedly account for the phenomenon of *enzyme specificity;* a given type of enzyme normally accelerates only one particular type of reaction. For example, the enzyme in the glucose-fructose reaction above, called *invertase,* is specific and catalyzes *only* that particular reaction. In living matter, there are actually almost as many different kinds of enzymes as there are different kinds of reactions. This specificity of enzymes is an important corollary of the more general phenomenon of *protein specificity,* about which more will be said in Chap. 4. Because of protein specificity, some proteins are enzymes and some are not. If a protein happens to have a surface into which some other molecules could fit, then that protein could function as an enzyme in reactions involving those molecules.

Several other characteristics of enzymatic reactions may now be noted. If we assume the general reaction

FIG. 2.10 Reactants A and B fit partially into the surface of the enzyme but reactant C does not. Hence the enzyme may speed up reactions involving A and B but not those involving C.

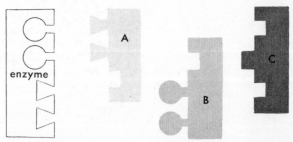

$A + B \longrightarrow C + D$ to be accelerated by an enzyme, we may write

$$A + B + enz \longrightarrow A \cdot B \cdot enz$$
$$C \cdot D \cdot enz \longrightarrow C + D + enz$$

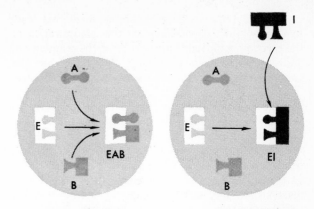

reaction of A and B possible with aid of enzyme E

reaction of A and B blocked by enzyme inhibitor I

FIG. 2.11 The principle of enzyme inhibition. The enzyme E normally speeds up reactions involving reactants A and B. But if an inhibitor molecule I, which fits into the surface of E, is supplied from the outside, then I may combine with E preferentially, thus preventing the normal reaction of E, A, and B. Poisons may be what they are because of such inhibiting effects. On the other hand, if the reaction of E with A and B gives an abnormal, disease-producing result, then a beneficial chemical may be introduced which acts like I and so prevents the disease.

Note here that the enzyme molecule reappears unchanged at the end of the reaction, free to combine with a new set of starting substrates. We conclude again that enzymes and catalysts in general are not themselves affected by the reactions. Because of this, very small amounts of enzymes, used over and over, can catalyze large quantities of substrates.

Note further that a given enzyme can speed up a reaction in *either* direction; the reaction sucrose $\longrightarrow$ glucose + fructose is accelerated by the *same* enzyme, namely, invertase, that speeds up the reaction glucose + fructose $\longrightarrow$ sucrose. This is understandable if we keep in mind that enzymes are primarily passive reaction platforms. Thus, like heat, enzymes only influence reaction *speeds;* other factors govern the direction of a reaction, as we shall see presently.

Many substances which are not normally present in living matter may, if introduced into living matter, combine with given enzymes and so act as poisons. For by attaching to enzymes, such poisons prevent the normal substrates from combining with the enzymes. Since enzymes are present only in rather small amounts, small quantities of such poisons, or *enzyme inhibitors,* may block certain normal reactions completely. This may be fatal. On the other hand, enzyme inhibition also accounts for the beneficial effect of many drugs (Fig. 2.11).

Enzymes may be classified according to the kind of substrate they affect. For example, any enzyme accelerating reactions of compounds called carbohydrates is referred to as a **carbohydrase.** Invertase, above, is a carbohydrase. Analogously, **proteinase** and **lipase** are enzymes that catalyze reactions of proteins and of fatty substances (= lipids), respectively. A suffix -*ase* always signifies that the substance in question is an enzyme. Note, however, that names of enzymes need not necessarily end in -*ase.* Enzymes may also be classified according to the nature of the reaction they catalyze. For example, one distinguishes "splitting" and "synthesizing" enzymes, "transferring" enzymes (*transferases*), and "rearranging" enzymes (*mutases*). In writing an enzymatic reaction symbolically, the name of the enzyme is conventionally put over the reaction arrow. Thus,

$$\text{glucose + fructose} \xrightarrow{\text{invertase}} \text{sucrose}$$

We have found that, like thermal agitation, enzymes increase the rate of contact among molecules, and so they increase the rate of reactions. But thermal agitation and enzymes are not the only two conditions to do so. A third is the *concentration* of the molecules present.

MASS ACTION

Every chemical reaction has three basic attributes: it takes place at a certain *speed,* it proceeds in a certain *direction,* and it has a certain *duration.* What determines these attributes specifically for any given reaction?

As noted above, the speed of a reaction is determined by the environmental temperature and by catalysts. But it should be readily apparent that reaction speeds will depend also on the concentration of the reacting compounds present; for if the temperature and the enzymes remain constant, then the greater the concentration of the starting compounds, the more frequently will contacts among the compounds become possible and the faster the reaction will therefore be. We may say that, other factors being equal, *the speed of a reaction is proportional to the concentrations of the participating molecules.* This is known as the **law of mass action** (Fig. 2.12).

This law actually predicts more than the speed of reactions. By implication, it also predicts the direction and the duration of reactions. In principle, all *chemical reactions are reversible;* i.e., if they can occur in one direction, they can also occur in the opposite direction. Suppose that we consider a fairly common reaction of biological importance, namely, the reversible reaction

$$\text{1 glycerin + 3 fatty acids} \rightleftharpoons \text{1 fat + 3 water}$$

If glycerin, fatty acids, fat, and water molecules come into mutual contact, in which direction will the reaction proceed? Will fat form or will fat disappear? The law of mass action gives the answer: if glycerin and fatty acids are present in higher concentrations than fat and water, then the reaction will go to the *right;* but if fat and water are present in higher concentrations, then the reaction will proceed to the *left.* Put differently, if more collisions occur between glycerin and fatty acids, more fat and water will form; and if more collisions occur between fat and water, more glycerin and fatty acids will form.

FIG. 2.12 The principle of mass action. At left, few molecules are present, and the concentration is low. Collisions are therefore infrequent; hence reaction speed is also low. At right, at the same temperature as at left, many molecules are present, and the concentration is high. Collisions at right are therefore frequent; hence reaction speed is high.

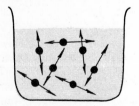

low concentration:
few collisions, hence slow reaction

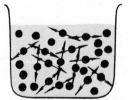

high concentration:
many collisions, hence fast reaction

Mass action clearly determines the direction of a reaction. How long will such a reaction continue in a given direction; i.e., what is the duration of reaction? Suppose that we started out with high concentrations of glycerin and fatty acids and a zero concentration of fat and water:

$$\text{glycerin + fatty acids} \longrightarrow$$

The reaction proceeds to the right at a certain speed. But as glycerin and fatty acids are transformed, their concentrations decrease. And as the first few molecules of fat and water appear, they can react together and start some reaction to the *left:*

$$\text{glycerin + fatty acids} \longrightarrow\!\!\!\longleftarrow \text{fat + water}$$

The *net* accumulation of fat will therefore now occur at a slower pace than at the beginning. With time, the net reaction to the right will become slower and slower; as more and more fat and water form, reacting increasingly to the left, less and less glycerin and fatty acids remain, reacting decreasingly to the right. An *equilibrium* will be reached when the left-hand reaction occurs as fast as the right-hand one. No further *net* increase of fat and water will take place thereafter, and the net reaction stops:

$$\text{glycerin + fatty acids} \rightleftharpoons \text{fat + water}$$

In short, a reaction continues in a given direction until an equilibrium point is reached. At that point certain quantities of reactants are present, and so long as the equilibrium is maintained, the reaction in one direction occurs as fast as in the other. Hence the net quantities of all substances present do not change.

This holds if the reaction system is left to itself and nothing is added or removed. Suppose, however, that we removed fat (or water) as fast as it formed. Then, because fat (or water) is not allowed to accumulate, a reaction to the left cannot take place. The reaction to the right will therefore continue. An equilibrium point will not be reached, and all the glycerin and fatty acids present initially will eventually be converted into fat and water. The reaction to the right will proceed to completion and the yield of fat and water will then be maximal.

Reactions often proceed to completion, i.e., to maximum yield, if one of the substances formed is an escaping gas ($\uparrow$) or a relatively insoluble precipitate ($\downarrow$); for either is equivalent to removing one of the end-products as fast as it is formed. For example,

$$H_2CO_3 \longrightarrow H_2O + CO_2 \uparrow$$
$$Ca^{++} + CO_3^{=} \longrightarrow CaCO_3 \downarrow$$

Another way of preventing establishment of an equilibrium in the glycerin-fat reaction above would be to keep *adding* glycerin and fatty acids to the reaction system. The concentrations of glycerin and fatty acids then would always remain high, and according to the law of mass action, the reaction would always be "driven" to the right. More and more fat and water would form as more and more glycerin and fatty acids were added.

Note that the rules of mass action also apply to the energy changes of exergonic and endergonic reactions. Consider the reversible reaction

$$A \rightleftharpoons B + \Delta H$$

Proceeding to the right, the reaction is exergonic. ΔH here is as much an endproduct as B, and if ΔH escapes as fast as it is produced, the reaction to the right will not reach equilibrium but will proceed to completion. Equilibrium could be reached only if the reaction were completely energy-insulated, i.e., if none of the energy produced could escape the system. Such insulation cannot be achieved in practice, and reactions of this type always do tend to go to completion. The reverse reaction is endergonic. Here ΔH must be added continuously if all of B is to be converted into A. If the supply of ΔH is stopped prematurely, the reaction to the left will cease and the reverse reaction to the right will supervene and proceed to completion.

We may now conclude with the following summary. If chemical reactions occur in water, the participating substances will be more or less completely dissociated acids, bases, and salts as well as whole, nondissociated molecular compounds. Reactions will be possible if sufficient activation energy is made available. If it is, the chemical changes can be in the nature of synthesis, decomposition, exchange, and rearrangement. The speed of the reactions will be determined by the environmental temperature, by catalysts, and by mass action, and mass action will also determine the directions and durations of the reactions. Finally, as the reactions proceed, reaction energy either will be required or will be released.

The foregoing account suffices for a preliminary understanding of biological reactions, which, as succeeding chapters will show, are an outgrowth of chemical ones.

REVIEW QUESTIONS

1. Define element, atom, compound, ion, molecule, chemical energy, chemical bond, valence.

2. What is an electrovalent bond? How is such a bond formed? Explain in terms of atomic structure. What is a covalent bond? How is such a bond formed? Again explain in terms of atomic structure.

3. In what kinds of chemical reactions may compounds participate? Give specific examples.

4. Consider the following equation:

$$Ca(OH)_2 + 2\ HCl \longrightarrow CaCl_2 + 2\ H_2O$$

a. Identify the different atoms by name and determine the valence of each.

b. Rewrite the equation to show the bonds, ionic, molecular, or both, within each compound.

c. Is the equation balanced?

d. Is this an exchange, synthesis, decomposition, or rearrangement reaction?

5. Define dissociation, electrolyte, acid, base, salt. Is H_2SO_4 an acid, a base, or a salt? How does sodium sulfate (Na_2SO_4) dissociate? The magnesium ion is Mg^{++} and the nitrate ion is NO_3^-; write the formulas for magnesium hydroxide, nitric acid, and magnesium nitrate.

6. What does the pH of a solution indicate? What would you expect the pH of a solution of NaCl to be? Of HCl? Of NaOH? Compared with pure water, how many more or fewer grams of H^+ ions will there be in a liter solution of (*a*) pH 5 and (*b*) pH 10? The pH of human blood is 7.3; what is the actual H^+ ion concentration per liter?

7. What is the biological significance of dissociation and pH? What are buffers?

8. Review the role of environmental heat in chemical reactions. What is activation energy? Reaction energy? How does the external energy requirement differ for exergonic and endergonic reactions?

9. What is a catalyst? What is an enzyme and

how does it work? Why is invertase ineffective in accelerating the reaction glycerin + fatty acids $\longrightarrow$ fat + water? What kind of enzyme does such a reaction actually require? Review the general operational characteristics of enzymes in biological reactions.

10. State the law of mass action. How does this law govern the speed, the direction, and the amount of a chemical reaction? Under what conditions is a reaction reversible? Irreversible?

SUGGESTED COLLATERAL READINGS

Substantial additional information on topics dealt with in this chapter may be found in virtually any modern introductory college text of chemistry. The student desiring such information is urged to consult such texts, available in all college and most public libraries. The works listed below represent sample selections. Many other, equivalent books may be similarly adequate. The article by Pfeiffer is a good semi-popular account on enzymes.

Daniels, F., and R. A. Alberty: "Physical Chemistry," Wiley, New York, 1955.

Maron, S. H., and C. F. Prutton: "Principles of Physical Chemistry," 3d ed., Macmillan, New York, 1958.
Noller, C. R.: "Textbook of Organic Chemistry," Saunders, Philadelphia, 1958.
Pauling, L.: "College Chemistry," Freeman, San Francisco, 1950.
Pfeiffer, J. E.: Enzymes, *Sci. American,* vol. 179, 1948.
Sienko, M. J., and R. A. Plane: "Chemistry," 2d ed., McGraw-Hill, New York, 1961.

PART 2
THE WORLD OF LIFE

A good plan of procedure in a study of living things is to begin with a characterization of the broad domain with which biology deals, namely, the whole living world in time and in space.

Just what is life? How was it created originally in the distant past? How did first life become the living world of today? Clearly, in any characterization of the living world as a whole, the **origin of life** must be a major topic.

Within the world of life, the basic units are living **cells,** i.e., the smallest bits of substance capable of displaying all the attributes which we collectively call "living." What is this cellular substance? What is it made of, and what are its life-producing properties? These questions will have to be answered as fully as possible in any broad characterization of life.

Single cells or physically joined collections of cells form individual living creatures, or **organisms.** What is the nature of all such organisms? What structural and functional features are common to them, and in which ways are cells actually combined to form an organism? Moreover, what, exactly, distinguishes a living organism from a dead one or from an inanimate object? A characterization of the living world certainly must deal with these issues in detail.

It is obvious also that individual organisms do not exist in isolation. They always form larger groups such as families, societies, populations, and, above all, **species** and **communities.** Groups of this sort live in and indeed are greatly influenced by particular kinds of geographic environments which serve as homes or habitats. Evidently, the fundamental relation of different kinds of organisms to one another and to their physical environment must be examined.

The following five chapters are devoted to these topics. We begin at the beginning, with the origin of life.

THE ORIGIN
OF LIFE

3

It is thought today that life originated principally through a series of chemical reactions; atoms combined into simple compounds, these combined into more complex ones, and the most complex compounds eventually formed in turn became organized into "living" wholes.

The details of these processes are at present known only partly. Some of the existing knowledge results from a backward projection of living types and living activities encountered today. For example, biologists deduce from viruses, bacteria, and other primitive existing forms what the earliest living forms might have been like. Other clues come from astronomy, physics, and geology, sciences which contribute information about the probable physical character of the ancient earth. Important data are also provided by ingenious chemical experiments designed to duplicate in the laboratory some of the steps which many millennia ago may have led to the beginning of life.

All this, supplemented here and there by reasonable speculation, today enables us to give a fairly good account of living origins. By tracing these origins as in this chapter, we gain important glimpses into the very nature of life. The understanding obtained actually provides the fundamental basis for the later discussion of all living processes.

CHEMICAL EVOLUTION

THE EARLY EARTH

Living creatures on earth are a direct product of the earth. There is every reason to believe that living things owe their origin entirely to certain physical and chemical properties of the ancient earth. Nothing supernatural appeared to be involved—only time and natural physical and chemical laws operating within the peculiarly suitable earthly environment. Given such an environment, life probably *had* to happen. Put another way, once the earth had originated in its ancient form, with particular chemical and physical properties, it was then virtually *inevitable* that life would later originate on it also. The chemical and physical properties of the earth permitted certain chemical and physical reactions to occur, and one result of these reactions was something *living*. We may infer, moreover, that if other solar systems possess planets where chemical and physical conditions resemble those of the ancient earth, then life would originate on these other planets as well. Indeed, it is now believed strongly that life occurs not only on this earth but probably widely throughout the universe as well.

The life-producing chemical and physical properties of the early earth were a result of the way the earth and our solar system as a whole came into being to begin with. Available evidence indicates that the solar system is anywhere from 5 to 10 billion years old. Several hypotheses have been proposed to explain how the sun and the planets were formed. According to one, now widely accepted, the whole solar system started out as a hot, rapidly rotating ball of gas. This gas was made up of free atoms. Hydrogen atoms probably were the most abundant, and other, heavier kinds were present in lesser quantities. The sun was formed when most of this atomic gas, hence most of the hydrogen, gravitated toward the center of the ball. Even today, the sun is composed largely of hydrogen atoms. A swirling belt of gas remained outside the new sun. Eddies formed in this belt, and in time it broke up into a few smaller gas clouds. These spinning spheres of fiery matter were the early planets.

The earth thus probably began as a glowing mass of free hydrogen and other types of atoms. These eventually became sorted out according to weight. Heavy ones, such as iron and nickel, sank toward the center of the earth, where they are still present today. Lighter atoms, such as silicon and aluminum, formed a middle shell. The very lightest, such as hydrogen, nitrogen, oxygen, and carbon, collected in the outermost layers (Fig. 3.1).

At first, temperatures were probably too high for the formation of compounds—bonds would have been broken as fast as they might have formed. But under the influence of the cold of cosmic space, the earth began to cool down gradually. In time, temperatures became low enough to permit the formation of relatively stable bonds between atoms. Compounds then appeared in profusion and free atoms disappeared.

With this we reach the beginning of the chemical history of the earth, which henceforth will accompany the physical history. As far as they are known or suspected, what were the life-producing chemical reactions?

THE FIRST COMPOUNDS

Among the lightest and most abundant materials in the surface gas of the early earth were, as noted above, atoms of hydrogen, oxygen, carbon, and nitrogen. Consequently, when temperatures became low enough to allow formation of compounds, the atoms of these four elements must have played a conspicuous role. (And it is therefore not a coincidence that, even today, some 95 per cent or so of the substance of every living creature consists of just these four elements.)

What simple compounds could have formed from the four elements? On the basis of their known chemical properties and their presumed relative abundance on the early earth, H, C, O, and N should have joined into some half dozen different combinations:

water, H—O—H, H_2O

methane, $H—\overset{\displaystyle H}{\underset{\displaystyle H}{C}}—H$, CH_4

ammonia, $H—N\langle\overset{\displaystyle H}{\underset{\displaystyle H}{}}$, NH_3

carbon dioxide, O=C=O, CO_2
hydrogen cyanide, H—C≡N, HCN
hydrogen molecules, H—H, H_2

We have evidence that at least the first three of these compounds actually came into being not only on the early earth but on other planets as well. For example, on the cold, distant planet Jupiter, water, methane, and ammonia are present today in the form of thick surface layers of permanently frozen solids. Apparently, these compounds must have formed there as on earth, but at that great distance from the sun the surface of the planet probably froze before much additional chemical change could occur. On the hot earth, by contrast, the early compounds could interact further and give rise to new compounds in the later course of time.

Moreover, there is every reason to believe that, under the conditions prevailing on the early earth, simple compounds which theoretically *could* have appeared actually *did* appear. On this basis, the formation of H_2, H_2O, CH_4, NH_3, CO_2, and HCN must have

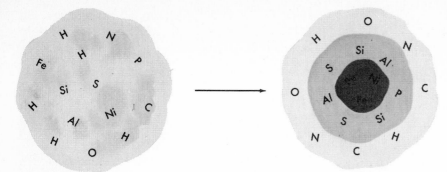

FIG. 3.1 The elements composing the early earth became sorted out according to weight. Heavy elements like iron (Fe) sank to the center; lighter ones like silicon (Si) formed a middle shell; and very light elements like hydrogen (H) collected into an outer mantle.

been a strong probability. Practically all of the hydrogen molecules (and any free hydrogen atoms still present) must soon have boiled off the surface layers of the earth, for the gravitational attraction of the comparatively small planet could not have been great enough to hold these extremely light substances. The other compounds remained and constituted a hot, gaseous *atmosphere.*

In time, as the gas ball which was the earth continued to cool, temperatures became low enough to allow some of the gases to liquefy and some of the liquids in turn to solidify. Heavy substances near the center of the earth probably tended to liquefy and solidify first. But the pressure produced by the weight of the overlying materials generated so much heat that any tendency to solidify was counteracted. To this day the earth contains a hot, thickly flowing, deformable center. On the other hand, the middle shell of lighter substances did congeal, and a solid, gradually thickening crust developed. As the crust thickened and cooled, it wrinkled and folded and gave rise to the first mountain ranges. Overlying this crust was the outer atmospheric mantle, which at temperatures then prevailing still remained gaseous.

Then the rains started. All the water on earth up to this stage was in the atmosphere, forming clouds probably hundreds of miles thick. The solidifying crust underneath at first was sufficiently hot that any liquid water would boil away instantly. But eventually the crust became cool enough to hold water in liquid form. Then rain began falling in unceasing, centuries-long downpours. Basins and shallows filled up and torrential rivers tore down from the mountains. The oceans formed in this way.

Dissolved in these seas were quantities of the atmospheric CH_4, NH_3, CO_2, and HCN, compounds which persist as gases at temperatures at which water is liquid. Also accumulating in the ocean were salts

and minerals. At first there were none, but as the rivers eroded the mountainsides and dissolved them away and as violent tides battered the shores and reduced them to powder, salts and minerals came to be added to the ocean in increasing quantities. Moreover, massive submarine bursts of molten lava probably erupted frequently through the earth's crust, and they too added their substance to the mineral content of the world's waters. Thus the oceans acquired their saltiness relatively early and to a small extent they became saltier still during subsequent ages (Fig. 3.2).

The formation of large bodies of liquid water containing the early atmospheric gases and many minerals in solution was the key event which made the later origin of life possible. Water was and is now the most essential single component of living matter. On an average, two-thirds and often as much as 90 per cent or more of anything living is water; and the presence of water in bulk over three-fourths of the earth's surface today is of profound importance in the economy of living things. This fundamental role of water in living matter traces primarily to two properties of water.

First, water is virtually the best of all possible solvents. It dissolves a greater variety of substances and greater quantities of each substance than practically any other liquid. This means that it is an excellent medium for chemical reactions. Chemical processes also occur in gases and solids, but many more can occur in liquids and much more readily. Since living processes are based on chemical processes, the abundant supply of liquid water on the early earth was a promising circumstance.

Second, water was originally the only good source of hydrogen and oxygen. Both elements have exceedingly useful properties, and the construction of a living system on a chemical basis virtually demands their availability. But, as noted, free hydrogen and free oxygen became unavailable soon after the origin of the

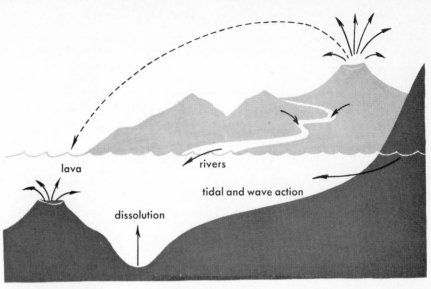

FIG. 3.2 The original sources of oceanic salt. Some was derived from volcanoes, both submarine and terrestrial; some was dissolved out of the sea bottom; a third source was tidal action, which crumbled and dissolved the shore lines; and a good deal of salt also came from the land surface, leached out by rain and rivers.

earth. Water molecules then came to serve as the principal suppliers. Water remains today virtually the only usable source of hydrogen and one of the important sources of oxygen.

Thus, oceanic water set the stage for the formation of living matter. The actors on this stage were the various gases and minerals dissolved in water, plus water itself. And the title role was played by the carbon atoms present in gases such as methane.

EARLY ORGANIC COMPOUNDS

Properties of Carbon

Carbon is a most versatile element. With a covalence of 4, carbon atoms can link up with as many as four other atoms of the same or of different kinds. Carbon is bonded to four hydrogens in methane, as noted, but any or all of these hydrogen atoms may be replaced rather readily by other atoms. For example, in reactions of methane with chlorine or chlorine-containing compounds, one may obtain new compounds such as CH_3Cl, CH_2Cl_2, $CHCl_3$, and CCl_4 (the last two being respectively known as chloroform, an anesthetic, and as carbon tetrachloride, a solvent used in cleaning fluids).

Apart from bonding possibilities such as these, carbon atoms may link directly to other carbon atoms, a most interesting and important bonding property. When carbon joins carbon, short or long *chains* of atoms may be formed.

$$-\overset{|}{\underset{|}{C}}-\overset{|}{\underset{|}{C}}-\overset{|}{\underset{|}{C}}-\overset{|}{\underset{|}{C}}-\overset{|}{\underset{|}{C}}-$$

To be sure, bare chains with open bonds do not exist as such, but they form parts of whole molecules in which various other atoms or groups of atoms are attached to the carbons. For example, if the carbons of two or more methane molecules are joined into a chain, then hydrogen atoms will be bonded to the carbons, as, for example, in

$$H-\overset{H}{\underset{H}{C}}-\overset{H}{\underset{H}{C}}-\overset{H}{\underset{H}{C}}-\overset{H}{\underset{H}{C}}-H$$

Alternatively, one or more types of atoms other than hydrogen may be attached to such chains.

Chains are by no means the only possible kinds of carbon-to-carbon combinations. If we imagine that one end of a carbon chain becomes connected to the other end, then a carbon *ring* will be the result. Benzene is one of such ring-containing compounds:

$$\begin{array}{c} H \\ | \\ C \\ \end{array}$$

Many additional types of configurations exist. For example, carbon chains can be branched, rings and chains can become joined to one another, and any of these "patterns in carbon" can extend into three as well as two dimensions. Such carbon structures form molecular "skeletons," as it were, and the other atoms bonded to the carbons may be thought of as the "flesh" on the skeletons.

No other element even approaches the self-bonding versatility displayed by carbon. Clearly, carbon-to-carbon combinations introduce the possibility of tremendous *complexity* as well as *variety* into molecular structure. Actually, carbon-containing substances display more complexity and more variety than all other chemicals put together.

In view of these properties of carbon, the events which must have taken place in the oceans of the early earth are not difficult to envisage. Compounds like methane undoubtedly reacted with a good many of the other simple compounds present, and a large variety of different carbon-containing compounds must have come into existence. Included in these reactions must have been many in which compounds like methane were joined to one another or to other carbon-containing types. The result was the appearance of new kinds of compounds which contained two or more *linked* carbon atoms.

This development was a critical happening in the early history of living matter—the compounds with linked carbons eventually became the stuff out of which much of living matter was constructed. Today, carbon-to-carbon combinations occur almost exclusively within living matter or in materials derived from living and once-living matter. Because of this, such complex carbon chemicals are called **organic compounds.** This contrasts with water, mineral substances, metallic materials, and other **inorganic compounds,** which do not contain linked carbons. Inorganic substances make up the nonliving world, but very many are also found in the living world.

What were some of the first organic compounds?

Compounds of Carbon

Among the numerous varieties of organic materials which undoubtedly formed in the early seas, five particular varieties came to have special significance in later events (as judged by hindsight from the vantage point of the present). These five varieties are:

1. sugars
2. glycerin
3. fatty acids
4. amino acids
5. nitrogen bases

Representations of the structural makeup of these compounds are given in Fig. 3.3. Note that in each case a carbon skeleton—either a chain or a ring structure—is the basis of the compound and that various groupings of hydrogen, oxygen, and nitrogen make up the remainder.

Sugars are members of a larger class of organic compounds known as **carbohydrates.** The carbon skeleton of a sugar is a relatively short chain. Chains consisting of five and six carbon atoms are particularly common in living matter. The general name given to a C_5 sugar is **pentose.** An important specific example of a pentose is the sugar *ribose* ($C_5H_{10}O_5$). A C_6 sugar is referred to generally as a **hexose,** a specific example being the widely occurring *glucose* ($C_6H_{12}O_6$). In sugars, as in carbohydrates as a group, the only elements present are H, C, and O.

This is true also for glycerin, which contains three carbon atoms in a chain, and for the fatty acids. In the latter, however, the carbon chains may vary in length from 2 to 20 or more atoms. One end of a fatty acid molecule always terminates in a —COOH group, termed the *carboxyl* group, which endows the molecule with its acid properties (see Chap. 2).

Carboxyl groups also characterize the amino acids, which in addition carry nitrogen-containing *amino* groups, —NH_2. In an amino acid molecule, the carboxyl and amino groups are bonded to a carbon atom. To this atom is usually also attached a carbon skeleton which may vary in structure considerably. For example, it may consist of a few or of many carbon atoms and these may form either a chain, a ring, or a chain-ring combination (symbolized as —R— in Fig. 3.3).

Nitrogen is also an invariable component of the nitrogen bases, a group of compounds which includes two major subgroups, the **pyrimidines** and the **purines.** In both, the molecular skeleton is always a ring structure, the rings in these cases containing carbon as well as nitrogen atoms. A single carbon-nitrogen ring characterizes the pyrimidines; a double ring, the purines.

On the basis of these structural configurations and given the conditions which presumably prevailed on the primitive earth, we may guess how the five categories of organic compounds might have come into being. Simple chain compounds such as sugars, glycerin, and fatty acids could have formed through reactions of methane with itself and with water. Similarly, inter-

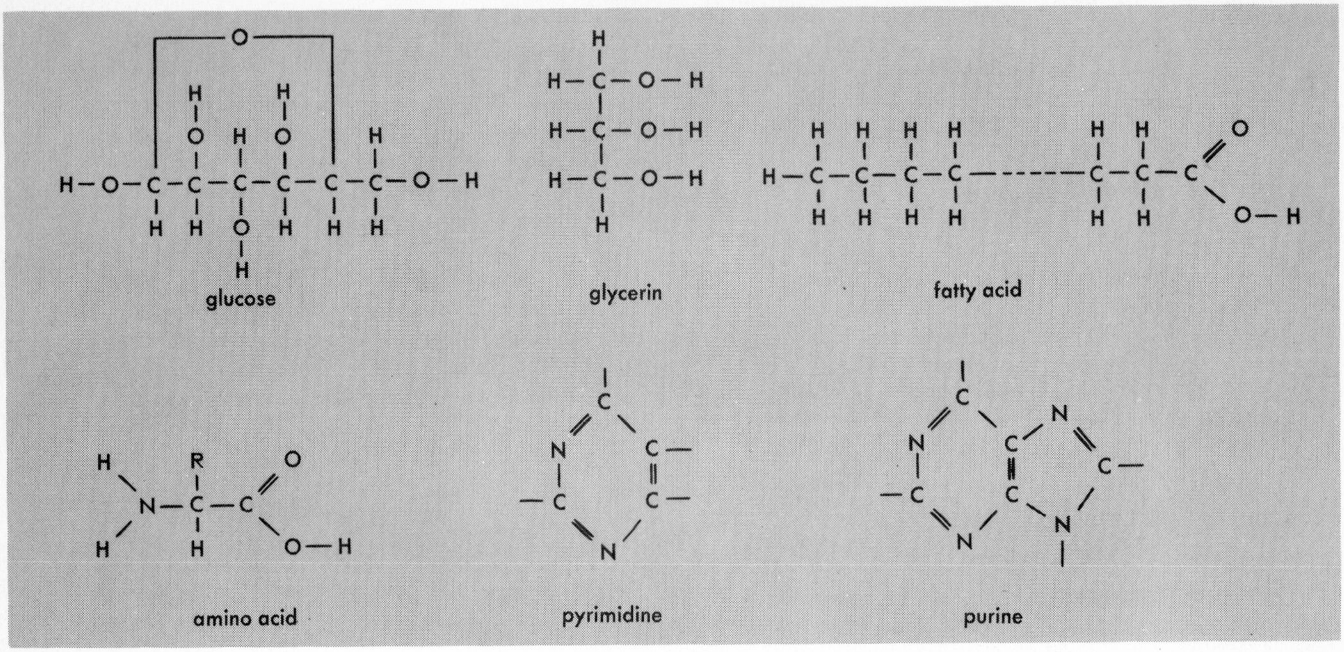

FIG. 3.3 The chemical structure of various types of compounds which are found in living systems today and which probably played conspicuous roles during the original formation of living systems. Glucose is one of many sugars. Purines and pyrimidines collectively may be referred to as nitrogen bases.

actions of methane, water, and ammonia could have given rise to amino acids and conceivably also to nitrogen bases. Moreover, if cyanide existed in the early oceans, as is probable, the —CN combination would have been a far better and more likely raw material for the formation of the carbon-nitrogen rings present in nitrogen bases. Figure 3.4 summarizes the chemical events which could have given rise to the organic compounds here discussed.

However, regardless of how possible such events are on paper, we may well ask how likely it is that they really took place. What source, for example, would have supplied activation energy and reaction energy?

Two different sources of energy were undoubtedly available. One of these was the sun. Although the dense cloud layers of water vapor at first must have prevented sunlight from reaching the earth's surface (which must have made the earth quite dark for long ages), the ultraviolet rays, X rays, and other high-energy radiations of the sun must have penetrated the clouds well. Some of this radiation could have provided the necessary energy for reactions among methane,

ammonia, hydrogen cyanide, and water. Solar radiation certainly is known to support various chemical reactions today.

Moreover, a second energy source must have been the powerful electric discharges in lightning, which must have occurred almost continuously in the early cloud-laden, storm-lashed atmosphere. Like solar radiation, lightning is capable of activating and sustaining chemical reactions. Either lightning or solar energy could have acted directly on the gas molecules of the atmosphere, as still happens today to some extent. The resulting aerial chemicals could then have been washed down into the seas by rain. Alternatively, reactions could have taken place directly in the waters of the ocean, where methane and all other necessary ingredients were dissolved.

But even assuming that adequate energy sources and appropriate simple compounds might have been available, could organic materials really have formed? They could indeed, as was demonstrated in the early 1950s through dramatic and now classic laboratory experiments. In these experiments, the presumable

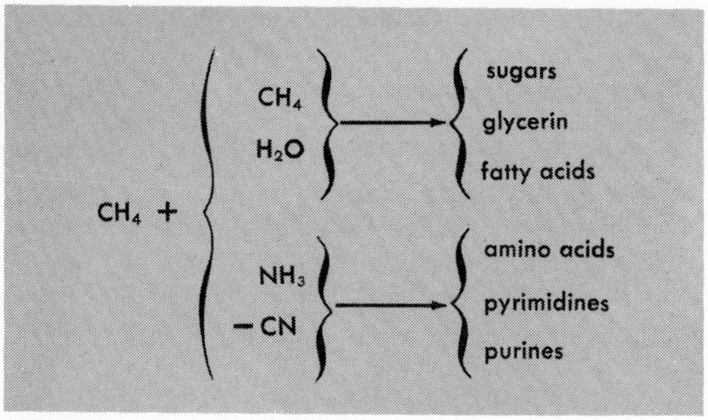

FIG. 3.4 Summary of early reactions. Interaction of methane with itself, water, ammonia, and, perhaps, cyanide probably resulted in the compounds shown on the right.

environment of the early earth was duplicated in miniature. Into a flask were put inorganic mixtures containing water, methane gas, and ammonia gas, and electricity was discharged through these mixtures for several days to simulate the lightning discharges of the early earth. When the contents of the flask were then examined, many amino acids, fatty acids, and other simple organic compounds were actually found to be present.

Thus there is excellent reason to think that, under the impact of early energy sources, simple gases and other inorganic materials not only could but probably did react with one another and gave rise to a variety of organic compounds which accumulated in the ancient seas. These organic substances were not very complex as yet, but they contained the all-important carbon-to-carbon combinations. This was the key which was to open the door to life, for it made possible the later synthesis of even larger molecules, with larger carbon skeletons and many novel chemical properties.

LATER ORGANIC COMPOUNDS

What were these new organic molecules, formed from the simpler types already present at this point? Based again on hindsight, we know that five major and several minor groups of new molecules must have arisen which later came to have particular significance in the origin of life. The five major groups were:

1. adenosine phosphates
2. polysaccharides
3. fats
4. proteins
5. nucleic acids

Adenosine Phosphates

These substances are derivatives of a highly important class of compounds known as *nucleosides.* A nucleoside consists of two parts, namely, a sugar and a nitrogen base. The sugar can be a pentose, and the nitrogen base can be either a pyrimidine or a purine. If the pentose is *ribose* and if this C_5 sugar is joined to a pyrimidine known as *adenine,* then the resulting nucleoside is called **adenosine.** We may postulate, therefore, that various sugars present in the early seas combined with various nitrogen bases and that the nucleosides so formed included molecules of adenosine (Fig. 3.5).

Adenosine (like other nucleosides, as we shall see) could further combine with *phosphates,* which were and are now inorganic mineral constituents of the ocean. More specifically, one, two, or three phosphate groups could become attached serially to the pentose portion of adenosine. Depending on the actual number of phosphates attached, three types of **adenosine phosphates** would be formed: *adenosine monophosphate,* **AMP** for short; *adenosine diphosphate,* **ADP** for short; and *adenosine triphosphate,* **ATP** for short (see Fig. 3.5).

ribose (*pentose sugar*) + adenine (*pyrimidine*) → adenosine (*nucleoside*)

adenosine + 1 phosphate → adenosine monophosphate (AMP)

adenosine + 2 phosphates → adenosine diphosphate (ADP)

adenosine + 3 phosphates → adenosine triphosphate (ATP)

FIG. 3.5 The formation and general composition of adenosine and of adenosine phosphates.

These compounds, the last two most particularly, today play an extremely important role as sources of activation and reaction energy in living matter. ADP differs from ATP only in having one phosphate group less. Thus, if a third phosphate group is added to ADP, ATP will be formed. Such an addition requires a great deal of energy. The necessary energy may be provided by various exergonic, i.e., energy-yielding, reactions. Particularly good sources are decomposition reactions of organic materials. For example, if sugars or fatty acids become decomposed chemically under appropriate conditions and in the presence of ADP and phosphate, then the energy yielded by the decomposition reaction may suffice to combine ADP and phosphate into ATP.

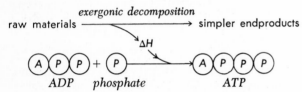

The ATP so produced represents a rich store of energy, since the energy (ΔH) made available by the exergonic reaction is now "trapped" as bond energy in ATP. At some later time, therefore, ATP may serve as an energy donor. If the bond between the second and the last phosphate group is broken, a large amount of bond energy becomes available for the support of other chemical reactions—energy-requiring synthesis reactions, for example:

In other words, the energy-transferring activities of ATP under appropriate conditions make possible the synthesis of more complex compounds at the expense of energy obtained originally from decompositions.

This pinpoints the significance of the adenosine phosphates in living matter today: they trap energy produced by exergonic reactions and then provide energy wherever it may be required. Very possibly, adenosine phosphates may have been of like significance in the early seas, before living matter existed. For example, if simple organic compounds already present underwent chemical decomposition, energy which could have been trapped in the adenosine phosphates would have become available. These could later become the energy donors for many new synthesis reactions. Physical energy sources such as the sun probably continued to play their reaction-supporting role. But the adenosine phosphates provided an alternative, namely, a readily usable *chemical* energy source which could make reactions independent of solar or electrical energy.

It was this alternative which was to prove essential for the origin of life; we know now that many reactions, particularly those involving synthesis of complex organic compounds, cannot occur with energy from physical sources. Such reactions require chemical energy specifically—largely energy supplied by adenosine phosphates. And these reactions are precisely the ones which produce and maintain life (see Chap. 16 for full discussion).

Polysaccharides and Fats

Polysaccharides are combinations of a few or many sugar molecules, all usually of the same kind. For example, if many glucose molecules become joined together end to end, the result is a large molecule containing a very long carbon chain. Such supermolecules are polysaccharides; they still belong to the general category of organic compounds called carbohydrates. The number of sugar units present in different polysaccharides varies considerably. In the polysaccharide *glycogen*, for example, only one or two dozen glucose units are joined, but as many as 2,000 are present in the polysaccharide *cellulose*.

The general chemical process in which molecular units of similar or identical type are synthesized into a single larger molecule is known as **polymerization**. Cellulose is said to be a *polymer* of glucose, specifically, a *high* polymer; glycogen is a *low* polymer of glucose. It is clear that polymerization can yield very large molecules indeed, and we shall find presently that this process of forming supermolecules by repeated linking of small units also occurs in several other biologically important instances.

Polymerization of sugars in the early seas may well have been mediated by energy from ATP. The endproducts later proved to be of considerable significance; polysaccharides became building materials in the construction of living matter. Also, like the sugars themselves, polysaccharides constituted excellent raw materials which could yield energy through chemical decomposition. They still function today as building materials and sources of chemical energy.

Fats are combinations of glycerin and fatty acids. One fat molecule is formed by the union of one glycerin molecule with three fatty acid molecules. The nature of a fat therefore varies with the nature of its fatty acids. Fats too proved to be very good sources of chemical energy, and as building materials they came to be at least as useful as polysaccharides.

If adenosine phosphates, polysaccharides, and fats had been the only complex organic compounds formed in the early seas, living matter would never have originated. That it did originate is a consequence primarily of the two remaining groups of compounds mentioned above, the proteins and the nucleic acids. Both types are not merely large; they can be huge. Molecular weights frequently are in the millions, and molecules of proteins and nucleic acids actually include the largest chemicals known. The general term *macromolecules* is often applied to them. Both groups attain their molecular size through polymerization.

Proteins

These compounds are polymers of amino acids. In many cases, a tremendous number of amino acid units—in the order of 100,000 or more—can be present in a protein molecule. The amino acids in a protein are not all of the same type. As noted earlier, amino acids differ according to the different structures of their carbon skeletons. Some two dozen different types of amino acids actually exist, and any or all of these types may be present in a protein. Moreover, a protein may contain any number of amino acids of *each* type and the different numbers of units of all two dozen types may be joined into a chain in practically any *sequence*. As a result, a virtually unlimited number of structural varieties of proteins exists.

Because of their structural variety, proteins today exhibit two properties essential to the maintenance of living matter. We may infer therefore that early proteins must have exhibited the same properties and that these must have been essential to the origin of living matter. First, differently structured proteins represented an array of highly diverse building materials which could be used in many different construction jobs. Living matter is a chemical "construction," and actual formation of living matter could have become possible only after protein "bricks" of widely different sorts were available. As noted earlier, polysaccharides and fats, as well as water and other inorganic materials, similarly came to serve as important bricks. But proteins provided building materials of far greater diversity, and

they alone made possible the construction of something so elaborate that it could have the properties of life. Even today, the structural diversity of different living things and the diversity of the various parts within a given living thing are due primarily to the differences in the many protein building materials present.

Second, in addition to this structural role, proteins came to play a crucial functional role; some proteins could serve as enzymes and could enormously speed up reactions among other molecules (see Chap. 2). We note that, with the appearance of the first proteins, the chemical tempo on the early earth could quicken substantially. Reactions which previously might have taken centuries now could occur within seconds or minutes. Living matter as it now exists can be sustained only through fast reactions, and enzymes make the necessary speed possible. Moreover, by their presence in living matter, different enzymes actually determine what kinds of reactions can occur at all; for without an enzyme a given reaction would occur so slowly that in effect it would be nonexistent. Clearly then, since "living" is strictly a function of enzyme-accelerated reactions, we may conclude that proteins had to be present when life originated. Early proteins speeded up certain reactions, and we now know these reactions as those which characterize living matter.

Nucleic Acids

If any single entity could qualify as "the secret of life," that entity would unquestionably have to be the nucleic acids. To be sure, inasmuch as we can actually make such an identification today, it is really no longer possible to speak of any "secret." In any event, before nucleic acids had appeared on the early earth and regardless of what other substances might have been present, life could not possibly have originated. But after nucleic acids had appeared, the origin of life became a virtual certainty.

Nucleic acids (Fig. 3.6) are complex derivatives of nucleosides, already encountered. As we have seen,

FIG. 3.6 The formation and general composition of nucleic acids.

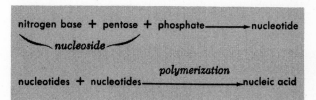

a nucleoside consists of a nitrogen base and a pentose. If a single phosphate group is added to the pentose portion of a nucleoside, then a **nucleotide** is formed. Several different varieties of nucleotides exist, depending on which particular nitrogen base and pentose is present. A nucleic acid is a high polymer of nucleotides. More specifically, a molecule of nucleic acid is formed when up to hundreds or thousands of nucleotide units are polymerized into a chain. Some nucleic acids therefore can be fully as large as, or even larger than, the most complex proteins. Nucleic acids too exist in virtually unlimited numbers of structural varieties; a nucleic acid molecule may contain any number of each of the different types of nucleotides and these units may be chained together in any sequence.

Information codes. Nucleic acids exhibit three remarkable properties. First, they are known to function as chemical *information carriers.* The specific sequence of different nucleotides in a nucleic acid chain spells out information, just as the sequence of letters in a word spells out information. In a nucleic acid, the information is in chemical code. That is, a given segment of the chain, containing a particular sequence of nucleotides, stands for one element of a message; the adjoining segment, consisting of another particular sequence of nucleotides, stands for a second part of the message; etc. Therefore, depending on the specific nucleotide sequence a nucleic acid happens to have, the acid will carry a specific bit of information "written" in chemical code. Differently structured nucleic acids accordingly carry different bits of information.

How do we know that a nucleotide sequence really does represent information? And if it does, what does it "say"?

In the most general terms, any set of objects can justifiably be considered to contain information if the objects can elicit consistent effects. For example, a set of letters contains information when it consistently generates mental images of certain objects or ideas in a human viewer; a given set of dial positions on a motor contains information when it consistently makes the motor run at a particular speed. In the case of letters, the information is "written" in visual code; in the case of dials, the code may be mechanical or electrical, for example. Similarly, a set of atoms or groups of atoms may be regarded to contain chemically coded information which may make other atoms behave in particular ways. In this sense, a nucleotide sequence may likewise be said to contain information.

Research in recent years has shown what kind of information the nucleic acids actually carry. The compounds contain sets of instructions on *how to build proteins.* More specifically, a given sequence of nucleotides determines what *kinds* of amino acids will make up a protein and in what *sequence* these amino acids will be joined. Imagine that a certain segment of a long nucleotide sequence is chemically so constituted that a particular kind of amino acid may become attached there. Similarly, the adjoining segment may permit another kind of amino acid—and only that kind—to become attached. In this manner, certain sequences of amino acids may become attached to given sequences of nucleotides; and when the amino acids then become linked together (with energy supplied by ATP), the protein so formed will have been built according to the chemical instructions present in the nucleic acid. Put another way, a nucleic acid serves as a "blueprint" which specifies the amino acid sequence in a protein. Differently structured nucleic acids consequently control the formation of differently structured proteins (Fig. 3.7; see also Chap. 18 for a more detailed discussion).

In all living creatures today, proteins are formed according to building instructions carried by nucleic acids. The significance of this is crucial, for, as noted, proteins function as building materials as well as enzymes which control virtually all reactions in living matter. Therefore, the very nature of living matter both

FIG. 3.7 Information codes and protein synthesis. If 1-2-3-4-5 represents a portion of a nucleic acid chain, the chemical characteristics of the nucleotide segment 1-2 could be such that only amino acid *a* could attach there. Similarly, only amino acid *b* might be able to attach to the nucleotide segment 2-3, amino acid *c* to the segment 3-4, etc. If then the amino acids become linked to one another and form a protein, the sequence of the amino acids will have been determined by the coded information contained within the nucleic acid chain.

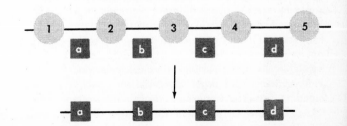

in its structural and its functional aspects is ultimately determined by the nucleic acids. In short, nucleic acids control life.

We may conclude that the origin of nucleic acids on the early earth must similarly have led to controlled formation of proteins, hence to enzymatically controlled reactions among many other compounds then present. Such control in itself did not yet constitute life, but it proved to play a critical role in the eventual creation of life.

Reproduction. The nucleic acids also played a second major role. These compounds were, as under proper conditions they still are today, *replicating* molecules; i.e., they could make exact replicas of themselves and so they could *reproduce.* At first glance it may seem utterly fantastic that a mere molecule should be able by its own efforts to make a copy of itself. But, as modern research shows, the process is no more unbelievable than that mere molecules should carry coded instructions on how to make other molecules. Indeed, nucleic acid reproduction is simply another instance of building other molecules according to coded information. In this case the "other molecules" are nucleic acids themselves.

Imagine again a long sequence of nucleotide units. Such a sequence automatically has built into it information about its own chemical structure, just as a sentence of words has built into it information about its own grammatical structure. If the sentence is to be reproduced, duplicate sets of words will have to be lined up in a sequence which matches that of the original sentence. In such a duplicating process, information transfer takes place. A man or a machine must first become informed about the structure of the existing sentence. Then, on the basis of this information, he or it must select appropriate duplicate words from a large pool of possible words and must put the selected words into the correct sequence. The new sentence now contains the information also present in the old.

Similarly, if a nucleotide sequence is to be reproduced, a duplicate set of individual nucleotides must be joined in a sequence which matches the original sequence exactly. The remarkable and quite unique property of nucleotide sequences is that they may carry out their own duplication, without intervention of any other controlling agency; under appropriate conditions they may select and arrange duplicate nucleotides on their own. Nucleic acids are said to be *self-duplicating.* In a given nucleotide sequence, for example, nucleotide 1 may attach to itself another nucleotide 1, if such a duplicate unit happens to be present in the vicinity as a raw material; nucleotide 2 similarly permits attachment of another nucleotide 2. In this manner, and provided that all needed duplicate nucleotides are available as raw materials, an existing molecule of nucleic acid may control the lineup of a matching set of nucleotides. If the matching set then links together into a chain, an exact replica of the original nucleic acid will have formed (Fig. 3.8).

In rough outline, this is how nucleic acid reproduction is believed to occur now (see Chap. 18 for further detail) and to have occurred in the early seas. The mechanism also gives us a clue how the first nucleic acids might have arisen. With energy obtained from the chemically related adenosine phosphates, various types of individual nucleotides must have formed in abundance. Later, sets of a few nucleotide

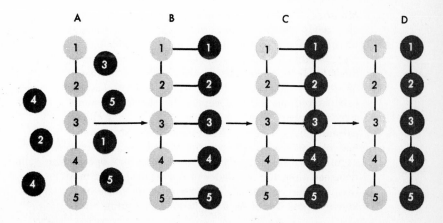

FIG. 3.8 Diagrammatic symbolization of nucleic acid reproduction. *A,* a preexisting nucleic acid molecule (light shading) surrounded by raw materials needed for the construction of a nucleic acid duplicate (dark shading). *B,* a raw material of a given type has affinity for a corresponding component of a nucleic acid, and the raw materials therefore attach in matching sequence to the preexisting nucleic acid. *C,* the correctly positioned raw materials link up with one another. *D,* the new nucleic acid molecule so created separates from the original "model." Model and replica are identical in composition.

units each might have joined at random into relatively short sequences. Such small nucleic acid molecules could then have reproduced, duplicate nucleotides being amply available as raw materials. In time, small nucleic acid molecules could have joined one another and such progressive polymerization could eventually have given rise to very large nucleic acids. Reproduction would have occurred at all stages of these progressive molecular enlargements. Consequently, even the most complex nucleic acids would have reproduced their kind. Adenosine phosphates could have been the energy source in both polymerization and reproduction.

We note that reproduction of nucleic acids represents a shortcut of the original process of nucleic acid creation. As just pointed out, the first nucleic acids probably came into existence through random polymerization of random nucleotides. But with the appearance of the first nucleic acids, blueprints became available which could accelerate the subsequent formation of more nucleic acids. Each slowly and randomly created first nucleic acid could serve as a model for the rapid and no longer random creation of an exact duplicate. The duplicate could then serve as a model in its turn. In this way, descendants of the first nucleic acids have followed one another in an unbroken succession of molecular generations right down to the present.

Moreover, as one nucleic acid generation gave rise to the next, it passed on its information on how to construct particular proteins. With this *inherited* information, each generation of nucleic acids could re-create the protein types of its ancestors and so could exercise the same control over the same enzyme-dependent reactions. This repeated and controlled recurrence of a given set of chemical processes, generation after generation, later was to become a major characteristic of life.

Mutation.   Indirectly through their reproduction, nucleic acids also displayed a third property which later became a characteristic of life. As a class, nucleic acids are exceedingly stable molecules. That is, unlike most other kinds of compounds, nucleic acids are not easily affected by the many physical and chemical hazards encountered on earth. Occasionally, however, minor structural changes may be produced by various chemical and physical agents. For example, the structure of one of the nucleotides present may become altered slightly; or a short sequence of nucleotides may become detached from the remainder of the sequence and may then become reattached, but in a different place or in inverted position; or an error may occur during repro-

duction and a "wrong" nucleotide unit might become incorporated accidentally into an otherwise "correct" sequence. When any alteration of this sort takes place, the altered nucleic acid molecule is itself very stable and, during its later reproduction, the changed condition is transmitted faithfully into the replica. Such stable changes, inheritable from one nucleic acid generation to the next, are called **mutations** (Fig. 3.9). Because "mutation" means altered nucleic acid structure, it also means altered information content; once a nucleic acid has mutated, it will henceforth control the production of a different type of protein.

We may infer, therefore, that nucleic acid reproduction on the early earth produced not merely a succession of identical molecules, but that some of the descendant molecules became different from the ancestral types through occasional mutations. A single ancestral type so could in the course of time give rise to altogether new and diverse types such as had never existed before. The new *mutants* could then control the formation of new and diverse types of proteins. As a result, new sets of enzyme-requiring reactions came under the ultimate control of nucleic acids.

Evidently, the origin of nucleic acids introduced a radically novel dimension into the chemistry of the

FIG. 3.9 Nucleic acid stability and mutation. The properties of a parental nucleic acid molecule are passed on unchanged to descendant molecules; if a mutation alters the properties of one of the descendants, then the altered condition is stable and is itself passed on unchanged.

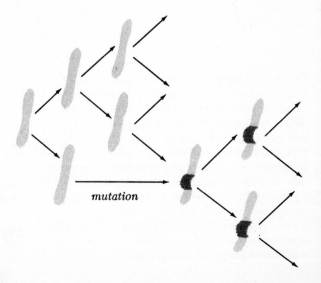

mutation

earth. First, the macromolecules possessed a structure large and stable enough to serve as a repository of information which could determine protein structure. Second, nucleic acids also carried information about their own structure, and they were replicable. This led to a succession of molecular generations with the same properties, hence to a perpetuation of given enzyme-requiring reactions over long periods of time. As a result, some of the chemistry of the earth ceased to occur randomly and became oriented into fixed, controlled, and persisting channels. Third, nucleic acids were complex enough to stay intact as stable wholes despite the introduction of occasional structural errors. This made the molecules mutable and led to the occasional appearance of new nucleic acids displaying new properties; i.e., a mechanism became available which could deflect the channeled chemistry of the earth into new channels.

Indeed, with the formation of nucleic acids, all the basic ingredients for the eventual origin of a living entity were assembled. Events up to this point may be described collectively as *chemical evolution:* the production and gradual accumulation in the early seas of all the various compounds which later came to function as components of living matter. As we have seen, the most essential of these compounds included at least

seven categories of substances, namely, inorganic materials such as water and dissolved mineral substances, and organic materials such as adenosine phosphates, carbohydrates, fats, proteins, and nucleic acids (Fig. 3.10).

The events which followed subsequently may be described as *biological evolution:* the actual putting together of the chemical components into the first living units.

BIOLOGICAL EVOLUTION

The first truly living units, and still the basic units of all living matter today, unquestionably were **cells.** These are microscopic watery drops composed of a multitude of organic and inorganic compounds, including nucleic acids and proteins in all cases. Each such drop is surrounded by a fine membrane and displays all the characteristics and properties by which we define "being alive."

If we say that the biological evolution of cells followed chemical evolution, this does not mean that chemical evolution simply stopped at one point and biological evolution then took over. On the contrary, chemical evolution continued and indeed goes on even

FIG. 3.10 Summary of later chemical evolution. Interactions shown to the left of the arrows probably resulted in the compounds shown on the right. The chief properties of these compounds are indicated to the right of the reactions.

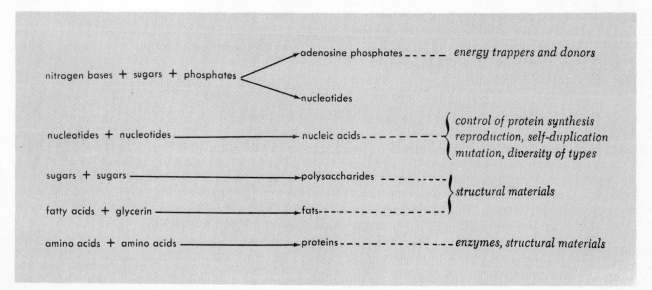

now. What is meant instead is that at some stage of chemical evolution an *additional* kind of creation took hold. Molecules no longer gave rise just to new molecules only, but some of the molecules also produced something entirely new, something hitherto completely nonexistent, namely, fully living cells. These in turn then produced more cells through processes of multiplication which are still going on today. Thus the new dimension of biological evolution became *superimposed* on the still continuing older dimension of chemical evolution.

How did the first cells arise?

THE FIRST CELLS

The nature of the events which resulted in cell formation can be deduced in general outline only; the details are not yet clear. Conceivably, the same end result may have been achieved in several different ways.

Cell Formation

The creation of the first cells may be envisaged to have occurred in the following way. By one means or another, sets of all the key compounds already present in the early ocean must have collected together in tiny spaces, and each set of materials so accumulated must have remained aggregated in a cohesive drop. By virtue of the various properties of the aggregated materials, the drop would have been alive.

If this describes the overall process, we may ask first whether or not such aggregates could actually have formed by known physical and chemical means. Certain possibilities which might appear reasonable theoretically must probably be regarded as unlikely in practice. For example, it is probably unlikely that aggregation of the necessary compounds could have occurred directly in the open ocean. The concentration of compounds must have been quite low and the open water must therefore have been too dilute a solution to provide a reasonable chance for repeated aggregation of just the right sets of materials. Moreover, even if such aggregation could have occurred, it is difficult to imagine how the aggregated materials could have been kept together in open water for any length of time. After making chance contacts, the compounds most likely would have dispersed again.

It is physically and chemically more plausible to assume that the critical aggregations took place along the shores of the ocean. The solid ground available there would have provided appropriate surfaces to which oceanic molecules could have adhered. Many organic compounds are known to be readily *adsorbed* to various surfaces, a property which we often recognize as stickiness. For example, sugars, fats, and proteins stick very readily to many kinds of surfaces, and nucleic acids are extraordinarily adsorbable. Also, finely divided sand and clay particles are excellent adsorbing materials and such particles must have been abundant along the ocean shore. Accordingly, it is reasonable to think that some of the organic compounds which had formed in the ocean were washed to the shore, where some of them became adsorbed more or less at random to various surfaces. This process might have occurred progressively. The adsorbing surfaces could have trapped those molecules which did happen to make contact, and other molecules of the same or of different types might or might not have become added later. The concentrations of the molecules so would have increased slowly, a process which would have been reinforced by considerable evaporation of water in the tide zone.

Moreover, it is not necessary to assume that nucleic acids, proteins, complex polysaccharides, and large molecules generally first had to be formed in the open ocean and then had to become aggregated along the shore. On the contrary, it is physically and chemically more plausible to think that the first aggregations involved only the relatively simple organic compounds. Large molecules later could have become synthesized directly within, and indeed as a consequence of, the simple accumulations. For if microscopic organic pockets could become established along the shore, and if these accumulated high enough concentrations of adenosine phosphates, nucleotides, amino acids, sugars, and fatty acids, then such systems probably would have been adequate for the production of larger molecules within them. The synthesis of large molecules such as nucleic acids and proteins today is known to require direct availability and very close proximity of all the needed raw materials and energy sources. Indeed, recent experiments show that if concentrated mixtures of amino acids are heated under nearly dry conditions, proteinlike complexes are formed. Similarly, mixtures of other appropriate starting compounds heated under almost dry conditions can yield products having some of the characteristics of nucleic acids.

It is unlikely, therefore, that something as complex as a nucleic acid could have formed by the chance accumulation of enough ATP and nucleotides in the open ocean. It is more likely that nucleic acids arose *after* ATP and nucleotides had already become collected together in a small enough space and in high enough concentrations to provide an adequate and perhaps fairly dry chemical environment for synthesis. And after nucleic acids had become synthesized, they themselves could then have directed the synthesis of the first proteins, again right within the aggregations already present. Some of the proteins would subsequently have acted as enzymes and so would have facilitated the rapid formation of a wealth of new compounds, e.g., polysaccharides out of sugar raw materials.

Moreover, some of the proteins and also some of the fats and carbohydrates would have represented building materials. These could have become organized into a structural framework which ramified through and around the aggregated drop. Many proteins are known to precipitate out of solution and to form solid granules or threadlike fibrils, for example. Also, as will be shown in Chap. 4, mixtures containing proteins or protein-fat complexes may, as a consequence of their physical state, form membranous surface films (e.g., like the "skins" on custards). Polysaccharides like cellulose similarly may form fibrils or films. Thus the aggregated drops on the ocean shore could well have developed external boundary membranes and some measure of internal scaffolding. They would henceforth have been distinctly individual units marked off from the surrounding ocean water, and they would have remained individualized even if they absorbed more water and were later washed back into the open ocean. Indeed such units would have been primitive cells (Fig. 3.11).

Undoubtedly, numerous trials and errors must have occurred before the first actual cells left their places of birth. Many and perhaps most of the aggregations on the shore probably were "unsuccessful." In given cases, for example, the right kinds of starting ingredients might never have come together; or the right amounts of ingredients might never have accumulated; or the mixture might have dried up completely; or it might have been washed out to sea prematurely and dispersed. Clearly, numerous hazards must have led to many false starts and to many incomplete endings. Yet when an appropriate constellation of materials did form a persisting aggregate, the formation of a cell would have been a likely result. And this probably happened not just once but many times in the course of centuries or millennia and in widely different places of the world.

In one sense, therefore, chance must have played a role in cell formation: many aggregations never became cells, and those that did formed by the chance accumulation of the right ingredients. But in another sense, cell formation was not simply an enormously "lucky accident," a one-time occurrence of very remote probability. On the contrary, given an early earth so constituted that certain compounds could form and given these compounds and their special properties, then cell formation *had* to take place sooner or later, repeatedly and inevitably. The only element of chance here was time; the uncertainty was not in the nature of "if," but in the nature of "when" and "how often." Accordingly, the origin of cells was as little an accident as is the eventual appearance of sevens and elevens in a succession of dice throws. Best estimates at present

FIG. 3.11 The possible origin of the first cells. Appropriate chemical ingredients might have accumulated by adsorption in microscopic pockets along the seashore (1) and these ingredients could have become concentrated progressively (2). Under relatively dry conditions and perhaps with the aid of ATP, which might have been present, nucleic acids and proteins could have become synthesized (3). The proteins would then have permitted the occurrence of enzymatically accelerated reactions and the formation of structural membranes and internal fibrils (4). Finally, primitive cellular compartments might have been washed out to sea (5).

suggest that the first cells probably arose some 3 billion years after the origin of the earth, i.e., some 2 billion years ago.

It is not necessary to assume that cells were formed exclusively by the processes just described or even that the above outline corresponds in detail to the actual events of the distant past. The important consideration at this stage of knowledge is mainly that we *can* envisage processes of cell formation which are plausible within the limits of the physics and chemistry of the earth. This in itself represents a major advance over knowledge available just two or three decades ago. In another two or three decades we are quite likely to have far surer knowledge, plus, perhaps, the ability to duplicate in the laboratory some of the key steps of cell formation.

The units we have called cells above were *alive*. What justifies use of this term?

Cell Properties

All aggregates which became *living* cells must necessarily have shared the same broad chemical composition. They all must have contained at least water, various mineral substances, adenosine phosphates, carbohydrates, fats, proteins, and nucleic acids. Only aggregates possessing these substances would have displayed the collection of properties we call "life." It is not a coincidence that all living things today still must, and do, possess these same seven categories of components.

As we have seen, many of the specific activities of the chemical components of cells required the use of raw materials—inorganic and simple organic materials present in the early ocean. In biological terminology, these oceanic raw materials constituted *nutrients*. The absorption of such nutrients by the early cells represented a simple form of **nutrition.** It is customary to reserve the term *food* especially for organic nutrients.

As more and more food molecules were withdrawn and used by more and more cells, the rate of global food utilization must eventually have become greater than the rate of food formation from methane, ammonia, and the other atmospheric constituents. In time, therefore, free molecular foods must have disappeared completely from the ocean, and that environment then became as exclusively inorganic as it still is today. Evidently, almost as soon as it originated, living matter began to affect and to change the physical character of the earth. This influence gradually intensified, and it continues even now. Moreover, the depletion of the free

foods by the cells in the early ocean later had profound effects on the cells themselves, a consideration we shall return to below.

For the moment, we recognize that the earliest cells did have access to ample oceanic supplies of nutrients of all kinds. Such nutrients served in two major capacities. As pointed out earlier, one portion of the nutrients became the source of the chemical energy which could be transferred from the bonds in sugars, fats, and other foods into the bonds of adenosine phosphates. The latter, and particularly ATP, then functioned as readily available internal energy sources for all cellular activities. Biologically, the process of gathering, transferring, and finally packaging energy as ATP inside cells is called **respiration.** Beginning with the very first cells and continuing right to the present, respiration was the absolutely essential power generator, the "motor," which maintained life.

One of the byproducts of respiration was, and still is, carbon dioxide (CO_2). In time, more and more respiring cells produced more and more of this gas, which passed from the cells into the ocean. Some of it dissolved there and the remainder escaped into the atmosphere. As a result, a gas probably present previously in some quantity now became an abundant constituent of the atmosphere. This was another instance of environmental change brought about by biological processes. Atmospheric carbon dioxide is known to be a screen against high-energy solar radiation. The progressive accumulation of the gas in the early atmosphere must therefore have meant that certain forms of solar energy were gradually becoming unavailable on the earth's surface. As we shall see, atmospheric carbon dioxide was to affect the further development of living matter in other ways as well.

The second major role of the nutrients obtained from the ocean was to serve as starting ingredients in **synthesis** reactions. With appropriate nutrients and adequate supplies of ATP, early cells could synthesize duplicate nucleic acids, could manufacture more proteins, and indeed could make more of every cellular component. Such additional materials in cells could then serve, for example, as replacements for components which might have become damaged or destroyed, e.g., by chemical decomposition in respiration. Structural integrity of a cell so could be maintained by internal *self-repair*. Moreover, as additional synthesized materials accumulated within a cell, they led to increase of cell size. In this way, *growth* became a consequence of synthesis reactions.

Indeed, with a profusion of different molecules available within cells, entirely new synthesis reactions became possible; the products of one process of synthesis could become the starting materials in another. New endproducts with new properties could appear in this manner and could affect cellular structure, behavior, or both. As a result, cells could undergo internal molecular *development* (Fig. 3.12).

All such reactions, we already know, were under the ultimate control of the nucleic acids. These governed the structural nature of the proteins produced, hence also the functional nature of the enzymes which were required in all the reactions. The cellular nucleic acids which then served and still serve today as ultimate reaction controllers are called **genes.** Because of genes, reactions in cells were prevented from proceeding in random directions. Cells so maintained stable characteristics. This meant that nutrition, respiration, synthesis, and all the other activities of cells could *continue as before.* Genes were, as they are now, the fundamental preservers of **steady states,** the guardians of optimal operating conditions within cells, the maintainers of life in the dimension of time. It is because of this "policing" function of genes that cells today still exist at all and that they all still exhibit the same basic characteristics as the first cells.

As an early cell produced gene-controlled nucleic acid duplicates and other synthesized materials, a stage of growth must eventually have been reached at which the enlarging cellular mass became unstable physically. It would then have split into fragments, just as too large a drop of quicksilver splits into smaller droplets. But whereas small quicksilver droplets simply remain as they are, the derivatives of split cells were still cells. The latter possessed all the characteristics of the parent, including, in particular, the capacity to grow. Evidently, the growth-promoting activities of genes led first to internal molecular and then to total cellular **reproduction.** This process not only multiplied the number of cells but also maintained an indefinitely continued succession of cellular generations. All cells today are products of this succession.

As cell numbers increased progressively through reproduction, the drain on the free molecular foods in the ocean must have become correspondingly severe. This must have meant that *competition* became a new condition for cellular existence. By withdrawing food molecules from the sea, cells in effect began to compete for available supplies. Under such circumstances, it would have been highly advantageous if the cells

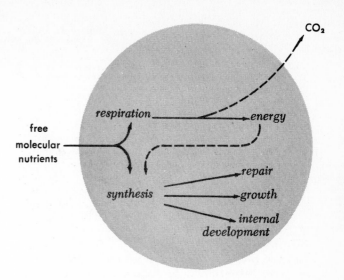

FIG. 3.12 The two basic uses of food materials in early cells.

could have changed their properties to some extent, i.e., if they could have adjusted, or **adapted,** to the new environmental conditions. For example, it might have become possible for properly adapted cells to utilize existing foods more efficiently or at a faster rate than cells which had not changed their properties. Or some cells might have adapted by developing altogether new ways of producing or obtaining foods.

Since cellular properties were gene-determined, any change of properties would have been contingent on changes of genes. Actually there were at least two major ways by which the gene content of early cells could have become altered. One way would have been a consequence of occasional fusions among cells. If two cells happened to drift into contact, probably a fairly frequent occurrence, the cells might have fused together. Such fusions could have been partial and temporary or total and permanent. In the first case, some of the genes present in the two cells could have become mutually interchanged. In the second case, all the genes of both cells would have become pooled together. In either event, the result would have been a change in the gene content of the cells, hence a stable alteration of cellular properties. Some of these new properties then might have been such that the cells could cope successfully with altered environmental conditions. A process of adaptation accomplished as above by interchanging or pooling genes among cells still occurs today; we call it *sex* (Fig. 3.13).

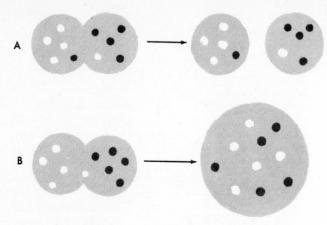

FIG. 3.13 Sexuality in early cells. Temporary partial fusion of two cells (A) might have led to partial exchange of genes. Alternatively, permanent total fusion of two cells (B) would have resulted in a total pooling of genes. In either case, the resulting cells would have contained new gene combinations, which would have controlled new combinations of cellular properties.

The second major way in which the gene content of cells could have become altered was mutation, already discussed. Equally or even more effectively than sex, mutations could endow cells with often radically new properties. These could permit some cells and their offspring to obtain food despite increasing competition. We shall presently examine the principal new food-procuring methods developed by early cells.

Gene changes brought about by sex and mutations were, as they still are today, quite random. Only chance determined which cells would fuse and which genes would then be exchanged or pooled. Similarly, only chance determined what gene would mutate and in which way. Consequently, any new property acquired by an early cell could have been more or less advantageous, or more or less disadvantageous, or actually without adaptive significance. The environment determined what was or was not advantageous. If an altered cellular property permitted a cell to compete more successfully in its particular environment, then that property was adaptively advantageous. If competitive capacity was lessened, then the gene change and the new property it controlled were disadvantageous.

Sex and mutation thus provided early cells with a mechanism of adaptation. Through it, some strains of cells could develop significant advantages over other strains in the competition for food. Well-adapted, well-fed strains would then have been able to multiply faster and to produce larger numbers of offspring, whereas poorly adapted strains might not even have found enough foods to multiply at all. In subsequent generations, therefore, well-adapted strains would have made up the vast bulk of the existing cell population and poorly adapted strains would frequently have become extinct. Such shifts in the nature of populations, leading in the course of many successive generations to the appearance of types with many new characteristics, constitute **evolution.**

We find, in summary, that by virtue of their particular chemical components and internal makeup, early cells could carry out six fundamental activities. They could *nourish* themselves, they could *respire*, and they could *synthesize*, the latter activity also permitting growth and internal development. Further, they could maintain controlled internal *steady states*, they could *reproduce*, and through processes of sex and mutation they could evolve and so *adapt* to long-term changes in the environment. These various activities collectively define life. With the appearance of the first cells, therefore, the earth possessed individualized *living* units: single-celled **organisms.**

EARLY ORGANISMS

Cells and Viruses

In the earliest cells, gene-forming nucleic acid molecules probably were suspended free within the cell substance or, judging from primitive cells today, were aggregated into tiny nucleic acid clumps. It must have happened on occasion that such clumps, along with other cell components, broke free from a cell into the open ocean. This could have occurred, for example, after an accidental temporary rupture in the boundary membrane of a cell or after a cell died and disintegrated. In this free state, a nucleic acid clump would have been simply a lifeless and inert chemical aggregate, for it lacked its normal cellular "housing." But it must have happened often that such inert aggregates by accident met up with other early cells and entered them. Within these host cells, the inert aggregates could become active again; i.e., the living machinery of the host could again provide the means for nucleic acid control activities and reproduction.

Such nucleic acid clumps, escaped from one cell, existing free for a time in an inert state, and then reentering and being reactivated by another cell, may have been the ancestors of the modern **viruses.** Viruses today behave exactly that way. First, they consist mainly of nucleic acids, the only other structural component being an external mantle of protein (Fig. 3.14). Note therefore that viruses are *not* cells and *not* organisms; they are considerably less than cells or organisms. Second, we know that at least some viruses arise as fragments broken off from the nucleic acid components of a given cell. Such fragments then direct the cell to manufacture protein mantles around them. The so-formed viruses subsequently escape from the host, often disintegrating the host cell in the process. Then they exist free in air or water. We know also that all modern viruses are quite inert in the free state and that they become reactivated if, and only if, they enter some new cell. In such *infections,* a virus becomes attached to the surface of the new host and then the nucleic acid mass of the virus is squeezed out from the protein mantle, through the cell surface, into the cell interior. The empty mantle itself does not enter the host. Within the host cell, the viral nucleic acids now may use the living apparatus of the cell for renewed virus formation; the nucleic acids reproduce and new protein mantles are manufactured around them.

Viruses can therefore be classified as infective *parasites.* Modern viruses are known to be highly complex in structure and behavior, and it is likely that their distant ancestors were far less complex. Indeed, such ancestors may have been naked nucleic acids. If so,

formation of viruslike nucleic acid units and transfer from cell to cell could have occurred as soon as cells themselves were in existence.

Such transfers must have had important consequences. For example, some cells would have lost certain properties and other cells would have gained them; the transferred nucleic acids were genes, and as they became shuffled among cells, so did the activities which these genes controlled. Therefore, in addition to sex and mutation, transfer of viruslike nucleic acids would have constituted a third way in which the gene content of cells could have become altered. This process similarly must have promoted cellular evolution and must have contributed to the emergence of a great variety of different cell types. It is known that certain kinds of modern viruses still transfer genes from one cell to another. The phenomenon is called *transduction,* and we shall deal with it in Chap. 18.

Early Cell Types

Among the early single-celled organisms, two main structural types came to have particular significance in later evolution. As already noted briefly, the first cells probably possessed freely suspended gene-forming nucleic acids. These compounds usually became associated closely with proteins, forming complexes we now call **nucleoproteins.** In some of the descendants of the early cells, the nucleoproteins apparently aggregated together into loose clumps. In each cell, such a clump

FIG. 3.14 The shape and structure of modern viruses. Virus types of many other shapes are known. The diagram shows the typical composition of viruses, with nucleic acid in the center and a protein shell on the outside. The photograph is an electron micrograph. *(Photograph courtesy of Dr. R. M. Herriott and Dr. J. L. Barlow, The Johns Hopkins University, and J. Gen. Physiol., vol. 36, p. 17.)*

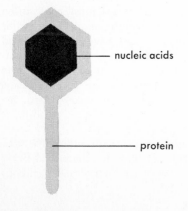

nucleic acids

protein

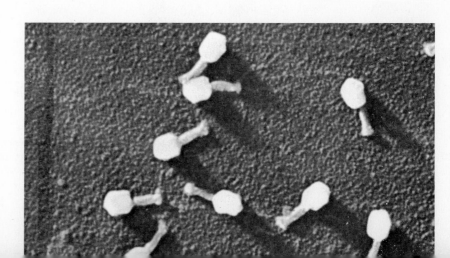

then remained embedded within the cell substance and in direct contact with it.

The group of organisms characterized by this type of internal cellular arrangement may be referred to collectively as the **Monera.** Representatives of this group are still in existence today; the most familiar of the Monera are the *bacteria* (Fig. 3.15). The exact ancestry of modern bacteria is somewhat in doubt. However, in structure as well as function, bacteria now living are very close to our conception of what the first Monera might have been like. Conceivably, therefore, the latter may have been the ancestors of modern bacteria.

Another group now living and probably descended from the first Monera are the *blue-green algae.* It will be shown in Chap. 8 that these primitive cellular organisms are not always blue-green and indeed are probably not really true algae. Instead they resemble bacteria in many ways, including the way in which the gene-containing nucleoprotein is arranged within their cells. We may say, therefore, that the first cells on earth probably gave rise to an early group of Monera and that these in turn were the ancestors of the modern Monera, represented today chiefly by the bacteria and the blue-green algae.

In a second major cellular type descended from

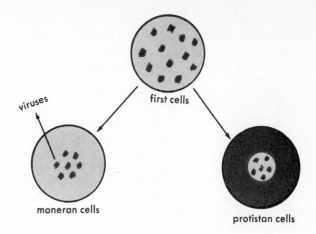

FIG. 3.16   The earliest cells (containing nucleoprotein, as indicated) probably gave rise to two structural types, one without nuclear membrane and referred to as moneran cells, one with nuclear membrane and referred to as protistan cells. Viruses may have formed from nucleoproteins which escaped from the cells.

the first cells, the gene-containing nucleoproteins in each cell also condensed together into a loose mass. In addition, however, a fine membrane formed around this mass. As a result, the nucleoprotein was no longer in direct contact with the rest of the cell substance. Such a membrane-enclosed nucleoprotein aggregate within a cell is now known as a cell *nucleus.* Early cells which evolved a distinct gene-containing nucleus may be referred to collectively as the **Protista.** These came to be the ancestors of the vast majority of modern organisms, i.e., of all except the Monera (Fig. 3.16).

Within both the early moneran and protistan groups, abundant diversification must have occurred and many new types of organisms must have arisen through evolution. We may surmise, moreover, that this evolutionary branching out must have been promoted and oriented by a powerful environmental stimulus already referred to, namely, the gradual disappearance of free molecular foods from the ocean. Indeed, unless new ways of procuring foods could have evolved, the ever-increasing multitude of reproducing, food-using cells would soon have nourished itself into extinction. Early cells evidently did not succumb, but on the contrary gave rise to the far-flung, richly diversified living world of today. What were the nutritional inventions which made this possible?

FIG. 3.15   The dispersed nucleic acid of bacteria. The name of the bacteria shown here is *Escherichia coli.* Some of the cells occur as single individuals; others are joined into chains. Staining makes the nucleoproteins appear as dark bodies. Note the dispersion of these bodies throughout the cytoplasm of a bacterial cell. *(Courtesy of the Society of American Bacteriologists, from A. G. Smith, J. Bacteriol., vol. 59, 1950.)*

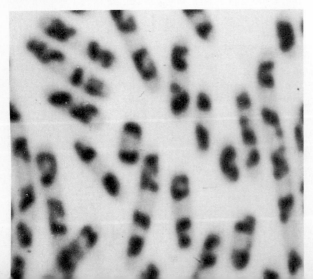

NUTRITIONAL EVOLUTION

Heterotrophism

One of the first evolutionary responses to dwindling food supplies probably was the development of **parasitism.** If foods could not be obtained from the open ocean, they still could be obtained within the bodies of living cells. As already noted, a virus, for example, could penetrate right into a cell and use the foods accumulated in such a host. Similarly, a small cell could solve its food-supply problem if it could manage to invade a larger cell. Methods of infecting cellular hosts undoubtedly evolved early, and today all viruses as well as many of the descendants of the first Monera and Protista are infective and parasitic.

For many of the early organisms, parasitism undoubtedly was an effective new way of life. Another new way which required relatively little evolutionary adjustment was **saprotrophism.** Here an organism drew food molecules not from the decreasing supply in the ocean but from the bodies of dead cells or disintegrated cellular material. Many early bacterial groups probably adopted this comparatively easy method of getting food and became the ancestors of the many modern saprotrophic bacteria. Note that organic *decay* is a result of the nutrient-gathering activities of saprotrophic organisms. Before the evolution of saprotrophism, decay was unknown on earth. Today, saprotrophic types—especially bacterial saprotrophs—are so abundant that virtually any substance begins to decay almost immediately after exposure to air or water.

A third new process which permitted survival despite dwindling food supplies was **holotrophism,** i.e., the process of *eating* other living cells whole. This became possible through evolution of cellular mouths or equivalent engulfing structures, of devices to extract usable food molecules from the swallowed organisms, and of means of hunting for food organisms. Note, incidentally, that the difference between cellular eating and cellular parasitism is largely defined by the final result. In both cases, one cell gets inside another, but in one instance the larger host lives off the guest and in the other instance the guest lives off the host (Fig. 3.17).

But all three of these new food-gathering procedures were ultimately self-limiting. Parasitism, saprotrophism, and holotrophism, collectively known as *heterotrophic* forms of nutrition, merely changed the distribution of already existing organic matter; they did not add any new food to the global supply. Clearly, if totally new food sources had not become available, life would have had to cease sooner or later.

Autotrophism

What was needed, fundamentally, was a new way of making organic substances, preferably right within cells. The original way, in which sun and lightning formed food compounds out of materials such as methane, ammonia, and water, was no longer adequate, if it occurred at all at that late period. But the raw materials for a new process were still available in

FIG. 3.17 The three noncreative, heterotrophic methods of obtaining food. In parasitism, one organism obtains food from another living one (a small parasitic cell is shown inside a larger host cell). In saprotrophism, food is obtained from dead organisms or from organic derivatives of other organisms. And in holotrophism, one organism eats another, in whole or in part, and obtains food in this manner. These three methods are noncreative because they merely redistribute already existing foods and do not create new supplies.

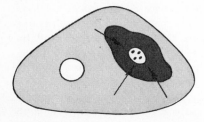

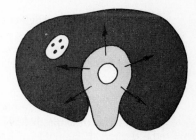

parasitism   saprotrophism   holotrophism

abundance. Water was in inexhaustible supply and, in addition to methane or hydrogen cyanide, there now existed, directly within cells, an even better source of carbon: carbon dioxide, byproduct of respiration. Given CO_2 and water, organic molecules could be manufactured in cells, provided that new external sources of energy could be found. Internal energy in the form of ATP was still available, to be sure; but ATP was itself an organic compound and was therefore among the very substances which would have disappeared if new external energy had not made possible their continued manufacture. Organisms which evolved means of utilizing external energy in the production of organic compounds are collectively known as *autotrophs*. Two broad categories of them came into existence.

Chemosynthesizers. Some of the early Monera, particularly certain bacterial types, found new external sources of energy in sulfur, in iron, in nitrogen, and in a number of other metallic and nonmetallic materials obtainable from the environment. Several groups of the early bacteria must have evolved in such a way that they could absorb various inorganic molecules into their cell substances and there make them undergo various chemical reactions. In these reactions, chemical bonds were broken and bond energy became available. Such energy was then used within the cells to combine CO_2 and water into food molecules, specifically, carbohydrates. The whole process is called **chemosynthesis** (Fig. 3.18). Certain bacteria living today still manufacture foods in this manner (see Chap. 12).

Judging from the results some 2 billion years later, early chemosynthesis apparently was only a limited solution of the energy- and food-supply problem. Possibly it depended too much on particular inorganic materials available only in particular localities. A more generally useful solution required a steady, more nearly universal external energy source. Such a source was the sun.

Photosynthesizers. High-energy solar radiations such as ultraviolet and X rays no longer were a sufficient energy source for the amount of food production required. Similarly, the earlier permanent cloud cover had disappeared by now and lightning too became inadequate as an energy source. But solar radiation of lower energy content, especially *light*, now beamed down to earth as predictably and dependably as could be desired. If sunlight could be used, the energy problem, hence the food problem, would be solved. Sun-

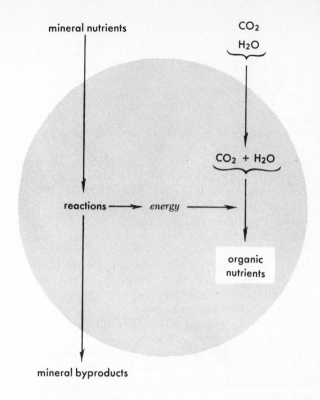

FIG. 3.18 The general pattern of chemosynthesis. With energy obtained from inorganic nutrients, the organism creates new organic nutrients out of carbon dioxide and water.

light actually did become the ultimate energy supplier for the vast majority of organisms, and it has played that role ever since.

Utilization of light energy within cells requires a cellular light-trapping device. Many kinds of photosensitive compounds are known to be able to absorb light and to trap more or less of its energy. By chance reactions, such compounds may have formed very early in the open ocean, along with all the others we have discussed. And it is likely that some of these substances were among the many materials which collected together and formed cells. Alternatively, light-trapping compounds might have been manufactured directly within cells already in existence, as one of the new materials produced by cellular synthesis. In some such way, some of the early cellular organisms came to possess substances which were more or less efficient in trapping the energy of sunlight. This energy could be then used to transform CO_2 and water into organic food compounds.

One of the early light-trapping substances has been perpetuated to the very present. It is green, and we call it *chlorophyll*. The new process, in which sunlight and chlorophyll promote the transformation of CO_2 and water into foods, is called **photosynthesis** (Fig. 3.19).

With this new source of organic compounds assured, it did not matter that free molecular foods in the ocean finally disappeared. Photosynthesizing cells could make foods for themselves; holotrophic organisms could eat such cells and then each other; parasites could invade photosynthesizers or eaters; and saprotrophs in turn could find foods in the dead bodies of any of these. Consequently, excepting only the chemosynthesizers, which made their own foods, all other organisms were saved from premature extinction by photosynthesis. Today, photosynthesis still supports all living creatures except the chemosynthesizers.

We note that, sooner or later after the appearance of the first cells, five kinds of food-getting methods were evolved: parasitism, saprotrophism, holotrophism, chemosynthesis, and photosynthesis. Only the last two added to the net global supply of foods. The Monera apparently adopted all methods except eating, and the Protista, all methods except chemosynthesis. Moreover, there is good evidence (see Chap. 9) that individual protists could obtain food by two or three of the pro-

FIG. 3.19 The general pattern of photosynthesis. With energy obtained from the sun and by means of energy-trapping molecules such as chlorophyll, the organism creates organic nutrients out of carbon dioxide and water.

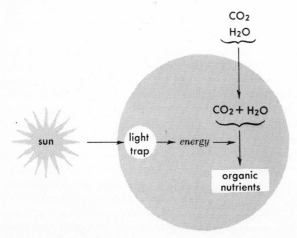

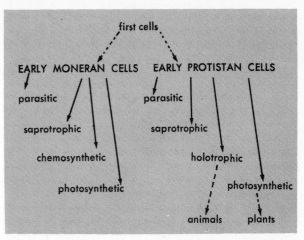

FIG. 3.20 Summary of nutritional evolution. This shows how the earliest living things became diversified according to the methods of food getting they evolved.

tistan methods. For example, it was quite common for a single-celled protist to be able to eat *as well as* to photosynthesize. Numerous descendants of such types still exist among the modern Protista. Furthermore, the evidence also indicates that some of the early protists with multiple means of nutrition eventually lost all except one of these means. Thus, one group perfected the photosynthetic method and lost the holotrophic capacity in the course of evolution. Distinct *plants* later arose from this stock. Conversely, another ancient group specialized in the holotrophic method and lost photosynthetic capacity (hence also its green color). This stock eventually gave rise to distinct *animals* (Fig. 3.20).

THE OXYGEN REVOLUTION

As photosynthesis occurred to an ever-increasing extent, it brought about far-reaching changes in the physical environment. As we shall see later, a byproduct of photosynthesis is free molecular oxygen (O_2), a highly reactive gas which combines readily with other substances. Before the advent of photosynthesis, free oxygen had not existed since the early days of the earth, when oxygen atoms were still uncombined. Later, such small quantities of free oxygen as might occasionally have formed would have combined quickly with materials in the vicinity. Now, increasingly large amounts of free oxygen escaped from photosynthesizing cells into the ocean and from there into the atmosphere. The gas must have reacted promptly with everything it could, and this probably initiated a slow, profound "oxygen revolution" on earth (Fig. 3.21).

Oxygen probably reacted with methane and transformed it into carbon dioxide:

$$CH_4 + 2 O_2 \longrightarrow CO_2 + 2 H_2O$$

Oxygen also must have reacted with ammonia and with any cyanide present, and molecular nitrogen (N_2) must have formed:

$$4 NH_3 + 3 O_2 \longrightarrow 2 N_2 + 6 H_2O$$
$$4 HCN + 5 O_2 \longrightarrow 2 N_2 + 2 H_2O + 4 CO_2$$

These events ultimately transformed the ancient atmosphere into the modern one, which no longer contains methane, ammonia, and cyanide. Instead, it consists mainly of water vapor, carbon dioxide, and molecular nitrogen, plus large quantities of free molecular oxygen itself.

At higher altitudes, under the impact of high-energy radiation from space, oxygen molecules combined with one another. The result was a layer of *ozone* (O_3). This layer, several miles up, has been in existence ever since. Ozone formed an even better screen than carbon dioxide against deep penetration of high-energy radiation. Consequently, organisms which evolved after the establishment of the ozone layer lived in an environment more or less completely free of high-energy radiation. This is why modern advanced plants and animals are comparatively unadapted to such radiation and are killed by even small doses of it. By contrast, the earliest organisms had evolved before the large-scale formation of ozone and had become more or less well adapted to space radiation. Some of their

FIG. 3.21 The "oxygen revolution." Oxygen resulting from photosynthesis reacted with other materials as shown and brought about the changes indicated.

$$CH_4 + 2 O_2 \longrightarrow CO_2 + 2 H_2O$$
$$4 NH_3 + 3 O_2 \longrightarrow 2 N_2 + 6 H_2O$$
$$O_2 + 2 O_2 \longrightarrow 2 O_3, \text{ ozone}$$
$$\text{metals, minerals} + O_2 \longrightarrow \text{ores, rocks}$$
$$\text{organisms} + O_2 \longrightarrow \text{aerobic respiration}$$

modern relatives among the Monera and Protista still display this radiation resistance. They now can withstand exposures to X rays and similar radiation that would kill an army of men.

Free oxygen also reacted with the solid crust of the earth and converted most pure metals and mineral substances into *oxides*—the familiar ores and rocks of which much of the land surface is now made. A few relatively unreactive metals like gold resisted the action of oxygen, but others could not. And if today we wish to obtain pure iron or aluminum, for example, we must smelt or otherwise process appropriate ores to separate out the firmly bound oxygen.

Free oxygen, finally, made possible a new, much more efficient form of respiration. The earliest cells decomposed food molecules without oxygen, a method of energy liberation and ATP formation called *fermentation,* or *anaerobic* (without air) respiration. However, if oxygen is available, it may participate in respiration. The amount of energy then obtained per unit amount of food consumed is much greater than in fermentation. When free environmental oxygen began to accumulate in quantity, newly evolving organisms developed means to utilize this gas. An *aerobic* (with air) form of respiration then came into existence, and it soon became the standard way of extracting energy from foods.

We note that the effects and activities of the early organisms greatly altered the physical character of the earth and also the biological character of the organisms themselves. So it has been ever since, even if never again so dramatically and incisively: the physical earth creates and influences the development of the biological earth, and the biological earth then reciprocates by influencing the development of the physical earth.

We have traced the major stages of the earth's early history as they are understood today (Fig. 3.22). In this history, no one point really qualifies as a "beginning" of life. The cell is the major product of the first 3 billion years, and we regard this product as being alive. But the earlier organic compounds dissolved in the ocean already possessed the properties which eventually made life possible. Such compounds in turn did not originate their characteristic properties, but acquired them when they were formed from various simpler compounds. The potential of life clearly traces back to the original individual atoms, and the creation of life out of atoms was but a step-by-step exploitation of their properties. Each of the steps spanned literally eons of chemical and later also of biological evolution,

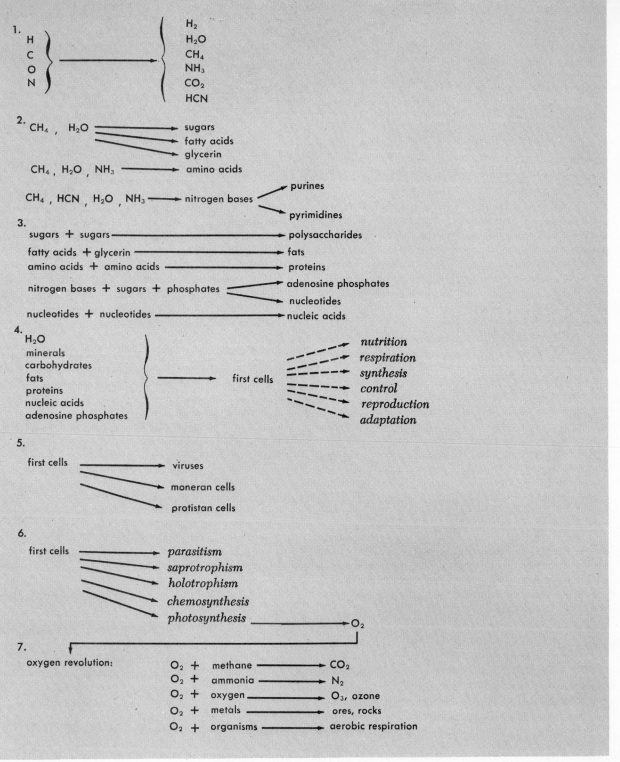

FIG. 3.22 Overall summary of the events of "genesis" described in this chapter.

and any one step overlapped and intergraded with the next unimaginably slowly.

Thus, unlike Athena, who sprang fully formed and armed from Zeus's head, life did not burst forth from the ocean finished and ready. Instead, life *developed,* and here is perhaps the most dramatic illustration that small beginnings may have surprisingly large endings. Development has been the hallmark of life ever since; life today is still unceasingly forming and molding. Indeed, it will never be finally "finished" until its last spark is extinguished.

REVIEW QUESTIONS

1. Which gases in the early atmosphere of the earth may have contributed to the formation of simple organic compounds? What were some of these compounds and what evidence do we have that they could actually have formed?

2. Review the role of (*a*) temperature, (*b*) water, (*c*) organic compounds, and (*d*) enzymes in the origin of life.

3. Review the chemical composition and general structure of adenosine phosphates, carbohydrates, fats, proteins, and nucleic acids. What are sugars, amino acids, fatty acids, purines, and nucleosides?

4. What are the principal properties of nucleic acids and what roles have these properties probably played in the origin of life? What are genes?

5. How may the first cells have evolved? What are viruses and how could they have evolved?

6. What distinguishes moneran and protistan cell types and how could both have arisen from the first cells?

7. With what properties were the first cells probably endowed and what is the nature of these properties?

8. What are nutrients? What factors may have contributed to their disappearance from the early ocean and in what different ways did early organisms then obtain foods? Review the general nature of each of these ways.

9. What was the physical character of the earth at the time it formed, before life originated, and after life originated? Review the principal events of the oxygen revolution.

10. Review the whole step-by-step sequence of events by which cellular life is now believed to have originated.

SUGGESTED COLLATERAL READINGS

The following are excellent key accounts of the probable origin of the earth and of life. The article by Miller describes the experiments referred to above in which inorganic gases were transformed into organic substances found in living matter.

Gamow, G.: The Origin and Evolution of the Universe, *Am. Scientist,* vol. 39, 1951.

Miller, S. L.: A Production of Amino Acids under Possible Primitive Earth Conditions, *Science,* vol. 117, 1953.

Oparin, A.: "The Origin of Life," 3d ed., Dover, New York, 1945.

Schrödinger, E.: "What Is Life?" Macmillan, New York, 1945.

Urey, H.: The Origin of the Earth, *Sci. American,* vol. 187, 1952.

Wald, G.: The Origin of Life, *Sci. American,* vol. 191, 1954.

CELLS

4

The immediate result of the original life-producing processes was the *cell*. The first cells were the first *unicellular organisms,* and an enormous array of other unicellular organisms later descended from them. Early single cells also evolved into multicellular complexes, and from these first *multicellular organisms* many others later descended in turn. The living world now in existence is a varied collection of unicellular and multicellular organisms.

Today, therefore, as in the past, the basic unit of all living things still is the cell. Different cells differ vastly in virtually all their features; it is an important conclusion of biological studies that no one kind of cell is ever exactly like any other. Moreover, no one cell is ever exactly the same from moment to moment, for the substance of a living cell is not a static, passive material. New materials enter a cell continuously; wastes and manufactured products leave continuously; and substances in the cell interior are continuously transformed chemically and redistributed physically. As a result, living matter is in persistent internal turmoil. To the human observer a tree may appear to be a rather placid, inactive structure; but if the cellular components of the tree could be seen, they would all be noted to be in constant, violent motion, colliding with one another and interacting and changing. Consequently, the tree as a whole changes continuously, and so indeed does every kind of living material.

However, despite such differences between cells and changes within cells, all cells nevertheless share certain very basic features. Representing the universal heritage passed on by the very first cells on earth, the common features are partly *chemical,* partly *physical,* and partly *biological.* We shall examine each of these three aspects of cellular organization in this chapter.

CHEMICAL ORGANIZATION

Regardless of where, when, or how we examine the structure of any cell, we ultimately find it to consist entirely of chemical compounds. And regardless of what particular function of a cell we examine, that function is ultimately always based on the properties of the cellular compounds.

Four of the most widely distributed chemical elements on earth make up approximately 95 per cent of the weight of cellular living matter: oxygen, 62 per cent; carbon, 20 per cent; hydrogen, 10 per cent; and nitrogen, 3 per cent. About 30 other elements contribute the remaining 5 per cent of the weight. The elements listed in Table 2 occur in virtually all types of cells. Trace amounts of others are found only in particular types, and still other elements may become incorporated into living matter accidentally, along with nutrient materials. All these elements, we recall, are present in the ocean; having originated in water, cellular living matter reflects the composition and content of water.

TABLE 2
The relative abundance of chemical elements in living matter

element	symbol	weight, per cent
oxygen	O	62
carbon	C	20
hydrogen	H	10
nitrogen	N	3
calcium	Ca	2.50
phosphorus	P	1.14
chlorine	Cl	0.16
sulfur	S	0.14
potassium	K	0.11
sodium	Na	0.10
magnesium	Mg	0.07
iodine	I	0.014
iron	Fe	0.010
		99.244
trace elements		0.756
		100.00

Virtually all the elements occur in the form of *compounds.* As already noted, cells consist of two great classes of compounds: mineral, or *inorganic*, compounds and more or less complex carbon-containing *organic* compounds.

THE INORGANIC COMPONENTS

Directly or indirectly, all inorganic compounds in cells are of mineral origin; i.e., they are supplied in finished form by the external physical environment. **Water,** the most abundant cellular mineral, is present in amounts ranging from 5 to 90 or more per cent. For example, the cellular water content of certain plant seeds is 5 to 10 per cent; of bone and of timber, 40 to 50 per cent; of muscle, 75 per cent; of brain, milk, and mushrooms, 80 to 90 per cent; and of algae and jellyfish, 90 to 95 or more per cent. As a general average, cellular matter is about 65 to 75 per cent water, overall.

Mineral solids constitute the other inorganic components of cells. Such solids are present in amounts ranging from about 1 to 5 per cent, on an average. A considerable fraction of the minerals may exist in the form of hard bulk deposits, either as crystals within cells or as secreted precipitates on the outside of cells. Such deposits are often silicon- or calcium-containing substances. For example, diatoms and the surface cells of certain grasses (as well as many other kinds of organisms) are reinforced externally with glasslike silica; the hard part of bone is largely a deposit of calcium phosphate, secreted in layers around individual bone-forming cells; clam shells consist of calcium carbonate, secreted to the exterior by sheets of cells.

All other cellular minerals are in solution, either free or combined with organic compounds. These inorganic constituents exist largely in the form of *ions*. The most abundant positively charged inorganic ions are H^+, hydrogen ions; Ca^{++}, calcium ions; Na^+, sodium ions; K^+, potassium ions; and Mg^{++}, magnesium ions. Abundant negatively charged mineral constituents include OH^-, hydroxyl ions; $CO_3^=$, carbonate ions; HCO_3^-, bicarbonate ions; $PO_4^\equiv$, phosphate ions; Cl^-, chloride ions; and $SO_4^=$, sulfate ions. Note that the mineral constituents of cells are also major constituents of the ocean and of rocks and ores. This is not a coincidence, for rocks are dissolved by water, water finds its way into the ocean and into soil, and living matter draws its mineral supplies from these sources.

THE ORGANIC COMPONENTS

In Chap. 3 we have identified organic compounds as those in which the molecules contain linked carbon atoms. We may now define organic substances more precisely as all compounds of carbon in which the principal bonds are carbon-to-carbon and carbon-to-hydrogen links. Thus, carbon dioxide (CO_2), carbonic acid (H_2CO_3), and compounds derived from them are not organic, since the carbon is bonded primarily to oxygen. But methane (CH_4), with its carbon-hydrogen

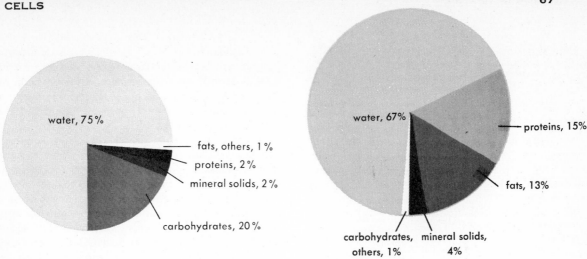

FIG. 4.1   The average overall composition of plant cells (left) and animal cells (right).

bonds, is considered to be an organic compound. Virtually all organic compounds we shall be concerned with contain numerous carbon-to-carbon bonds.

Cells contain hundreds of different categories of organic constituents. Of these, four broad categories in particular are found in all types of cells, and they form the organic basis of living matter. We have already identified the four categories, partly under different names and in different groupings: *carbohydrates,* which include sugars and polysaccharides; *lipids,* which include fatty acids, fats, and derivatives of these; *proteins,* which include amino acid polymers; and *nitrogen base derivatives,* which include adenosine phosphates and nucleic acids.

Like mineral compounds, some of these organic substances may contribute to the formation of hard parts. For example, wood, horn, and *chitin* (the external covering of insects, many fungi, and of numerous other organisms) are predominantly organic. More generally, however, organic materials are dissolved or suspended in cellular water, some in ionized, some in nonionized form. Their relative abundance varies considerably for different types of cells and for different types of organisms. For example, in a plant such as corn, carbohydrates make up about 18 per cent of the total weight, proteins about 2 per cent, and all other organic constituents together not more than about 1 per cent. By contrast, an animal such as man contains about 15 per cent protein, about 15 per cent fat, and other organic components to the extent of about 1 per cent (Fig. 4.1). In both cases, evidently, the inorganic matter (mainly water) far outweighs the organic. It is also generally true that, per unit weight, plant cells contain less organic matter and more water than animal cells.

Carbohydrates

Organic compounds in this group are so called because they consist of carbon and of hydrogen and oxygen in a 2:1 ratio, as in water. The general atomic composition of the simplest carbohydrates may be represented as $(CH_2O)_n$, where n is any whole number. If n equals 5, the carbohydrate is a pentose sugar; a specific example is *ribose* ($C_5H_{10}O_5$), already referred to in Chap. 3. If n equals 6, hexose sugars result. Common examples are *glucose* (Fig. 4.2), *fructose,* and *galactose,* all widely encountered among cells and all having the atomic formula $C_6H_{12}O_6$. Note again that differences between such compounds lie not in the numbers and types of atoms present, but in the patterns in which the atoms are bonded together.

Carbohydrates such as pentoses and hexoses are collectively called **monosaccharides,** because each represents a single sugar unit. If two monosaccharides become joined, a "double sugar" or **disaccharide** results. For example, a polymer of two glucose units forms the disaccharide *maltose,* malt sugar; a combination of glucose and fructose forms *sucrose,* the cane or beet sugar used familiarly as a sweetening agent; and a union of glucose and galactose forms *lactose,* milk sugar. All three of these disaccharides have the atomic formula $C_{12}H_{22}O_{11}$, and their formation is described by the same equation:

$$2\ C_6H_{12}O_6 \longrightarrow H_2O + C_{12}H_{22}O_{11}$$

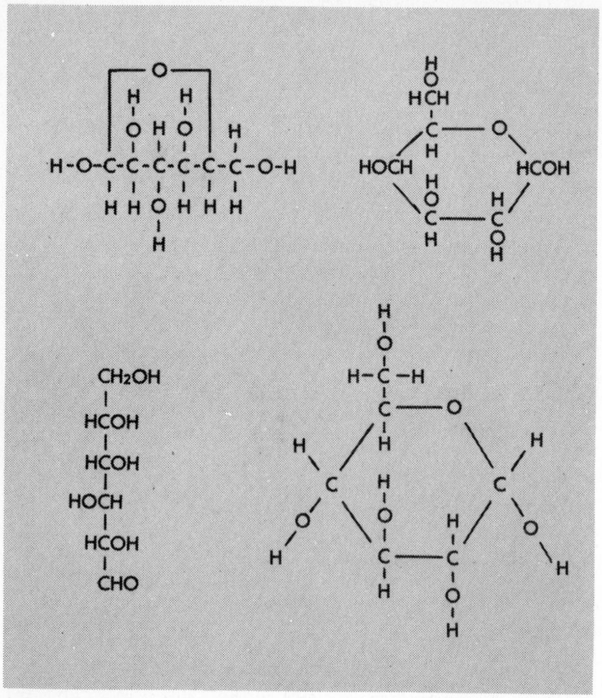

FIG. 4.2 Four ways of writing the structural formula of glucose. Note that the structure may be depicted as either a chain or a ring.

Two or more disaccharide molecules may polymerize into even larger carbohydrates, producing the "multiple sugars" or **polysaccharides** already referred to in Chap. 3. In addition to *cellulose* (about 2,000 glucose units) and *glycogen* (about 12 to 18 glucose units) mentioned earlier, other important polysaccharides include *amylose*, a chain of some 300 to 1,000 glucose units, and *amylopectin*, a branched chain of glucose units. Varied mixtures of amylose and amylopectin form the *starches* found in many plants and plantlike organisms.

The cellular functions of the specific carbohydrates here named illustrate the general functions of carbohydrates as a group. For example, ribose is a structural component of adenosine phosphates and some nucleic acids; cellulose is deposited as a supporting wall around plant cells; starch, glycogen, and the disaccharides serve largely as storage foods in cells, usable either as donors of chemical energy or as raw materials in synthesis reactions; and glucose is the principal form in which carbohydrates are transported from cell to cell, as in the sap of plants and the blood of animals.

Lipids

It will be recalled from Chap. 3 that a fat molecule is formed by a combination of one glycerin molecule and three fatty acid molecules. A fatty acid in turn is a carbon chain carrying a terminal carboxyl (—COOH) group (Fig. 4.3).

Fatty acids vary greatly in chain length. The simplest is *formic acid*, HCOOH. This compound occurs occasionally in cellular excretions such as sweat and urine and also plays a protective role in some ants, where the compound may be squirted out as an irritant spray against potential enemies. A series of increasingly complex fatty acids is formed by successive addition of —CH_2— groups to HCOOH. For example, addition of one such group produces *acetic acid*, CH_3COOH, the active ingredient of vinegar. Acetic acid serves a vital function in all cells, being an important intermediate in the respiratory decomposition of foods. Beyond acetic acid, many fatty acids may be represented by the general formula $CH_3(CH_2)_nCOOH$, where n is any number other than zero. In almost all such fatty acids of living matter, n is an even number. As we shall see, this is because the cellular fatty acids are synthesized from acetic acid building units which themselves are 2-carbon, i.e., even-numbered, chains. Very common fatty acids in this category, present as components of most plant and animal fats, are *palmitic acid*, $CH_3(CH_2)_{14}COOH$ (or $C_{16}H_{32}O_2$), and *stearic acid*, $CH_3(CH_2)_{16}COOH$ (or $C_{18}H_{36}O_2$).

Fatty acids like these are said to be **saturated**; all available bonds of the carbon chains are filled with hydrogen atoms. This contrasts with **unsaturated** fatty acids, characterized by the presence of one or more double bonds in a carbon chain. Such double bonds can become single bonds by the addition of more hydrogen:

A widely occurring example of an unsaturated fatty acid is *oleic acid*, $CH_3(CH_2)_2CH{=}CH(CH_2)COOH$ (or $C_{18}H_{34}O_2$). If the double bond of this acid is converted to a single bond by addition of 2 H, then the result is the saturated compound $CH_3(CH_2)_{16}COOH$, i.e., stearic acid, as above.

The physical nature of a fat is determined by the chain lengths and the degrees of saturation of the fatty acids present. Fats containing fatty acids that are short-chained, unsaturated, or both tend to be volatile or oily liquids. For example, oleic acid is oily, and fats containing oleic acid tend to be similarly liquid. By contrast, fats containing long-chained and saturated fatty acids tend to be hard tallow. This is the case, for example, in *tristearin,* a common animal fat containing three stearic acids per fat molecule.

In cells, fats and fatty acids function as important storage foods and thus as potential energy donors and as raw materials for synthesis. Also, these lipids are major structural components of cells. For example, they play a particularly significant role in the formation of bounding membranes, where they probably contribute to controlling the movement of materials into and out

FIG. 4.3 The formation of a fat molecule. Three fatty acid molecules combine with one glycerin molecule, resulting in three water molecules and one fat molecule.

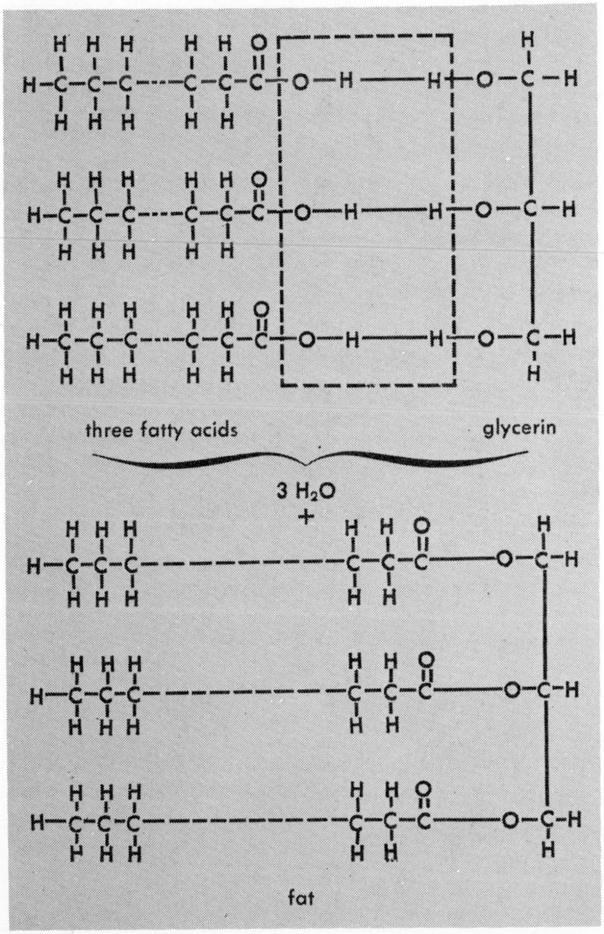

of cells. Numerous other functions are exercised by chemical derivatives of fats and fatty acids, and we shall discuss some of them later in this chapter.

Proteins
The ways in which these high polymers of amino acids can differ structurally has already been outlined in preliminary fashion:

1. A protein may contain any or all of the two dozen or so naturally occuring *types* of amino acids.

2. A protein may contain virtually any *number* of each of these types of amino acids.

3. The specific *sequence* in which given numbers and types of amino acids are joined into a chain can vary almost without restriction.

In a protein molecule, the particular union which holds any two adjacent amino acids together is known as the **peptide bond.** It consists of the atomic grouping

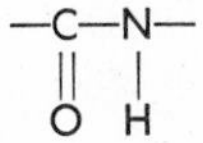

$$-\overset{\|}{\underset{O}{C}}-\overset{\|}{\underset{H}{N}}-$$

(or —CONH—), and it is formed when one water molecule is extracted from two amino acid molecules:

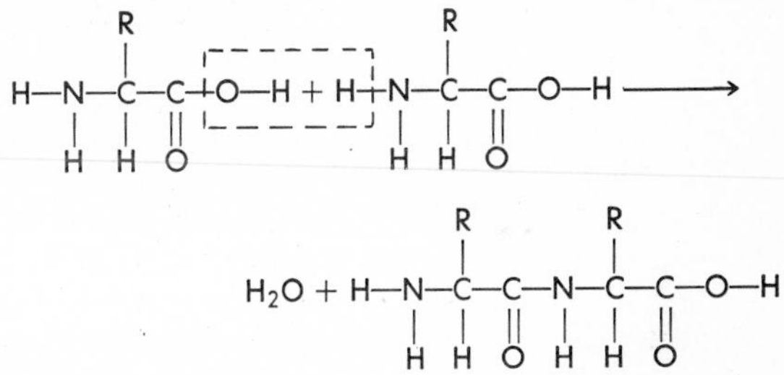

The resulting "double amino acid," or **dipeptide,** now contains a peptide bond. If a third amino acid is joined to the dipeptide in similar fashion, another water molecule will be removed and another peptide bond will be formed. In this manner, successive additions of amino acids will produce a highly polymerized **polypeptide** chain. Such chains are the basis of protein structure.

A polypeptide chain has the physical form of a longitudinally twisted ribbon. That is, if a line were drawn through all the —R— portions of the consecutive amino acids present, that line would mark out a spiral. Such a spiral, called an *alpha helix,* has quite uniform geometric characteristics for all kinds of polypeptide chains. For example, there are on the average 3.6 amino acid units per turn of the spiral. Accordingly, a polypeptide chain of some 18 amino acid units forms an α helix with five complete turns (Fig. 4.4).

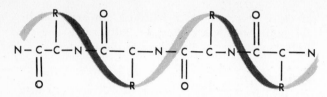

FIG. 4.4 The α helix. Shown here is a portion of a polypeptide chain, illustrating the primary structure of a protein molecule. If a line is drawn to connect all —R— fractions of the consecutive amino acid units, such a line marks a spiral called an α helix.

Extended polypeptide chains held together by peptide bonds represent the fundamental or *primary structure* of all proteins. Many kinds of proteins display only this primary composition, and their molecules consist simply of single, variously long polypeptide chains. However, superimposed on the primary structure, many other kinds of proteins also display a *secondary structure*, maintained by so-called **disulfide bonds**. Some amino acids, notably *cystine,* contain a sulfur group, —SH. If two cystine units come to lie side by side, their sulfur groups may become joined and may then form a "disulfide bridge," —S—S—. For example, if a long cystine-containing polypeptide chain is folded back on itself, two cystine units may come to lie side by side and establish a disulfide bridge between them. Such a bond will then hold the chain in the folded condition. Similarly, two (or more) separate polypeptide chains may run in parallel and may be held together by disulfide bridges. Any configuration resulting from such disulfide bonds establishes the secondary structure of a protein (Fig. 4.5).

Analogously, a *tertiary structure* is produced by so-called **hydrogen bonds**. A hydrogen bond is formed when a hydrogen atom is shared between, for example, an oxygen atom of one amino acid and a nitrogen atom of another amino acid. More specifically, the hydrogen atom in the —COOH group of one amino acid unit

may become bonded to the amino nitrogen of another amino acid unit. The H then shared by O and N links the two amino acid units together (Fig. 4.6). In a protein molecule, hydrogen bonds of this sort may produce numerous geometric configurations. For example, two or more straight polypeptide chains may become united end to end, forming very long threadlike structures, or may become united side by side, forming bundles of threadlike structures. Or a single long chain may become variously folded, looped, or coiled. Any configuration so held together by hydrogen bonds is referred to as the tertiary structure of a protein.

In gross external shape, therefore, proteins may be grouped into two general categories: **fibrous** proteins, in which the peptide, disulfide, and hydrogen bonds give rise to extended, threadlike formations; and **globular** proteins, in which the bonds produce folded and looped formations (Fig. 4.7). By and large, fibrous proteins are relatively insoluble in water; they form solid, large, often microscopically visible complexes excellently suited to serve as "bricks" in the structural framework of cells. Indeed, they form the foundation of the cellular framework, other construction materials such as carbohydrates and fats being largely secondary additions. Good examples of structural proteins are *myosin,* the characteristic protein of muscle; *keratin,* the characteristic protein of hair and skin; and *collagen,* the fiber-forming protein produced by cells in bone, cartilage, tendons, and other connective tissues. By contrast, globular proteins are largely soluble in water. Most of the functionally important proteins belong to this category. For example, enzymes are almost entirely globular. Such proteins have exceedingly varied molecu-

FIG. 4.6 The hydrogen bond. Two amino acid units are linked by a hydrogen bond: a common hydrogen atom is part of the —COOH group of one amino acid unit as well as the —NH₂ group of the second amino acid unit. Hydrogen bonds maintain the tertiary structure of a protein molecule.

FIG. 4.5 The disulfide bridge. Shown here are two disulfide bridges linking two polypeptide chains. Disulfide bridges maintain the secondary structure of a protein molecule.

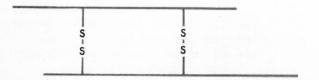

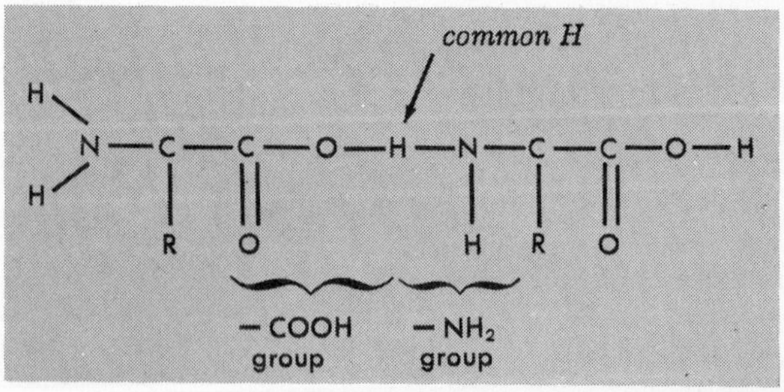

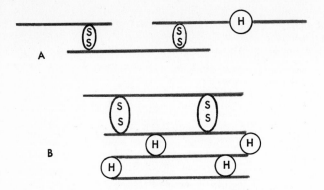

FIG. 4.7 Fibrous proteins consist of extended arrays of polypeptide chains held together by disulfide and hydrogen bonds (A). In globular proteins, on the other hand, the polypeptide chains are in folded patterns, again held together by disulfide and hydrogen bonds (B).

lar shapes and are consequently well suited to serve as enzymes.

Of the three types of bonds in proteins, the peptide bond is the strongest and the hydrogen bond is the weakest. Indeed, hydrogen bonds may be disrupted readily by changes in the physical and chemical environment of a protein. Excessive heat, pressure, electricity, heavy metals, increased acidity, and many other conditions may disrupt hydrogen bonds. When the bonds are disrupted, the particular geometric configuration of a protein will no longer hold together as before and the molecule will lose its specific tertiary structure. For example, an originally highly folded globular protein may now stretch out and become a straight, fibrous protein. Such changes in physical configuration are called **denaturation.** If the environmental effect is mild and of brief duration, denaturation may be temporary and the protein may subsequently revert to its original *native* state. But if the environmental effect is drastic and persisting, then denaturation becomes permanent and irreversible and the protein will be *coagulated* (like boiled egg white). Any biological property a protein may have in the native state is usually lost after denaturation. For example, specific enzyme function depends on specific protein configuration; and if the latter is lost, the former is likely to be lost as well. This is also a major reason why undue heat or virtually any undue environmental change kills cells.

Inasmuch as proteins can vary not only in primary structure, i.e., in amino acid numbers, types, and sequences, but also in secondary and tertiary configura-

tions, it is clear that the number of theoretically possible protein types is astronomical. Indeed, no two types of living organisms contain exactly the same types of proteins. This is not the case for carbohydrates or fats. Even a highly complex carbohydrate, for example, is the same whether we obtain it from mushrooms or mangoes, from mice or from men. A given lipid, similarly, is the same lipid regardless of where we find it. Not so for proteins, however. Even twin organisms have slightly different proteins. The structural differences between proteins are the greater the more unrelated two organisms are evolutionally. We say that proteins have a high degree of *specificity:* the proteins of a given living unit have a unit-"specific" character; i.e., they are unique for that unit.

Protein specificity has major well-known consequences. For example, transfer of protein from one organism into the cells of another amounts to the introduction of foreign bodies and disease may result. Thus, the proteins of plant pollen may produce allergy in man. Blood of one person mixed with blood of another, if not of compatible type, may produce protein shock and death. Bacteria, partly because their proteins differ from those of other organisms, may produce many diseases if they infect given hosts. And portions of one organism, when grafted onto another organism, normally do not heal into place because the two sets of proteins differ. Moreover, because proteins are specific, enzymes are specific. Different enzymes represent structurally different proteins, and that is why any given enzyme can catalyze only one particular type of reaction.

In 1954, the exact internal structure of a protein was unraveled for the first time. The protein involved in this historic achievement was insulin, the hormone of the pancreas. An insulin molecule was shown to consist of two parallel polypeptide chains held together by two disulfide bridges. One chain was found to contain 30 amino acid units, the other 21 units; and the identity and sequence of these units was established precisely (Fig. 4.8). Containing only 51 amino acid units per molecule, insulin is certainly among the smallest proteins. Most other proteins are huge by comparison; they contain hundreds of amino acid units in innumerable configurations. In view of this it is not surprising that, since 1954, the exact structure of only a few other proteins has been determined.

Nucleic Acids
We have found in Chap. 3 that these most critical constituents of cells are nucleotide polymers, a nucleo-

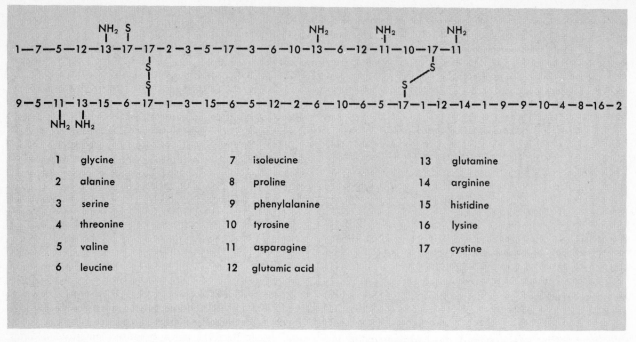

FIG. 4.8 The structure of the insulin molecule. The molecule consists of two poly-peptide chains held together by two disulfide bridges. The numbers represent amino acid units the names of which are listed below the diagram. Note that disulfide bridges are formed by the amino acid cystine.

tide being a nitrogen-base–sugar–phosphate complex. We have also found that the nitrogen base can be either a purine or a pyrimidine and that the sugar is a pentose.

When the nitrogen base is a purine, it is usually one of two kinds: **adenine** or **guanine**; and when the nitrogen base is a pyrimidine, it is usually one of three kinds: **cytosine**, or **thymine**, or **uracil**. The molecular skeletons of these compounds have been given in Fig. 3.3. (Note that the purine adenine is related chemically to the adenosine of adenosine phosphates.) Depending on which one of these purines or pyrimidines is present in a given nucleotide, five major types of nucleotides may be distinguished: adenine-pentose-phosphate, guanine-pentose-phosphate, cytosine-pentose-phosphate, thymine-pentose-phosphate, and uracil-pentose-phosphate.

The pentose can itself be one of two kinds. One kind is **ribose**; the other is **deoxyribose**. The principal difference between these two 5-carbon sugars is indicated by their names: "deoxy"-ribose contains one oxygen atom less than ribose. Therefore, according to the kind of sugar present, two types of nucleotides may be distinguished: *ribose nucleotides* and *deoxyribose nucleotides*.

If we now distinguish nucleotides on the basis of both their specific nitrogen base content and their specific sugar content, we find that eight major varieties of nucleotides exist:

ribose nucleotides	*deoxyribose nucleotides*
adenine-ribose-phosphate	adenine-deoxyribose-phosphate
guanine-ribose-phosphate	guanine-deoxyribose-phosphate
cytosine-ribose-phosphate	cytosine-deoxyribose-phosphate
uracil-ribose-phosphate	thymine-deoxyribose-phosphate

Note that adenine, guanine, and cytosine occur in both groups of nucleotides. But uracil is found only in association with ribose; and thymine, only in association with deoxyribose.

Hundreds of nucleotides joined together into a chain form a nucleic acid molecule. In any such molecule, all nucleotides present are *either* ribose nucleo- tides *or* deoxyribose nucleotides, but not both. On this basis, we may distinguish between **ribose nucleic acid, RNA** for short, composed entirely of ribose nucleotides, and **deoxyribose nucleic acid, DNA** for short, com- posed entirely of deoxyribose nucleotides. DNA spe- cifically is the type of nucleic acid which forms genes and which probably played the key role during the origin of life. RNA functions as an intermediary be- tween genes and the cellular sites of protein synthesis (see Chap. 18 for details).

What is the bonding pattern which unites the nucleotides in nucleic acid molecules? We may discuss this best for DNA, the structure of which has been analyzed more fully than that of RNA. It is believed, however, that the basic pattern of molecular structure is quite similar for both kinds of nucleic acids.

Available evidence indicates that a DNA molecule is a *double chain of nucleotides,* one chain parallel to the other. In each single chain, the nucleotide units appear to be joined in such a way that the phosphate group of one unit links to the sugar of the next and that the purines and pyrimidines stick out laterally. If we symbolize a nucleotide as $P—D—N$, where P stands for phosphate, D for deoxyribose, and N for nitrogen base, then in a single chain

$$—P—D—P—D—P—D—P—D—$$
$$\quad\;\; |\qquad\; |\qquad\; |\qquad\; |$$
$$\quad\;\; N\qquad N\qquad N\qquad N$$

The evidence further suggests that two such single chains are linked into a double chain by the two sets of N's, which are held together pairwise by compara- tively weak (hydrogen) bonds:

As noted, N stands for nitrogen base, and in DNA such bases are either the purines adenine or guanine or the pyrimidines cytosine or thymine. Which are bonded to which in a double chain as above? Purines, contain- ing skeletons of double carbon-nitrogen rings, are larger molecules than pyrimidines, which possess only single- ring skeletons (Fig. 3.3). Therefore, if an $—N·N—$ combination in a double chain as above consisted of two pyrimidines, it would be smaller than if it con- sisted of two purines. Actually, all $—N·N—$ combina-

tions are of the same overall size; in a double chain, one N of a pair is always a pyrimidine, the other, a purine. Any such two together take up the same amount of space, and the $—P—D—P—D—$ chains to which they are attached are therefore parallel.

Specifically, four different $—N·N—$ combinations occur in DNA, as outlined in Fig. 4.9. Note that *adenine is always paired with thymine, guanine always with cytosine.* The chemical properties of these purines and pyrimidines, and the space available between the parallel $—P—D—$ chains, are such that only combi- nations shown in Fig. 4.9 can be formed.

But there is apparently no limit to the number of times each of these combinations can occur in a long double chain. Nor, apparently, are there restrictions as to their sequence. Thus $A·T$, $T·A$, $G·C$, and $C·G$ may be regarded as an alphabet of four symbols, and "words" of any length may be constructed by using these symbols as often as desired and in any order. Evidently, the possible number of compositionally dif- ferent DNAs is practically unlimited. This is reminiscent of the situation in proteins, where an alphabet of about two dozen amino acids gives rise to a virtually unlim- ited number of different polypeptide chains.

A final structural characteristic of DNA is that its double chain is not straight but spiraled into a helix (Fig. 4.10).

DNA structure as outlined here is not yet as firmly established as protein structure. The above conception of the makeup of DNA may be considered to be a preliminary working model, and indeed it is designated as the **Watson-Crick model** after the investigators who proposed it. The model answers three important ques- tions. First, it shows that DNAs can be just as *specific*

FIG. 4.9 The Watson-Crick model of DNA structure. *P*, phosphate; *D*, deoxyribose; *A, T, G, C*, purines and py- rimidines. A *P—D—A* unit represents one of the nucleo- tides. In this $—P—D—P—D—$ double chain, four kinds of purine-pyrimidine pairs are possible, that is, *A·T, T·A, G·C,* and *C·G.* Each of the four may occur very many times, and the sequence of the pairs may vary in unlim- ited fashion.

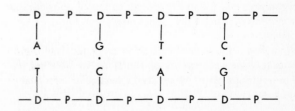

FIG. 4.10 A DNA double chain is spiraled as shown in this diagram. The two spirals symbolize the —P—D—P—D— chains, and the connections between the spirals represent the purine-pyrimidine pairs.

as proteins: different sequences of nitrogen-base pairs would represent different DNAs. This accounts for the observation that no two organisms have exactly identical genes, genes being composed of DNA. Variations in gene types are actually just as great as variations in protein types, as is to be expected if the function of nucleic acids is to control protein synthesis (see Chap. 3). Second, the Watson-Crick model shows how DNA might actually accomplish control of protein synthesis and indeed how a specific DNA would govern the formation of a specific protein. Third, the model suggests how DNA could reproduce. We shall deal with these functional aspects of nucleic acids in Chap. 18.

Other Constituents

Carbohydrates, lipids, proteins, and nitrogen-base derivatives such as nucleic acids and adenosine phosphates form the organic bulk of living matter. However, hundreds of other types of organic substances exist in cells. Although such substances are often present in very small quantities only, they may nevertheless be of extreme importance in the maintenance of life. Some of these constituents are not related chemically to the four main categories above. Others are derivatives of one of the four groups, and still others are combinations of two or more of the basic four. Also, some are dissolved or suspended in the water of cells and others contribute to the formation of hard bulk deposits (see below).

Few of these organic constituents occur universally in all types of cells. More usually, they are special components of particular cell types only, serving special functions. Of such special materials found in various organisms, the following categories are of considerable importance structurally, functionally, or both.

Pigments. These most conspicuous chemicals of organisms serve a wide variety of functions, as we shall see. Three groups of pigments are of particular significance (Fig. 4.11).

One group includes pigments known as **tetra-pyrrols.** A so-called pyrrol molecule contains a skeleton of five atoms, namely, carbon and nitrogen atoms, and the five are arranged as a ring. Four such pyrrol rings joined together form a tetrapyrrol. In some cases, the four joined pyrrol rings form a straight chain. Tetra-pyrrols of this type include red, blue, green, and other varieties of pigments found, for example, in certain algae (see Chap. 9), in the shells of robin and other bird eggs, and in mammalian feces and urine. In other tetrapyrrols, the four pyrrol rings are joined to form a larger ring in turn, and in the center of this larger ring is usually present a single atom of a metal. A major pigment of this type is green *chlorophyll,* the central metal atom here being magnesium. As will be shown in Chap. 9, several varieties of chlorophyll distinguished by minor chemical differences exist in different photosynthetic organisms. In another important type of ring-like tetrapyrrol, the central metal atom is iron and such pigments are red. They include the *cytochromes,* which are vital participants in the respiration of all cells (see Chap. 16), and the *haemes,* which are components of *haemoglobin,* the red oxygen-transporting substance in the blood of many animals (e.g., man, and vertebrates generally; see Chap. 15).

A second large group of pigments in organisms comprises the **carotenoids.** They produce red, orange, yellow, and brown colors. Carotenoids are essentially long chains of carbon atoms with carbon rings attached at both ends of the chains (Fig. 4.11). Two subgroups of these pigments are the *carotenes* and the *xantho-phylls.* Carotenes have the general formula $C_{40}H_{56}$, and it may be noted that vitamin A is a derivative. Named after the carrot, in which carotenes are abundant, the pigments also occur widely in all leaves and are responsible for the red, yellow, or cream-white colors of, for example, tomatoes, pumpkins, egg yolk, butter, milk, and other plant and animal products. Xanthophylls contain oxygen in addition to carbon and hydrogen. They are as widely distributed as the carotenes. For example, a common xanthophyll of leaves is *lutein* ($C_{40}H_{56}O_2$), which is responsible for the yellow colors in autumn foliage. An important xanthophyll in brown and other algae is *fucoxanthin* ($C_{40}H_{56}O_6$; see Chap. 9).

A third major group of pigments comprises the **anthocyanins,** found among plants but not among animals. An anthocyanin molecule is composed of several rings of atoms, the rings being joined in complex ways (Fig. 4.11). Anthocyanins produce the deep reds and blues of plants, as in many flowers, fruits, and roots

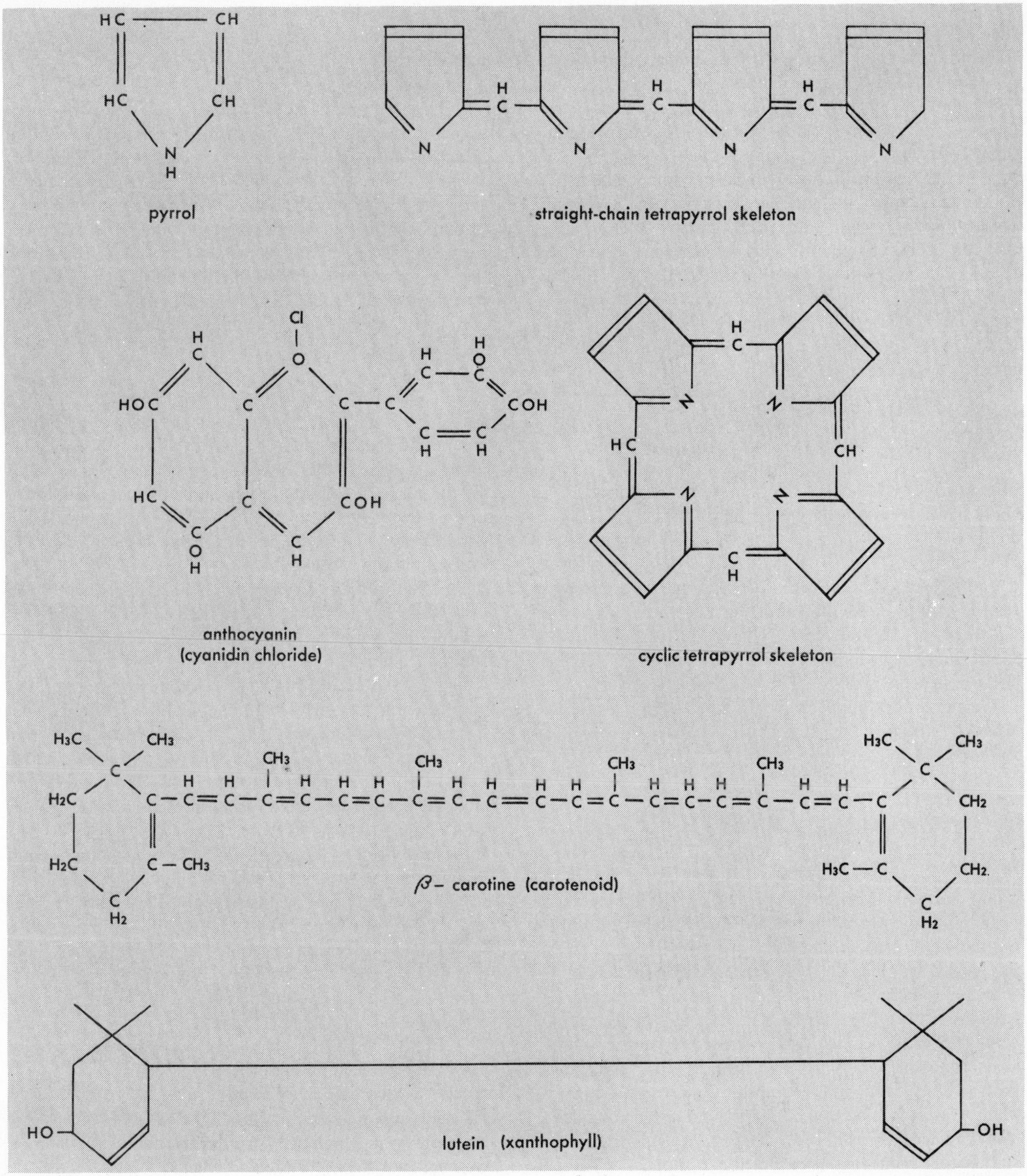

FIG. 4.11   The chemical structure of various pigments and related organic compounds.

(e.g., beets). The pigments are also manufactured in fall foliage, where they account for the red coloration. Anthocyanins are soluble in water; hence they occur in solution in the water of cells. By contrast, carotenoids and chlorophyll are fat-soluble, and these pigments are associated with the fatty constituents of plant cells.

Most conspicuous in animals, but not in plants, is a pigment known as **melanin.** It is responsible for all yellow-brown, brown, and black animal colors. Thus, melanin occurs abundantly in hair, in skin, in the inner layers of eyes, and, in many animals, also in some of the interior membranes of the body. Melanin is a chemical derivative of the amino acid *tyrosine.* Specialized pigment cells produce melanin, which accumulates in granules within such cells. If only a few melanin granules are present, the cell appears to be yellowish or brownish in color; a black color is produced by dense masses of granules.

In addition to the pigments here named, many others are found in specific types of organisms. We shall have occasion to discuss some of them in later contexts.

Carbohydrate derivatives. Most organisms possess several groups of complex organic substances which are all more or less distantly related to carbohydrates. Many of these substances are constituents of cellular surface structures (Fig. 4.12).

One important group of this kind comprises derivatives of **uronic acids.** If a sugar molecule is modified so that the

$$\begin{array}{c} \text{H} \\ | \\ \text{—C—OH} \\ | \\ \text{H} \end{array}$$

group normally present at one end of the molecule is changed to a carboxyl group, —COOH, then the resulting molecule is a uronic acid. For example, if the starting sugar is glucose, then the modified molecule is so-called *glucuronic acid;* if the starting molecule is galactose, then the modified molecule is *galacturonic acid.* Differently constituted polymers of various uronic acids function widely as cell "cement"; i.e., they hold groups of cells together in multicellular organisms. In plants, for example, uronic acid polymers such as *pectic acid* and various *pectins* are important cementing substances between cells and are also components of cell walls. In animals, analogously, *hyaluronic acid* aids in

binding cells to one another. Moreover, related complex compounds called *mucopolysaccharides* are major ingredients of various types of mucus and other slime substances.

In many animals and in fungi, a chief component of external cell walls and surface skeletons (as in insects) is **chitin,** a celluloselike carbohydrate derivative. If one of the —OH groups in a glucose molecule is replaced by an amino group, —NH$_2$, the resulting compound is *glucosamine.* A high polymer chain formed from glucosamine units represents the principal ingredient of chitin. Similarly celluloselike is *hemicellulose,* a polymer of pentose sugars and uronic acids. This compound is one of the common components of cell walls in plants.

Lipid derivatives. Chemically related to fats are the **waxes,** in which long fatty acids are joined to certain compounds other than glycerin. Waxes occur most abundantly in plants, where they form covering films on the surface cells of leaves and other exposed plant parts. Two other types of fat-derived surface components of plant cells are **cutin** and **suberin.** Cutin is present in the cuticles of plant cells, and suberin is a secretion product of cork cells (see Chap. 10). Being fatty in character, wax, cutin, and suberin all are insoluble in water, and in one form or another they function primarily as waterproofing and evaporation-resisting materials. Similarly related to fats are the **sterols,** complex ring structures which form the molecular framework of a number of vitamins and of animal hormones. Among the sterols is also *cholesterol,* which may play a role in forming the solid deposits responsible for hardened arteries, gallstones, and kidney stones.

Variously derived constituents. Certain cellular components, some of them very abundant, are chemically so complex that their detailed molecular structure is as yet known only incompletely. A good case in point is **lignin,** a major reinforcing material in plant parts functioning as antigravity supports. For example, the substance of wood is approximately 50 per cent lignin, the remainder being largely cellulose.

Of the vast array of other chemicals which go into the makeup of different cells and organisms, some are known to play major functional roles, as in the case of vitamins and hormones. We shall deal with these later in appropriate contexts. Most other cellular chemicals we shall not have occasion to discuss.

We may now sum up. Carbohydrates, lipids, pro-

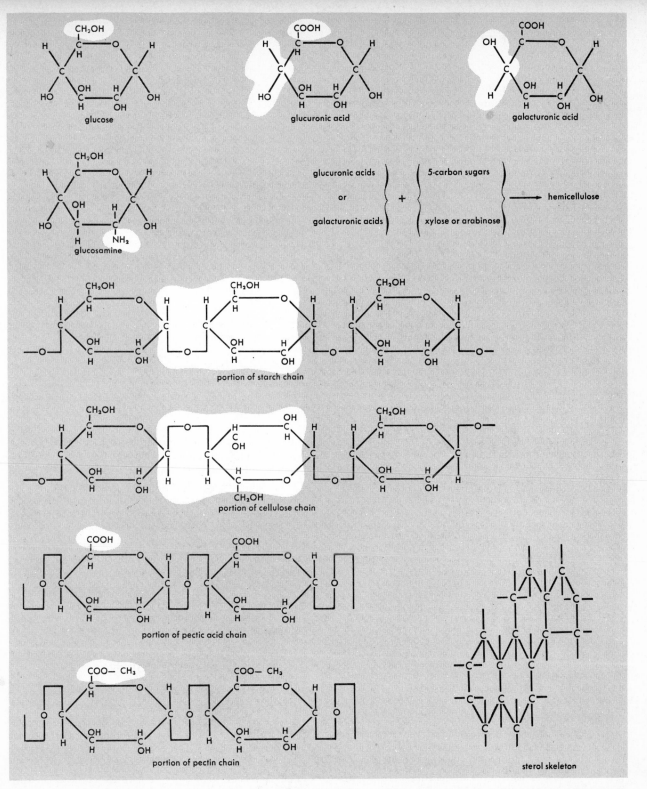

FIG. 4.12   The chemical structure of various carbohydrate derivatives. White areas emphasize chemical differences between related compounds.

teins, nucleic acids, various related substances, together with water and other inorganic materials, plus numerous additional compounds found specifically in particular types of cells—all these are the chemical bricks out of which cells are made. The water component dissolves many of the other components, and we already know the chemical consequences of this. As shown in Chap. 2, some of the dissolved materials exist in dissociated form, some remain molecular. Many proteins present function as enzymes, and these, plus the temperature of the environment, permit numerous chemical reactions at various speeds, in various directions, and in various amounts. As a result of such reactions, energy exchanges occur, concentrations change, and chemical compositions as such become changed.

New sets of reactions then become possible among the altered constituents, and such reactions alter chemical conditions in turn. If, as is normally the case, changes in the external environment occur at the same time, the diverse chemical events in cells will be affected accordingly. Living matter consequently is forever in chemical flux.

Apart from containing many substances in water solution, the cell contains numerous materials which are not dissolved but which remain in suspension. These materials include, for example, the fats and many other lipid components and very large molecules such as the complex polysaccharides, the fibrous proteins, and the nucleic acids. Because it consists partly of dissolved and partly of suspended components, the cell substance exhibits a particular *physical* organization superimposed on and resulting from the chemical organization. We now turn our attention to these physical characteristics of the cell substance.

PHYSICAL ORGANIZATION

Any system composed of particles contained in another medium can be classified as belonging to one of three categories, depending on the size of the particles. If the particles are small enough to dissolve in the medium, then the system is a true **solution.** (In a water solution crystals can readily form, and such a system is therefore also called a *crystalloid.*) If the particles are large, e.g., the size of soil grains, they soon settle out by gravity at the bottom of a container. Such a system is a coarse **suspension.** But if the particles are of intermediate size, they neither form a solution nor settle out. Such a system is a **colloid** (Fig. 4.13).

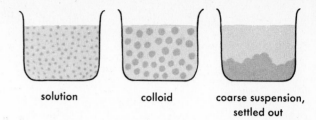

| solution | colloid | coarse suspension, settled out |

FIG. 4.13   The size of the particles in water determines whether they will form a solution, a colloid, or a coarse suspension which settles out.

The particles in a colloid range in diameter from $1/1,000,000$ to $1/10,000$ millimeter (mm). The larger figure corresponds very nearly to the limit of vision under a good microscope. In biological practice, the unit $1/1,000$ mm = 1 micron (μ) is frequently used. Hence the colloidal range is from $1/1,000$ to $1/10$ μ.

Any diphasic system is a colloid if one of the two components consists of particles of appropriate size. Eight general types of colloid systems are possible: a gas within either a solid or a liquid; a liquid within either a liquid, a solid, or a gas; and a solid within either a liquid, a solid, or a gas. Liquids within liquids are called *emulsions.* Among common colloidal systems are milk and mayonnaise (colloidal fat and protein in water), fog (colloidal water in air), cigarette smoke (colloidal ash in air), cheese (colloidal air in fat-protein), and ruby glass (colloidal gold in a solid).

The cell substance is partly a true solution, partly a colloidal system. Water is the medium in which many materials are dissolved, and it is also the **liquid phase** in which many insoluble materials of colloidal size are dispersed. This colloidal **dispersed phase** includes, for example, solids such as the fibrous proteins and liquids such as the oily fats. Therefore, insofar as living matter is a colloidal system, it is of both the solid-within-liquid and the liquid-within-liquid type.

CELLULAR COLLOIDS

What properties of living matter result from its colloidal nature? What, first, prevents the colloidal particles from settling out?

As noted earlier, the molecules of a liquid are under continuous thermal agitation; the more intense the agitation, the higher the temperature. When the liquid freezes, molecular motion is reduced sharply. Above the boiling point, molecules move so rapidly that many escape, i.e., the liquid vaporizes at great rate. If

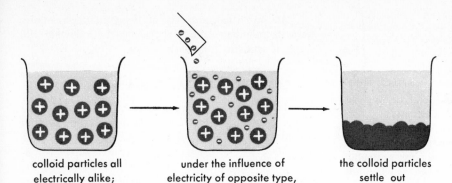

colloid particles all
electrically alike;

under the influence of
electricity of opposite type,

the colloid particles
settle out

FIG. 4.14 Colloid particles carry similar electric charges—in this illustration, positive ones (left). These charges make the particles repel one another and thus keep them suspended. If electricity of the opposite type is added (middle), the colloid charges are neutralized and the particles settle out (right).

dispersed particles are present in a liquid, they are buffeted and bombarded constantly by the molecules of the liquid. Very large particles are unaffected by these tiny forces, and they fall straight to the bottom of a container. But smaller bodies of colloidal size may be pushed back and forth, up and down. Gravitational pull may thereby be counteracted partly or wholly and the particles thus may be kept suspended. This random movement of small particles, called **Brownian motion,** is easily demonstrable under the microscope.

Brownian movement aids in keeping colloidal particles from settling out, but they cannot remain suspended by this force alone. Colloids stay dispersed mainly because of their **electrical charges.** All solid particles of a given colloidal system are either electropositive or electronegative. Since like charges repel, the particles are kept apart. If the charge is neutralized by electricity of opposite type, the colloid particles do settle out (Fig. 4.14).

Cellular colloids undergo reversible **sol-gel transformations,** also called *phase reversals.* If large numbers of colloidal particles are added to the system or, alternatively, if water is gradually withdrawn, the particles are brought closer together and come into contact with one another eventually. Rod-shaped particles then pile up like a log jam; round or irregular particles interlock in intricate ways. In effect, the original dispersed phase now is a continuous spongelike network which holds water within its meshes, in discontinuous droplets. This is the *gel* state of a colloid. The quasi-solid, pliable aspect of living matter, as in skin, or of protein colloids generally, as in Jello and gelatin, is due to the gel condition. We may understand, therefore, how even systems like jellyfish, which contain as much as 90 per cent or more water, can maintain definite form and shape.

Conversely, addition of water to a colloidal system or removal of dispersed particles results in greater fluidity, the *sol* state of a colloid (Fig. 4.15). In cells, sol and gel states alternate normally and repeatedly with local variations of particle concentrations.

Increased temperature may convert a gel into a sol; at higher temperature, colloidal particles in a gel become more agitated and the gelled meshwork is disrupted (e.g., liquefaction of Jello by heating). Many other physical and chemical influences, such as low or high pH or pressure, affect sol-gel conditions. For example, cream, a sol, when churned (i.e., when put under pressure), yields butter, a gel. Butter in turn can be creamed, i.e., returned to the sol state.

FIG. 4.15 Phase reversals. A gel may be transformed into a sol by either addition of more liquid (top) or withdrawal of solid particles. And a sol may be transformed into a gel by either addition of more solid particles (bottom) or withdrawal of liquid.

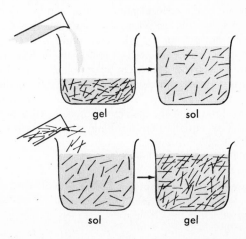

gel   sol

sol   gel

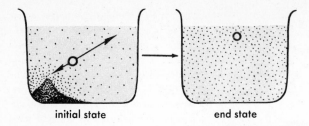

initial state   end state

FIG. 4.16 Diffusion. In the initial state, particles are distributed unevenly (left). A given particle (for example, the circled one) will therefore have more freedom of movement in the direction of lower concentrations. This eventually leads to an even distribution of particles, as in the end state shown at right.

All colloids **age.** The particles in a young, freshly formed colloidal system are enveloped by layers of *bound water;* water molecules are held against the particle surfaces by electrochemical attraction. It is largely because of these forces that water within a gel does not "run out" through the gel meshes. With time, however, the binding capacity of the particles decreases and some of the water does run out. The colloid "sets," i.e., contracts and gelates progressively; examples are exudation of water from long-standing milk curd, custard, mustard. Such aging of colloids may be a factor contributing to the aging of living systems.

Migratory movements occur in colloids, and also in true solutions, as a direct result of the thermal agitation of the particles. If ions, molecules, or colloidal particles are unevenly distributed, more collisions take place in more concentrated regions. For example, if a particle in the circle in Fig. 4.16 is displaced by thermal agitation or by Brownian bombardment *toward* a region of higher concentration, it will soon be stopped in its track by collision with other particles. But if it is displaced *away* from a high concentration, its movement will not be interrupted as soon, since neighboring particles are farther apart. On an average, therefore, a greater number of particles is displaced into more dilute regions than into more concentrated ones. In time, particles throughout the system will become distributed evenly. This equalization resulting from migration of particles is called **diffusion.**

Diffusion plays an important role in living matter. For example, it happens often inside a cell that particles are unevenly distributed. Diffusion will then tend to equalize the distribution. Evidently, this is one way through which materials in cells can migrate about.

An important property of living matter resulting from its colloidal makeup is that, as the following will show, it tends to form *membranes.*

MEMBRANES AND PERMEABILITY

The boundary between a colloidal system and a different medium (air, water, solid surfaces, or another colloid of different type) is called an *interface.* The molecules there are usually subjected to complex physical forces which act on and from both sides of the interface. The result is that the molecules at the interface pack together tightly and become *oriented* in parallel, in layers, or both; an interfacial membrane forms (e.g., the "skins" on puddings, custards, boiled milk; Fig. 4.17). On the surfaces of cells, such molecular skins are called **plasma membranes.** If the plasma membrane on the surface of a cell is punctured, a new membrane develops over the opening within seconds, before appreciable amounts of the interior can flow out.

Plasma membranes are the gateways through which the molecular traffic into and out of living matter must pass. How do materials get through such membranes?

Plasma membranes have different **permeability** to different substances. Most membranes are completely permeable to water; i.e., water molecules can pass through freely in either direction. As for other materials, organic or inorganic, there is no rule by which their passage potential can be determined beforehand. In

FIG. 4.17 A diagrammatic representation of an interfacial membrane. Where two different colloidal systems meet, the molecular particles become oriented in some regular manner, and this is a major factor in the formation of an interfacial film. In the diagram, the horizontal line separates the two colloidal systems.

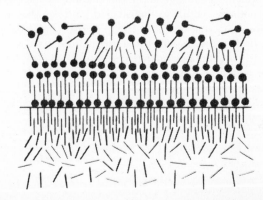

general, three classes of materials can be distinguished: those that can pass through a membrane in either direction; those that can pass in one direction but not in the other; and those that cannot penetrate at all. These categories vary considerably for different membranes.

In the past, traffic through living membranes has been compared with traffic through nonliving ones like cellophane. Such nonliving membranes let water or small ions through, but not proteins, for example. Particle penetration here can be explained rather readily in terms of diffusion. Ions, for example, would strike the barrier; most of them would bounce off, but some would pass through *pores* in the membrane. If the ion concentration were greater on one side of the membrane than on the other, more ions on an average would migrate into the dilute side, thus equalizing concentrations.

However, a hypothesis postulating diffusion through pores is generally inadequate for living membranes. If cellular membranes were indeed passive, inert films with holes like cellophane, then it should not matter if such a membrane were poisoned; being nonliving, it could not be affected by a poison. But experiments actually show that the activity of cellular membranes *is* stopped or severely impaired by poisons, indicating that such membranes are not simply passive films. Moreover, if living membranes actually contained small holes, then the size of a particle should determine whether or not it could pass through such holes. However, particle size is often of little importance. For example, under certain conditions large protein molecules may pass through a given membrane whereas very small molecules sometimes may not. Again, the molecules of the three sugars glucose, fructose, and galactose, all $C_6H_{12}O_6$, have the same size, yet they are passed through living membranes at substantially different speeds.

Clearly, membranes are highly *selective*; i.e., they act as if they "knew" which substances to transmit and which to reject. Moreover, it is now known that active, energy-consuming work is often done by a living membrane in transmitting materials and that complex chemical reactions take place in the process. Therefore, rather than visualize a passive membrane with small holes, we are led to consider plasma films as dynamic structures in which entering or leaving particles are actively "handed" across from one side to the other. Fatty components of membranes are thought to contribute particularly to these processes.

Accordingly, if we encounter a situation where materials other than water pass through a living membrane, we will be quite wrong if we simply say off-handedly that this can be explained "by diffusion." Diffusion does play some role in most cases, but actually a minor one; active work by the membrane usually plays the all-important role.

Membranes also account for a final property we must discuss.

OSMOSIS

When a membrane separates one colloid or solution from another or from a different kind of medium, it often happens that the membrane is permeable to some of the particles present on either side of the membrane and is impermeable to others. If, initially, the transmissible particles are unequally concentrated on the two sides, diffusion will equalize the concentration, as we have seen. What happens when *nontransmissible* particles are unequally concentrated? For simplicity, let us assume that transmissible substances are not present at all and that we deal only with water containing nontransmissible particles. What events occur in such a system? Consult Fig. 4.18:

1. In the initial state, relatively more water molecules are in contact with the membrane X on the A side than on the B side, since fewer of the solid particles occupy membrane space on the A surface than on the B surface.

2. Therefore, more water molecules, on an average, are transmitted through the membrane from A to B than from B to A.

FIG. 4.18 Osmosis. In the initial state, because A is less concentrated than B, water will be pulled from A into B. This eventually leads to the isotonic end state, where concentrations in A and B are equal. From this point on, no further net migration of water occurs (i.e., just as much water moves from A into B as from B into A). A semipermeable membrane is represented by x.

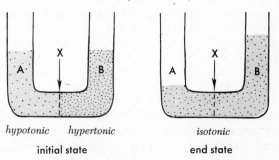

hypotonic   *hypertonic*   *isotonic*

initial state   **end state**

3. As a result, the water content decreases in *A* and increases in *B*. Particles in *A* become crowded into a smaller and smaller volume, and more and more of them therefore take up membrane space on the *A* surface. On the *B* side, the increasing water content permits the spreading of the particles into progressively larger volumes, thus reducing particle concentration along the *B* surface of the membrane.

4. A stage will be reached at which the number of particles along the *A* surface equals that along the *B* surface. From then on, the number of water molecules transmitted from *A* to *B* equals the number transmitted from *B* to *A*. Thereafter, no further *net* shift of water occurs.

This *movement of water is called* **osmosis.**

Note that the extent of osmosis depends on the *concentration differential,* the relative *numbers* of particles in *A* and *B*. Actually, it makes no difference whether the particles involved are transmissible or not. If, as normally happens in living matter, both kinds are present, transmissible particles on the more concentrated side will eventually diffuse over to the other side until concentrations are equal; but before this equality is reached, transmissible particles still exert a temporary osmotic effect. Nontransmissible particles, not being able to penetrate the membrane, exert a permanent osmotic effect.

If the difference in particle number is great enough (for example, if *A* contains pure water only and *B* contains water and a large number of particles), then the *A* side may dehydrate completely and collapse, while the *B* side might burst and so collapse also. Since this does not normally happen in living systems, their parts, clearly, must be in general osmotic equilibrium. The concentration of particles must be the same on both sides of membranes, or as often stated, the two sides must be **isotonic** to each other. If the initial concentration on an arbitrary *A* side is lower than on a *B* side (as in Fig. 4.18), then the *A* side loses water. The *B* medium here is said to be **hypertonic** to *A*, that is, initially more highly concentrated than the *A* medium. The *B* side, having the higher initial concentration of particles, gains water. The *A* medium is said to be **hypotonic** to the *B* medium.

Note that the net effect of osmosis is to pull water *into* the region of higher colloidal concentration, i.e., from the hypotonic to the hypertonic side. The process will continue until the two sides are isotonic. And note that osmosis will occur whenever certain particles cannot or do not pass through a membrane. Then nothing migrates through the membrane except *water* (plus any particles present which *can* diffuse through).

Like diffusion, osmosis plays an important role in living matter. It is one agency by which water is distributed and redistributed across membranes. As in diffusion also, care must be taken in explaining given membrane phenomena simply as "osmosis." Sometimes the event in question actually is osmosis, but many times it is not. In this connection, it is particularly poor practice simply to dismiss given events at membranes unthinkingly as "diffusion and osmosis."

We may conclude generally that, in its physical organization, the living matter of cells is a mixed colloidal system bounded by variously permeable membranes, undergoing localized sol-gel transformations, and being kept in constant internal motion by molecular bombardments, by diffusion displacements, and by osmotic forces. As a result of these properties, living matter is subjected to a continuous physical flux equally as profound as the chemical flux. Indeed, physical changes initiate chemical ones, and vice versa; and from any small-scale point of view, living matter is therefore never the same from moment to moment.

It should be clear, however, that a living cell cannot be simply a loose collection of structural bricks displaying given chemical and physical properties; a random pile of such bricks does not make a living structure any more than a mere pile of real bricks makes a house. First and foremost, if the whole is to be living, the components must be organized into a specific variety of larger microscopic bodies and these in turn into appropriately structured cells. Indeed, superimposed on and resulting from its chemical and physical organization, the cell substance displays a highly characteristic *biological* organization. We shall examine it in what follows.

BIOLOGICAL ORGANIZATION

The generalization that all living organisms consist of cells and cell products is known as the **cell theory.** Principal credit for its formulation is usually given to the German biologists Schleiden and Schwann, whose work was published in 1838. But the French biologist Dutrochet had made substantially the same generalization as early as 1824. The cell theory rapidly became one of the fundamental cornerstones of modern biological science, and, with minor qualifications, it still has that status today.

Cells came to be recognized early as the "atomic" units of living matter, structurally as well as functionally. In 1831, the English biologist Robert Brown discovered the presence of nuclei within cells, and in 1839 the Bohemian biologist Purkinje coined the general term "protoplasm" for the living substance out of which cells are made. Virchow in 1855 concluded that *"omnis cellula e cellula"*—new living cells can arise only by reproduction of preexisting living cells. This important recognition of the continuity of life, and thus of the direct derivation of all cells from ancient cellular ancestors, introduced the notion of history into the study of cells. Ever since, the study of cells has revolved around three interrelated problems: cell *structure,* cell *function,* and short- and long-range cell *development.* The first of these concerns us here particularly.

THE BASIC DESIGN

Examination of living or killed cells under various kinds of microscopes shows that cells vary considerably in size, ranging in diameter from about 2 μ to as much as several millimeters and more. However, the order of size of the vast majority of cells is remarkably uniform. A diameter of 5 to 15 μ is fairly characteristic of cells generally. We surmise that, notwithstanding the exceptions, cells can be neither much smaller nor much larger than a certain norm. Too small a size presumably would not provide enough room to accommodate the necessary parts, and too large a size would increase the maintenance problem and at the same time reduce the efficiency of compact operation.

The two fundamental subdivisions of most cells are the **nucleus** and the living substance surrounding the nucleus, called the **cytoplasm.** The nucleus is bounded by a **nuclear membrane,** the cytoplasm by a **cell membrane,** also called *plasma membrane.* Surrounding the cell membrane in many cases is a **cell wall** (Fig. 4.19).

Most cells contain a single nucleus each, but there are many exceptions. As already noted in Chap. 3, bacteria and blue-green algae do not contain distinct nuclei at all. Conversely, many other single-celled organisms normally contain more than one nucleus. *Binu-*

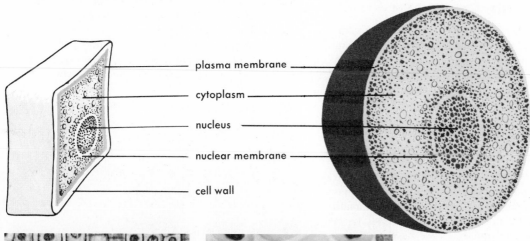

plasma membrane

cytoplasm

nucleus

nuclear membrane

cell wall

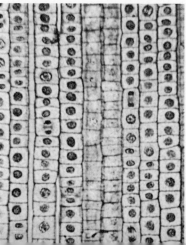

FIG. 4.19 The general structure of cells. The diagrams represent sections through a plant cell (left) and through an animal cell (right). The photos show cells from the root of a plant (left) and red blood cells of a bird (right). Note the darkly stained nucleus in the center of the cells. *(Photo of root cells, courtesy of Dr. M. S. Fuller, Brown University; photo of blood cells, General Biological Supply House, Inc.)*

cleate and *multinucleate* cells are found with some frequency among multicellular organisms also.

There are exceptions too concerning the individuality of cells, normally maintained by the cell membrane. In certain cases, e.g., in latex-forming cells of rubber trees and in the embryos of many animals, cell membranes at first form boundaries between individual cells. But at a later stage of development these boundaries dissolve, the result being a fused, continuous living mass with nuclei dispersed through it. Such a structure, in which cellular individuality has been lost, is called a **coenocyte** in plants and a **syncytium** in animals.

Despite variations in the number of nuclei or the occasional loss of the structural discreteness of cells, the fundamentally cellular character of living matter is undeniable even in such exceptional cases. And in all other cases the cellular character is unequivocal, for there we deal with distinct bits of living matter, each bounded by a plasma membrane and often a cell wall and containing one nucleus.

NUCLEUS AND CYTOPLASM

A nucleus typically consists of three kinds of components: the more or less gel-like nuclear sap, or **nucleoplasm,** in which are suspended the **chromosomes,** and one or more **nucleoli** (Fig. 4.20). The chromosomes are the principal nuclear structures. Indeed, a nucleus as a whole may be regarded primarily as a protective housing for these slender, threadlike bodies. Chemically, chromosomes consist largely of protein and of nucleic acids, intimately associated into complexes called *nucleoproteins*. DNA is the principal nucleic acid of the nucleoproteins, but RNA is also present. Functionally, chromosomes are the carriers of the genes which, as noted on previous occasions, are the ultimate controllers of cellular processes. Particular cell types may not contain formed nuclei, as we have seen, and thus they may not contain formed chromosomes; but all cell types contain genes.

Chromosomes are conspicuous only during cell reproduction, when they become thickly coated with additional nucleoprotein. At other times such coats are absent and chromosomes then are very fine filaments not easily identifiable within the nuclear sap. The exact number of chromosomes within each cell nucleus is an important species-specific trait. For example, cells of human beings contain 46 chromosomes each. Analogously, cells of every other type of organism have their own characteristic chromosome number. A cell rarely contains more than in the order of 100 chromosomes. Therefore, since there are several million different kinds of organisms, many kinds share the same chromosome number. To be sure, possession of the same *numbers* of chromosomes does not mean possession of the same *types*.

A nucleolus ("little nucleus") is a spherical body which also consists largely of nucleoprotein. But the only type of nucleic acid present here is RNA. As we shall see in a later chapter, nucleoli are derivatives of chromosomes and they appear to play an important role in the control of protein synthesis within cells. Given cell types contain a fixed number of nucleoli per nucleus.

The whole nucleus is separated from the surrounding cytoplasm by the nuclear membrane. This structure, like most other living membranes, is constructed mainly of proteins and lipids. It governs the vital traffic of materials between cytoplasm and nucleus.

FIG. 4.20 Electron micrograph of a cell nucleus. The whole round structure covering most of the photograph is the nucleus; cytoplasm is outside it. Note the nuclear bounding membrane. Within the nucleus, the dark patches are the gene-containing chromatin and the two large, rounded, clear areas are nucleoli. *(Courtesy of Dr. W. G. Whaley, University of Texas, and Am. J. Botany, vol. 47, p. 401.)*

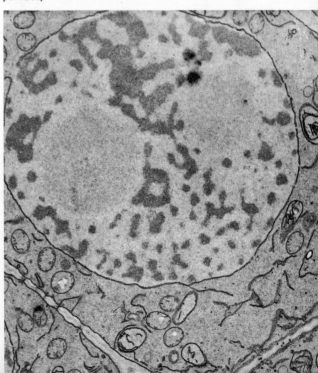

Examination with the electron microscope shows that the nuclear membrane is actually a double layer pierced by tiny pores (Fig. 4.21). The functional significance of such an architecture is not yet clear.

If the nucleus, by virtue of its genes, is the control center of cellular functions, then the cytoplasm is the executive center. In it the directives of the nucleus are carried out. But it should be emphasized at once that such a functional distinction between nucleus and cytoplasm should not be taken too rigorously. Although the nucleus primarily controls, it also executes many directives of the cytoplasm; and although the cytoplasm primarily executes, it also influences many nuclear processes. As we shall see later, a vital reciprocal interdependence binds nucleus and cytoplasm, and experiment has repeatedly shown that one cannot long survive without the other.

Cytoplasm consists of a semifluid **ground substance,** which is in a sol or a gel state at different times and in different cellular regions, and in which are suspended large numbers of various formed inclusions. Such inclusions may be shaped into granules, rodlets, filaments, or droplets. Each of these may have various sizes and chemical compositions and may have a variety of functions. Particular cell types often possess unique inclusions not found elsewhere. The following inclusions are widespread among many or all cell types:

Mitochondria. Found universally in all cells, these bodies have a predominantly fat-protein composition. In addition to RNA-nucleoprotein, they are known to contain *respiratory enzymes,* i.e., enzymes required in energy-producing reactions. Mitochondria are the principal chemical "factories" in which cellular respiration is carried out.

Under the light microscope, mitochondria appear as short rods or thin filaments averaging 0.5 to 2 μ in length. The electron microscope shows that the surface of a mitochondrion consists of two fine membranes (Fig. 4.22). The inner one is greatly folded, the folds projecting into the interior of the mitochondrion. These folds, known as *mitochondrial cristae,* are believed to be the specific locations where energy-producing reactions take place (see also Chap. 16).

Ribosomes. These bodies are exceedingly tiny granules, visible under the electron microscope (Fig. 4.23). Present in all cells studied, ribosomes contain RNA-nucleoprotein (hence the "ribo-" portion of their name) and enzymes required in many synthesis reactions. It is believed that ribosomes are the principal "factories" which carry out cellular protein synthesis.

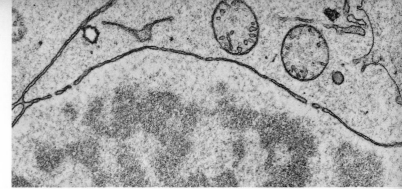

FIG. 4.21   Electron-micrographic close-up of a nuclear membrane. Note the double-layered condition of the membrane and the pores in it. Portions of the nucleus are shown at the bottom of the photograph. *(Courtesy of Dr. W. G. Whaley, University of Texas, and Am. J. Botany, vol. 47, p. 401.)*

FIG. 4.22   Electron micrograph of two mitochondria, one cut in cross section, the other longitudinally. Note the double-layered mitochondrial membrane and the interior cristae, which are infoldings of the inner layer of the membrane. *(Courtesy of Dr. W. G. Whaley, University of Texas, and Am. J. Botany, vol. 47, p. 401.)*

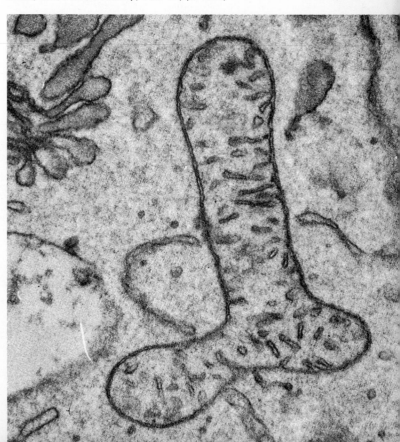

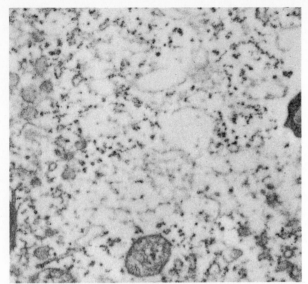

FIG. 4.23 Electron micrograph of portion of cytoplasm showing ribosomes (fine dark granules). *(Courtesy of Dr. W. G. Whaley, University of Texas, and Am. J. Botany, vol. 47, p. 401.)*

Golgi bodies. These structures are probably universal in cells, but they do not have the same appearance in all cases. Thus, depending partly on the position of cells within an organism and partly on the way in which cells are prepared for microscopic study, Golgi bodies appear variously as complexes of droplets or as stacks of thin platelike layers, or as mixtures of these and other configurations (Fig. 4.24). Golgi bodies are believed to function in the manufacture of cellular secretion products, for these structures are particularly conspicuous in actively secreting cells. For example, whenever gland cells are producing their characteristic secretions, the Golgi bodies of such cells become very prominent.

Plastids. These round, oval, or disk-shaped bodies are found in the cells of plants and other photosynthetic organisms. Three kinds of plastids may be distinguished on the basis of their pigment content. Plastids of one kind are without pigment, and they are referred to as **leucoplasts.** Colorless plastids of this sort may function in the storage of starch, in which case they are given the name *amyloplasts.* In a second kind of plastid, pigments are present, but the pigments do not include chlorophyll. Instead, carotenes and xanthophylls are abundant. Plastids of this type are known as **chromoplasts.** For example, carrots and tomatoes owe their color to pigments localized in chromoplasts. The

FIG. 4.24 Electron micrograph of portion of cytoplasm showing two Golgi bodies. Each such body consists of stacks of parallel lamellae. *(Courtesy of Dr. W. G. Whaley, University of Texas.)*

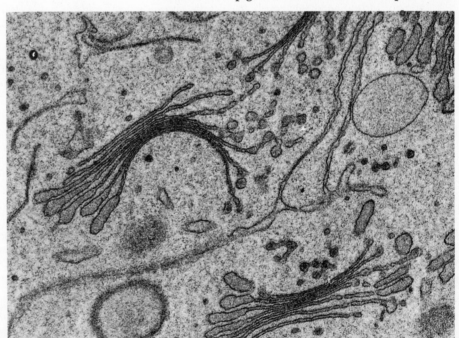

third variety of plastid contains pigments like the chromoplasts, but chlorophyll is present also. Such green plastids are called **chloroplasts** (Fig. 4.25).

Averaging 4 to 6 μ in diameter, chloroplasts contain a structural framework composed largely of protein. This framework is arranged as a stack of parallel layers, each layer being separated from the next by a definite space. Set into this framework are smaller bodies, so-called **grana**. Each of these again has a

framework of parallel protein layers, but here the layers are stacked more densely than in the chloroplast as a whole. Present within the framework of the grana are nucleoproteins, enzymes, chlorophyll and the other pigments, and indeed the whole chemical machinery necessary for food manufacture; grana are the "factory" locations where photosynthesis takes place.

Centrioles. In the cells of some algae, some fungi, and all animals, a single small granule is located just

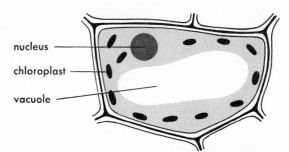

nucleus

chloroplast

vacuole

FIG. 4.25 Diagram of a cell showing disposition of chloroplast (left). Electron micrograph showing section through a whole chloroplast (bottom left). Note laminate structure and denser grana. A higher magnification of one of the grana in a chloroplast is shown (bottom right). Note that the lamellae of the chloroplast are continuous through the grana. *(Photographs courtesy of Dr. A. J. Hodge, California Institute of Technology, and J. Biophys. Biochem. Cytol., vol. 1, p. 605.)*

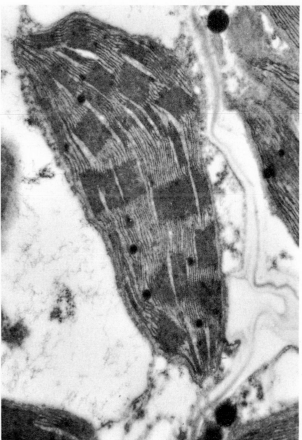

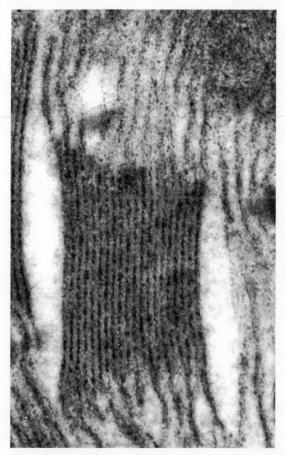

outside the cell nucleus. As will be shown later, such centrioles function in cell reproduction.

Apart from the inclusions just listed, cytoplasm generally contains additional **granules** and fluid-filled droplets bounded by membranes, called **vacuoles**. Such cytoplasmic granules and vacuoles perform a large variety of functions. They may be vehicles transporting raw materials from the cell surface to interior processing centers (e.g., *food vacuoles*) or finished products in the opposite direction (e.g., *secretion granules*); they may be places of storage (e.g., *starch granules, fat vacuoles, water vacuoles, pigment granules*); they may be vehicles transporting waste materials to points of elimination (e.g., *excretory vacuoles*); or they may be special processing centers themselves.

In addition to all these, cytoplasm may or may not contain a variety of long, thin **fibrils** made predominantly out of protein (e.g., *contractile myofibrils, conducting neurofibrils*). Various other inclusions, unique to given cell types and serving unique functions, may also be present. In general, every function a cell performs, common or not, is based on a particular structure in which the machinery for that function is housed.

Cytoplasm as a whole is normally in motion. Irregular eddying and streaming occur at some times, and at others the substance of a cell is subjected to cyclical currents, a movement known as **cyclosis**. The formed inclusions, as well as the nucleus, are swept along passively in these streams. The specific cause of such motions is unknown, but there is little doubt that they are a reflection of the uninterrupted chemical and physical changes which take place on the molecular level. Whatever the specific causes may be, the apparently random movements might give the impression that nothing is fixed within a cell and that cytoplasm is simply a collection of loose particulate bodies suspended in "soup."

But this impression is erroneous, as examination under the electron microscope shows. The ground substance of cytoplasm, which under the light microscope does appear to be a fluid, structureless soup, actually turns out to be highly structured and organized. A network of exceedingly fine membranes can be shown to traverse the cytoplasm from plasma membrane to nuclear membrane and in many cases also from cell to cell. This network is known as the **endoplasmic reticulum** (Fig. 4.26). Linked to it are the nucleus, the mitochondria, the ribosomes, and all the other cytoplasmic inclusions. Thus, little is really "loose" in a cell. When cytoplasm as a whole streams and moves, the endo-

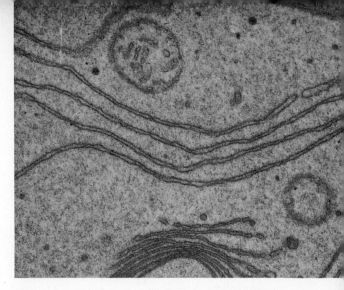

FIG. 4.26 Electron micrograph showing portion of endoplasmic reticulum. Note that the reticulum consists of an array of double membranes. *(Courtesy of Dr. W. G. Whaley, University of Texas.)*

plasmic reticulum streams and moves too and the formed inclusions are carried along, still held to the ultramicroscopic network. Evidently, even though the contents of a cell may shift position and the cell as a whole may be deformable, an orderly structural integration of the interior persists nevertheless. Indeed, this is essential if cellular functions are to be orderly and integrated.

THE CELL SURFACE

Every cell as a whole is bounded by a *cell* (or *plasma*) *membrane*. Composed predominantly of protein and lipid substances, this important structure is far more than a passive outer skin. It is an active, highly selective, semipermeable membrane which regulates the entry and exit of materials into and out of a cell. The membrane therefore plays a critical role in all cell functions, since directly or indirectly every cell function necessitates *absorption* of materials from the exterior, *excretion* of materials from the interior, or both. We shall have occasion in many later contexts to consider some of the specific activities of cell membranes.

Nearly all plant cells possess a *cell wall* around the cell membrane. Usually composed of cellulose, hemicellulose, and pectic substances (but of chitin in many fungi), cell walls vary in thickness depending on the functions of cells and their position within the plant body. A **primary cell wall** is that part of the wall which is formed while a cell grows and develops. Mature,

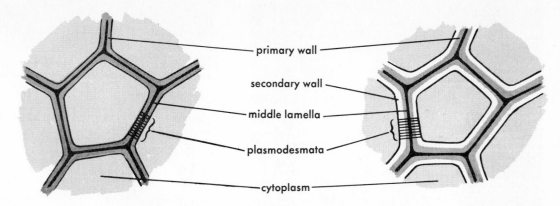

FIG. 4.27   Diagram of plant cells showing plasmodesmata and primary and secondary cell walls.

nongrowing cells often deposit additional materials on the inner surfaces of their primary walls, and such additions form a **secondary cell wall** (Fig. 4.27).

In multicellular plants, adjacent cells are held together by a thin layer called a **middle lamella**, composed of pectic cementing substances. In many cases, adjacent cells are interconnected also by fine strands of cytoplasm known as **plasmodesmata**. These pass through the cell walls and the middle lamella, thus forming minute but continuous cytoplasmic bridges between one cell and the next. Parts of the endoplasmic reticulum are included in such plasmodesmata.

Thin cell walls are more or less elastic; thicker ones, more or less rigid. These envelopes maintain *cell shape* and, as we shall see, aid in mechanical *support* against gravity. Plant cells exposed directly to the external air also secrete **cuticles** on their exposed surfaces, in addition to cell walls. As noted earlier in this chapter, such cuticles are made of waxy and fatty materials. They make the exposed cells relatively impermeable to water (Fig. 4.28).

Walls of cellulose and cuticles of wax are not found among animal cells, but in many cases animal cells too surround themselves with walls or cuticles. For example, a coat of **chitin** is found on the skin cells of insects and other invertebrates. Analogously, the surface cells of mammalian skin and hair secrete external coats made of the protein **keratin**. Skeletal **shells** of lime, glass (silica), or organic substances are among other external covers manufactured by many plant and animal cell types (Fig. 4.29).

Many cell types have the capacity of locomotion, and among these, many are equipped with distinct locomotor structures on the cell surface. Such structures are principally **flagella**, long, slender projections. The base of a flagellum is anchored in the cytoplasm of a cell, on a distinct granule known as a *kinetosome* or

FIG. 4.28   Portion of a leaf showing epidermal cells with thick, dark walls and a waxy cuticle on their exposed surfaces. *(Courtesy of Dr. M. S. Fuller, Brown University.)*

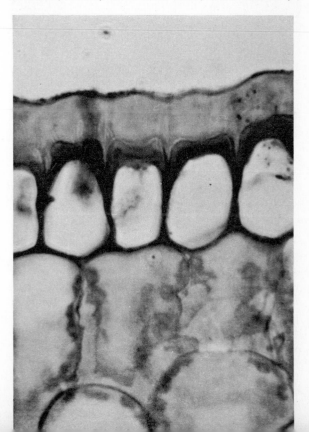

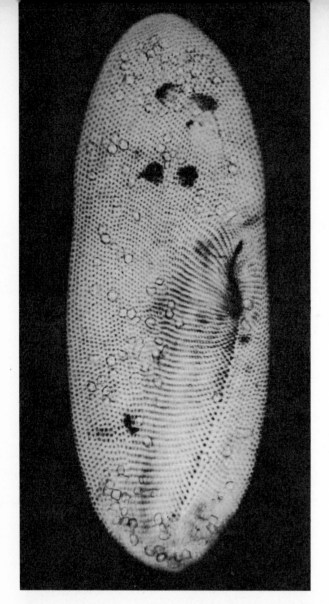

FIG. 4.29 Cell walls in protozoa. Left, the outer covering of the ciliate protozoan *Paramecium*, made of complex, chitinlike organic materials. The dark dots represent tiny holes through which cilia project. Right, silicaceous shells secreted around radiolarian protozoa. *(General Biological Supply House, Inc.)*

blepharoplast. This granule controls the motion of the flagellum. Most often flagella are at the "forward" end of a cell; i.e., the flagellum leads the cell and its motion pulls the cell along behind it. If a flagellum has a smooth external surface, it is said to be of the *whiplash type;* if it possesses exceedingly fine side branches set on the main stem like the bristles of a brush, it is said to be of the *tinsel type*. A cell may possess either or both types of flagella. In most cases, a cell bears from

one to four flagella, all originating from the same surface region. But in some cases the number is very much larger and each flagellum then originates at a separate surface point. Such flagella are usually called **cilia** (Fig. 4.30).

Internally, all flagella have the same structure. The electron microscope reveals a flagellum to be a bundle of eleven exceedingly fine fibrils. Two of the fibrils are central and nine are arranged in a ring around the central two. All the fibrils connect with the kinetosome at the base of the flagellum. How flagellar motion is actually produced is as yet understood only poorly.

The above account outlines some of the main organizational features characteristic of cells generally. As we have seen, certain of the components of the

FIG. 4.30 Diagram, types of flagella and their insertion in cells. Bottom left, electron micrograph of dried flagellum, showing the 11 constituent filaments. Bottom right, the ciliate protozoan, *Tetrahymena*, stained to show the cilia and their arrangement on the body surface. (Bottom left, *courtesy of Dr. W. Koch, University of North Carolina, and Am. J. Botany, vol. 43, p. 811*; bottom right, *courtesy of Dr. N. Williams, Iowa State University.*)

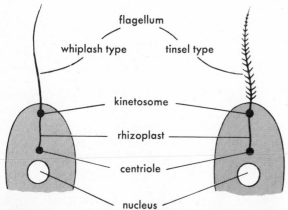

TABLE 3

Some structural components of cells and their correlated functions

structure	function
nucleus	
chromosomes	ultimate control of cell activities
nucleolus	control of protein synthesis
nuclear membrane	traffic control to and from cytoplasm
cytoplasm	
mitochondria	site of respiration
ribosomes	site of protein synthesis
Golgi bodies	site of secretion synthesis
chloroplasts	site of photosynthesis
centrioles	auxiliary to cell division
granules ⎱ vacuoles ⎰	transport, storage, processing centers
fibrils	contraction, conduction
surface	
plasma membrane	traffic control to and from cell
cell walls ⎱ cuticles ⎰	protection, support, cell shape
cilia ⎱ flagella ⎰	locomotion, current creation

nucleus, the cytoplasm, or the cell surface may be associated directly with well-circumscribed cell functions. Photosynthesis and respiration, for example, are distinct functions performed in distinct cytoplasmic structures; see Table 3 for a summary of such correlations. But many cell functions cannot be localized so neatly. For example, cellular reproduction requires the cooperative activity of many or all of the cell components present. Functions of this kind cannot be referred to any particular part of a cell; they must be referred to the cell as a whole.

Note in this connection that, whereas many cell structures are bulky enough to be visible under the microscope, even more are not visible; individual molecules in a cell "function" no less than larger molecular aggregates. Note also that *each* cellular structure performs a function, and as the structures differ among cells, so do the functions.

Singly and in multiple combinations, cells form organisms. The ways in which cells are joined into organisms and the general nature of organisms will be the topics of the next chapter.

REVIEW QUESTIONS

1. What are inorganic compounds? Organic compounds? What principal classes of each occur in living matter and in what relative amounts? Which of these substances are electrolytes and which are nonelectrolytes?

2. Review the chemical composition and molecular structure of carbohydrates and fats. What are monosaccharides, disaccharides, and polysaccharides? Give examples of each. What are saturated and unsaturated fatty acids? In what kinds of reactions may carbohydrates and fats participate and what general roles do they play in living matter?

3. What are proteins and how are they constructed? In what ways do proteins differ from carbohydrates and fats? Discuss fully and carefully. What is the primary, secondary, and tertiary structure of proteins and what is protein specificity? How is a coagulated protein different from a native or a denatured protein? Review the general biological roles of proteins.

4. What is the chemical composition and molecular structure of nucleic acids? In chemical terms, what are DNA and RNA? What is their relation to nucleoproteins? How are nucleotides related to DNA and RNA? What different kinds of nucleotides occur in living matter?

5. What main classes of pigments occur in organisms? How do these substances differ chemically? What are some of their functions? What derivatives of carbohydrates and fats are common in organisms?

6. What is a colloidal system? How does such a system differ from a solution? What kinds of colloidal systems are possible and what kinds are found in living matter? Review the properties of colloidal systems.

7. Define diffusion and show how and under what conditions this process will occur. What is the biological significance of diffusion?

8. How and where do plasma membranes form? What are the characteristics of such membranes? What roles do they play in biological processes?

9. Define osmosis. Show how and under what conditions this process will occur. Distinguish carefully between osmosis and diffusion. Cite examples of biological situations characterized by isotonicity, hypertonicity, and hypotonicity.

10. What are the structural subdivisions of cells? What are the main components of each of these subdivisions, where are they found, and what functions do they carry out?

11. List cytoplasmic inclusions encountered in all cell types and inclusions found only in certain cell types. What is cyclosis? How do plant and animal cells differ structurally?

12. What structures are found on the surfaces of various cell types? Which of these structures are primarily protective? What do they protect against? What are the functions of other surface structures? How do the surfaces of plant and animal cells differ?

SUGGESTED COLLATERAL READINGS

The articles cited below are good semipopular accounts dealing with a variety of cellular constituents.

Bushwell, A. M., and W. H. Rodebush: Water, *Sci. American,* vol. 194, 1956.

Crick, F. H. C.: Nucleic Acids, *Sci. American,* vol. 197, 1957.

Doty, P.: Proteins, *Sci. American,* vol. 197, 1957.

Frank, S.: Carotenoids, *Sci. American,* vol. 194, 1956.

Frieden, E.: The Enzyme-Substrate Complex, *Sci. American,* vol. 201, 1959.

Kamen, M. D.: A Universal Molecule of Living Matter, the Tetrapyrrol Ring, *Sci. American,* vol. 202, 1960.

Linderstrom-Lang, K. U.: How Is a Protein Made? *Sci. American,* vol. 189, 1953.

Nord, F. F., and W. J. Schubert: Lignin, *Sci. American,* vol. 199, 1958.

Pauling, L., R. B. Corey, and R. Hayward: The Structure of Protein Molecules, *Sci. American,* vol. 191, 1954.

Pfeiffer, J. E.: Enzymes, *Sci. American,* vol. 179, 1948.

Preston, R. D.: Cellulose, *Sci. American,* vol. 197, 1957.

Robertson, R. N.: Electrolytes in Plant Tissue, *Endeavour,* vol. 16, 1957.

Schmitt, F. O.: Giant Molecules in Cells and Tissues, *Sci. American,* vol. 197, 1957.

Vallee, B. L.: The Function of Trace Elements in Biology, *Sci. Monthly,* vol. 72, 1951.

The following texts include excellent accounts of the composition and the properties of cells.

Giese, A. C.: "Cell Physiology," Saunders, Philadelphia, 1957.

DeRobertis, E. D. P., W. W. Nowinski, and F. A. Saez: "General Cytology," 3d ed., Saunders, Philadelphia, 1960.

The following compilation contains abstracts from original research papers in major areas of biology; the cell is among the topics treated.

Gabriel, M. L., and S. Fogel (eds.): "Great Experiments in Biology," Prentice-Hall, Englewood Cliffs, N.J., 1955.

ORGANISMS

5

All living things in nature exist in the form of whole, individual organisms, some of which are unicellular and some of which are multicellular. In the multicellular ones, cells are usually joined together into distinct **tissues,** tissues in turn are often combined into **organs,** and organs may be united into **organ systems.** These subdivisions of organisms will occupy our attention in the first part of this chapter.

The second part will concentrate on the whole organism. What is basic and common to all organisms, unicellular and multicellular, to qualify them as "living" things? If one cell suffices for life in some cases, why are many joined cells necessary in other cases? Besides, compositional characteristics alone do not show how a living organism differs from a dead one. What must organisms *do* to be living? And how, if at all, are the activities of organisms fundamentally different from those of machines? In short, we shall inquire here into the general **nature of organisms** and thus into the essential meaning of our concept of "life."

TISSUES, ORGANS, ORGAN SYSTEMS

As a multicellular organism matures, most of its cells *specialize* in various ways; i.e., they develop the capacity to carry out particular functions. Some cells specialize to a relatively minor extent, and each is then able to perform several comparatively simple functions. Other cells, however, become highly specialized, and each is then capable of performing just one or two comparatively complex functions. We shall return to this phenomenon of functional specialization below. The important point for the present is that specialization in function is always accompanied by specialization in structure. Thus, maturing cells become diversified in appearance and extremely specialized cells come to differ from one another drastically. Moreover, such cells also come to differ greatly from the basic microscopic organization of cells described in the preceding chapter. The characteristics of very highly specialized cells are usually fixed and irreversible; i.e., a cell specialized in one way cannot change and become respecialized in another way.

Tissues are formed by variously specialized cells. A tissue may be defined as an aggregation of cells in which each *cooperates* with all others in the performance of a particular group function. In a **simple tissue,** all cells are of the same type. Two or more different cell types are present in a **composite tissue.** The cells of a tissue need not necessarily be in direct physical contact, but this is actually the case in most instances. Tissues may be highly or less highly specialized, according to the degree of specialization of the component cells.

An *organ* is an aggregation of tissues all of which cooperate in the performance of a group function. Analogously, an *organ system* is a cooperating aggregation of organs. Several organ systems may be present in an organism. But note that not all multicellular organisms necessarily possess organs and organ systems. In some of the most primitive multicellular organisms, the whole body consists of but a single tissue. More advanced organisms usually possess several tissues. Some of these tissues often form an organ. Numerous organs and sets of organ systems occur only in the most advanced organisms.

We shall examine the general internal organization of highly advanced multicellular organisms, and we shall select flowering plants and mammals as illustrative examples.

THE PLANT PATTERN

Cell Types

Among the least specialized and most abundant cell types present in plant tissues are so-called **parenchyma** cells (Fig. 5.1). Such cells may variously photosynthesize, manufacture numerous chemical constituents of living matter, store some of these constituents, and transport others in solution from one parenchyma cell to another. Above all, parenchyma cells remain so indistinctly specialized that, under appropriate stimulation, they may specialize further and develop into a large variety of other cell types. Groups of parenchyma cells collectively may even develop into whole roots or stems or into complete new plants. Evidently, parenchyma cells retain more or less *embryonic,* undeveloped characteristics even in an adult plant.

Parenchyma cells are usually packed closely to-

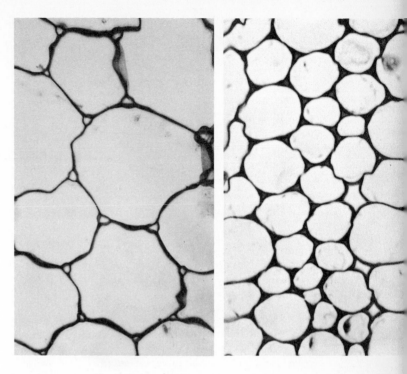

FIG. 5.1   Left, parenchyma; right, collenchyma. *(Courtesy of Dr. M. S. Fuller, Brown University.)*

gether, and the pressure the cells exert on one another gives them a typically 14-sided shape. The cell walls of parenchyma cells remain relatively thin and consist most often of primary wall only. When such cells become more specialized and develop into other cell types, secondary walls may be formed inside the primary ones. Given points along these walls may remain thin, however, and such points are known as **simple pits.** Opposing pits in two adjacent cells form a **simple pit pair.** The two pits here are separated by the middle lamella and a thin layer of primary wall on either side. These dividing layers constitute a **pit membrane.** Transport of materials from cell to cell takes place particularly through such pit pairs (Fig. 5.2).

A somewhat more specialized variant of parenchyma cells is a cell type called **collenchyma** (see Fig. 5.1). These cells possess quite thick, yet nevertheless fairly elastic, primary walls. Wall thickenings are especially noticeable at the corners of the prismatic cells. Collenchyma cells are abundant in developing leaves and stems, where the thick cell walls aid materially in support against gravity.

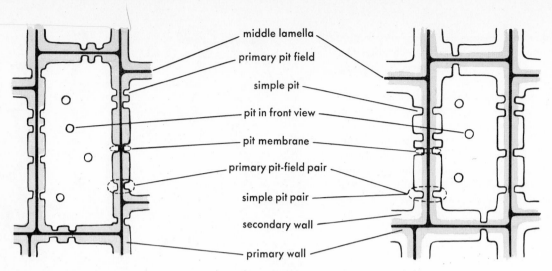

middle lamella

primary pit field

simple pit

pit in front view

pit membrane

primary pit-field pair

simple pit pair

secondary wall

primary wall

FIG. 5.2   Diagram of cells showing pit modifications of cell walls. Left, cell with primary wall only; right, cell with primary and secondary walls.

Many body parts of a plant are covered externally by various types of **epidermal cells.** They have greatly diversified shapes, and they serve not only as protective coverings but also in procurement, manufacture, and storage of nutrients. In epidermal cells of stems and leaves, the parts of the cell walls which face the atmosphere are usually thickened by the deposition of waxy cuticles. As a group, epidermal cells are not very highly specialized, and in this and other respects they rather resemble parenchyma cells.

Two particular kinds of epidermal cells are somewhat more specialized than others (Fig. 5.3). One kind, known as **guard cells,** occurs on the surfaces of leaves and green stems. Guard cells are sausage- or crescent-shaped, and they are placed pairwise in such a way that the concave side of one faces the concave side of another. Along these concave sides the cell walls are thicker than elsewhere. The open space left between two such paired cells is a **stoma.** Through changes of osmotic conditions within guard cells stomata may be

FIG. 5.3   Epidermal specializations. Left, surface view of epidermis showing a pair of chloroplast-containing guard cells enclosing a stoma; right, root epidermis with root hairs. (*Left, Ward's Natural Science Establishment, Inc.; right, courtesy of Dr. M. S. Fuller, Brown University.*)

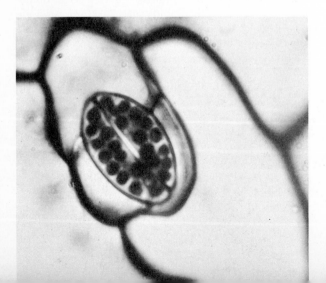

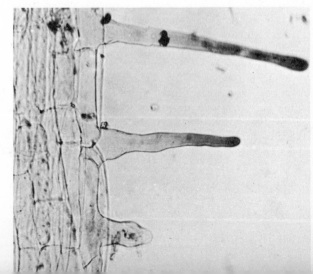

opened or closed, an important feature which controls the entry and exit of atmospheric gases through the body surface of a plant. We shall discuss this process in greater detail in a later chapter.

Another special kind of epidermal cell is found on the surfaces of roots, at certain stages of root development. Present there are so-called **root-hair cells**. Like epidermal cells of roots generally, these cells are without cuticles. As their name indicates, they possess fingerlike extensions of the cell cytoplasm, on the side exposed to soil. Such "hairs" greatly increase the surface area of the cells, a significant feature in nutrient absorption. This too will be discussed in detail later.

Among the most highly specialized cells of multicellular plants is a group which functions primarily in providing mechanical support. The cell type is known as **sclerenchyma** (Fig. 5.4). Such cells possess thick primary walls and also very thick, lignin-impregnated secondary walls. Cells of this type are strong, quite inelastic, and well suited to lend rigidity and hardness to mature, nongrowing body parts of a plant. Two variant forms of sclerenchyma may be distinguished, viz., **fibers** and **sclereids**. Fibers are greatly elongated, and they usually have tapered ends. The cells function mainly in lending support to elongated plant parts such as stems. Sclereids have more varied and irregular shapes. Their main function is to provide rigidity or hardness. Once a cell begins to develop as a distinct sclerenchyma type, it can thereafter no longer respecialize as any other type. In this respect, sclerenchyma cells are like all other highly specialized cell types. Often, indeed, sclerenchyma cells manufacture their walls and then the nucleus and the cytoplasm disintegrate altogether. Only the walls are left, and mature sclerenchyma may therefore be wholly nonliving and no longer "cellular" in character at all.

Several highly specialized cell types serve particularly in transport of water. One group of such cells, found largely in stems, is known as **tracheids** (Fig. 5.5). Mature tracheids are spindle-shaped and comparatively huge. They may be up to 5 mm long and 0.03 mm

FIG. 5.5 Types of tracheids showing various kinds of secondary thickenings.

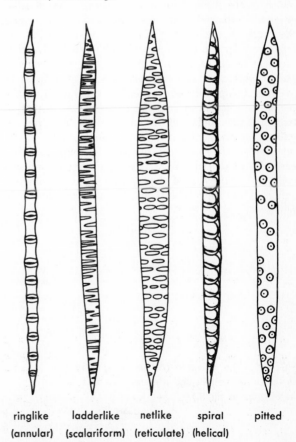

FIG. 5.4 Sclerenchyma. The diagram depicts fibers in longitudinal view (A), in cross section (B), and a section through a part of a sclereid (C) as well as a whole sclereid (D).

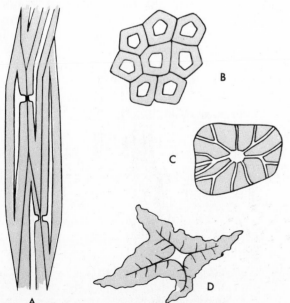

A

B

C

D

ringlike   ladderlike   netlike   spiral   pitted

(annular)   (scalariform)   (reticulate)   (helical)

wide. Their cell walls contain primary as well as secondary layers, both rigid and impregnated with lignin. In many cases the secondary wall lines the primary layer completely, as an uninterrupted inner coat. In other cases the secondary wall is incomplete and is deposited in the form of rings or spiral bands or transverse bars or networks. Such incomplete patterns add strength yet still permit a long tracheid to bend without breaking. Like a sclerenchyma cell, a mature tracheid has lost its nucleus and cytoplasm and is represented only by its nonliving walls.

Liquid transport from one tracheid into the next occurs through elaborate **bordered pits** in the cell walls, specialized regions similar in some respects to the simple pits of parenchyma cells (Fig. 5.6). In a bordered pit, the primary cell wall of a tracheid is very thin except at a small central area. Here primary-wall material forms a **torus**, a small round or oval plug attached to the pit membrane. The secondary wall overhangs the pit around its rim and is absent in the region of the torus. Thus if water pressure in an adjacent cell pushes the pit membrane and the torus into the tracheid, the torus is prevented from moving too far inward by the rim of the secondary wall. The torus in effect functions like a valve. Like the simple pits of parenchyma cells, bordered pits most frequently occur in pairs, the pit of one tracheid joined directly to the pit of an adjacent cell. If the adjacent cell is another tracheid, the double pit is known as a **bordered pit pair**; if the adjacent cell is parenchymatous, the double pit is referred to as a **half-bordered pit pair**. In either case the pits permit easy passage of liquid between cells, and in the case of the rigid tracheids the pluglike action of the torus guards against entry or exit of too much water.

Serving like tracheids in water conduction are highly specialized, cell-derived structures called **vessels** (Fig. 5.7). A vessel develops from embryonic cells which are placed end to end and form a continuous column often many feet long. Each cell here gives rise to a **vessel element**. As the cell matures it produces primary and secondary cell walls as well as bordered pits, just as in tracheids. The secondary walls may be incomplete and may be deposited in spiral bands or in rings or in other patterns. Eventually the nucleus and the cytoplasm disintegrate and disappear. Moreover, the transverse end walls, where one cell of the column abuts against the next, may develop one or more openings or may dissolve altogether. In effect, therefore, the mature vessel elements in a column become a continuous nonliving hollow tube, with remnants of transverse cross walls still present in places. Such a final structure is a vessel.

Specialized for the conduction of organic compounds are cellular complexes called **sieve tubes** (Fig. 5.8). A sieve tube usually develops from a column of embryonic cells placed end to end, much as in the development of vessels. Each of these embryonic cells divides, and one of the two resulting cells is a **sieve-tube cell**. Remaining joined to it, the other cell forms one or more smaller **companion cells**. Subsequently, primary cell walls (only) are deposited; they are quite thin where the sieve-tube cell is attached to the companion cells. Also, many simple pits form in these regions. As the sieve-tube cell continues to mature, **sieve areas** appear at various points of its wall. These areas represent modified pits, and they are actually openings or perforations in the cell wall. Passing through these openings are strands of cytoplasm which interconnect the sieve-tube cell with adjacent cells. In

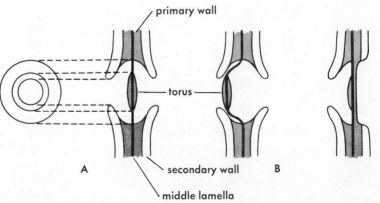

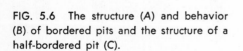

FIG. 5.6 The structure (A) and behavior (B) of bordered pits and the structure of a half-bordered pit (C).

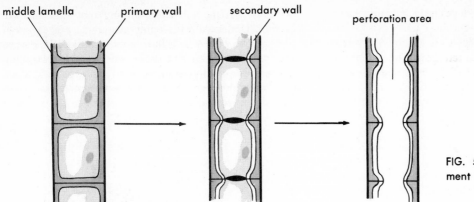

FIG. 5.7 The develop-
ment of a vessel.

some plants comparatively large sieve areas develop only on the end walls, where one sieve-tube cell in the column abuts against others above and below. Food conduction through a long sieve tube depends particularly on the cytoplasmic bridges between adjacent sieve-tube cells.

A characteristic feature of mature sieve-tube cells is the absence of a nucleus. This body persists through the period of cell maturation, but then it disintegrates and disappears. Thereafter, such nuclear activities as are required appear to be carried out by the persistently nucleated companion cells. These maintain a close cooperation with their associated sieve-tube cell. Thus if a mature sieve-tube cell stops functioning for any

reason, its associated companion cells also stop functioning and die.

The cell types described above represent some of the most widespread and abundant types known to exist in flowering plants. The description shows how, superimposed on a common basic organization, different cells may come to vary in the fine details of their specialized organization.

Tissues and Organs

In various groupings and combinations, the cell types above are the structural building blocks of numerous plant tissues. This is well illustrated if we examine

FIG. 5.8 Sieve tubes and their development (left to right).

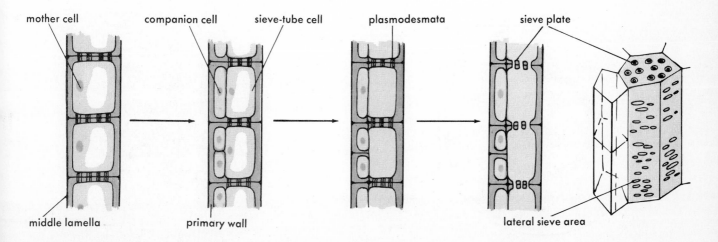

the tissues which typically develop in a young stem-root system (Figs. 5.9 and 5.10).

In such a system, the tissues are arranged in a concentric, radially symmetrical pattern. The outermost tissue is the **epidermis,** a protective cover one cell layer thick and composed of various kinds of epidermal cells. In the stem portion, such cells include guard cells; in the root portion, nutrient-absorbing root-hair cells are present. Underneath the epidermis are several layers of parenchyma cells which form a tissue called the **cortex.** This tissue is green and food-producing in stems, non-green and food-storing in roots. In both root and stem, the cortex also transports water. Adjacent to the inner-most layer of the cortex is the **endodermis.** In most

FIG. 5.9   Top, the typical arrangement of tissues in a stem; a portion of a section through a bean stem is shown at right. Bottom, the typical arrangement of tissues in a root; a section through a buttercup root is shown at right. *(Top photo, Ripon Microslides; bottom photo, Carolina Biological Supply Co.)*

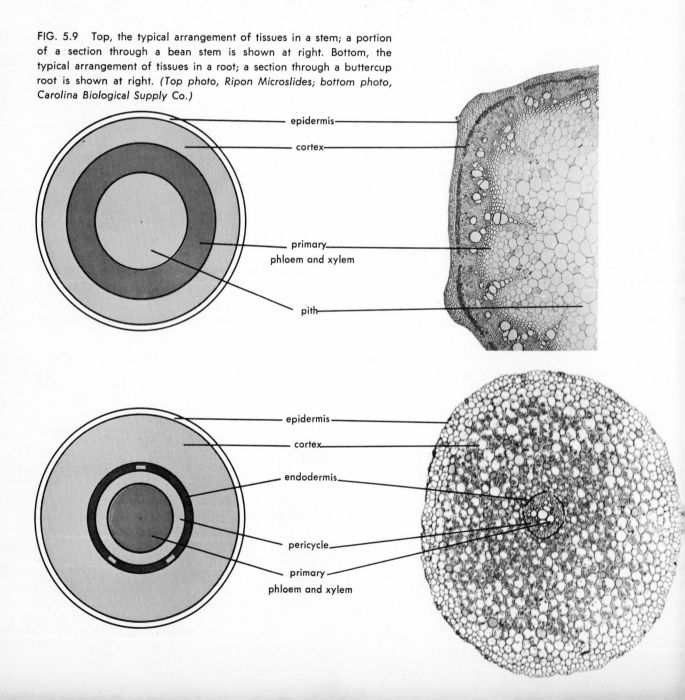

Tissues	Epidermis	Cortex	Endodermis	Pericycle	Phloem	Xylem	Pith
Cell types	epidermal cells	parenchyma	endodermal cells	parenchyma	parenchyma	parenchyma	parenchyma
	guard cells	collenchyma	passage cells	sclerenchyma	sclerenchyma	sclerenchyma	sclerenchyma
	root-hair cells	sclerenchyma			companion cells	tracheids	
					sieve-tube cells	vessel elements	

FIG. 5.10   The principal cell types composing each of the tissues in a mature stem and root.

stems the endodermis is developed very incompletely, and in some it may not be present at all. But in roots the endodermis is usually quite prominent. It is composed of a single layer of fairly large cells, most of them impregnated with suberin on their outer surfaces. In certain regions of the root, small groups of endodermis cells do not manufacture suberin. These are called *passage cells;* as we shall see later, they play an important role in water transport through the root.

Toward the inside of the endodermis is a group of tissues known collectively as the **stele.** The arrangement of these stelar tissues differs greatly for different plant groups, and we shall discuss various specific arrangements in Chap. 10. Here we shall be concerned only with the basic or primitive arrangement from which all others are probably derived. The outermost tissue of the stele, directly adjacent to the endodermis, is the **pericycle.** In most stems the pericycle, like the endodermis, is developed very incompletely, and in some stems it may not be present at all. But in roots the pericycle is fairly conspicuous, being composed here of one or more layers of parenchyma cells.

Toward the inside of the pericycle, a second tissue of the stele is the **primary phloem.** This is a highly composite tissue consisting of parenchyma cells, sclerenchymatous fiber and sclereid cells, companion cells, and sieve-tube cells formed into sieve tubes. Primary phloem is a conducting tissue; it transports organic materials and food stuffs over long distances. By virtue of its transporting function, primary phloem is also referred to as a *vascular tissue.*

A third tissue of the stele is located typically toward the inside of the primary phloem. This tissue is the **primary xylem.** It too is highly composite; it consists of parenchyma cells, sclerenchymatous fiber cells, tracheids, and, above all, vessel elements formed into vessels. These components make primary xylem both a vascular and a supporting tissue; it functions in long-distance conduction of water and dissolved inorganic nutrients, and it supports a plant against gravity. Note that possession of the two vascular tissues, primary phloem and xylem, defines a group of plants appropriately called "vascular plants." Note also that another name for xylem is *wood.* However, if only a little is present, as is usually the case in primary xylem, this tissue usually represents too little wood to make a plant distinctly "woody" in external appearance.

The last of the basic tissues to be considered here is the **pith.** It is not present in roots, and in stems it is located right at the center, surrounded by primary xylem. Pith is composed of parenchyma cells; as in the cortex, pith cells store foods and conduct water from cell to cell.

Clearly, these various tissues are not "just there," but are organized in a definite structural pattern. Because of this structural pattern, functional cooperation among the tissues becomes possible. The main cooperative functions of the tissues are, in the stem, support against gravity, conduction, and manufacture of organic nutrients and, in the root, support in soil, conduction, and absorption of inorganic nutrients. Group functions performed by several tissues are characteristic of *organs,* and we may note that stems and roots actually are two of the kinds of organs found in a plant.

Two other sets of organs occur in vascular plants, namely, *leaves* and *reproductive organs*. As we shall see later (e.g., Chap. 10), these organs are formed largely from the same kinds of cell types and tissue types which form stems and roots. In at least one instance among plants, several whole organs cooperate functionally and form a still more complex organization, viz., an *organ system*. This is the case in cones and flowers. As we shall see, these consist of several reproductive and other associated organs, all contributing to the one overall function of propagation.

A far more elaborate organization, including many more than one type of organ system, is characteristic of advanced animals.

THE ANIMAL PATTERN

Tissue Types

Two general classes of animal tissues may be distinguished, viz., **connective tissues** and **epithelia.** Often not included in these two groups are three specific tissues, namely, *blood, nerve tissue,* and *muscle tissue.* The first two of these will be dealt with separately in Chaps. 21 and 22. A discussion of muscle tissue will be included here.

Connective tissues. In these, the cells are usually separated from one another by greater or lesser amounts of intercellular spaces which are variously filled with fluid and solid materials. Another identifying characteristic is the relatively unspecialized nature of the cells. With appropriate stimulation, they may trans-

form from one connective tissue cell type into another. In these respects, the cells are roughly equivalent to the parenchyma and parenchymalike cells of plants. On the basis of the types of intercellular deposits present, two major varieties of connective tissues, each with several subvarieties, may be distinguished: *loose* and *hard* connective tissues.

The basic variant of the loose connective tissues may be considered to be **fibroelastic tissue** (Fig. 5.11). In it, the most conspicuous components are large numbers of threadlike fibers, some of them tough and strong (and made of the protein collagen), some of them elastic. These fibers are suspended in fluid and form an irregular, loosely arranged meshwork. The cells of the tissue are dispersed throughout the mesh. Materials secreted by the cells give rise to the fibers outside them. The cells are of various types. Many are so-called *fibrocytes,* generally spindle-shaped and believed to be the chief fiber-forming cells. Other cells, the *histiocytes,* are capable of amoeboid locomotion and of engulfing foreign bodies (e.g., bacteria in infected regions). Also present are *pigment cells, fat cells,* and *mesenchyme cells.* The latter are embryonic, undeveloped, and relatively quite unspecialized; they may develop into any of the other cell types of the tissue. (Note that most of the other cells present may also transform into one another. For example, a fibrocyte might become a fat cell, then perhaps a histiocyte, then a fibrocyte again, and then a pigment cell. The specializations of any of these cells evidently are not fixed.)

By virtue of its cellular components, fibroelastic

FIG. 5.11 Fibroelastic connective tissue. Note the conspicuous fibers forming a meshwork and the cells (small dark dots) embedded in the meshwork (left). Some of the cells, namely, fibrocytes, are shown in enlarged view growing in tissue culture (right). *(Photograph of tissue, General Biological Supply House, Inc.)*

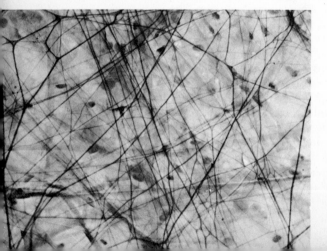
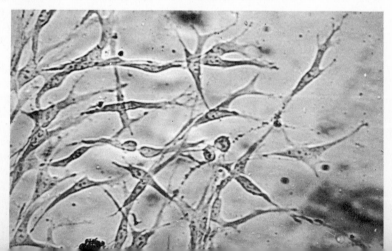

tissue functions in food storage and in body defense; and by virtue of its fibers, the tissue is a major binding agent which holds one body part to another. For example, fibroelastic tissue connects skin to underlying muscle; the tough fibers provide connecting strength, yet the elastic fibers still permit the skin to slide over the muscle to some extent. In man, fat stored in fibroelastic tissue under the skin is responsible for the generally rounded contours of females and is partly responsible for the obese appearance of overweight persons.

The relative quantities of both the cellular and the fibrous components may vary greatly, and on the basis of such variations one may distinguish other types of loose connective tissue (Fig. 5.12). For example, **tendons** are dense tissues containing only fibrocytes and tough collagen fibers, the fibers being arranged as closely packed parallel bundles. Tendons typically connect muscles to cartilage or bone. A **ligament** is similar to a tendon, except that both collagen and elastic fibers are present and that these are arranged in more or less irregular manner. Another variant of fibroelastic tissue is **adipose tissue,** of which fat cells are the most abundant components. Each fat cell contains a large fat droplet which fills almost the entire cellular space. A large collection of such cells has the external appearance of a continuous mass of fat. Still another variant of fibroelastic tissue occurs in several (but not all) types of **tissue membranes,** in which the cellular components are numerous and fairly densely packed and the intercellular components are minimal. Various other types of loose connective tissues are known in addition. These occur in special locations or at special times during animal development.

In the hard connective tissues, the cellular com-

FIG. 5.12 Variants of fibroelastic connective tissue. Top left and right, tendon and ligament. Bottom left, adipose tissue. Bottom right, pigment cell. In adipose tissue, note the virtual absence of fibers and the large fat droplets in each of the closely packed cells. (Bottom left, courtesy of Dr. B. J. Serber, College of Medicine, New York University; bottom right, courtesy of Dr. R. Brenner, Brown University.)

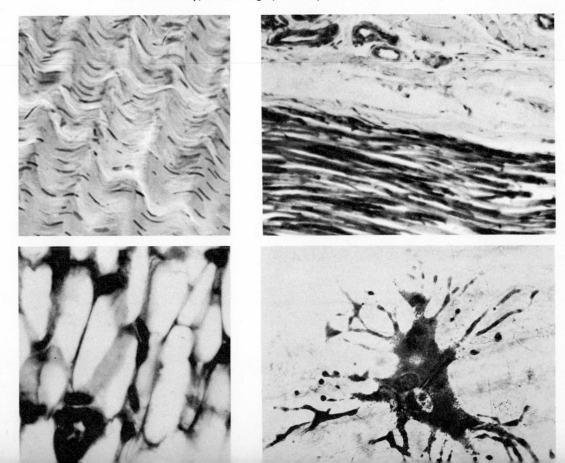

ponents secrete organic and, especially, inorganic materials which form a solid precipitate around the cells. Thus the cells appear as islands embedded in hard intercellular deposits. The chief variants of this tissue type are **cartilage** and **bone** (Fig. 5.13). Calcium phosphate is the main inorganic constituent of bone. The functions of cartilage and bone are twofold; they support (e.g., the long bony rods of the appendages, which hold other tissues around them) and they protect (e.g., the flat bony plates of the skull, which cover the underlying brain).

Among vertebrate animals, cartilage is the sole supporting tissue in forms such as lampreys and sharks. In these, the skeleton remains permanently cartilaginous. In other vertebrates, man included, much of the skeleton is preformed in cartilage during early embryonic development, but later most of these supports are gradually replaced by bone (regions which do not become bony include, for example, the cartilage of the nose). In man, replacement of cartilage by bone is usually not completed until approximately the twentieth year of life (Fig. 5.14).

The brief descriptions above show that, as a group, connective tissues serve largely in forming the structural scaffolding of the animal body. Primarily functional parts of the body are formed chiefly by the epithelial tissues.

Epithelia. An epithelium is a tissue in which the cells are cemented directly to one another and so form a single-layered sheet, a multilayered sheet, or an irregular, compact, three-dimensional aggregate (Fig. 5.15).

Sheets consisting of a single layer of cells are called **simple epithelia.** Distinctions among them are made principally on the basis of cell shape. If the cells are flattened and are joined along their edges, the tissue is known as a "pavement" or *squamous* epithelium. Many tissue membranes are of this type. If the cells have the shape of cubes, the tissue is a *cuboidal* epithelium. The walls of ducts and glands frequently consist of such tissues. Analogously, if the cells are prismatic and are joined along their long sides, the tissue is a *columnar* epithelium. A good example of this type is the innermost layer of the gut, the so-called *intestinal mucosa* (Fig. 5.16).

Intergradations between such cell shapes are very common, and many simple epithelia therefore cannot be classified into definite categories. If several epithelial layers of a given type are stacked into a multilayered sheet, the term **stratified epithelium** is often applied. Such complex epithelia thus may be of stratified squamos, stratified cuboidal, or of stratified columnar type. The epidermis, i.e., the outermost tissue of the skin, is a good example of a mixed stratified epithelium; the cells are squamous along the outer surface and become increasingly cuboidal with increasing distance from the surface (Fig. 5.17).

In contrast to the connective tissues, the epithelia are all fairly highly and permanently specialized. Once their cells are mature, they do not thereafter change in their basic structural characteristics. Also, by the time maturity is reached, the cells have acquired given fixed functions which are then performed throughout the life of the animal.

FIG. 5.13 Left, histological section through cartilage. Note the many cartilage-producing cells, surrounded by their own secretions. Right, histological section through bone. Bone-producing cells are located in the dark patches, arranged in concentric patterns. Hard bone substance, light in the photo, surrounds the cells. *(Left, General Biological Supply House, Inc.; right, Ward's Natural Science Establishment, Inc.)*

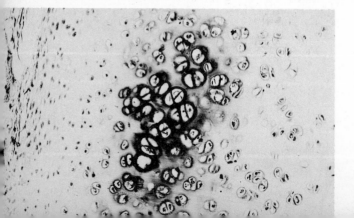
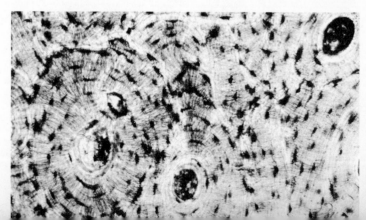

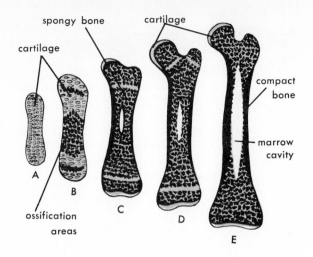

FIG. 5.14 The growth of a bone. *A*, cartilage rod, foreshadowing future bone. *B*, bone-forming cells give rise to three centers of ossification (black areas). *C*, spongy bone replaces all of cartilage, except in regions near joints (white bands); compact bone begins to form at surface of shaft, and marrow cavity in center of shaft. *D*, compact bone (solid black) extensive, marrow cavity enlarging. *E*, mature bone; cartilage layers near joints have been replaced by bone; in shaft, marrow cavity large, and spongy bone largely replaced by compact bone.

In most respects quite like an epithelium is **muscle tissue,** undoubtedly the most abundant tissue in most animals. In a man, as much as two-thirds of the total body weight is muscle weight. Muscle is also one of the most characteristically "animal" tissues, and there is no general body function that does not involve muscular contraction in some way.

Three types of muscle tissue may be distinguished: *smooth* muscle, *striated* muscle, and *cardiac* muscle (Fig. 5.18). In the smooth variety, the cells are elongated and spindle-shaped. Contraction of lengthwise intracellular *fibrils* shortens and thickens the cell. Many of such cells may be oriented in parallel, forming a muscular layer. For example, the intestinal wall of vertebrates contains two such layers. In one, the cells are aligned longitudinally and in the other they are placed circularly (Fig. 5.19). Contraction of the one shortens and widens the gut; contraction of the other lengthens and narrows it. Contraction of both maintains firmness and a tubular shape. In vertebrates, smooth muscle is generally not connected with the skeleton and is not under voluntary nervous control. Contractions take place relatively slowly.

Striated, "skeletal," or "voluntary" muscle is made up of syncytial units. Each such unit, a **muscle fiber,** develops through repeated division of a single cell, and in this process the boundaries between daughter cells disappear. The resulting fiber therefore contains many

FIG. 5.15 Epithelia. Left, surface view of frog epidermis. Note the close packing of the cells and the angular cell outlines, produced by pressure of cells against one another. Right, section through an epithelium which forms a compact sheet many cell layers thick. *(Ward's Natural Science Establishment, Inc.)*

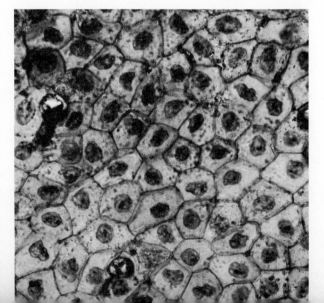

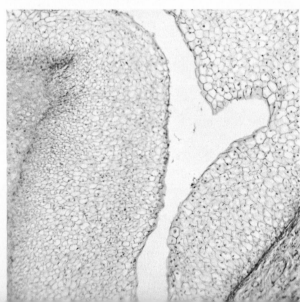

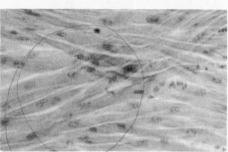

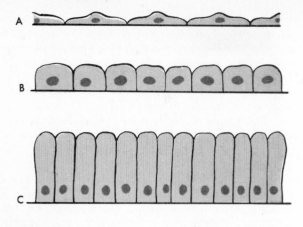

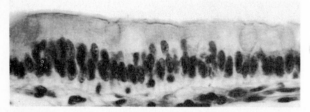

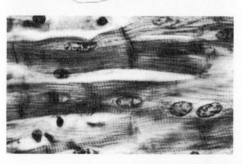

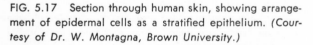

FIG. 5.16 Simple epithelia. Diagram: *A*, squamous epithelium; *B*, cuboidal epithelium; *C*, columnar epithelium. Photo: the intestinal mucosa of a frog, a columnar epithelium lining the inner surface of the gut wall. (*Photograph, General Biological Supply House, Inc.*)

FIG. 5.18 Top, a few fibers of skeletal muscle. Note the cross striations, and the many nuclei within each fiber. Middle, smooth muscle. Note the spindle-shaped cells. Bottom, heart muscle. Note the branched fibers, the nuclei, the faint longitudinal fibrils within each fiber, and the faint cross striations. (*General Biological Supply House, Inc.*)

FIG. 5.17 Section through human skin, showing arrangement of epidermal cells as a stratified epithelium. (*Courtesy of Dr. W. Montagna, Brown University.*)

FIG. 5.19 Cutaway diagram of a section of gut, showing the outer longitudinal and the inner circular layer of smooth muscle.

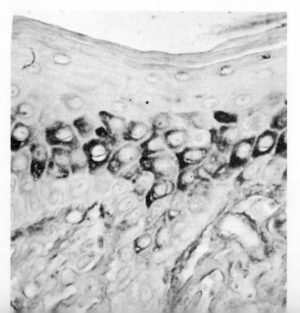

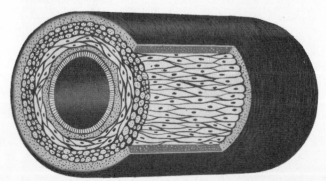

nuclei embedded in a continuous mass of muscular cytoplasm. The whole fiber is elongated, and its internal contractile fibrils are aligned longitudinally. Under the microscope these fibrils exhibit cross striations (alternate dark and light bands), hence the name of this type of muscle tissue (see Fig. 5.18). More will be said about the internal fine structure of this muscle type in Chap. 17.

A group of parallel muscle fibers makes up a **muscle bundle.** Such a bundle is enveloped by layers of loose connective tissue. Several bundles form a **muscle,** which is enclosed within a connective tissue sheath of its own. At either end, a muscle may merge gradually into *tendon.* Like smooth muscles, striated muscles may be arranged into consecutive layers, each contracting in a different direction (e.g., the layers of the human body wall).

Cardiac muscle composes the bulk of the heart. Like smooth muscle, it is not under voluntary control; like striated muscle, its fibers are syncytial. Indeed, cardiac fibers are themselves fused together in intricate patterns (see Fig. 5.18). Consequently, the whole heart is a continuous, multinucleate mass of contractile living matter.

Living muscles are never completely relaxed. Mild contractions occur all the time, groups of cells or fibers working in relays. A definite *muscle tone* is thereby maintained, and it is through this that muscles preserve body shape and posture and provide structural support in general. (Note here that numerous animals, e.g., worms, do not possess skeletons; muscles then are the principal supporting structures.) Stronger contractions, above and beyond tonic ones, produce movement of internal organs or locomotion. We shall see in Chap. 17 how muscular contractions are believed to be brought about.

Organs and Organ Systems

The manner in which various tissues are joined cooperatively into an organ may be illustrated by considering a structure such as the small intestine of mammals (Fig. 5.20).

The wall of this organ consists of four main layers formed by at least six or seven different tissues. The innermost layer is the **mucosa,** composed principally of a simple columnar epithelium as noted above. Its chief function is to complete the digestion of foods and to absorb the digested nutrients from the cavity of the gut. Adjoining the mucosa toward the outside is the **submucosa,** a layer of fibroelastic connective tissue in which are present numerous blood vessels, lymph vessels, and nerve fibers. The principal function of the

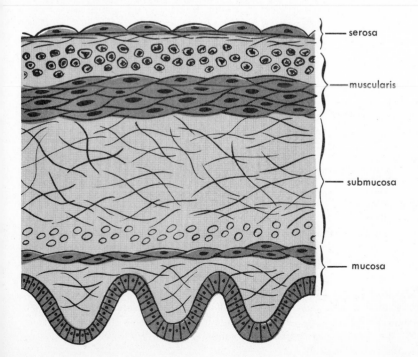

— serosa

— muscularis

— submucosa

— mucosa

FIG. 5.20 Cross section through a portion of the intestinal wall, diagrammatic. The four principal tissue layers are indicated. The mucosa consists of columnar epithelium and connective tissue; the submucosa, of connective tissue, nerve, muscle, and blood vessels; the muscularis, of inner circular and outer longitudinal muscles; and the serosa, of connective tissue and squamous epithelium. Note that the mucosa is usually far more extensively folded than suggested in the diagram.

submucosa is to transfer nutrients from the mucosa into the blood and lymph streams for further distribution into other parts of the body. Surrounding the submucosa is the **muscularis,** the chief muscle tissue of the gut wall. As already noted above, this tissue is composed of smooth muscle, and it contains an inner circular and an outer longitudinal sublayer. More nerve tissue is present between these two muscle layers. The muscularis maintains the tubular shape of the gut, and it also produces a series of gut movements which play important roles in digestion (see Chap. 14). The outermost layer of the intestinal wall is the **serosa,** composed of an inner sublayer of fibroelastic tissue and an outer sublayer of squamous epithelium. The serosa as a whole is the limiting membrane of the gut, and it is continuous with the membranes which keep the entire intestine in place within the body.

All these component tissues of the small intestine cooperate in performing the one group function of food processing. The small intestine is therefore an organ. Several dozens of organs, each similarly constructed out of two or more tissues, may be identified in animals as complex as vertebrates. Of these organs, given groups cooperate in carrying out given complex functions, and so they form organ systems. For example, numerous organs in addition to the small intestine function in food processing: mouth, stomach, liver, pancreas, salivary glands, large intestine, and others. Together these organs constitute the *alimentary system.* In this instance, as in most others, the component organs are interconnected physically. But this is not always the case. For example, the endocrine system consists of a series of hormone-producing glandular organs which are not interconnected physically.

The vertebrate body, that of man included, contains a total of ten organ systems:

the **integumentary** system, including skin and skin appendages such as hair, feathers, scales, nails, and skin glands, which serves as outer cover and protective device for the whole animal

the **circulatory, breathing,** and **excretory** systems, which ferry foods, gases, and wastes between the skin and the body interior, and within the interior

the **alimentary** system, which processes available foods into usable ones

the **skeletal** and **muscular** systems, which provide support, protection, and the means of motion

the **reproductive** system, which propagates the animal

the **nervous** and **endocrine** systems, which coordinate the activities of all organs and systems into a harmonious pattern

In various animal groups, some or others of these systems may not be present. As already noted, for example, worms of all kinds do not possess skeletal systems. Many primitive animals do not possess circulatory or breathing or excretory systems. In all such animals, as indeed also in plants, the functions which are performed elsewhere by systems are performed by individual cells or individual tissues or individual organs.

What is the significance of these various degrees of internal elaboration in various groups of organisms? An organism consisting of but a single cell is just as completely alive as one consisting of ten organ systems. Accordingly, if life is an attribute of any whole organism, is the structural simplicity or complexity of organisms simply a fortuitous circumstance, a chance result of evolution? Does structural organization just happen to be what it is in each case, without any particular functional meaning beyond the observed meaning that it sustains life?

In attempting to answer this problem, we are led to consider a most fundamental question, namely, what does "being alive" actually mean? The next section will outline an answer.

THE NATURE OF ORGANISMS

FUNCTIONAL CHARACTERISTICS

Plant or animal, unicellular or multicellular, *every* organism is a variation on the functional themes elaborated a few billion years ago. All organisms perform the various activities which the very first cells had already performed. These activities, considered now more systematically than in Chap. 3, may be grouped into two broad categories of functions, namely, **metabolism** and **self-perpetuation.**

Metabolism comprises the functions of **nutrition, respiration,** and **synthesis** and all processes associated with these three. Nutrition provides the raw materials for life. Respiration extracts energy from some of the raw materials. With a portion of this energy, synthesis transforms the other raw materials into structural components of living matter. The remainder of the energy and all the structural components then make self-perpetuation possible (Fig. 5.21).

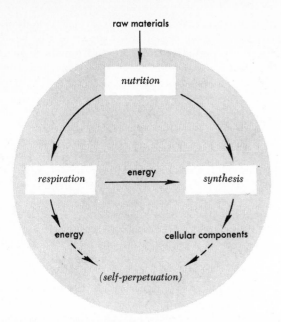

FIG. 5.21 The interrelations of the main processes of metabolism and the main results of metabolism.

In principle, metabolism occurs in inanimate machines also. A machine may be designed to take on "nourishment" in the form of fuel and raw materials. The fuel may provide operating energy, and, with it, the raw materials may then be processed into nuts, bolts, shafts, and other structural components out of which such a machine is built. If for one reason or another any one of these processes should stop, the machine would cease to operate even though it was still whole and intact. Similarly, if a metabolic function of an organism is stopped, the organism becomes non-operational and dies.

Metabolism may therefore be said to run the machinery of life. But metabolism, having equivalents in inanimate nature, is not the distinguishing feature of living nature. That distinguishing feature is, rather, self-perpetuation. Self-perpetuation ensures that the machinery *continues* to run indefinitely, *without* outside help, and *despite* internal or external changes which would otherwise stop its operation.

Based on the energy and the structural components supplied by metabolism, self-perpetuation itself includes three principal activities: **steady-state control, reproduction,** and **adaptation** (Fig. 5.22). All three allow the organism to cope with the disruptive and destructive effects of the *environment* in far greater measure than the operations of any machine can do. It is primarily this which puts the organism into the category of the living and the machine into that of the inanimate.

Fundamentally, *steady-state* controls permit the organism to receive *information* from within itself and from the external environment and to act on this information in a *self-preserving* manner. The information is received in the form of **stimuli** and the self-preserving actions are **responses.** Thus, with the aid of energy and building materials, steady-state controls cause the organism to procure fresh nutritive raw materials when past supplies are used up; adjust respiration and synthesis in rate and amount according to the requirements of the moment; channel the energy of respiration into protective physical responses like movement and into protective chemical responses like poison manufacture;

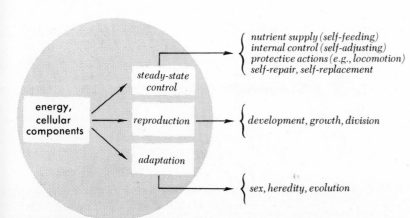

FIG. 5.22 The interrelations of the main processes of self-perpetuation and the main results of these processes.

and channel the products of synthesis into repairing damaged parts of the organism, into completely replacing irreparable parts, and into constructing additional parts, hence into growth.

Many machines of advanced, modern design similarly have ingenious steady-state controls built into them. For example, such controls may make a machine automatically self-"feeding" and self-adjusting. But no machine is as yet self-protecting, self-repairing, or self-healing to any major extent, and no machine certainly is self-growing. On the other hand, it is known today how, theoretically, such a fully self-controlled, self-preserving machine could be built. If it is ever built, it will have steady-state controls conceivably quite as effective as the ones which have been standard equipment in living organisms for a billion years.

Steady-state controls permit an organism to live as long as it inherently can. Life span is invariably limited because, like any other parts of an organism, those which maintain steady states are themselves subject to wear and tear, to breakdown, and to accidental destruction. When some of its controls become inoperative for any such reason, the organism suffers disease. Other, still intact controls may then initiate self-repair. In time, however, so many controls break down simultaneously that too few remain intact to effect repairs. The organism then is in an irreversibly *unsteady state* and it must die. In this regard, the organism again resembles a machine; even the most carefully serviced apparatus eventually becomes scrap, and the destructive impact of the environment ultimately can never be denied.

But unlike a machine, the organism here outwits the environment. For before it dies, the organism may have *reproduced.* With the help of energy and raw materials, the living organism has grown in size, which subsequently permits subdivision and growth in numbers. Reproduction in a sense anticipates and compensates for unavoidable individual death. And through reproduction over successive generations, the tradition of life may be inherited and carried on indefinitely (Fig. 5.23).

Reproduction implies a still poorly understood capacity for *rejuvenation.* The material out of which the offspring is made is part of the parent, hence is really just as old as the rest of the parent. Yet the one lives and the other dies. Evidently, there is a profound distinction between "old" and "aged." Reproduction also implies the capacity for *development,* for the offspring is almost always not only smaller than the parent but also less nearly complete in form and function.

In its capacity for reproduction, the organism far outclasses any inanimate system. No machine self-reproduces, self-rejuvenates, or self-develops. However, it may be noted once again that the theoretical knowledge of how to build such a machine now exists. A device of this kind would metabolize, maintain steady states, and eventually "die" but, before that, would reproduce. It would be *almost* living. If it had the additional capacity for adaptation, it would be fully living—and here too the theoretical know-how is already available.

Adaptation is the final requirement for circumventing destructive effects of the environment. Steady-state controls and reproduction as such cannot counteract major, long-term environmental change. Over thousands and millions of years, climates may become

FIG. 5.23 Reproduction: growth in size, followed by subdivision and growth in numbers. The bacteria shown here are named *Bacillus megatherium,* and they are stained to show the cell walls. These organisms have grown in length for a period of time and, as the transverse partitions show, are now in various stages of reproduction by subdivision. Repeated at intervals, reproduction may maintain the bacterial succession indefinitely. *(Courtesy of Dr. C. F. Robinow and the Society of American Bacteriologists.)*

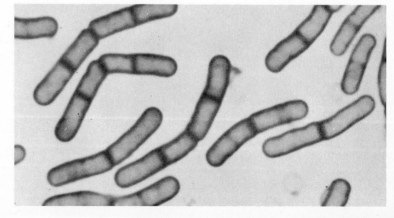

altered profoundly; ice ages may come and go; mountains, oceans, vast tracts of land may appear and disappear. Moreover, living organisms themselves may in time alter the nature of a locality in major ways. Consequently, two related organisms many reproductive generations apart could find themselves in greatly different environments. And whereas the steady-state controls of the ancestor may have coped effectively with the early environment, these same controls, if inherited unchanged by the descendant, could be overpowered rapidly by the new environment. In the course of reproductive successions, therefore, organisms must change *with* the environment if they are to persist. They actually do change through adaptation. *Evolution* is the means of adaptation, and evolution in turn is made possible through mutation and also through sex and heredity (Fig. 5.24).

To define, then, the fundamental meaning of "living," we may say that **any structure which metabolizes and self-perpetuates is alive.** And we find further that *the metabolic functions of nutrition, respiration, and synthesis make possible the self-perpetuative functions of steady-state control, reproduction, and adaptation.*

A first implication of this is that any structure which does not satisfy the above *in every particular* is either nonliving or is dead if it was once alive. Every nonliving or dead object on earth sooner or later decomposes and crumbles to dust under the impact of the environment. But every living object metabolizes and self-perpetuates and so may avoid such a fate. We come to realize that living matter, though soft and weak to the touch, is actually far more durable than the strongest steel, far more permanent than the hardest granite. Oceans, mountains, even whole continents have come and gone several times during the last 2 billion years, but living matter has persisted indestructibly during that time and, indeed, has become progressively more abundant.

A second implication of the definition above is that the property of life basically does not depend on a particular substance. *Any* substance of whatever composition will be "living" provided that it metabolizes and self-perpetuates. It happens that only one such substance is now known. It is shaped into organisms, and it is a complex mixture of many inorganic and organic compounds, as outlined in the preceding chapter. We call this type of material "living matter," or often also *protoplasm.* But if some day we should be able to build—as we almost surely will—a fully metabolizing and self-perpetuating system out of nuts,

FIG. 5.24 Illustrating the process of adaptation, or change *with* the environment. The upper figure is a drawing of a placoderm, a type of fish long extinct but very common some 300 million years ago. Fishes of this group were the ancestors of modern fish, of which one, a haddock, is shown in the lower figure. Evidently, in this evolutionary history, as in most others, descendants changed as their physical and biological environment changed and remained adapted to this changing environment. (Placoderm, Chicago Natural History Museum; haddock, U.S. Fish and Wildlife Service.)

bolts, and wires, then it too will have to be regarded as being truly alive. Similarly, if some day we should encounter on another planet out in space a metabolizing and self-perpetuating entity made up of hitherto completely unknown materials, it also will have to be considered living. It may not be "life as we know it," i.e., life based on cells, genes, proteins, fats, water, etc.; but in any case it will be truly living if it metabolizes and self-perpetuates.

A third implication is that a comprehensive study of organisms must deal with at least three major topics:

1. the **living material,** which possesses the properties of life and out of which organisms are made
2. **metabolism,** which maintains living processes
3. **self-perpetuation,** which endows organisms with potential immortality

A glance at the table of contents will show that the remainder of this book is structured along these very lines.

The above characterizes organisms from the functional standpoint. What are their structural characteristics?

STRUCTURAL CHARACTERISTICS

Levels of Organization

During the process of genesis in the early seas, the keynote and central running theme were progressive *aggregation*. As we have seen in Chap. 3, atoms aggregated into simple compounds, simple compounds aggregated into complex ones, and these plus others eventually aggregated into cells. These combinatorial events were a progressive expression of the inherent bonding potential of atoms. We recall the energy requirement in making such potentials actual.

The successive stages of aggregation may be regarded as successively higher **levels of organization of matter**. Each such level features new properties over and above those found at lower levels. For example, a molecule exhibits new properties over and above those of the individual atoms. Similarly, a cell exhibits important properties in addition to those of the molecular aggregates which compose it. Such additional properties in a sense represent the dividend on the energy required to raise one level to the next higher.

The aggregative tendencies which led to higher organizational levels did not cease to operate with the formation of cells and of single-celled organisms. Multicellular organisms arose in due course, and, within them, a number of supracellular levels came to be established—tissues, organs, and organ systems. Moreover, aggregation has carried beyond the organism. A few individual organisms of one kind together may make up a **family**. Large numbers of organisms of one kind make up a **population**. All organisms, families, and populations of the same kind together form a **species**. Different species aggregate into a local **community**. And the sum of all local communities represents the whole living world (Fig. 5.25).

Each of these living levels features properties

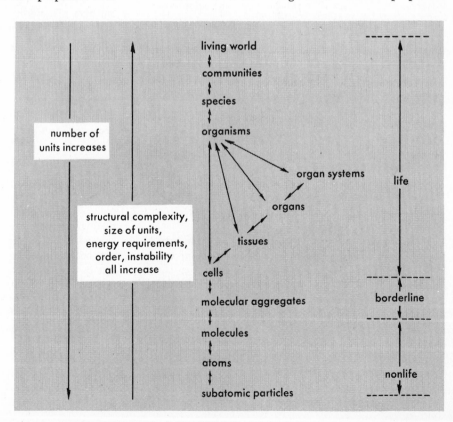

FIG. 5.25 The hierarchy of levels in the organization of matter.

above and beyond those of lower ones. Also, each of these levels is structurally more complex than lower ones, for it combines the complexities of all lower levels and has an additional complexity of its own. Moreover, each level includes fewer members than the preceding. Thus there is only one living world, but there are uncountable numbers of atoms. We note that, from atom to living world, matter is organized into a *hierarchy* of structural levels.

From this, we arrive at *structural* characterizations of life, nonlife, and death. Up to the level of the molecular aggregate, matter is nonliving. At all higher levels matter is living, provided that, at *each* such level, metabolic and self-perpetuative functions are carried out. To be living, a society, for example, must metabolize and self-perpetuate on its own level, as well as on every subordinate level, down to the molecular aggregate.

As life is organized by levels, so is death. Structural death occurs when one level is disrupted or decomposed into the next lower. For example, if a tissue is disaggregated into separate cells, the tissue ceases to exist. Structural death of this sort always entails functional death also, i.e., disruption of the metabolic and self-perpetuative processes of the affected level. But note that disruption of one level need not necessarily mean disruption of lower levels. If a tissue is decomposed into cells, the cells may carry on as individuals; if a family is disrupted, the member organisms may survive on their own (Fig. 5.26). On the other

hand, death of one level does always entail death of higher levels. If many or all of its tissues are destroyed, the whole organ will be destroyed; if many or all of its families are dismembered, a society may cease to exist. In general, the situation is comparable to a pyramid of cards. Removal of a top card need not affect the rest of the pyramid, but removal of a bottom card usually topples the whole structure. We recognize that neither life nor death is a singular state but is organized and structured into levels.

The aggregation of living matter into a hierarchy of levels has a number of operational consequences. As already noted, energy must be expended to create a higher organizational level. Energy must also be supplied thereafter to maintain the organization. For example, if the energy supply to the cell, the organ, or the organism is stopped, death and decomposition soon follow and reversion to lower levels occurs. Similarly, maintenance of a family or a society requires work over and above that needed to maintain the organization of subordinate units.

This requirement is an expression of the **second law of thermodynamics**, one of the most fundamental laws of nature: *if left to itself, any system tends toward a state of greatest disorder.* "Randomness," "stability," and "probability" are equivalent to this meaning of disorder. When we say that a system has a higher level of organization, we also say that the system exhibits a high degree of order, that it is nonrandom. The second law tells us that such a system is unstable and improb-

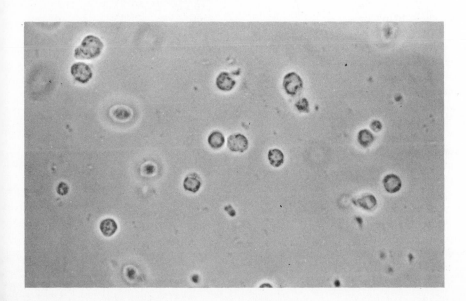

FIG. 5.26 Disaggregated tissue cells of a mouse embryo, cultured in nutrient solution. Originally these cells were part of a compact tissue. Disaggregation destroyed the tissue level of organization but did not destroy the cellular level; the individual cells shown here remain alive. *(Courtesy of Dr. Clifford Grobstein, Stanford University.)*

able and that if we leave it to itself it will eventually become disordered and therefore more stable. Living systems are the most ordered, unstable, and improbable systems known. If they are to avoid the fate predicted by the second law, a price must be paid. That price is energy—energy to push the order up, against the constant tug to tear the order down.

With each new level attained, the energy expenditure nets new properties. One of these is united, integrated function: nonaggregated structure means independent function and, by extension, **competition**; aggregated structure means joint function and, by extension, **cooperation**. Atoms, for example, may remain structurally independent, and they may then be in functional competition for other, suitable atoms with which they might aggregate. Once they do aggregate into a compound, they have lost structural independence and cannot but function unitedly, as a single cooperative unit. Similarly, cells may remain independent structurally and they may compete for space and raw materials. But if they aggregate into a tissue, they surrender their independence and become a cooperative, integrated unit.

This generalization applies at every other organizational level as well (Fig. 5.27). The results on the human level are very familiar. Men may be independent and competing, or they may give up a measure of independence, form families and societies, and start cooperating. Note here that sociological laws governing human society are based on and are reflections of the more fundamental laws governing the organization of all matter, from atoms to the whole living universe.

Note also that competition and cooperation are not in any basic sense willful, deliberate, planned, or thought out; atoms or cells neither think nor have political or economic motives. Structural units of any sort simply *function* as their internal makeup dictates. And the automatic result of such functioning among independent units may be competition; among aggregated units, cooperation. To be sure, human beings may *decide* to compete or to cooperate, but this merely channels, reinforces, makes conscious, and is superimposed on what they would necessarily do in any event. *Reasoned* cooperation is the most recent result of the ancient aggregative tendency of matter; the evolution of reason may be regarded as nature's way of ensuring the possibility of a very close cooperation among organisms.

Specialization

An important consequence of cooperation is **operational efficiency**: the cooperating aggregate is more efficient in performing the functions of life than its subordinated components separately and competitively. For example, a given number of nonaggregated cells

FIG. 5.27 Photomicrograph through mammalian skin, showing the base (follicle) of a hair. Many different types of tissues may be seen; they cooperate to produce and maintain this organ. In so doing, these tissues surrender much of their freedom and independence of action. (*Courtesy of Dr. William Montagna, Brown University.*)

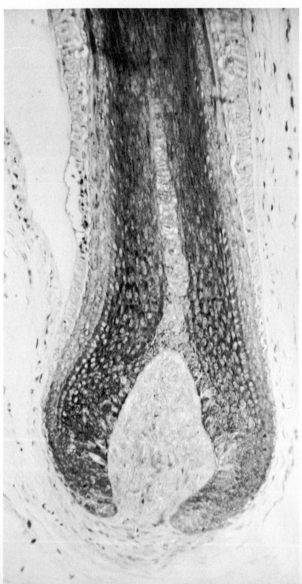

must expend more energy and materials to survive than if that same number of cells were integrated into a tissue. Similarly for all other organizational levels.

One underlying reason for this difference is that, in the aggregate, duplication of effort may be avoided. For example, in a set of nonaggregated cells, every cell is exposed to the environment on all sides and must therefore expend energy and materials on all sides to cope with the impact of the environment. However, if the same cells are aggregated into a compact tissue, only the outermost cells are in direct contact with the environment and inner cells then need not channel their resources into protective activities.

In addition to avoiding duplication of effort, aggregation permits continuity of effort. Such continuity is not always possible in nonaggregated units. We may illustrate this by contrasting unicellular and multicellular organisms, for example. A unicellular organism must necessarily carry out all survival functions within its one cell. In many instances, however, the performance of even one of these functions requires most or all of the capacities of the cell. For example, in a bacterium, an amoeba, or a single-celled alga, the *entire* cell surface is designed to serve as gateway for entering raw materials and departing wastes. The *entire* substance of the cell functions to distribute materials within it. And *all* parts of the cell may be required directly in locomotion or in feeding, for example (Fig. 5.28).

Very often, therefore, two such functions cannot be performed at the same time. In an amoeba, because locomotion and feeding *each* necessitate action by the *whole* cell surface, performance of one of these functions more or less precludes the simultaneous performance of the other. We shall find, moreover, that reproduction too involves the operational equipment of the *whole* cell, and in an amoeba this necessitates temporary suspension of both feeding and locomotion. Mutual exclusion of some functions by others is a common occurrence in all unicellular forms.

In multicellular forms, by contrast, continuity of effort becomes possible through **division of labor.** In such an organism, the total job of survival may be divided up into several subjobs and each subjob becomes the continuous responsibility of particular cells only. For example, some cells may function in feeding, continuously so, and other cells may function in locomotion, again continuously so. Indeed, division of labor in many cases is so pronounced that given cells

are permanently limited in functional capacity; they can perform *only* certain jobs and no others. Thus, nerve cells can conduct nerve impulses only and are quite unable to reproduce or move. Muscle cells can move by contracting, but they cannot conduct nerve

FIG. 5.28 An amoeba. Like all other unicellular organisms, this protozoon carries out all metabolic and self-perpetuative functions within the confines of its single cell. Note nucleus (dark central body), excretory vacuole (light spherical body), and the pseudopods—fingerlike extensions which function in locomotion and feeding. (*Carolina Biological Supply Co.*)

impulses; and normally they do not reproduce. Most cells in many multicellular organisms have analogous limitations. Each group of cells is more or less restricted in its functional *versatility* and exhibits a particular **specialization** (Fig. 5.29).

Specialization in turn makes possible further gains in operational efficiency: a given vital function can be performed far more effectively by a specialized cell than by a nonspecialized cell. For example, a tracheid or a vessel element of plants is so highly specialized that it is unable to carry out any functions except those of support and conduction. But these two it performs so extremely efficiently that its expenditure of energy and materials is in effect zero; it is nonliving altogether and its continued maintenance costs nothing. By contrast, a parenchyma cell is less highly specialized and more versatile, and it must expend correspondingly more energy and materials to maintain this versatility. It is therefore correspondingly less efficient in the performance of any one function; a tracheid is far more efficient as a conducting structure than a parenchyma cell. On the basis of this line of reasoning, we may conclude that the most versatile and least specialized cells of all are unicellular organisms.

Consider another example. All unicellular organisms are sensitive to environmental stimuli. But such organisms, which must perform all survival functions within their single cells, are not specialized for any one of these functions. Consequently, although they are sensitive to stimuli, the degree and range of sensitivity are quite modest. By contrast, many multicellular organisms possess highly specialized sensory cells. Such cells can be exceedingly sensitive and may respond to even very weak stimuli. Moreover, there may be several kinds of sensory cells, some specialized specifically for light stimuli, others for sound stimuli, still others for mechanical stimuli, etc. In short, the degree as well as the range of sensitivity can become enormously greater in cells which can specialize than in cells which cannot. Analogously for all other functions.

We may now understand the fundamental significance of multicellularity and of the existence of tissues, organs, and organ systems. First, multicellularity makes possible division of labor, which avoids duplication of effort and permits continuity of effort. Second, division of labor leads to specialization, which permits any given effort to become highly effective. The overall result is an enormous saving of energy and materials and an enormous gain in operational efficiency. This gain basically is what has favored more and more aggregation in matter generally and in living matter particularly, and this is why evolution has produced multicellular organisms with as many as ten organ systems rather than only bigger and better unicellular organisms.

But note again that a price must be paid for gains in efficiency. Part of this price is increased energy expenditure which is necessary to maintain a higher level of organization despite the second law of thermodynamics. Another part is loss of independence of the aggregated units, and a third part is loss of functional versatility of the units. In a multicellular organism, the individual specialized cell does not and indeed cannot perform all the functions necessary for survival. That is why, when some cells are separated away from the whole organism, as in injury, for example, such cells must usually die. The specialized cell has lost independence mainly because it is not very versatile, because it can do only some of the jobs necessary for survival. And the whole job of survival can be carried out only by the whole multicellular system, which possesses the required versatility by virtue of its many differently specialized cells.

Note also that loss of functional versatility in a specialized cell is never total. A cell cannot be so completely specialized that it performs just a single function. Certain irreducible "housekeeping" functions must be carried out by every living cell of a multicellular organism. Every such cell must absorb food materials and excrete waste products, must respire and synthesize, and must be responsive at least to its immediate environment. These functions cannot be special-

FIG. 5.29 The principle of specialization. The single-celled organism (left) must carry out all required functions (symbolized by letters) within the limits of one cell. In the multicellular organism (right), on the other hand, each cell may specialize to carry out a single function only, with resulting gains in efficiency.

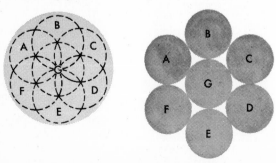

ized. Performed continuously and simultaneously in every cell, they are the bedrock of cellular survival. Specialization only affects additional functions, and the fewer of such additional functions a cell performs, the more specialized it is. Analogously, a cell can never be completely unspecialized and be so versatile functionally that it could survive under any or all conditions. All cells, even the most independent, still depend on very *particular* environments, for example. Cells therefore may only be more or less highly specialized; and within limits, the relative degree of functional versatility is an inverse measure of the relative degree of specialization.

Most multicellular organisms actually consist of cells which exhibit widely different degrees of specialization. In view of the earlier discussion about comparative efficiencies, would it not be most efficient if a multicellular organism consisted exclusively of highly specialized cells? Probably not, because certain functions need not be performed continuously. For example, it would be quite wasteful to maintain a permanent set of specialized scar-tissue cells—the organism might never sustain an injury. Analogously, it is a decided advantage that, in many multicellular organisms, reproductive structures become fully developed only during seasons when reproduction actually occurs. Thus, the actual design of the multicellular system permits the greatest possible economy of energy and materials. The most critical and continuously required functions are the responsibility of sets of permanently specialized cells. But less critical functions, and those required intermittently or only under unusual circumstances, are carried out by initially more versatile, less highly specialized cells.

In this structural characterization, we have found organisms to be ordered, organized aggregates above a certain level of complexity, carrying out functions of metabolism and self-perpetuation at every level. An important corollary is that a whole organism is more than the sum of its parts. To cite an analogy from the nonliving world, a collection of carbon atoms, for example, may be either soot, graphite, or diamond, according to *how* the atoms are grouped together. Each different grouping here endows the whole with unique properties over and above those of the sum of the individual carbon atoms. Similarly, an integrated cellular aggregate possesses properties not exhibited by a mere random heap of cells. The difference is a result of *organization*, of pattern of arrangement. Just as a cell is the sum of its molecules *plus* internal organization, so also is a multicellular whole the sum of its cells *plus* organization. Only through its specialized organization does the multicellular aggregate become "organism."

Reflecting the specializations of its molecules, cells, tissues, and organs, the whole organism is itself specialized. It is able to live in a *particular* environment only and to pursue only a *particular* way of life. In effect, it is a dependent, necessarily cooperating unit of a higher living level: the population, the whole species, the community of several species, the physical environment which encompasses all. The next chapters will examine the place of the organism within these higher levels.

REVIEW QUESTIONS

1. Review the structural and functional characteristics of moderately and highly specialized cell types among plants. Which cell types function primarily in conduction? In mechanical support? What cell types are unique to roots? To aerial portions of a plant?

2. Describe the development and structure of xylem vessels and of sieve tubes. What is a stele? What justifies the designation of a stem or a root as an organ?

3. What basic types of tissues are characteristic of animals? Describe the structural characteristics and principal variants of these tissues and give examples. Show how such tissues are combined to form specific organs.

4. Describe the development and structure of bone. What types of muscle tissue are there and how are they distinguished?

5. Define "cell" (*a*) structurally and (*b*) functionally. Define tissue, organ, organ system, organism. Name and state the function of the various organ systems of man. Which familiar organs belong to each of these systems? How many organ systems are present in a flowering plant?

6. What is metabolism? Self-perpetuation? What

are the principal component functions of each of these, and what specific roles do these functions play in the maintenance of life?

7. What are the fundamental differences between inanimate and living systems? Discuss carefully and fully.

8. Define living, cellular specialization, death.

9. Review the hierarchy of levels in the organization of matter and discuss how living matter is characterized in terms of levels. Review the relation of levels of organization to energy, to aggregation, to complexity, to competition and cooperation, and to operational efficiency.

10. In terms of cellular specializations, how does a cell of a single-celled organism differ from a cell of a multicellular organism? Cite examples of specialization on the tissue, organ, organism, and species levels of organization.

SUGGESTED COLLATERAL READINGS

The following texts are suggested for further reading on cells, tissues, and organs:

DeRobertis, E. D. P., W. W. Nowinski, and F. A. Saez: "General Cytology," 3d ed., Saunders, Philadelphia, 1960.

Esau, K.: "Anatomy of Seed Plants," Wiley, New York, 1960.

Greep, R. O. (ed.): "Histology," McGraw-Hill–Blakiston, New York, 1954.

Maximov, A. A., and W. Bloom: "A Textbook of Histology," 6th ed., Saunders, Philadelphia, 1952.

Sharp, L. W.: "Fundamentals of Cytology," McGraw-Hill, New York, 1943.

Wilson, E. B.: "The Cell in Development and Heredity," 3d ed., Macmillan, New York, reprinted, 1947.

Two of the topics discussed in this chapter are dealt with in the following articles:

Kemeny, J. G.: Man Viewed as a Machine, *Sci. American*, vol. 192, 1955.

McLean, F. C.: Bone, *Sci. American*, vol. 192, 1955.

Parker, G. H.: Criteria of Life, *Am. Scientist*, vol. 41, 1953.

Penrose, L. S.: Self-reproducing Machines, *Sci. American*, vol. 200, 1959.

SPECIES

6

Being a specialized entity, every organism depends on other organisms for some essential product or process; no organism can survive in strict isolation. Cooperative aggregations of organisms are as ancient as organisms themselves, and as the ones evolved, so did the others. Moreover, the same principles and consequences of aggregation described previously for levels of organization below the individual organism hold also for the levels above.

In this chapter, we shall focus attention on one of the major supraorganismic levels of the living world, namely, the **species.** Important subunits within species are **populations,** and specialized types of populations are **societies.** We shall examine the nature of these subunits as well.

SPECIES CHARACTERISTICS

THE SPECIES CONCEPT

The smallest organizational group formed by individual organisms of the same kind is the *family*. This is a rather temporary type of association characteristic of only very few kinds of organisms, namely, some of the vertebrate animals (see below). Also more or less temporary and typical of only certain animal organisms are larger associations of families of the same kind into *tribes* or *herds*. But, whether or not like organisms form families and herds, they always form a next higher grouping, namely, local *populations*.

A population (or, in precise technical terminology, a **Mendelian population**) is a relatively permanent association of organisms of the same kind. It is encountered among all types of organisms; the dandelions in a field, the pines in a forest, the earthworms in a plot of soil, the minnows in a pond, and the people in a village—all are examples of local populations. Individual organisms multiply and die, emigrate or immigrate, but collectively the population persists. It may split into subpopulations or it may fuse with adjacent sister populations, yet the basic characteristics of the group as a whole do not thereby change. Structurally, the geographic extent of a population may vary vastly, from the space in a laboratory test tube to a space of continental or oceanic proportions. Likewise, population density may vary greatly. Functionally, the fundamental unifying link of a population is that *its members interbreed more or less preferentially with one another.* However, fairly frequent interbreeding with members of sister populations does occur in addition. A population thus is a reproductively cohesive unit that is integrated more loosely with other such units (Fig. 6.1).

The sum of all the populations of the same kind and therefore the sum of all the organisms of the same kind forms a **species.** For example, all the corn plants on earth, all the bullfrogs on earth, all the human beings on earth, each group represents a species. Even more so than the population, the species is a universal, very permanent, self-perpetuating level of organization.

If "species" is defined as above as the sum of all organisms of the same kind, what does the phrase "of the same kind" actually mean? Is a pygmy of the Ituri Forest in Africa the "same kind" of organism as a 7-ft member of the neighboring Watusi tribe, and is either the "same kind" of organism as a New York businessman? Is the fishlike bullfrog tadpole the "same kind" of organism as a bullfrog adult? Clearly not, and we may note that the definition of species as "the totality

of organisms of the same kind" is wanting because the word "kind" is exceedingly vague.

As a second approximation, therefore, we might say that a species is the sum of all organisms specialized structurally and functionally the same way. This would help to put Pygmies, Watusis, and New Yorkers into the same species, where they should be, but we could not properly put men and women, for example, or bullfrog tadpoles and adults, into the same species. Men and women or bullfrog tadpoles and adults clearly are not specialized in the same way. The basic difficulty here is that every single organism actually differs in many structural and functional respects from every other organism and no two are ever exactly alike. Even identical twins differ structurally and functionally to some extent, however small. We say that organisms exhibit **individual variation** (Fig. 6.2).

Yet that men and women and tadpoles and frogs naturally "belong together" is clearly evident, and biologists usually have little trouble in recognizing a species and distinguishing between species. Underlying this basic distinctiveness of a species is a relatively close historical link between its member organisms. *Relatedness* is as good a criterion of group character, and

FIG. 6.2 Individual variation. These two umbrella birds belong to the same species, namely, *Cephalopterus ornatus.* But they are members of different populations, and the structural differences between the birds are quite pronounced. Technically, these birds are said to belong to different subspecies of the same species. *(New York Zoological Society.)*

FIG. 6.1 The interrelation between individuals, populations, and species. Interbreeding occurs frequently among the individuals of a population and occasionally among the populations of a species. Individuals of two different species usually do not interbreed in nature.

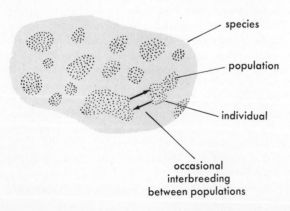

often a better one, than structure and function. We may say, therefore, as a third approximation, that a species is a collection of structurally and functionally similar organisms which are more closely related to one another than to any other organisms.

But note that even this definition still has elements of vagueness, for the phrase "more closely related than" may be interpreted with considerable latitude. All organisms on earth are related to one another; yet all are different from one another. In this stream of historical relation and difference, it is often difficult or impossible to decide exactly where one species ends and the next related one begins. Relatedness puts bullfrog tadpoles and adults into the same species, but this would also put grass frogs into the same species as bullfrogs. Yet it should not.

Evidently, what is needed is a distinguishing feature other than relatedness which introduces discontinuity into the continuous stream of historical relation and individual variation. Such a distinguishing feature is the breeding pattern among organisms. As a fourth and most nearly adequate definition, we may regard a species as *a group of closely related, structurally and functionally similar organisms which interbreed with one another, but which in nature do not usually interbreed with organisms of other groups.*

Thus, whereas interbreeding between populations *within* a species occurs regularly, interbreeding *between* species is relatively rare. Closely related plant species in nature may cross-mate comparatively more commonly than animal species, in most of which cross-mating does not occur at all. For example, all bullfrog populations on earth are in actual or potential reproductive contact and so are all grass frog populations. Bullfrogs and grass frogs may and do coexist in the same localities; yet despite this constant proximity they do not interbreed. They represent different species.

Evidently, some kind of *reproductive barrier* exists between species. In many cases, as between bullfrogs and grass frogs, the barrier is *biological* and interbreeding then is impossible regardless of how close the organisms are. Bullfrogs and grass frogs have incompatible structures and functions, and sperms from one cannot successfully fertilize the eggs of the other. In numerous other cases, the eggs and sperms of different species *are* compatible, yet effective biological barriers still exist. For example, the breeding season in one group may occur a few weeks earlier or later than in another, or the members of one group may be active only at night, those of another only in the daytime.

Interbreeding will be impossible under such circumstances.

In still other instances, the reproductive barriers are not biological but *environmental*. Impassable mountains, unfordable rivers, pronounced climatic differences, or merely great distances between one territory and another may make contact between groups impossible and reproductive isolation will be the consequence. In given cases, interbreeding might still occur if the isolating condition were removed, but in nature such removals do not normally occur. Therefore, when two different species *do not* interbreed in nature, this does not always mean that they *cannot* interbreed. In many cases, members of different species may be brought together in the laboratory and there they interbreed perfectly well. For example, swordtails and platys, two species of tropical fish (Fig. 6.3), may have offspring in the laboratory quite readily. But in nature they almost never do because they normally live in different parts of a river and simply do not meet.

The development of new environmental isolating conditions is the usual cause of **speciation**, i.e., the origin of new species by the splitting of one into two. For example, if an original parent species ranges over a given large territory, physical barriers may arise in

FIG. 6.3   Platyfish female at top, swordfish male at bottom. These animals belong to different species, and in nature they do not interbreed. But they can and do interbreed in the laboratory. *(Courtesy of the Genetics Laboratory, New York Zoological Society.)*

the course of time which may prevent interbreeding between populations at opposite ends of the territory. With reproductive contact so lost, evolution in the now isolated populations may henceforth follow entirely different courses. In effect, the parental species will be split into two new ones (Fig. 6.4). At first, the descendant species will still be rather similar structurally and functionally. In time, however, evolutionary changes are likely to introduce progressively pronounced differences, including biological barriers to interbreeding. These would add to and reinforce the environmental ones already in existence. Speciation by this means is the principal way in which new species evolve. Such a process takes, on an average, about 1 million years. In Chap. 29 we shall hear more about speciation and we shall find also that the concept of "species" has important genetic aspects.

VARIATIONS

In each species, a basic set of structural and functional characteristics is common to all member organisms. For example, no matter in what way or to what degree human beings might differ, they never differ so much that their human status cannot be recognized. Because such common and unique traits do exist, species can be used as fundamental units in classifying organisms, as will be shown in Chap. 8.

As noted, however, superimposed on the common traits, individual variations among the member organisms are equally characteristic of species. Indeed, the range of individual variations within one species may be directly continuous with the range within a closely related species. It may happen, therefore, that two

FIG. 6.4 If two populations of the same species are too far apart, the migratory range of one may not intersect that of the other. Individuals of population A therefore cannot meet individuals of population B, and interbreeding does not occur. If the reproductive separation persists a long time, two new species may arise in this manner from the original one. Distance is often a major factor in speciation.

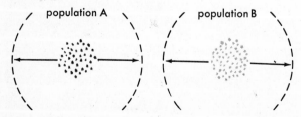

population A   population B

organisms from two different species might differ less in structure and function than two organisms from the same species.

Two classes of variations may be distinguished, *inheritable* and *noninheritable* ones. The first are produced by gene mutations and are controlled by genes. They may therefore be transmitted to offspring. Noninheritable variations are the result of developmental processes within organisms and are not controlled genetically. They therefore disappear from a species with the death of the individuals which exhibit them. Evidently, only inheritable variations can be significant in species evolution. If a man is an athlete, his muscular system is likely to be developed much more than in the average person. This is an individual variation and a noninheritable one. The degree of muscular development does not depend on heredity, primarily, but only on whether or not a person goes in for athletics. On the other hand, the blood type, the skin color, and the hair color are examples of hereditary variations. They are part of the genetic inheritance from parents and earlier forebears and will, in turn, influence the traits of future offspring generations (Fig. 6.5).

Many variations exist which are inherited but which may be modified subsequently in noninheritable fashion. For example, body weight is a general, inherited species characteristic. But what the *actual* weight of an individual will be depends partly on his eating habits. Similarly, a generalized level of intelligence is characteristic of the human species and is inherited, but actual mental capacities depend greatly on the thought training of each individual and on other noninherited factors.

In many and probably in the majority of instances, the variations within a species are correlated with variations in the environment. Among birds and mammals, for example, man not excepted, clear-cut structural differences accompany differences in climatic temperatures. In warm climates, for example, individuals of many animal species tend to have smaller body size, longer ears, tails, and other protrusions, and darker body colors than fellow members of the species living in cold climates. Such structural variations are said to be *adaptive;* i.e., they are advantageous to the individuals in the different environments. Smaller bodies and longer ears, for example, make for a large body surface relative to the body volume. Under such conditions evaporation from the skin surface is rapid and the cooling effect of this enhanced evaporation is of considerable benefit in a warm climate. The converse

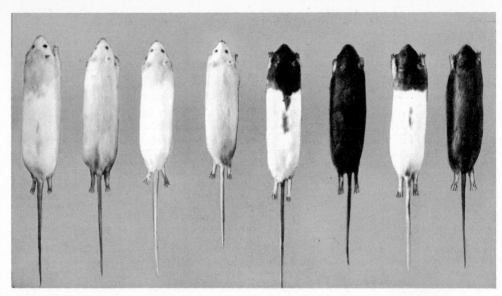

FIG. 6.5 Inheritable variations. These are litter-mate rats, produced by the same two parents. Considerable variation in coat color is evident. Such differences arise because even brothers and sisters of the same family may be different genetically. Hereditary (i.e., gene-controlled) variations tend to be more pronounced, the less related the given members of a species. *(American Museum of Natural History.)*

FIG. 6.6 Courtship of fur seals. Female on left, male on right. Sexual dimorphism is illustrated strikingly here, the male being far larger and darker in color than the female. Special forms of polymorphism of this sort occur very widely among animals. See also Fig. 20.9. *(Courtesy of V. B. Scheffer, U.S. Fish and Wildlife Service.)*

is true in the cool climate. In many instances it may be very difficult to recognize the adaptive value of a variation. And some variations conceivably may be *nonadaptive*, without inherent advantage to the possessors. Human eye color may possibly (but not certainly) be in this category.

Because of the individual variations of its members, a species is said to exhibit **polymorphism**, i.e., to be composed of individuals of "many shapes." The sexual differences between the males and females of most organisms are instances of *dimorphism*, a form of polymorphism (Fig. 6.6). But polymorphism may be far more pronounced. Two individuals may be so different structurally and functionally that their common traits become evident only through the most careful study. Many coelenterate species are highly polymorphic. For example, *Physalia*, the Portuguese man-of-war, is a colonial coelenterate common on the surface of warm seas (Fig. 6.7). A colony is made up of several dozens or hundreds of individuals and several classes of polymorphs are present: *feeding* individuals, with ten-

FIG. 6.7 Model of *Physalia*, the Portuguese man-of-war. Each tentacle suspended from the gas-filled float represents a portion of a single coelenterate individual. The several different types of tentacles here indicate the high degree of polymorphism encountered in this colony. (*American Museum of Natural History.*)

tacles and mouths adapted for the ingestion and digestion of small fish; *protective* individuals, whose long trailing tentacles are equipped with batteries of sting cells which paralyze prey and ward off predators; individuals modified into the air-filled *float*, which buoys the whole colony; *reproductive* individuals, which manufacture sex cells and propagate the species. A more familiar example of pronounced polymorphism is the variety of individuals found in insect societies: queens, drones, soldiers, workers, and others, all structurally and functionally very dissimilar (see below).

All instances of polymorphism are expressions of organismic *specialization*. And where organisms exhibit great polymorphic diversity, a high degree of cooperative interdependence is also in evidence. In *Physalia*, for example, only the feeding individuals can feed and the whole colony depends on that. Only the protective individuals can protect and all other polymorphs depend on that also. And only the whole, tightly integrated colony is a self-sufficient unit. Indeed, such units display all the elements of a primitive **society**. In one form or another, a high degree of polymorphism is always characteristic of societies, as the following section will show.

SOCIETIES

A society is subordinated to the species; it is a special type of population *within* a species. In most cases, the only identifying feature of a population (apart from localized geography) is the preferential interbreeding of the member organisms. In some cases, however, a population is a far more closely knit group, the unifying link being not only interbreeding but also a particularly great structural or functional interdependence of the member organisms. Such a strongly cooperating group is a *social* population.

Societies are characteristic only of animals. Also, all societies have evolved independently of one another and the most advanced societies occur in the most advanced animals: insects and vertebrates. Structural or functional polymorphism is pronounced in both groups, as is cooperative interdependence of the member organisms.

INSECT SOCIETIES

Highly developed societies occur among termites, ants, bees, and wasps. In these, each member organism is structurally adapted from birth to carry out specific functions in the society. Insect societies, organized somewhat differently in each of the four groups just named, operate in fixed, stereotyped, largely unlearned behavior patterns. In its rigid, inflexible ways, the insect society resembles a human dictatorship, except that among insects there is no dictator, no rule by force. Each member is guided by inherited, instinctive reactions and is unable to carry out any functions other than those for which built-in instincts exist. Insects *can* learn, though only to a limited extent. For example, a bee may be taught to respond differently to different colors and scents, and it may learn a new route to its hive if the hive has been moved.

Social insects have this in common: they build intricate *nests*, and their societies are stratified into *structurally* distinct castes. In each of the four groups, different species form societies of different degrees of complexity. We may profitably examine the organization of a few of the more complex associations.

Honeybees

A colony of honeybees (Fig. 6.8) is made up of three social ranks: a *queen*, tens or hundreds of male *drones*, and from 20,000 to 80,000 *workers*. The queen and the stingless drones are fertile, and their main functions are reproductive. The smaller-bodied workers are all sterile females. They build the hive, ward off enemies, collect food, feed the queen and the drones, and nurse the young.

When a hive becomes overcrowded, the queen together with some drones and several thousand workers secedes from the colony. The emigrants swarm out and settle temporarily in a tree or other suitable place until a new hive is found (Fig. 6.9). In the old

FIG. 6.9 A swarm of bees, emigrated from a parental hive and searching for a new hive. (*U.S. Department of Agriculture.*)

hive, meanwhile, the workers which remain behind raise a small batch of the old queen's eggs in large, specially built honeycomb cells. These eggs develop into new queens. The first one to emerge from its cell immediately searches out the other queen cells and stings their occupants to death. If two new queens happen to emerge at the same time, they at once engage in mortal combat until one remains victorious. The young queen, her succession now undisputed, soon mates with one of the drones. In a nuptial flight high into the air, she receives millions of sperms which are stored in a receptacle in her abdomen. The sperms from this single mating last through the entire egg-laying career of the queen.

Among the eggs laid individually into honeycomb cells (Fig. 6.10), some escape fertilization, even in a young queen. None is fertilized in an older queen once her sperm store is exhausted. Unfertilized eggs develop into drones. Fatherless development of this sort, or **natural parthenogenesis**, is widespread among social insects and a number of other animal types, e.g., roti-

FIG. 6.8 Honeybees. Worker on left, queen in middle, drone on right. (*U.S. Department of Agriculture.*)

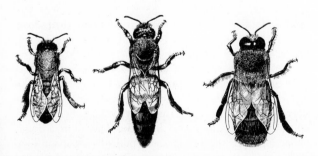

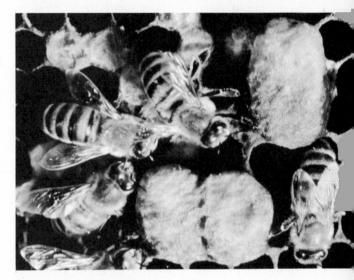

FIG. 6.10 Top left, queen bee laying eggs, surrounded by attendants. Top right, nurse bee feeds and cleans the larvae in the brood cells. Bottom left, a worker bee just hatching out from its brood cell. Bottom right, two enlarged brood cells, capped over with wax, in which queen bees are being raised. *(All photos copyright © Walt Disney Productions.)*

fers, water fleas, brine shrimp (see Chap. 11). Fertilized eggs develop into larvae and these either into queens or into workers, depending on the type of food the larvae receive from their worker nurses. Larvae to be raised into workers are fed a "regular" diet of plant pollen and honey. Queens form when the larvae receive an especially rich royal jelly, containing pollen, honey, and comparatively huge amounts of certain vitamins (e.g., pantothenic acid). But new queens are not raised while the original queen remains in the hive, healthy and fertile. If the queen produces eggs faster than honeycomb cells can be built, she receives less food from her attendants. Egg production then slows down. Conversely, if she is behind in her egg laying, she is fed more intensively.

In the six weeks or so of its life, a worker bee does not perform the same duties continuously. The age of a bee determines what work it can do; housekeeping tasks are performed by young bees, foodcollecting trips are made by older ones. On a foodcollecting trip, the bee gathers pollen, rich in protein, and nectar, a thin sugar solution. Pollen is carried home in *pollen baskets* on the hind legs. Nectar is swallowed into the *honey crop*, a specialized part of the alimentary tract, where saliva partially digests the sugar of nectar. On arriving at the hive, the bee first passes a security check on the way in, then unloads its pollen into one cell and regurgitates its nectar into another. Other bees which happen by pack the pollen tight and start converting nectar into honey. They rapidly beat their wings close to a nectar-filled cell, a process which is continued until most of the water has evaporated. Every now and then a bee samples the product (probably more a matter of hunger than of professional pride in the work). And when the honey is just right (or when all the bees standing by have had their fill?) the cell is sealed up with wax. This is the principal food store for the winter. Pollen is unobtainable at that time and, being perishable, cannot be stored as readily.

Bees and other social insects possess remarkable powers of orientation and communication. On food-collecting trips, bees have been shown to navigate by the sun. They are able to relate the position of their hive with the direction of polarized light coming from the sun; hence they may steer a beeline course home from any compass point. On arrival in its hive, a scouting bee which has found a food-yielding field of flowers communicates with its fellow workers by means of an *abdominal dance,* a side-to-side wiggle of the hind portion of the bee's body. The violence of the dance gives information about the richness of the food source. Flight distance is indicated by the duration of the dance, and flight direction, by the specific body orientation the dancing bee assumes on the honeycomb surface.

In winter, bees cling together in compact masses. Animals in the center always work their way out; those near the surface work their way in. A clump of bees thereby withstands freezing, even when exposed to very low temperatures. Smoke calms bees, as is well known. The animals react to smoke by rushing to their food stores and gorging themselves with honey. They are too busy at that time to sting an intruder. This is probably an inherited adaptive response to fire. Smoke might indicate a burning tree, and it is of obvious advantage if the bees are well fed when they are forced to abandon their nest. Similarly adaptive is the expulsion of all drones from the colony at the approach of winter. Not contributing to the well-being of the colony, males merely use up food which is at a premium in the cold season. Reactions such as these might

appear to be thought out. Yet bees probably do not "reason" at all.

Other Insect Societies

Structurally polymorphic castes, functionally polymorphic division of labor, and group behavior are in evidence among other social insects also. Many species of ants and termites include, in addition to sterile wingless workers, sterile wingless *soldiers.* These are strong-jawed, heavily armored individuals which accompany work crews outside and keep order within the nest. Soldiers in many cases cannot feed themselves and are cared for by workers. Besides a winged fertile queen (Fig. 6.11) and one or several winged fertile males (*kings*), ant and termite societies may maintain structurally distinct lesser "royalty," probably developed by overfeeding larvae; not enough to produce queens, but more than enough to produce workers.

Agricultural societies occur among both termites and ants (Fig. 6.12). Certain termite species make little garden plots of wood, excrement, and dead termites. There they plant and rear fungi for food. *Leaf-cutting ants,* similarly, prepare pieces of leaves upon which fungi are grown. The fungi are systematically pruned and cared for by gardening details.

Dairy ants exist which keep aphids, tiny green insects (plant lice), as food suppliers. The aphids secrete honeydew, a sugar- and protein-containing mixture, on which the ants depend. A common species of garden ant, for example, places "domesticated" plant lice on the roots of corn. The aphids feed there, and the ants thereafter milk these "ant cows" by gently stroking them. At the approach of winter, the aphids are car-

FIG. 6.11 A queen ant. (*Ward's Natural Science Establishment, Inc.*)

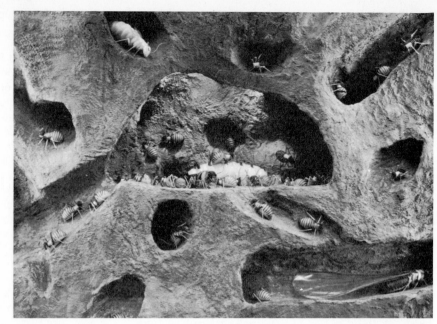

FIG. 6.12   Portion of termite nest. In central chamber note queen, her abdomen swollen with eggs, being cared for by workers. Winged king in lower right corner, larval queen in upper left corner. *(Courtesy of C. E. Simmons, Buffalo Museum of Science.)*

ried into the ant nest and are put back on corn roots the following spring (see Fig. 7.8).

Certain desert ants, called *honeypot ants,* collect nectar from flowers and feed it to some of their fellow workers which are kept within the nest. These "living bottles" become greatly distended and serve as bacteria-free storage bins; during the dry season they dispense drops of honey to their thirsty mates.

Slave-making ants exist which can neither build

nests, feed themselves, nor care for their larvae. They form workerless soldier societies capable only of making raids on other ant species. These victims are robbed of their pupae. The captive pupae mature, and the emerging slaves then care for their masters, performing all the functions they would have carried out in their own nest.

Tropical *army ants* (also called *driver* or *legionary* ants, Fig. 6.13) march across country in raiding expe-

FIG. 6.13   Army ants. Left photo shows queen; the right, a marching column. If such a column is made to travel in a circle, as in the photo, then these ants will continue to circle endlessly. Unless they are diverted by an outside force, they may march themselves to death. Each ant evidently is governed by inherited instinct so completely that it is capable only of following the ant before it and is incapable of thinking itself out of an even slightly altered situation. *(American Museum of Natural History.)*

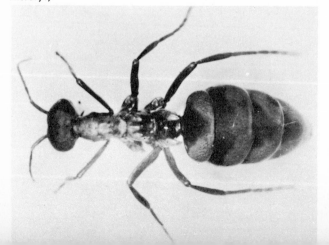

ditions. They travel in columns, and larger-bodied "officer" ants march alongside. Everything living in the path of such columns is devoured, even large animals, including man, if they should be unable to move away. The instinctive, unreasoned nature of insect behavior is shown particularly well in these ants. If a column of army ants is made to travel in a circle, so that the first animals of the column come to march right behind the last, then these ants will continue to circle, endlessly. And unless they are diverted by an outside agency, they may march themselves to death. Each ant evidently is so completely "disciplined" from birth that it is capable only of following the ant before it and is incapable of thinking itself out of even a slightly changed situation.

Among insect societies generally, the fixed nature of each individual constitutes a potential long-range disadvantage. Death of a queen bee and the destruction of honeycomb cells which contain larvae still young enough to be reared into queens usually spell the end of a bee colony; new workers are not produced, and old ones die out. Local eradication of the fungus on which agricultural termites depend and the destruction of their gardens spell the end of the termite colony, its members not being equipped to grow any other food. The victims of slave-making ants could better preserve their colony if all the workers could be mobilized into defending soldiers at the moment of attack.

Among insects, destructive social crises of this sort are offset by the establishment of numerous colonies and by enormous reproduction rates. The safety of the species lies in the number of its individuals. We recognize, however, that it would be immediately advantageous if, in addition to safety through numbers, the society were organized more flexibly; if each member could perform the functions of every other member and if the colony as a whole could learn to adopt new ways of life in the face of changed environmental conditions. Flexible social organization is actually in evidence to greater or less degree among vertebrate groups.

VERTEBRATE SOCIETIES

In contrast to insects and apart from individual differences associated with the sexual dimorphism of males and females, the members of vertebrate societies are more or less alike at birth in structural and functional potential. Later polymorphism is predominantly functional and behavioral and is based on variations in physical strength, in developed skills, in mental acuity, and in some cases on social tradition. As in insects, on the other hand, the main determinant of behavior is inherited instinct, tempered here with a more or less thin veneer of *learning* and *reasoning*. Learning goes hand in hand with *training*, and both are made possible largely by **family** groupings. The subdivision of the vertebrate society into family units and also into herds is one of its main distinctions.

Schools of fish, flocks of birds, packs of European wolves, herds of deer are among the most primitive of the associations within the vertebrate group. Functional polymorphism is not particularly pronounced. In travel, the individual which happens to be in the lead position, usually a male, guides the group temporarily. Other males, often stationed along the outskirts of the group, may take the lead in frequent rotation. The advantages of such associations are largely protective. Many eyes see more than two; a closely huddled herd stays warm; a group is more effective in attack and in defense. Family life within such groups may or may not be evident. There is hardly any in schools of fish. But a duck or a doe trains its young. Families tend to maintain their own physical space within the society. For example, in a herd of seals resting on an island, males take up stations at more or less regular intervals, and each male gathers his family around him. The individual patriarch jealously guards his territory, driving off bachelor males and keeping a sharp eye on his females (see Fig. 7.35). Social life among beavers is more cooperative and rather more advanced. *Several* families may pool their efforts in woodcutting and dam building. All share the benefits of this teamwork, which clearly serves more than mere protection.

Social herding very often is associated with extensive animal **migrations**. These may be undertaken in search of richer or safer pastures, in response to seasonal changes in climate, or to reach geographically fixed breeding grounds. Eels, seals, salmon, and many types of birds are among familiar migrants. When not migrating, solitary individuals or families of these animals may be dispersed widely over a considerable territory. At specific times, as if on cue, individuals draw together from far and near to a common jumping-off point, and then they travel together to their destination, as a band.

These occurrences are among the most intriguing in all biology. How do these animals know where to gather before the journey? How do they time their arrival there, often exactly to the day? And what leads them unerringly to their destination, thousands of miles away in many cases? The navigation problem is sufficiently puzzling among types which make the same trip every year, like seals and birds. If nothing else, a remarkable memory for landmarks, prevailing winds, or ocean currents may be indicated. The problem becomes even more puzzling, however, when none of the migrating animals has ever been at its destination. This is the case among eels.

The spawning grounds of both European and American eels are situated in the deep waters of the Sargasso Sea, southeast of Bermuda and northeast of Puerto Rico. The eggs hatch there, and the near-microscopic larvae, or *elvers,* then travel toward the coasts; larvae of American eels turn west, those of the European eel turn east. The spawning beds of the American type lie farther west. Differences in the direction of ocean currents probably contribute to the initial separation of the two species.

Elvers of the American species travel for about a year before they reach continental waters—and maturation of the larvae requires just 1 year. The voyage of European elvers lasts 3 years—and their maturation requires precisely 3 years.

In coastal estuaries the elvers change into adults. The glassy transparency of the larval body changes to an opaque brown-gray, and the fishlike larval shape changes to the characteristic elongated form of the adult. Adult males remain in estuaries. Females ascend rivers and settle in headwaters and in lakes. Some 7 to 15 years now pass. Then the females migrate back to the estuaries, rejoin the males, and all head out into the Atlantic. Reproductive organs mature during this migration, and upon arrival in the Sargasso, the females spawn and the males fertilize the eggs. The adults then die.

How do the adults find their breeding grounds? It is hardly conceivable that they memorized the route in reverse when they made the trip as immature larvae, a decade earlier. And how do the larvae find coastal waters from which to ascend rivers?

In eels particularly, and in migrating animals generally, all the evidence has clearly not been assembled as yet. But much is known, and almost that much remains unexplained. Whatever the mechanics of migrations might be, however, the adaptive value of banding together during travel is clear.

Not all vertebrate societies migrate and not in all cases are families grouped into herds. Solitary families are common among both monogamous and polygamous species. Fish such as sticklebacks, birds such as parrots, and mammals such as bears and wolverines are monogamous and may mate for life. Such family groups are organized like human families.

Solitary polygamous families may approach the numerical proportions of flocks or herds, as in chickens. Such a group is usually made up of a single dominant male, a series of females, their young, and sometimes a few unrelated young bachelor males. The rule of the dominant male is frequently challenged by the bachelors. If one of these succeeds in defeating his opponent in battle, the loyalty of the females is transferred to the winner. In this way the group is assured of continuously fit, healthy leadership.

An interesting social organization exists among the females of a polygamous family. In a flock of chickens, for example, hens are ranked according to a definite **peck order.** A given hen may peck without danger all hens below her in social rank but may be pecked in turn by all hens above her in the scale. If a new hen is introduced into the flock, she undertakes, or is made to undertake, a pecking contest with each fellow hen. Winning here and losing there, she soon finds her level in the society. A high ranking carries with it certain advantages, such as getting first to the food trough and obtaining a position of prestige on the perch. Very-high-ranking birds often are so aggressive that they persistently reject the attentions of the rooster. More submissive hens then produce most of the offspring. Social rankings of a similar nature are found also among female elephants as well as in most other polygamous families.

Human society had its prehistoric beginnings in the solitary nomadic family. Later arose associations of families into clans and tribes, groupings roughly equivalent to herds among other mammals. With the family as its foundation, the society of the village, the city, and the nation gradually emerged. Today, the trend is toward large-scale associations of nations, a process of social consolidation which may eventually encompass the entire species.

The success of vertebrate societies as a whole lies primarily in the functional versatility of the individual. In the insect society, as we have noted, reproduction of the majority is suppressed, and reproduction of the minority serves not only toward the new formation of individuals, but also toward the new formation of the whole society. Thus, among insects, the fate of the society hinges on the fate of a single female, and her genes alone provide continuity from one social generation to the next. By contrast, virtually all members of a vertebrate society are reproducers. Social continuity consequently is the responsibility of many, and reproduction of any one individual is less vital for the propagation of the society.

The phenomenon of "society" as a whole appears to be bound up with advanced evolutionary status; both insects and vertebrates are elaborately evolved groups. And although different in origin and detailed organiza-

tion, remarkably similar patterns of social behavior are in evidence. Ants and man are unique among animals in making deliberate war, in practicing slavery, in pursuing agriculture, and in domesticating other organisms.

Society in all its forms, like the population generally, is subordinated to the larger species. Populations of social and nonsocial organisms in turn are subordinated to the still larger local community, an aggregation which will occupy our attention in the next chapter.

REVIEW QUESTIONS

1. What is a population, a society, a species? Make sure that you understand the interrelation of these units.

2. How do new species arise and in what general ways are two sister species different?

3. What are individual variations? Distinguish between inheritable and noninheritable variations and give examples of each. Why are noninheritable variations without direct importance in species evolution? What are adaptive variations?

4. Define polymorphism and give several examples. What varieties of polymorphism are encountered within societies?

5. Review the organization of some insect and vertebrate societies and contrast these organizations. What is the social significance of family groupings and where do the latter occur? What is the significance of animal migrations? Of peck orders?

SUGGESTED COLLATERAL READINGS

The following texts include discussions of populations and species:

Allee, W. C.: "Animal Aggregations," University of Chicago Press, Chicago, 1931.
Elton, C.: "Animal Ecology," Macmillan, New York, 1937.
Hesse, R., W. C. Allee, and K. P. Schmidt: "Ecological Animal Geography," 2d ed., Wiley, New York, 1951.

Among many popular books and articles on social animals, the following are recommended:

Collias, N.: Social Life and the Individual among Verte-

brate Animals, *Ann. N.Y. Acad. Sci.*, vol. 51, 1950.
Guhl, A. M.: The Social Order of Chickens, *Sci. American,* vol. 194, 1956.
Haskins, C. P.: "Of Societies and Men," Norton, New York, 1951.
Imms, A. D.: "Social Behavior in Insects," Methuen, London, 1947.
Krough, A.: The Language of the Bees, *Sci. American,* vol. 179, 1948.
Tinbergen, N.: "Social Behavior in Animals," Wiley, New York, 1953.
Von Frisch, K.: "Bees, Their Vision, Chemical Senses, and Language," Cornell University Press, Ithaca, N.Y., 1950.

COMMUNITIES

7

Communities of organisms represent the highest level of living organization; the sum total of all communities on earth encompasses the whole living world. Communities consist partly of free-living organisms, partly of parasites and other organisms which live in *symbiotic* associations. We shall examine the nature of **communities** generally and of **symbiosis** specifically in the first two parts of this chapter. In the concluding part, we shall deal with the different geographical **habitats** in which differently specialized kinds of communities make their home.

COMMUNITY CHARACTERISTICS

A community (often referred to technically as a **biota**) is a local association of populations of several *different* species. A pond with its various plant and various animal populations is a community; so is a forest, a meadow, a section of ocean shore, or a village with its people, trees, grasses, bacteria, cats, dogs, and other organisms (Fig. 7.1). Note that a community almost always contains plants as well as animals, a virtual necessity for community survival.

All communities have certain general characteristics in common, and their maintenance is governed by similar forces.

CYCLES AND BALANCES

Like other living entities, a community grows, develops, passes through a relatively stable mature phase, reproduces, and ultimately dies. The time scale is in hundreds and thousands of years.

Such communal life cycles result from an interplay between organisms and their environment. Being specialized, different organisms are adapted to, and must therefore live in, different environments. The physical character

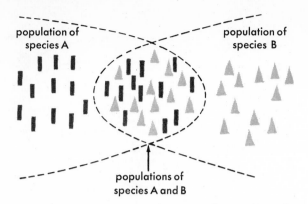

population of
species A

population of
species B

populations of
species A and B

FIG. 7.1 When the territorial ranges of several species overlap, populations of these different species may coexist within a given limited area. The organisms in such an area represent a community.

of a given region consequently determines what types of organisms can settle there originally. Temperature, winds, amount of rainfall, the chemical composition of the surroundings, latitude and altitude, soil conditions, and other similar factors decisively influence what kinds of plants will be able to survive in a given locale. Vegetation in turn, as well as the physical character of the locale, has a selective effect on the types of animals that may successfully settle in the region.

By its very presence, however, a given set of organisms gradually alters local conditions. Raw materials are withdrawn from the environment in large quantities and metabolic wastes are returned. To the extent that these wastes differ from the original raw materials, the environment becomes altered. Moreover, the components of dead organisms also return to the environment, but not necessarily in the same place or necessarily in the same form in which they were obtained. In time, organisms thus bring about profound redistributions and alterations of vast quantities of the earth's substance.

This means that later generations of the original organisms may find the changed local environment no longer suitable. The members of the community must then resettle elsewhere or die out. A new community of different plants and animals may come to occupy the territory, and as this community now alters the area according to its own specializations, type replacement may eventually follow once more. We note how closely the nonliving and the biological components of the environment are interlinked; change in one produces change in the other.

In a community, as on all other levels of living organization, **turnover** as above occurs continuously. Individuals of the various populations emigrate or die out and are replaced by others. The important point is that this flux is automatically self-adjusting. As a result the community remains internally *balanced* and exhibits a numerical steady state; i.e., in all populations present, the numbers of individuals remain relatively constant. In a large, permanent pond, for example, the number of algae, frogs, minnows, and any other organisms, plant or animal, will be more or less the same from decade to decade. Annual fluctuations are common, but over longer periods of time, constancies of numbers are characteristic in most natural communities.

Three main factors create and control these striking numerical balances: **food, reproduction,** and **protection.** They are the principal links which make the members of a community interdependent.

COMMUNAL INTERDEPENDENCE

In every stable community, green plants produce their own food and grow; herbivorous animals eat the plants; carnivorous animals eat each other or herbivores; the elimination products and the dead bodies of all plants and all animals replenish the ocean or the soil; and this, plus solar energy and raw materials from the environment, then makes new plant growth possible (Fig. 7.2).

In such cycles, a pound of soil does not make a pound of new living plant matter; for many of the components of soil are completely unusable in the construction of the living matter of plants. Similarly, a pound of plant food cannot make a pound of new living animal matter; for much of what a plant consists, cellulose, for example, cannot be digested or used otherwise by animals. Therefore, as raw materials are transferred from soil to plants and from plants to animals, these transfers are not 100 per cent efficient. More than a pound of soil is needed to make a pound of plant matter, and more than a pound of plant matter is needed to make a pound of animal matter. Similarly, more than 300 lb of antelope meat or even lion meat is required to produce a 300-lb lion.

This inescapable condition leads to the establishment of **food pyramids** in the community (Fig. 7.3). So many tons of soil can support only so many *fewer* tons of grass. Grass in turn supports herbivores which together weigh less than the grass. And only a relatively small weight of carnivores can find sustenance in such

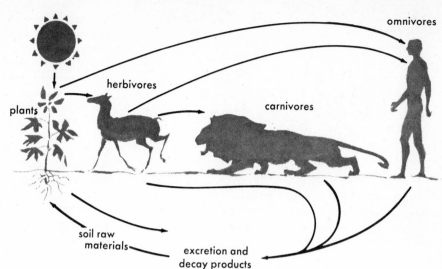

FIG. 7.2 The basic nutritional links in a community.

a community. Several acres of ground thus might just suffice to support a 150-lb man. Such a pyramid of total weights also delineates a pyramid of individual numbers and individual sizes, for prey is generally smaller than predator; hence the balanced community may contain millions of individual grasses, but only one man.

Pyramids of this sort are one of the most potent factors in balancing communal populations; significant variations of numbers at any level of a pyramid entail automatic adjustments at every other level. For ex-

FIG. 7.3 The general pattern of food pyramids. Soil and ocean support plant life; herbivorous animals subsist on the plants; and carnivorous animals subsist on the herbivores.

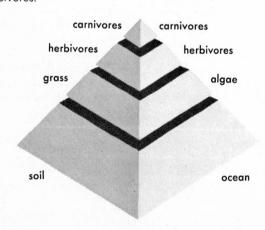

ample, overgrowth of land by plants soon results in nutritional depletion of soil, since more raw materials are withdrawn from the soil. This depletion eventually leads to a starvation of the plants and decimation of their numbers. But the bodies of the dead plants now enrich the soil again, and the fewer plants which still live make less total demand on the raw materials once more present in soil. These living plants therefore can become well nourished. Hence they may reproduce relatively rapidly, and this circumstance increases their numbers again (Fig. 7.4). The cycle then is reintroduced and repeated.

Analogous cycles occur among animals. For example, overpopulation of carnivores soon results in the depletion of herbivores, since a greater number of herbivores is eaten. This depletion leads to starvation of carnivores, hence to a reduction of their numbers. Underpopulation of carnivores then results in overpopulation of herbivores, since fewer herbivores are eaten. But the fewer carnivores can be well fed. They may therefore reproduce relatively rapidly, and this increases their numbers again (see Fig. 7.4). As a general result, although the numbers of all kinds of organisms undergo short-term fluctuations, the total quantities remain relatively constant over the long term.

The territory of a given community usually supports more than one food pyramid. Each of these is characterized by a different **food chain**, culminating in a different carnivore. For example, a lion would find it extremely expensive in terms of locomotor energy to live on insects, worms, or even lizards and mice. Big-

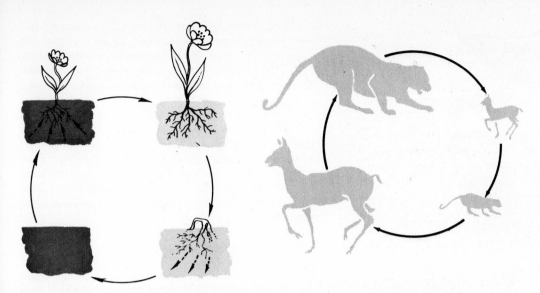

FIG. 7.4 Left, population balance in plants. A large plant population on land reduces the soil nutrients available (top). This eventually leads to starvation of plants and reduction of their numbers (lower right). But the dead plants now enrich the soil (lower left), and this again permits an increase in the number of living plants. Through continued repetition of such a cycle, the size of the plant population is maintained fairly constant over the long term. Right, population balance in animals. A large carnivore population reduces the herbivore population by predation (top). This eventually decreases the food supply of carnivores and leads to starvation and decrease of the carnivore population (bottom right). This in turn then permits the herbivore population to flourish again (bottom left), which also permits an increase in the numbers of carnivores. The cycle repeats in this manner.

ger prey, like antelope or zebra, is obviously more appropriate. On the other hand, insects and worms are suitable food for small birds; and small birds, lizards, and mice provide adequate diet for larger predator birds. In this example, two food pyramids are based on the same plot of land. The pattern is generally much more complex. Different types of plants in one territory may sustain many different herbivores. These may form the basis of different, intricately interlocking animal food chains. As in the case of elephants, a herbivore may itself represent the peak of a food pyramid (Fig. 7.5).

It may be noted also that, in a balanced community, the total living matter yields just enough dead matter and other raw materials to replenish the soil or the ocean. This permits the continued existence of the various food pyramids above ground or in water. In such delicate nutritional interdependencies, minor fluc-tuations are rebalanced fairly rapidly. But serious inter-ference, by disease, by man, or by physical factors, is likely to topple the whole pyramid. If that happens, the entire community may cease to exist.

A second link between the members of a commu-nity is reproductive interdependence. A familiar and most important example of this is the pollinating activity of insects. In some well-known cases of remark-able specialization, a given insect visits only one or a few specific flower types for pollen and nectar. The flowers (e.g., snapdragons) in turn are structurally adapted to facilitate entry of the insect. Such intimate reciprocity testifies to a closely correlated evolutionary development of animal and plant. It is fairly obvious how such interdependence contributes to population balance: reduction of the insect population entails reproductive restriction of the plant, and vice versa. Similarly significant in balancing the reproductive

FIG. 7.5 Several different food chains, each culminating in a different organism, may be supported by a single plot of ground.

growth of plant populations is the seed-dispersing activity of birds and mammals, man in particular.

Other examples of reproductive dependence are many. Birds such as cuckoos lay eggs in nests of other birds. Insects such as gall wasps embed their eggs deep in the tissues of particular plants, where the hatching larvae find food and protection. Other insects deposit eggs on or under the skin of various animals. Certain wasps, for example, kill tarantulas and lay their eggs in them (see Fig. 7.15).

Reproductive growth and geographical expansion of a community are intimately correlated with nutritional balances. In new territory, a pioneer association of populations will first form a small food pyramid, occupying perhaps only part of the available territory. The pyramid may still be too "low" to support any big herbivores or carnivores. Abundance of food and ab-

sence of competition promote high reproduction rates and a rapid increase of numbers at all levels of the pyramid. The base of the pyramid therefore widens, and a larger area of the territory will be occupied. Sizable herbivores and even a few larger carnivores may gradually be assimilated into the community. As a result, the rate of predation will increase, which in turn will slowly decrease the net reproductive population gain. A turning point will be reached eventually. Prior to it the community grows at an increasing rate; after it the community still grows, but at a decreasing rate. Net expansion finally comes to a standstill, and from then on the pyramid retains relatively stable proportions (Fig. 7.6).

In such a growth pattern, it is assumed that territorial and numerical expansion can follow its inherent trend without external restriction. Yet geographical and biological barriers often delimit an area. A small forest may be surrounded by water or by land on which trees cannot grow; a meadow may be ringed in by forest, or a valley by high mountains. In such cases, growth of the community is stopped before its inherent potential is fully expressed. The food pyramid on such a limited territory may never become high enough to support large herbivorous or carnivorous members. One searches in vain for stag in a tiny forest, for large fish in a small pond. But the one is likely to abound in worms, mice, and small birds; the other in algae, protozoa, and frogs.

In a community incapable of further expansion, steady reproduction may produce a centrifugal **population pressure**. This condition may be relieved by emigration of the overflow population. If emigration is not possible or if it is not sufficiently effective, numbers will be decimated by starvation or even sooner by epidemic diseases. The latter spread rapidly through an overpopulated, undernourished, spatially delimited community. Even if disease affects only one of the component species, the whole communal web is likely to be disrupted.

The third main link among the members of a community is protective interdependence. Plants in forest and grassland usually protect animals by providing shelter against enemies and adverse weather. If the opportunities for protection are reduced, both the animal and the plant population may suffer. For example, if an overpopulation of insects makes available plant shelter inadequate, the insects will become easier prey for birds and bats. But this circumstance may also decimate the plant populations, for their major pollinating agents may no longer be sufficiently effective.

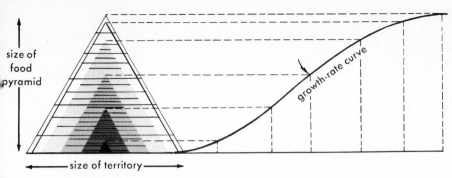

size of food pyramid

growth-rate curve

size of territory

FIG. 7.6 Population growth and geographical expansion. As the number of individuals increases, more territory will be occupied and the food pyramid will become wider and higher (left part of diagram). Rates of population increase are indicated in the curve at right; increasing rates are in evidence prior to a turning point (arrow), decreasing rates thereafter.

Given animals in many cases are protected from other animals by *camouflage*. Such a protective device may involve body color or body shape or both (see Fig. 11.1). Probably the most remarkable instance of color camouflage is the phenomenon of **mimicry**, widespread particularly among butterflies and moths. In certain of these animals, pigmentation patterns exist which are virtually indistinguishable from those of other, unrelated species. Usually those species are mimicked which are strong or fast and have few natural enemies. The advantage is that an animal resembling even super-

ficially another more powerful one will be protected too, by scaring off potential predators.

Insects also display a variety of structural camouflages. For example, the individuals of certain species possess the detailed shape of leaves, of branches, or of thorns (Fig. 7.7). This serves not only defensively but also as a disguise against potential victims.

Other protective devices vary widely in type. Various birds and some mammals mimic the song and voice of other species, either defensively or as an aggressive lure. The hermit crab protects its soft ab-

FIG. 7.7 The shape of many insects mimics that of plant parts on which these animals habitually live. Left, a praying mantis, colored green, resembling a thin stem. Middle, a leaf insect, whose resemblance to a leaf is exceptionally striking. Right, a dead-leaf butterfly, which, when its wings are folded, remarkably resembles a leaf. (Right, General Biological Supply House, Inc.; others, U.S. Department of Agriculture.)

domen in an empty snail shell of appropriate size. Schools of small pilot fish scout ahead of large sharks, leading their protectors to likely prey. Significant protection is also afforded by man, through domestication, game laws, parks, and sanctuaries.

These various examples illustrate how the member populations of a community are specialized nutritionally, reproductively, and protectively. Carnivorous populations cannot sustain themselves on plant food and not even on every kind of animal food. Herbivorous populations require plants and are incapable of hunting for animals. The populations of green plants depend on soil or ocean, and the populations of saprotrophs cannot do without dead organisms. These are profound specializations in structure and function, and they imply loss of individual self-sufficiency as well as a need for cooperative interdependence. Communal associations of populations evidently are a necessity. They are but extensions, on a higher biological level, of the necessarily cooperative aggregation of cells into tissues, organs, and organisms.

Indeed, the development of "community" appears to be as integral a part of organic evolution as the development of individual organisms. Events were probably *not* such that a particular organism first evolved structurally and functionally in a certain way and then happened to find the right community into which it could fit. Rather, the community probably existed from the very beginning, and all its member populations evolved together; the community itself evolved. The histories of the bumblebee and the snapdragon are linked as intimately as the histories of every man's hand and foot.

A community within a given territory includes not only free-living organisms in loose cooperative association but also organisms which live together in more or less permanent *physical* contact. Two individuals of different species may be joined so intimately that one lives right *within* the other. All such instances of physically intimate living together of members of different species are instances of **symbiosis,** a special form of communal life.

SYMBIOSIS

THE PATTERN

A free association in which an animal habitually shelters under a plant might, in a relatively simple evolutionary step, become an association in which the animal and the plant have entered a more permanent protective union. A plant which depends on some animal for seed dispersal might advantageously live in, or on, the animal altogether, not only at the time of seed production but throughout life. A soil bacterium or a scavenging protozoon living on the undigested elimination products of larger forms might find a surer food supply if it could adapt to an existence right in the gut cavity of its supplier.

Among ancestral populations of free-living forms, ample opportunity existed for the development of such symbiotic relationships. These opportunities were exploited to the full, and many associations arose in which two organisms of different species came to live together in intimate, lasting physical contact. Today there is no major group of organisms which does not include symbiotic species, and there is probably no individual organism which does not play **host** to at least one **symbiont.**

The phenomenon of symbiosis is expressed in two basic patterns. In **facultative** associations, two different organisms "have the faculty" of entering a more or less intimate symbiotic relationship. But they need not necessarily do so, being able to survive as free-living forms. In **obligatory** associations, on the other hand, one organism *must* unite symbiotically with another, usually a specific one, if it is to survive. The ancestors of obligatory symbionts have invariably been free-living organisms which in the course of history have lost the power of living on their own. Before becoming obligatory symbionts, they formed facultative associations with organisms on which they came to depend more and more.

Symbionts affect each other in different ways. Thus, **mutualism** describes a relationship in which both associated partners derive some benefit, often a vital one, from living together. **Commensalism** benefits one of the partners, and the other is neither helped nor harmed by the association. **Parasitism** is of advantage to the parasite but is detrimental to the host to greater or lesser extent. These categories intergrade imperceptibly, and in many boundary cases clear-cut distinctions cannot be made.

MUTUALISM

An example of a loose mutualistic association is the tickbird-rhinoceros relationship. The tickbird feeds on skin parasites of the rhinoceros, and in return the latter is relieved of irritation and obtains warning of danger when the sharp-eyed bird flies off temporarily to the security of the nearest tree. Another example is the relationship between dairy ants and aphids, already cited in Chap. 6 in the section on insect societies. The ant obtains food from the aphid, and the aphid in turn secures protection, food, and care from the ant. These two examples also illustrate the difference between facultative and obligatory mutualism. Both tickbird and rhinoceros can get along without each other if necessary; but the ant cannot do without its aphids and the aphid cannot do without its ants (Fig. 7.8).

A somewhat greater degree of physical intimacy is exhibited in the mutualistic symbiosis of sea anemones and hermit crabs. Sea anemones attach themselves to empty snail shells, and hermit crabs use these shells as protective housings. The sea anemone, an exceedingly slow mover by itself, is thus carried about on the shell of the hermit crab—an obvious advantage to the anemone in its search for food and in geographic dispersal. The hermit crab in turn benefits from the disguise. Moreover, since the anemone is not a dainty eater, scraps of food become available to the crab when the anemone catches prey. This is a facultative association; sea anemones and hermit crabs may and largely do live on their own.

An example of rather more intimate mutualism is provided by *lichens,* grayish and yellowish incrustations commonly found on rock surfaces and on tree bark (Fig. 7.9). These crusts are associations of photosynthe-

FIG. 7.9 Mutualism. The photograph shows lichens, mutualistic associations of algae and fungi. *(J. Carel and Larousse Publishing Co., Paris.)*

sizing single-celled algae and saprotrophic threadlike fungi. The meshes of the fungal threads support the algae, and they also hold rain water like a sponge. The algae produce food for themselves and for the fungus. The fungus in turn contributes water, nitrogenous wastes, and respiratory carbon dioxide, substances which allow for continued photosynthesis and food production. Lichens may consequently survive in relatively dry terrestrial environments. The fungus may live alone in a water-sugar medium, and the alga may persist by itself in mineral-containing water. Separately, they are merely two types of organisms not particularly different from many others like them. But together they become a combination of considerable evolutionary importance. Lichens were among the first organisms capable of eking out a terrestrial existence. Contributing to the crumbling of rock and the formation of soil, they paved the way for a larger-scale colonization of the land.

The most intimate forms of mutualism involve organisms which live directly within other organisms. For example, the roots of certain vascular plants, particularly legumes like soybeans, clover, and peas, form important mutualistic associations with so-called *nitrogen-fixing bacteria.* The bacteria invade the hosts through the root hairs, and the infected root cells respond by increasing in size and number. The result is the development of **root nodules.** In them, the host

FIG. 7.8 Mutualistic symbiosis. The photo shows a carpenter ant protecting a larva of a tree hopper insect. The larva benefits from the protection and in return secretes sugary honeydew, which is licked off by the ant and serves as its food. *(Courtesy of E. W. Teale.)*

provides nutrients for the bacteria and the bacteria in turn fix atmospheric nitrogen; i.e., they make this essential element chemically usable for both themselves and the host plant. This is a major source through which usable nitrogen becomes available to living organisms (see Chap. 12).

Analogously invasive forms of mutualism occur in associations between algae and various other organisms. For example, many free-living protozoa, (e.g., a species of *Paramecium*) and coelenterates (e.g., several species of *Hydra*) harbor green single-celled algae within their translucent bodies. Known as **zoochlorellae**, the algae supply food and oxygen, as in lichens, and in turn receive protection, water, and other materials essential for continued photosynthesis.

In the gut of termites live flagellate protozoa which secrete an enzyme capable of digesting the cellulose of wood. Termites chew and swallow wood, the intestinal flagellates then digest it, and both organisms share the resulting carbohydrates. Thus, to the detriment of man, termites may exploit unlimited food opportunities open to very few other animals. And the protozoa receive protection and are assured of a steady food supply.

Virtually every animal which possesses an alimentary canal houses billions of intestinal bacteria, particularly in the lower gut. These bacteria draw freely on materials not digested or not digestible by the host, and as a result of their activities, they initiate fecal decay (see Chap. 14). The host generally benefits from the auxiliary digestion carried out by the bacteria and in many instances is also dependent on certain of the bacterial byproducts. For example, man and other mammals obtain many vitamins in the form of "waste" materials released by the bacterial symbionts of the gut.

Mutualistic associations may sometimes develop into parasitic ones. In the course of successive generations, a relationship originally beneficial to both partners may change into an association in which one partner gradually comes to live at the expense of the other. For example, a given beneficial intestinal symbiont might easily "develop a taste" for gut-wall tissue or might become capable of penetrating through the gut wall into the blood stream. In effect, the host would then support a parasite.

COMMENSALISM

Just as the chance association of two free-living organisms may develop into mutualism, so an analogous chance association may develop into commensalism. As far as can be demonstrated, the commensal neither harms nor helps its host, and the host appears neither to resist nor to foster the relationship in any way.

Among plants, commensalism is illustrated by numerous **epiphytes**. An epiphyte is a plant which grows on another host plant, but the latter is neither harmed nor helped. Tropical ferns and plants closely related to the pineapple, e.g., the *bromeliads*, frequently occur as epiphytes on jungle trees. The symbionts obtain water and minerals from pockets in the host tree. In many cases, such epiphytes also possess modified cup-shaped leaves which catch rain water. Aerial roots of the epiphyte then may grow into these cups and absorb the water collected there (Fig. 7.10).

Animal commensalism is illustrated, for example, by a species of small tropical fish. Individuals of this species find shelter in the cloacas of sea cucumbers. The fish darts out for food and returns, to the utter indifference of the host. The so-called suckerfish provides another example. This fish (Fig. 7.11) possesses a dorsal fin which is modified into a holdfast device. By means of it, the fish attaches to the underside of sharks and thereby secures scraps of food, wide geographic dispersal, and protection. The shark neither benefits nor suffers in any respect. In still another example, barnacles may attach to the skin of whales, an association which secures geographic distribution and wider feeding opportunities for the sessile crustaceans. In this instance, a trend toward parasitism is in evidence; in some cases the barnacles send rootlike proc-

FIG. 7.10 Epiphytes. The photograph shows ferns growing epiphytically on a tree trunk. *(Paul Popper, Ltd., London.)*

FIG. 7.11 Commensalistic symbiosis. Shark with three suckerfish attached to underside. (*New York Zoological Society.*)

FIG. 7.12 Mistletoe, parasitic on branch of pine tree. (*U.S. Forest Service.*)

esses into the whale, outgrowths which eat away bits of host tissue.

These and most other existing commensalistic unions tend to be facultative; for a symbiont is not likely to be allowed to impose on a host in intimate, obligatory fashion unless the host derives at least some benefits from such an imposition and therefore fosters the association, or unless the symbiont has overcome the host's defenses and is frankly parasitic. Consequently, although obligatory commensalistic associations may have evolved quite often, most of them have probably been unstable; they would soon have changed either into mutualism or into parasitism.

We note that both commensalism and mutualism may develop into parasitism. Also, commensalism may first become mutualism, then parasitism. Finally, of two associated organisms, one may be parasitic from the outset. Evidently, all symbiotic roads may eventually lead to parasitism, and none, or virtually none, leads away from it. Parasitic symbiosis is by far the most stable, by far the most widespread.

PARASITISM

Parasitic Ways of Life

It has probably become apparent in the above that symbiosis revolves largely, though not exclusively, around the problem of food. We might suspect, therefore, that symbiosis in general and parasitism in particular would be most prevalent among organisms in which competition for food is most intense. This is actually the case. Although some parasitic green plants do exist (e.g., mistletoes, Fig. 7.12), photosynthesizing organisms by and large are not under competitive pressure for basic nutrients; air, water, and sunlight are present everywhere in inexhaustible quantities. Para-

sitism flourishes primarily among organisms which must obtain food from others: in viruses, in bacteria, in fungi, and in animals.

All viruses are parasitic. Of the bacteria, those which are not photosynthetic or saprotrophic are parasitic. Among fungi, some are saprotrophic, the rest are parasitic. And in animals, many major groups are wholly parasitic; virtually all others include important parasitic subgroups (see Chaps. 9 and 11).

As we have seen in Chap. 3, parasitism is almost as old as life itself. So advantageous and economical is the parasitic mode of living that many parasites may be infested with smaller parasites of their own and these in turn may support still smaller ones. For example, a mammal may harbor parasitic worms; these may be invaded by parasitic bacteria; and the bacteria may be infected by *bacteriophages*, i.e., viruses which parasitize bacteria (Fig. 7.13). **Hyperparasitism** of this

FIG. 7.13 Electron micrograph of the remnants of a bacterium after attack by bacteriophages. The virus parasites are the small rodlets with knobbed ends. (*R. W. G. Wyckoff, "Electron Microscopy," Interscience Publishers, Inc., 1949*).

sort, i.e., one parasite inside another, is very common. It represents a natural exploitation of the very condition of parasitism. Inasmuch as the parasite is generally smaller than the host and inasmuch as one host may support many parasites, parasitic and hyperparasitic relationships form inverted food pyramids contained within the pyramids of the larger community.

The first problem a potential parasite faces is the defense mobilized by a potential host. Attachment to the outer body surface can be prevented only with difficulty, particularly if the host does not possess limbs. Numerous **ectoparasites** exploit this possibility. Equipped with suckers, clamps, or adhesive surfaces, they hold onto skin or hair, and with the aid of cutting, biting, or sucking mouth parts, or with rootlike outgrowths, they feed on the body fluids of the host. Examples are leeches, lice, ticks, mites, lampreys, and many fungi.

Endoparasites, within the body of the host, must breach more formidable defenses. Cellular enzymes of a host, digestive juices and strong acids in the alimentary tract, antibodies in the blood, white blood cells and other cells which engulf foreign bodies in amoeboid fashion (e.g., histiocytes), these are among the defensive agents which guard against the invader. Overcoming such defenses means *specialization:* development of resistant outer coverings, as in bacteria and fungi; tough cuticles, as in most parasitic worms; development of cyst walls and calcareous capsules; development of hooks or clamps with which to hold onto the gut wall; development of enzymes which, when secreted, erode a path through host tissues.

Specialization of the parasite also involves the selection of *specific* hosts. Highly advanced parasites cannot pick a host at random, even if many similar ones offer the same type of nutrients. During the evolution of a parasite, structural and functional specializations have developed in adaptation to particular hosts only. Thus, most parasites enter a host's body by fixed routes, then settle in fixed regions, as if, in the course of time, they had learned to channel their attack through points of weakness characteristic of particular hosts.

Breaching the host's defenses is a perennial problem to the parasite. No sooner has it developed an avenue to a comfortable existence than the infected individual is discriminated against in his environment; healthy hosts which have evolved a resistance to the parasite have a better chance of surviving. For example, large-scale infection of a population with parasites will lead to the preferential survival of those hosts which, through random mutations, develop specific means of combating the infectious agents. Hence if a parasite is to prevail against host defenses continually improved by evolution, it too must readjust and evolve. Through its own random mutations, it must develop new means of attack.

We recognize that parasite and host evolve *together,* first the parasite, then the host being one jump ahead. The very fact that free-living organisms exist at all today signifies that they are resistant to a good many potential parasites by which they are constantly besieged. The very fact that parasites continue to exist signifies that free-living organisms are not completely resistant—and they probably can never be, in view of the evolutionary inventiveness of the parasites.

It may be noted in this connection that it is to the obvious advantage of the parasite to keep the host alive. We find, indeed, that the virulence of a parasite often decreases with time. When a parasite-host relationship is first established, the invader is likely to be *pathogenic,* i.e., disease-producing. Two parallel evolutionary trends tend to reduce this pathogenicity. One is natural discrimination against infected hosts, as indicated above; the least resistant will be eliminated through plagues and epidemics. At the same time, less virulent populations of a given parasite will be favored; for when a parasite kills a host, the killer is generally killed as well. Therefore, the more harmful the parasite, the more difficult is its perpetuation. Many parasites are only mildly pathogenic, or not at all, often indicating long association with a particular host.

Parasitic Degeneracy

Once established in the body of a host, the parasite may pursue a life of comparative ease. Embedded in food, it needs no locomotor equipment, few sense organs, no fast nervous reflexes. Indeed, structural and functional *degeneracy* is a nearly universal characteristic of parasites. Here we encounter the ultimate expression of the principle that loss of self-sufficiency tends to be proportional to the degree of interdependence of organisms.

Structural degeneracy is exhibited, for example, by mistletoes. The dwarf mistletoe, common on western cone-bearing trees, has only the slightest vestiges of leaves. Moreover, absorption of water and inorganic materials from the host occurs not through true roots, but through rows of parenchyma cells which grow like fungus filaments through the host tissue. Among animal parasites, structural degeneracy is pronounced in tapeworms, for example. These parasites (see Fig. 7.16) possess only a highly reduced nervous system, a greatly reduced muscular system, and not even a vestige of a digestive system. Almost like blotting paper, the worms soak up through their body walls the food juices in the host gut. Even more degenerate is the adult of *Sacculina,* a crustacean which parasitizes its not too remote relatives, crabs. The parasitic adult is little more than a formless, semifluid mass of cells which spreads through a crab like a malignant tumor. The invader later produces sperms and eggs, and fertilized eggs then develop into recognizably typical, free-swimming crustacean larvae. These attach to crabs, enter them, and change into the degenerate adults.

Degeneracy also extends to metabolic activities. In particular, the synthetic capacities of a parasite are almost invariably restricted. For example, in the presence of nitrogen sources and simple carbohydrates like glucose, a *free-living* soil bacterium or fungus may synthesize amino acids, proteins, vitamins, numerous antibiotics useful to man, in short, all the complex compounds which make up the living matter of the organism. By contrast, an obligately *parasitic* bacterium or fungus promptly dies when given nitrogenous and simple organic substances alone. It has reduced synthesizing capacities and has become dependent on its host to supply it with most of the components of its living substance in prefabricated form.

In this respect, the modern virus is the most degenerate. It cannot metabolize or self-perpetuate at all except within living host cells. Removed from cells, it becomes a lifeless crystal of complex chemicals; and it may resume metabolic and self-perpetuative activities only when it is reintroduced into living host cells (Fig. 7.14). Other parasites may be free-living at least at some stage of their life cycle, but viruses are never free-living. Their parasitism is total, complete, obligatory. It should be noted here, however, that viruses actually cannot be considered to be in the same category as other parasites; for, as shown in Chap. 3, viruses are chemical complexes and not cellular organisms like other parasites. Moreover, the ancestors of all other parasites were free-living organisms, whereas the ancestors of viruses probably were the genetic substances of bacteria. These substances were never free-living to begin with.

In parasitic organisms, degeneracy is probably an adaptive advantage, for the degenerate condition may be more economical than the fully developed condition

FIG. 7.14   Crystals of a virus. In this state viruses are nonliving. They exhibit living properties only when present within host cells. *(Courtesy of R. W. G. Wyckoff, "Electron Microscopy," Interscience Publishers, 1949).*

of the free-living ancestor. A tapeworm, for example, being structurally degenerate, may concentrate all its resources into parasitizing the host; it need not divert energy and materials into maintaining elaborate nervous, muscular, or digestive systems, which are unnecessary anyway in this parasitic way of life.

Parasite Reproduction

In one respect parasites are far from degenerate: reproduction. In this function they are as prolific as the most prolific free-living forms. The practical necessity of an enormous reproductive potential is correlated with a major problem confronting the parasite, particularly the endoparasite, namely, how to get from one host to another. The problem is severely compounded by the requirement that not any new host will do. Another individual of the same host species must be found.

Parasites succeed in two ways, both of which involve reproduction: **active transfer** and **passive transfer.** In the former, one stage of the life cycle of the parasite is free-living *and* motile; i.e., this stage transfers from one host to another through its own powers of locomotion. For example, the adult phase may be parasitic and the free-living embryo or larva may be capable of locomotion, as in *Sacculina*. Or the larval phase may be the parasite, the adult then being free-living and capable of locomotion. This is the case in a number of parasitic insects which deposit their eggs within or on individuals of other species (Fig. 7.15).

Passive transfer is encountered among parasites in which *no* phase of the life cycle is capable of locomotion. Propagation here is accomplished by wind, by water, or by **intermediate hosts.** The latter offer a means of transfer which is not quite as chancy as random distribution by wind or water. What is involved here is well illustrated in the propagation of tapeworms.

These parasites of man (Fig. 7.16), like numerous others, exploit one of the easiest routes into and out of the host, namely, the alimentary tract. Entering through the host's mouth by way of eaten food and leaving through the anus by way of feces, some, like

FIG. 7.15 A caterpillar of a sphinx moth, parasitized by the pupae of another insect species. *(Courtesy of E. W. Teale.)*

tapeworms, spend their adult life directly in the gut cavity of the host. Others utilize the gut as a springboard from which to invade interior tissues. The problem is to transfer offspring from one human host to another by passive means. Tapeworms accomplish a first phase of this readily; namely, mature eggs are released to the outside with the host's feces.

Since man does not eat feces, the eggs evidently cannot reach new human hosts directly. However, tapeworms ingeniously take advantage of the food pyramids of which man is a member; man eats beef, and cattle eat grass. A ready-made pathway from grass to man thus exists, and the transfer chain becomes complete if, as happens on occasion, human feces are deposited on grass. Tapeworm eggs clinging to such vegetation may then be eaten by cattle.

In the intestine of a cow, a tapeworm egg develops into an embryo and such an embryo bores a path through the gut wall into the cow's bloodstream. From there the embryo is carried into beef muscle, where it encapsulates and matures. If man then eats raw or partially cooked beef, the capsule surrounding the young tapeworm is digested away in the human gut and the free worm now hooks on to the intestinal wall of its new host (Fig. 7.17).

This history illustrates a very widely occurring phenomenon. Many kinds of parasites utilize well-established food pyramids in transferring to new hosts. Often there is more than one intermediate host, as in the life cycle of the Chinese liver fluke (Fig. 7.18). The adults of this parasite infest the liver of man. Fertilized eggs are released via the bile duct into the gut of the host and pass to the outside with the feces. If the feces get into ponds or rivers, as happens frequently, some of the eggs may be eaten by snails.

In the tissues of a snail, each egg develops into a larva, called a **miracidium.** This larva then develops into another larval type, called a **sporocyst.** The latter subsequently gives rise to many **redia** larvae, which feed on snail tissue and grow. Then *each* of the rediae produces yet another set of many larvae, called **cercariae.**

These fourth-generation larvae escape from the snail and swim about freely. If within a short time they happen to find a fish, they bore into it and encapsulate in muscular tissue. And if man subsequently eats raw or incompletely cooked fish, the young adult flukes find their way from the human gut into the liver.

Note that this cycle involves two intermediate hosts, the snail and the fish. Transfer is partly passive

 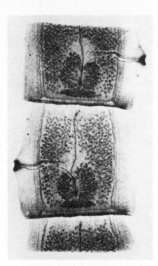 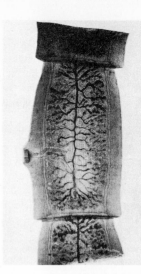

FIG. 7.16   Tapeworm. Left, head. Middle, segmental sections near middle of body. Right, segmental sections near hind end of body. Tree-shaped structures in middle and right are reproductive organs. Note testes filling segments in middle and genital pores opening on the sides of the segments. The uterus filled with eggs is conspicuous in right. *(General Biological Supply House, Inc.)*

FIG 7.17   The life cycle of a tapeworm. Ripe sections of the worm pass with the feces from the human gut. Eggs are released from these sections in the gut of cattle. Tapeworm embryos then encapsulate in beef muscle, and the embryos become adults in the intestine of man.

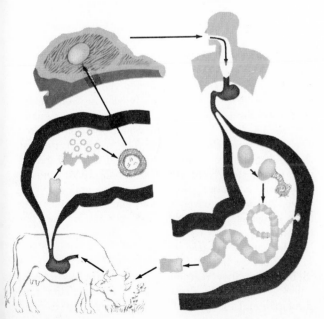

(man to snail, fish to man), partly active (snail to fish). Note particularly the multistage, larva-within-a-larva type of development. Characteristic of flukes generally, it constitutes a highly efficient method of enormously increasing the number of reproductive units. A single fluke egg is estimated to yield a final total of some 10,000 cercariae—and a single adult fluke may produce many tens of thousands of eggs. Hence the chances become fairly good that at least some of the millions or billions of larvae will reach final hosts.

Through active locomotion, through physical agents such as air and water, and through routes involving food pyramids and intermediate hosts, parasites have solved their transfer problems most successfully. So successfully, indeed, that there are many more individual parasites in existence than free-living organisms.

A community consists of various kinds of free-living and various kinds of symbiotic populations. Which particular ones of each type actually compose a given community, hence the very nature of the community itself, is determined largely by the type of physical *environment* in which organisms exist. We shall examine the different communal environments in the following section.

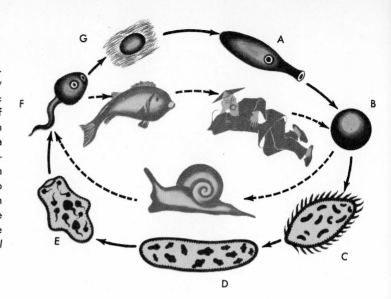

FIG. 7.18 Photo: Chinese liver fluke, adult. Note sucker at anterior (narrow) end of body and dark-stained reproductive organs. Diagram: life cycle of a liver fluke. *A*, adult in liver of man. *B*, egg, passing out with feces and eaten by snail. *C*, in the snail, the egg develops into a miracidium larva. *D*, from it develops a sporocyst. *E*, from each sporocyst larva in turn form many redia larvae. *F*, each redia gives rise to many cercaria larvae. *G*, cercariae escape from the snail and encapsulate in fish muscle. The encapsulated larvae then grow into adults in the gut and liver of man. (*Photo, Ward's Natural Science Establishment, Inc.*)

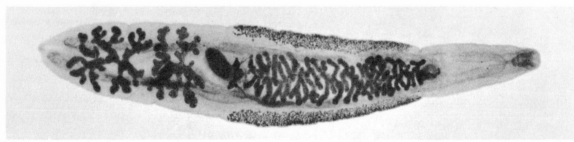

COMMUNITY HABITATS

With the possible exception of the most arid deserts, the high, frozen mountain peaks, and the perpetually icebound polar regions, probably no place on earth is devoid of life. The subdivisions of this planetary environment represent homes, or **habitats,** in which communities live. The two principal habitats are the **aquatic** and the **terrestrial.** Both range from equator to pole and from a few thousand feet below to a few thousand feet above sea level. **Ocean** and **fresh water** are the principal components of the aquatic habitat and **air** and **soil** of the terrestrial.

THE OCEANIC HABITAT

The Ocean Basin
Even the land dweller will appreciate readily that the sea is not a single, unified environment. Indeed, an examination of its structure and of its content of living matter shows clearly that this birthplace of life comprises nearly as many distinct subenvironments as the land.

All ocean basins have roughly the form of an inverted hat (Fig. 7.19). A gently sloping **continental shelf** stretches away from the coast line for an average distance of about 100 miles (discounting often extreme deviations from this average). The angle of descent then changes more or less abruptly and the shelf grades over into a steep **continental slope.** Characteristically, this slope is scored deeply by gorges and canyons, carved out by slow rivers of mud and sand discharging from estuaries. Several thousand feet down, the continental slope levels off into the ocean floor, a more or less horizontal expanse known as the **abyssal plain.** Mountains rise from it in places, with peaks sometimes so high that they rear up above sea level as islands. Elsewhere, the plain may be scarred by deep rifts, e.g., the Japan and Philippine Deeps along the western edge

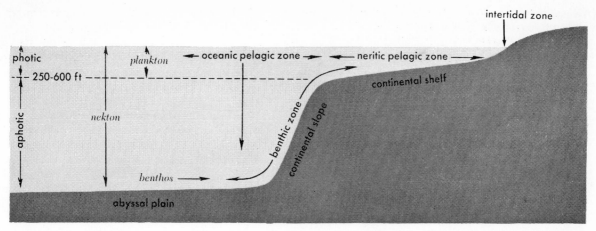

FIG. 7.19   The structure of an ocean basin.

of the Pacific. These plunge 35,000 ft down and are the lowest parts of the earth's crust.

Three major environments may be distinguished in such a basin. The sea floor from the shore out to the edge of the continental shelf forms the **littoral** zone. Its most important subenvironment is the narrow **intertidal** belt, between the high- and low-tide lines. Beyond the littoral, the sea floor along the continental slope and the abyssal plain constitutes the **benthonic** environment. The third principal environment is the **pelagic**—the water itself which fills the ocean basin. This environment includes a **neritic** subdivision over the littoral zone and an **oceanic** subdivision over the benthonic zone.

A most important vertical subdivision of the pelagic environment is brought about by the sun. Acting directly or via the overlying medium of air, the sun produces "weather" in the surface layers of the sea: waves, currents, storms, evaporation, seasons, daily climatic rhythms, and other changes. Deep water is not so affected. Moreover, sunlight penetrates into water only to an average depth of about 250 ft and to at most 600 ft in certain seas. Within this sunlit layer, called the **photic zone,** light dims progressively to zero with increasing distance from the surface. The most significant consequence of this circumstance is that photosynthesizing vegetation can exist only in the uppermost layers of the sea. Animal life directly dependent on plant foods therefore must similarly remain near the surface. As a result, the top 250 ft or so of the oceans contains a concentration of living matter as dense as any on earth. In sharp contrast, the **aphotic zone,** i.e., the dark region underneath the photic zone, is com-

pletely free of photosynthetic organisms and contains only animals, bacteria, and possibly fungi.

On the basis of its relationship to these various environments, marine life has been classified into three general categories: **plankton, nekton,** and **benthos.** Plankton includes all passively drifting or floating forms. Most of them are microscopic and are found largely in the surface waters of the sea, i.e., in the photic zone. Even though some of these forms possess locomotor systems, they are nevertheless too weak or too small to counteract currents and movements of water. Nekton comprises the active swimmers, capable of changing stations at will. All nektonic types are therefore animals, and they are found in all waters, along the surface as well as in the sea depths. The benthos consists of crawling, creeping, and sessile organisms along the sides and the bottom of the ocean basin.

The Photic Zone

Since photosynthetic organisms do not possess powerful locomotor systems like muscles, such organisms in open water can stay within the range of sunlight only if they float. And since living material is slightly heavier than water, passive floating is possible only if an organism possesses a special floating device or if it is small enough to be buoyed up by the salt water.

Thus, the predominant marine photosynthesizers are planktonic. They include teeming trillions of algae which, as a group, probably photosynthesize more food than all land plants combined. Collectively called **phytoplankton,** this oceanic vegetation represents the richest pasture on earth; directly or indirectly, it forms the nutritional basis of all marine life.

Most of the algal types included in this "grass of the sea" are microscopic (see also Chap. 9). Unquestionably the most abundant are the *diatoms*. Each of these single-celled organisms is enclosed within a delicate, intricately sculptured, silicon-containing shell (Fig. 7.20). Reddish *dinoflagellates* (see Chap. 9) also abound in surface waters, sometimes in populations so dense that they tint acre upon acre of ocean with a coppery hue (e.g., "red" tides). Other marine algae include many types of variously pigmented forms, and some of these, as well as countless numbers of marine bacteria, are bioluminescent. They emit flashes of cold light, which dot the night seascape with a billion pin points of greenish fire.

Surrounded on all sides by raw materials and bathed in sunlight, the passively drifting phytoplankton community inhabits a highly favorable, chemically rather stable environment. The death rate resulting from animal feeding is high, but rapid reproduction suffi-

FIG. 7.20 The finely sculptured silica shell of a diatom. Other examples of these single-celled components of phytoplankton are illustrated in Chap. 9, Fig. 9.14. *(General Biological Supply House, Inc.)*

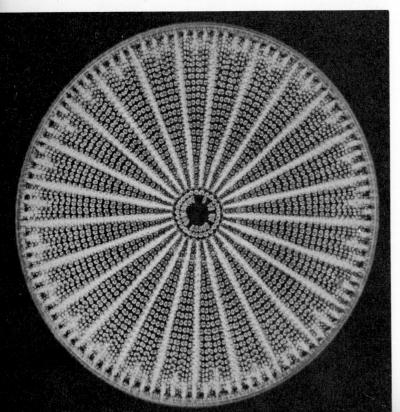

ciently offsets it. Physical and climatic changes do not affect an algal cell too greatly. In winter, the temperature of surface waters may fall below the freezing point, but the salts of the ocean prevent actual freezing. Cold merely reduces the rate of metabolic processes and algal life continues at a slower pace.

Indeed, low temperatures promote algal growth. When surface temperatures are high, as in tropical waters throughout the year and in northern and southern waters in summer, pronounced **temperature layering** of water prevents much vertical mixing. A warm-water layer is less dense and thus lighter than a colder layer below it; it "swims" on top of the colder layer without mixing. Under such conditions, organisms in the warm layer deplete the surface waters of mineral raw materials and at death these materials sink down without being brought back to the surface by vertical mixing. As a result, the amount of surface life is limited, and warm seas are actually relatively barren (Fig. 7.21).

By contrast, when surface and deeper waters have roughly the same low temperature, vertical mixing becomes possible and minerals are recirculated more rapidly. Surface life may therefore be more abundant. The perennially cold arctic, antarctic, and subpolar waters actually support huge permanent populations of algae. And, as is well known, the best commercial fishing grounds are in the high north and south, not in the tropics, and the best fishing seasons are spring and fall, not summer.

FIG. 7.21 Temperature layering of surface water, as in summer, leads to the formation of a thermocline and poor vertical circulation of water (left). In early spring, late fall, and winter, surface waters acquire the same temperature as deeper layers; hence the thermocline disappears, and vertical mixing becomes possible.

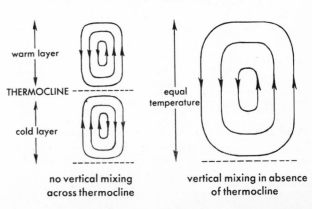

warm layer

THERMOCLINE -------

cold layer

equal temperature

no vertical mixing across thermocline

vertical mixing in absence of thermocline

In certain circumscribed regions, phytoplankton also includes larger, multicellular algae: flat, sheetlike seaweeds, often equipped with specialized air bladders which aid in keeping the organisms afloat. Such seaweeds may sometimes aggregate in considerable numbers over wide areas, particularly if a region is ringed in by ocean currents and therefore remains relatively isolated and stagnant. The Sargasso Sea in the mid-Atlantic is a good example. This sea has figured prominently in marine lore. For example, stories are told of ships trapped in "floating jungles," rapidly overgrown by plants, and sunk without a trace. Such accounts are wholly legendary, since the organisms are nowhere dense enough to prevent a ship's passage.

Yet the Sargasso *is* unique from a biological standpoint. The comparative isolation of the region has led to the evolution of distinct plants not found elsewhere on earth, and an equally distinct fauna finds shelter and food in this vegetation (Fig. 7.22). Buoyancy in the Sargasso, as in other tropical and subtropical waters, is particularly great, since a high rate of surface evaporation produces a correspondingly high, buoyancy-promoting salinity of the water.

Living side by side with the photosynthetic phytoplankton in the open waters of the photic zone are the small nonphotosynthetic forms. These include bacteria and members of the **zooplankton,** such as

FIG. 7.22 Sargassum weed, a brown alga. The bulbous structures are air bladders. A species related to the one shown in the photograph forms the principal seaweed of the Sargasso Sea. *(General Biological Supply House, Inc.)*

protozoa, eggs, larvae, tiny shrimp and other crustacea (particularly *copepods*), and countless other small animals carried along by surface drift (Fig. 7.23). They feed directly on the microscopic vegetation; hence as the phytoplankton waxes and wanes, so does the zooplankton. A good part of the nekton, largely fishes and marine mammals, comes into these waters to feed either on zooplankton or on phytoplankton directly.

Nearer to shore, in the neritic waters above the littoral zone, the problem of remaining afloat is not so critical for a photosynthesizer as in open water, for here even a bottom dweller is likely to be within the range of sunlight. The problem, rather, is to remain attached to solid ground, for close to shore the force of waves and of ground swells is considerable. In the intertidal belt, moreover, an even more profound problem is the ebbing of water twice daily and the consequent rhythmic alternation between aquatic and essentially terrestrial conditions. Also, in waters in and for miles beyond estuaries, fresh water discharging from rivers mixes with ocean water, a circumstance introducing additional environmental inconstancies. Being the meeting ground of water, land, and air, the intertidal belt is actually among the most violently changing environments on earth.

Vegetation here and in the littoral and the overlying neritic region as a whole is again largely algal. In addition to the single-celled and small planktonic types, attached multicellular forms abound. Most of these are equipped with specialized holdfasts which anchor the organisms to underlying ground. Green, brown, and red algae are particularly common. For example, the soft, slippery mats of vegetation encrusting rocks along the shore are familiar to many, as is *Fucus,* a common leathery brown alga found in dense populations on coastal rock (Fig. 7.24). We shall hear more about specific kinds of marine vegetation in Chap. 9.

Animals in coastal waters include representatives of virtually all major groups. In addition to the abundant planktonic types, sessile and creeping animals occur which are variously adapted to rocky, muddy, or sandy bottoms. The animals make use of all conceivable dwelling sites—for example, tide pools left on rock by ebbing water, crevices and hollows in and under rock, burrows in sand or mud, the sheltered water among vegetation and among sessile animal growths, empty shells and other skeletons of dead animals, and flotsam and jetsam along the shore and in deeper water. Among the very abundant nektonic animals in these regions, largely fish, many normally do not stray very far from

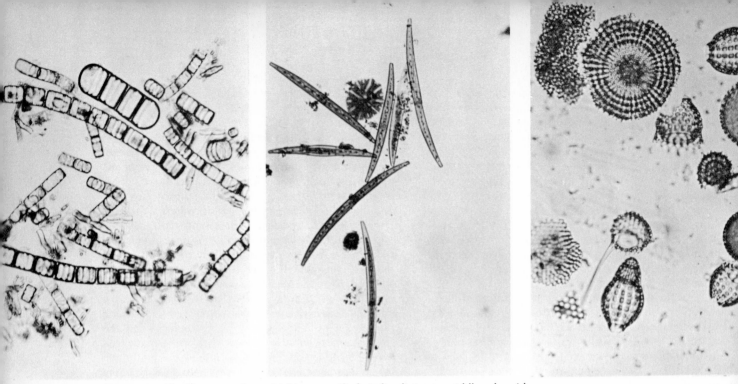

FIG. 7.23 Plankton organisms, highly magnified. Left, diatoms; middle, desmids; right, radiolaria. *(Courtesy of Clay-Adams, Co., Inc.)*

FIG. 7.24 A portion of *Fucus*, a common brown alga found attached to rocks on the seashore. Note the air bladders along the leaflike body. The bulbous structures at the ends of the body contain sex organs. *(General Biological Supply House, Inc.)*

a particular home, even though an efficient locomotor system would permit them to do so. They foray into surrounding waters for food and mates, but they always tend to return to the same base of operations. However, another group of nektonic animals consists of perpetual wanderers without permanent homes.

The Aphotic Zone

The contrast between the surface environments within reach of the sun and those underneath is dramatic. As the ones are forever fluctuating, so the others are perennially steady and relatively unchanging. The deep ocean is still little explored, and, for many, this "last frontier" has acquired a romance and mystery all its own. Several unique physical conditions characterize this world of the sea depths.

First, the region is one of eternal night. In the total absence of sunlight, the waters are pervaded with a perpetual blackness of a kind found nowhere else on earth.

Second, seasons and changing weather are practically absent. Localized climatic changes do occur as a result of occasional submarine volcanic activity or, more regularly, through deep-sea currents. These produce large-scale shifts of water masses and, incidentally, bring oxygen to even the deepest parts of the ocean.

Being beyond the influence of the sun, the deep waters are cold, unchangingly so. Temperatures range from about 10°C at the top of the dark zone to about 1°C along the abyssal plain.

Third, water pressure increases steadily from the surface down, 1 atmosphere (atm) for every 33 ft of descent. Thus, in the deepest trenches of the ocean, the pressure is about a thousand times as great as at sea level.

And fourth, a continuous slow rain of the dead remnants of surface organisms drifts down toward the sea bottom. Much of this material, particularly the organic fraction, dissolves completely during the descent. But much microscopic mineral matter reaches the abyssal plain, where it forms ever-thickening layers of ooze. Accumulating over the millennia, the older layers eventually compress into rock. Vertical-bore samples of such rock have revealed a great deal of the past history of the oceans and their once-living surface inhabitants.

Contrary to early beliefs that life should be impossible in such an environment, a surprisingly rich diversity of organisms has been found to exist virtually everywhere in the free water and along the floor of the deep sea. Apart from containing bacteria and perhaps fungi, the community is characteristically *animal*—photosynthesizing organisms are confined to the sunlit surface. Virtually all animal groups are represented, many by—to us—strange and bizarre types uniquely adapted to the locale (Fig. 7.25).

If a deep-sea animal is to avoid death from explosion or implosion, its internal pressure must equal the external pressure of the water. A few of the nektonic animals, toothed whales, for example, are adapted to resist the harmful effects of rapid changes of external pressure. These animals are capable of traversing the whole ocean from bottom to surface. They may therefore feed directly on the rich food supplies in surface waters. But the bulk of the deep-sea nekton is adapted to particular water pressures only, and given animals are rigidly confined to limited pressure zones at given depths. Such animals must therefore obtain food either from the dead matter drifting down from the surface—a meager source, particularly in deeper water—or from within the nekton itself.

This last condition makes the deep sea the most

FIG. 7.25 Deep-sea fishes. Left and middle, two kinds of oceanic angler fishes. The animal at left is a female. The structure above the eye is a parasitic male, which is carried about permanently attached. This neatly solves the problems of finding mating partners in the dark. The "beard" of the animal in the middle is probably luminescent. Many of these large-mouthed, dagger-toothed fishes are surprisingly small, as the angler fish photo at the right indicates. *(Right, courtesy of D. M. Owen, Woods Hole Oceanographic Institute; left and middle, American Museum of Natural History.)*

fiercely competitive environment on earth. The very structure of the animals underscores their violently carnivorous, "eat-or-be-eaten" mode of existence. For example, most of the fishes have enormous mouths equipped with long, razor-sharp teeth, and many can swallow fish larger than themselves.

Since the environment is pitch-black, one of the critical problems for these animals is to *find* food to begin with. A highly developed pressure sense provides one solution. Turbulence in the water created by nearby animals can be recognized and, depending on the nature of the turbulence, may be acted upon either by flight or by approach.

Another important adaptation to the dark is bioluminescence. Many of the deep-sea animals possess light-producing organs on the body surface, of different shapes, sizes, and distributions in different species. The light patterns emitted may include a variety of colors and probably serve partly in species recognition. Identification of a suitable mate, for example, must be a serious problem in an environment where everything appears equally black. Another function of the light undoubtedly is to warn or to lure. Some of the bioluminescent lures have evolved to a high degree of perfection. Certain fish, for example, carry a "lantern" on a stalk protruding from the snout (Fig. 7.26). An inquisitive animal attracted to the light of the lantern will discover too late that it has headed straight into powerful jaws.

THE FRESHWATER HABITAT

Physically and biologically, the link between ocean and land is the fresh water. Rivers and lakes were the original invasion routes over which some of the descendants of ancestral marine organisms reached land and, in the process, evolved into terrestrial forms. Certain of the migrant types never completed the transition but settled along the way, in fresh water.

Among such organisms, some adapted to the brackish water in estuaries and river mouths or to a life spent partly in the ocean, partly in fresh water (e.g., salmon, eels). Very many types could leave the ocean entirely and adapt to an exclusively freshwater existence. The descendants of these organisms include representatives of virtually all groups present in the ocean. Certain of the freshwater types later managed to gain a foothold on land. Of these, some continued to spend part of their lives in or near fresh water (e.g., mosses, frogs), but more became wholly terrestrial. And among the terrestrial forms, some subsequently returned to water and adapted secondarily to an aquatic existence (e.g., reed grasses, many insects). Thus, organisms which inhabit the fresh water today constitute a rich and major subdivision of the biological world.

Three main conditions distinguish the freshwater environment from the ocean environment. First, the salt content is substantially lower. If an organism has

FIG. 7.26 Two kinds of deep-sea angler fishes with stalked, luminescent "lanterns" over the mouth. Note the vertical position of the mouth in the animal at left. This facilitates catching prey lured to the light of the lantern. *(American Museum of Natural History.)*

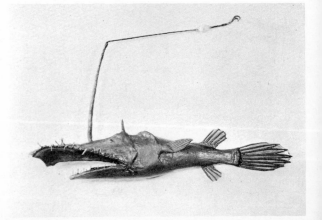

evolved in and still lives in the sea, the internal salt concentration of its body matches that of the marine environment. If such an organism moves to fresh water, the external salt concentrations will be much lower than the internal. As a result, water will be pulled by osmosis from the environment through the body surface into the organism. The amount of water in the organism will therefore tend to increase and the substance of cells will tend to become diluted.

Freshwater organisms evidently require, and they actually possess, means of counteracting this tendency of shipping too much water. Where rigid cell walls are present, as in plants, such walls protect against internal dilution. The walls withstand the outward pressure generated by the accumulation of water within cells; once such cells contain given amounts of water, no more can be drawn in osmotically because the walls will not permit any further cell enlargement. Where cell walls are not present, as in animals, water balance is maintained by the excretion of any excess internal water. Excretory systems and also digestive systems and gills serve in this function. In animals inhabiting estuaries, where external salt concentrations fluctuate almost continuously, and in organisms whose life cycle includes both marine and freshwater phases, water- and salt-balancing mechanisms are particularly well developed.

A second general condition characterizing much of the freshwater environment is the presence of strong, swift currents. Where these occur, passively floating life so typical of the ocean surface is not likely to be encountered. On the contrary, the premium will be either on maintaining firm anchorage along the shores and bottoms of rivers or on ability to resist and to overcome the force of currents by muscle power.

Indeed, the vegetation found in swift rivers consists almost entirely of plants possessing rootlike holdfasts or actual roots. Since true roots are characteristic only of terrestrial plants, the presence of such plants in rivers means that some ancestral land plants have adapted secondarily to a life in water. Pertinent examples are reed grasses, water foxtails, wild rice, and watercress (Fig. 7.27). By contrast, where fresh water is not flowing strongly, as in lakes, ponds, bogs, and marshes, not only rooted but also floating planktonic vegetation may be exceedingly abundant. In stagnant or near-stagnant water, algal communities forming continuous layers of green surface scum are particularly conspicuous.

Among animals, analogously, those in quiet fresh

FIG. 7.27 Portions of cattails, plants adapted secondarily to water. (R. H. Noailles, Museum of Natural History, Paris.)

waters include both planktonic and nektonic types, but those in swiftly flowing water are either attached and sessile or nektonic and swimming. The eggs of nektonic animals cannot swim, to be sure, but they are enveloped by sticky jelly coats which adhere firmly to plants or other objects in the water (Fig. 7.28). And the young are strongly muscled from the moment they hatch.

We may note in this connection that most modern fishes and vertebrates in general probably are an evolutionary product of the fresh water, not of the ocean. The ancestors of vertebrates were marine. They laid small, relatively yolk-free eggs which developed rapidly, and the adults were small and not very muscular. Some of the descendants of these forms then evolved adaptations which permitted them to become successful in fresh water. Principally, eggs enlarged and became very yolky. Well supplied with food in this manner, the eggs could develop slowly and for a relatively long period,

FIG. 7.28 Frog eggs. Note the jelly coat surrounding each egg. This jelly holds the egg masses together and attaches them to vegetation and other objects in the water. (General Biological Supply House, Inc.)

which allowed ample time for the elaboration of internal structures, muscular systems included. At hatching, therefore, the young were already well muscled and could maintain station against river currents.

The first fish probably arose in this way, as forms well adapted to the freshwater environment. Some of these early fishes stayed in fresh water and their descendants may still be encountered there today. Others, however, invaded the ocean, returning along the reverse route their ancestors had taken. Marine fishes so came into being, and today they are among the dominant life forms of the ocean. A third group of the early freshwater fishes took the path to land, and from these eventually evolved the modern land vertebrates—amphibia, reptiles, birds, and mammals, including man. Large, yolky eggs are still characteristic of vertebrates today, a silent reminder of their probable freshwater origin (see also Chaps. 11 and 30).

A third major distinction between fresh water and ocean is that the former, with the exception of only the very large lakes, is affected much more by climate and weather than any part of the latter. Bodies of fresh water often freeze over in winter and may dry up completely in summer. Water temperatures change not only seasonally but also daily, frequently to a considerable extent. Gales or flood conditions may bring bottom mud and silt to the surface and upset the freshwater habitat in major ways. A large number of factors may alter flow conditions and produce, for example, stagnant water or significantly altered chemical content

or situations facilitating infectious epidemics. We note that the fresh water shares the environmental inconstancies of the land in very large measure. Notwithstanding the aquatic nature of the freshwater habitat, its living component reflects the ebb and flow of land life as much as that of ocean life.

THE TERRESTRIAL HABITAT

That land environments differ vastly in character is eminently clear to a land dweller as efficient and far-ranging as man. It should also be clear that, regardless of which particular subdivision of the terrestrial environment one considers, the sustaining foundations of all land life are *air* and, directly or indirectly, also *soil*. Air and soil are to the terrestrial habitat what the surface waters of the ocean are to the marine.

Like air, soil is itself a terrestrial home, providing a habitat for a vast array of subsurface organisms. And by creating the conditions necessary for the survival of all other terrestrial organisms, soil becomes a major agency which transforms terrestrial environments into life-sustaining "habitats." Two other agencies play a vital role here: annual *temperature* and *rainfall*. As these vary with geographic latitude and altitude, they divide the soil-covered land surface into a number of distinct habitat zones, or **biomes**: *desert, grassland, rain forest, deciduous forest, taiga,* and *tundra*.

In the tropics are found representatives of the first three of the six biomes just named. They are characterized here by comparatively high annual temperatures and by daily temperature variations which are greater than the seasonal variations. Differences in the amount of precipitation largely account for the different nature of these habitats.

A **desert** (Fig. 7.29) usually has less than 10 in. of

FIG. 7.29 The desert habitat. In this particular view, Joshua trees are the predominant plants. (Courtesy of E. P. Haddon, U.S. Fish and Wildlife Service.)

rain per year, concentrated largely in a few heavy cloudbursts. Desert life is well adapted to this. Plants, for example, grow, bloom, are fertilized, and produce seeds, all within a matter of days after a rain. Since the growing season is thus greatly restricted, such plants stay relatively small. Leaf surfaces are often reduced to spines and thorns, minimizing water loss by evaporation (see also Chap. 10). Desert animals too are generally small, and they include many burrowing forms which may escape the direct rays of the sun under the ground surface. In most deserts, the "warm-blooded" mammals and birds are comparatively rare or are absent altogether; maintenance of constant body temperature is difficult or impossible under conditions of great heat and practically no water. By contrast, animals which match their internal temperature to the external, the so-called "cold-blooded" forms, can get by much more easily.

Grassland, as everyone well knows, is not an exclusively tropical biome but extends into much of the temperate zone as well (Fig. 7.30). The more or less synonymous terms "prairie," "pampas," "steppe," "pusz-ta," and many other regional designations underscore the wide distribution of this biome. The common feature of all grasslands is intermittent, erratic rainfall, amounting to about 10 to 40 in. annually. Grasses of various kinds, from short buffalo grass to tall elephant grass and thickets of bamboo, are particularly adapted to irregularly alternating periods of precipitation and dryness. Grassland probably supports more species of animals than any other terrestrial habitat. Different kinds of mammals are particularly conspicuous.

In those tropical and subtropical regions where torrential rains fall practically every day and where a well-defined rainy season characterizes the winter, plant growth continues the year round. Lush **rain forests** have developed here (Fig. 7.31), typified particularly by the

FIG. 7.31 Top, the habitat of the rain forest. Many dozens of different plant types, coexisting in dense formations, are generally characteristic of it. Bottom, a subtropical palm forest. The trees of such forests may retain their foliage the year around. (Top, National Park Service; bottom, U.S. Forest Service.)

FIG. 7.30 Grassland habitat. The photograph shows a landscape in Arizona. (U.S. Department of Agriculture.)

communal coexistence of up to several hundred different species of trees. Rain forests are the "jungles" of the adventure tale. They cover much of central Africa, south and southeast Asia, Central America, and the Amazon basin of South America. Trees in such forests are normally so crowded together that they form a continuous overhead canopy of branches and foliage, which cuts off practically all the sunlight, much of the rain water, and a good deal of the wind. As a result, the forest floor is exceedingly humid and quite dark, and it is populated by plants requiring only a minimum of light. Animal communities too are stratified vertically, according to the several very different habitats offered between canopy and ground. The tropical rain forest is singularly quiet during the day, but it erupts into a cacophony of sound at night, when the largely nocturnal fauna becomes active.

In the temperate zone, apart from extensive grasslands and occasional deserts, the most characteristic biome is the **deciduous forest** (Fig. 7.32). The fundamental climatic conditions here are cold winters, warm summers, and well-spaced rains bringing some 30 to 40 in. of precipitation per year. The biome is characterized also by seasonal temperature variations which are greater than the daily variations. Winter makes the growing season discontinuous, and the flora is adapted to this. Trees are largely deciduous, i.e., they shed their leaves and hibernate; and small annual plants produce seeds which withstand the cold weather. A deciduous forest differs from a rain forest in that trees are spaced farther apart and in that far fewer species are represented. Compared with the hundreds of tree types in the one, there may be only some ten or twenty in the other. Maple, beech, oak, elm, ash, and sycamore are among the common trees of a deciduous forest. The many familiar animal types in this biome include deer, boars, raccoons, foxes, squirrels, and, characteristically, woodpeckers.

North of the deciduous forests and the grasslands, across Canada, northern Europe, and Siberia, stretches the **taiga** (Fig. 7.33). This is a biome of long, severe winters and of growing seasons limited largely to the few months of summer. Hardy conifers, spruce in particular, are most representative of the flora, and moose, wolves, and bears of the fauna. The taiga is preeminently a zone of forests. These differ from other types of forests in that they usually consist of a single species of tree. Thus, over a large area, spruce, for example, may be the only kind of tree present. Another conifer species might be found in an adjacent, equally large area. Occasional stands of hardy deciduous trees are often intermingled with conifers. An accident of geography makes the taiga a habitat characteristic of the northern hemisphere only: little land exists in corresponding latitudes of the southern hemisphere.

The same circumstance makes the **tundra,** most polar of terrestrial biomes, a predominantly northern phenomenon (Fig. 7.34). Much of the tundra lies within the Arctic Circle. Hence its climate is cold and there may be continuous night during the winter season and continuous daylight, of comparatively low intensity, during the summer. Some distance below the surface, the ground is permanently frozen. Above ground, frost can form even during the summer—plants often freeze solid and remain dormant until they thaw out again. The growing season is very brief, as in the desert, but in the tundra the limiting factor is temperature, not water supply. Plants are low, ground-hugging forms, and trees are absent. Lichens, mosses,

FIG. 7.32 The habitat of the deciduous forest. In this type of forest, characteristic of the temperate zone, the trees lose their leaves during the winter. (*National Park Service.*)

FIG. 7.33 The habitat of the taiga. Note the predominance of a single species of tree over large areas, characteristic of the taiga generally. (*National Park Service.*)

FIG. 7.34 The habitat of the tundra. Note complete absence of trees in both views. *(Courtesy of U. C. Nelson and H. C. Oberholser, U.S. Fish and Wildlife Service.)*

FIG. 7.35 The polar and subpolar habitat, based on the sea. The photo shows a group of fur seals on an island in the far north. Note the polygamous, familial organization: a single male, several females, and their young. *(Courtesy of V. B. Scheffer, U.S. Fish and Wildlife Service.)*

coniferous and other shrubby growths, and herbs with brilliantly colored flowers, all blooming simultaneously during the growing season, are characteristic of the habitat. Conspicuous among the animals are hordes of insects, particularly flies, and a considerable variety of mammals: caribou, arctic hares, lemmings, foxes, musk oxen, and polar bears. Birds are largely migratory, leaving for more southern latitudes with the coming of winter.

Life does not end at the northern margin of the tundra but extends farther into the ice and bleak rock of the soilless polar region. Polar life is almost exclusively animal. And it is not really terrestrial anyway but is based on the sea (e.g., walrus, seals, penguins; Fig. 7.35).

The horizontal sequence of biomes between equator and pole is repeated more or less exactly in a vertical direction, along the slopes of mountains (Fig. 7.36). Here too temperature and precipitation are the decisive variables. On a high mountain in the tropics,

FIG. 7.36 The sequence of habitat zones between equator and pole is repeated altitudinally between the foot and the top of a mountain.

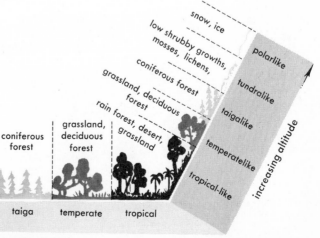

for example, the succession of biomes from mountain base to snow line is tropical rain forest, deciduous forest, coniferous forest, and lastly, low shrubby growths and lichens. The farther north a mountain is situated, the more northern a biome covers its base and the fewer biomes cover its slopes. In the taiga, for example, the foot of a mountain is coniferous forest and the only other biome higher along the slopes is the zone of low shrubby plants. Thus, habitat zones which are spread over thousands of miles latitudinally are telescoped altitudinally into a few thousand feet.

The foregoing should make it clear that the nature of any kind of habitat, terrestrial, freshwater, or marine, is determined by a few persistently recurring variables. Among them are solar light, solar heat, geographic latitude, vertical depth and altitude, rainfall, wind and

water currents, and the chemical composition of the locale. As such environmental variables differ in different geographic regions of the world, the living communities present there differ accordingly. All oceans do not contain communities composed of the same kinds of organisms, and, analogously, all bodies of fresh water do not contain the same types of communities. Variations in the species composition of communities on different continents are even more pronounced, and a global pattern of geographic distribution is actually in evidence. Continental land areas harbor broadly distinct "supercommunities," each characterized by the presence of particular species of plants and animals. In one or two cases the boundaries between such supercommunities are fairly sharp, but more often they are quite diffuse. Based especially on the types of mam-

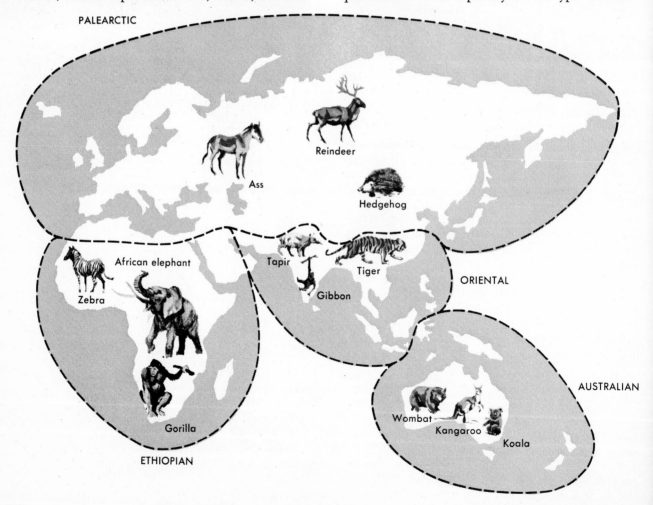

PALEARCTIC

Reindeer

Ass

Hedgehog

African elephant

Tapir

Tiger

Zebra

Gibbon

ORIENTAL

Gorilla

AUSTRALIAN

Wombat

Kangaroo

Koala

ETHIOPIAN

mals and birds present, six major **biogeographic regions** can be identified. The locations and the most characteristic mammals of these regions are given in Fig. 7.37. This figure indicates, for example, that the widely separated communities of Alaska and Northern Mexico by and large resemble each other more than the directly adjacent communities of Northern Mexico and Southern Mexico.

This concludes our general characterization of the living material. We have found in this series of chapters that both living and nonliving substances have a common ancestry in the very same atoms which once composed the early earth. In one case these atoms interacted far more extensively and intensively than in the other, and the outcome was a form of matter we call living. This matter is identified by its content of unique kinds of compounds, nucleic acids and proteins above all, and by its unceasing chemical and physical dynamism, a consequence of its molecular content. Biological properties are the further result. Thus, by virtue of its compounds and their interactions, this living material becomes arranged into a hierarchy of structural levels and it performs the fundamental functions of metabolism and self-perpetuation on all these levels. The levels of organization range from cellular to multicellular units and from individual organisms to complex communities and supercommunities of organisms. Throughout this range, the ever-recurring theme is progressive aggregation and the ever-recurring result is progressive interdependence, cooperation, specialization, and greater economy and efficiency in maintaining and perpetuating life.

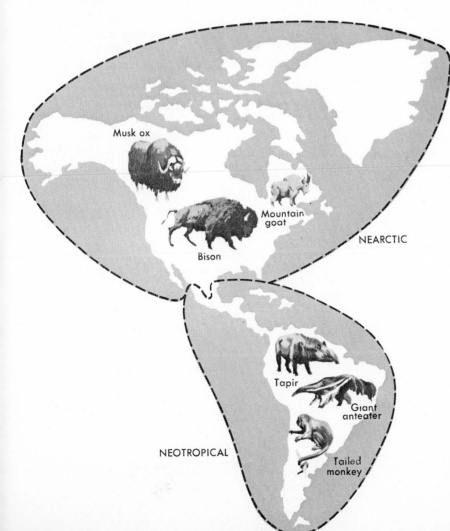

Musk ox

Mountain goat

Bison

NEARCTIC

Tapir

Giant anteater

NEOTROPICAL

Tailed monkey

FIG. 7.37 The six biogeographic regions. For each supercommunity, three representative and characteristic mammals are indicated.

REVIEW QUESTIONS

1. Define community, communal succession, food pyramid, food chain, mimicry. Review the nutritional, reproductive, and protective links which hold the members of a community together. How are long-range numerical population balances maintained? In what ways are populations, species, and communities specialized?

2. What are the various forms of symbiosis and how are they defined? Give concrete examples of each. What is an epiphyte? A lichen?

3. Which broad groups of organisms include or consist entirely of parasites? What is hyperparasitism, ectoparasitism, endoparasitism?

4. What general structural and functional characteristics distinguish parasites from free-living organisms? How do parasites transfer from host to host?

5. Describe the life cycles of tapeworms and liver flukes, and review the general significance of intermediate hosts.

6. What is the structure of an ocean basin? What are the major subenvironments in such a basin, and what role does the sun play in creating some of these subenvironments? What physical conditions characterize the various subenvironments?

7. Define plankton, nekton, and benthos. Give specific examples of each. Where in the ocean are each of these types of organisms found? Why is life in tropical waters generally less abundant than in temperate and subpolar waters?

8. What physical and biological conditions characterize the sea depths?

9. Review the essential physical differences between oceanic and freshwater environments. What major types of plants occur in fresh water, and in what general ways are they adapted to this environment? What major types of plants are terrestrial?

10. What are the main terrestrial habitats and what physical and biological conditions characterize each of them? In what way are latitudinal terrestrial habitats related to altitudinal habitats?

SUGGESTED COLLATERAL READINGS

The texts cited at the end of Chap. 6 are valuable references for most topics dealing with communities. Recommended also are the following books:

Beebe, W.: "Edge of the Jungle," Little, Brown, Boston, 1950.

Berrill, N. J.: "The Living Tide," Dodd, Mead, New York, 1951.

Carson, R.: "The Sea around Us," Oxford University Press, London, 1951.

Coker, R. C.: "This Great and Wide Sea," 2d ed., University of North Carolina Press, Chapel Hill, N.C., 1949.

Daubenmire, R. F.: "Plants and Environment," Wiley, New York, 1959.

Ommanney, F. D.: "The Oceans," Oxford University Press, London, 1949.

Tiffany, L. H.: "Algae, the Grass of Many Waters," 2d ed., Charles C Thomas, Springfield, Ill., 1958.

Various aspects of symbiosis are popularly described in the following:

Bigger, J. W.: "Man against Microbe," Macmillan, New York, 1939.

Burnet, F. M.: Viruses, *Sci. American,* vol. 184, 1951.

Cleveland, L. R.: An Ideal Partnership, *Sci. Monthly,* vol. 67, 1948.

De Kruif, P.: "Microbe Hunters," Harcourt, Brace, New York, 1928.

Luria, S. E.: The T2 Mystery, *Sci. American,* vol. 192, 1955.

Lwoff, A.: The Life Cycle of a Virus, *Sci. American,* vol. 190, 1954.

Zinsser, H.: "Rats, Lice, and History," Little, Brown, Boston, 1935.

The following articles deal with the relation of various organisms to their various environments:

Deevey, E. S.: Life in the Depths of a Pond, *Sci. American,* vol. 185, 1951.

Nicholas, G.: Life in Caves, *Sci. American,* vol. 192, 1955.

Ryther, F. H.: The Sargasso Sea, *Sci. American,* vol. 194, 1956.

Vevers, H. G.: Animals of the Bottom, *Sci. American,* vol. 187, 1952.

Walford, L. A.: The Deep-sea Layers of Life, *Sci. American,* vol. 185, 1951.

PART 3
THE LIVING ORGANISMS

This series of chapters is devoted to an examination of the main groups of organisms in existence today, their habits, structures, and internal organization. A preliminary objective will be to become familiar with the ways in which main groups are named and distinguished. Subsequently, each of the groups so identified will be studied systematically, with attention also on the principal subgroups.

Note that this part of the book serves a dual role. First, it leads to an appreciation of the vast diversity of the living creatures on earth. This in turn promotes an understanding of how life is achieved in innumerable and often highly different ways and under enormously varied environmental circumstances. Second, these chapters also provide the essential background for the remainder of the book. The processes of life, namely, metabolism and self-perpetuation, reside in specific individual organisms. Therefore, if the processes are to be interpreted and understood, it is clearly necessary that their containers themselves be known and understood.

KINDS OF
ORGANISMS: MONERA

8

Organisms can be classified on the basis of their specializations into more or less well-defined types or categories. The discipline dealing specifically with such classification is called **taxonomy** or **systematics**. In the first part of this chapter we shall examine the general scheme of taxonomic classification and the major groups of organisms actually identified within this scheme. In the second part, we shall begin the detailed discussion of the major groups and shall concern ourselves particularly with the group known as the Monera.

THE TAXONOMIC SYSTEM

CLASSIFICATION

Organisms are named and distinguished on the basis of their specializations in *structure, function, development,* and *evolutionary history.* The practice of cataloging organisms by such criteria is in universal use; it was originated by Karl von Linné (Linnaeus), a Swedish naturalist of the early eighteenth century. The "Linnaean" system of taxonomy, now greatly elaborated, consists essentially of a hierarchy of graded **taxonomic ranks.** In this hierarchy, any given rank usually contains several categories of lower ranks as components. If certain specializations are common to a large group of organisms, this group may be assigned a particular taxonomic rank. Within such a rank, several smaller groups can usually be distinguished on the basis of finer differences in their specializations; such smaller groups are then assigned the next lower rank. Each lower-ranking group in turn may be subclassified further into a succession of progressively lower ranks.

The lower the rank of a group, therefore, the more similar are the organisms within the group. Accordingly, if two organisms can be classified into the same low-ranking group, such organisms will be structurally, functionally, and developmentally quite similar and they will have had similar evolutionary histories. Evidently, the Linnaean system not only provides a convenient classification but also tells a great deal about the nature and the evolutionary interrelation of organisms. The Linnaean system consequently is far more than a mere naming scheme. That is why it is in universal use today and why other systems of classification, which *were* mere naming schemes, have not survived beyond the time of Linnaeus.

Within the living world as a whole, the highest taxonomic rank usually recognized is the **kingdom.** By tradition going back directly to Linnaeus, organisms are classified into two kingdoms, namely, the plant kingdom and the animal kingdom. It is highly questionable whether this 250-year-old tradition is still justifiable today, and there are good reasons to name kingdoms on a different basis. We shall return to this point below.

The next highest rank within a kingdom is the **division** or the **phylum.** The two terms are equivalent. In precise usage, the term "division" is reserved for major groups within the plant kingdom and the term "phylum" for major groups within the animal kingdom. But, because in certain instances the distinction between "plant" and "animal" is far from clear and because the line of separation between the two kingdoms is therefore obscure (see below), it is difficult in many cases to decide whether to use the term "division" or the term "phylum." We shall arbitrarily and uniformly use the designation "phylum" throughout this book.

The phylum rank describes a broad grouping of historically more or less closely related organisms, all characterized by fairly similar structural and functional body organization. For example, all fungi as a group represent a phylum and all sponges as a group represent a phylum.

Within a phylum, the next highest rank is the **class.** For example, sponges may be subdivided into classes on the basis of their skeletons, one group having calcium skeletons, another silicon skeletons, and a third horny skeletons. Similarly, the phylum *Chordata* includes all animals which possess an internal skeleton, the *notochord,* at least as embryos. This phylum contains the class of *mammals.* Such animals share the possession of a notochord with all other chordate classes, e.g., the birds, the reptiles, and the fishes. But mammals are set off from other chordate classes by their possession of hair and by their nursing young with milk. Each other class has its own distinguishing features.

Using such criteria of likenesses and differences among and within groups, one may recognize **orders** within a class, **families** within an order, **genera** within a family, and **species** within a genus. The species normally is the lowest unit. We have already seen in Chap. 6 how this important rank is characterized. Because the species encompasses all organisms of the same kind and because it is a fundamental and reasonably permanent level of organization in nature, it can also become the base on which the whole pyramid of technical classification is built.

According to Linnaean tradition and internationally accepted rules, a species is always identified by *two* technical names. These names are in Latin or are latinized and are used uniformly all over the world. For example, the species of grass frogs is known technically as *Rana pipiens;* the species to which we belong is *Homo sapiens.* Such species names are always underlined or printed in italics, and the first name is capitalized. This first name always identifies the genus to which the species belongs. Thus, the human species belongs to the genus *Homo* and the grass-frog species to the genus *Rana. Homo sapiens* happens to be the only presently living species within the genus *Homo,* but the genus *Rana* contains *Rana pipiens* as well as many other frog species.

Sometimes it is desirable to make finer distinctions between two consecutive ranks. In that case an additional rank may be interpolated between the original two and the prefix *sub-* or *super-* is then added to one of the main ranks. For example, between an order and a family, the order may contain several **suborders,** each suborder several **superfamilies,** and each superfamily several families. (Note, incidentally, that the taxonomic meaning of the term "family" differs from the social meaning.)

A complete classification of an organism tells a great deal about the nature of that organism. For example, suppose we knew nothing else about corn plants and men except their taxonomic classifications. Then we would know that the characteristics of these organisms are as listed in Table 4. Evidently, even brief taxonomic characterizations such as these place an organism rather well, and we may note that a full, detailed classification would describe an organism completely.

Within a phylum, the member organisms often differ radically in their ways of life. Consider, for example, the different ways of a desert plant like a cactus, an aquatic plant like a water lily, and an underground

TABLE 4

Descriptive classification of corn plants and men

taxonomic rank	corn plant	man
Phylum	Tracheophyta: plants with vascular tissues	Chordata: animals with notochords
Subphylum	Pteropsida: types with large leaves	Vertebrata: types with vertebral columns
Superclass	Spermatophyta: seed producers	Tetrapoda: terrestrial; four limbs, bony skeletons
Class	Angiospermae: flowering plants; seeds inside fruits	Mammalia: types with hair and milk glands
Subclass	Monocotyledonae: parallel-veined leaves; single seed leaf; flowerparts in threes or multiples	Eutheria: offspring develop within female parent, nourished by placenta
Order	Graminales: grasses	Primates: fingers; flat nails
Family	Graminaceae: leaves in two rows on round or flattened stem	Hominidae: upright posture; flat face; stereoscopic vision; large brains; hands and feet
Genus	*Zea:* corn plants	*Homo:* double-curved spine; long life span and long youth
Species	*Zea mays:* cultivated, domesticated corn plants	*Homo sapiens:* well-developed chins; high forehead; thin skull bones

plant like an onion bulb; or consider the different ways of a fish and a man. Nevertheless, all organisms within a phylum use the same kinds of structures in solving the different problems of their different environments. Thus, the spines of a cactus, the surface float of a water lily, and the white, tear-producing layers inside

an onion bulb, all are basically the same kinds of structures, namely, leaves; they all have evolved along different paths from one ancestral type of foliation. Analogously, the fins of a fish and the arms of a man are basically the same kinds of structures which have evolved from one common ancestral type of body appendage.

Whenever given body parts of different organisms have evolved from a common ancestral starting point, as in the example just cited, and whenever they have developed embryologically in like fashion, we say that such body parts are **homologous** (Fig. 8.1). If abundant homologies can be shown to exist between two organisms, these organisms are likely to be related rather closely. Hence studies of homology aid greatly in classifying organisms. It may be noted that homologous structures may or may not function the same way. For example, the fins of fish and the arms of man do not function in the same manner, yet they are homologous. Whenever two structures do function in like fashion they are said to be **analogous**. Bird wings and bat wings are analogous. They also happen to be homolo-

FIG. 8.1 Comparison of limb structure of bird wing (top), human arm (middle), and bat wing (bottom). These three limbs are homologous, having evolved from the same ancestral vertebrate appendage and developing in the embryo in initially the same way.

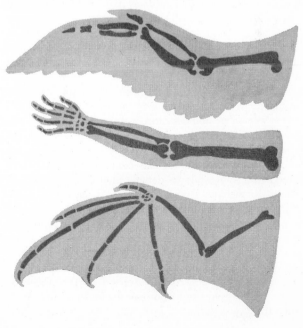

gous, but note that analogous structures need not always be homologous as well. For example, bird wings and insect wings are analogous inasmuch as both are used for flying, but they are not homologous. Since organisms on the whole differ far more in their structural and developmental features than in their functional features, homologies have much greater significance in taxonomic studies than analogies.

In some cases it is not universally agreed whether, on the basis of homologies, a given group of organisms represents a distinct phylum or a superphylum containing several smaller phyla or a class within a larger phylum. Indeed, general agreement among biologists becomes better with the lower taxonomic ranks and worse with the higher ranks. The higher-rank categories actually are being reshuffled more or less constantly. This is probably as it should be, for these rankings incorporate our knowledge of the evolution of organisms; and as this knowledge improves, the rank categories must be adjusted accordingly. A specific instance of such an adjustment will be considered presently.

THE MAJOR LIVING GROUPS

Within the framework of the taxonomic system outlined above, how are existing organisms actually classified?

As noted above, it is rather doubtful whether the simple subdivision of the living world into plant and animal kingdoms is still adequate today. Work during the past few decades has shown that certain groups of organisms really fit into neither the plant nor the animal category and should in fact be regarded as something else. At the same time, several other groups fit into both categories. For example, traditional views notwithstanding, bacteria really have very little in common with either plants or animals, and certain unicellular flagellate organisms can be regarded equally well as plants *or* animals (see below).

A basic difficulty in this connection is that it is practically impossible to define "plant" or "animal" in adequate fashion. Every fundamental feature customarily used to define "plant" is encountered among at least some "animals" also, and vice versa. To be sure, no one has much difficulty in deciding whether advanced organisms like cabbages and cats are plants or animals. But such a difficulty does exist with primitive organisms, i.e., those closely related to the ancestral types which give rise to both cabbages and cats. Such ancestral types possessed both plantlike and animallike

features *simultaneously,* as is true of their primitive descendants today. And if we go even farther back in time, the very first organisms on earth probably possessed neither plantlike nor animallike features at all (cf. Chap. 3), as is again true of their present-day descendants.

The point is that plants and animals, clearly so recognizable, were not in existence right from the beginning. Rather, some of the early organisms *evolved* in plantlike or animallike directions slowly and gradually; and a definite, finalized "plant" status or "animal" status was attained only relatively late in evolutionary history. Therefore, a division of the living world merely into plant and animal kingdoms is too simple. It does not take into account this gradual evolutionary development, and it allows no place for those primitive organisms which still are neither "plant" nor "animal" or which are both.

In view of this, attempts have been made in recent years to establish alternative classifications which do reflect our present knowledge of evolution. One such alternative scheme, in part already referred to in Chap. 3, recognizes not two but four basic categories of organisms. Each of the four has a taxonomic rank roughly equivalent to a kingdom, although it may not be desirable to use this rank designation so long as it is technically still reserved for "plants" and "animals."

The four basic categories are the **Monera,** the **Protista,** the **Metaphyta,** and the **Metazoa.** Detailed distinctions between these groups will be described in later chapters; here we shall limit ourselves to brief characterizations.

Monera and Protista go back farthest in evolutionary history. Both groups are believed to be descended, independently, from the very first cells on earth. As pointed out in Chap. 3, Monera include all those organisms in which the cells do not possess nuclear membranes. **Bacteria** and **blue-green algae,** all basically unicellular, are modern representatives of the group.

Protista do possess nuclear membranes around their nuclei. Ancient protists undoubtedly were unicellular, and primitive modern ones still are. Other modern protists are multicellular, however, and in their structural organization they reach the tissue and organ level of complexity. Apart from "inventing" nuclear membranes, ancient Protista probably developed several additional new features. Among them are the possession of true chromosomes and chloroplasts; the capacity of moving by amoeboid and flagellary locomotion; and the ability to acquire food by both plantlike and animallike methods, i.e., photosynthesis and eating. Modern protists have inherited these features. Many are still plantlike and animallike simultaneously. But others have lost the plantlike ways of life and are now more or less "animal" in character. Conversely, still others have lost the animallike modes of living and are now more or less distinctly "plant." The major groups among modern Protista are the **algae,** the **slime molds,** the **fungi,** and the **protozoa.**

The Metaphyta and Metazoa are both believed to have evolved from ancient protists. More specifically, certain ancient green algalike stocks probably were the ancestors of the Metaphyta, and other ancient algal types or protozoa or both may have been ancestors of the Metazoa. The derivation is far less certain in the latter case than in the former. Metaphyta and Metazoa all are exclusively multicellular, their structural complexity reaching the level of complicated organs and organ systems. Moreover, both Metaphyta and Metazoa typically have life cycles which include more or less distinct *embryos,* a characteristic not in evidence (or at best only vaguely suggested) in the Protista.

Metaphyta are almost exclusively photosynthetic and sessile, and they are unmistakably "plants." They include the **bryophytes,** or moss plants, and the enormous and far more important group of **tracheophytes,** or vascular plants. Metazoa are exclusively nonphotosynthetic and largely motile, and they are unmistakably "animals." The main groups of Metazoa and also the main groups of all other organisms are listed in Table 5. Probable evolutionary relations of these major categories are diagramed in Fig. 8.2.

FIG. 8.2 The four main categories of organisms and their probable evolutionary interrelations.

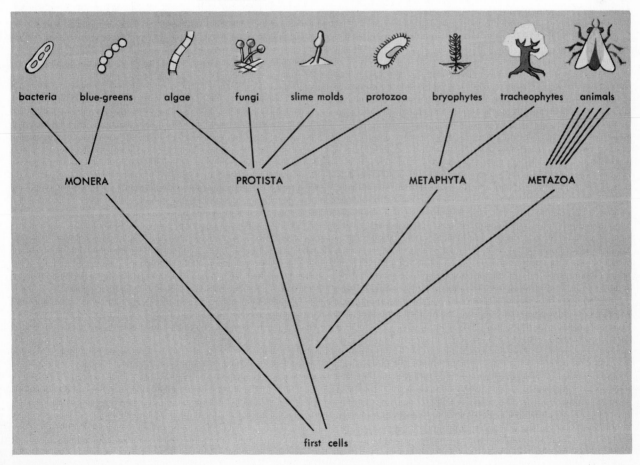

TABLE 5
*The main categories of living organisms**

category	probable ancestors	main subgroups
Monera	first cells and ancient Monera	bacteria blue-green algae
Protista	first cells and ancient Protista	algae fungi protozoa slime molds
Metaphyta	ancient Protista (early algal types)	bryophytes (moss plants) tracheophytes (vascular plants, e.g., ferns, seed plants)
Metazoa	ancient Protista (early algal and protozoan stocks)	sponges coelenterates (e.g., jellyfish) various categories of "worms" mollusks (e.g., clams, snails, squids) arthropods (e.g., insects, spiders, lobsters) echinoderms (e.g., starfish, sea urchins) vertebrates (fishes, amphibia, reptiles, birds, mammals)

* Protozoa and all Metazoa are traditionally regarded as "animals"; all other groups listed are usually designated as "plants."

Note that, in this four-part classification, every living creature has a proper place. Monera and Protista include organisms which are plantlike, animallike, neither, or both, as well as some of the organisms traditionally regarded as "true" plants (e.g., advanced algae) and "true" animals (e.g., most protozoa). And the Metaphyta and Metazoa include the remainder of the "true"

plants and animals. Throughout the remainder of this book, an otherwise unqualified reference to "plants" is specifically to Metaphyta; similarly, a reference to "animals" is specifically to Metazoa.

Another point may be emphasized in this context. All available evidence indicates that living evolution has the general pattern of a greatly branching *bush* (Fig. 8.3). All presently living organisms are *contemporaries,* appearing at the uppermost branch tips of the bush. Ancestral types, mostly long extinct, appear lower on the bush, where branches join. Thus, a particular common ancestor may give rise to *several* different types of descendants, each inheriting the characteristics of the common ancestor and evolving innovations of its own. And a particular descendant living today may become a common ancestor of new and different types living tomorrow.

A corollary of the above is that the pattern of evolution is *not* that of a "ladder" or a "scale." Many uninformed persons still speak of a "scale of evolution," implying a straight-line progression from one organism directly to the next, usually from some "low" type like an alga or a protozoon to some "high" type like a tree or a man. Such statements are based on wholly erroneous notions. A glance at Fig. 8.3 shows that a straight-line "scale" simply does not exist; only a branching pattern is in line with the actual evidence. Moreover, trees and men did not descend from algae and protozoa.

FIG. 8.3 The bush pattern of evolution. The uppermost tips of the branches represent currently living forms, and branches terminating below the top represent extinct forms. Fork points such as B and C are ancestral types. B is more ancient and of higher taxonomic rank than C. A represents the archancestor of all living types.

Instead, all these organisms are modern contemporaries which have evolved coequally and along entirely separate paths from some ancient, long-extinct protistan ancestor. Finally, among currently living organisms, there simply are no "higher" and "lower" types, since all rank equally high (or equally low) on the evolutionary bush. There are only *different* types, with different histories and different characteristics.

With these various considerations as a general background, we may now proceed in this and subsequent chapters to a more specific study of the Monera, the Protista, the Metaphyta, and the Metazoa.

MONERA

As noted, the representatives of this major category are descendants of possibly the most ancient and most primitive living creatures on earth.

Monera as a group are distinguished from all other organisms largely by negative features. A moneran cell does *not* possess an organized nucleus with a distinct surrounding membrane so characteristic of all other cell types. Gene-containing DNA-protein forms one or more clumps, and these clumps do *not* contain chromosomes of the type found in other organisms. Moneran-cell cytoplasm does *not* appear to contain vacuoles, and it can *not* be observed to undergo the cyclosis and streaming movements typical of other cell types. Many Monera are photosynthetic, and these do *not* possess highly organized chloroplasts like those found in all other photosynthetic cells. Instead, the structural unit of photosynthesis appears to be a disk of protein-containing material, 0.05 μ in diameter, much resembling a single layer of a single granum in a true chloroplast (cf. Chap. 4). Such a unit carries photosynthetic pigments; it may therefore be called a **chromatophore.** Many chromatophores are distributed more or less uniformly throughout a photosynthetic moneran cell (Fig. 8.4).

Such features of nonpossession may reflect the evolutionary antiquity of the moneran stock. Evidently, at the time this stock arose, the internal elaboration and specialization of cellular structure had not yet progressed very far. To be sure, quite a number of identifying traits are of a positive nature, but they tend to be less fundamental than those listed above.

Within the moneran category, the bacteria form the phylum *Schizophyta;* and the blue-green algae, the phylum *Cyanophyta.* The exact evolutionary rela-

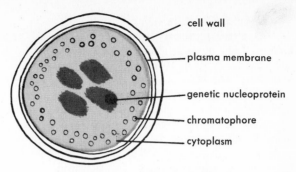

FIG. 8.4 Diagrammatic representation of a moneran cell.

tion of one phylum to the other is still relatively obscure. Some moneran groups exhibit traits intermediate between those of the schizophytes and the cyanophytes; hence these groups could be, and often are, assigned to either phylum. It is likely, therefore, that the separation of the Monera into just two phyla may not represent a natural, ultimately correct classification. Nevertheless, there is little doubt that Monera as a whole do form a clearly identifiable natural category which can be distinctly set off from the three other major branches of life.

PHYLUM SCHIZOPHYTA: BACTERIA
(about 2,000 species)

These organisms probably were first observed on June 10, 1675, by the Dutch lensmaker Anton van Leeuwenhoek. On that day, using one of his primitive microscopes, Leeuwenhoek discovered a multitude of very tiny "animalcules" in drops of rainwater he had collected earlier. From his notes and drawings, we know that at least some of the microbes he saw probably were bacteria. For almost two centuries thereafter, bacteria remained merely objects of curiosity. They did not receive much scientific attention until Louis Pasteur and Robert Koch demonstrated that the microorganisms could produce disease in man and other animals. Since then, and especially during the last few decades, our knowledge of bacteria has grown by leaps and bounds. This is partly because the bacteria play a major role in the economy of nature and of man, partly because they are eminently suitable test organisms in genetic and biochemical research. Indeed, much of our present understanding of the molecular basis of life has come from studies on bacteria.

General Characteristics

As a group, schizophytes are the smallest cells known. They average about 1 to 3 μ in length, as compared with about 10 μ for most cell types of other organisms. The structure of a representative bacterial cell is diagramed in Fig. 8.5. As in all Monera, a nuclear membrane is absent; genes occur in spherical or dumbbell-shaped clumps of nucleoprotein, one or more of which may be present. The cytoplasm is non-vacuolated, but it may contain granules composed of, for example, fatty materials or polysaccharides. A rigid cell wall surrounds the cytoplasm of many bacteria. Such a wall consists of polysaccharides, proteins, and frequently also lipids. Very often, the cell wall in turn is surrounded by a gelatinous capsule of different composition in different cases. Some of the usual constituents of such a capsule are polysaccharides, galactose, fructose, glucose, uronic acids, and amino acids. In many instances, it is the presence or absence of a capsule which determines whether a bacterium will be disease-producing or not.

FIG. 8.5   Diagrammatic representation of a bacterial cell.

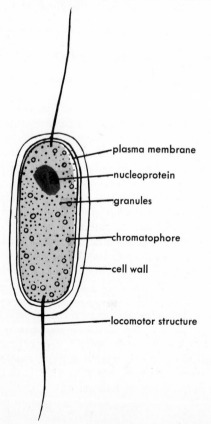

plasma membrane

nucleoprotein

granules

chromatophore

cell wall

locomotor structure

Many bacteria are motile, flagella often being the locomotor structures. Note that bacterial flagella are structurally unique, for each is composed of just a single thin fibril. By contrast, flagella in all other organisms are each composed of 11 fibrils, organized into a bundle (cf. Chap. 4). Given bacteria may possess one or more flagella at one end of the cell or a flagellum at each end of the cell or many flagella distributed over the entire cell surface (Fig. 8.6).

Bacterial cells are of many different shapes (Fig. 8.7), but three shapes are most common: the spherical or **coccus** type, the straight-rod or **bacillus** type, and the curved-rod or **spirillum** type. Cells may occur singly, but in many cases two or more cells are aggregated together into colonies. These may be filamentous, disk-shaped, or three-dimensional. In each colonial species, the form of the colony is determined by the planes of cell division. Among cocci, for example, if a cell divides and the two resulting daughter cells remain stuck together, the pair is said to be a **diplococcus** type of aggregate. If further cell divisions in the same plane produce a filamentous chain of cells, the colony is of the **streptococcus** type. If, in a diplococcus, the plane of the next division in both cells occurs at right angles to the plane of the first division, then a disk of four cells results, designated as a colony of the **tetracoccus** type. Analogously, three divisions in the three planes of space produce an eight-celled, cuboidal colony of the **sarcina** type. Successive divisions in random planes produce an irregular clump of cells known as a colony of the **micrococcus** or **staphylococcus** type.

In their usual state, bacterial cells are said to be in a *vegetative* condition. Some bacteria may also exist in an alternative state; i.e., they may transform into **endospores**. Formation of an endospore involves development of a membrane or wall within a bacterial cell. This wall encloses an oval or spherical portion of the cell substance, including genetic material and some of the cytoplasm. The part of the cell outside the wall eventually degenerates, but the part within persists as the endospore. Such a condition represents a *dormant* state; an endospore does not feed or multiply. The wall of the endospore is highly resistant to injurious physical and chemical agents. Bacteria so protected may therefor survive in environments which would kill vegetative cells. Under favorable conditions, an endospore may germinate; i.e., the wall breaks open and a normal vegetative cell emerges (Fig. 8.8).

With the exception of animallike eating, all possible forms of food procurement occur among the bacteria. Some species are photosynthetic or chemosynthetic, and these produce their own food. The photosynthesizers possess unique varieties of chlorophyll, and, as noted earlier, true chloroplasts are absent. Moreover, bacterial photosynthesis is chemically unique, different from photosynthesis in all other organisms. For example, bacterial photosynthesis never produces oxygen as a byproduct. We shall discuss this further in Chap. 12.

Most bacteria depend on other organisms for food. Of these, some are free-living saprotrophs in soil or ocean, and the rest are parasitic, commensalistic, or mutualistic symbionts. Also, some bacteria must have oxygen for respiration; others can do without it and respire by fermentation; and still others may survive both with and without oxygen. In most of these types,

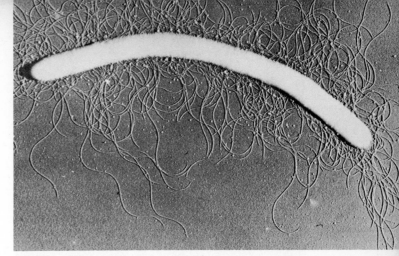

FIG. 8.6 Electron micrograph of *Proteus vulgaris*, a flagellate bacterium. Note the numerous locomotor flagella. (*Society of American Bacteriologists and courtesy of Dr. C. F. Robinow and Dr. J. Hillier.*)

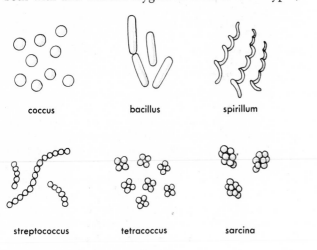

coccus   bacillus   spirillum   diplococcus

streptococcus   tetracoccus   sarcina   staphylococcus

FIG. 8.7 Diagram at left: cell shapes and growth habits of bacteria. Photographs: bottom left, cocci, growing in chains; bottom middle, bacilli; bottom right, spirilla. (*Photographs, General Biological Supply House, Inc.*)

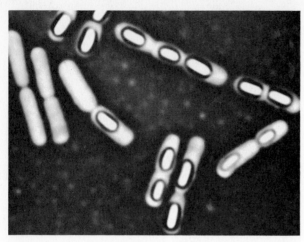
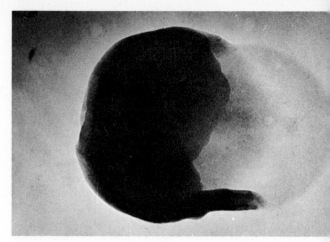

FIG. 8.8   Left, thick-walled endospores within rod-shaped bacterial cells. Right, electron micrograph of a germinating spore of the bacterium *Bacillus mycoides*. Note the bacterial cell emerging from the coat of the endospore. *(Left, courtesy of Dr. C. F. Robinow, University of Western Ontario, from "The Cell," Academic Press, New York, vol. IV; right, courtesy of Dr. G. Knaysi, Dr. R. F Baker, and Dr. J. Hillier, J. Bacteriol., vol. 53, 1947, and Society of American Bacteriologists.)*

reserve foods are stored in the form of the polysaccharide *glycogen*. We may note, incidentally, that bioluminescence is fairly common among bacteria (Fig. 8.9).

Primarily as a result of their varied nutritional activities, bacteria as a whole have come to be of major significance to all other life on earth. Three general groups are of particular importance: those saprotrophic bacteria which, in soil and ocean, bring about *decay;* those chemosynthetic bacteria which supply *usable*

FIG. 8.9   Test-tube culture of bioluminescent bacteria. The continuous light they emit is strong enough to illuminate part of a printed page. *(Carolina Biological Supply Co.)*

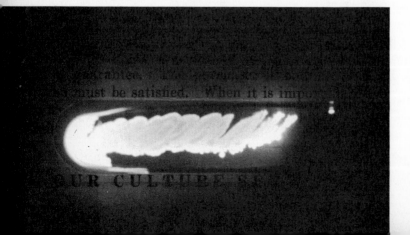

nitrogen compounds for other organisms; and those parasitic bacteria which produce disease, the *pathogenic* bacteria. We shall hear more about each of these groups in later chapters.

As implied by their name, schizophytes ("fission plants") reproduce by fission or cell division. This is an enormously effective process, for under good circumstances bacterial cells may divide every 20 min or so. In just 6 to 7 hr, therefore, a single bacterium may give rise to 1 million offspring. In view of this, it may be easily appreciated that bacteria probably outnumber all other living organisms on earth. It was discovered recently that some bacteria may mate and undergo a sexual process. This subject will be discussed further in Chap. 24.

The Main Groups

Reflecting our still very limited knowledge of bacterial evolution, the taxonomic subclassification of the bacteria is possibly the least stabilized of all the phyla of living organisms. Ten or so subgroups can be distinguished. The following are most important.

Pseudomonadales: pseudomonads. These organisms are probably the most primitive bacteria now living. Members of the group are generally flagellate, and cells of all three basic shapes are represented. In addition to other types, pseudomonads include the photosynthetic and chemosynthetic bacteria. The former belong to three families: the *purple sulfur bacteria,* the *purple nonsulfur bacteria,* and the *green sulfur bacteria.* Among the chemosynthesizers are the *sulfur bacteria,* the *iron bacteria,* the *hydrogen bacteria,* the *nitrifying bacteria,* and many others. We shall have more to say about all these photosynthetic and chemosynthetic types in Chap. 12, for they are of considerable general importance (Fig. 8.10).

Eubacteriales: true bacteria. These organisms form by far the largest and most studied group. Virtually all structural types are included, some with flagella, some without, some living as single cells, others in various colonial aggregations. Cell walls are generally rigid. The organisms are partly saprotrophs, living free in virtually all environments, and partly symbionts of all possible kinds. Among the latter are most of the pathogenic bacterial parasites, including many of particular concern to man. Certain individual species, e.g., *Escherichia coli,* a commensal widely occurring in animal intestines, have been studied so extensively that, biologically, they are among the best-known organisms of all kinds (see Fig. 8.10).

Actinomycetales: branching bacteria. These microbes typically form branched filamentous colonies superficially resembling certain fungi. Motility is generally lacking. Some members of the group are quite familiar through their metabolic excretion products: the actinomycetes include the organisms which produce streptomycin, aureomycin, and similar antibiotics (Fig. 8.11).

Spirochaetales: spiral bacteria. These forms are all unicellular and have the shape of spirals making at least one complete turn (see Fig. 8.11). In some cases the cells are veritable giants, reaching lengths of up to 0.5 mm. Tapered ends, often extended into very fine processes, are relatively common. The cells are quite flexible, and they may propel themselves by whirling and spinning around their long axes. Locomotion here is evidently not brought about by flagella. The best-known spirochete is probably *Treponema pallidum,* causative agent of syphilis.

Myxobacteriales: gliding slime bacteria. Organisms in this group occur as single cells, each a flexible, motile rod. Flagella are absent, but the cells are somehow able to creep or glide along a surface, leaving a layer of secreted slime behind them. At times the organisms *swarm;* i.e., they migrate into a mass and then stop moving. Such *resting cells* become embedded in secreted slime, and the whole aggregate forms a *fruiting body.* In some cases, fruiting bodies may be stalked and assume shapes of considerable complexity (Fig. 8.12). In this behavior the myxobacters greatly resemble certain of the protistan slime molds (see Chap. 9).

FIG. 8.10 Left, Pseudomonadales: *Spirillum.* Middle, Eubacteriales: *Bacillus.* Right, Eubacteriales: *Azotobacter. (General Biological Supply House, Inc.)*

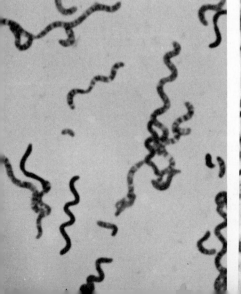
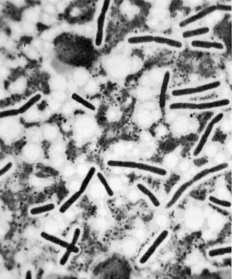
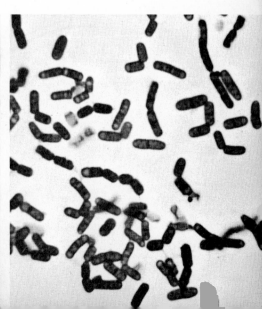

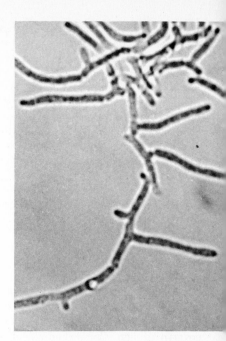

FIG. 8.11 Left, a spirochete; right, filamentous branching growth of actinomycetous bacteria. (Courtesy of Dr. C. Robinow, University of Western Ontario, and Academic Press, Inc., New York.)

Beggiatoales: gliding bacteria. Like the myxobacters, the beggiatoas also are flexible, gliding cells, but they form filamentous colonies and do not aggregate into fruiting bodies (see Fig. 8.12). Some beggiatoas resemble sulfur bacteria in that they use sulfur compounds in their metabolism. Propulsion of a colony is accomplished by slow rolls and by jerking or oscillating movements. These interesting, so far unexplainable motions are identical with the movements of certain blue-green algae. Moreover, in certain gliding bacteria (e.g., *Beggiatoa*) and certain cyanophytes (e.g., *Oscillatoria*), the structure of the cellular colonies and the manner in which they are formed are also quite indistinguishable. Indeed, the only essential difference between these types is that one is photosynthetic whereas the other is not. Thus, genera like *Beggiatoa* could be—and often are—regarded as colorless cyanophytes, perhaps evolved from pigmented cyanophyte ancestors by loss of pigments. In view of this, inclusion of beggiatoas among the bacteria must be considered provisional.

Two additional groups are almost certainly not bacteria but may nevertheless be closely related. One of these groups comprises the **Rickettsiae.** These organisms are like bacteria in certain respects and like viruses in others. Beyond this, their evolutionary affinities are completely unknown. Moreover, considerable uncertainty still exists as to whether rickettsias are "organisms" at all, i.e., are cellular in nature. In a general way their spherical or rodlike structure does resemble that of bacteria. But rickettsias are far smaller than even small bacteria, being in the size range of large viruses. Rickettsias resemble viruses further in that they are obligate intracellular parasites, unable to carry out living functions outside the cells of specific hosts. Such hosts appear to be arthropods only, particularly ticks and lice. Several rickettsias are pathogenic. For example, one species is the causative agent of Rocky

FIG. 8.12 Fruiting body of a myxobacterium. (Courtesy of Dr. I. K. Ross, Yale University.)

Mountain spotted fever and another of epidemic typhus fever, both diseases of man. Ticks in the first case and body lice in the second transfer the rickettsias to man.

Another group with possible affinities with bacteria includes the viruses themselves. They are definitely neither cells nor organisms but intracellular parasitic chemicals consisting of nucleic acids and proteins. As noted in Chap. 3, at least some of the viruses now in existence may be descendants of ancestral nucleic acid fragments which broke away from the genetic material of early bacterial cells. If so, the cells of other organisms very possibly may have given rise to viruses too, in similar fashion. Indeed, virus creation of this sort may still be taking place today.

PHYLUM CYANOPHYTA: BLUE-GREEN ALGAE
(about 2,500 species)

The name of these organisms, "blue-green algae," is somewhat misleading, for some cyanophytes actually are not blue-green. Many are of black, purple, red, yellow, green, blue, or various intermediate shades. These colors are produced by different proportions of several pigments present in different species. The pigments include a variety of chlorophyll called *chlorophyll a, carotene,* various *xanthophylls,* and two phycobilins, namely, blue *c-phycocyanin* and red *c-phycoerythrin.* These last two are unique to the cyanophytes, not being found in any other group of organisms.

Cyanophytes occur in virtually all environments containing water. Cyanophytes range from the tropics to the poles and are present in soil, fresh water, and the ocean. In open aquatic habitats they often form part of the plankton. Extensive growths of blue-green algae frequently occur in areas which are wetted only intermittently, e.g., tidal flats, stream banks, tree bark, and rocks sprayed with sea water. Some cyanophytes live in the icy waters of glaciers; others, in hot springs where temperatures reach 85°C or more. Apart from such free-living forms, some blue-green algae live in symbiotic association with other organisms.

The cell interior of a cyanophyte consists of a colorless central region and a surrounding pigmented region (Fig. 8.13). The central portion contains the genetic DNA-protein as well as granules believed to be phosphate-containing crystals. This region is not separated from the surrounding parts by any membrane or other structure. In the outer cytoplasm are found the various pigments referred to above, as well as *cyano-*

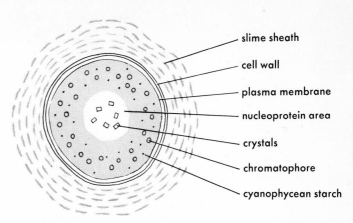

FIG. 8.13 Diagrammatic representation of a cell of blue-green algae.

phycean starch. This is the unique food-storage compound of the cyanophytes. It is not the same as the starch found in other organisms, and its chemistry is known only poorly.

The cytoplasm of a cyanophyte cell is enclosed in a wall which contains *cellulose* and frequently also *pectin.* In some cases the pectin may dissolve immediately after being secreted by the cell, but in others it may persist and form a thick gelatinous sheath around the cell wall. Flagella are entirely lacking in the phylum. Where locomotion occurs, it is of the gliding, jerky type described above for the beggiatoas. Cyanophytes reproduce mainly by cell division. Sexual processes are entirely unknown in the group, a feature quite unique in the whole living world.

If beggiatoas are regarded as bacteria, then all of the cyanophytes are photosynthetic. Oxygen is a byproduct, and this form of photosynthesis is actually universal for all except the bacterial photosynthesizers. Like some of the bacteria, some blue-green algae are able to fix atmospheric nitrogen, i.e., incorporate aerial nitrogen into the amino acids and proteins of their bodies. This ability makes such organisms important producers of nitrogen compounds usable by other forms of life (see Chap. 12).

Like bacteria, the cyanophytes are essentially unicellular. However, again as in bacteria, the cells frequently do not separate entirely after division, with the result that colonies are formed. Depending on the degree of cell separation, colonies may consist of loosely grouped cellular aggregates or of tightly joined cells forming filaments. The arrangement of the cells in a

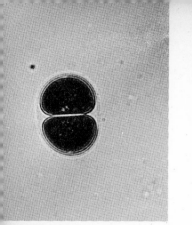
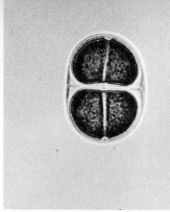
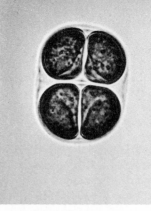
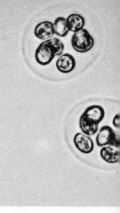

FIG. 8.14 Chroococcales. Left to right, three stages in the growth of *Chroococcus* and two colonies of *Gloeocapsa*. (Courtesy of Dr. M. S. Fuller, Brown University.)

colony and the way in which newly produced cells are added to the colony constitute the basis for cyanophyte classification. Three main subgroups are recognized: the *Chroococcales,* the *Chamaeosiphonales,* and the *Hormogonales.*

All of the Chroococcales (Fig. 8.14) are unicellular, but the cells often form loose colonies held together by the gelatinous slime sheaths secreted by the organisms. *Chroococcus* and *Gloeocapsa,* frequently encountered in moist places, are two representative types. In both, the cells have conspicuous sheaths. After a cell divides, its sheath very often does not break and groups of associated daughter cells then retain a common sheath around them. The division planes are random in the two genera mentioned, but in other genera division takes place only in two or three planes. If divisions occur in two planes, a flat layer of cells results, as in *Merismopedia;* but if divisions occur in three planes, the colony is cuboidal, as in *Eucapsis.*

Chamaeosiphonales too are either solitary or colonial, but unlike the Chroococcales, they regularly produce true spores (see Chap. 24). A representative type

of this group is *Chamaesiphon,* a fresh-water epiphyte on green algae and other organisms (see Fig. 8.14).

The Hormogonales (Fig. 8.15) are distinctly filamentous, cell divisions always being restricted to a single plane. The cells are joined so intimately that groups of them may be enclosed within a common wall. Such cell groups are called **hormogones.** In many cases, two neighboring hormogones in a multicellular filament may be joined by means of a unit known as a **heterocyst.** Such a unit often is larger than the cells on either side, and it appears to be a transparent cell with a double wall. A filament may break readily at these heterocysts, and their main function may be to make such breaks possible. The separated hormogones then may settle elsewhere and grow into new offspring filaments. In contrast with the other two groups, the Hormogonales are motile and display the jerky, rolling type of movement referred to earlier.

Two common representatives of the Hormogonales are *Oscillatoria,* so named after its characteristic locomotion, and *Nostoc* (Fig. 8.15). The latter is found in clear fresh water, where it forms gelatinous balls of up to 50 cm in diameter. Such balls are composed of many filaments and their surrounding sheaths. When colonies of *Nostoc* are mature, the hormogones between heterocysts often enlarge, fill with reserve foods, and enter a dormant state. In this condition the organisms may survive through the winter season. *Nostoc* also lives mutualistically with fungi, the combinations representing some of the *lichens.*

This discussion concludes the account of the Monera. In the next chapter we shall deal with the Protista, which arose side by side with the Monera but became, in the process of evolution, far more inventive and progressive.

FIG. 8.15 Hormogonales. Portion of a colony of *Nostoc.* Note the gelatinous sheaths. (General Biological Supply House, Inc.)

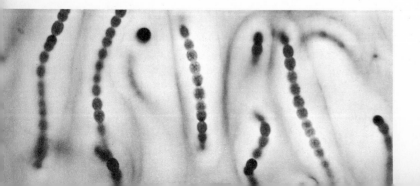

REVIEW QUESTIONS

1. Review the hierarchy of taxonomic ranks. What rules are in force in the naming of species and other taxonomic ranks? Review the classification of any organism.

2. What are the main categories of organisms in existence today? What distinguishes these categories from one another? What are the major subgroups within each category? How are the main categories probably related evolutionally?

3. Which of the organisms in Question 2 have traditionally been regarded as plants and which as animals? What are customary definitions of "plant" and "animal"? Show how these definitions are inadequate.

4. Define homology, analogy. Give specific examples. Why is it incorrect to speak of "higher" and "lower" organisms?

5. Review the identifying characteristics of (a) Monera, (b) bacteria, and (c) blue-green algae. What features distinguish (b) and (c)?

6. Describe the general structure of a bacterial cell. How do bacteria (a) feed and (b) move? How are bacteria distinguished in shape and in growth patterns? What is an endospore?

7. Name some of the main subgroups of bacteria and review the characteristics of each. What are (a) Rickettsiae and (b) viruses?

8. Describe the general structure and the biochemical characteristics of a cyanophyte cell. How do cyanophytes (a) feed and (b) move?

9. Name the three main subgroups of blue-green algae and review the characteristics of each. What are the names of representative genera?

10. Define hormogone, heterocyst. Where do cyanophytes occur in nature?

SUGGESTED COLLATERAL READINGS

The biology of the Monera is described in detail in the following texts:

Henrici, A. T., and E. J. Ordal: "The Biology of the Bacteria," Heath, Boston, 1948.

Pelczar, M. J., and R. D. Reid: "Microbiology," McGraw-Hill, New York, 1958.

Stanier, R. Y., M. Doudoroff, and E. A. Adelberg: "The Microbial World," Prentice-Hall, Englewood Cliffs, N.J., 1957.

Thimann, K. V.: "The Life of Bacteria," Macmillan, New York, 1955.

Bacteria and viruses are discussed popularly in the following books and articles:

Bigger, J. W.: "Man against Microbe," Macmillan, New York, 1939.

Burnet, F. M.: Viruses, *Sci. American,* vol. 184, 1951.

Clayton, R. K., and M. Delbruck: Purple Bacteria, *Sci. American,* vol. 185, 1951.

De Kruif, P.: "Microbe Hunters," Harcourt, Brace, New York, 1928.

Luria, S. E.: The T2 Mystery, *Sci. American,* vol. 192, 1955.

Lwoff, A.: The Life Cycle of a Virus, *Sci. American,* vol. 185, 1951.

Perret, J.: Biochemistry and Bacteria, *New Biol.,* vol. 12, 1952.

Postgate, J.: The Sulphur Bacteria, *New Biol.,* vol. 17, 1954.

PROTISTA

9

The very first organisms on earth were cells, and early biological evolution may be regarded as a thoroughgoing exploitation of this newly achieved unicellular way of life. One result of this exploitation was the origin of the ancestral Monera and, later, of their modern descendants. Another early result must have been the evolutionary "invention" of a basic *protistan* cell type. This type must have proved to be enormously modifiable and exceedingly rich in evolutionary potentialities, far more so than the basic moneran type; in time, the protistan cell type probably gave rise to all other life forms on earth, namely, all modern Protista as well as the ancestors of all Metaphyta and all Metazoa.

What were the fundamental traits of this ancestral protistan type, as inferred from its modern descendants? In other words, what are the common features of all the Protista now in existence?

BASIC CHARACTERISTICS

The various evolutionary innovations which distinguish the basic protistan cell type almost certainly did not develop all at once, but must have accumulated gradually during millions of years. In their totality, these innovations affect all cell characteristics, i.e., structure, function, and development (Fig. 9.1).

1. The ancestral protistan type evolved a true cell **nucleus** with a distinct nuclear membrane, the latter separating the gene-containing nucleoproteins from the cytoplasm. Such a structure is not present in the Monera; its adaptive advantage will become clear in Chap. 18.

2. The gene-containing nucleoproteins do not occur in clumps as in Monera, but are organized into clearly identifiable **chromosomes.** The cells of each species contain a given fixed number of these filamentous bodies. Moreover, chromosomes produce **nucleoli,** which are also evolutionary "inventions" of the protistan stock.

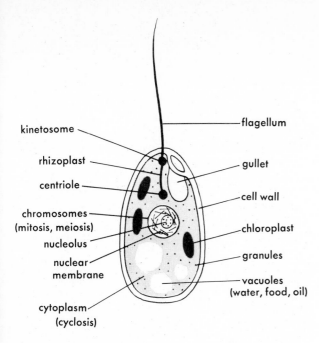

kinetosome

flagellum

rhizoplast

gullet

centriole

cell wall

chromosomes
(mitosis, meiosis)

chloroplast

nucleolus

nuclear
membrane

granules

vacuoles
(water, food, oil)

cytoplasm
(cyclosis)

FIG. 9.1 Diagrammatic representation of the basic protistan cell type.

3. A new method of cell division is in evidence. This method includes a process known as **mitosis,** about which more will be said in Chap. 23. Note here that mitosis is contingent on the presence of chromosomes, hence does not occur in the Monera. Chromosomes are also essential in another divisional process, **meiosis,** and this component of sex (Chap. 23) likewise originated with the Protista.

4. The typical **size** of the protistan cell is substantially larger than that of the moneran type. Also, the protistan cytoplasm often streams and undergoes **cyclosis** and it contains **vacuoles,** some contractile and serving excretory functions, other noncontractile and serving various storage functions.

5. Ancestral protists probably invented true plastids, particularly **chloroplasts,** far more complex in structure than the chromatophores of the Monera. Chlorophyll *a* is universally present in photosynthetic Protista. Since this pigment also occurs in the cyanophytes, it may represent an inheritance from the very earliest cells, shared alike by Monera and Protista. This may also be true of carotenoids and xanthophylls, some of which are identical in Monera and Protista. However, Protista developed very many new additional

pigments, as is well illustrated in the case of the chlorophylls. Whereas cyanophytes possess only chlorophyll *a*, Protista always possess chlorophyll *a* plus at least one other variety of chlorophyll (named *b, c, d, e,* as we shall see).

6. Ancient protists undoubtedly originated the cytoplasmic granules known as **kinetosomes.** From these in turn grew the complex **flagella** composed of 11 fibrils each, not merely of one each as in the Monera. Locomotion by means of flagella or by the variants called *cilia* became one of the standard methods of protistan propulsion. Further, kinetosomes can divide within a protistan cell and produce more of such granules; that is how offspring cells produced by cell division acquire kinetosomes. Moreover, these bodies need not always be associated with flagella but may assume other functions connected with movement, notably movement of internal cell components. One such kinetosome derivative is the **centriole,** typically present in protistan cells and located often outside, but in many cases inside, the nucleus. As we shall see in Chap. 23, the centriole plays a role in the movement of chromosomes during mitosis and meiosis. Centrioles have been largely lost in some advanced Protista and all Metaphyta, but they have been retained by the Metazoa.

7. The basic protistan cell type undoubtedly could exist in several alternative vegetative states (Fig. 9.2). The free-swimming **flagellate** state represents one of these. By successive cell divisions, a parental cell in this state can give rise to many, similarly flagellate, single-celled individuals. Another possible state is the **amoeboid** condition, which arises when a flagellate cell casts off its flagellum (but retains its kinetosome). Such a cell then may settle on a surface and move along it by characteristic amoebalike locomotion. At some later time, even after one or more cell divisions have produced many individuals, a new flagellum may develop from the kinetosome, amoeboid motion may cease, and the free-swimming flagellate state may be resumed.

By loss of flagella, two different nonmotile or sessile states may also arise. One may be referred to as the **coccoid** condition. Here the nonmotile cell ceases to divide its cytoplasm (except during specialized reproductive processes) but continues to divide its nucleus. The result is a progressively more and more multinucleate but still unicellular organism. When such an organism reproduces, all or part of it becomes partitioned off simultaneously into numerous cells, each of which contains one nucleus. These *spore* cells may de-

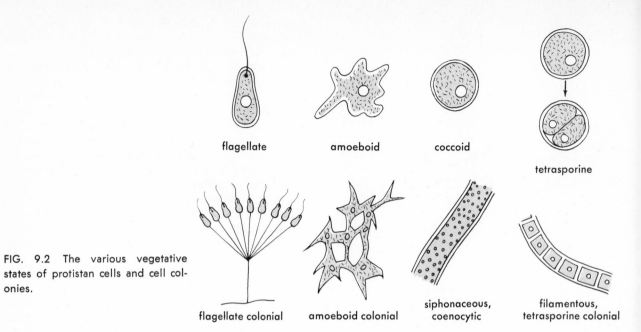

flagellate   amoeboid   coccoid

tetrasporine

FIG. 9.2 The various vegetative states of protistan cells and cell colonies.

flagellate colonial   amoeboid colonial   siphonaceous, coenocytic   filamentous, tetrasporine colonial

velop flagella, disperse by active locomotion, then settle and grow into new nonmotile coccoids. A fourth possible state is the **tetrasporine** condition, again sessile, in which the cell simply remains as it is, nonmotile and uninucleate. After such a cell divides, the daughter cells tend to remain sticking together, since they are nonmotile. Successive divisions here produce multicellular aggregates. In some cases, individual cells may sometimes redevelop flagella and disengage from the aggregate.

Of these four different states, the flagellate condition is probably basic and primitive, all others being derived. The possibility of existing in such alternative vegetative conditions must have endowed the ancestral protists with vast evolutionary opportunities. And within numerous groups of protists today, many or even all of the alternative states are still in evidence. But other protistan groups are specialized in just one of the ancestral states and through mutation have lost the capacity of existing in any other.

8. These various states of the ancestral protists have each evolved independently into **multicellular** sublines. Thus, in addition to the unicellular members in the several states, different protistan groups today variously include motile *flagellate colonies,* motile *amoeboid colonies,* sessile *coccoid colonies,* and sessile *tetrasporine colonies.*

Ancestral tetrasporine colonies in particular displayed rich evolutionary potentialities. Since they were sessile and their cells were joined directly and tightly, such colonies could hold together well and could grow to extremely large size, well beyond the microscopic range of the other types of colonies. Moreover, depending on the planes of cell division, they could form one-dimensional filaments, or two-dimensional disks and sheets, or three-dimensional compact masses. All such tetrasporine organizations are encountered today among modern protists. Indeed, structurally advanced tetrasporine colonies are quite indistinguishable from, and are actually identical with, **tissues.** Undoubtedly, this level of organization originated with the Protista.

Furthermore, as we shall see later, the whole category of Metaphyta most probably arose from an ancestral protistan stock which had reached an advanced, tetrasporine, tissue level of organization.

9. Depending on environmental conditions, either unicellular or multicellular protists of virtually any vegetative type could temporarily enter one of several *protective* or *dormant* stages (Fig. 9.3). For example, motile cells could cease to be motile and become **encapsulated.** Nonmotile cells could encapsulate directly. Here the cell secretes a thick wall around itself, and such a protective shell enables the organism to survive unfavorable conditions. Later, the wall may break open

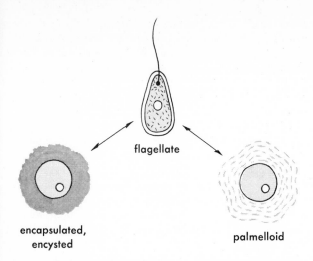

flagellate

encapsulated,
encysted

palmelloid

FIG. 9.3 The protective, or dormant, states of protistan cells.

and the emerging cell may reassume its active state. Another common protective condition is the **palmelloid** stage, in which a nonmotile protist (or one which has become nonmotile) secretes a surrounding sheath of pectin-containing gelatinous material. This material is hygroscopic and holds water. The palmelloid stage is therefore adaptively very advantageous under conditions of drought or temporary lack of environmental water generally. If the palmelloid stage lasts long enough, the cells may divide and produce larger groups of cells lying more or less closely together, embedded within a common mass of jelly.

10. Early protists could undoubtedly reproduce by several methods, one such method involving sex cells, another spore cells. Protista did not invent reproduction, to be sure, but they developed and still maintain a number of reproductive features which set them apart from Metaphyta and Metazoa. One such feature is the virtually universal presence of **unicellular reproductive structures.** That is, even in multicellular Protista (only a few groups excepted), single cells are or give rise to reproductive cells. Moreover, the unicellular reproductive structures are almost invariably *exposed.* In Metaphyta and Metazoa, by contrast, reproductive structures are always multicellular, with several or many cells forming a reproductive *organ.* In such organs, the reproductive-cell-producing tissue is unexposed, a sterile protective tissue forming an external covering.

11. Ancestral unicellular Protista probably could obtain food by all possible methods of nutrition except chemosynthesis. They could **photosynthesize,** feed as

holotrophs by swallowing bulk food, subsist as **saprotrophs** by absorbing molecular food from dead organic matter, or live as **symbionts** of various kinds in association with living hosts. Indeed, one and the same individual probably possessed the capacity to nourish itself, successively or simultaneously, by two or even more of these methods. As we shall see, this is still the case today in many of the unicellular protists.

Chloroplasts served in photosynthesis; the general cell surface served in saprotrophic or symbiotic absorption of food molecules; and flagellary as well as amoeboid motion aided in eating bulk foods. In the amoeboid state, fingerlike extension of the cell, so-called *pseudopodia,* flow around a microscopic speck of food on all sides (see Fig. 5.28). In this manner food is engulfed and forms a food vacuole within the cell. In the flagellate state, the beat of the flagellum creates tiny water currents which sweep food particles toward the cell. At or near the base of the flagellum is a pit or depression in the cell surface, the so-called *gullet,* into which food is propelled (see Fig. 9.1). At the bottom of the gullet, a vacuole forms around a food particle and such a vacuole then is carried into the cell interior by cytoplasmic streaming.

Clearly, the motile states served not only in locomotion, effecting geographical dispersal, but also and perhaps mainly in feeding. It must have been of immense adaptive advantage if, at night or at the dimly lit bottoms of natural waters, an ancestral protist could transform into a motile state and actively hunt for food. In the presence of light, however, photosynthesis could occur and energy could then be saved by resumption of one of the sessile states. In this sense, ancestral protists undoubtedly were, and some of their modern descendants still are, both plantlike and animallike simultaneously. But other modern protists are more distinctly "plant" or more distinctly "animal." These groups must have evolved when, through chance mutations, some of the ancestral protists lost one or the other method of nutrition. Moreover, Metaphyta must have arisen from some of these newly evolved, permanently photosynthetic and sessile stocks, and Metazoa from some of the newly evolved, permanently bulk-feeding and motile stocks. We may note that loss mutations may be induced experimentally in certain modern plantlike-plus-animallike protists, leading to a conversion to either purely plantlike or purely animallike organisms. Such experiments undoubtedly duplicate the ancient natural process of nutritional evolution among protists.

We may conclude that different ancestral Protista probably did not vary too greatly in the most basic features of their newly evolved intracellular organization, which they all had in common, but that they could vary quite considerably in the characteristics of their vegetative states and in their methods of nutrition. And as different combinations of these variants became specialized and permanently fixed in the evolution of different lines of descent, the several specific groups of modern Protista came into being. As has been noted, these groups are the *algae,* which are largely photosynthetic, and the *protozoa,* the *slime molds,* and the *fungi,* which are nonphotosynthetic.

ALGAE

This group of organisms represents a superphylum containing several distinct phyla. Considered as a whole, living algae still retain the various vegetative states of the protistan ancestors. Primitive algae tend to be unicellular and both plantlike and animallike in their nutrition. But more advanced types are multicellular, sessile, and, like the Metaphyta, able only to photosynthesize.

Although structural features provide useful distinctions between the algal phyla, the main differences are primarily biochemical: types of chlorophyll and other pigments present, the chemical composition of the cell wall, and the chemical nature of stored foods. On the basis of their chlorophyll content, three main groups of algae may be recognized. All three possess chlorophyll *a,* but in addition, one possesses chlorophyll *b,* the second chlorophyll *c* (or in some cases *e*), and the third chlorophyll *d.* In conjunction with other pigments present, these chlorophylls produce characteristic visible colors: some shade of green in the *a* plus *b* types, brown in the *a* plus *c* types, and red in the *a* plus *d* types. We may therefore distinguish a *green line,* a *brown line,* and a *red line* of algae (Table 6).

THE GREEN LINE
PHYLUM CHLOROPHYTA: GREEN ALGAE
(about 6,000 species)

The phylum is identified by chlorophylls *a* and *b* and various carotenes and xanthophylls, by comparatively rigid cell walls consisting usually of an inner cellulose layer and an outer pectic layer, by reserve foods stored as starch, and by flagellate cells or stages which, wherever present, bear two (or more rarely four) equally long anterior flagella, all of the whiplash type. We may note that these characteristics occur in precisely this combination only in the green algae and the Metaphyta. Early stocks of the former are therefore believed to have been in the specific ancestors of the latter.

The pigments of the green algae are contained in chloroplasts of various shapes and numbers. Typically present on the chloroplasts are small, often highly refractile bodies called **pyrenoids.** These have a protein composition and around them accumulate deposits of starch. For this reason, pyrenoids are believed to be specific starch-synthesizing centers. Many flagellate algal cells possess an **eyespot** near the anterior end. This small structure consists of a cup containing a photosensitive pigment, namely, a carotene derivative called *haematochrome,* which is chemically related to vitamin A; and of a "lens," a transparent, light-concentrating body lying in the pigmented cup. A functional connection, if not also a structural one, is believed to exist between the eyespot and the nearby kinetosomes of the flagella. By virtue of this complex of photosensory and locomotor structures, the cell may be able to distinguish regions of light and dark and may move accordingly.

Chlorophytes include three main lines of evolutionary descent distinguished by their principal vegetative states: a *flagellate* line, a *coccoid* line, and a *tetrasporine* line. Each is represented by both unicellular and colonial forms. Given life cycles frequently include temporary encapsulated and palmelloid stages and, in a few cases, amoeboid stages.

The flagellate line is represented by single-celled types such as *Chlamydomonas,* which exhibits most of the characteristics of green algal cells in most nearly typical form (Fig. 9.4). Different species of *Chlamydomonas* occur in soil, in freshwater ponds and pools, in quiet streams, and in the ocean. Very closely related to *Chlamydomonas* is *Polytoma,* which is virtually identical to *Chlamydomonas* except that it is colorless and nonphotosynthetic (Fig. 9.5). It lives as a saprotroph. As we shall see, paired types of this sort are also encountered among most of the other algal phyla. Undoubtedly, such paired photosynthetic and colorless forms represent branch lines descended from a relatively recent common ancestor, one line having retained and the other lost the photosynthetic method of nutrition. In certain cases, experiment may duplicate such

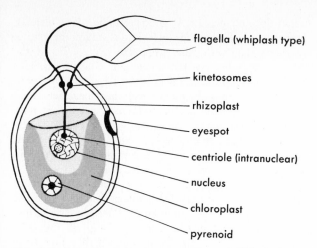

FIG. 9.4 Diagrammatic representation of *Chlamydomonas,* a unicellular, flagellate, green alga.

- flagella (whiplash type)
- kinetosomes
- rhizoplast
- eyespot
- centriole (intranuclear)
- nucleus
- chloroplast
- pyrenoid

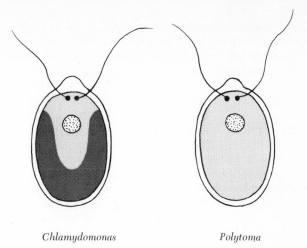

Chlamydomonas   *Polytoma*

FIG. 9.5 The green photosynthetic alga *Chlamydomonas* greatly resembles the nongreen saprophytic alga *Polytoma.* The latter does not possess a chloroplast.

TABLE 6

Comparative biochemical characteristics of algae

group	phylum	chloro-phyll	other pigments	food-storage compounds	cell walls
green line	Chlorophyta	*a, b*	carotenes xanthophylls	starch	cellulose, pectin
	Charophyta	*a, b*	carotenes xanthophylls	starch	cellulose, pectin
	Euglenophyta	*a, b*	carotenes xanthophylls	paramylum, fats	usually none
brown line	Chrysophyta	*a, c (e)*	carotenes xanthophylls (lutein, fucoxanthin)	leucosin, fats	pectins, cellulose, silica, or none
	Pyrrophyta	*a, c*	carotenes xanthophylls	starch, polysaccharides, fats	cellulose or none
	Phaeophyta	*a, c*	carotenes xanthophylls (fucoxanthin)	laminarin, mannitol	cellulose, algin
red line	Rhodophyta	*a, d*	carotenes xanthophylls (lutein) *r*-phycocyanin *r*-phycoerythrin	floridean starch	cellulose, pectins

evolutionary processes. For example, it has been possible to convert given photosynthetic algae into variant strains which lack chlorophyll. Such animallike variants thrive perfectly well if a readymade source of food is supplied from the outside. Very probably, experiments of this sort also simulate the ancient natural process through which original flagellate protists may have given rise separately to plantlike and animallike descendants.

Cells rather like *Chlamydomonas* form flagellate colonies, in which the daughter cells remain joined after division. Among the green algae, such flagellate colonies are usually composed of fixed numbers of cells—4, 8, 16, 32, 64, or larger multiples. If there are relatively few cells, they form disks or cupshaped colonies; and if the cell number is comparatively large, the colony is usually a hollow sphere, as in *Volvox*. In this organism, the cells exhibit a high degree of coordination. A network of fibrils, presumably impulse-conducting, joins the kinetosomes of the many cells, and their flagella beat in an integrated pattern which produces coordinated locomotion (Fig. 9.6).

Chlorophytes in the coccoid line of evolution typically are sessile and unicellular, and vegetative cell divisions do not occur. A good example is *Chlorella*, probably used more extensively in studies of photosynthesis than any other organism (Fig. 9.7). At the time of reproduction, the nucleus of *Chlorella* divides several times and each offspring nucleus, together with some of the surrounding cytoplasm, becomes partitioned off as a *spore* cell. In *Chlorella* such spores are nonmotile, but in many close relatives of *Chlorella* the spores are flagellate and motile. Note, in any case, that division of the cell occurs only during spore formation, never during the adult vegetative stage.

Many chlorophytic coccoids attain extraordinary sizes and exhibit a remarkable internal specialization of their one sessile cell. For example, *Acetabularia*, growing in warm seas, may be 2 to 3 in. long (see Fig. 9.7). The alga consists of a stalk, an umbrella-like cap at the top, and fine outgrowths at the bottom of the stalk which anchor the organism on the sea floor. The whole is one cell, a single nucleus being situated in the base of the stalk. At the time of reproduction, the nucleus migrates into the cap, where it divides several times. Spores then form as in *Chlorella*. Other coccoid algae become highly multinucleate as adults, yet they too remain undivided single cells. Such algae usually have tubular bodies, which may be branched in many different ways. Tubular or *siphonaceous* algae of this sort are capable of indefinite extension in length. A good example is *Bryopsis* (see Fig. 9.7).

The tetrasporine line of evolution is the most diversified of the chlorophytes. Unicellular types include the common *Protococcus*, which usually grows on perpetually moist tree bark in the form of loosely aggregated colonies. More highly organized colonies are formed by types in which cell divisions occur in one or more fixed planes. Divisions in one plane produce the many *filamentous* green algae (Fig. 9.8). In some of these, the reproductive cells are either nonmotile altogether or amoeboid, but never flagellate. To this group belongs, for example, the common freshwater alga *Spirogyra*. Other filamentous algae are characterized by flagellate reproductive cells. Representatives of this group are *Ulothrix* and *Oedogonium*, both superficially rather like *Spirogyra*.

The group with flagellate stages has been the more progressive from an evolutionary standpoint, for from it arose not only filamentous types but also more complexly structured organisms. For example, cell divisions in two planes may produce a branched filament as in *Cladophora* or a flat sheet of cells as in the common sea lettuce *Ulva* (see Fig. 9.8). Cell divisions occur in

FIG. 9.6 *Volvox*, a colonial green alga consisting of many flagellate cells. The cells are arranged as a single-layered sphere, with each cell in direct contact with the water environment. In the interior of the sphere are several offspring colonies, which develop there and eventually burst through the parent. (*Courtesy of Dr. M. S. Fuller, Brown University.*)

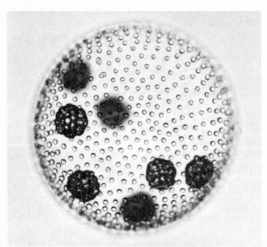

FIG. 9.7 Green algae of the coccoid line of evolution. Left, *Chlorella*; middle, *Acetabularia*; right, *Bryopsis*. (Left and right, courtesy of Dr. M. S. Fuller, Brown University; middle, General Biological Supply House, Inc.)

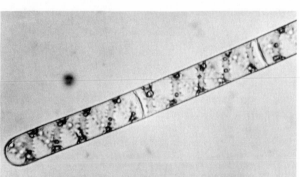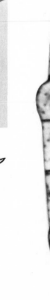

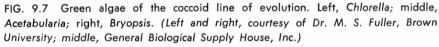

FIG. 9.8 Green algae of the tetrasporine line of evolution. Top left, terminal cells of a *Spirogyra* filament; middle, *Oedogonium*; right, *Cladophora*; bottom left, *Ulva*. (Top left, middle, and right, courtesy of Dr. M. S. Fuller, Brown University.)

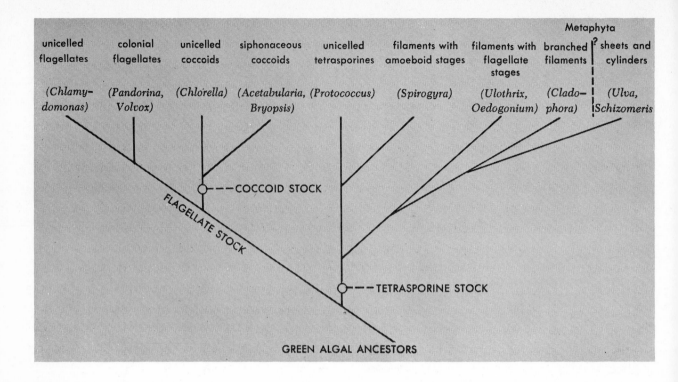

unicelled flagellates	colonial flagellates	unicelled coccoids	siphonaceous coccoids	unicelled tetrasporines	filaments with amoeboid stages	filaments with flagellate stages	branched filaments	Metaphyta sheets and cylinders
(Chlamy-domonas)	*(Pandorina, Volvox)*	*(Chlorella)*	*(Acetabularia, Bryopsis)*	*(Protococcus)*	*(Spirogyra)*	*(Ulothrix, Oedogonium)*	*(Clado-phora)*	*(Ulva, Schizomeris)*

FLAGELLATE STOCK

○---COCCOID STOCK

○---TETRASPORINE STOCK

GREEN ALGAL ANCESTORS

FIG. 9.9   The probable evolutionary affinities of various groups within the green algae.

three planes in *Schizomeris*, which possesses a solid cylindrical body several cell layers thick. These algae may be regarded as having attained the tissue level of organization; and because of their biochemical traits and their complex tetrasporine body construction, early stocks of such algae are believed to have been the specific ancestors of the Metaphyta (Fig. 9.9).

PHYLUM CHAROPHYTA: STONEWORTS
(about 250 species)

Because many of their characteristics, biochemical traits included, are similar to those of the green algae, the organisms in this group are often given the status of a class within the Chlorophyta. But the stoneworts probably warrant phylum rank inasmuch as at least four of their features are distinct from those of the chlorophytes.

As indicated by the representative genera *Chara* and *Nitella* (Fig. 9.10), the four identifying features of stoneworts are the following: a complex filamentous

body organization, with rootlike, stemlike, and leaflike portions; a nodal arrangement of the branches; a pattern of body growth which is strictly terminal, rather than diffuse as in chlorophytes; and the presence of multicellular sex organs surrounded by layers of sterile

FIG. 9.10   Stoneworts. The photograph shows a whole specimen of *Nitella*. (Courtesy of Dr. P. Green, University of Pennsylvania.)

cells. In this last respect, stoneworts are quite unlike other Protista but quite like Metaphyta. However, charophytes lack many important traits which Metaphyta possess; hence the stoneworts cannot be readily included among the metaphytes. Stoneworts *are* protists, but highly advanced protists. They may conceivably have evolved in parallel with the ancestors of the Metaphyta from some complexly organized tetrasporine stocks of green algae. But charophytes may not have gone as far in their evolution as the ancestral metaphytes.

PHYLUM EUGLENOPHYTA: EUGLENOIDS
(about 350 species)

By virtue of its pigments, this phylum belongs to the green-line stock of algae. But the organisms differ in several important respects from other green-line algae (Fig. 9.11). First, euglenoids are almost exclusively unicellular flagellates. Other vegetative states either have never developed or have been lost. Second, there may be a single anterior flagellum, or two flagella of equal length, or one long and one short flagellum, or even three flagella. In all cases the flagella are of the tinsel type and are therefore distinct both in number and structure from those of the green algae. Third, the cells are naked, without rigid cell walls, and very pliable and deformable. Fourth, the characteristic food storage compound is not starch, but partly fatty material and partly a polysaccharide, called *paramylum*, chemically related to starch. Like green algae, euglenoids possess gullets, eyespots, and pyrenoids.

Paired green and colorless euglenoids are common. For example, *Euglena* is a green photosynthesizer, interesting also in that it can and probably must occasionally feed as a saprotroph, whether light is present or not. *Astasia*, on the other hand, is a colorless saprotroph otherwise entirely similar to *Euglena*.

THE BROWN LINE
PHYLUM CHRYSOPHYTA: GOLDEN-BROWN ALGAE
(about 6,000 species)

Class Chrysophyceae: yellow-brown algae
Class Xanthophyceae: yellow-green algae
Class Bacillariophyceae: diatoms

This is an enormously diversified phylum, including more different structural types than any other algal group. Moreover, early chrysophytes, particularly the early yellow-browns, may have been ancestral not only to all other chrysophytes but also to all other brown-line phyla, as well as to some of the slime molds, fungi, protozoa, and perhaps even sponges.

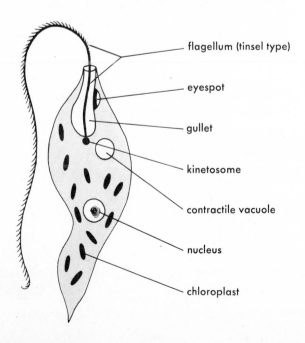

flagellum (tinsel type)

eyespot

gullet

kinetosome

contractile vacuole

nucleus

chloroplast

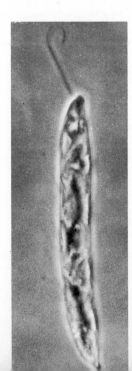

FIG. 9.11 Diagram and photograph of *Euglena*. The genus *Astasia* is entirely similar except that chloroplasts are lacking. *(Photograph, courtesy of Dr. M. S. Fuller, Brown University.)*

Chrysophytes are identified by various pigments which are slightly different in the different classes (see below). Foods are never stored as starch, but are stored partly as *oils* and partly as the polysaccharide *leucosin*. Cell walls may be absent or present. In the latter case the wall is in two halves, the rim of one half tightly overlapping the rim of the other, like lid and box. Such walls are composed of pectic substances plus cellulose in some cases and silicon compounds in the majority of cases. Formation of encapsulated dormant stages, here called *statospores*, is further characteristic of the phylum.

Organisms in the class Chrysophyceae probably are the modern descendants of the original chrysophyte ancestors. Their pigments are chlorophyll *a* plus at least one other chlorophyll of still undetermined type; carotenes; and xanthophylls, which include the yellow *lutein* and the brown *fucoxanthin*. The last two endow these algae with a characteristic yellow-brown color. Four major evolutionary lines of yellow-browns are known, i.e., flagellate, amoeboid, coccoid, and tetrasporine lines. Each of these has unicellular and colonial representatives (Fig. 9.12).

The flagellate forms display various kinds of flagellation patterns. These organisms, as also the amoeboid forms, include many paired photosynthetic and color-less types. Some of the colorless flagellate chrysophyceans may have evolutionary affinities with certain of the primitive fungi. Analogously, colorless amoeboid chrysophyceans may have contributed to the evolution of slime molds and amoeboid protozoa; note that a colorless chrysophycean amoeba, for example, is virtually indistinguishable from a protozoan amoeba. Two groups of the yellow-brown flagellates are partially enclosed within intricately sculptured external skeletons. In the *coccolithophoridae*, the skeleton is composed of calcium compounds, and in the *silicoflagellates*, of silicon compounds (Fig. 9.13). These algae are marine and often form important components of plankton. They may be derived from ancestral stocks which, by loss of chlorophyll, may also have given rise to certain protozoa, i.e., the Foraminifera and the Radiolaria, respectively.

Organisms in the class Xanthophyceae are characterized by chlorophylls *a* and *e* (the latter quite similar to but not identical with chlorophyll *c*), by carotenes, and by xanthophylls of still undetermined nature. Paired photosynthetic and colorless types are again known. Moreover, the yellow-green algae display almost the same wide array of flagellate, amoeboid, coccoid, and tetrasporine types as the yellow-brown algae. Also, the xanthophyceans too have probably contributed to the evolution of other groups, notably the protozoa and slime molds.

Diatoms, forming the class Bacillariophyceae, possess chlorophylls *a* and *c*, carotenes, and xanthophylls which include the brown fucoxanthin. Whereas the

FIG. 9.12 Diagrammatic representation of various Chrysophyceae. *Chrysamoeba* belongs to the amoeboid stock; *Epichrysis,* to the coccoid stock; and *Phaeothamnion,* to the tetrasporine stock.

FIG. 9.13 Diagrammatic representation of two groups of flagellate unicells within the Chrysophyceae. On the right, A represents a sectional view; B, an external view.

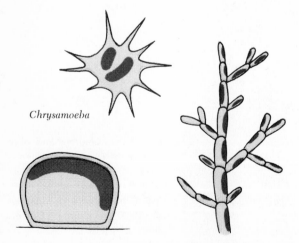

Chrysamoeba

Epichrysis   *Phaeothamnion*

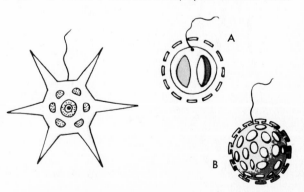

silicoflagellate   coccolithophoridae

other two classes are highly varied in vegetative types, the diatoms are relatively unvaried. They actually represent just one principal vegetative condition, namely, a tetrasporine state which is mostly unicellular and occasionally primitively colonial. A diatom possesses a conspicuous rigid cell wall or shell, composed as in other chrysophytes of two tightly fitting halves and consisting of pectic and silicon-containing compounds (Fig. 9.14). These shells are finely sculptured in a great variety of bilateral or radial patterns (see also Fig. 7.20).

In contrast to the other two classes, the diatoms are of major economic importance. As already noted in Chap. 7, diatoms are the most abundant single group of plankton organisms, and as such they support much of the flora and fauna of the oceans and the fresh water. The silica shells of dead diatoms make up large tracts of the ocean floor. Geologically uplifted parts of this floor are the source of *diatomaceous earth*, mined for its abrasive and various other properties. For example, it is a common component of tooth paste. More-

over, much of the petroleum used in industry today is probably derived from the oils synthesized and stored by diatoms of past ages.

PHYLUM PYRROPHYTA: FIRE ALGAE
(about 1,000 species)

Class Cryptophyceae: cryptoflagellates
Class Dinophyceae: dinoflagellates

The pigments in this phylum are chlorophylls *a* and *c*, carotenes, and several xanthophylls which include at least three of unique composition. Foods are variously stored in the form of starch, starchlike carbohydrates, and fats and oils. Cell walls are absent in some of the Dinophyceae. In others, as well as in the Cryptophyceae, walls composed of cellulose are present.

The evolutionary affinities of the Cryptophyceae are uncertain and the inclusion of this group in the

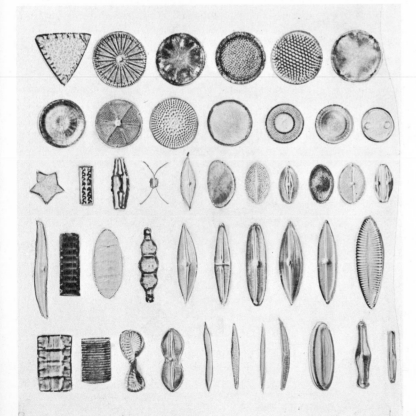

FIG. 9.14 An array of diatoms. A close-up of a single diatom is shown in Fig. 7.20. *(General Biological Supply House, Inc.)*

Pyrrophyta must be regarded as provisional. The organisms are very largely biflagellate unicells. A gullet is conspicuous near or at the base of the flagella. Paired photosynthetic and colorless types are represented, for example, by *Cryptomonas* and *Chilomonas*, respectively (Fig. 9.15).

The Dinophyceae (Fig. 9.16) are by far the more important class, for they constitute a major component of plankton. The vast majority of the Dinophyceae are dinoflagellates, i.e., motile flagellate types. Most of them are unicellular, but some are colonial. All remaining Dinophyceae represent amoeboid, coccoid, and tetrasporine evolutionary lines, but in this class these types are not nearly as elaborately developed as in other algae groups.

Most of the dinoflagellates possess cellulose walls formed into distinct interlocking "armor" plates (e.g., *Peridinium, Ceratium*). Two flagella are present, one directed backward in swimming, the other undulating within a transverse groove formed by the armor. Different nutritional variants are common. For example, *Ceratium* is photosynthetic, *Blastodinium* is a colorless parasite in animals, and *Noctiluca* either photosynthesizes or feeds like an animal. Paired photosynthetic and colorless types are known as well, and these have probably contributed to the evolution of other protistan groups. Many marine dinoflagellates are bioluminescent (e.g., *Noctiluca*). On occasion, some dinoflagellates proliferate locally in fantastic numbers. For example, the reddish *Gymnodinium* often produces so-called red tides (hence the name of the phylum, which literally means "fire plants").

PHYLUM PHAEOPHYTA: BROWN ALGAE
(about 1,000 species)

The identifying pigments of these algae are chlorophylls *a* and *c*; carotenes; and several xanthophylls, of which three are unique to the phylum and one is the brown fucoxanthin, present in amounts sufficient to mask all other pigments. Foods are stored partly as *laminarin*, a unique polysaccharide, partly as *mannitol*, a complex alcohol. The cell walls are composed of an inner layer of cellulose and an outer layer of *algin*, a pectic material unique to the brown algae.

Phaeophytes are exclusively multicellular and sessile. With the exception of three rare freshwater species, all others are marine. Colorless forms are unknown and photosynthesis is the only food-procuring process. These plantlike organisms represent tetrasporine filaments and more highly advanced organizations of the tissue grade of construction (Fig. 9.17). In the filamentous forms (e.g., *Ectocarpus*) and also in some of the more complex tissue-level forms, growth proceeds from cells at the base of the body. In the remaining types, distinct apical cells are present at the upper tip of the body and give rise to all other cells by continual division.

Most of the seaweeds are brown algae. The majority of species live in shallow water and in the intertidal zone, attached to rocky bottoms by holdfasts. Ebb tides may expose the organisms to air for several hours, but their algin coating retains considerable amounts of

FIG. 9.15 Cryptophyceae. The photograph shows an individual of *Cryptomonas*. *(Photograph courtesy of Dr. M. S. Fuller, Brown University.)*

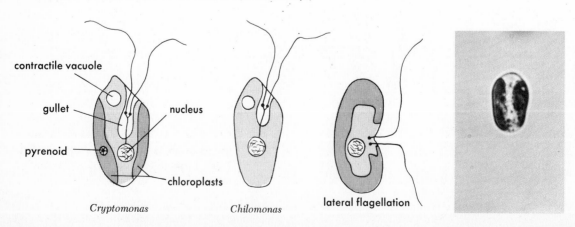

Cryptomonas   *Chilomonas*   lateral flagellation

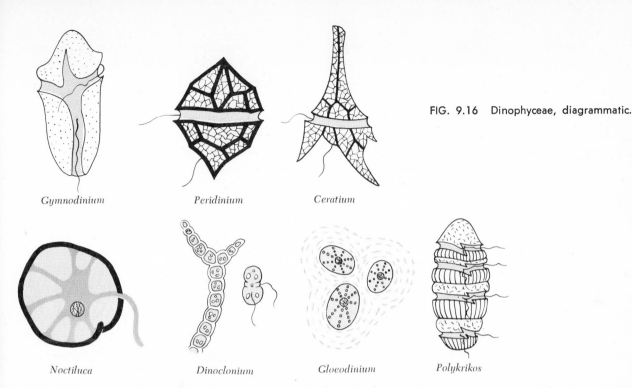

FIG. 9.16 Dinophyceae, diagrammatic.

Gymnodinium   *Peridinium*   *Ceratium*

Noctiluca   *Dinoclonium*   *Gloeodinium*   *Polykrikos*

water and protects the algae from desiccation. The most familiar of the brown algae is probably the rockweed *Fucus*, found along many shores. Undoubtedly the most spectacular of the seaweeds are the giant kelps, growing along the North American west coasts. For example, the kelp *Macrocystis* sometimes attains lengths of more than 100 yards, which makes it longer than a full-grown blue whale. *Laminaria*, the commonest of the kelps, is of worldwide distribution. Torn pieces of it, along with other algae, may often be found washed up on beaches, particularly after a storm. We may note that brown algae are the source of many

FIG. 9.17 Brown algae. Left to right, *Fucus, Ascophyllum, Laminaria, Macrocystis.* In left middle, note the conspicuous air bladders. In right middle and far right, note holdfasts, stipes (stalks), and leaflike blades (considerably bunched up in far right). *(Far left, left middle, and right middle, Jean Carel and Larousse Publishing Co., Paris; far right, General Biological Supply House, Inc.)*

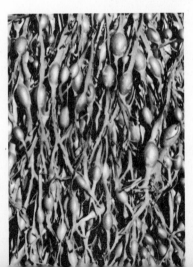

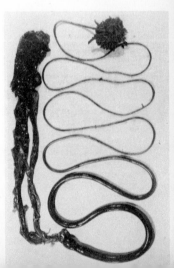

substances useful to man, e.g., iodine, which the algae concentrate, and algin, which finds wide use in many manufacturing processes (e.g., ice cream). Because of this, extensive kelp beds in shallow waters are harvested regularly by special cutting and collecting machines.

THE RED LINE
PHYLUM RHODOPHYTA: RED ALGAE
(about 3,000 species)

The members of this phylum possess chlorophylls *a* and *d*, carotenes, xanthophylls (one of which is lutein), and the pigments *r-phycocyanin* and *r-phycoerythrin*. The last two occur uniquely in this phylum, and they are chemically not the same as similarly named pigments in the blue-green algae. Red algae (Fig. 9.18) store food in the form of *floridean starch*, chemically very much like glycogen but with somewhat different physical properties. The cell walls are composed of an inner layer of cellulose and an outer layer of pectin. Some rhodophytes, particularly the *stony coralline algae* (e.g., *Corallina*), deposit calcium compounds on their outer surfaces. Such algae contribute importantly to the formation of coral reefs.

The cells of the simpler red algae are typically uninucleate, but in the larger forms they are usually multinucleate. Some red algae are parasitic and these are colorless or very nearly so, containing very few chloroplasts. All red algae are sessile. A few genera are unicellular (e.g., *Porphyridium*), but most are multicellular. Like the brown algae, the red algae represent filamentous and more advanced tetrasporine organizations. In some cases, growth by increase in cell number is accomplished by the division of virtually all cells of the organism. In other cases, distinct apical cells are alone specialized for continued division. The evolutionary origin of the red algae is difficult to trace. They are not obviously related to any of the other algal phyla and must have arisen, in ways unknown to us, from some early ancestral unicellular stocks.

Red algae are exclusively marine. They live in somewhat deeper water than the brown algae. The red pigment *r-phycoerythrin* appears to be an adaptation to this dimmer environment; *r-phycoerythrin* absorbs blue light particularly well, and the "blue" wavelengths of sunlight actually penetrate deeper into water than "red" wavelengths. Indeed, *r-phycoerythrin* has been found to play an important auxiliary role in the photosynthesis of these algae. Rhodophytes are lacier and more delicate than the sturdy brown algae. The latter are adapted to withstand pounding surf, but in deeper water the red algae are not so subject to wave action.

Some of the red algae are used commercially. The pectin of the genus *Gelidium* is the source of agar-agar, which is used as a medium for culturing microorganisms. *Porphyra, Rhodymenia,* and *Chondrus crispus,* the Irish moss, are among several types prized as vegetables in various parts of the world.

FIG. 9.18   Red algae. Left, *Porphyridium*, a unicellular type. Middle, *Corallina*, one of the stony coralline types. Right, *Polysiphonia*, a highly branched, delicately structured type. *(Left, courtesy of Dr. M. S. Fuller, Brown University; middle and right, General Biological Supply House, Inc.)*

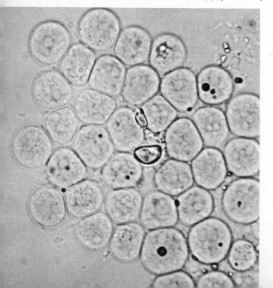

The probable evolutionary relationships of all the algal groups are outlined in Fig. 9.19.

PROTOZOA

Whereas algae are far more plantlike than animallike, protozoa are far more animallike than plantlike. These organisms are entirely without chlorophyll, and their nutrition is accomplished variously by holotrophic bulk feeding, by saprotrophism, and by symbiosis. Because the evolution of protozoa was characterized by a loss of group-identifying pigments, it is difficult to determine the detailed ancestry of these organisms. There is little question, however, that protozoa are descendants of the ancestral unicellular protists described earlier in this chapter. By loss of photosynthesis, such ancestral types may have given rise to protozoa early and directly, or later and indirectly, via various algal groups.

The unicellular condition is almost universal, but a few protozoan genera form colonies. As a group, therefore, protozoa have largely exploited the unicellular motile ways of life of the protistan ancestors, without developing any of the sessile coccoid and tetrasporine patterns so characteristic of algae. Two main lines of protozoa are flagellate, and in one of them the flagella are shortened to cilia; these two groups are the *Mastigophora*, or flagellate protozoa, and the *Ciliophora*, or ciliate protozoa. A third line is amoeboid; it

FIG. 9.19 The probable evolutionary affinities of all major algal divisions. The letters in the diagram indicate the types of chlorophyll present.

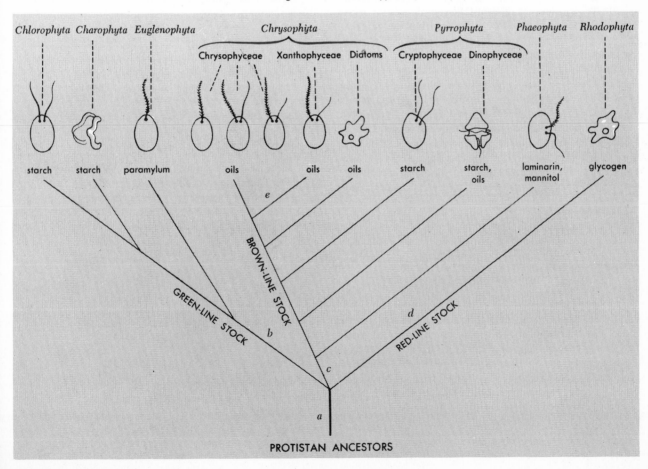

comprises the *Rhizopoda*. In a fourth line, the *Sporozoa*, the members are probably derived from flagellate and amoeboid stocks, but today they are entirely parasitic and their active locomotion is therefore greatly restricted. In all four groups, encapsulated states occur as temporary phases of given life cycles.

In traditional taxonomy, protozoa are ranked as a single phylum and each of the four groups above forms a class. However, the distinctions among the four groups are probably great enough that each should perhaps be accorded independent phylum rank. Protozoa as a whole then become a superphylum, like algae. The number of existing protozoan species has been underestimated fairly consistently. Figures often quoted are in the order of 15,000, but there are known to be more than that many foraminiferan species alone. Moreover, very many animals harbor at least one unique parasitic protozoan species, which means that protozoa could well number in the hundreds of thousands of species. As a conservative figure, at least 100,000 species of protozoa may be presumed to exist.

The protozoan cell is either naked or is surrounded by a nonrigid cuticle composed of chitin or chitinlike substances. Cellulose is not present. In many cases, shells of various inorganic compounds are secreted as external skeletons. Foods are stored as glycogen and fats. Many protozoa are free-living, but many in each phylum are symbiotic and particularly parasitic. As noted, Sporozoa are exclusively parasitic. In free-living flagellate and ciliate types, gullets are usually well developed; rhizopod protozoa use pseudopodia as feeding structures. Contractile vacuoles are present in most cases. Protozoa are largely uninucleate, but all ciliates and some amoeboid types are multinucleate, often highly so.

PHYLUM MASTIGOPHORA: FLAGELLATE PROTOZOA

Also called *zooflagellates*, these organisms are generally regarded as the most primitive groups of protozoa. The ancestors of the group may have been close kin to the early photosynthesizing flagellate protists which gave rise to the algae. In addition, however, numerous zooflagellates may have arisen later from some of the Chrysophyta and other established algal groups. In any of these possible derivations, loss of chlorophyll must have been a first step, and holotrophic, saprotrophic, or symbiotic ways of life must have been adopted subsequently. Parasitic zooflagellates are particularly common today.

The most primitive zooflagellates now in existence are largely free-living and holotrophic, and they greatly resemble colorless flagellate algae. For example, the collar flagellate *Proterospongia* resembles certain flagellate chrysophytes. *Proterospongia* feeds on debris and microorganisms. Food is trapped within the collar of these cells, and the flagellum then creates a current which sweeps the food toward the cell body, where it is engulfed. Groups of individual collar flagellates may form loose colonial aggregates of various types (Fig. 9.20). In many of the free-living zooflagellates, the flagella may be lost temporarily and the organisms then become amoeboid. In some cases, moreover, the flagellate and amoeboid conditions are associated so intimately that an organism is flagellate and amoeboid simultaneously; the front end of the cell bears a flagellum and the hind end produces pseudopodia. Such interrelations between the two motile states support the generally accepted conclusion that at least some flagellate and amoeboid protozoa may be related very closely. Indeed, the Mastigophora and Rhizopoda are sometimes classified together as a single group.

Free-living zooflagellate stocks undoubtedly gave rise to the many symbiotic forms. These are highly specialized and adapted to specific hosts, and any algal

FIG. 9.20 The colonial zooflagellate *Proterospongia*. These cells are embedded in secreted jelly. Photo of glass model. (*American Museum of Natural History.*)

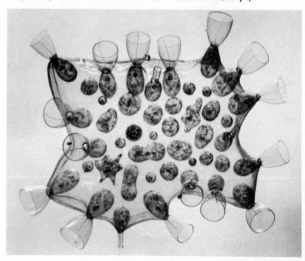

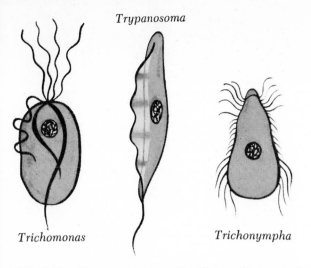

Trypanosoma

Trichomonas

Trichonympha

FIG. 9.21   Three types of zooflagellates, diagrammatic.

characteristics have become largely obscured (Fig. 9.21). For example, *Trichonympha,* a wood-digesting symbiont in the gut of termites, possesses hundreds of flagella inserted in enlarged, ribbon-shaped kinetosomes. Interestingly, this type of superflagellation has developed also in the motile sperm cells of primitive coniferous plants (e.g., cycads, ginkgoes). The same adaptive forces may have oriented this parallel evolution. Zooflagellates like *Trichonympha* must move through the thick, viscous contents of a termite gut; the plant sperms, analogously, move through the thick, viscous living substance of female reproductive organs. In both cases, numerous "paddles" in the form of flagella are adaptively useful. Other specialized symbiotic zooflagellates include, for example, *Trichomonas,* a commensal in the gut of man and other vertebrates, and *Trypanosoma,* different species of which live parasitically in the bloods of various vertebrates. One such species causes sleeping sickness in man.

PHYLUM RHIZOPODA: AMOEBOID PROTOZOA

Also known as *Sarcodina,* these organisms are almost certainly derived from quite a number of evolutionary sources. As noted, likely ancestors probably include free-living zooflagellates and algal groups such as Chrysophyta and Dinophyceae. Sarcodine protozoa comprise the **Lobosa,** characterized by inconstant and changing body contours; the **Heliozoa,** which have permanent shapes and pseudopodia stiffened internally by fine solid spikes; the **Foraminifera,** which possess calcareous shells; and the **Radiolaria,** equipped with silica shells.

Some of the Lobosa are naked cells, and among these are the familiar *Amoeba* and other "typical" amoebae. The group includes parasitic forms such as *Entamoeba histolytica,* which causes amoebic dysentery in man. Other Lobosa enclose their bodies in various shells. For example, a chitinous housing is present in *Arcella,* the organism extruding pseudopods through an opening in the shell. *Diffugia* cements tiny sand particles to a chitinous envelope (Fig. 9.22). The Heliozoa are so named because stiff spikes radiate from the spherical cell body like sun rays. Covering the spikes is pseudopodial cytoplasm on which food is trapped and engulfed. The Foraminifera manufacture calcareous shells of many different forms, all resembling tiny snail shells (Fig. 9.23). Pseudopods are extruded through holes in these shells, hence the name of the

FIG. 9.22   Sarcodina. The photograph shows *Pelomyxa,* a multinucleate sarcodine protozoon related to *Amoeba.* A representative of *Amoeba* is shown just above *Pelomyxa.* In both organisms, note the food-trapping pseudopodia. Some paramecia are shown on the right; these ciliate protozoa are favorite food organisms of *Pelomyxa.* (Photograph, Carolina Biological Supply Co.)

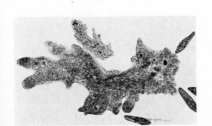

Arcella

Diffugia

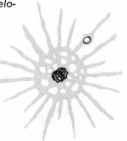

Heliozoan

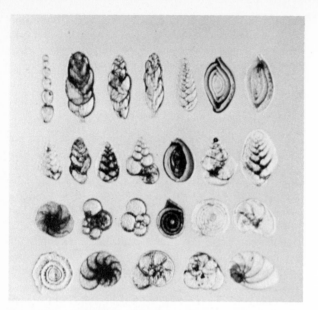 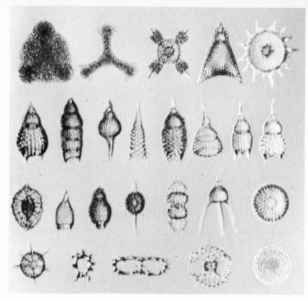

FIG. 9.23 Sarcodina. Left, Foraminifera. Right, Radiolaria. The shells of the former are made of calcium salts; those of the latter, of silicon compounds. (General Biological Supply House, Inc.)

group, which means "hole bearers." Foraminiferan shells may accumulate in given tracts of ocean floor in such numbers that they form the predominant bottom deposit in such regions. This is true also of the silica shells of the Radiolaria. Foraminiferan deposits may become transformed into chalk; radiolarian deposits, into flint. When either of these is uplifted geologically, it may contribute massively to the formation of land (e.g., the chalk cliffs of Dover).

PHYLUM CILIOPHORA: CILIATE PROTOZOA

These organisms are undoubtedly the most advanced and structurally the most complex protozoa. An evolutionary derivation of the phylum from flagellate, particularly zooflagellate, stocks is likely; organisms with traits intermediate between those of zooflagellates and ciliates are known. The Ciliophora include two main groups: **Ciliata,** which are permanently ciliated, and **Suctoria,** which are ciliated only during young stages.

The Ciliata (Fig. 9.24) move and feed by means of their cilia, which in most cases are arranged in orderly rows. In the so-called **holotrichous** ciliates, the ciliary rows are longitudinal and the cilia are of roughly equal size all over the cellular body. *Paramecium* is a familiar representative of this group. In **heterotrichous** ciliates, the ciliary rows are also longitudinal but the cilia in the gullet region are longer and thicker than those elsewhere on the body. A representative of this group is *Stentor*. In **hypotrichous** ciliates, typified by *Euplotes*, for example, ciliary rows are not present. Instead, localized groups of thick cilia, here called *cirri*, occur on the underside of the flattened body. In all the three groups just named, cell division is transverse; i.e., anterior and posterior daughter cells are formed. This is not the case in a fourth group of ciliates, the **peritrichous** types, of which *Vorticella* is a member. These organisms possess transverse ciliary rows and cell division cuts the body longitudinally into left and right offspring.

In all ciliates, the cilia originate from kinetosomes which are components of a complex system of intracellular conductile fibrils. These coordinate the beat of the cilia. All ciliates are also uniquely characterized by the possession of *two* kinds of nuclei. The so-called **micronucleus** functions principally in sexual processes; the **macronucleus** controls metabolism, development, and all other cellular processes (Fig. 9.25). Several of

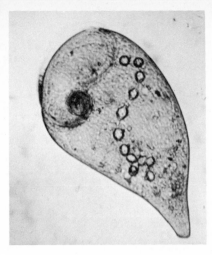

Euplotes

Vorticella

FIG. 9.24 Ciliates. Far left, the holotrich *Paramecium*. Left middle, the heterotrich *Stentor*. Right middle, the hypotrich *Euplotes*. Far right, the peritrich *Vorticella*. At far left, note the elaborate surface, including cilia, the gullet pocket leading into the organism from the anterior (upper) end, the food-containing vacuoles, and one of the nuclei, at mid-body. At left middle, note prominent chain of nuclei, the dark anterior whorl of the gullet, and the posterior holdfast. *(Far left, American Museum of Natural History; left middle, Dr. Roman Vishniac, New York.)*

both kinds of nuclei may be present in a single organism. This nuclear specialization is paralleled by a very high degree of cytoplasmic specialization. For example, in addition to the permanent ciliary apparatus and its conductile fibrils, ciliates typically also possess permanent gullets, excretory vacuoles, and contractile fibrils.

Some ciliates are sessile, either as solitary or as colonial forms, and very many are symbiotic, particularly parasitic. Suctoria are organized quite like ciliates generally, except that as adults they are sessile and unciliated. They feed by means of tentaclelike protrusions which capture and suck up the contents of other protozoa. Cell division produces offspring which are ciliated and free-swimming. Such young eventually settle and become adults by shedding the cilia (Fig. 9.26).

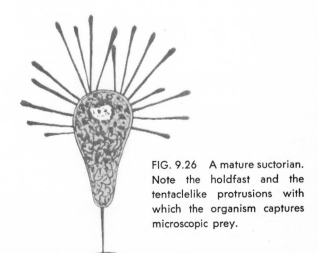

FIG. 9.25 *Paramecium*, stained to reveal the macronucleus (large dark central body) and the micronucleus (small dark body partly overlapping the macronucleus on the top). *(Carolina Biological Supply Co.)*

FIG. 9.26 A mature suctorian. Note the holdfast and the tentaclelike protrusions with which the organism captures microscopic prey.

PHYLUM SPOROZOA: SPORE-FORMING PROTOZOA

These organisms display affinities to both the flagellate and the amoeboid protozoa, and this phylum too probably has had multiple origins. But it is uncertain whether Sporozoa arose directly from algal types or indirectly via protozoan types. In adaptation to their exclusively parasitic ways of life, their life cycles have become exceedingly complex. This has largely obscured any resemblance to possible ancestral stocks.

FIG. 9.27   The life cycle of the sporozoan malarial parasite *Plasmodium*. The organism is injected by an *Anopheles* mosquito into the human blood stream in the form of flagellate sporozoite cells (1). Sporozoites enter red corpuscles, transform into amoeboid cells, and undergo multiple fission (2) to (4). The corpuscles then rupture and release the amoeboid cells, a process accompanied by a characteristic attack of fever. Amoeboid cells then may reinfect other red corpuscles, undergo fission, and by repeated reinfections bring about repeated fever cycles (5), (6). Some of the amoeboid cells eventually transform into gamete producers (7), (8), and these are sucked up by a mosquito, along with blood. In the gut of the mosquito, gametes form, fertilization occurs, and the amoeboid zygote penetrates through the gut wall into the blood of the insect (9), (10). Here the zygote encysts, undergoes multiple fission, and forms many flagellate sporozoites. These escape from the cyst, find their way into the salivary glands of the mosquito, and are then injected into human blood when the insect bites man.

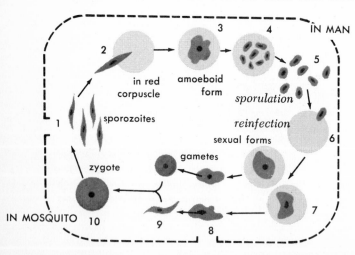

As indicated by the name of these protozoa, their life cycles include spore-forming stages; i.e., a single cell may undergo *multiple fission* and become divided up simultaneously into numerous smaller cells. Such spore cells distribute the species and continue the life cycle. In some Sporozoa the spores are naked and amoeboid; in others, the spores are encapsulated. The most familiar sporozoan genus is undoubtedly *Plasmodium*, various species of which cause malaria in mammals and birds. In human malaria, the *Anopheles* mosquito is the specific intermediate host of the sporozoan parasite. The life cycle of this sporozoan is outlined in Fig. 9.27.

SLIME MOLDS

PHYLUM MYXOPHYTA

Class Myxomyceteae: multinucleate slime molds with flagellate swarmers

Class Acrasieae: multicellular slime molds with amoeboid swarmers

Class Labyrinthuleae: multicellular slime molds without fruiting bodies

This phylum represents the culmination of the colonial amoeboid state: the vegetative body of a slime mold is a naked, creeping, amoeboid mass, in some cases as much as 1 ft in diameter.

Because certain stages of the life cycle exhibit protozoan traits and others fungal traits, there has been much discussion in the past as to whether slime molds are a special group of protozoa or a special group of fungi, whether they are more plantlike than animallike or vice versa, and thus whether they are within the province of botanists or zoologists. This uncertainty has been reflected in the many ways in which slime molds have been classified. However, all such uncertainties disappear once it is recognized that slime molds are *Protista* first and foremost, hence organisms which by definition share many traits with all other members of this category. And since they are also *colorless* Protista, they automatically have much in common with the other colorless Protista, namely, the protozoa and the fungi. Slime molds actually feature their own special combination of common protistan traits and newly developed traits. The predominant characteristic resulting from this combination of traits is that of a highly advanced amoeboid colony.

The evolutionary origin of the phylum remains obscure. Any ancestral group or groups, photosynthetic or not, which could have given rise to protozoan amoebae, or even to protozoan flagellates, or to primitive fungi, could qualify also as the ancestral stocks of the slime molds. Inasmuch as the ones are unknown, the others are still unknown as well. From the nature of existing slime molds, it is highly probable that a multiple origin must be postulated for the phylum, with a different derivation for at least each class.

Adult slime molds of the class Myxomyceteae exist in the form of **plasmodia,** naked amoeboid sheets with irregular and slowly shifting contours (Fig. 9.28). Each such plasmodium contains hundreds or thousands of nuclei, but internal cell boundaries are absent and the whole organism is a continuous living mass. Some myxomycetes are parasitic in flowering plants, but most are free-living in moist wooded areas, where they creep over fallen leaves and rotting logs like supergiant amoebae (e.g., *Physarum*).

When a myxomycete plasmodium reproduces, its amoeboid life ceases and for a time it becomes rather funguslike. More specifically, the plasmodial mass flows together into one or more heaped mounds or grows into one or more upright stalks each of which

FIG. 9.29   Fruiting bodies of the slime mold *Arcyria.* (General Biological Supply House, Inc.)

develops a bulbous upper tip. Such structures are *fruiting bodies,* or *sporangia* (Fig. 9.29). Within a fruiting body spore cells then form, each typically containing one nucleus and its own wall. The spores secrete protective capsules and eventually escape from the fruiting bodies and scatter. In suitable environments they may germinate and produce *swarmers,* i.e., single flagellate cells. Such cells greatly resemble colorless algal flagellates or protozoan zooflagellates. Swarm cells may undergo successive cell divisions, and eventually they fuse pairwise, i.e., undergo a sexual process. Thereafter the flagella are cast off and each cell becomes exclusively amoeboid. Such amoebae subsequently grow into adult vegetative plasmodia in one of two ways. Either a single amoeba divides its nucleus repeatedly, the cytoplasm enlarging but remaining undivided, or many sister amoebae fuse together and lose their cell boundaries, cytoplasmic growth and nuclear divisions then following.

Slime molds in the class Acrasieae resemble the myxomycetes in many respects, but they feature several distinct characteristics. The adult vegetative body is a **pseudoplasmodium;** i.e., it is a true cellular colony composed of hundreds or thousands of uninucleate amoeboid cells which do not lose their cell boundaries. Second, stalked fruiting bodies are again formed, but the method of formation is unique. In a stalk just being developed, the inner cells become immobile and cells around the young stalk stream upward. Some of these cells then add themselves to the lower completed por-

FIG. 9.28   Plasmodium of the myxomycete *Physarum.* (Carolina Biological Supply Co.)

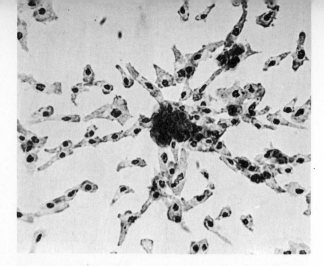

FIG. 9.30 The amoeboid cells of a slime mold, *Dictyostelium*, migrating together and eventually forming a compact aggregate. A reproductive structure will then develop from the aggregate. *(Courtesy of Dr. J. T. Bonner, J. Exp. Zool., vol. 106, p. 7.)*

tions of the stalk and become immobile as well. Other cells on the outside move higher and some of these add themselves to the stalk in turn. In this manner the stalk builds from the base upward. Eventually, cells moving upward along the outside of the completed stalk accumulate at the tip in the form of a bulbous sporangium.

Spores are produced as in myxomycetes. However, the products of spore germination are never flagellate, but are solitary uninucleate amoeboid cells. Such amoebae divide and increase in number. Eventually they all migrate into a common multicellular mass,

FIG. 9.31 *Labyrinthula.* Single cell on slime track on left, colony on right.

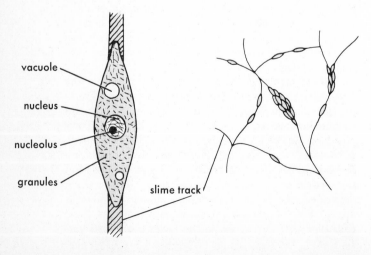

vacuole
nucleus
nucleolus
granules
slime track

which represents a new pseudoplasmodial generation (Fig. 9.30). It has been shown, particularly in *Dictyostelium,* that a hormonal substance, **acrasin,** is secreted by some of the migratory amoebae. This substance affects and orients other amoebae in the vicinity and guides their migration into a compact aggregate (see Chap. 27).

Organisms in the class Labyrinthuleae are poorly known. Multicellular pseudoplasmodia appear to be typical, but fruiting bodies are not. Motile unicellular swarmers are again a phase of the life cycle. These swarmers possess eyespots, suggesting algal affinities. On the other hand, the locomotion of the swarmers is neither flagellate nor amoeboid. Indeed, clearly identifiable locomotor structures are not visible at all and the cells appear to be sliding along a surface without noticeable change of shape. Just how their propulsion is accomplished is unknown (Fig. 9.31).

FUNGI

PHYLUM MYCOPHYTA
(90,000 species)

Class Phycomycetes: nonseptate fungi
    water molds, downy mildews, blights, bread molds
Class Ascomycetes: sac fungi
    yeasts, molds, powdery mildews, truffles, cup fungi
Class Basidiomycetes: club fungi
    rusts, smuts, bracket fungi, mushrooms, toadstools, puffballs, stinkhorns
Class Fungi Imperfecti: provisional collection of types with incompletely known reproductive patterns, not yet assignable to any of the above groups.

This very large and highly diversified phylum has representatives in almost every available habitat on earth, and many fungi are of major economic or medical significance to man. Fungi are partly free-living saprotrophs, partly symbionts of all possible types. They store foods in the form of glycogen and as lipids. Primitive members of the division are aquatic, and they produce flagellate reproductive cells. More advanced fungi are terrestrial, with nonmotile reproductive cells dispersed passively by wind, water, and animals.

As a group, fungi may be regarded as a culmination of the sessile *coccoid* state in protistan evolution. That is, the vegetative body of a fungus is multinucleate, without internal cell boundaries. Phycomycetes are without internal partitions of any kind; in the other classes internal walls do develop, but these partitions, or **septa,** are incomplete, leaving pores through which the living substance may flow (Fig. 9.32). Thus the fungus body is always a continuous mass which may grow in size and increase the number of nuclei by nuclear divisions. Cytoplasmic divisions do not occur in the vegetative state. True cells, with complete individual boundaries and one nucleus each, are formed only during reproduction.

The living mass of a fungus is bounded externally by a rigid wall composed of cellulose in some of the primitive fungi and of chitin in others. Excepting only some of the primitive fungi, which are more or less spherical, the basic unit of the fungus body has the form of a tubular, often branched filament. Such a unit is called a **hypha.** As it grows, it may extend in length and branch increasingly. Numerous hyphae may be intermeshed into an irregular network, a so-called **mycelium** (Fig. 9.33). Hyphae may also pack together in more orderly patterns, producing, for example, structured bodies like mushrooms.

As in the case of all other protists, the evolutionary origin of fungi is obscure. Traditional hypotheses regard either protozoa or algae as the ancestral stocks, but there is really no reason why slime molds should not also be included as possible ancestors. For just as slime molds share traits with protozoa and fungi and also algae, so fungi share traits with protozoa and algae and also slime molds. Such resemblances merely indicate the protistan character of all these groups. Actually, the flagellate stages of the primitive fungi strongly suggest a multiple origin of the phylum. Figure 9.34 outlines the probable evolutionary interrelations of groups within the phylum.

Class Phycomycetes

This is undoubtedly the most primitive fungal class. Within it, the most primitive fungi in turn are the aquatic Phycomycetes. Some of these are free-living, some are parasitic.

FIG. 9.32 The incomplete partitions in the hyphae of the ascomycete *Neurospora*. Note the continuity of the cytoplasm through the pore in the transverse partition. *(Courtesy of Dr. A. J. Shatkin and Dr. E. L. Tatum, Rockefeller Institute, and J. Biophys. Biochem. Cytol., vol. 6, p. 423.)*

FIG. 9.33   A mycelium of a fungus. *(Courtesy of Dr. M. S. Fuller, Brown University.)*

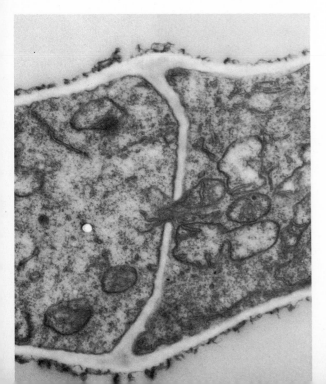

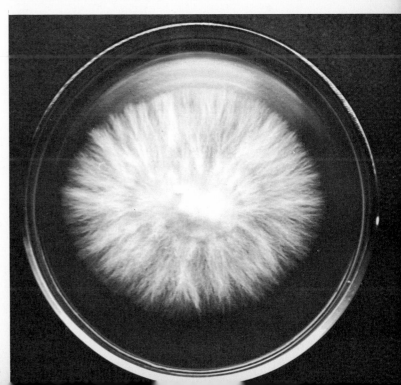

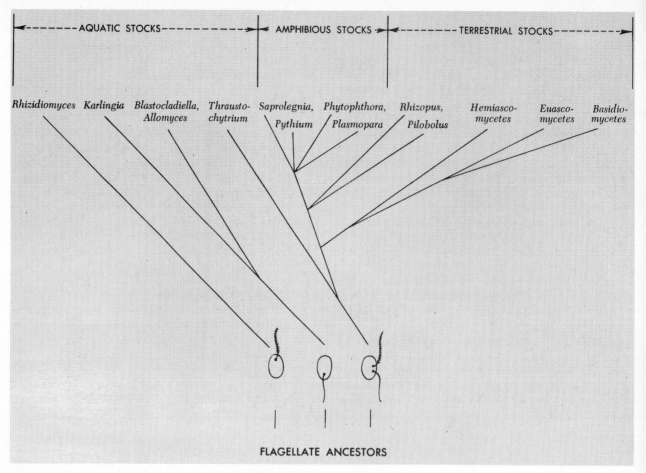

FIG. 9.34 Probable evolutionary interrelations of various fungal groups.

In the aquatic Phycomycetes (Fig. 9.35), the vegetative body is often microscopic and consists in many cases of little more than a multinucleate cell. In some cases such a body is drawn out at one point into fine branching extensions, so-called **rhizoids,** which air particularly in nutrient uptake. Cell walls are composed either of chitin only or of chitin and cellulose or of cellulose only. When such a fungus reproduces, the body becomes subdivided internally into numerous cells, each containing one nucleus. Such spore cells develop one or two flagella each and are then known as **zoospores.** They disperse by swimming in water. Eventually they settle, lose the flagella, and grow into new adult fungi by repeated nuclear divisions.

Other members of the aquatic Phycomycetes are structurally more complex. In some (e.g., *Blastocladiella*), the body consists of two multinucleate compartments, one vegetative and functioning in nutrient uptake, the other reproductive and producing zoospores. In still more advanced types, filamentous hyphae with branches are in evidence and in many cases such hyphae are formed into mycelial meshworks.

These structurally more complex Phycomycetes (see Fig. 9.35) illustrate a progressive transition from strictly aquatic to amphibious to strictly terrestrial ways of life. For example, *Saprolegnia* is a water mold growing saprotrophically in calm fresh waters. But this fungus may also live in well-irrigated soils. By contrast, *Pythium*, some species of which cause root rot in young vascular plants, is found in soil more often than in bodies of water. Yet regardless of where they are found, fungi like *Saprolegnia* and *Pythium* are still basically aquatic types and they produce zoospores.

Distinctly amphibious types are represented, for example, by *Phytophthora*, best known as the causative agent of late blight in potatoes. Under favorable conditions, this fungus may develop sporangia which produce zoospores. But when lack of environmental water or too high a temperature prevents swimming zoospores from carrying out their dispersal function, the sporangia do not produce zoospores. Instead, they may become detached from the fungus and, after passive dispersal, may later produce hyphae called **germ tubes.** Such germ tubes grow directly into new fungi. Similarly adapted to either aquatic or terrestrial conditions is one species of *Plasmopara*, which causes downy mildew in grapes. This fungus has sporangia which may form either zoospores or germ tubes. But another species of *Plasmopara*, causative agent of downy mildew in onions, does not develop zoospores at all. It forms only sporangia which grow by formation of germ tubes. It

may therefore reproduce without any free water and it is fully terrestrial.

The most advanced members of the Phycomycetes are also strictly terrestrial. They form neither zoospores nor germ tubes, but they always produce nonmotile, encapsulated spores which are well adapted to dispersal on dry land. The bread mold *Rhizopus* illustrates the pattern. This fungus grows on stale bread as a mycelium, and many stalked sporangia develop from it as upright outgrowths. At such a stage, the bread appears to be covered with white fuzz. The multinucleate mass within each sporangium then subdivides into numerous uninucleate spore cells, and these encapsulate. During spore maturation, the sporangia turn black externally. The spores eventually break free and become scattered passively. In suitable environments, each spore germinates into a new mycelium (see also Chap. 24).

Many fungi closely related to the bread molds grow saprotrophically on animal dung. One of these is *Pilobolus*, the "ballthrowing" fungus as its name indi-

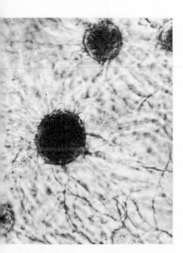

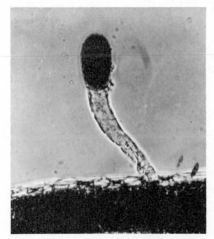

FIG. 9.35 Aquatic Phycomycetes. Top left, *Karlingia*; note the rhizoids radiating out from the globular unicellular fungus body. Top right, *Blastocladiella*; note the terminal sporangium on the hypha. Bottom left, *Saprolegnia*; a terminal portion of a hypha is shown. Bottom middle, *Phytophthora*; note the globular sporangia on the hyphae. Bottom right, *Pythium*; note the mass of zoospores just escaped from the sporangium. (Courtesy of Dr. R. Emerson, University of California, Berkeley, and Mycologia, vol. 50, p. 589.)

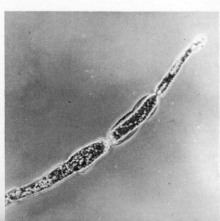

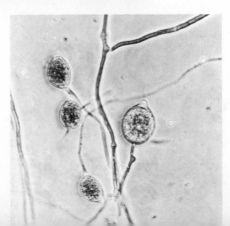

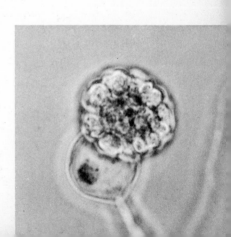

cates (Fig. 9.36). Pilobolus forms mycelia on horse dung. Governed by the daily cycle of light and darkness, sporangia develop the night before spores are to be released. At first light the next morning, the spores are ready to be dispersed. The tip of a maturing sporangium has then attained an angle of 45° from the horizontal, the exact angle at which ballistic projectiles may travel the greatest distance. Now the cell just below the mass of mature spores squirts a jet of water against the spores, which thereby become scattered. If they land on grass, a horse may ingest them. Such spores then pass through the alimentary tract of the animal and reemerge with fresh dung. On it the spores subsequently germinate into new mycelia.

Class Ascomycetes

In all probability, this class arose from a relatively advanced ancestral stock of the terrestrial Phycomycetes. Ascomycetes are similarly terrestrial and motile stages are absent. As already noted, the hyphae are incompletely septate; i.e., transverse partitions with central holes develop at intervals along a hyphal fila-

FIG. 9.36 Terrestrial Phycomycetes. The photograph shows several sporangium-bearing stalks of *Pilobolus*, growing on horse dung. *(Courtesy of Dr. I. K. Ross, Yale University.)*

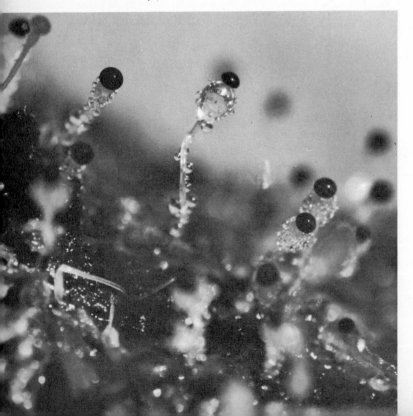

ment. The living mass between two consecutive septa most often contains one nucleus, but in many cases more than one is present.

The spores of Ascomycetes are usually of at least two types (see also Chap. 24). Most members of the class form **conidia,** spore cells which are divided off, often in chainlike series, from the ends of hyphae or specially modified hyphae. But regardless of whether or not they produce conidia, all Ascomycetes form **ascospores** within elongated or oval sacs called **asci** (Fig. 9.37). Such asci develop only after fertilization, i.e., after fusion of a male and a female sex cell. The resulting fusion product, a *zygote,* then either gives rise directly to a single ascus or produces a radial array of special hyphae each of which forms an ascus at its end. Within an ascus the ascospores later develop.

Ascomycetes are grouped into two major subclasses on the basis of the number of asci formed by the zygote. Fungi in which a single ascus develops from the zygote are members of the subclass *Hemiascomycetes.* The best known of these fungi are undoubtedly the *yeasts,* long important to man in the manufacture of bread and wine. Most yeasts are secondarily reduced, unicellular fungi. But some do develop the mycelial body, and nearly all produce the ascospores so characteristic of the subclass (Fig. 9.38).

In the second and larger subclass, the *Euascomycetes,* a zygote grows out into several ascus-forming hyphae. These hyphae and their asci are usually more or less packed together and are surrounded by supporting hyphae. The whole complex constitutes a *fruiting body.* Three general types of such fruiting bodies are known (Fig. 9.39). A **cleistothecium** is spherical, without external openings and with asci in the interior arranged either randomly or in some orderly pattern. A **perithecium** is a flask-shaped fruiting body with an opening at the neck of the flask. And an **apothecium** is a cup- or saucer-shaped fruiting body, the asci forming an orderly layer lining the inner surface (Fig. 9.40).

Among the cleistothecial types is *Penicillium,* source of the antibiotic penicillin. Another group in this category comprises the *powdery mildews,* all obligate parasites living in grapes, hops, grasses, roses, apples, and various cereal plants. These fungi are not severely damaging, but by depriving the hosts of food they reduce crop yield, vigor, or both. Perithecial fruiting bodies are formed, for example, in the pink bread mold *Neurospora crassa,* an important laboratory organism which has contributed greatly to our understanding of gene action and metabolism. Of considerable eco-

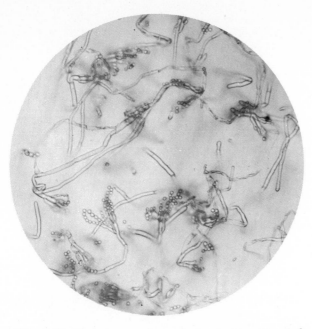

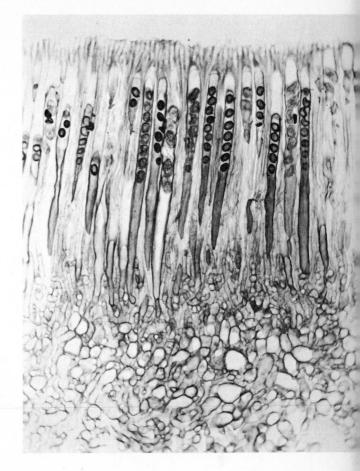

FIG. 9.37 Two types of spores in Ascomycetes. Left, hyphae of *Penicillium*, with conidia formed in chains on many of the terminal branches. Right, layer of asci in a cup fungus, with ascospores in the asci. *(Left, General Biological Supply House, Inc.; right, Carolina Biological Supply Co.)*

nomic significance are perithecial types such as *Cerato-cystis ulmi*, causative agent of the Dutch Elm disease; *Venturia inaequalis*, causative agent of apple scab; *Endothia parasitica*, which has made chestnut trees extinct in North America; and *Claviceps purpurea*, the

FIG. 9.38 Yeast cells. Note budding. *(General Biological Supply House, Inc.)*

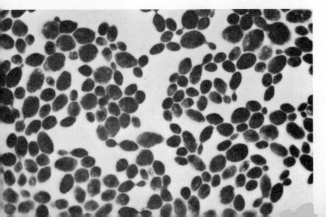

ergot fungus in rye. Apothecial fruiting bodies are characteristic of the cup fungi. Included in this group are *Monolinia fructicola*, which causes brown rot in peaches; the edible *morels;* and the subterranean *truffles*, which are highly prized by gourmets and are hunted in France by specially smell-trained pigs and dogs. The fruiting bodies of truffles are rounded masses with irregular ascus-containing internal cavities.

Lichens, Fungi Imperfecti

Lichens are symbiotic associations of algae and fungi (see Chap. 7). The fungal members are Ascomycetes in the vast majority of cases. Among the algal members are *Nostoc, Gloeocapsa*, and other blue-green algae, as well as various coccoid green algae. In a lichen, the fungus forms a mycelial framework within which the algae are held and supported. Some lichens are crustlike or **crustose;** others are leaflike or **foliose;**

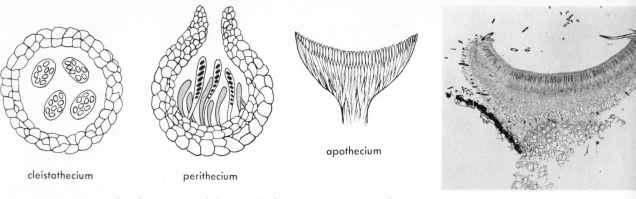

cleistothecium   perithecium   apothecium

FIG. 9.39 Diagram, the three types of fruiting bodies in Ascomycetes. Photo, an apothecium. Note the ascus layer, a high-power view of which is shown in Fig. 9.37. *(Photo, Carolina Biological Supply Co.)*

FIG. 9.40 Euascomycetes. Left, the cup fungus *Peziza* (a section of which is shown in Fig. 9.39). Right, a morel. *(Left, courtesy of Dr. I. K. Ross, Yale University; right, courtesy of New York Botanical Garden.)*

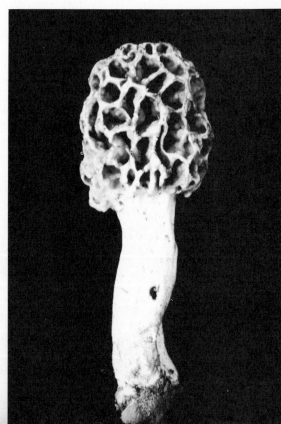

and still others are branching or **fruticose** (Fig. 9.41). They are often epiphytic on trees, but more commonly they live independently on rock. Here they are important soil formers; they aid in the fragmentation of rock surfaces through acids produced by their metabolism and also through acids formed when lichens decay.

Most of the Fungi Imperfecti are probably Ascomycetes too. Fungi in this artificial class are at present known only by their conidial, i.e., spore-forming, stages. Whenever the sexual stages are discovered in a given species, that species may be assigned to one of the three other classes of fungi. In the past, such discoveries have increased the membership of the Ascomycetes most, that of the Basidiomycetes somewhat, and that of the Phycomycetes not at all. Correspondingly, the membership of the Fungi Imperfecti is steadily decreasing.

Class Basidiomycetes

Available evidence suggests that this class of fungi has evolved from ascomycete ancestors, specifically from some early stock of the Euascomycetes. Basidiomycetes are again incompletely septate, with filamentous hyphae forming mycelia and fruiting bodies. The identifying feature of the class is the formation of **basidiospores**, produced on often club-shaped bodies called **basidia** (Fig. 9.42). A basidium is considered by some to be a modified type of ascus. But whereas ascospores develop *inside* an ascus, basidiospores develop on the *outside* of a basidium. Like the growth of asci, that of basidia is similarly contingent on prior fertilization and zygote formation. Sexual processes are rather unique in Basidiomycetes and distinct from those in other fungi and Protista generally. We shall discuss this subject in Chap. 24.

The class contains two principal subclasses. In the *Heterobasidiomycetes,* a basidium is partitioned transversely or longitudinally into two, three, or four cells. Each such cell produces one basidiospore. In the *Homobasidiomycetes,* a basidium is one cell and produces four basidiospores in most cases. Both subclasses are extremely large groups; together they comprise some 25,000 species.

Among the Heterobasidiomycetes are the *jelly fungi,* common saprotrophs on dead tree branches and decaying logs (Fig. 9.43). Much of the fungus body here is a hygroscopic gelatinous mass which swells considerably when wetted. Hyphae within the jelly produce the basidia. The most important Heterobasidiomycetes from an economic standpoint are the *rusts* and *smuts.* Both groups are parasites of vascular plants

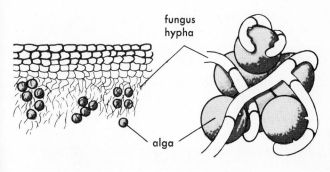

FIG. 9.41 Lichens. Left, a foliose species. Middle, a fruticose species. Right, the interrelation between the algal cells and the fungal hyphae. (*Left, Jean Carel, Paris; middle, courtesy of Dr. M. S. Fuller, Brown University.*)

FIG. 9.42 Types of basidia. Unicellular basidia, as in *A*, are characteristic of the subclass Homobasidiomycetes. Two-, three-, or four-celled basidia, as in *B, C, D*, are characteristic of the subclass Heterobasidiomycetes.

FIG. 9.43 Heterobasidiomycetes. Top, jelly fungus. Bottom, wheat-rust lesions on stems. Right, corn smut. *(Top, courtesy of Dr. C. M. Christensen, University of Minnesota, and University of Minnesota Press; below, right, from E. C. Stakman and G. Harrar, "Principles of Plant Pathology," The Ronald Press Co., New York, 1957.)*

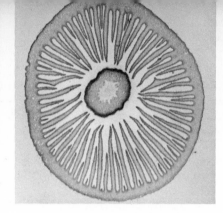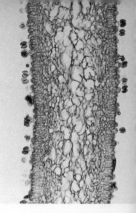

FIG. 9.44 Homobasidiomycetes. Far left, mushroom with gills on the underside. Left middle, a bracket fungus. Right middle, section through the cap of a mushroom, showing the arrangement of the gills. Far right, close-up of a gill. Note the mycelial meshwork in the interior, and the spores, attached to basidia and projecting from the surface. *(Far left and left middle, courtesy of Dr. M. S. Fuller, Brown University; right middle and far right, General Biological Supply House, Inc.)*

(e.g., black stem wheat rust, corn smut; see also Chap. 24). The Homobasidiomycetes include the best known fungi of all, namely, the *mushrooms* (Fig. 9.44). A typical mushroom of commerce is *Agaricus campestris*. The mycelium of this fungus, present in soil, develops stalked fruiting bodies with caps, on the underside of which are radially arranged **gills**. Club-shaped basidia are exposed along the surfaces of the gills. Mature basidiospores fall into the soil, where they germinate into new mycelia. After sexual processes

have taken place, numerous hyphae of such mycelia develop cooperatively into the stalked mushrooms.

Not all mushrooms possess gills and not all are soil inhabitants. Very many are parasitic on woody plants, e.g., the *bracket fungi,* and many others bring about decay of fallen trees. Apart from mushrooms, Homobasidiomycetes also include *puffballs, stinkhorns,* and *bird's nest fungi* (Fig. 9.45). All these are saprotrophs, and their basidia are formed within closed, rounded fruiting bodies. Spore release can take place

FIG. 9.45 Homobasidiomycetes. Left, puffball. Middle, stinkhorns. Right, bird's-nest fungi. The globular bodies within the latter are reproductive dispersal units. *(Left, R. H. Noailles, Museum of Natural History, Paris; middle, courtesy of Dr. C. M. Christensen, University of Minnesota; right, courtesy of Dr. H. J. Brodie, University of Alberta, and Nat. Hist. Mag., vol. 61, p. 407.)*

only when the fruiting bodies decompose or when they break open. Such mechanical release is brought about by the spores themselves, for they are frequently so numerous that masses of them erupt right through the outer layers of a fruiting body. Indeed, giant puffballs, which may reach diameters of several feet, probably have the distinction of being reproductively the most prolific of all living organisms. A single giant puffball may manufacture as many as 100 *trillion* spores. It has been estimated that were each of these spores to grow into a mature fungus, a mass of living matter nearly 1,000 times the earth's size would be produced.

The probable evolutionary interrelations of all major protistan groups are outlined in Fig. 9.46.

FIG. 9.46 The probable interrelations of the various main groups within the Protista. The horizontal line separates photosynthetic forms below from the non-photosynthetic forms above. Where a phylum contains both photosynthetic and non-photosynthetic types, the name of the group appears with the more abundant types. The letters in conjunction with the algal groups refer to the variants of chlorophyll present. Note that, in virtually all cases, exact interrelations are not yet known and that the lines of interconnection must be regarded as provisional. Note also that the various algal groups have undoubtedly contributed to the evolution of the other protistan lines, interrelations which are not indicated.

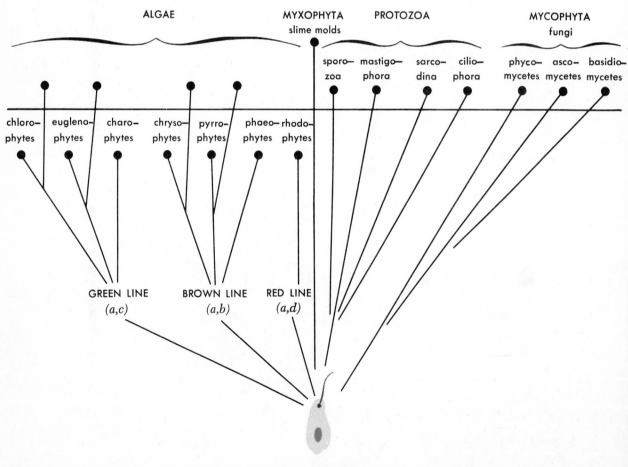

ancestral protista

REVIEW QUESTIONS

1. What are the unifying features of the Protista? Why should the various protistan groups no longer be classified simply as "plants" and "animals"? Describe the probable ancestral type from which Protista are believed to have evolved.

2. What are the group characteristics of the algae? What are the special characteristics of the green-line, brown-line, and red-line algal groups? Review here the (a) pigments, (b) food-storage compounds, and (c) cell-wall compounds of these organisms.

3. What is the probable evolutionary significance of pairs of algae where one is photosynthetic and the other not? Give specific examples of such pairs for three or four algal phyla.

4. In what ways are (a) charophytes and (b) euglenophytes similar to chlorophytes and in what ways are they different?

5. Describe the characteristics of chrysophytes generally and of each chrysophyte class specifically. What groups are included among the Pyrrophyta and what features identify each of these groups?

6. Review the identifying features of brown algae and of red algae.

7. Describe the group characteristics of protozoa. What are the phyla of protozoa and what are their distinguishing features?

8. What differentiates the classes of slime molds? Review the life cycles of these organisms. What justifies the inclusion of slime molds within the Protista? Which features of slime molds are protozoalike and which are funguslike?

9. Review the structural characteristics of fungi generally. What are the possible evolutionary relations of this phylum to other Protista? Name the main groups within the fungi and the possible evolutionary relations of these groups to one another.

10. Describe the general characteristics of the various fungal classes. What different types of fruiting bodies are encountered among the Euascomycetes? What are Fungi Imperfecti? Lichens?

SUGGESTED COLLATERAL READINGS

The following books provide additional information about the biology of the Protista:

Alexopoulos, C. J.: "Introductory Mycology," Wiley, New York, 1952.

Bold, H. C.: "Morphology of Plants," Prentice-Hall, Englewood Cliffs, N.J., 1957.

Bonner, J. T.: "The Cellular Slime Molds," Princeton University Press, Princeton, N.J., 1959.

Chapman, V. F.: "Seaweeds and Their Uses," Methuen, London, 1950.

Christensen, C. M.: "The Molds and Man," University of Minnesota Press, Minneapolis, 1951.

Gray, W. D.: "The Relation of Fungi to Human Affairs," Holt, New York, 1959.

Haupt, A. W.: "Plant Morphology," McGraw-Hill, New York, 1953.

Hyman, L.: "The Invertebrates," vol. 1, "Protozoa through Ctenophora," McGraw-Hill, New York, 1940.

Smith, G. M.: "Cryptogamic Botany," vol. 1, "Algae and Fungi," 2d ed., McGraw-Hill, New York, 1955.

Various activities of algae are discussed interestingly in the following articles:

Bonner, J. T.: A Colony of Cells, Sci. American, vol. 182, 1950.

Brook, A. J.: Water-blooms, New Biol., vol. 13, 1957.

Fogg, G. E.: Famous Plants: Chlorella, New Biol., vol. 15, 1953.

Hutner, S. H., and J. A. McLaughlin: Poisonous Tides, Sci. American, vol. 199, 1958.

Isaac, P. C. G., and M. Lodge: Algae and Sewage Treatment, New Biol., vol. 26, 1958.

Jane, F. W.: Famous Plant-Animal: Euglena, New Biol., vol. 19, 1955.

Lewin, R. A.: Flagella—Variations and Enigmas, New Biol., vol. 19, 1955.

Milner, H. W.: Algae as Food, *Sci. American,* vol. 189, 1953.

Newton, L.: Famous Plants: *Fucus, New Biol.,* vol. 17, 1954.

Pringsheim, E.: The Cultivation of Algae, *Endeavour,* vol. 9, 1950.

Weiss, F. J.: The Useful Algae, *Sci. American,* vol. 187, 1952.

Popular accounts on fungi and other protists may be found in the following articles:

Abraham, E. P.: The Antibiotics in Microbiology, *Endeavour,* vol. 18, 1959.

Avery, G. S., Jr.: The Dying Oaks, *Sci. American,* vol. 196, 1957.

Bonner, J. T.: The Growth of Mushrooms, *Sci. American,* vol. 194, 1956.

Emerson, R.: Molds and Man, *Sci. American,* vol. 186, 1952.

Ingold, C. T.: Famous Plants: the Mushroom, *New Biol.,* vol. 18, 1955.

Lamb, I. M.: Lichens, *Sci. American,* vol. 201, 1959.

Maio, J. J.: Predatory Fungi, *Sci. American,* vol. 199, 1958.

Milne, L. J., and M. J. Milne: The Eelgrass Catastrophe, *Sci. American,* vol. 184, 1951.

Niederhauser, J. S., and W. C. Cobb: The Late Blight, *Sci. American,* vol. 200, 1959.

Russell, P. F.: The Eradication of Malaria, *Sci. American,* vol. 186, 1952.

METAPHYTA

10

This category includes all the green, terrestrial, multicellular plants. Specifically, the group comprises two phyla, the *Bryophyta*, or moss plants, and the *Tracheophyta*, or vascular plants. The latter are far more important, abundant, and spectacular, and they will occupy most of our attention.

GENERAL CHARACTERISTICS

As noted earlier, Metaphyta as a whole have probably evolved from ancestral, green freshwater algae. Such a relationship is strongly suggested by the presence of **chlorophylls** *a* and *b*, by cell walls made of **cellulose** and **pectic substances,** by the deposition of food stores in the form of **starch,** and by the presence of two **whiplash flagella** in motile cells (or more than two in certain advanced metaphytes). All Metaphyta are highly elaborate, three-dimensional tetrasporine types with true tissues, organs, and, in some cases, also organ systems.

Directly or indirectly, most characteristics which distinguish the Metaphyta uniquely from the Protista are adaptations to terrestrial ways of life. For example, in the absence of support against gravity by the buoyant action of water, Metaphyta possess specialized **skeletal tissues** not present in any of the Protista. Such tissues reach their most advanced form in the sclerenchymas and woods of the tracheophytes. The problem of mechanical support is minimized further by the generally **upright, radial** construction of metaphytes, although this is not an invariable feature. Such a design distributes the weight equally around the vertical axis and permits lower portions of the body to support upper ones directly.

In the absence of open water around all surfaces, Metaphyta possess specialized **absorbing tissues** which project into soil. These are either *rhizoids* or more elaborate *roots*. Since they are present only in specific regions of the plants, metaphytes possess more or less specialized nutrient-distributing or conducting tissues, the most highly developed being the *vascular* tissues.

Permanent exposure to air introduces the problem of desiccation. Metaphytes cope with it through **waxy cuticles** on exposed surfaces, which let light pass but not water or atmospheric gases. But since gases must be exchanged, impervious cuticles cannot form a complete, unbroken coating over external surfaces. Indeed, Metaphyta possess gas-transmitting surface pores or **stomata.**

The dangers of desiccation have elicited adaptive responses also in the structures and processes of reproduction and in life cycles. The reproductive structures arise from single cells, but the mature structures are always **multicellular.** They are *organs* composed of at least two specialized tissues. One is an external sterile tissue, consisting of one or more layers of cells, which protects against desiccation, and the other is an internal spore- or sex-cell–producing tissue. Mature spores are nonmotile and encapsulated in all Metaphyta. Female sex cells, eggs, are equally nonmotile. Male sex cells, sperms, are naked and motile in primitive metaphytes, and release of such cells is timed to coincide with wet or rainy conditions. In advanced metaphytes, however, even the male sex cells are nonmotile and their release has become independent of external water (see Chap. 25). The general sessilism of metaphytes has been accompanied by a loss of kinetosomes from all cells except only those sperm cells which are motile. Centrioles, derivatives of kinetosomes, are usually absent as well.

The life cycle of metaphytes always includes a distinct **embryonic phase,** a characteristic not generally encountered in any of the Protista. The embryo prolongs the developmental period, and this provides time for the elaboration of the many specialized tissues of the adult metaphyte. Since such internal elaboration is an adaptation to land life, as we have seen, the embryo too is evidently an evolutionary response to the requirement of terrestrial life.

Finally, Metaphyta invariably possess a life cycle consisting of two different, successive adult generations. One produces sex cells only, and it is called the **gametophyte generation.** The sex cells participate in fertilization, and a new adult develops thereafter. This adult produces spores only, and it is therefore called the **sporophyte generation.** Spores subsequently grow into new gametophytes. The adult plants of these two generations are structured quite differently, both externally and internally; they represent excellent examples of polymorphism (see Chap. 6). As will be shown in Chap. 23 Metaphyta did not "invent" life cycles with such *alternation of generations;* Protista did so, in adaptation to their own problems of aquatic life. However, as will be shown in Chap. 25, Metaphyta turned the alternating generations they inherited to their own adaptive advantage and actually made them one of the foundations of their signal success as terrestrial plants.

There are excellent reasons to believe that Metaphyta became what they are, not because their aquatic ancestors suddenly developed a taste for terrestrial life, but because they probably tried, with all the evolutionary means at their disposal, to remain aquatic. Undoubtedly, the chlorophyte ancestors were occasionally subjected to prolonged droughts, not an unusual hazard in freshwater habitats. The plants successfully became adapted to these hazards by a variety of evolutionary innovations. These permitted them to survive through periods of drought and thus allowed them to persist as basically aquatic forms. Almost incidentally, however, gradual perfection of the adaptations to temporary terrestrial living must eventually have produced plants which could survive away from open water altogether and which so could be permanently terrestrial. At least two such groups must have evolved from the green algae, separately and independently. One culminated in the bryophytes, the other in the tracheophytes.

BRYOPHYTES

PHYLUM BRYOPHYTA: MOSS PLANTS
(about 25,000 species)

Class Bryopsida: mosses
Class Hepaticopsida: liverworts
Class Anthoceropsida: hornworts

The members of this phylum are distributed all over the world. In general, they occur in more or less shady, perpetually moist places, where the danger of drying out is minimized and where rain water is amply available as a medium for the swimming sperms. Bryophytes often inhabit bogs and swamps, the peat moss *Sphagnum* being particularly common in such areas. Some bryophytes grow in the cold regions of the world, high on mountains and in the tundra; others grow in deserts, near hot springs, and in the tropics. In tropical rain forests, bryophytes occur abundantly as epiphytes on the leaves, branches, and trunks of trees. Several species of bryophytes are completely aquatic, being adapted secondarily to a floating or submerged life in fresh water. But bryophytes do not include any marine forms.

Terrestrial bryophytes frequently are important soil formers and soil protectors. They may settle where lichens have begun to convert bare rock surfaces into small patches of soil and, by their metabolism and decay after death, then contribute to a further transformation of rock into soil (see Chap. 12). Moreover, many bryophytes rather rapidly form dense, soil-covering carpets, which not only prevent erosion of soil but also help in maintaining its water content; water is retained well between the plants in a carpet. In addition, many bryophytes absorb water directly through their leaves, which spares the fluid supplies of soil. The rapid formation of extensive bryophyte beds is a result of the remarkable propagative powers of these plants (see Chap. 25). In their own way, therefore, bryophytes play an important role in the small-scale economy of nature.

As a group, bryophytes are distinguished from tracheophytes by a life cycle in which the gametophyte generation is always *dominant*. That is, this generation lasts longer, is physically larger and more conspicuous, is nutritionally independent, and in general represents the "main" plant. Casual reference to a "moss," for example, is a reference to the gametophyte generation. By contrast, the sporophyte generation is small and short-lived, and this plant is invariably *attached* to the gametophyte. Moreover, it is nutritionally dependent on the gametophyte, drawing many or all required inorganic and some required organic nutrients from it. Thus the sporophyte is essentially a parasite.

Class Bryopsida

This class is probably the most primitive, and early mosses may have been ancestral to the other bryophyte classes.

The gametophyte body of a moss generally consists of two parts (Fig. 10.1). One is a branched network of green filaments lying on or close to the ground. Each such filament, rather reminiscent of some of the green algae, is a **protonema.** Extending from it in places into the soil are filamentous, nongreen **rhizoids.** The second and structurally quite different part of the body consists of one or more upright green **shoots,** which develop from buds growing upward on the protonema. A shoot is composed of a **stem** to which are attached radially arranged **leaves.** At maturity, a shoot also bears **sex organs** at its tip. The common moss *Funaria* illustrates this typical organization rather well. From the protonema of *Funaria* extend numerous branched, multicellular rhizoids. Upright shoots, from 1 to 3 cm high, grow from the protonema where the rhizoids join it.

The stem of the shoot consists of an outer **epidermis,** which is one cell layer thick, green, and without stomata (Fig. 10.2). Underlying this epidermis is a **cortex** composed of several layers of parenchyma cells. These contain chlorophyll only during the early stages of shoot development. The center of the stem is filled with elongated, thin-walled cells in which the cell substance degenerates during development. Such cells, reminiscent of the vascular elements of tracheophytes, undoubtedly function in water and nutrient transport. The leaves of *Funaria* have a well-defined midrib which contains several layers of sclerenchymatous supporting cells. A single layer of green cells on each side of the midrib forms the leaf blade. Other mosses possess considerably more complex leaves. In the pigeon-wheat moss *Polytrichum,* for example, a leaf consists of many layers of differently specialized cells. As indicated in Fig. 10.2, such a leaf also contains air spaces near the upper surface, which permit even deep-lying green cells to exchange gases directly with the external atmosphere.

As a shoot matures, sex organs develop at its tip (see Chap. 25). Male organs are known as **antheridia;** female organs, as **archegonia.** In *Funaria* and many

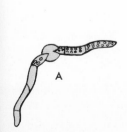
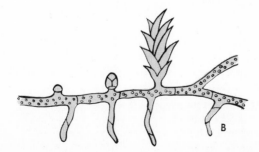

FIG. 10.1 *A*, germinating spore of a moss, showing rhizoid and growing protonema; *B*, protonema of a moss, showing rhizoids, buds, and young shoots.

usually contains stomata. Parenchymatous cells make up the interior of the stalk, and a column of such cells also continues into the sporangium, where it forms a central **columella.** Between it and the sporangial epidermis is the spore-producing or **sporogenous tissue.** During its early development, the sporophyte is green and depends on the gametophyte mainly for water and mineral nutrients. But as the sporangium matures, chlorophyll largely disintegrates and the sporophyte then is nutritionally completely dependent on the gametophyte.

A ripe sporangium consists of an outer cup-shaped **capsule** covered by a **lid.** The rim of the capsule under the lid is studded with flexible **teeth.** When the sporangium is dry and brittle, the lid falls away and the mature spores within the capsule become exposed. Spore dispersal is accomplished partly by wind and partly by the teeth around the rim of the capsule. These

FIG. 10.3 *A,* moss gametophyte with attached sporophyte. Note calyptra atop spore capsule. *B, C,* views of teeth along the rim of the spore capsule in two stages of spore dispersal.

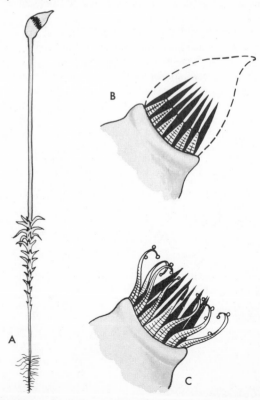

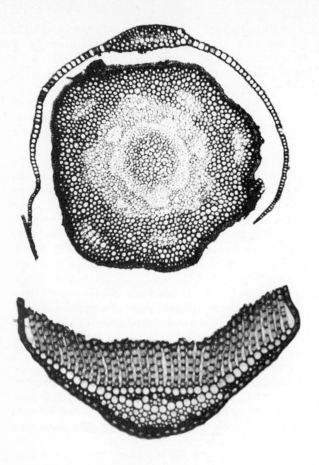

FIG. 10.2 Top, cross section through a stem of the moss *Polytrichum.* Note the thick-walled cortex cells and the thin-walled inner cells. Bottom, cross section through a leaf of the moss *Polytrichum.* Note the columns of cells along the upper surface and the air spaces between the columns. *(Courtesy of Dr. M. S. Fuller, Brown University.)*

other mosses, a single plant may form both types of sex organs. In another group of mosses (e.g., *Polytrichum*), male and female organs are produced on different plants. After an egg is fertilized, a process to be described in Chap. 25, it is retained in the archegonium. By repeated division it develops into the *embryo* of the sporophyte generation, growing atop the shoot of the gametophyte (Fig. 10.3). A mature sporophyte consists of an expanded **foot,** which anchors the base of the sporophyte to the tip of the gametophyte; a **stalk;** and a terminal spore-producing organ or **sporangium.** The external tissue of a sporophyte is an epidermis, which

teeth are hygroscopic, and they flex into and out of the capsule with changes in humidity. Thus they may flip spores out of the capsule (see Fig. 10.3).

Class Hepaticopsida

Whereas mosses are characteristically vertical and radially symmetrical, liverworts are prostrate, horizontal plants with clearly differentiated dorsal (top) and ventral (bottom) surfaces. On the basis of body organization, two groups of liverworts may be distinguished. One is said to be **foliose**; i.e., the body is leafy as in mosses. The leaves here are almost always without midribs. The other group is said to be **thallose**; i.e., the body forms a sheet, or *thallus*, flat on the ground (Fig. 10.4).

Foliose liverworts are rather elaborate externally, but internally they are relatively uncomplicated. For example, *Porella* is a leafy liverwort often epiphytic on trees. The plant lies flat, and it consists of a stem which usually bears three rows of leaves, one row ventral and two rows dorsolateral. The stem is composed of a central cylinder of large, thin-walled cells and of an outer cortical tissue containing smaller cells with somewhat thicker walls. A leaf is composed of a single layer of polygonal, parenchymatous cells. The sex organs of *Porella* arise on the dorsal surfaces. Antheridia form where leaves join the stem, but archegonia are usually terminal.

A sporophyte, attached to the archegonium, consists of foot, short stalk, and sporangium (Fig. 10.5). Present in the sporangia of *Porella* and indeed of most liverworts are so-called **elaters.** These are thin, elon-

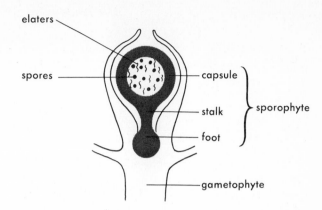

FIG. 10.5 Diagrammatic representation of a sporophyte of a liverwort (*Porella*).

gated, hygroscopic filaments possessing spirally thickened inner walls. They are interspersed among the maturing spores. When a sporangium of *Porella* becomes ripe, the capsule breaks open. Spores are exposed in this manner, and they are scattered partly by wind, partly by the elaters. The latter twist and coil as they dry, and such jerky motions flip spores out of the capsule. Elaters are not found among mosses, but they do occur in hornworts.

In contrast to foliose types like *Porella*, thallose liverworts are relatively simple externally, but internally they are organized quite elaborately. *Riccia* and *Marchantia* are good illustrations (see Fig. 10.4). The thallus of these plants is characteristically ribbon-shaped and lobed, with a median furrow along the upper surface. From the underside project numerous rhizoids. At the forward margin of a thallus is a *growing point* consisting of a cluster of a few cells. As these divide off new cells to either side, two lobes are formed. The growing point thus comes to be located in a notch between these lobes. Later the cells of the growing point may become separated into two groups, each of which may initiate the formation of a thallus branch. A growth pattern of this sort is said to be **dichotomous;** i.e., it leads to the formation of two equal branches from one main branch.

Internally, a thallus is stratified dorsoventrally into three distinct zones, each composed of one or more tissues (Fig. 10.6). The bottom zone is largely absorptive and consists mainly of nongreen rhizoids. The middle zone is nongreen parenchyma functioning in storage and conduction of nutrients. The upper zone is

FIG. 10.4 Comparison of general body shapes of a foliose liverwort (*Porella*) and a thallose liverwort (*Marchantia*).

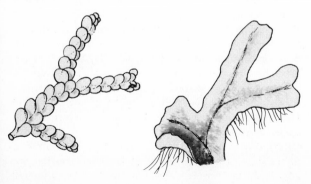

Porella   *Marchantia*

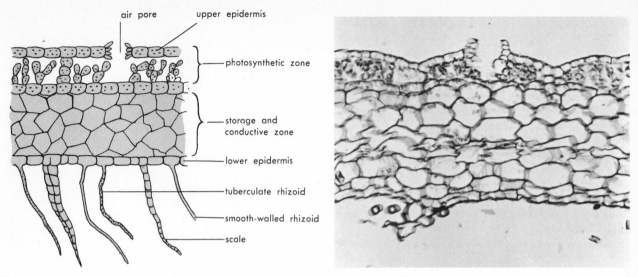

air pore — upper epidermis

— photosynthetic zone

— storage and conductive zone

— lower epidermis

— tuberculate rhizoid

— smooth-walled rhizoid

— scale

FIG. 10.6 Diagram and photomicrograph of the internal structure of a thallus of *Marchantia. (Photograph courtesy of Dr. M. S. Fuller, Brown University.)*

photosynthetic. Its architecture includes elaborate air chambers and air pores, as indicated in Fig. 10.6. In types like *Marchantia,* the location of the internal air chambers is revealed externally by fine diamond-shaped markings on the surface of the thallus.

In *Riccia* and related genera, the sex organs develop in the median furrow of the thallus, where water is likely to collect and provide a pathway for the sperms. Both antheridia and archegonia may develop in a single plant, in different regions. In other thallose liverworts, groups of archegonia are located in so-called **receptacles** which, after fertilization, grow upward on stalked extensions of the thallus. *Marchantia* is representative of a third group, in which both types of sex organs are in receptacles, both becoming raised on stalks after fertilization (Fig. 10.7). Antheridial receptacles are shaped like scalloped disks, with male sex organs set in the upper surface. An archegonial receptacle is roughly umbrella-shaped, and its rim is extended into (usually) nine fingerlike processes. The female sex organs are on the underside of the umbrella. An adult sporophyte is quite small. A foot anchors it to archegonial tissues, and a short, thick stalk connects the foot with a spherical sporangium. Embryo sporophytes are green, but as they mature they lose most of their chlorophyll. Adult sporophytes thus depend on the gametophytes for nutrients. As in the foliose liverworts, elaters aid in spore dispersal.

Class Anthoceropsida

The hornworts, of which the best known is probably *Anthoceros,* are characterized by thallose gametophytes which are irregularly scalloped along the margins but are without notches and without surface furrows or midribs. Rhizoids are present on the underside. Internally, there is little or no differentiation of tissues. The cells of the thallus are parenchymatous, and each possesses a single large chloroplast with a conspicuous pyrenoid. This contrasts sharply with the cells of the other bryophyte classes, which possess numerous chloroplasts each and do not contain pyrenoids. The central portions of a hornwort thallus are usually several cell layers thick, but there are no air chambers or air pores. Sex organs of both types are formed within the same individual of *Anthoceros,* embedded deep in the thallus.

In sharp contrast with the simply constructed gametophyte, the sporophyte of *Anthoceros* is differentiated to a remarkably high degree (Fig. 10.8). The foot is anchored within the thallus. A stalk connects the foot with a rod-shaped sporangium, which projects upward from the thallus to a height of several inches. The sporangium consists of a central cylindrical columella surrounded by sporogenous tissue containing elaters. Surrounding this tissue in turn is a green parenchymatous cortex, and covering the whole on the outside is an epidermis. The cells in this layer secrete conspicuous waxy cuticles on their outer surfaces. The

FIG. 10.7 Sex-organ—bearing stalks in *Marchantia*. Left, stalk bearing fingerlike processes in which female sex organs are located. Right, structure containing male sex organs. *(Carolina Biological Supply Co.)*

epidermis also contains stomata which are formed by pairs of guard cells as in vascular plants. Such stomata lead into air spaces between the cells of the underlying cortex.

A sporophyte retains its chlorophyll throughout its existence and therefore requires only inorganic supplies from the gametophyte. Mature sporophytes split open lengthwise from their upper ends down, and spores may then escape with the aid of the elaters.

TRACHEOPHYTE CHARACTERISTICS

Vascular plants represent the largest group of photosynthetic organisms and, after the insects, the second largest group of all types of organisms. The phylum is identified uniquely by independent and **dominant sporo-**

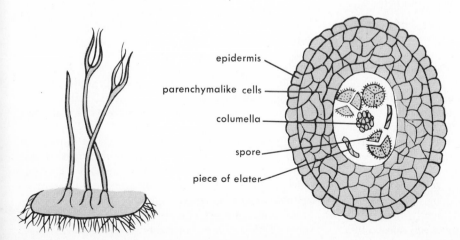

epidermis

parenchymalike cells

columella

spore

piece of elater

FIG. 10.8 *Anthoceros.* Left, whole view of thallus with attached sporophytes. Right, cross section through a sporophyte.

phytes and by gametophytes which are either independent or dependent but never dominant. Where the gametophytes are independent they are exceedingly small plants, reminiscent in general structure of simple thallose bryophytes such as *Anthoceros*. Casual reference to a tracheophyte is always a reference to the sporophyte generation. The phylum is further characterized by the presence of two distinct and specialized vascular tissues, the water-conducting **xylem** and the food-conducting **phloem**. A third unique feature of the phylum is that the body of virtually all sporophytes is clearly subdivided into **roots, stems,** and **leaves,** each such body part representing a true organ.

ARCHITECTURE

Tracheophytes possess a main axis which is vertical, and the radial symmetry around this axis is conspicuous. Such an organization not only permits efficient nutrient absorption from all sides around the plant, but also provides a mechanically balanced body design which anchors the plant safely and gives it maximum internal support along the vertical axis. Many tracheophytes also taper upward, which allows the greatest weight to rest on the broadest foundation. In addition, specially developed supporting structures are present: collenchyma, sclerenchyma, and the cellulose and lignin of wood. In effect, the size of the plant need be limited only by the inherent strength of its supporting materials. This strength is comparatively much greater than that of animal skeletons; woody plants include the largest living things of all, living and extinct animals not excepted. Thus, tracheophytes have solved the gravity problem far more efficiently than bryophytes, which solve it mainly by staying small and close to the ground. This serves well enough, to be sure, but the cost of such conservatism is lack of spectacular success on land.

Large size necessitates long-distance nutrient conduction and a functional subdivision of nutrient-providing regions in the subterranean and aerial parts of the plant. The characteristic root-stem-leaf organization of the tracheophyte is a specific adaptation to this requirement. Roots absorb from the ground; leaves photosynthesize; and stems interconnect, conduct, and support.

Surfaces are necessary for the absorption of raw materials. For a given mass of absorbing tissue, the best architectural arrangement is consequently that which offers the largest area. Indeed, roots are most often highly branched, rather than thick and compact; and leaves, similarly, are flat and thin or needle-shaped. A large surface is also required for illumination by sunlight. However, the sun is not stationary but arcs across the sky every day. A given mass of stationary light-receiving tissue will therefore be illuminated most if it is flat and thin, if it is subdivided into many small plates, and if the plates are set at many different angles. Leaves are fairly widely spaced, usually in nonobstructing formations. In many plants, leaves turn toward the sun if the heat is not too great and turn away from the sun if it is. Another well-known adaptation is the ability of tracheophytes to grow toward the light even if they are planted away from it (see also Chap. 19).

Large surfaces for illumination and absorption also constitute large surfaces for evaporation. However, waxy cuticles are present on the exposed aerial surfaces. Such coats let sunlight through readily, and they prevent the escape of internal water. But in so doing they also bar the entry or exit of gases from and to the atmosphere. Yet gas exchange must occur. The dilemma is resolved by the stomata, which permit gas exchange and therefore also a certain amount of evaporation. Nevertheless, the greater part of the tissue is protected by wax and a large surface is still available for illumination. Waxy surfaces are additionally advantageous in that they allow rain or dew to run off.

In the stationary plant in which water is vital and in which food cannot be produced during the night and often also not during the winter, *storage* of water and food is likely to be of major importance. Indeed, water storage is a function of every living tracheophyte cell. Every such cell is **succulent;** it contains a large amount of water, much of it in vacuoles. This condition also makes the cells highly **turgid:** the comparatively large amounts of water are confined by rigid cell walls and this constraint puts the water under considerable pressure. Such cellular turgor gives tissues additional mechanical support and permits even "soft" plant parts like leaves to maintain their shape well. But if water is in insufficient supply, succulence, turgor, and mechanical support may all become reduced and the plant may wilt.

Food storage to some extent is also a function of every living plant cell, parenchymatous cells most particularly. Many tracheophytes have actually developed enlarged body parts with greatly proliferated parenchymatous tissues, adapted especially for food storage. Stems and roots are modified more frequently for this function than leaves, probably partly because leaves must maintain their food-producing role and cannot be spared for a storing role, partly because massive food stores can be supported physically far better in the ground than in the air, and partly because leaves are temporary, relatively short-lived organs. Indeed, storage stems frequently are underground, and in this location they may aid also in protecting the plant against drastic temperature fluctuations and in easing the problem of mechanical support.

Some of the principal types of modified stems are (Fig. 10.9): **rhizomes,** horizontal underground stems common particularly in primitive tracheophytes; **tubers,** locally expanded ends of rhizomes, often adapted for food storage, as in potatoes; **bulbs,** shortened, usually underground stems to which thickened storage leaves are attached, as in onions; **corms,** shortened, bulky, underground storage stems which superficially resemble bulbs but which possess scalelike leaves on the outer

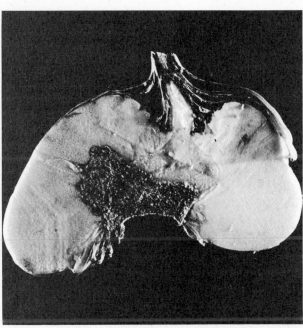

FIG. 10.9 Some types of stems. Top left, a bulb. The central vertical stem is surrounded by leaves, which form the bulk of the bulb. Top right, a corm. Leaves are borne at the top. Bottom left, a tuber. Bottom right, a runner. *(Courtesy of Dr. M. S. Fuller, Brown University.)*

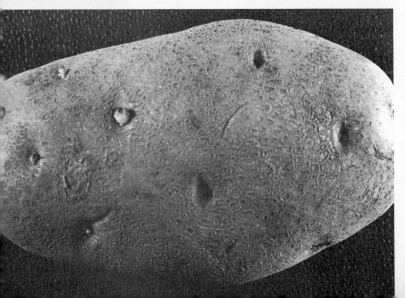

surfaces, as in gladioli; **runners**, horizontal stems flat on the ground and supported by the ground, as in strawberries; and **twining stems**, which wind around upright or other objects and obtain support from them, as in beans.

Variant types of roots include (Fig. 10.10): **fibrous roots**, in which numerous branch roots lead off from the stem base into soil in all directions, as in grasses; **taproots**, single, thick, vertical storage roots from which small branch roots may lead off, as in carrots; **adven-**

FIG. 10.10 Some types of roots. Top left, fibrous roots. Top right, taproots. Bottom left, prop roots. Bottom right, adventitious roots. (Top left and top right, U.S. Department of Agriculture; bottom left, Brooklyn Botanical Garden; bottom right, Jean Carel, Paris.)

titious roots, which sprout from any region of the plant (except a root), even from regions near the tip of the stem; **prop roots,** which are adventitious roots specially adapted to provide mechanical support, as in banyan trees and older corn plants; and **aerial roots,** which are not in contact with the ground at all and which absorb water from sources available above ground, as in the epiphytic orchids. Such roots have a many-layered epidermis, the cells of which die and become specialized for water uptake, prevention of water loss, and protection against mechanical injury.

These various examples suggest, and the prodigious success of tracheophytes clearly proves, that the basic structure of these plants is adapted very adequately to both the general and the specific character of their particular terrestrial environment. But a suitable body design is only one requirement for a successful sessile way of terrestrial life. Another requirement is adaptability to potentially lethal changes in local weather, for a plant rooted to the ground cannot escape extremes of temperature. It can only attempt to protect against them. Water poses the key problem here. In summer heat and in deserts, the plant is in danger of having too little internal water. And in winter cold or at high latitudes and altitudes there is likely to be too much water, for water freezes and kills.

HEAT PROTECTION

The heat problem is one of internal *water conservation,* and it affects the exposed stems and leaves far more than the underground roots.

Tracheophytes living in dry, warm or hot climates are *xerophytes;* they have developed various structural adaptations guarding against excessive water loss by evaporation (Fig. 10.11). For example, waxy cuticles over exposed surfaces are greatly thickened, sometimes becoming even thicker than the epidermal cells which secrete them. Stomata are often reduced in number. And they may be located mostly or entirely on the underside of leaves, where shade and somewhat lower temperatures reduce evaporation and where settling dust is not likely to clog them. Or they may be sunk deep into microscopic epidermal pits, which provide shade except when the sun shines straight into them and which again protect against clogging by dust.

Under near-desert conditions, the rate of evaporation may nevertheless be too high. Water vaporization can be held down, however, by reduction of the *area* of exposed parts in proportion to their volume. Thus,

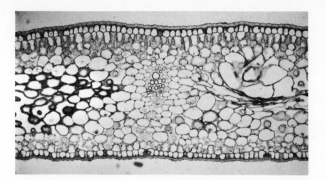

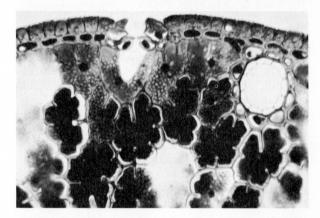

FIG. 10.11 Adaptations to dry conditions. Top, section of leaf with thick cuticles on both upper and lower epidermis. Bottom, section of pine leaf showing sunken stoma (top center of photograph) and lobed parenchyma cells in interior. *(Courtesy of Dr. M. S. Fuller, Brown University.)*

plants may possess but a few large leaves (e.g., ferns) or small scalelike or needle-shaped leaves. In the extreme case, well exemplified by cacti, leaves may be reduced to thorny spines and massive stems may take on most of the function of food manufacture. Moreover, exposure may be reduced by development of underground stems, horizontal rhizomes being particularly common in xerophytes. Water-storing capacity may be increased through bulky, succulent leaves, as in many ornamental house plants. Through adaptations such as these, tracheophytes are able to survive even in the hottest, driest regions provided that at least *some* water is available at *some* time. Quite a number of tracheophytes have overcome their water-conservation problem by adapting secondarily to an aquatic habitat and living as *hydrophytes* (see Fig. 7.27).

A summer day may be excessively hot and dry, and the tracheophyte may droop and begin to wilt. But if there is moisture on the following day, conditions within the plant are soon restored to normal. By contrast, winter frost for even an hour is likely to kill; below the freezing point, water which is not firmly bound in colloidal gels is transformed into ice crystals. Such crystals may tear and disrupt the molecular framework of cells. Therein lies a potentially lethal effect of cold.

COLD PROTECTION

Probably in response to yearly cold seasons or outright winters, tracheophytes have developed major adaptations which profoundly affect their whole way of life. On the basis of these adaptations, we may distinguish three groups of vascular plants: **perennials, biennials,** and **annuals.**

In perennials, major or all portions of the plant body persist through successive winters. At the approach of winter, such plants may manufacture large quantities of colloidal materials within their cells. This increase in the amount of colloid particles leads to a conversion of much of the living substance of cells into a gel state. As a result, little water remains free inside cells and freezing is successfully forestalled. In evergreen plant groups, such winterproofing, or **winter hardening,** is particularly effective. Even leaves can be retained, and vital processes carry on as in summer though at a slower pace (provided water replacement is not made impossible by frozen conditions in other parts of the plant). Conifers like pines are good examples of evergreen perennials.

Other perennials are *deciduous* plants; they cannot protect their foliage against the cold and they shed leaves in the fall. But the rest of the plant lives on. Buds and embryonic leaves have developed during the preceding summer, and these sprout the next spring into new foliage. In the absence of mature leaves during the cold season, little or no food can be produced. However, such plants accumulate food reserves at other seasons and store them in root and stem. Flowering trees living in the temperate zone are familiar examples of deciduous perennials.

Still other perennials are soft-bodied and *herbaceous* (e.g., asparagus, dandelions). In such plants, the leaves as well as the aerial parts of the stem die off in the fall. But the roots and a short underground piece of stem survive. Reserve foods in these underground body parts last through the winter and suffice in spring for the development of a new aerial shoot. Leaves and a mature stem then grow from this shoot. Since the aerial portions of these plants persist only through a relatively short growing season, they never become very extensive; bulky wood is neither required nor formed and the plants remain nonwoody herbs.

The above patterns (Fig. 10.12) give evidence of an adaptive trend in perennials: it is more economical to retrench when life becomes difficult than to maintain elaborate aerial structures against heavy odds. This trend does not halt here, however. Winter retrenchment goes even further in biennial and annual herbaceous plants.

In biennials (e.g., carrots), leaves die off in a first winter, after procuring extensive food reserves which are stored in bulky roots. The roots and portions of the shoot survive that winter, and from them a new plant develops the following spring. This second-year plant flowers and forms seeds. At the approach of the second winter, the entire plant dies, roots included. Only the seeds survive, and these subsequently initiate a new two-year cycle (Fig. 10.13).

The annual plant (e.g., wheat) flowers and produces seeds every year. The whole plant dies in the fall, and its seeds give rise to a new generation the following spring (Fig. 10.13).

Evidently, vascular plants have found several

FIG. 10.12 The perennial patterns of plants. In one pattern, as in conifers (left), the whole plant survives the winter. In another pattern, as in deciduous plants (center), foliage is shed in the cold season but the rest of the plant survives. In a third pattern, as in herbaceous perennials (right), only the roots and a small piece of stem survive the winter.

evergreen   deciduous   herbaceous perennial

workable solutions to the problem of cold. They may winterproof the whole body or some part of the body, or they may rely entirely and most economically on a handful of hardy cells: seeds. These often contain as little as 5 per cent water and are therefore adapted excellently to withstand the rigors of winter.

Thus, in numerous and very elegant ways, tracheophytes have made the most of their difficult terrestrial environment. Actually, there are only two types of land environments to which a tracheophyte cannot adapt: the glacial regions, as at very high altitudes and latitudes, and the permanently arid regions, as in some deserts.

TRACHEOPHYTE STRUCTURE

PRIMARY GROWTH: STEM AND ROOT

A tracheophytic sporophyte begins its life history as an embryo. This is an elongated, multicellular structure with a **shoot apex** at one tip and a **root apex** at the other (Fig. 10.14). At these apices, specific cells called **apical meristems** remain permanently embryonic. They continue to divide, and new cells formed by them are added behind each tip to the embryonic tissues already present. Thus the whole embryo continues to elongate.

New cells produced by the apical meristems soon become organized into three fundamental embryonic tissues, the **primary meristems.** These are the **protoderm** on the outside, the **procambium** in the center, and the **ground meristem** between protoderm and procambium (see Fig. 10.14). While these three tissues develop, primary meristems, formed somewhat earlier and thus situated farther away from the apices, begin to specialize as adult stem and root tissues. Therefore, even in a mature sporophyte, a small zone immediately behind each apex is always meristematic, and in a zone behind this primary meristem, the three embryonic tissues are always in process of developing into adult tissues. Consequently, a lengthwise view of a shoot or a root exhibits an orderly sequence of zones which indicates the sequence of stages each adult stem or root tissue has passed through during its development (Fig. 10.15).

The nature of the adult tissues developed from the three primary meristems has already been discussed in

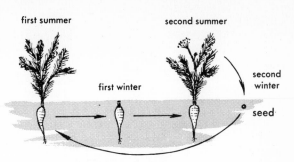

THE BIENNIAL PATTERN

THE ANNUAL PATTERN

FIG. 10.13 The biennial and annual patterns of plants. In a biennial, only the roots and a small piece of stem survive the first winter, and only seeds survive the second winter. In an annual, the whole plant dies every year and is perpetuated only by seeds.

Chap. 5. Figure 10.16 indicates which adult tissues are formed by which of the primary meristems.

In the stem region, the protoderm-derived epidermis is cutinized and contains paired green guard cells which enclose stomata. Wax cuticles and stomata are absent in the root, but present there are root-hair cells, usually in a distinct zone some distance behind the root apex. Root hairs are temporary structures. Ahead of the root-hair zone, hairs have not yet developed; behind it, they have already disappeared. Thus the root-hair zone advances as the root apex advances. Also present in the root is a **root cap,** several layers of cells which envelop the root tip externally (Fig. 10.17). A root cap is formed by the apical root meristem. Such a cap is an important adaptive device, for as the root tip advances, hard soil grains would soon macerate unprotected meristem tissue. In the presence of a root cap, however, cap cells wear off instead and the growing tip is shielded effectively. New cap cells continue to be formed by the root meristem.

The adult cortex and the endodermis are formed from the embryonic ground meristem. The stem cortex

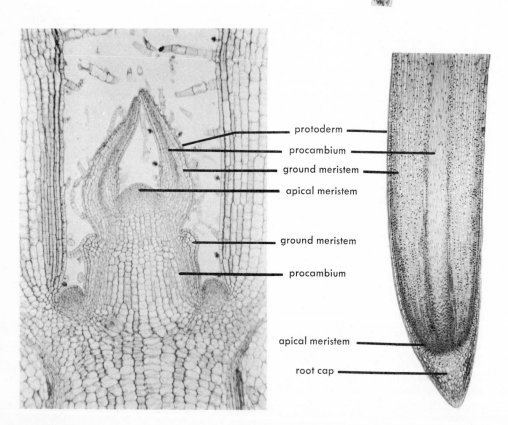

apical shoot meristem
protoderm
procambium
ground meristem
seed coat
cotyledons (seed leaves)

apical root meristem

FIG. 10.14 The apical and the primary meristems. Right, longitudinal section through a seed, showing the embryo within. Bottom left, longitudinal section through a shoot apex. Bottom right, longitudinal section through a root apex. In all cases, note the basic meristematic tissues and their position. *(Courtesy of Dr. M. S. Fuller, Brown University.)*

protoderm
procambium
ground meristem
apical meristem

ground meristem

procambium

apical meristem

root cap

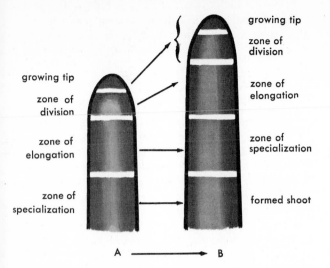

growing tip

zone of division

zone of elongation

zone of specialization

growing tip

zone of division

zone of elongation

zone of specialization

formed shoot

A ⟶ B

FIG. 10.15 The lengthwise development of a growing shoot. The condition depicted in A changes to that of B after a period of growth. Note how any given zone transforms into that originally below it. The growth pattern is comparable in a growing root.

frequently is photosynthetic. The endodermis may be reduced or absent in stems, but it is always present in roots. Passage cells without suberin coats are conspicuous here.

The procambium develops into three adult tissues of the stele, namely, the pericycle (frequently reduced or absent in stems), the primary phloem, and the primary xylem (or primary wood). A fourth adult tissue of the stele, the pith, is a derivative of ground meri-

stem, not of procambium. These stelar tissues are arranged in different ways in the roots and stems of different tracheophytes (Fig. 10.18).

The most primitive type of stele is a **protostele,** characterized by the absence of pith. Three variant forms of it are known. A *haplostele* is the simplest type. Xylem here forms a central cylinder; phloem develops as a sleeve surrounding the xylem; and the pericycle in turn surrounds the phloem. An *actinostele* is quite similar, except that the central xylem column is alternately grooved and ridged in a vertical direction, which gives a cross-sectional view a somewhat starlike appearance. The number of "arms" varies from about two to six. The third type of protostele is known as *plectostele*. Here the xylem is in the form of several separate lengthwise ribbons or plates embedded in phloem. With only a few exceptions, the roots of almost all tracheophytes are actinostelic. The stems of various primitive tracheophytes contain protosteles of all three types. However, most tracheophytes do not contain protosteles at all, but contain stems with pith.

One stele type with pith is a **siphonostele.** Several variants of it are known; all are characterized by a central column of pith and sleeves of vascular tissues which surround the pith completely. Related to siphonosteles are stele types collectively called **dictyosteles.** In these, the xylem and phloem tissues are arranged as distinct and separate *vascular bundles* grouped in more or less circular patterns within the stem. Pith is ringed in by such a circle of bundles but is continuous with the stem cortex outside the ring of bundles. A third stele type with pith is an **atactostele.** Vascular bundles are present here as well, but these bundles are

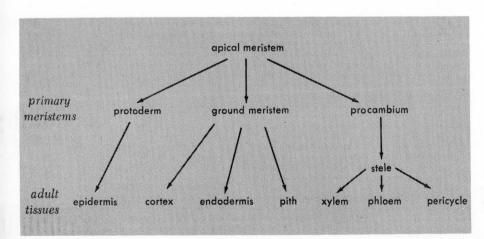

primary meristems

apical meristem

protoderm   ground meristem   procambium

stele

adult tissues

epidermis   cortex   endodermis   pith   xylem   phloem   pericycle

FIG. 10.16 The primary meristems and the principal adult tissues derived from them.

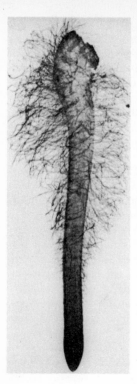
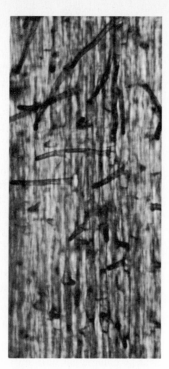

FIG. 10.17 Left, a root showing root-hair zone; at lower tip, note thickening formed by the rootcap. Right, a high-power view of a portion of the root-hair zone, showing epidermal cells and individual root hairs. *(General Biological Supply House, Inc.)*

scattered randomly throughout the stem, and it is often difficult to differentiate precisely between pith and cortex.

PRIMARY GROWTH: LEAVES AND BRANCHES

Stem and root growth is continuous as a result of the persisting production of new cells at the shoot and root apices. Leaf growth, on the other hand, is usually limited. A leaf may be considered to be a *modified branch stem,* which in most cases does not possess an apical meristem of its own.

A **leaf bud** forms from embryonic tissue just below and lateral to the shoot apex. Sometimes a single cell but more often several cells give rise to the leaf bud. These embryonic cells divide repeatedly, most divisions occurring along the margins of the expanding and flattening blade. The surface layer of the embryonic leaf is protoderm, which becomes continuous with the protoderm of the stem. The inner mass is ground meristem, similarly continuous with the corresponding tissue of the stem. During this early developmental phase, a column of procambium branches away from the center of the stem and grows laterally through the ground meristem of the stem into the ground meristem of the leaf. This procambial column is a **leaf trace** (Fig. 10.19).

In due course, the embryonic tissues of the leaf differentiate into adult tissues. In some exceptional cases among ferns, the leaves do retain meristematic tissues at the tips and such leaves may grow continuously, like stems. But in the vast majority of cases, *all* leaf tissues

FIG. 10.18 Some types of steles of vascular plants: white areas, cortex; cross-hatched areas, pericycle; gray areas, phloem; black areas, xylem; stippled areas, pith. The first three stele types shown are collectively known as protosteles, i.e., steles without pith.

haplostele

actinostele

plectostele

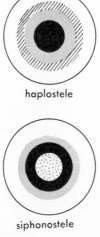

siphonostele

dictyostele

atactostele

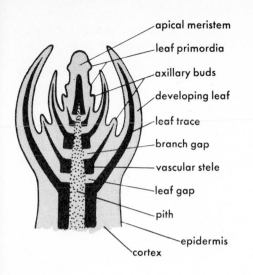
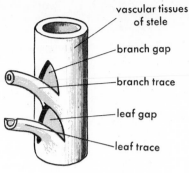

apical meristem
leaf primordia
axillary buds
developing leaf
leaf trace
branch gap
vascular stele
leaf gap
pith
epidermis
cortex

vascular tissues
of stele
branch gap
branch trace
leaf gap
leaf trace

FIG. 10.19 Left, diagrammatic representation of the distribution of vascular tissues in a shoot apex. Right, three-dimensional views of a section of a vascular cylinder in a region where leaf and branch traces emerge. Note that the vascular tissues of both leaves and branches leave gaps in the stele.

soon become adult. At that time the leaf has attained its final size, and it does not grow thereafter (Fig. 10.20).

Leaf protoderm develops into epidermis. As in the stem, leaf epidermis is cutinized and contains green guard cells enclosing stomata. The interior ground meristem gives rise to adult parenchymatous **mesophyll** tissue. This is usually the chief food-producing tissue of the plant; all mesophyll cells contain chlorophyll. In leaves of some primitive tracheophytes, mesophyll cells may be packed more or less close together, with or without occasional air spaces between cells. In most tracheophyte leaves, however, mesophyll is organized into two distinct zones. Just underneath the upper epidermis in horizontally placed leaves and underneath the whole epidermis in most upright and needle-shaped leaves, mesophyll cells are arranged in compact layers, or **palisades**. Elsewhere, mesophyll is **spongy**; i.e., it is organized into loose cellular strands and layers. The whole is honeycombed extensively with air spaces. These connect with one another and lead to the exterior of the leaf through open passages in the palisade tissue and the stomata. This structural arrangement brings the greater part of every mesophyll cell into direct contact with fresh external air.

The procambial leaf traces develop into vascular xylem and phloem. Two fundamental leaf types may

FIG. 10.20   Cross section of a leaf. (Courtesy of Dr. M. S. Fuller, Brown University.)

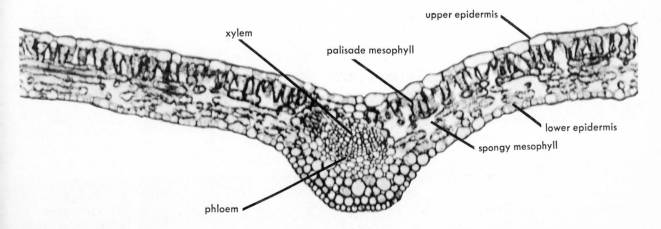

xylem
palisade mesophyll
upper epidermis
lower epidermis
spongy mesophyll
phloem

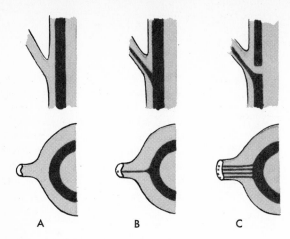

FIG. 10.21   Microphylls and megaphylls. Top row, longitudinal views; bottom row, cross-sectional views. *A*, microphyll without vascular trace. *B*, microphyll with vascular bundle. *C*, megaphyll. Note the many vascular bundles and the leaf gap in the megaphyll. Leaf gaps are not associated with microphylls.

be distinguished on the basis of the amount of vascular tissue formed. In a so-called **microphyll**, the vascular tissue is the equivalent of a single vascular bundle. In a **megaphyll**, by contrast, the vascular tissue is equivalent to numerous vascular bundles. Microphylls occur only in primitive tracheophytes; megaphylls are characteristic of most vascular plants (Fig. 10.21).

Megaphylls leave distinct **leaf gaps** in the stele of the stem. Such a gap forms when a leaf first develops. When a stem elongates beyond the region where a procambial leaf trace branches away laterally into a leaf bud, the stem procambium newly forming above the base of the leaf trace does not connect directly with that leaf trace. Instead, a small discontinuity is left in the stem procambium just above the base of the leaf trace. This discontinuity becomes the leaf gap, and in the adult condition it is usually filled with parenchymatous tissue. Microphylls do not produce leaf gaps.

A microphyll is composed of a leaf blade only. But a mature megaphyll usually consists of a **petiole**, a thin basal stalk which attaches the whole leaf to the stem; two **stipules**, small appendages which grow out near the base of the petiole in many species; and a **lamina**, the leaf blade itself. In the lamina, the vascular tissue together with greater or lesser amounts of supporting fiber tissue forms **veins** (Fig. 10.22). These may be either *parallel* to one another or *reticulate*, i.e.,

arranged in the form of a network. In external form, a lamina may be *flattened, needle-shaped*, or *scalelike* (Fig. 10.23).

The geometric arrangement of leaves on a stem is known as **phyllotaxis**. Several different phyllotactic patterns may be distinguished. Leaves are said to be *alternate* if single leaves grow out at successive levels of the stem. In such cases the leaf bases mark out a spiral which winds up along a stem. The geometric characteristics of such spirals are quite distinct for given species. Leaves are *opposite* if two leaves grow out at the same level of the stem, and they are *whorled* if more than two are attached to the same level. In these instances, the regions of the stem where leaves grow out are called **nodes**, and the leaf-free regions between two consecutive nodes are called **internodes** (see Fig. 10.23).

In tracheophyte species living in the temperate zone, the plant body may become dormant during the winter. As noted earlier, growth ceases and the leaves are shed in many cases. A fallen leaf leaves a perma-

FIG. 10.22   The pattern of veins in a leaf. A close-up of a portion of the vein pattern is shown at right. *(Brooklyn Botanical Garden.)*

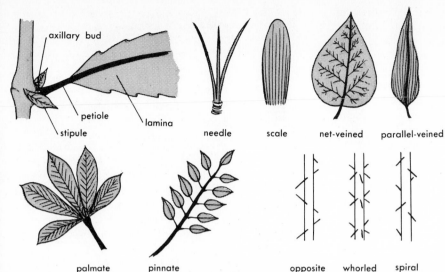

FIG. 10.23   Leaf types and leaf arrangements.

nent **leaf scar** on the stem. In such species also, the apical shoot meristems are protected during the winter by **bud scales.** These are modified leaves or leaf parts produced at the approach of winter around an apical meristem. The scales are densely placed and make up an apical or **terminal bud** on a dormant stem in winter condition (Fig. 10.24). When apical growth resumes the following spring, bud scales fall off and leave densely placed **bud-scale scars** on the stem. By counting the number of stem regions where such scars occur, it may often be possible to determine the age of the plant.

In some tracheophytes, particularly in primitive types, stems branch **dichotomously;** i.e., a given stem splits terminally into two equal branches. This is brought about by a vertical subdivision of the shoot apex, and each branch so acquires its own apical meristem. More commonly, however, branching is **monopodial;** i.e., a given stem produces one or more subordinate *lateral branches.* A lateral branch arises from a **branch bud,** developed in the apical shoot meristem in the so-called *leaf axil.* This is the region where a leaf joins the stem, specifically the angle between the upper leaf or petiole surface and the stem. Wherever a leaf bud is formed, a branch bud forms in the leaf axil. Such branch buds always produce their own **branch gaps** in the stele of the parent stem (see Fig. 10.19).

Branch buds often do not mature immediately. Some may remain dormant for many years and some may not develop at all. Accordingly, a leaf may or may not be accompanied by a branch stem. Dormant branch buds are usually clearly visible just above leaf scars in wintering stems. When a branch bud does mature, it develops an apex of its own and grows in every respect like the parent stem. We note again that an important difference between a leaf and a branch is that one does not and the other does acquire an apex in the bud stage.

FIG. 10.24   Diagram, stem with dormant buds. Photo, terminal dormant bud of the horse chestnut. *(Photo, Jean Carel, Paris.)*

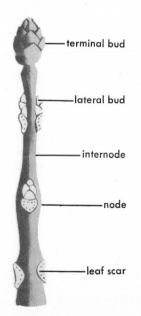

— terminal bud

— lateral bud

— internode

— node

— leaf scar

Roots may form branches also, but the process of development here differs from that of stem branches. At varying distances behind the apex of the main or primary root, **lateral roots** may be formed (Fig. 10.25). Such branch roots originate in the pericycle. Cells in localized regions of the pericycle divide and form a pad of tissue, the so-called **root primordium.** As such a primordium develops further, it pushes out through the peripheral tissues of the primary root. By the time it emerges through the epidermis, a root cap and the primary meristems have been formed. Later a stele with vascular tissues matures, and these tissues become continuous with the corresponding tissues of the primary root. Thereafter the lateral root is fully established and continues to grow like a primary root.

SECONDARY GROWTH

The whole organization of the tracheophyte plant body described up to this point represents the result of **primary growth:** all body parts are direct derivatives of the apical meristems and the three primary meristems of the embryo. As we have seen, primary growth is essentially growth in *length,* and any increase in the thickness of stems and roots comes about mainly through enlargement of cells in a lateral direction. In many tracheophytes, primary growth is typically the only means of increasing body size. However, large numbers of tracheophytes are capable of growing not only in length but also in thickness, through lateral increase of cell *number.* These plants have evolved processes of **secondary growth,** superimposed on the earlier processes of primary growth. Apart from comparatively enormous increases in stem and root girth, the gross result of such secondary growth is the development of *bark* and of secondary *wood.*

Secondary wood tends to be formed in relatively large quantities and new layers are added each year to those accumulated previously. Such plants develop into shrubs and trees and become recognizably *woody* in character. To be sure, primary growth also produces wood, i.e., primary xylem. But in the vast majority of cases primary wood is formed in such small amounts that the plant is left in a *herbaceous* condition; and if a distinctly woody appearance is to develop, secondary wood must be formed by secondary growth. Thus the term "woody plants" refers largely to plants in which secondary growth occurs.

In such woody plants, young shoots and roots develop as in all other cases through primary growth.

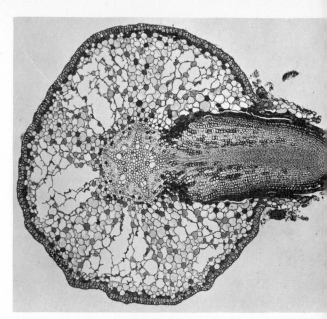

FIG. 10.25 Cross section of a root with outgrowing lateral root. Note that the lateral root originates in the pericycle region of the primary root. *(Courtesy of J. Limbach, Ripon Microslides.)*

Later too, the plant continues to elongate through primary growth at each apex, and the regions immediately behind each apex maintain the characteristic primary organization of nonwoody roots and stems. More specifically, in plants in which secondary growth occurs the primary root pattern is actinostelic and the primary stem pattern is typically dictyostelic. Transformation of these primary patterns into secondary ones begins only in older regions, well behind each apex; as is well known, even woody plants have early shoots and later growing tips which remain "green." Since leaves bud off near the shoot apex and do not possess apices of their own, they do not participate in secondary development at all.

The transformation of roots and stems from primary to secondary states is brought about by **secondary meristems,** or **cambia.** Two kinds of cambia develop: a **vascular cambium** and a **cork cambium.** Each arises from different primary tissues, and the process of formation differs somewhat in root and stem.

The Vascular Cambium

In a root, the vascular cambium forms between the primary xylem and phloem in the stele (Fig. 10.26).

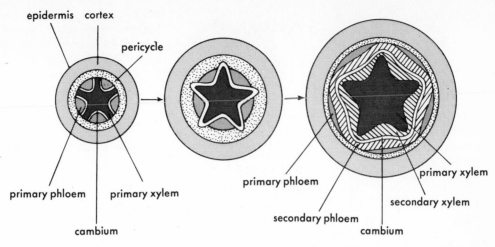

FIG. 10.26   The development of cambium and of cambium-derived tissues in the root. In some roots, pith is in the center (not shown here).

As noted earlier, if only primary growth occurs in a root, embryonic procambium eventually transforms completely into adult actinostelic tissues. But if secondary growth occurs as well, a layer of procambium cells between the primary xylem and phloem remains permanently embryonic and relatively unspecialized.

These cells form the vascular root cambium, which ultimately rings in the primary root xylem completely.

In a stem, part of the vascular cambium again forms between primary xylem and phloem, from procambium which has remained undifferentiated (Fig. 10.27). Since the primary vascular tissues in the dictyo-

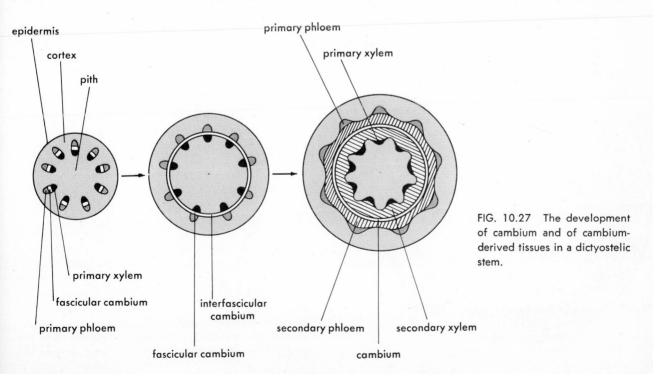

FIG. 10.27   The development of cambium and of cambium-derived tissues in a dictyostelic stem.

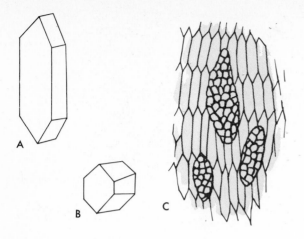

FIG. 10.28 Cell types of cambium. A, fusiform initial. B, ray initial. C, tangential view of cambium layer, showing arrangement of fusiform initials and islands of ray initials.

FIG. 10.29 Cross section of a three-year-old woody stem. (Courtesy of J. Limbach, Ripon Microslides.)

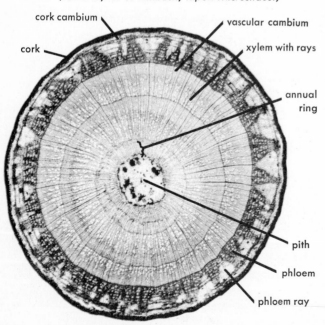

cork cambium

cork

vascular cambium

xylem with rays

annual ring

pith

phloem

phloem ray

stelic stem are in the form of circularly grouped bundles, with xylem toward the inside and phloem toward the outside, procambium layers between these xylem and phloem areas are arranged like an incomplete tube, interrupted between neighboring bundles. This discontinuous tube soon becomes continuous, for layers of parenchyma between neighboring bundles acquire the properties of a cambium. As a result, the vascular cambium eventually formed in the stem is a complete tube. This cambial tube of the stem is continuous with the similar tube of the root; and as the stem-root axis continues to elongate through primary growth at the apices, the open-ended cambial tube lengthens apace as progressively more cambium develops behind the apices.

Vascular cambium in both root and stem contains two types of meristematic cells (Fig. 10.28). The less-abundant type comprises so-called **ray initials**. As these continue to divide, they bud off new cells toward both the inside and the outside of the cambial layer. The new cells on the inside form persistently lengthening strands of tissue extending toward the center of the stem. Such strands are **xylem rays**. Analogously, new cells deposited toward the outside of the cambial layer become tissue strands called **phloem rays**. Both kinds of rays function in lateral transport of nutrients within stem and root.

All other cells of the cambium, vastly more numerous than the ray initials, are known as **fusiform initials**. They too continue to bud off new cells toward both the inside and the outside. Indeed, the combined activity of all the fusiform initials generates whole *layers* of new cells at both sides of the cambium. Layers produced toward the inside soon mature into all the various cellular components of xylem tissue; layers budded off toward the outside form all the various components of phloem tissue (see Chap. 5). Vascular tissue so generated by cambium is called **secondary xylem** (or **secondary wood**) and **secondary phloem**. These tissues are traversed in places by the xylem and phloem rays (Fig. 10.29).

Clearly, as secondary xylem continues to be formed in successive concentric layers within the cambial tube, it comes to press against the primary xylem and the pith already there. These early tissues may become compressed somewhat, and thereafter any new secondary xylem produced expands the net thickness of the stem or the root. Analogously, as secondary phloem develops in concentric tubes from the cambial tube outward, it increases the thickness of stem or root still

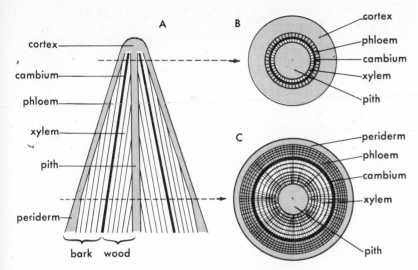

FIG. 10.30 A, diagrammatic longitudinal view of a shoot, showing the formation of successive tissue layers to the outside and inside of the cambium. A cross section at the level of the upper broken line would appear as in B; at the level of the lower broken line, as in C.

more and pushes out all the primary phloem, the cortex, and the epidermis. Since these early primary tissues are adult and cannot grow by cell division and since they therefore cannot keep pace with the ever-expanding girth of stem or root, they ultimately rupture.

Note that successive concentric tubes of secondary xylem and phloem become progressively longer, inasmuch as the cambial tube which generates them becomes longer itself as the stem-root axis gradually elongates. Also, the smallest amounts of secondary tissue are always near the apices, where cambial activity is just beginning; the largest amounts are accumulated at the stem-root juncture, the region which has grown for the longest period and is the oldest. This is therefore the region of greatest girth, and from here the stem *tapers* upward and the root tapers downward (Fig. 10.30).

The Cork Cambium

Also known as **phellogen,** this secondary meristem originates in the stem, usually in the cortex, just underneath the epidermis (Fig. 10.31). In the root, cork cambium arises from outer layers of the pericycle. The cells of this tissue first proliferate by cell division, and this pushes the endodermis, the cortex, and the epidermis outward, usually resulting in their loss from the root. An outer layer of the enlarged pericycle then differentiates as cork cambium.

The cork cambium of both stem and root, like the vascular cambium, produces new cell layers toward the inside and outside. Layers budded off toward the inside are called **phelloderm.** The cells here differentiate as

parenchyma. Layers formed toward the outside are called **phellem** or **cork.** During their maturation, cork cells deposit heavy suberin coats on their walls and accumulate many tannin compounds in their interior. The living substance of these cells then disintegrates, and mature cork consequently is wholly nonliving. Cork, cork cambium, and the inner phelloderm are collectively referred to as the **periderm.**

Cork cells are usually packed close together, and intercellular spaces are absent. Because of this and as a result of the chemical makeup of cork cells, the outer covering of a woody plant is quite impervious to water and air. At various places, however, the cork cambium produces loosely arranged cork cells separated by intercellular spaces. Such spongy regions are known as **lenticels.** They permit the interior living tissues of the root and the stem to exchange gases with the atmosphere (Fig. 10.32).

As root and stem girth continues to increase through secondary growth, vascular growth in particular, the original epidermal and cortical tissues tear and are soon sloughed off. Periderm first develops in the fissures, and eventually a continuous layer of periderm comes to surround the entire circumference of stem or root. Soon, however, further increases in stem and root diameter cause a rupturing and flaking off of the original periderm. New cork cambium then differentiates in the pericycle of roots and in the secondary phloem of stems, and new cork is produced. This tissue later ruptures and flakes off in turn, and the cycle of new formation and flaking off repeats indefinitely. The pericycle of roots itself disappears later, and secondary

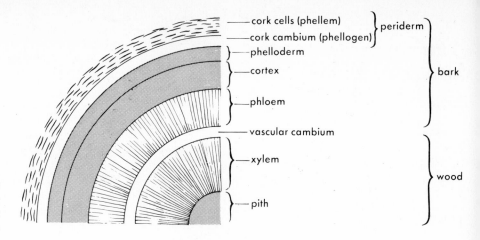

cork cells (phellem) ⎫ periderm
cork cambium (phellogen) ⎬
phelloderm ⎭
cortex ⎫ bark
phloem ⎬
vascular cambium ⎭
xylem ⎫ wood
pith ⎭

FIG. 10.31 Diagram, right: the position of the cork cambium and its products in a woody stem. Photograph, bottom: the structure of the periderm. (Photograph, courtesy of Dr. M. S. Fuller, Brown University.)

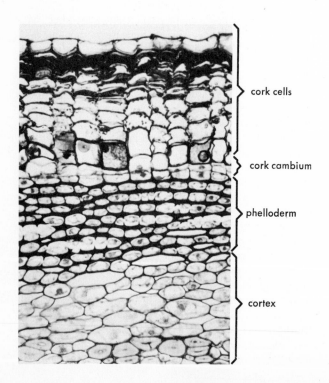

cork cells

cork cambium

phelloderm

cortex

phloem in both root and stem ultimately becomes the chief source for the regeneration of cork cambium.

The Woody Condition

As has been shown in the above account, **wood** fills most of the space inside the tube of vascular cambium. All tissues outside the tube of vascular cambium are collectively called **bark.**

Note that in a mature woody section of a stem nothing is left of the original primary tissues except the central pith, possibly some primary xylem around the pith, and the microscopically thin layer of vascular cambium at the line of juncture between wood and bark. In a mature woody root the pattern is similar, except in some cases in which pith is absent from the beginning. Thus the concentric components of a woody section are, from the outside inward: periderm, secondary phloem, vascular cambium, secondary xylem, and usually pith.

Secondary phloem is produced less abundantly than secondary xylem. Moreover, older xylem accumulates and persists in the core of the trunk, whereas older phloem toward the surface of the trunk continually flakes off as the trunk thickens. Therefore, only a thin rind of young phloem is present within bark at any given time. As a further result, the vast bulk of a trunk is nonliving; all the tracheids and vessels in wood, as well as the cork layer in bark, are devoid of living substance.

Just as only *young* phloem is functional, so also only *young* xylem is functional. Older xylem, though present, in time gradually blocks up with resins and gums, and water conduction through these channels

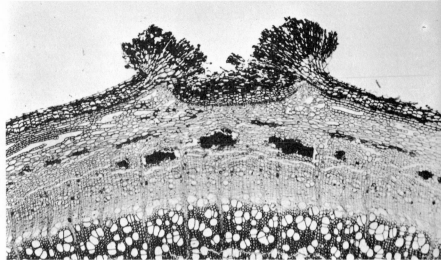

FIG. 10.32 Lenticels. External and cross-sectional views. *(External view, courtesy of Dr. M. S. Fuller, Brown University; section, courtesy of J. Limbach, Ripon Microslides.)*

is then no longer possible. Such central regions of a trunk are called **heartwood** (Fig. 10.33). The core of a tree may therefore be hollowed out without interfering with xylem conduction. But the outer, young wood of a tree, called the **sapwood,** must remain intact if a tree is to remain alive.

Annual rings are usually fairly conspicuous in an older tree growing in the temperate zone (see Fig. 10.33). Xylem vessels laid down during spring generally have a larger diameter than those formed in summer. In spring, melting snow provides the tree with much water. As a response to hormones (see Chap. 19) produced in developing leaves, wider conducting channels are then formed which accommodate the greater flow. The alternation of narrow summer and fall xylem and wider spring xylem is recognizable with the naked eye as concentric dark and light banding—annual rings. The number of rings indicates the age of a tree. Moreover, from the comparative widths of spring and summer rings it is also possible to estimate the amount of rainfall, hence general climatic conditions, during past seasons as far back in time as the tree has lived.

Through the secondary growth processes described, a young, green sporophyte is slowly transformed into a tall, thick, tapering woody tree. Note that such a plant can become really tall only because secondary tissues displace primary ones everywhere except near the apices. For although a plant *can* elongate through pri-

mary growth, such elongation will be greatly limited for obvious mechanical reasons if a corresponding increase in thickness cannot take place at the same time.

TRACHEOPHYTE GROUPS

PHYLUM TRACHEOPHYTA: VASCULAR PLANTS
(about 260,000 species)

Subphylum PSILOPSIDA: *Psilotum* (2 species)
Tmesipteris (1 species)
Subphylum LYCOPSIDA: club mosses, ground pines, quillworts (about 900 species)
Subphylum SPHENOPSIDA: horsetails, scouring rushes (25 species)
Subphylum PTEROPSIDA: large-leafed vascular plants
Class Filicineae: ferns (about 10,000 species)
Class Gymnospermae: cone-bearing seed plants (about 700 species)
Class Angiospermae: flowering seed plants (about 250,000 species)

Internal evidence from living tracheophytes as well as fossil data (see Chap. 30) indicate that ancestral Psilopsida probably were the first members of the

FIG. 10.33   Portion of a 12-year-old tree trunk, showing annual rings. *(United States Forest Service.)*

phylum, evolved in some independent way from an unknown green algal stock. Early psilopsids in turn appear to have given rise to four separate branch lines, represented today by the four subphyla listed above. Of these, the first three came to flourish soon after they evolved, but then they declined. Today they are little more than evolutionary relics. Pteropsida, on the contrary, started out relatively inconspicuously but subsequently increased in importance slowly and steadily. At present they are unquestionably the dominant group of plants. Flowering plants in particular include more species than all other Metaphyta and plantlike Protista combined.

PSILOPSIDA

The three living species in this subphylum are all xerophytes. *Psilotum* grows in tropical and subtropical regions of the Americas, either in soil pockets rich in

humus or epiphytically on trees. *Tmesipteris* is found in Australia, New Zealand, and New Caledonia as a hanging epiphyte on fern and other trees (Fig. 10.34).

The sporophyte body of the psilopsids is based on a horizontal rhizome, underground in the nonepiphytic plants. A unique distinguishing feature of the subphylum and unquestionably a highly primitive trait is the absence of true roots. The only absorptive structures present are *unicellular rhizoids*. The erect aerial stems growing upward from the rhizome are about 1 ft or more high and branch dichotomously. In adaptation to xeric habitats, the aerial stems possess a heavily cutinized epidermis with sunken stomata.

Internally, a psilopsid stem (Fig. 10.35) contains a parenchymatous cortex with chloroplast-containing layers and with sclerenchymatous strengthening layers more interiorly. An endodermis with passage cells is present. The steles of rhizomes are usually actinosteles. Siphonosteles may occur in aerial stems. Thick-walled

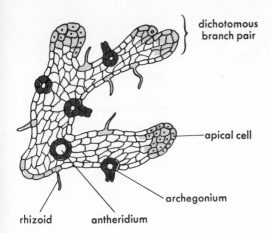

dichotomous branch pair

apical cell

archegonium

rhizoid   antheridium

FIG. 10.34 *Psilopsida*. Left, gameto-phyte of *Psilotum*, diagrammatic representation. Right, sporophyte of *Psilotum*. (*Right, courtesy of Dr. M. S. Fuller, Brown University.*)

sclerenchyma functions as pith in these cases. Secondary growth does not occur, and xylem contains tracheids only, not vessels. The leaves are always *microphylls*. In *Psilotum*, such leaves contain neither vascular tissue nor stomata. A single strand of vascular tissue and stomata are present, however, in the microphylls of *Tmesipteris*.

FIG. 10.35   Cross section of a stem of *Psilotum*. Note the epidermis with cuticle and stomata, the thick underlying cortex with a layer of sclerenchymatous cells, and the central actinostelic protostele with xylem in the core and surrounding phloem. (*Courtesy of Dr. M. S. Fuller, Brown University.*)

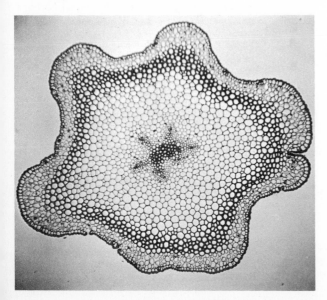

The sporangia of psilopsids are in bulbous cases developed on the aerial stems (see Fig. 10.34). Spores develop into gametophytes which are tiny independent plantlets. They consist largely of nongreen parenchymatous cells, and they are covered with rhizoids. These plants are saprotrophs living on tree trunks, in rocky crevices, and occasionally in soil. The sex organs of the gametophytes produce eggs and swimming, multiflagellate sperms. As in bryophytes, wet periods are required for fertilization.

LYCOPSIDA

These plants are comparatively the most abundant of the three relic subphyla. They still range in respectable numbers from the tropics to north-temperate regions. Many ancestral lycopsids were large woody trees, but their present-day relatives are invariably small and nonwoody. Vestiges of secondary growth are still encountered in the quillworts. Many lycopsids are creepers with prostrate rhizomes, others are erect, and some are epiphytes. In all cases, true roots are present and leaves are always microphyllous.

Horizontal as well as erect dichotomously branched stems are encountered in the club mosses and ground pines of the genus *Lycopodium* (Fig. 10.36). Roots here are frequently adventitious, the pericycle of the stem being the tissue from which such roots arise. In erect plants, adventitious roots sometimes originate near the shoot apex and grow down right *through* the stem cortex. All growth is primary. Roots are usually actinostelic; stems are actinostelic and plectostelic. Leaves contain air spaces in the mesophyll and stomata on both surfaces.

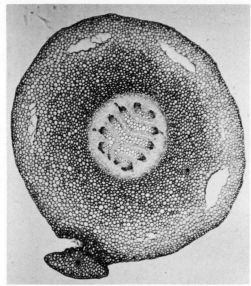
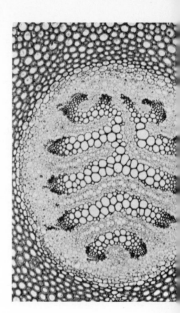

FIG. 10.36 *Lycopodium.* Left, whole plant. Middle, cross section through a stem. Right, the stele of a stem. This stele combines actinostelic and plectostelic features. *(Courtesy of Dr. M. S. Fuller, Brown University.)*

The sporangia of *Lycopodium* develop terminally on erect stems. Leaves bearing sporangia are called **sporophylls,** and a whole group of such sporophylls at the tip of a stem forms a **cone** or **strobilus.** Gametophytes are small, independent, soil-inhabiting plantlets, ovid or cylindrical in shape (Fig. 10.37). Their base is colorless and bears many rhizoids. Lobes containing green parenchyma project upward into the air. The gametophytes of many species are perennial, persisting for as long as 10 to 25 years. Such gametophytes possess marginal meristems and may therefore grow continuously. Sperms are flagellate and swimming, and wet conditions are required for fertilization.

The genus *Selaginella* includes a most interesting group of lycopsids; unusual or noteworthy features are exhibited by all body parts of the sporophytes and by the gametophytes as well. Living largely in damp, shady places in the tropics, the sporophytes are small and delicate, some of them erect and shrubby, others rhizomatous with erect branches (Fig. 10.38). Growth is primary. The stem epidermis is cutinized but is without stomata. Stems are haplostelic, but upright branch stems often contain *several* haplosteles *each.* If such branches are put into horizontal positions, all newly formed procambial tissues mature as a single stele, as

FIG. 10.37 Gametophyte of *Lycopodium,* diagrammatic representation. Note the sex organs in the aerial portions and the rhizoids in the subterranean portions.

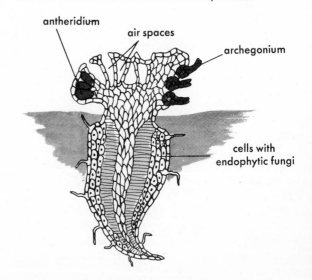

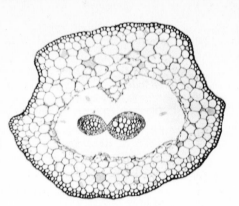
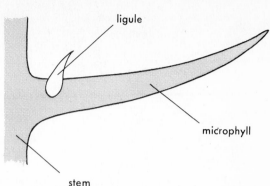

FIG. 10.38 *Selaginella*. Left, whole plant; note the rhizophores. Middle, cross section through a stem; note the two haplosteles situated in the large central air space. Right, the position of a ligule on a microphyll. *(Left, Jean Carel, Paris; middle, courtesy of Dr. M. S. Fuller, Brown University.)*

in originally horizontal stems. Each haplostele is surrounded on all sides by a large air space, and the stele is held in place only by endodermis cells which traverse the air space and interconnect cortex and stele.

Very young sporophytes develop roots like other lycopsids, but virtually all later roots form from so-called **rhizophores**. These are stemlike outgrowths produced from *axial meristems*, located where an upright stem forks into branches. A rhizophore arcs from such an axial meristem into the ground, and the part which enters the ground reorganizes structurally and functionally into a root.

The leaves are microphylls, with stomata usually only in the lower epidermis. Internally, the mesophyll is organized into distinct palisade and spongy layers. Each leaf also bears a **ligule,** a small tuft of tissue attached to the upper leaf surface near the juncture with the stem (see Fig. 10.38). Ligules are characteristic of lycopsids generally, but they are not present in *Lycopodium*. Neither the function nor the evolution of ligules is known.

Selaginella is *heterosporous;* i.e., it produces *two* types of spores: small **microspores** and larger **megaspores**. Among tracheophytes now living, this phenomenon is otherwise encountered only in advanced pteropsids (see below and Chap. 25). *Microsporangia* form microspores, and these grow into *microgametophytes*. The latter produce only swimming, flagellate sperms. Analogously, *megasporangia* form megaspores, and these develop into exclusively egg-producing *megagametophytes* (see Chap. 25). Both types of gametophytes are microscopic, consisting of but a few cells.

They are nongreen and they remain within their respective sporangia, nourished by food previously supplied by the parent sporophytes. Sperms must swim from a microgametophyte to a megagametophyte, and fertilization and embryonic development then take place there.

Quillworts of the genus *Isoetes* are the only surviving lycopsids still capable of secondary growth (Fig. 10.39). They do not become woody, however, and their secondary growth results from the activities of a *cortical* cambium. Quillworts are deciduous perennials. They live in marshy areas, with stems embedded in the ground. The stems are *corms*. Numerous roots project from the lower part of the corm, and the upper part bears dense clusters of erect microphylls which project into the air. This gives the quillwort part of its English name as well as a superficial resemblance to a patch of lawn grass.

SPHENOPSIDA

Like the lycopsids, the sphenopsids attained their evolutionary peak in past ages. The only surviving genus is *Equisetum*, and all living sphenopsids are members of it (Fig. 10.40). These plants range from the tropics to the temperate zone. They are characterized by an underground rhizome which bears erect aerial branches with microphylls. Roots are largely adventitious growing out along the rhizome. The underground portions are perennial, but the aerial structures of plants in the temperate zone are regrown each year.

Growth is exclusively primary. Roots are actino-

FIG. 10.39 *Isoetes*, aerial portions. *(Courtesy of Dr. R. H. Mohlenbrock, University of Southern Illinois, and Am. Fern J., vol. 50, p. 181.)*

stelic; stems are largely dictyostelic. The stems are conspicuously ribbed longitudinally, and the epidermal cells are not only cutinized but also coated with thick deposits of silica. Stomata occur between the ridges of the stem. The cortex consists of outer layers of scleren-

chyma and inner layers of photosynthetic parenchyma. Vertical air spaces and wide air canals pass through both cortex and pith. The vascular bundles are located under the ridges of the stem and each is enveloped by endodermis (Fig. 10.41).

Leaves have stomata on both surfaces, and numerous air spaces ramify through the inner mesophyll. The phyllotactic arrangement is characteristically *nodal* and *whorled*. Rhizomes are similarly nodal. In many forms the rhizome produces not only highly branched green aerial shoots but also unbranched nongreen sporangial shoots. In all sphenopsids the sporangia are in cones, as in lycopsids.

The gametophytes are small, independent plantlets. They have the appearance of miniature pincushions, with tiny wings or lobes projecting upward (Fig. 10.42). The lobes are green; the base usually is not. Rhizoids grow from the underside of the base. Sperms are flagellate and swimming and water is required for fertilization.

PTEROPSIDA

This largest subphylum of the tracheophytes has probably descended from early psilopsid stock as a fourth independent evolutionary line. Ferns were undoubtedly primitive, and an ancestral group of ferns then gave rise to the seed plants. Among these in turn, cone-bearing types evolved first and some of these were probably ancestral to the flowering types (see Chap. 30).

The subphylum as a whole is distinguished from the three others by the presence of **megaphylls**, large leaves with multiple vascular bundles, which always leave leaf gaps where they branch off from the stele.

FIG. 10.40 *Equisetum*. Left, a portion of whole plant. Note nodal and whorled arrangement of the branches and, above each node, the whorls of the tips of the microphylls. Right, enlarged view of a nodal region, showing the ribbing of the stem. *(Left, Jean Carel and Larousse Publishing Co., Paris; right, courtesy of Dr. R. Hauke, University of Rhode Island.)*

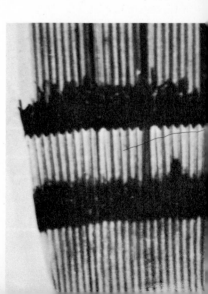

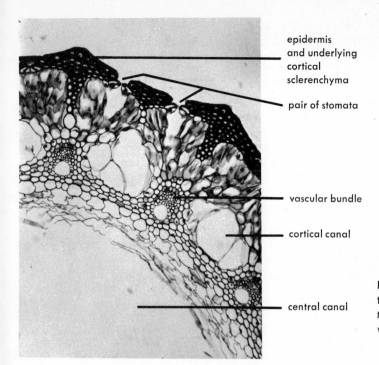

epidermis
and underlying
cortical
sclerenchyma

pair of stomata

vascular bundle

cortical canal

central canal

FIG. 10.41 Cross section of a portion of a stem of *Equisetum. (Courtesy of Dr. M. S. Fuller, Brown University.)*

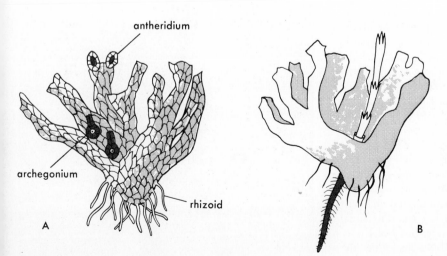

antheridium

archegonium

rhizoid

A

B

FIG. 10.42 The gametophyte of *Equisetum. A,* gametophyte with sex organs; *B,* gametophyte with young sporophyte.

With the exception of only a few pteropsids having protostelic stems, all other pteropsids possess stems with pith. Roots are mostly actinostelic.

Class Filicineae

Ferns are possibly even more abundant today than in the past. They range from temperate regions to the tropics, where they reach their greatest development. Tree ferns in such localities may attain heights of 50 to 60 ft, with leaves 10 to 15 ft long. (But note that tree ferns are nonwoody; secondary growth is absent from the entire class.) Other ferns are shrubby, and many are hanging epiphytes in rain forests. Deciduous forests and other well-watered temperate-zone areas harbor many fern species as abundant ground cover. Some few ferns are secondarily aquatic.

Most ferns are characterized by underground perennial rhizomes, with large, upright, complexly shaped leaves. These are regrown every year in most species of the temperate zone, but in some species the leaves last several seasons and thus are perennial. Leaves commonly exhibit *circinate vernation;* i.e., young leaves form tight coils, and as they grow by division of meristematic cells at the leaf tip they unroll and straighten up (Fig. 10.43).

The stem is frequently covered with fibrous remnants of leaf bases, giving it a somewhat "hairy" appearance. An epidermis is underlain by a thick cortex which is highly sclerenchymatous. As a result, fern stems may have a strength equivalent to that of wood, which permits some ferns to attain the proportions of trees. The vascular tissue can be variously protostelic, siphonostelic, or dictyostelic (Fig. 10.44). All variant types of these steles are encountered among ferns, plus some additional variants which do not exist in other plants. Growth is primary in all cases. Xylem contains not vessels, but tracheids only. In some species, primitive kinds of vessels are formed by a loss of pit membranes at the endwalls of adjacent tracheids. Continuous longitudinal channels arise in this manner.

Sporangia develop on the undersides of leaves, frequently in groups projecting from the lower leaf surface. Such groups may be covered over with a cap of sterile tissue, the **indusium.** A multisporangial structure of this kind is known as a **sorus.** Numerous sori may form in rows on a leaf (Fig. 10.45). Spores are discharged by a unique catapult mechanism described in Chap. 25. Gametophytes (see Fig. 25.10), are independent, green, and up to 1 cm in size. The body of these plantlets is a prostrate heart-shaped thallus. Rhizoids

project from the underside. This side also bears the sex organs. Sperms are flagellate and swimming.

Class Gymnospermae

Subclass Cycadophytae
    Order Cycadales—cycads (100 species)
Subclass Coniferophytae
    Order Ginkgoales—*Ginkgo* (1 species)
    Order Coniferales—conifers (about 600 species)
    Order Gnetales—(about 70 species)

The most distinctive features of this class are reproductive, and we shall discuss the details in Chap. 25. However, we may note here that gymnosperms are *heterosporous* (like *Selaginella*), with microspores and megaspores developed in microsporangia and megasporangia, respectively. The latter are borne on sporophylls which form *cones.* Moreover, reproduction includes a process of **pollination,** which circumvents the requirement of free external water for sperms. After

FIG. 10.43 Circinate vernation of a developing fern leaf. (*R. H. Noailles, Museum of Natural History, Paris.*)

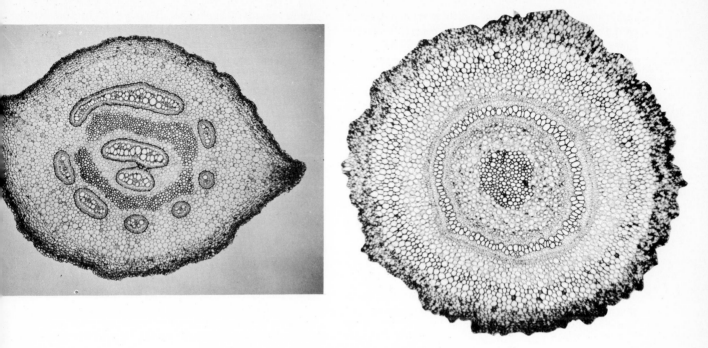

FIG. 10.44 Two types of steles in ferns. Left, stem with partly dictyostelic and partly plectostelic features. Right, siphonostele. *(Courtesy of J. Limbach, Ripon Micro-slides.)*

FIG. 10.45 Fern sori. In left photograph, note the small black sporangia projecting beyond the indusium in some of the sori. Indusia are not present in right photograph. *(Left, courtesy of Charles Neidorf, Fair Lawn, New Jersey; right, R. H. Noailles, Museum of Natural History, Paris.)*

fertilization, **seeds** are formed and these remain exposed or naked on the sporophylls of the cones; hence the name of the class, "naked-seed formers." Through the evolution of pollination, gymnosperms were the first Metaphyta to become reproductively quite independent of free water. This contributed immeasurably to their success as terrestrial plants.

Most gymnosperms are perennial evergreens. Primary growth produces actinostelic roots and dictyostelic stems. Active secondary growth occurs thereafter, however, and the woody habit is virtually universal in the class. Only tracheids form in xylem; vessels do not.

In the subclass Cycadophytae the cycads, or "sago palms," are the only living order. These plants flourished throughout the world in past ages, but today they are limited to isolated areas in tropical and subtropical regions. Many cycads are grown as ornamental plants in California, Florida, and some other states. As a group, cycads are smaller than conifers, averaging about 5 ft in height (Fig. 10.46). However, some species may become as tall as 60 ft. Stems are unbranched, with large leaves borne at the top. This

FIG. 10.46   A cycad. *(Jean Carel and Larousse Publishing Co., Paris.)*

gives cycads a superficial resemblance to tree ferns. Internally, the stem contains a wide pith, an extensive starch-storing cortex, and very little wood.

Members of the subclass Coniferophytae are generally much more massive than the cycads, and their other characteristics are largely opposite as well. For example, Coniferophytae possess small simple leaves, narrow pith, narrow cortex, and a very active cambium which deposits extensive accumulations of wood.

The order Ginkgoales consists of the single living species *Ginkgo biloba*, the maidenhair tree (Fig. 10.47). It is native to eastern Asia, but it is used throughout the world as a shade tree. It reaches heights of some 90 to 100 ft, and its trunk may have a diameter of 3 to 4 ft at the base. The tree is highly branched, with two types of branches. One consists of **long shoots** with very little foliage. From such long branches grow short ones, so-called **spur shoots,** which bear terminal groups of wedge-shaped leaves and sporangia.

The Coniferales, or conifers proper, are the dominant, most abundant, and most conspicuous gymnosperms. Their distribution is worldwide, but they are concentrated particularly in the temperate zone and the taiga of western North America and northeast Asia. The order includes pines, spruces, firs, cedars, yews, and redwoods, all of which are evergreens; and larches and bald cypresses, which are deciduous. All are relatively tall trees, with straight main stems and many branches. Giant redwoods reach heights of some 400 ft, which makes them the largest and most massive living things on earth. Because conifers develop very much wood in proportion to other tissues, they are used widely as lumber and in paper manufacture. The vascular tissues of conifers are characterized by the presence of **resin canals,** ducts formed by the activity of the vascular cambium. These channels secrete the aromatic gums and resins so characteristic of conifer wood. The compounds are largely excretion products, and they may play a role in process of winter-hardening (Fig. 10.48).

As in ginkgoes, pines and some other conifer species develop both long shoots and spur shoots, the latter bearing most of the leaves and the sporangial cones. But most species form only long shoots, with leaves and cones attached directly to them. Leaves are familiarly needlelike in many conifers, but cypresses and incense cedars, for example, possess scalelike leaves.

The order Gnetales includes three genera (*Ephedra, Gnetum, Welwitschia*), which may not be very closely related to one another or even to other gymno-

FIG. 10.47 *Ginkgo*. Left, whole view of maidenhair tree. Right, end of long shoot with leaf-bearing spur shoots. *(Left, courtesy of New York Botanical Garden; right, Jean Carel and Larousse Publishing Co., Paris.)*

FIG. 10.48 Pine wood. Left, transverse section; note resin canal near bottom of photograph. Middle, radial section; note pits in tracheids and xylem ray traversing upper part of photograph. Right, tangential section; note pits in tracheid walls and end view of a xylem ray in mid-region of photograph. *(Courtesy of J. Limbach, Ripon Microslides.)*

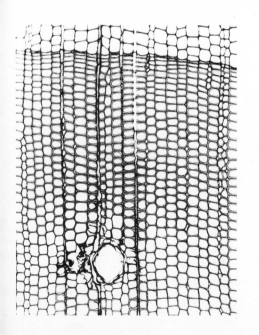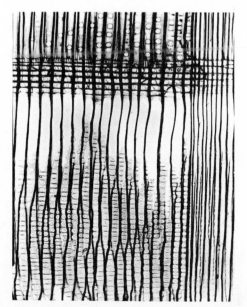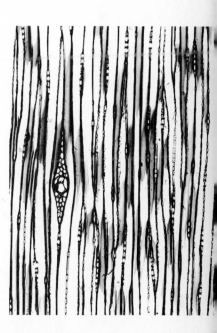

sperms (Fig. 10.49). One of the principal distinguishing features of the group is the presence of true xylem vessels, a trait not otherwise encountered among gymnosperms but typical generally of angiosperms. Gnetales may possibly represent remnants of one or more quite independent lines of pteropsid evolution.

Class Angiospermae

Subclass Dicotyledoneae (200,000 species)
Subclass Monocotyledoneae (50,000 species)

Flowering plants today inhabit virtually all environments except the open ocean. They include annuals, biennials, and virtually all possible kinds of perennials; herbaceous types, semiherbaceous types, and woody types; aquatic types, parasitic types, saprotrophic types, and partly carnivorous types. They enrich the world with unmatched beauty, color, and scent, but they also exude poison and stench. Some survive only for a few days; others live for centuries. Some are near-microscopic; others are gigantic. Some live in solitude in dusty deserts or wind-blown tundras; others form impenetrable jungles. They provide man and other animals with practically all of their food and most of their shelter, and in addition they provide man with much of his clothing, many of his drugs, and numerous of the other vital necessities which maintain his civilization. Angiosperms as a group display more adaptive plasticity and variety than any other group of plants,

major or minor; and far more so than in any other case, an unqualified reference to "plants" implies a reference to the flowering plants.

The class is distinguished from gymnosperms by the presence of xylem which contains tracheids as well as true **vessels.** In sclerenchyma tissue, the components are not only sclereids as in other tracheophytes, but also **fibers.** Reproductively, angiosperms are heterosporous, pollen-producing, and seed-forming. However, angiosperm sporangia are in **flowers,** not cones. Seeds are not exposed on sporophylls as in gymnosperms, but groups of them are developed and are retained within an **ovary;** hence the name of the class, "hidden-seed formers." After seed formation the ovary expands into a **fruit.** Details of these and other reproductive characteristics will be discussed in Chap. 25.

Evidence from living angiosperms indicates that their unknown ancestors probably possessed actinostelic roots, and dictyostelic stems without endodermis and with pericycles reduced or absent. They also must have possessed capacity of secondary growth. From such an ancestral stock, two independent evolutionary lines probably led to the two present subclasses, the "dicots" and the "monocots." Each retained most of the ancestral traits, but changed or added others. The probable evolutionary forces which promoted such changes will be outlined in Chap. 30.

Among the dicots, many have retained the capacity of extensive secondary growth. These constitute the

FIG. 10.49   Gnetales. Left, branches of *Ephedra* (microsporangiate on left, megasporangiate at right). Right, *Welwitschia.* (Left, from A. S. Foster and E. M. Gifford, Jr., "Comparative Morphology of Vascular Plants," W. H. Freeman and Co., San Francisco, 1959; right, Chicago Natural History Museum.)

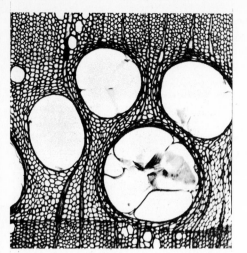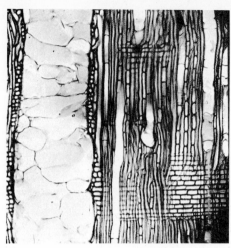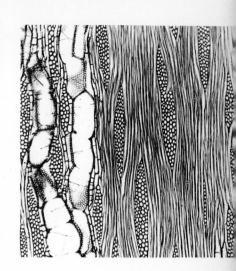

FIG. 10.50 Oak wood. Left, transverse section. Middle, radial section. Right, tangential section. In left photograph, note the large vessels into which parenchyma has grown. Such vessels appear in longitudinal section toward the left of the middle and the right photographs. Groups of xylem ray cells appear in longitudinal section in the middle photograph and in cross section in the right photograph. *(Courtesy of J. Limbach, Ripon Microslides.)*

woody dicots (e.g., oak, Fig. 10.50). Other dicots exhibit secondary growth only to a reduced degree; i.e., they become woody only in old, basal portions of the stem and root. Such plants are *semiherbaceous* dicots (e.g., sunflower, Fig. 10.51). A third group of dicots has lost secondary-growth capacity altogether. Such dicots are fully *herbaceous* (e.g., buttercup, Fig. 10.52).

The monocot subclass has changed rather more drastically from the ancestral condition. First, the primary stem has not remained dictyostelic as in the dicots, but has become atactostelic (e.g., corn, Fig. 10.53). Second, monocots have almost invariably lost the capacity of secondary growth; virtually all are herbaceous. The only exceptions are palms, in which a complex and rather atypical form of secondary growth is encountered.

Several other differences distinguish dicots and monocots (Fig. 10.54). Leaves are characteristically net-veined in dicots, parallel-veined in monocots. Flower parts and seed chambers in the ovary occur in fours, fives, or multiples of these numbers in dicots, but in threes or multiples thereof in monocots. In most dicots the early sporophyte embryo within the seed develops two embryonic seed leaves; in most monocots, only one such seed leaf is formed. These leaves nourish the embryo and the later seedling through stored food or

FIG. 10.51 Cross section through the stem of a sunflower. Note the circular arrangement of the vascular bundles. *(General Biological Supply House, Inc.)*

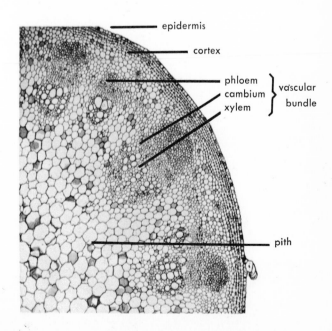

epidermis

cortex

phloem
cambium } vascular bundle
xylem

pith

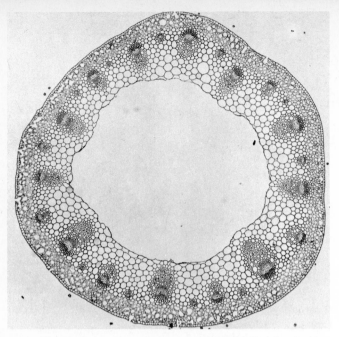

FIG. 10.52 Cross section through the stem of a butter-cup. Note the spacing of the vascular bundles and the hollow nature of the stem. *(Courtesy of G. H. Conant, Triarch Products.)*

FIG. 10.53 Cross section through the stem of a corn plant. Note the scattered arrangement of the vascular bundles. *(Courtesy of J. Limbach, Ripon Microslides.)*

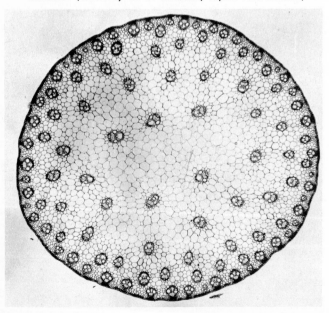

through photosynthesis, until the first adult leaves are mature. Seed leaves are called **cotyledons;** their number gives each subclass its name.

Each subclass contains numerous orders. Dicots are the more abundant and possibly the more primitive group. They include all the flowering trees and shrubs, including apple, peach, cherry, oak, chestnut, walnut, elm, and rubber trees, and many others; as well as strawberry, bean, cabbage, turnip, cotton, cocoa, coffee, avocado, celery, carrot, parsley, spinach, citrus, lilac, blueberry, cranberry, potato, tomato, tobacco, pepper, melon, cucumber, lettuce, goldenrod, rhubarb, and artichoke plants, and hundreds more. Monocots have at least equal economic importance, for in this subclass are wheat, corn, rye, rice, oat, barley, bamboo, sugar cane plants, and all other grasses; as well as palms, lilies, irises, pineapples, bananas, and orchids.

FIG. 10.54 Structural differences between dicots and monocots.

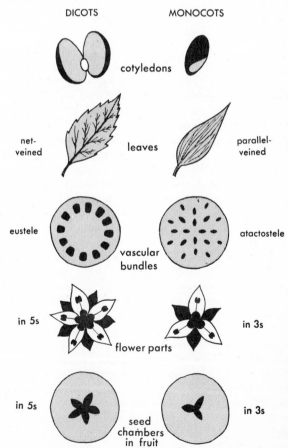

REVIEW QUESTIONS

1. Review the identifying characteristics of Metaphyta. How is this category distinguished from Protista? What is a gametophyte? A sporophyte?

2. Describe the group characteristics and the basic structure of all bryophytes. Name the classes of bryophytes and their identifying features. Define elater, thallus, rhizoid, protonema.

3. State the identifying characteristics of tracheophytes. How is this phylum classified into subphyla and classes? What is the probable evolutionary relation of (a) tracheophytes as a whole to bryophytes and Protista and (b) the subcategories within the tracheophyte phylum?

4. Review the architectural adaptations of tracheophytes to life on land. Name different modifications of (a) stems and (b) roots, and state the adaptive role of each such modification.

5. How do tracheophytes conserve water? How do they protect against (a) heat and (b) cold? What different groups of tracheophytes are perennial, biennial, and annual, and what are the life cycles of such plants?

6. Show how the sporophyte embryo of a tracheophyte develops into a mature plant by primary growth. Name specific tissues and indicate how they differentiate. Describe the organization of different types of steles.

7. Define leaf trace, leaf gap, mesophyll. What is the difference between a microphyll and a megaphyll? Describe the structure of a leaf. What types of leaves and leaf arrangements may be distinguished? How does a leaf develop?

8. Describe how a stem or a root grows in length. What is secondary growth? Show how a vascular cambium forms secondary xylem and phloem. Describe the activities of a cork cambium.

9. Define lenticel, ray initial, phellogen, periderm, fusiform initial, phloem ray, phellem, annual ring, heartwood, bark, wood.

10. Describe the complete structural organization of a mature woody plant in (a) the woody part of the stem, (b) the woody part of the root, (c) the nonwoody apical part of the stem, and (d) the nonwoody apical part of the root.

11. Describe the structure of the sporophytes of (a) psilopsids, (b) lycopsids, and (c) sphenopsids. In what aspects of the life cycle does *Lycopodium* differ from *Selaginella*?

12. Define the terms sporophyll, ligule, heterospory, rhizophore, circinate vernation, sorus, spur shoot, atactostele.

13. Review the identifying features of pteropsids. Describe the structural organization of a fern sporophyte. Show how the general life cycle of a seed plant differs from that of other tracheophytes.

14. How are gymnosperms subclassified? Describe the structural characteristics of gymnosperms. What are the identifying features of angiosperms? Name the subclasses of angiosperms and their identifying features. Name representative plants of each subclass.

15. Describe the internal structure of (a) a woody angiosperm, (b) a semiherbaceous angiosperm, and (c) a herbaceous angiosperm.

SUGGESTED COLLATERAL READINGS

For further data on the basic structure of tracheophytes, the text by Esau listed at the end of Chap. 5 is strongly recommended. Popular accounts of various tracheophytes and bryophytes are given in the following books and articles:

Anderson, E.: "Plants, Life, and Man," Little, Brown, Boston, 1952.

Biddulph, S. O.: The Circulatory System of Plants, *Sci. American*, vol. 200, 1959.

James, W. O.: Succulent Plants, *Endeavour*, vol. 17, 1958.

Mangelsdorf, P. C.: The Mystery of Corn, *Sci. American*, vol. 183, 1950.

Mangelsdorf, P. C.: Wheat, *Sci. American*, vol. 189, 1953.

Phillips, E. W. J.: The Biology and Properties of Wood, *New Biol.*, vol. 4, 1948.

Platt, R.: "Our Flowering World," Dodd, Mead. New York, 1947.

Richards, P. W.: Famous Plants: The Liverwort *Marchantia, New Biol.*, vol. 27, 1958.

Salaman, R. N.: The Social Influence of the Potato, *Sci. American*, vol. 187, 1952.

Schery, R. W.: "Plants for Man," Prentice-Hall, Englewood Cliffs, N.J., 1952.

Wardlaw, C. W.: The Banana, *New Biol.*, vol. 11, 1951.

Watson, E. V.: Famous Plants: *Funaria, New Biol.*, vol. 22, 1957.

White, D. J. B.: The Stem Apex of a Dicotyledon, *New Biol.*, vol. 16, 1954.

Williams, S.: Wood Structure, *Sci. American*, vol. 188, 1953.

METAZOA

11

The evolutionary origin of Metazoa is obscure. That they arose from ancestral Protista is hardly in doubt, but it is impossible at present to be sure exactly which protistan group was directly ancestral. Early traditional views held that Protozoa gave rise to the Metazoa, but there is little evidence to indicate whether or not this is actually correct. Metazoa may equally well have originated directly from ancestral protistan flagellates, for example, from groups which later also gave rise to chrysophyte algae. Indeed, there are some indications that different metazoan groups may have arisen independently from various different protistan stocks. All we can be reasonably sure of at present is that Metazoa evolved when some ancestral, unicellular, motile protistan group became multicellular, retaining and improving powers of locomotion but losing any photosynthetic capacity it or they may have possessed.

Metazoa are all *multicellular* and clearly "animal" in character. They are distinguished from their protistan relatives in that their bodies are composed of distinct tissues, organs, and usually several organ systems also. Metazoan cells typically possess centrioles, and, with the general exception of cells on the body surface, other cells are naked, without walls or cuticles. Metazoa also feature complex, multicellular reproductive organs, and animal development passes through distinct *embryonic* and, typically, *larval* phases.

The metazoan category is subclassified into some 20 to 30 phyla. In some cases universal agreement on phylum designations is lacking, hence the inexactness of the number of phyla.

GENERAL CHARACTERISTICS

NUTRITION AND MOVEMENT

Being nonphotosynthetic, all animals ultimately depend for food on photosynthesizers. Both in space and in time, therefore, animal life waxes and wanes in step with plant life. From the standpoint of food sources, two broad categories of animals may be distinguished: the **symbiotic** and the **free-living** types.

Some of the animal symbionts live in mutualistic or commensalistic associations with individuals of other species (Chap. 7). But most are parasites, on or within specific hosts. Free-living animals variously subsist on any usable foods available in the environment: living plants and animals, dead plants and animals, and many different kinds of derivatives of organisms, including in some cases decaying matter. Most of these free-living animals and also most of the symbiotic types are bulk-feeding holotrophs. In other words, they have mouths and they eat, or *ingest*. Associated with this form of food procurement is *digestion* and the elimination of unusable eaten material, or *egestion*. Ingestion, digestion, and egestion together constitute the process of **alimentation**.

Directly or indirectly, the whole way of life of an animal is oriented by this requirement of alimentation. One immediate consequence is the necessity of locomotion. Whereas a plant finds raw materials for photosynthesis practically all around it, prefabricated bulk food is in strictly limited supply and its location generally does not coincide with the location of the hungry animal. Therefore, an animal must either move toward food itself or remain stationary and feed on moving organisms which happen to pass by. Actively moving animals constitute the majority of Metazoa. Locomotion is accomplished on the principle of first-class levers, and propulsive power is provided by muscles which move variously formed body appendages. The most common methods of locomotion are quite familiar: swimming, creeping, walking, flying, each with numerous variants in different animal groups. But many Metazoa are specialized as permanently or temporarily sessile forms (e.g., sponges, corals, barnacles). Such animals generally use their locomotor structures to create water currents which sweep small food organisms toward them.

As we have seen, Metaphyta do not move and are very largely terrestrial. On the other hand, Metazoa, which typically do move, include relatively few terrestrial groups: some snails, some worms, arthropods such as insects and spiders, and vertebrates such as reptiles, birds, and mammals. All other metazoan groups are aquatic, and this is correlated in large measure with the requirement of locomotion. Propulsion can be accomplished with less effort in water than on land or in the air; friction is greatest on land, support against

gravity is least in the air. In water, however, an animal is buoyed up and comparatively little energy need be expended for locomotion. Added to the abundance of food in water and the general biological benefits of a water environment, these factors have contributed greatly to making aquatic life far more attractive to animals than life on land. (We may note, however, that although few groups of animals are terrestrial, these few include more species than all other living organisms combined.)

Because the supplies of bulk food are limited, animals tend to compete sharply and overtly for available food. As a result, some become predators, some become prey. Offense and defense evidently are basic expressions of the animal way of life. Correlated with this are variously furtive habits, stealth, cunning, and other forms of *behavior*. These also are primary consequences of alimentation and locomotion. Similarly correlated are many structural adaptations, of benefit to either the hunter or the hunted. For example, brute strength, speed, and body colorations which camouflage or warn are exceedingly prevalent, in water as on land. Many animals may even change their body colors according to the colors of their backgrounds (Fig. 11.1 and Chap. 7).

Correlated with the necessity of searching for food are specializations in animal eating habits. Thus, **herbivores** are specialized to eat plant foods; **carnivores** subsist on other animals; and **omnivores** eat both animal and plant foods, living or dead. In view of its abundance, plant food is easily come by. As a result, more herbivorous animal types exist than any other. Also, since plants do not put up a fight before being eaten, herbivores generally are of more or less gentle disposition and are more adept in defense than in offense.

A plant diet presents its own special problems. Cellulose cell walls, sclerenchyma, and xylem make plant tissues tough and difficult to tear. Plant juices may therefore have to be sucked out, as is the case in many herbivorous insects, which have sucking mouth parts. Alternatively, plant parts may be scraped off, as in many mollusks, which have mouths equipped with filelike raspers. Common devices for handling plant foods are teeth, which, as in rodents and cattle, are partly sharp, broad cutting teeth or flat-topped grinding teeth. Birds possess, instead of teeth, modified stomachs in which two muscular plates grind against each other like millstones. Herbivores generally have comparatively long intestines, which provide more time and more surface for the digestion of plant foods. A

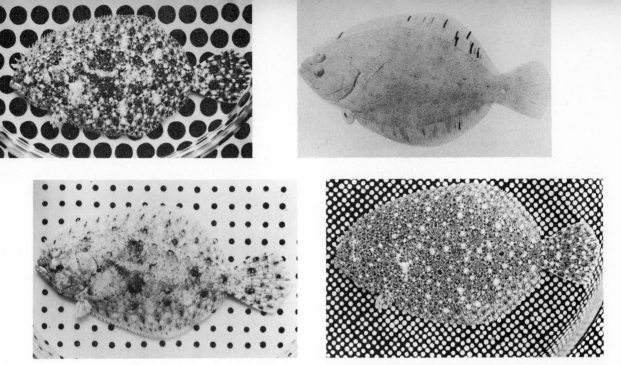

FIG. 11.1 A flounder against four different backgrounds. Note how the animal may adapt its skin pigmentation pattern to the color pattern of the environment. In such cases of adjustable camouflage, information about the environment is communicated to the skin via eyes, nerves, and hormones. Pigment cells in the skin respond to the information by contracting or expanding, thus altering the body coloration. (*U.S. Fish and Wildlife Service.*)

pound of fresh plant material consists largely of water and cellulose and of correspondingly less usable organic nutrients. Accordingly, herbivores generally eat more, and more often, than other animal types.

Carnivores are specialized to overcome not only herbivores but also smaller carnivores and omnivores. The food-catching devices of carnivores are varied and largely familiar: fangs, talons, sharp beaks, and needle-point teeth; poison-secreting stings which immobilize prey (scorpions); spider webs; tentacles with suction cups (squids), or tentacles with sting cells (coelenterates). Fast reflexes, excellent sense organs, and devices like growls, rattles, bioluminescent organs, and electric organs are among the many auxiliary adaptations for a carnivorous way of life. Virtually none of the carnivores kills wantonly, but only when hungry or challenged; it is to the carnivore's advantage to live amidst a thriving population of herbivores. Animal tissue is softer than that of plants and tears fairly easily; hence there is a predominance of sharp, pointed teeth among carnivores. Absence of cellulose from animal foods also tends to reduce chewing time and makes for easier

digestion and relatively shorter intestines. Nutritive values per pound of animal tissues are greater than in plant foods. Therefore, carnivores generally eat fewer, smaller meals.

Omnivores subsist on whatever nourishment they can find or catch. Many omnivores wait on the scene of battle between carnivore and herbivore, to scavenge among the remains. Others live on minute plant and animal debris in soil or water. A large variety of worms, crabs, lobsters, many types of insects, rats, bears, pigs, and man are among omnivorous animals. Their food-trapping devices, dentition, and alimentary structures combine herbivorous and carnivorous features, as might be expected.

Once the capacity of locomotion is given, it may be made to serve not only in food catching but also secondarily in numerous other animal activities. For example, locomotion plays a fundamental role in mate selection and reproduction, functions which the motile animal accomplishes far more readily than the sessile plant. Locomotion also is an important factor in protecting animals against environmental dangers, climatic changes among them. For example, as noted in Chap. 6, many animals carry out seasonal north-south migrations. Others remain at given latitudes permanently, yet through locomotion they are able to search out protective forests, caves, or self-constructed shelters like burrows, hives, nests, and houses.

But note that locomotion does not make animals completely independent of the climate; environmental temperatures do affect animals just as they do plants. Animals other than birds and mammals are designated, rather inappropriately, as being *cold-blooded*. They are not necessarily cold and they do not necessarily possess blood, but, as in plants, their internal body temperature matches that of the external environment (Fig. 11.2). In such an organism, the rates of internal chemical reactions are high on a warm day and the animal eats more, moves faster, and in general lives faster than on a cold day. The varying buzzing pitch of houseflies is a familiar indication of the influence of temperature on the tempo of living. In winter most cold-blooded animals die, but their protected eggs or larvae survive. In this respect they resemble annual plants. Other cold-blooded forms winter over successfully, either in deep water of oceans and lakes or sheltered on land in suitable sites above or below ground.

Birds and mammals maintain a constant internal body temperature, regardless of the temperature of the external environment. These animals are designated, again somewhat inappropriately, as being *warm-blooded*. Internal temperature here is kept constant by controls which balance heat gain against heat loss. Principal sources of heat gain are food, friction generated by moving parts, and to a variable extent also the heat of the external environment. Fat, fur, or feathers may aid in heat retention. Heat loss results from surface radiation, from evaporation, and from loss of warm body water, as in urination, sweating, and breathing. When food is scarce, as in winter, internal heat production clearly becomes more difficult. Many mammals then *hibernate*, and in this state they are more or less cold-blooded. Heat regulation is temporarily suspended, body temperature drops, and food requirements, hence also the need for locomotion, are reduced proportionately (Fig. 11.3).

Hibernating or not, birds and mammals derive an important adaptive advantage from being warm-blooded. They become highly independent of daily and seasonal variations in climate; they may therefore compete successfully against cold-blooded forms, which must slow down in every respect on a cold day. Moreover, warm-bloodedness in conjunction with locomotion permits the free spreading of mammals and birds between equator and pole, a factor which has contributed greatly to the preeminence of these types.

FIG. 11.2   In "cold-blooded" animals, heat is gained or lost according to the temperature of the external environment. The internal temperature therefore matches the external. In "warm-blooded" animals, heat is also gained or lost according to environmental temperatures; but decreased internal heat production compensates for heat gains and increased internal heat production compensates for heat losses. As a result, the internal temperature is maintained constant, regardless of the temperature of the environment.

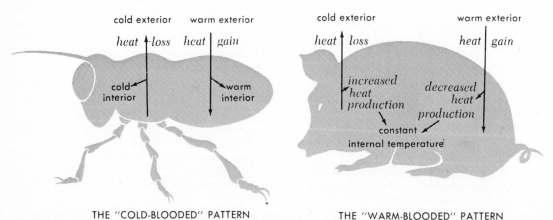

THE "COLD-BLOODED" PATTERN   THE "WARM-BLOODED" PATTERN

FIG. 11.3   A chipmunk, hibernating in its underground burrow. Note the accumulated store of acorns at the bottom of the nest. *(American Museum of Natural History.)*

ARCHITECTURE

The requirement of locomotion profoundly influences the entire structural organization of an animal. Most moving animals have an *elongated, bilaterally symmetrical shape* which is particularly suited for locomotion. For propulsion of any kind necessarily implies that one portion of the organism "goes first" and that another goes last. Mechanical balance will be greatest if the left and right sides are equivalent, i.e., if they are mirror images. Resistance by the propulsion medium will be least if the body is elongated in the direction of motion.

Moreover, the forward end enters new environments first. Sense organs for scouting and the chief nerve centers are therefore placed most advantageously at the front, and mouths should be located close to the sense organs. Thus the leading part of the animal becomes *head*. Analogously, elimination products of all kinds are best released at the hind end, where they do not impede forward progression. A general build of this sort is actually standard and nearly universal among moving animals (Fig. 11.4).

By contrast, sessile animals, and also many of the very slow movers, face their environment more or less equally from all sides, like plants, and their architecture reflects this. They are or tend to be *radially symmetrical* and a distinct head is usually not present (e.g., corals, starfish). In many sessile forms also, the intestine is looped into a U, which brings the mouth and the anus close together and both openings away from the region where the animal is attached to the ground.

How does an animal maintain its shape? Unlike a plant, an animal obtains relatively little mechanical support from the turgor of individual cells. Stiff outer walls are not present in the interior cells of the body, and the thin cell membranes withstand only moderate turgor pressure. Accordingly, whatever inherent rigidity an animal cell possesses is due largely to the semisolid consistency of its colloidal gels. This may suffice to preserve the shape of single cells, but a larger cellular

FIG. 11.4   Diagrammatic representation of the basic structure of a moving animal. This is a hypothetical animal, showing the position and function of various body parts and organs usually encountered in many elongated, worm-shaped types.

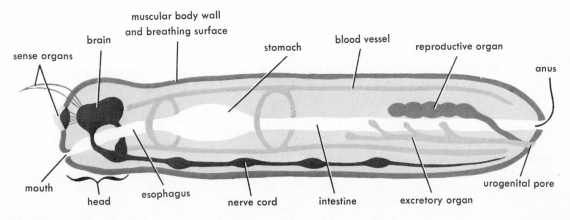

aggregation—a slice of fresh liver tissue, for example—sags badly.

The major supporting structures of animals are muscles and skeletons. That muscles function not only in motion but also in support is well illustrated in animals such as earthworms, which do not possess a skeleton. The same muscles which move such animals also hold them together and maintain their shapes. Moreover, even an animal with a skeleton would sag into a formless mass if muscles did not maintain a taut, firm organization. On the other hand, that skeletons function not only in support but also in locomotion is also clear. A large, heavy animal could neither hold its shape nor propel itself forward by muscles alone, without rigid supports.

Animal skeletons are either calcium-containing *calcareous* supports or silicon-containing *siliceous* supports or variously organic *horny* supports. Horny skeletons made of chitin are particularly common in invertebrate animals. Skeletons are organized either as **exoskeletons** or as **endoskeletons.** In an exoskeleton, the supporting material is on the outside of the animal and envelops it partly or wholly. Coelenterates, mollusks, and arthropods are among forms with such exoskeletons. In an endoskeleton, the supports are internal and soft tissues are draped over them. The main animal groups characterized by this type of skeleton are the echinoderms and the chordates, the latter including the cartilage- and bone-possessing vertebrates. Note that an endoskeleton permits an animal to become far larger than an exoskeleton. With increasing body size, an exterior skeletal envelope rapidly becomes inadequate to support deep-lying tissues. Interior supports, however, can buttress all parts of even a large animal. It is not an accident, therefore, that the largest animals are the vertebrates and that animals without skeletons or with exoskeletons are all comparatively small (Fig. 11.5).

Apart from affecting the general shape and form of animals, locomotion and alimentation also greatly influence all other aspects of animal architecture. In certain respects, metazoan structure matches that of Metaphyta. For example, all animals possess *integumentary* and *reproductive* structures, as do all plants. Also, most animals, particularly the larger ones, possess *circulatory* systems and blood, body parts which correspond to the vascular tissues of tracheophytes. However, most other features of animal structure do not have counterparts among plants; because of alimen-

tation and locomotion, the animal organization requires a number of structural systems not needed in plants.

For example, no plant possesses an *alimentary* system, for the obvious reason that the key process in plant nutrition is intracellular photosynthesis and that complex organ systems for catching and preparing foods are therefore not required. Analogously, no plant possesses structures specialized for the collection of environmental oxygen or for the excretion of metabolic wastes. Yet all but the most simply constructed animals possess both: lungs, gills, moist skins, and other specific body parts for breathing; and kidneys, lungs, gills, sweat glands, and other specific body parts for excretion. Such structures are necessitated by the shape of the animal body and, ultimately, by the requirement of locomotion. The light-requiring, stationary plant is built for maximum surface exposure. Virtually all its cells are in direct contact with the external environment, and each cell may therefore collect oxygen and excrete wastes on its own. By contrast, the moving animal for obvious mechanical reasons cannnot be built in the ramified shape of a tree, but must be constructed far more compactly, for minimum surface exposure. Most cells of an animal therefore cannot be in direct contact with the environment, and this necessitates specialized *breathing* and *excretory* systems operating in conjunction with the internal circulatory system (Fig. 11.6).

Above all, animals do not match plants in structures associated directly with the function of locomotion. Apart from the *muscular* and *skeletal* systems already mentioned, animals also possess elaborate equipment for internal coordination. Movement must be readjusted often, in response to rapid changes of external locale brought about by movement. Accordingly, animals possess systems for *chemical coordination,* such as blood, kidneys, and endocrine glands, and systems for *neural coordination,* such as sense organs, nerves, and brains.

We may emphasize here that neural activities of all kinds, including even the most sophisticated thinking of man, serve fundamentally and primarily toward the control of muscles and of movement in general. In line with this, a close parallelism exists in the degree of nervous and the degree of locomotor development. Sense organs, nerves, and brain centers tend to be greatly reduced in sessile and slow-moving animals but are highly developed in fast, agile types. For example, the sluggish starfish and sea urchins, though very ad-

FIG. 11.5 Top left, the calcareous exoskeleton of a snail. Top right, the horny exoskeleton of a stag beetle. Above, portion of the silica skeleton of a glass sponge. Bottom left, the calcareous endoskeleton of a sea urchin, seen from the underside. Bottom right, X-ray photograph of a girl, showing the human endoskeleton. *(Top left, above, bottom left, American Museum of Natural History; top right, U.S. Department of Agriculture; bottom right, Eastman Kodak Co.)*

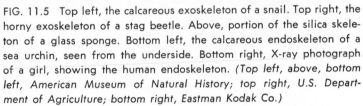

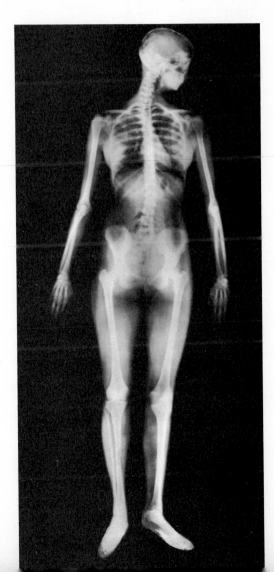

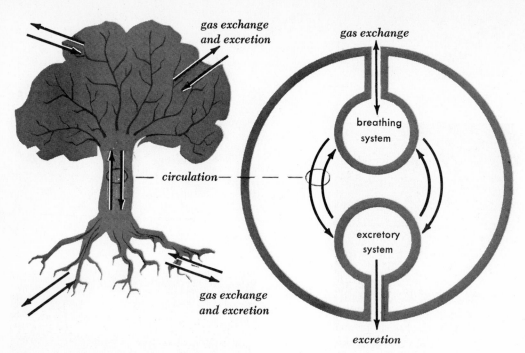

plants: ramified design;
most cells have direct access to environment

animals: compact design;
few cells have direct access to environment

FIG. 11.6 Diagram contrasting the ramified architecture of a plant and the compact architecture of an animal. Because of their respective architectures, the animal does, and the plant does not, require specialized breathing and excretory systems.

vanced in other ways, possess but a rudimentary nervous system. So do clams and snails. But their close relatives, the fast squids, possess eyes, nerves, and brains which in structure and functional efficiency match those of vertebrates.

In general, therefore, just as the plant body reflects a way of life based on photosynthesis and sessilism, so the architecture of the animal body reflects the way of life based on alimentation and locomotion.

The various animal organ systems (see also Chap. 5) are arranged in a definite structural pattern. Broadly speaking, every animal may be considered to be made up of three groups of layers. Each group forms a "tube" of a sort, and the three tubes are one within the other. The outermost tube is the external body wall, which includes the integumentary system and all derivatives. The innermost tube is the alimentary system and its derivatives. And the middle tube consists of all the other organs and systems between body wall and alimentary tract (see Fig. 11.4). This is more than a rough analogy; the three-layered picture of an animal has biological reality, for at an early stage of embryonic life animal embryos consist of just three single-celled layers. How this stage develops we shall discuss in Chap. 27. Here we may note that the outer embryonic cell layer is called **ectoderm**, the middle one **mesoderm,** and the inner one **endoderm**. These three cell layers, or *germ layers*, later produce the three "tubes" of the adult animal. Ectoderm forms the outer tube of skin, nervous system, and other structures. Mesoderm forms the middle tube of muscles, bones, circulatory system, excretory and reproductive systems, and others. Endoderm forms the inner tube of the alimentary system and associated structures (Fig. 11.7).

In the embryo, the three germ layers do not develop at the same time; the middle layer, mesoderm,

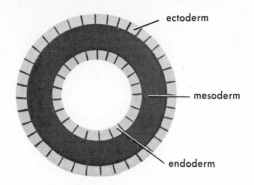

FIG. 11.7 Diagram showing the three germ layers of an animal embryo.

forms last. In certain animal embryos this mesoderm arises from cells produced by the ectoderm; in other animals, from cells produced by the endoderm; and in still other animals, from cells produced by both ectoderm and endoderm. Further, once the mesoderm layer is present, it may undergo several later fates. In one series of cases, it develops a large cavity within it. Such

a cavity, surrounded entirely by mesoderm cells, is called a **coelom**. When it forms, this region becomes the principal body cavity of the animal. In man, for example, the coelom in part is the cavity inside the abdomen, in which many organs lie (Fig. 11.8).

Animals can be classified into superphyla on the basis of how mesoderm forms, how extensive it becomes, and whether or not a coelom develops in it. Other criteria, particularly structural features of adult animals, are used to distinguish individual phyla within the superphyla. Apart from the separate single phylum of sponges, five superphyla may be recognized: the *radiates,* the *acoelomates,* the *pseudocoelomates,* the *schizocoelomates,* and the *enterocoelomates.* These groups will be the broad units of discussion in the following sections.

SPONGES AND RADIATES

In these groups, the mesoderm is not very well developed; in extreme cases it may even be absent altogether. When it does exist, it is formed from ectoderm

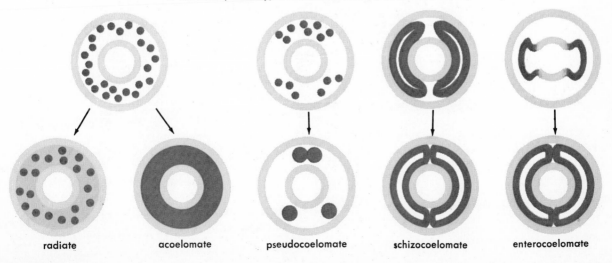

FIG. 11.8 Diagrammatic representation of the formation of mesoderm and the coelom in the five animal superphyla. In the radiates, jelly fills the space between ectoderm and endoderm, and individual mesoderm cells are embedded in the jelly. In acoelomates, mesoderm accumulates compactly and a coelom does not develop. In pseudocoelomates, mesoderm accumulates regionally and the body cavity is therefore not a true coelom but is bounded by ectoderm and endoderm. In schizocoelomates, the mesoderm splits into outer and inner layers, and in enterocoelomates, the mesoderm grows out as hollow pouches from the endoderm. In both cases, the end result is the same, namely, a mesoderm-lined, true coelomic body cavity.

radiate   acoelomate   pseudocoelomate   schizocoelomate   enterocoelomate

and consists largely of a solid mass of jelly within which are embedded relatively few cells (see Fig. 11.8). An additional characteristic of these animals is a basic *radial* body symmetry. This is particularly conspicuous in the radiates, or "Radiata," which are so named because of their symmetry. All other animals, by contrast, are basically bilaterally symmetrical and are often referred to collectively as "Bilateria." A third distinguishing feature of radiates is that they possess an alimentary system with but a *single* opening to the outside. The system is essentially a sac, and its one opening serves as both mouth and anus.

Sponges are primitive Metazoa, and it is generally agreed that they represent a separate branch of animal life, evolved independently and more or less directly from protistan ancestors. The identity of these ancestors is unknown; protozoan groups or chrysophyte or other algal groups are likely possibilities. The radiates are likewise relatively primitive, and their evolutionary origin similarly appears to trace directly and independently to (unknown) protistan stocks. Two fairly closely related phyla are included within the radiate superphylum, the coelenterates and the comb jellies.

PHYLUM PORIFERA: SPONGES
(15,000 species)

Class Calcarea: chalk sponges
Class Hexactinellida: glass sponges
Class Demospongiae: horn sponges

All sponges are sessile as adults, but their embryos are ciliated and free-swimming. The embryos, essentially saclike, are composed of two cell layers, the ectoderm and the endoderm. Jelly often forms a middle layer. When the embryos settle and become adult sponges, the neat arrangement of the cellular layers become greatly obscured. Nevertheless, the adults possess different cell types on the outside, the inside, and the middle (Fig. 11.9).

The outer cells are of several kinds, the most distinctive being those which secrete the intracellular skeletal elements called **spicules.** These have different characteristic shapes in different species and are the basis of sponge classification. In chalk sponges, the

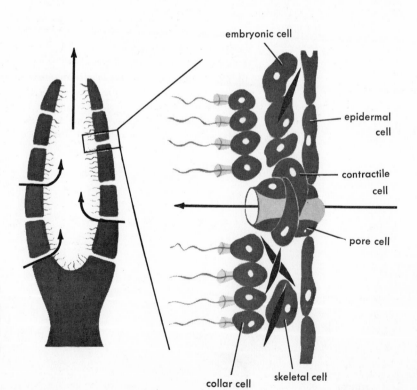

FIG. 11.9 The organization of a simple sponge, diagrammatic. Left, cross-sectional view showing the flow direction of water. Right, detail of a portion of the body wall.

embryonic cell

epidermal cell

contractile cell

pore cell

collar cell

skeletal cell

spicules consist of calcium salts; in glass sponges, of silica; and in horny sponges, of complex organic materials (Fig. 11.10).

The most characteristic cells on the inside of a sponge are the so-called **collar cells,** which are flagellate and remarkably like the collar flagellates of the protozoan phylum Mastigophora. These cells line a system of interconnecting channels which communicate with the environment through entry and exit pores located on the surface of the sponge body. The collar cells create a water current which flows through the entry pores into the channel system and out through the exit pores. Food present in the current is trapped by the collar cells (see Fig. 11.9).

All sponges are aquatic, and most of them are marine.

FIG. 11.10   Top left, the skeletal spicules of a calcareous sponge. Bottom left, the horny skeleton of a bath sponge. Right, a silicaceous rope sponge. (*Top left, Carolina Biological Supply Co.; bottom left, U.S. Fish and Wildlife Service; right, American Museum of Natural History.*)

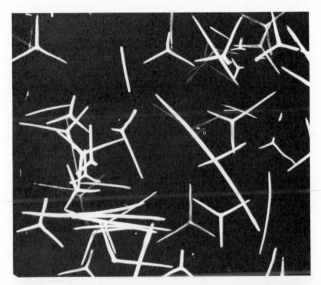

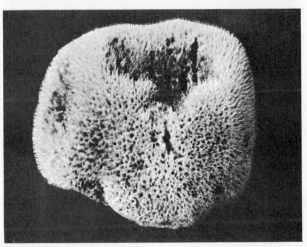

PHYLUM CNIDARIA: COELENTERATES
(10,000 species)

Class Hydrozoa: *Obelia, Hydra, Physalia*
Class Scyphozoa: jellyfishes
Class Anthozoa: sea anemones, corals

Coelenterates are characterized by a digestive cavity with a single opening, by tentacles which surround this opening, and by **sting cells,** unique to this phylum, located on the tentacles. The body consists of an outer ectodermal cell layer containing sensory cells of various sorts and an inner endodermal layer containing digestive amoeboid cells. Between these two cell layers is a jellylike layer of varying thickness, the **mesogloea.** In this middle layer is embedded a simply constructed nerve net (Fig. 11.11).

The embryo of coelenterates typically develops into a free-swimming, ciliated **planula** larva consisting of two cell layers. Such a larva eventually transforms into an adult, which is either a sessile, saclike **polyp** or a free-swimming, bell-shaped **medusa.** Hydrozoa characteristically pass through alternate polyp and medusa stages. In *Obelia*, for example, a larva grows into a sessile colony of polyps. Most of these are feeding polyps, but some develop as specialized reproductive polyps which produce medusae by budding. These medusae separate away as free-swimming stages. Eventually they develop sex organs, and after fertilization the egg develops into a larva which gives rise to a new polyp colony (Figs. 11.12 and 11.13).

In Scyphozoa, the polyp phase is greatly reduced. For example, in the common jellyfish *Aurelia*, the larva grows directly into a single reproductive polyp (**ephyra** larva) which buds off medusae. Such medusae develop

FIG. 11.11 Diagram: the basic structure of coelenterates. The outer body layer is epidermal, the inner is digestive, and the middle one, the so-called mesogloea, is largely jelly in which is embedded a simple nerve net. A single opening serves as both mouth and anus, and there are usually tentacles around this opening. The sessile phase of a coelenterate (the polyp) is as shown, and if the diagram is viewed upside down, it illustrates the motile phase (the medusa). Photo: microscopic cross section through the body of a coelenterate (Hydra). Note the two layers of cells, ectoderm on the ouside, endoderm on the inside. The cavity enclosed by endoderm is the alimentary sac. *(Photo, Ward's Natural Science Establishment, Inc.)*

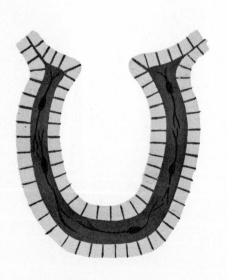
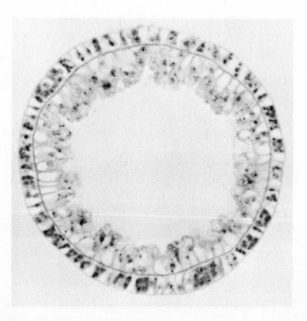

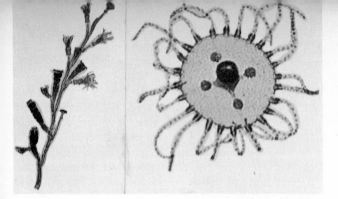

FIG. 11.12 *Obelia.* Left, a colony of polyps. Note feeding polyps with tentacles, and club-shaped reproductive polyps. The latter produce medusae. Right, a medusa. Dark region in center is the mouth. Note the four sex organs. *(Carolina Biological Supply Co.)*

FIG. 11.13 The life cycles of coelenterates. Polyp and medusa generations alternate in Hydrozoa like *Obelia;* polyp phases are suppressed in Scyphozoa like *Aurelia* and other jellyfish; and medusa phases are suppressed in Anthozoa like sea anemones.

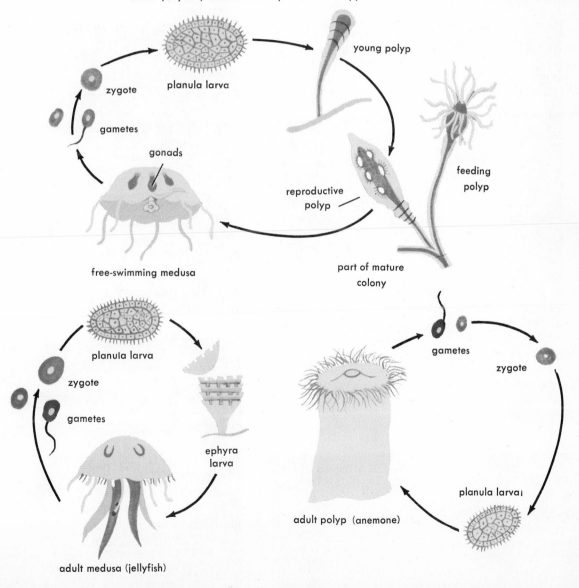

sex organs, and after fertilization new larvae form (see Fig. 11.13).

In Anthozoa, on the contrary, it is the medusa phase which is reduced. Indeed, that phase is absent altogether: the sessile adult is a feeding polyp which develops sex organs. After fertilization, larvae form, and these grow into new adult polyps (see Fig. 11.13).

Whether sessile or free-swimming, coelenterates are efficient carnivores which catch crustacea, small fish, and other prey by means of tentacles and sting cells. Most genera are marine, but some, like the famil-

iar *Hydra*, live in fresh water (see Fig. 27.24). Note that *Hydra* is a highly specialized form in which the characteristic hydrozoan life cycle does not occur. In particular, a medusa phase is suppressed. Hydrozoa also include specialized colonial types like *Physalia*, the Portuguese man-of-war, characterized by several different kinds of polyps whose forms and functions are quite distinct (see Fig. 6.7). Anthozoa manufacture often very elaborate exoskeletons of calcium salts. The group includes the builders of coral reefs and atolls (Fig. 11.14).

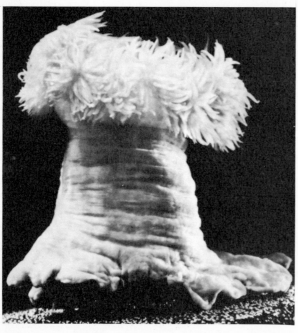

FIG. 11.14 Anthozoa. Top left, top right, two types of sea anemones. Bottom left, bottom right, various types of coral skeletons. *(Top left, Carolina Biological Supply Co.; top right, bottom left and right, American Museum of Natural History.)*

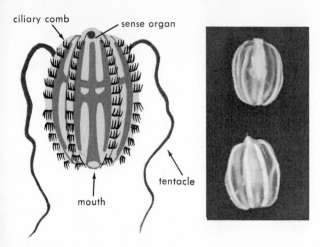

FIG. 11.15   Ctenophores, diagram and photo of structure. *(Photo, General Biological Supply House, Inc.)*

PHYLUM CTENOPHORA: COMB JELLIES
(100 species)

In some respects these animals resemble coelenterate medusae, but in others they are quite unique. (Fig. 11.15). The body is transparent and consists of ectoderm derivatives on the outside, a bulky gelatinous mesogloea underneath, and endoderm derivatives in the center. The digestive cavity leads from a single opening into eight pouches. The number eight is of considerable general significance in the phylum. For example, there are also eight nerve cords, which underlie eight external rows of comb plates, the locomotor organs of the animals. Ctenophores possess a pair of tentacles which are not equipped with sting cells and which may be withdrawn into ectodermal pouches. All ctenophores are marine, and many species are bioluminescent.

ACOELOMATES

This superphylum (and all subsequent ones as well) contains bilaterally symmetrical animals. In the embryos of acoelomates, the mesoderm develops from the ectoderm and this middle tissue remains a solid layer (see Fig. 11.8). Because, therefore, a coelom cavity does not form, the name of the group is "acoelomates," i.e., "without coelom."

The superphylum includes three phyla of worms: flatworms, proboscis worms, and spiny-headed worms. Considerable uncertainty exists about the evolutionary relation of these three groups to one another and about the derivation of acoelomates as a whole. Because flatworms possess an alimentary system with but a single opening, like radiates, and because of other similarities, some investigators think that acoelomates may have arisen from ancestral radiates. In particular, planula-like ancestors are assumed to have elongated into worm shapes and to have developed extensive mesodermal tissues. This view, widely held, contrasts with another which assumes that flatworms and acoelomates as a whole have originated directly from protistan ancestors. Evidence presently available is inadequate to decide between these alternatives.

PHYLUM PLATYHELMINTHES: FLATWORMS
(10,000 species)

Class Turbellaria: free-living flatworms
Class Trematoda: flukes
Class Cestoda: tapeworms

As a group, flatworms are distinguished by a body flattened top to bottom and, as noted above, by an alimentary system which resembles that of coelenterates; i.e., a single opening (on the underside of the body) serves as both mouth and anus. Moreover, the digestive cavity is lined with amoeboid cells which engulf small food particles and digest them intracellularly. All other acoelomate phyla, and indeed all other animals of any kind, possess alimentary tracts with two separate openings, i.e., separate mouth and anus.

The most familiar free-living flatworms are the *planarians* (Fig. 11.16). The body of these animals has definite front and rear ends, and the digestive opening is located in the middle, on the underside. An eversible **pharynx** breaks larger food into particles suitable for ingestion. A pair of **eyes** is present at the head end and the head also contains a concentration of nervous tissue, the **brain ganglion.** From it lead a pair of **ventral nerve cords,** which are interconnected at more or less regular intervals by transverse strands of nerves. The whole has the appearance of a ladder (Fig. 11.17). Circulatory and breathing systems are not present in flatworms, but these animals do possess excretory and elaborate reproductive systems. Locomotion is accomplished by undulating muscular movements, which result in swim-

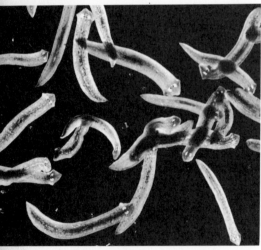

ming, or by the beat of cilia on the underside of the body, which propel the animal on a solid surface.

Turbellaria are largely free-living scavengers found in both ocean and fresh water. The *acoels* (see Fig. 11.17) are a group in which a digestive cavity is lacking and in which food is introduced from the alimentary opening directly into endodermal digestive cells. These animals are regarded as the most primitive of the flatworms. In *rhabdocoels*, the digestive cavity is straight and unbranched. In *triclads*, to which the planarians belong, the digestive cavity forms three pouches, one pointing anteriorly, two posteriorly. The largest of the turbellarians are the exclusively marine *polyclads*. They are characterized by highly branched digestive cavities and by free-swimming larvae which in several respects resemble the planulae of radiates.

The two remaining classes of flatworms are exclusively parasitic and of considerable general importance to man. We have already discussed their characteristic life cycles in Chap. 7.

PHYLUM NEMERTINEA: PROBOSCIS WORMS
(600 species)

These worms resemble flatworms in embryonic development and general structure, but they are unique in several important respects. First, they possess separate anterior mouth and posterior anal openings, connected by a straight alimentary tube. Second, they possess a simple closed circulatory system, blood moving forward in a dorsal vessel, backward in a ventral vessel. And third, they possess a unique and identifying **proboscis** apparatus. This is a long tubular organ

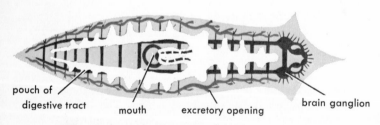

pouch of digestive tract   mouth   excretory opening   brain ganglion

FIG. 11.17 Left, the internal structure of a planarian. Right, the types of free-living flatworms, based on the structure of the alimentary cavity.

acoel   rhabdocoel   triclad   polyclad

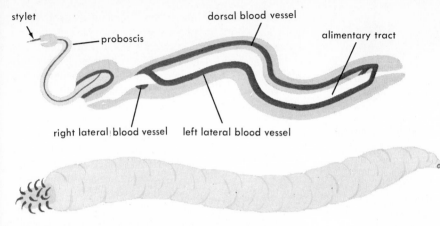

stylet

proboscis

dorsal blood vessel

alimentary tract

right lateral blood vessel   left lateral blood vessel

FIG. 11.18 Top, a proboscis worm, showing proboscis apparatus, one-way alimentary tract, and the primitive circulatory system. Bottom, an acanthocephalan. Both illustrations are diagrammatic.

lying inside a cavity above the mouth opening. It can be extruded rapidly and wrapped around suitable animal prey. In some cases, the tip of the proboscis contains a pointed stylet which pierces the body of a victim. A gland then secretes poison into a wound made by the stylet (Fig. 11.18). Proboscis worms occur in the ocean as well as in fresh water.

PHYLUM ACANTHOCEPHALA: SPINY-HEADED WORMS
(300 species)

All animals of this phylum are parasitic in vertebrates. They are so named because the head bears a retractile proboscis armed with hooks (Fig. 11.18). By means of this structure, the parasite clings to the intestinal lining of the host. Spiny-headed worms are without digestive systems, and they absorb food directly through their cuticles, like tapeworms.

PSEUDOCOELOMATES

In this superphylum, the embryonic mesoderm arises largely from ectoderm and does not become a solid middle layer. Instead, mesodermal tissues collect in limited regions in the space between ectoderm and endoderm. As a result, these animals do possess a body cavity, but this cavity is enclosed by ectoderm on the outside and by endoderm on the inside, not by mesoderm (see Fig. 11.8). The cavity is therefore a "false coelom," hence the name "pseudocoelomates." Another characteristic of the superphylum is that the adults in many cases are syncytial; i.e., the cells have lost their boundary membranes.

Pseudocoelomates include seven phyla. The first six described below comprise worm-shaped animals, and most of them exhibit a tendency toward superficial, external segmentation. In some classifications, these six phyla are considered to be classes within the single phylum *Aschelminthes*. But the group is actually relatively heterogeneous, and independent phylum rank for each major type can be justified.

The pseudocoelomates as a whole include some of the rarest and least known as well as some of the most abundant of all animals. Their evolutionary affinities to one another and to other superphyla are quite obscure. Various pseudocoelomate groups may have arisen independently from ancestral acoelomates or from even earlier stocks which have given rise to the acoelomates themselves. Alternatively, pseudocoelomates could be offshoots from later schizocoelomate ancestors. Actual lines of descent are simply not known; the general level of structural complexity of these animals suggests an evolutionary age at most as great as that of the acoelomates but probably somewhat greater than that of the schizocoelomates.

PHYLUM ROTIFERA: ROTIFERS
(1,500 species)

These microscopic animals are very largely free-living and are found predominantly in fresh water, where they are exceedingly common.

They possess an identifying anterior crown of cilia surrounding the mouth, hence the name "wheel bearers" for the phylum. The cilia are the organs of locomotion, and they also create food currents. The mouth leads into a muscular grinding organ, the mas-

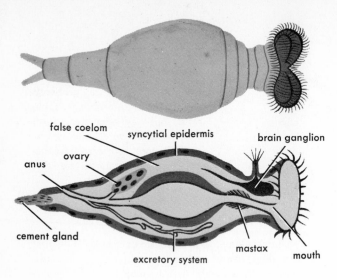

FIG. 11.19   The structure of a rotifer, diagrammatic. Top, dorsal external view. Bottom, sagittal section.

and of a series of nerve cords leading away from the ganglion. Rotifers possess excretory systems, but circulatory and breathing systems are absent (Fig. 11.19).

One of the long-known peculiarities of these animals is that the number of cells in late embryos and the number of nuclei in adults is constant for each species. Also, the nuclei occupy fixed positions in each individual. The body plan of each species may therefore be mapped out nucleus by nucleus.

During spring and summer, female rotifers produce eggs which develop into new females without being fertilized. These females in turn reproduce without fertilization and many generations of females succeed one another in this manner. In the fall, the females lay some eggs which are smaller than the rest. These hatch into small males, degenerate individuals lacking digestive systems but capable of producing sperms. Fertilization may then occur. The resulting eggs possess thick, hard shells and may resist unfavorable environments for very long periods. Under suitably favorable conditions, e.g., in the following spring, the shelled eggs develop into females (Fig. 11.20). In some types of rotifers males are unknown altogether, the species being propagated exclusively by unfertilized eggs. This phenomenon of egg development without fertilization is called **parthenogenesis.** We have already encountered it in the discussion on social insects (Chap. 6).

tax, and then into a straight intestine which terminates at the anus. At the hind end are located **cement organs,** which anchor the animal during feeding and which also make possible a second form of locomotion resembling caterpillarlike creeping. The nervous system consists mainly of a brain ganglion dorsal to the mouth

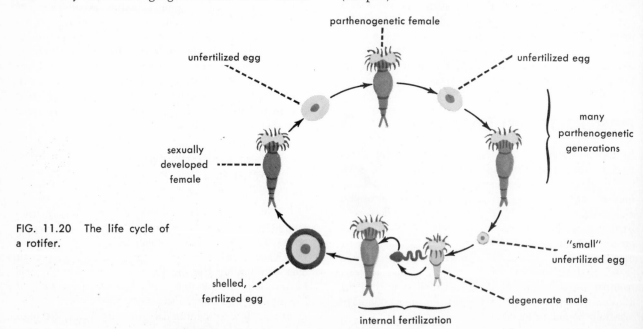

FIG. 11.20   The life cycle of a rotifer.

PHYLUM NEMATODA: ROUNDWORMS
(10,000 species)

It has been estimated that probably more individual roundworms exist than any other Metazoa except possibly insects. Many nematodes are free-living in water and soil, and they occur in such numbers that a spadeful of garden earth is likely to contain up to a million worms. Many nematodes are parasitic in plants and animals, and they are usually implicated when an animal is said to suffer from "worms." Man alone harbors some 50 species. Most of these are relatively harmless, but some cause serious diseases.

All nematodes are remarkably alike (Fig. 11.21). The body is slender and cylindrical, has tapered ends, and is covered with a tough chitinous cuticle. As in rotifers, the number of nuclei is constant for each species and cell boundaries are absent in the adult. The worms possess mouth, straight intestine, and anus. Circulatory and breathing systems are not present, and excretory systems are constructed relatively simply. Males are usually smaller than females.

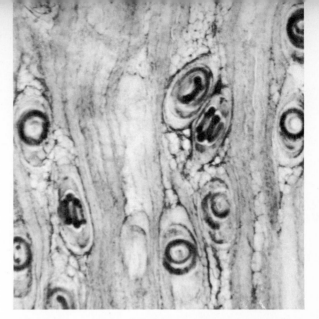

FIG. 11.22 Larvae of trichina worms, encapsulated in pig muscle. If infected pork is cooked improperly, the larvae are digested out in the intestine of the host and the worms then invade the host tissues. (*Ward's Natural Science Establishment, Inc.*)

FIG. 11.21 A mature female of the nematode *Paratylenchus*, which causes disease in plants. (*Courtesy of Dr. W. F. Mai, Cornell University.*)

Among the serious nematode pests of man are the *trichina worms*, introduced into the human body via insufficiently cooked pork (Fig. 11.22); the *hookworms*, which live in soil and infect man by boring through his skin; and the *filaria worms*, which are transmitted by mosquitoes and cause blocks in lymph vessels. The disease resulting from filarial infections is characterized by immense swellings and is known as *elephantiasis*.

PHYLUM NEMATOMORPHA: HAIRWORMS
(80 species)

These are very long, very thin animals which resemble nematodes in general structure (Fig. 11.23). Larval hairworms are parasitic in insects; adults are free-living but nonfeeding.

PHYLUM GASTROTRICHA
(200 species)

The phylum comprises microscopic marine and freshwater animals which move by means of cilia located on the underside of the body. In some species the body surface is covered with bristles, and this makes the animals resemble ciliate protozoa. However, the internal structure is in some respects like that of rotifers, in others like that of nematodes (Fig. 11.23).

PHYLUM KINORHYNCHA
(30 species)

Marine worms with surface spines and retractile proboscis, resembling nematodes in general structure (Fig. 11.23).

PHYLUM PRIAPULIDA
(3 species)

Thick-bodied marine worms living in mud and sand in coastal regions (Fig. 11.23).

PHYLUM ENTOPROCTA
(60 species)

One species of this group of minute, sessile animals is known to live in fresh water; the rest are marine (Fig. 11.24). The animals form shallow-water colonies which encrust rocks, shells, and seaweeds. Each entoproct is attached by a stalk; at the other end it possesses a crown of ciliated tentacles. The cilia create feeding currents. Mouth and anus lie side by side within the ring of tentacles, and the digestive tract is U-shaped. Entoprocts thus are the only pseudocoelomate animals not shaped like worms. The larvae of entoprocts are unique, types like them not being found in any other phylum.

SCHIZOCOELOMATES

In this important superphylum, the embryonic mesoderm has two sources. Early mesoderm forms from ectoderm, and such mesoderm is characteristic of larval stages. When a larva transforms into an adult, the early mesoderm largely degenerates and new adult mesoderm is developed from endoderm. Such later mesoderm subsequently splits into two layers, an outer one which comes to lie against the inner surface of the body wall and an inner one which surrounds the alimentary tract (see Fig. 11.8). The animals therefore have a true coelom, and since it arises by a splitting of mesoderm, the superphylum is named "schizocoelomates." The larvae of schizocoelomates are **trochophores** or typically trochophorelike (Fig. 11.25).

Of the seven phyla in the superphylum, two rank

FIG. 11.23   Various pseudocoelomates, diagrammatic.

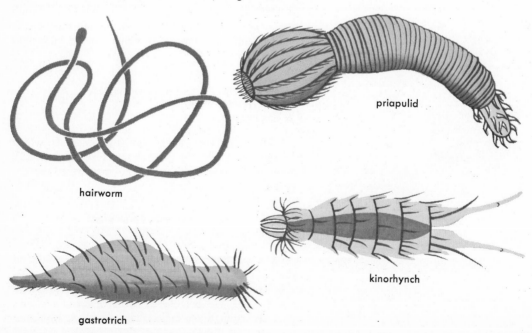

hairworm

priapulid

gastrotrich

kinorhynch

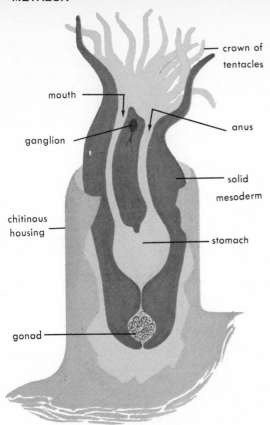

crown of
tentacles

mouth

ganglion

anus

solid
mesoderm

chitinous
housing

stomach

gonad

FIG. 11.24   The structure of an entoproct individual, diagrammatic cutaway. Note absence of true coelom and
position of anus within tentacle ring.

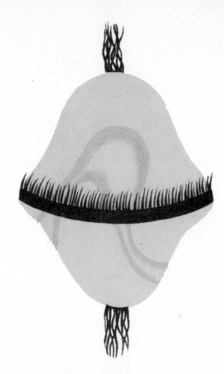

FIG. 11.25   Diagram of a trochophore larva. Note alimentary tract, also band and tufts of cilia.

first and second among Metazoa in numbers of species
(arthropods and mollusks). Two phyla are characterized by segmented bodies (annelids and arthropods).
That the various phyla are actually interrelated by
reasonably close evolutionary ties is probably better
established for schizocoelomates than for any other
superphylum. Several fairly good lines of evidence
indicate that a basic schizocoelomate stock probably
arose from ancestral acoelomates. This basic stock then
appears to have produced mollusks and four other
groups rather early, annelids later. Arthropods evolved
last, directly from annelids.

PHYLUM ECTOPROCTA
(2,500 species)

These are minute marine and freshwater animals
which resemble entoprocts superficially; i.e., they are

sessile, colonial, and form mats on rocks and seaweeds.
Moreover, they possess a U-shaped digestive tract, as
well as a crown of ciliated tentacles (Fig. 11.26). Because of these similarities, ectoprocts and entoprocts
used to be regarded as subgroups of a single phylum
(*Bryozoa* or *Polyzoa*). But the differences between the
entoprocts and ectoprocts are quite pronounced, and
each is now properly accorded the rank of a separate
phylum.

Ectoprocts are coelomate. The anus opens outside the ring of tentacles. Each animal is encased in a
calcareous or chitinous cup, from which the tentacles
may be protruded. Polymorphism is characteristic of
the group. Some individuals of a colony may mature
as highly modified animals which resemble the heads
of birds and are called **avicularia**. Each such animal
consists largely of a pair of muscle-operated jaws, which
prevent other organisms from settling on the colony.
Ectoprocts may reproduce by budding or by producing
sex cells. Fertilized eggs develop into free-swimming
trochophorelike larvae which disperse the species geographically. The larvae become adults through a very
drastic transformation in which almost all larval tissues

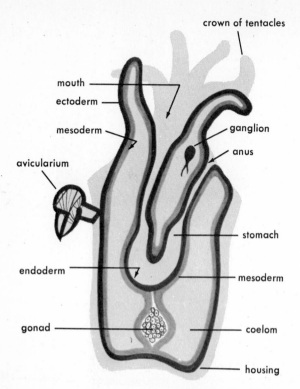

FIG. 11.26 The structure of an ectoproct individual, diagrammatic cutaway. Note presence of a true coelom and position of anus outside tentacle ring.

degenerate. Adult tissues are formed from the few larval remnants.

PHYLUM PHORONIDEA
(15 species)

These are wormlike, sedentary, tube-dwelling animals that live in the bottom of shallow seas. The straight tubular housing of a phoronid lies vertically in mud or sand. From the top protrudes a horseshoe-shaped crown of ciliated, food-catching tentacles. The digestive tract is U-shaped. Larvae are of the trochophore type, and in this and other respects phoronids resemble ectoprocts to some extent (Fig. 11.27).

PHYLUM SIPUNCULOIDEA
(250 species)

This group comprises small, flask-shaped animals found in sand or mud of shallow seas (Fig. 11.27). The narrow anterior part of the body bears a fringe of ciliated tentacles, and the whole foreregion of the animal may be retracted into a thicker hind part. The mouth, within the ring of tentacles, leads into a U-shaped, coiled intestine which terminates at an anus located dorsally behind the tentacle ring. The larva is of the trochophore type.

PHYLUM ECHIUROIDEA
(60 species)

The worm-shaped animals in this group (Fig. 11.27) possess an anterior proboscislike, nontentacled, mucus-secreting, food-catching organ, a mouth located at the base of the proboscis, and a coiled intestine leading to a posteriorly located anus. Echiurids are marine mud dwellers. Their larvae are of the trochophore type.

PHYLUM MOLLUSCA:
MOLLUSKS
(100,000 species)

Class Amphineura: chitons
Class Scaphopoda: tooth shells
Class Gastropoda: snails, slugs, whelks
Class Pelecypoda: clams, mussels
Class Cephalopoda: squids, octopuses, nautiluses

Among Metazoa, this enormous phylum is second only to the arthropods in number of species. Mollusks are mostly marine, but many snails and clams live in fresh water and one group of snails is terrestrial. Mollusks are exceedingly abundant in all aquatic habitats. As a group, they illustrate the general principle that successful phyla are highly diversified in structural adaptations and ways of life. We may also note that the phylum includes the largest of all nonvertebrate animals, namely, the giant squids, which may reach lengths of 50 ft.

Despite the external dissimilarities of the members of different classes, all mollusks share a common fundamental body organization. The molluscan body consists of a ventral, muscular **foot,** which is the principal organ of locomotion; a **visceral mass,** located dorsal to the foot, which contains most of the internal organs; and a **mantle,** a tissue layer which covers the visceral mass and which in most cases secretes a calcareous **shell** (Fig. 11.28). The larvae characteristically are trochophores. In most mollusks, the trochophore develops

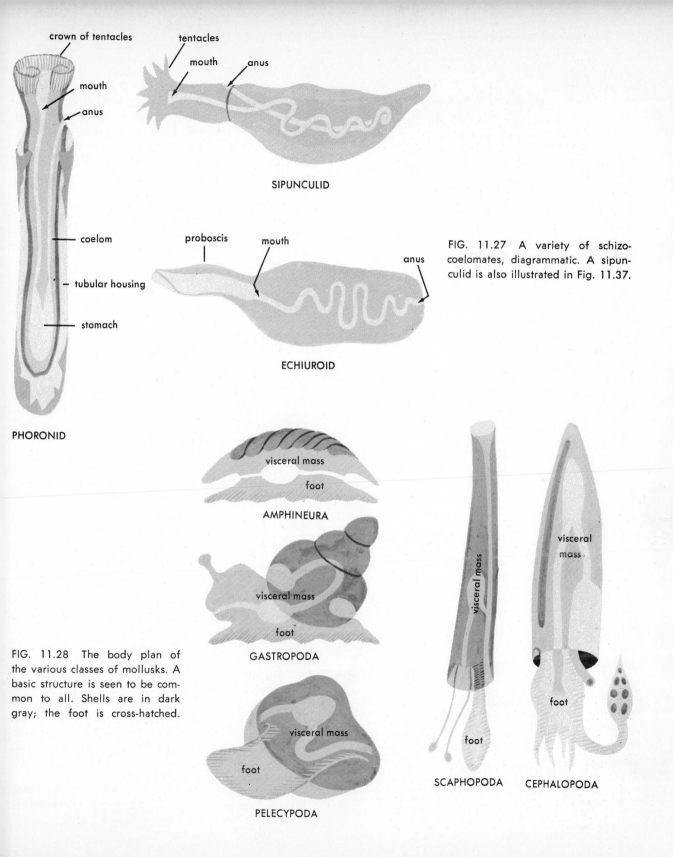

crown of tentacles

mouth

anus

coelom

tubular housing

stomach

PHORONID

tentacles

mouth

anus

SIPUNCULID

proboscis

mouth

anus

ECHIUROID

FIG. 11.27 A variety of schizo-coelomates, diagrammatic. A sipun-culid is also illustrated in Fig. 11.37.

visceral mass

foot

AMPHINEURA

visceral mass

foot

GASTROPODA

FIG. 11.28 The body plan of the various classes of mollusks. A basic structure is seen to be common to all. Shells are in dark gray; the foot is cross-hatched.

visceral mass

foot

PELECYPODA

visceral mass

foot

SCAPHOPODA

visceral mass

foot

CEPHALOPODA

FIG. 11.29 A chiton, member of the molluscan class Amphineura. The animal is seen from the dorsal side. Note the eight shell plates and the edge of the foot. *(American Museum of Natural History.)*

into a so-called **veliger** larva which eventually metamorphoses into the adults.

Class Amphineura

The animals of this class are probably the least specialized mollusks (Fig. 11.29). Chitons occur abundantly on rocks along the seashore, where they creep sluggishly with their broad foot. The dorsal surface of a chiton is protected by a shell of eight overlapping plates. Under the rim of this shell, in the so-called **mantle cavity**, are lateral **gills** for breathing. The head is greatly reduced, probably a specialized feature of

FIG. 11.30 Coiling of shell and torsion of internal organs in snails as a result of faster development on one side of the body.

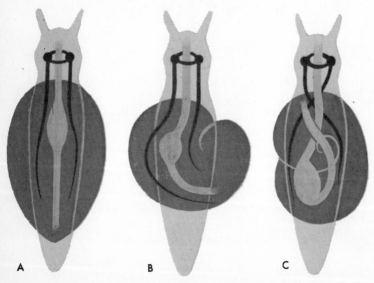

A   B   C

chitons. Between shell and foot is the visceral mass. It contains the alimentary system, which consists of an anterior mouth, a tubular digestive tract, and a posterior anus. Behind the mouth is a pharynx, in which is found a **radula,** a horny rasping organ characteristic of mollusks generally. When it is protruded through the mouth, the radula may move back and forth over algal vegetation and rasp off small fragments. Chitons possess a circulatory system with a simply constructed heart. The cavity in which this pumping organ is located represents the main part of the molluscan coelom. Also present in the visceral mass are excretory and reproductive organs and a nervous system. The latter consists of a ring of neural tissue which encircles the alimentary tract behind the mouth and of a ventral ladder-type array of nerve cords.

Class Scaphopoda

In these mollusks (see Fig. 11.28) the body is greatly elongated in a dorsoventral direction and the animal is tubular. The shell is a tube open at both ends and the foot of a scaphopod protrudes from the wider ventral end. The mouth is surrounded by delicate sensory and prehensile tentacles. Scaphopods are the least common of the mollusks. They are marine and live partly buried in sand or mud bottoms of shallow waters.

Class Gastropoda

Snails have the general architecture of chitons, with two major differences. First, a distinct **head** is present which bears retractile tentacles and eyes. Second, during embryonic development, the visceral mass becomes rotated through an angle of 180° relative to the foot. This makes the intestine U-shaped and brings the anus anteriorly above the mouth. Also, rotation twists the two main trunks of the ladder-type nervous system into a figure 8. Correlated with the visceral rotation, one side of the body, usually the left, grows much more slowly than the other. This unequal growth produces a coiling of the shell (Fig. 11.30).

Rotational development of this sort undoubtedly is an adaptation to the gastropod way of life. The shell is open only at one end; and when a snail withdraws into its shell, it is advantageous to have both mouth and anus near the opening. Shells are cumbersome even then, and we may note that in many gastropods the shells are reduced or absent altogether. In such animals, the visceral mass is more or less completely rotated back into the original position. Aquatic snails breathe by means of gills, like chitons, and in terrestrial snails parts of the mantle cavity have become adapted to function as lungs. Some land snails have returned secondarily to water and must surface periodically for air.

Class Pelecypoda

Clams are highly specialized mollusks adapted to a burrowing way of life. They are flattened from side to side, the hinge of the two shells, or **valves**, being dorsal (Fig. 11.31).

Lining the valves on the inside are the mantle tissues, which form two openings at the posterior end, one for the entry and one for the exit of water. In many species, these posterior tissues are drawn out into a long retractile tube, which may be pushed out into free water if the clam is embedded in several

FIG. 11.31   The internal structure of a clam. In this model, most of the gill flap is cut away to expose the organs of the visceral mass. Water enters via the incurrent siphon and passes over the gills, where food particles are strained out and conducted to the mouth, hidden under a flap of tissue. Water and elimination products of all kinds leave the clam via the excurrent siphon. The two adductor muscles control the closing of the valve shells. *(American Museum of Natural History.)*

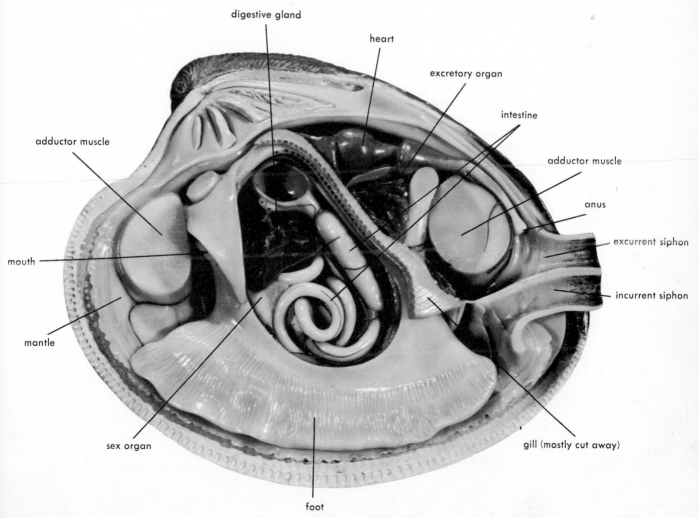

FIG. 11.32   A horse clam, showing the extensible tube containing the incurrent and excurrent siphons. When the animal is deeply embedded in mud or sand, the siphon tube may be extended upward into clear water. *(Courtesy of V. B. Scheffer, U.S. Fish and Wildlife Service.)*

inches of sand or mud (Fig. 11.32). Hanging freely into the mantle cavity are the gills, folds of ciliated tissue which function both as breathing organs and as food filters. Pelecypods subsist on microscopic food particles brought into the animals by the incoming water current. The gills strain and collect these particles and the cilia carry them to the mouth. This opening is located anteriorly between the left and right gills, in the visceral mass. The digestive tract within the visceral mass consists of stomach, digestive gland, and intestine. A radula is not present in this class of mollusks. The anus opens posteriorly and discharges into the outgoing water current.

The other organs of the visceral mass are largely as in other mollusks, except that the nervous system is

highly reduced, a feature undoubtedly correlated with the sluggish way of life of these animals. A head is not present either. The muscular foot, continuous with the visceral mass, may be protruded between the valves. Clams use the foot as a burrowing organ. By expanding the tip of the foot in sand and pulling the body after it, they may propel themselves forward (Fig. 11.33). Many pelecypods are permanently attached, however. This is true, for example, of oysters and also of the giant clam *Tridacna*, which may be 2 yd long and weigh ¼ ton.

Class Cephalopoda

All these most highly organized mollusks are marine, predatory animals (Fig. 11.34). Nautiluses have coiled, chambered shells, the animals living in the newest, largest chambers. Squids have a highly reduced horny shell embedded within the mantle. Octopuses are altogether without shells. Larval stages in cephalopods are suppressed, the young hatching as miniature adults.

Like scaphopods, cephalopods are elongated dorsoventrally. In squids, for example, the sucker-equipped tentacles represent the foot and the body represents the visceral mass (see Fig. 11.28). Within the wreath of tentacles is a highly developed head, with a large brain and large, vertebratelike eyes. The head also bears a mouth, which is equipped with strong horny jaws as well as a radula behind them. The digestive tract is U-shaped, the anus opening into the mantle cavity. This cavity opens to the exterior through a narrow muscular **funnel**. When the mantle contracts,

FIG. 11.33   The locomotion of a clam, diagrammatic. By successively extending its foot, anchoring it in sand, and then contracting and shortening it, a clam may propel itself forward slowly. The net distance covered in one propulsion cycle depends on how far the foot can be extended.

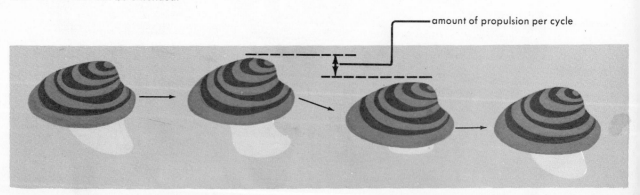

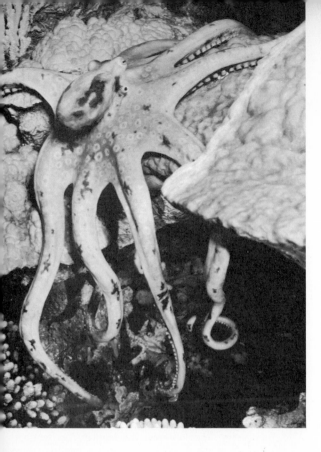

FIG. 11.34 Cephalopod mollusks. Left, an octopus. Note funnel, here visible under right eye. Right, the chambered nautilus. A section through the shell is shown. (*American Museum of Natural History.*)

water collected in the mantle cavity is squeezed out through the funnel with great force. The emerging water jet propels the squid in the opposite direction (Fig. 11.35). Speeds produced by such jet propulsion may match those of fish. Squids also possess a pair of horizontally placed fins, which are used for balancing and steering and for slow, sustained cruising.

PHYLUM ANNELIDA: SEGMENTED WORMS
(10,000 species)

Class Polychaeta: clamworms, tubeworms
Class Oligochaeta: earthworms
Class Hirudinea: leeches
Class Archiannelida

This phylum comprises animals in which the body is divided internally and externally into numerous **segments,** which are separated from each other by membranous partitions. Except for the segments of the head and the hind end, all others are more or less alike. The digestive, nervous, and circulatory systems

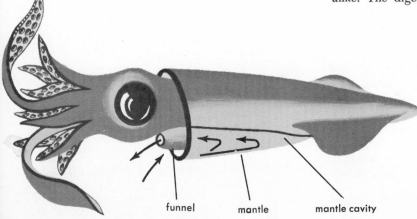

funnel   mantle   mantle cavity

FIG. 11.35 The jet principle of locomotion in a squid. Note the external mantle, the mantle cavity (with arrows), and the funnel, through which water is squirted out, propelling the squid in the opposite direction.

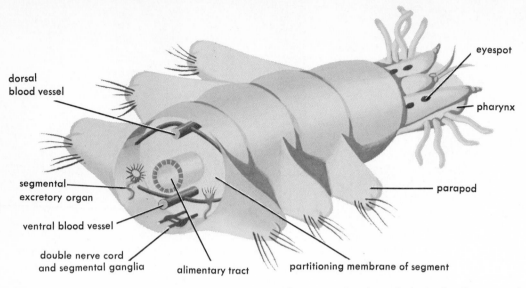

dorsal
blood vessel

eyespot

pharynx

parapod

segmental
excretory organ

ventral blood vessel

double nerve cord
and segmental ganglia

alimentary tract

partitioning membrane of segment

FIG. 11.36   Anterior part of the polychaete *Nereis* and cross section through the body, diagrammatic.

run uninterruptedly from front to rear, but all other organs are arranged on a segmental basis (Fig. 11.36). Where the life cycle includes larval stages, the larvae are trochophores, often indistinguishable from molluscan trochophores. Veliger stages are not present, however, and annelid trochophores elongate directly into segmented worms.

The first three segments of an annelid form the head, and the last segment represents the hind end. The mouth, located anteriorly in the head, leads into an alimentary tract which terminates in the last segment. The head also contains the brain ganglia, which form a ring around the pharynx. The rest of the nervous system is essentially of the ladder type, consisting of ventral nerve trunks thickened into ganglia in each segment. The circulatory system is composed principally of a longitudinal dorsal vessel, a longitudinal ventral vessel, and segmental connecting channels between these two. Blood flows forward dorsally and backward ventrally, propelled by peristaltic contractions of the dorsal blood vessel. Among oligochaetes, blood is kept in motion additionally by the connecting vessels of some of the anterior segments. These vessels are enlarged and function as pumping hearts. A pair of excretory organs with separate openings is found in each body segment. The cuticle-covered body surface of an annelid serves for breathing.

The Polychaeta (Fig. 11.37) form the largest and

FIG. 11.37   Polychaetes. Section through the tube of the parchment worm *Chaetopterus*. The head of the worm is on the left. Note the greatly elaborated parapodia, used to draw water currents through the tube. Between the arms of the U tube is a sipunculid worm, a member of another phylum. *(American Museum of Natural History.)*

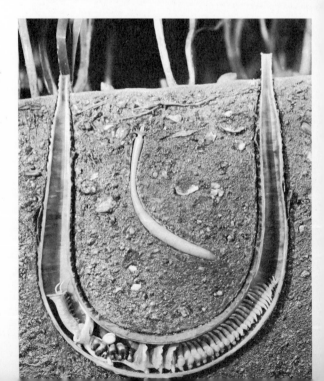

probably the most primitive class. These worms are mostly marine. Some are free-swimming. Others manufacture tubes in mud or sand in which they live permanently. And still others are burrowers. All are distinguished by the presence of a pair of fleshy lobes, the **parapodia,** on each body segment (see Fig. 11.36). Numerous chitinous bristles grow out from these lobes, hence the name "polychaetes," or "many-bristled," for worms of this class. Parapodia afford a large surface for breathing. The beating of the lobes also aids in locomotion or in drawing water in and out of tubes and burrows. Polychaetes are characterized further by the presence of eyes and of other specialized sense organs in the head segments. During the breeding season, the coelomic mesoderm in some or all body segments buds off reproductive cells which accumulate in the coelom. Such cells then reach the exterior through the excretory organs or by bursting through the body wall. Trochophore larvae are typical of the group.

The Oligochaeta include the familiar earthworms, which belong to the genus *Lumbricus*. Annelids of this class differ from polychaetes mainly in four ways. First, eyes and other head appendages are absent. Second, parapodia are absent and each body segment bears only a few bristles (Fig. 11.38). Third, each animal contains permanent male as well as female sex organs in specific segments. And fourth, free-swimming larval stages are suppressed. Oligochaetes live in the ocean, in fresh water, and on land. Some attain remarkable size. For example, the giant earthworms of Australia may reach lengths of over 10 ft and diameters of over 1 in.

Early oligochaete stocks have probably given rise to the Hirudinea, the class comprising the leeches (see Fig. 11.38). These animals are without bristles, and, unlike other annelids, they possess a fixed number of segments throughout life. Moreover, the external segmentation does not match the internal, external segments being the more numerous. Each end of the body is equipped with a sucker. The most familiar leeches are bloodsucking parasites, but we may note that not all members of the class pursue this way of life. The bloodsuckers possess digestive tracts equipped with spacious pouches, which may store enough food to make a single meal suffice for many months. These worms produce **hirudin,** an anticoagulant which prevents blood from clotting during ingestion.

Archiannelids are a minor group which may be either very primitive or very specialized and simplified.

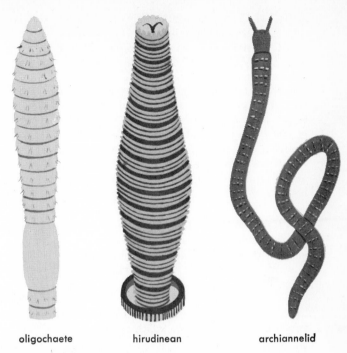

oligochaete   hirudinean   archiannelid

FIG. 11.38 Various annelids, diagrammatic.

These worms are unsegmented externally but segmented internally. In most species parapodia and bristles are absent. Cilia are present, however, a feature of the trochophore larva which is carried over into the adult (see Fig. 11.38).

The segmentation of annelids is a trait of considerable adaptive advantage. It permits the development of different specializations in different segments, just as, on a lower level of organization, division of living matter into cells makes possible divergent specializations. In modern annelids, to be sure, divergent segmental differentiation has not proceeded very far and most segments are still rather alike. However, the inherent possibilities were exploited to the utmost in another schizocoelomate phylum which almost certainly evolved from primitive annelid stock: the arthropods.

PHYLUM ARTHROPODA: JOINTED-LEGGED ANIMALS
(1 million species)

Class Onychophora: *Peripatus*
Class Crustacea: shrimps, lobsters, crabs, barnacles
Class Insecta: insects

Class Chilopoda: centipedes
Class Diplopoda: millipedes
Class Arachnida: spiders, scorpions, mites, ticks
Class Merostomata: horseshoe crabs

By almost any standard, this is today the most successful group of organisms in the whole living world. Arthropods are encountered in all environments in which life occurs at all, and in many tropical environments they maintain supremacy over even man. The insects are by far the most abundant and most diversified of all arthropods, being represented in the phylum by at least three-quarters of a million species.

General Characteristics

The body plan of arthropods as a whole is a highly elaborated variant of that of annelid worms (Fig. 11.39). A segmented design is fundamental, and the different segments are specialized in often greatly divergent ways. The body of an arthropod is composed of a **head,** a **thorax,** and an **abdomen.** The whole is covered by a chitinous exoskeleton which is molted at intervals. Jointed appendages are present on most or all segments. The head consists of six segments. Fused together in the adult, each head segment characteristically bears a pair of appendages having either a sensory or an ingestive function. The head also contains either or both of two kinds of eyes (Fig. 11.40). In so-called **simple eyes,** a single lens covers many light-sensitive cells. In **compound eyes,** many complete visual units are grouped together into a composite structure. Each visual unit here contains a separate lens and a light-sensitive cell. Compound eyes are unique to arthropods.

The alimentary tract consists of foregut, midgut, and hindgut. The first and last of these sections are lined with chitin, which is continuous with the exoskeleton; hence only the midgut functions digestively. Nervous structures include dorsal brain ganglia in the head, ventral nerve cords, and paired ganglia either in each segment or grouped together in head and thorax. The circulatory system is *open,* a dorsal tubular heart being the only vessel present. Blood flows out from it anteriorly, circulates freely through the body tissues, and reenters the heart posteriorly (Fig. 11.41). The excretory organs either are located in the head appendages, as in crustaceans, or are attached to the midgut and lead to the outside via the anus, as in insects.

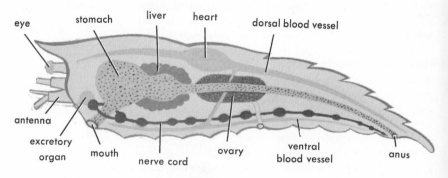

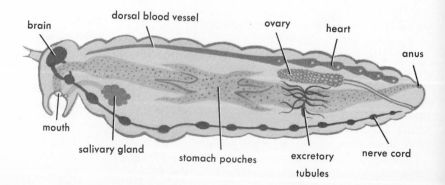

FIG. 11.39 The internal structure of a lobster (top) and a grasshopper (bottom), diagrammatic.

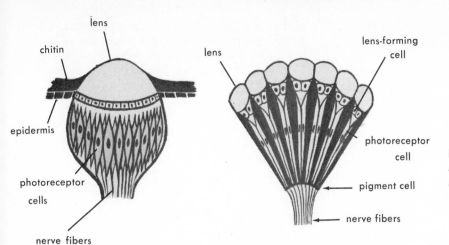

FIG. 11.40 Diagram of a simple arthropod eye (left) and a portion of a compound eye (right).

Breathing is accomplished in various ways in the different groups. Aquatic arthropods typically possess **gills** of some kind. In lobsters, for example, feathery gills are attached to the upper parts of the walking legs. Terrestrial arthropods like insects breathe by means of **tracheal tubes,** a unique, chitin-lined system of channels which originates on the body surface and ramifies to all interior tissues.

The fertilized eggs are large and extremely yolky. In many aquatic arthropods the eggs develop into free-swimming larvae. These resemble annelid worms to a considerable extent. This also holds for some terrestrial larvae, for example, the insect caterpillars. In other arthropods, the annelidlike stage is greatly abbreviated and when the larvae hatch they already look like miniature adults. All larval types develop through a series

FIG. 11.41 The open circulatory system of arthropods. Blood is pumped forward in an open-ended dorsal main vessel. After circulating freely through the body tissues, blood again enters the posterior end of the dorsal vessel.

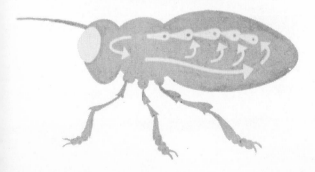

of molting steps, the last of which produces the adult. Insects do not molt after adulthood is attained, but crustaceans do molt throughout life.

Class Onychophora

The members of this small class are of great theoretical importance, for they indicate strikingly the close relation between annelids and arthropods.

The onychophoran *Peripatus* (Fig. 11.42), rather caterpillarlike in general appearance, possesses a head composed of three segments, as in annelids. These segments are fused, however, and their appendages include antennae, as in arthropods. Each body segment bears fleshy, parapodialike, unjointed legs, rather like annelids. But these legs terminate in claws, typical of arthropods. Like annelids, *Peripatus* possesses a pair of excretory organs in each body segment, leading to the outside by separate openings. But like terrestrial arthropods, *Peripatus* breathes by means of tracheal tubes. Also as in arthropods, the circulatory system of *Peripatus* is a single, open, dorsal vessel; yet as in

FIG. 11.42 *Peripatus.* This animal combines annelid and arthropod features. *(Carolina Biological Supply Co.)*

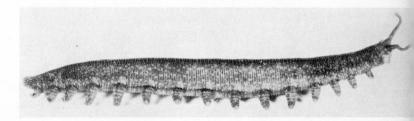

annelids, the reproductive ducts are ciliated, a feature not found elsewhere among arthropods.

Onychophora evidently represent a unique mixture of annelid and arthropod traits. Indeed, these animals are sometimes ranked as a separate phylum, sometimes as a subphylum within arthropods. Whatever the ranking, there is little doubt that they are remnants of an evolutionary line which branched off the ancestral arthropod stock, very soon after that stock itself had evolved from annelid ancestors.

Class Crustacea

This large group of arthropods is represented by some 50,000 species. Most crustaceans are aquatic and most of these are marine. Many are microscopic and planktonic, but others, like the giant crabs, may be some 12 ft across from one leg tip to the other. Most crustaceans are free-living and free-swimming, but some are parasitic either as larvae or as adults. Barnacles are sessile as adults. In their internal structure, crustacea display a typically arthropod organization. Externally, they show particularly clearly how different segments may become specialized for different functions. The segmental appendages of the lobster *Homarus* may serve to illustrate this point.

The body of a lobster consists of 21 segments (Fig. 11.43). The six segments of the head and the eight of the thorax are fused into a **cephalothorax** and are covered dorsally and laterally by a chitinous, lime-impregnated shield, the **carapace.** By contrast, the seven abdominal segments are marked off from one

another distinctly. During embryonic stages, all segments bear paired appendages which are rather alike and which later specialize in different ways. The first head segment is without appendages in the adult, but it bears a pair of stalked **compound eyes.** On the second and third segments are two pairs of sensory **antennae.** The excretory organs open at the bases of the second pair. Toothed chitinous **jaws** are present on the fourth segment. The fifth and sixth are equipped with **maxillae,** which pass food to the mouth.

To each of the first three segments of the thorax are attached a pair of **maxillipeds,** which aid in macerating food and also in passing it to the mouth. Moreover, the second and third maxillipeds are each equipped with a feathery gill. A pair of large pinching **claws** is present on the fourth thoracic segment, and on the remaining four segments of the thorax are **walking legs.** At the base of each of these is a gill protected by the overhanging carapace.

In the abdomen, the first segment contains a pair of sperm-transferring structures in the male and greatly reduced appendages in the female. On each of the next four segments is a pair of **swimmerets,** small paddlelike structures used in forward locomotion. In female lobsters, the swimmerets also serve as attachment sites for eggs. The next-to-last segment bears platelike **uropods.** These, together with the similarly platelike last segment, the **telson,** form a fan-shaped tail structure used in backward locomotion.

Inasmuch as all these segmental appendages originate in the embryo in like manner, they are mutually

FIG. 11.43   Dorsal view of a crayfish, a freshwater crustacean structurally very much like the marine lobster. Note the antennae, eyes, large claws, walking legs, uropods, and telson. The fused cephalothorax, covered by the carapace, is clearly set off from the abdominal segments. *(Carolina Biological Supply Co.)*

homologous. Later, their functions come to differ. This varied functional exploitation of segmental homologies lies at the root of the wide adaptability of arthropods generally and of crustaceans specifically.

Class Insecta

This largest of all animal groups differs from other arthropods in a number of distinct ways (Fig. 11.44).

First, the head is marked off clearly from the thorax and the thorax from the abdomen. The head again consists of six fused segments. On the first are a pair of compound eyes as well as one or more simple eyes. Only a single pair of antennae is encountered in insects, located on the second head segment. The mouth parts on the remaining four head segments vary greatly in structure, according to whether the animal feeds by *biting* like a grasshopper, by *sucking* like a housefly, or by *piercing and sucking* like a mosquito.

The thorax consists of three segments, each bearing a pair of walking legs. Also, in all except the most primitive insects (which are flightless) and secondarily flightless insects like fleas, each of the last two thoracic segments typically bears a pair of wings. Both pairs may be membranous, as in dragonflies and butterflies; the first pair may be heavily chitinized, as in beetles; or the second pair may be reduced to tiny stalks, as in houseflies and mosquitoes. The abdomen of insects characteristically is without appendages. The segments here vary in number in different groups and in many cases are fused.

FIG. 11.44   The external structure of an insect.

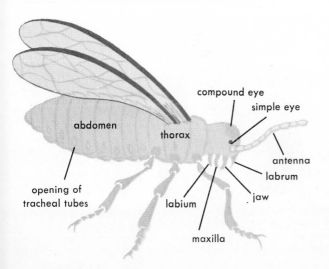

Insects become adults by *metamorphosis,* which can be either **incomplete** or **complete.** In the former the larva resembles the adult in general features and reaches adult condition gradually, in the course of five molting steps. Grasshoppers, earwigs, termites, true bugs, aphids, and many other insect types belong to this group. In the second case, the larva is annelid- or caterpillarlike. It eventually transforms into a **pupa,** and the pupa in turn becomes the adult. Butterflies, moths, houseflies, beetles, bees, and ants are in this group (Figs. 11.45, 11.46). Note that, in either group, only the adults fly.

Insects are classified into some 20 orders, each representing a very wide range of ways of life. For example, the order of beetles includes parasites, commensals, carnivores, herbivores, omnivores, aquatic types, subterranean types, arboreal types, diurnal and nocturnal types, and dozens of others, each adapted to a particular, often highly specialized mode of living. Analogous diversity is in evidence within most other orders. Incidentally, beetles alone number some 300,000 species. They form the largest of all orders within the largest of all classes within the largest of all phyla.

Classes Chilopoda, Diplopoda

Centipedes and millipedes (Fig. 11.47) are exclusively terrestrial. The two groups resemble each other in many ways, but they are nevertheless sufficiently distinct to be ranked as separate classes. In both groups, the rather wormlike or caterpillarlike animals are subdivided into numerous segments. The first six form the head and their appendages resemble those of insects. However, compound eyes are usually absent and clusters of simple eyes are typical. Body segments bear walking legs, *one* pair per segment in centipedes, *two* pairs per segment in millipedes. The first pair in centipedes is modified into poison claws. Centipedes are carnivorous, whereas millipedes are largely herbivorous. Despite the comparatively greater number of legs in millipedes, these arthropods cannot run as fast as centipedes. In their general internal structure, centipedes and millipedes are rather like insects.

Class Arachnida

This class similarly comprises terrestrial arthropods. The various types of arachnids within the group differ structurally in many ways, but they share a number of features which distinguish them from other arthropods (Fig. 11.48). Thus, in spiders, scorpions, and allied arachnids, the body is composed of a fused

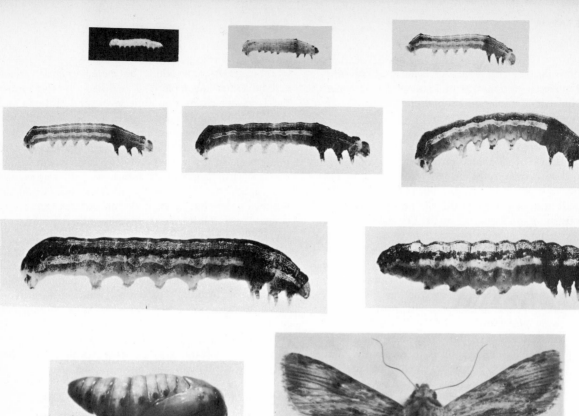

FIG. 11.45 Complete metamorphosis in insects. Note, top left to bottom right, the successive annelidlike larval stages (caterpillars), the pupa (next-to-last stage), and the winged adult stage. Each stage is connected to the preceding and succeeding one through a molt. In insects with incomplete metamorphosis, the larvae look like miniature adults. (Courtesy of Dr. D. Bodenstein, University of Virginia.)

FIG. 11.46 The molting of insects. Left, adult just emerging from cocoon, which has broken open along back. Top right, a moth just emerged from its cocoon. The adult exoskeleton has not yet hardened, and during the ensuing hours the abdomen pumps fluid into the wings. The abdomen thus becomes smaller and the wings larger, as at bottom right. The exoskeleton then hardens. (Left, U.S. Department of Agriculture; others, courtesy of H. Lou Gibson, Rochester, N.Y.)

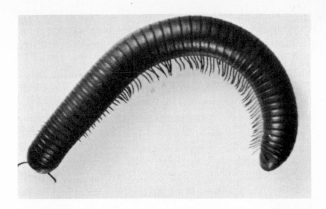

FIG. 11.47   Left, a centipede. Right, a millipede. Note the two pairs of legs per segment in millipedes, the single pair per segment in centipedes. *(Carolina Biological Supply Co.)*

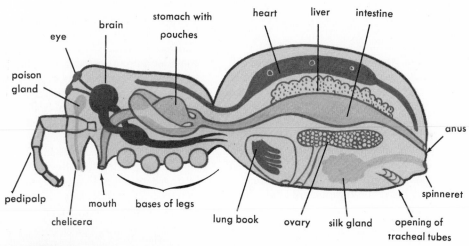

FIG. 11.48   Top, the internal structure of a spider, diagrammatic. Left, a tarantula. *(Left, General Biological Supply House, Inc.)*

cephalothorax and an abdomen. The head is without compound eyes, without antennae, and without true jaws. Instead, there are simple eyes, sensory bristles, and two pairs of appendages. One of the latter is sensory; the other is used for seizing and tearing prey. These are the **cheliceras** on the third head segment and the **pedipalps** on the fourth. In spiders, the cheliceras are sharp-pointed poison-injecting claws and the pedipalps serve a sensory function. In scorpions, it is the pedipalps which function in tearing prey apart. The thoracic segments bear four pairs of walking legs, a feature which distinguishes arachnids from insects most readily. The abdomen is without segmental appendages, but spiders possess several pairs of posterior **spinnerets**, organs which secrete web-forming silk. Arachnids have reduced abdominal tracheal tubes, and in addition they breathe by means of unique **lung books,** leaflike, richly vascularized plates of tissue present in an abdominal pouch. This pouch communicates with the outside through a slitlike opening.

Class Merostomata

Closely related to the arachnids and often classified with them are the marine *horseshoe crabs,* or king crabs. These are represented by five living species, all belonging to the genus *Limulus* (Fig. 11.49). The animals are archaic "living fossils"; they probably are survivors of an early branch of the aquatic stock which also gave rise to the modern arachnids. Horseshoe crabs possess compound as well as simple eyes, and they breathe by means of **gill books.** These are similar to and may well represent the forerunners of the lung books of the arachnids.

ENTEROCOELOMATES

Mesoderm in this superphylum arises exclusively from endoderm. At an early embryonic stage, the endoderm produces hollow pouches which grow into the space between ectoderm and endoderm. Eventually, these pouches fill the entire available space, and they also separate off from the endoderm which produced them. The cavities so enclosed completely by the mesodermal pouches are the coelom (see Fig. 11.8). Since the mesoderm and coelom here arise from the endoderm, which itself produces the gut (or *enteron*), the group is named "enterocoelomates."

Six phyla are included in the superphylum: lamp shells, arrowworms, beard worms, acorn worms, echinoderms, and chordates. The evolutionary interrelation of the last four is reasonably clearly established, but the relation of the first two to one another and to the other four is obscure. Similarly obscure is the derivation of the whole enterocoelomate stock. The origin of all mesoderm from endoderm is unique, as is the method of coelom formation. As will be shown in Chap. 27, various other embryological features additionally distinguish enterocoelomates from other superphyla. Because of such clear-cut differences, many investigators believe that enterocoelomates represent one or, more probably, several separate branches of metazoan evolution, arisen independently from acoelomate or radiate or perhaps even protistan ancestors. Inasmuch as enterocoelomates include the chordates and chordates include man, this superphylum is of very special interest.

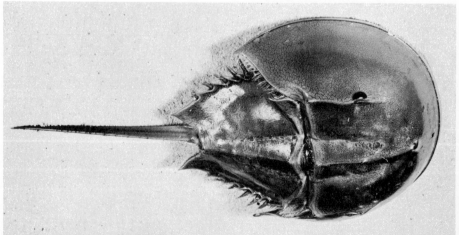

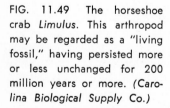

FIG. 11.49 The horseshoe crab *Limulus*. This arthropod may be regarded as a "living fossil," having persisted more or less unchanged for 200 million years or more. (Carolina Biological Supply Co.)

PHYLUM BRACHIOPODA: LAMP SHELLS
(250 species)

These are surviving remnants of a once very abundant group. The genus *Lingula* is considered to be the most ancient type of "living fossil" known. Brachiopods are all marine. They resemble clams superficially, but whereas in clams the valves are on the left and the right of the animal, in brachiopods they are dorsal and ventral, opening anteriorly. A muscular stalk protruding posteriorly between the valves attaches the animal to rock. Internally, two large, coiled arms are studded with short, ciliated tentacles. The beat of the cilia on the tentacles creates feeding and breathing currents (Fig. 11.50).

Although brachiopods possess an enterocoelous body cavity, certain other features of their embryonic development are like those of schizocoelomates. For example, the development of the brachiopod mouth follows the schizocoelomate, not the enterocoelomate, pattern. Also, the ciliated tentacle arms of brachiopods resemble the similar arms of the schizocoelomate phoronids. Such trait combinations make brachiopods a transitional group between schizocoelomates and enterocoelomates, and the exact evolutionary affinities of brachiopods are therefore quite uncertain.

PHYLUM CHAETOGNATHA: ARROWWORMS
(30 species)

These are small, transparent, marine animals (Fig. 11.50). Although relatively few species are known, individual arrowworms at given seasons become so enormously abundant that they form an important constituent of the food of marine fish. The chaetognath body is roughly torpedo-shaped. It is equipped with lateral "fins," used presumably in balancing. Internal transverse partitions mark the body into head, trunk, and tail, and a longitudinal partition divides the body cavity into left and right halves. Around the mouth are curved bristles, which aid in catching minute food organisms as the arrowworms dart about in shallow water. The anus is located at the junction of trunk and tail. The evolutionary affinities of this group are unknown, but the developmental pattern clearly indicates that the chaetognaths may be placed with the enterocoelomates.

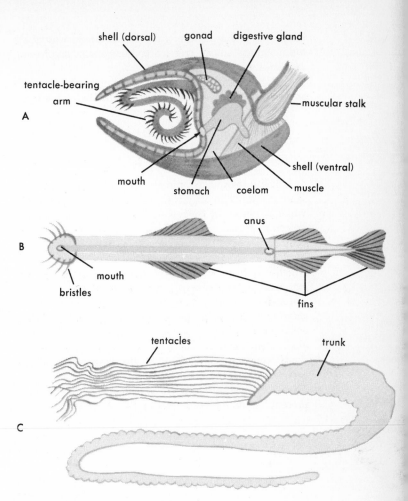

FIG. 11.50 *A*, diagram of the internal structure of a brachiopod. *B*, outline drawing of a chaetognath. *C*, outline drawing of a pogonophoran beard worm.

PHYLUM POGONOPHORA: BEARD WORMS
(25 species)

These marine animals (Fig. 11.50) live largely in the abyssal plains of deep oceans. The greatly elongated cylindrical body of a beard worm is housed in a secreted tube and the tube is embedded in the sea floor. One or more tentacular arms at the front end of the animal project from the tube into the open water. The tentacles not only catch food organisms but also form a temporary basket or cavity in which food is digested. Digestion products are then absorbed directly into blood vessels present in the tentacles. Mouth, intestine, and anus are entirely absent and beard worms are quite unique among free-living Metazoa in not having any trace of an alimentary tract.

Pogonophora are distinctly enterocoelomate and appear to be fairly closely related to the hemichordates.

PHYLUM HEMICHORDATA: ACORN WORMS
(100 species)

These wormlike animals are marine and live in sand or mud. The body consists of an anterior **proboscis,** which is used in burrowing, and of a **collar** and a posterior **trunk** (Fig. 11.51). The mouth is situated ventrally, where the proboscis joins the collar. Behind the collar are many pairs of **gill slits,** where water which has been taken in by mouth is expelled to the exterior. In the process, oxygen is absorbed from the water into blood which travels past the gill slits. A short internal rod of tissue projects forward from the collar and probably supports the proboscis. The nervous system includes two nerve cords in the trunk, one dorsal and one ventral, the dorsal cord in some species extending into the collar as a thickened, hollow tube. These cords connect with a network of nerve cells present under the epidermis of the worms.

The embryos and larvae of some hemichordates are remarkably like those of some echinoderms (Fig. 11.52). This is one of the main clues indicating close relationship between these two phyla. Hemichordates probably represent an early offshoot of an ancestral evolutionary stock which also gave rise separately to the beard worms, the echinoderms, and the chordates.

PHYLUM ECHINODERMATA: SPINY-SKINNED ANIMALS
(6,000 species)

Class Asteroidea: starfishes
Class Ophiuroidea: brittle stars
Class Echinoidea: sea urchins, sand dollars
Class Holothuroidea: sea cucumbers
Class Crinoidea: sea lilies, feather stars

The members of this phylum are exclusively marine, and their unique identifying feature is a so-called **water-vascular system** for locomotion. The embryos and larvae are bilateral, but the adults are radially symmetrical.

A starfish of the familiar genus *Asterias* is composed of a central region from which five **arms** radiate out. In other genera, there may be as many as 20 or

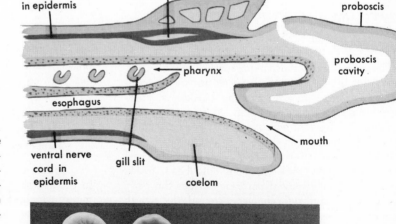

FIG. 11.51 Top, section through the anterior part of a hemichordate, diagrammatic. Bottom, model of the hemichordate *Dolichoglossus.* Note proboscis, collar, trunk, and the gill slits in anterior part of trunk, just behind collar. *(Bottom, American Museum of Natural History.)*

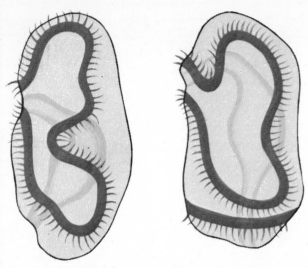

FIG. 11.52 Although the adults of echinoderms and hemichordates are very dissimilar, their larvae in many cases are quite alike. On the left is a diagram of an echinoderm larva; on the right, a diagram of a hemichordate larva.

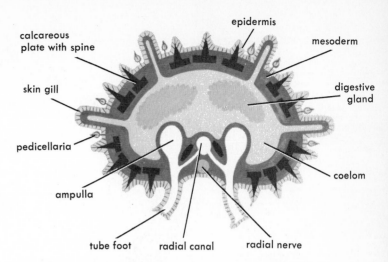

FIG. 11.53 Cross section through the arm of a starfish, diagrammatic.

more arms. The shell-like skeleton is an endoskeleton made up of small flat **calcareous plates** which are held together by muscles and connective tissue (Fig. 11.53; see also Fig. 11.5). Short **calcareous spines,** some of them movable, project from the skeletal plates. Covering the skeleton are epidermal tissues, which are studded with many tiny fingerlike protrusions, the **skin gills.** The internal cavities of these gills are parts of the coelom and communicate with the interior body cavity through spaces left among the skeletal plates. Also present on the body surface are numerous very small pincers, the **pedicellariae.** These protect the skin gills from interference by small animals.

The water-vascular system (Fig. 11.54) communicates with the outside through a **madreporite,** a sievelike device located excentrically on the upper surface of the animal. A series of ducts leads from the madreporite into five **radial canals,** one passing into each arm. Short side branches from these canals connect with the hollow, muscular **tube feet,** which project from the underside of the arms. At the base of each tube foot is a muscular sac, the **ampulla,** which may force water into the foot and so make it stiff. Tube feet may be used both as walking structures and as suction devices with which a starfish may hold onto rocks or food organisms (Fig. 11.55).

The mouth is on the undersurface in the center of the body, and in the center of the upper surface is a small **anal pore.** Connecting mouth and anus is a **stomach,** into which open five pairs of **digestive glands,** one pair from each arm. Starfishes feed largely on clams. The tube feet, working in relays as suckers, pull on the valves of a clam until the clam is exhausted and opens it housing. The stomach of the starfish then turns inside out through the mouth and digests the soft tissues of the clam. Starfishes are without brain,

FIG. 11.54 The components and the internal arrangement of the water-vascular system in a starfish. Water enters and leaves the system through the sievelike madreporite (sieve plate) at the upper side.

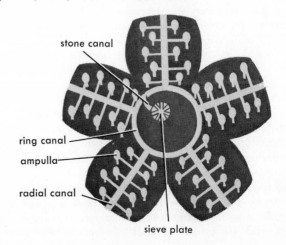

FIG. 11.55 Starfish. Left, view from top. Note the madreporite as a round spot in the angle between the two lower arms. Right, view from below, showing tube feet. (Left, Carolina Biological Supply Co.; right, Woody Williams, Inverness, Calif.)

and the nervous system is not very elaborate. It consists of a ring of nerve tissue around the mouth, from which nerve trunks radiate into each arm. The circulatory system is also greatly reduced. Excretion is accomplished partly by diffusion, partly by migrating amoeboid cells. These are dispersed freely in the body cavity, and they carry wastes to and through the epidermis.

The members of the other echinoderm classes largely resemble starfishes in their general features (Fig. 11.56). Among the brittle stars, the five arms are elongated and slender and their sinuous movements aid materially in locomotion. In some ophiuroids the arms are branched. Echinoids are without arms, but their bodies nevertheless are organized on a plan of five or multiples of five. For example, sea urchins possess five bands of long slender tube feet and a mouth equipped with five radially placed teeth. Long movable spines are characteristic of these animals. The sea cucumbers are elongated along the mouth-anus axis, and they are further distinguished by a highly reduced skeleton, a leathery body covering, and a circlet of tentacles around the mouth. Five longitudinal bands of tube feet are typical of most members of this class.

Crinoids are stalked, sessile, deepwater forms characterized by numerous feathery arms.

The early embryonic development of echinoderms is similar to that of chordates, and little doubt exists that echinoderms and chordates are fairly closely related.

PHYLUM CHORDATA: CHORDATES
(50,000 species)

Subphylum Urochordata: tunicates
Subphylum Cephalochordata: lancelets
Subphylum Vertebrata: vertebrates
    Class Agnatha: jawless fishes
    Class Placoderms: armored fishes (extinct)
    Class Chondrichthyes: cartilage fishes
    Class Osteichthyes: bony fishes
    Class Amphibia: amphibians
    Class Reptilia: reptiles
    Class Aves: birds
    Class Mammalia: mammals

Because this phylum includes man and the animals most directly important to man, it is unquestionably

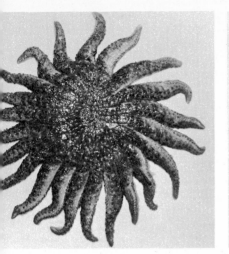
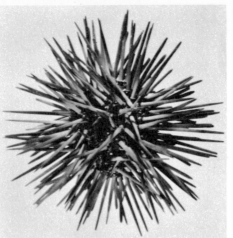
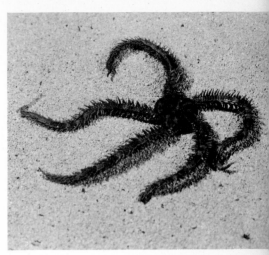

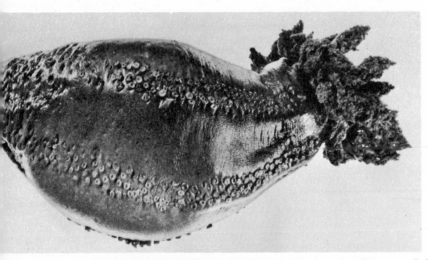

FIG. 11.56 Top left, a many-armed starfish. Top middle, a sea urchin. Top right, a brittle star. Left, a sea cucumber. In left, note the leathery skin, the tentacles surrounding the mouth, and the rows of tube feet. (Top left, V. B. Scheffer, U.S. Fish and Wildlife Service; top middle, left, Carolina Biological Supply Co.; top right, American Museum of Natural History.)

the most interesting from almost any standpoint. The phylum also has a special evolutionary significance, for it comprises what is by far the most progressive group of animals. Other phyla may include more species and may be more diversified; but only among chordates do we encounter, within one and the same phylum, types as primitively organized as tunicates and types as complexly organized as men. Evidently, the ancestral chordate body plan was richer in major evolutionary potentialities than the body plans of other phyla.

Chordates are characterized by the possession of a **notochord**, a hollow **dorsal nerve cord**, and paired **gill slits** (Fig. 11.57). These structures are present either throughout life or only at some stage of development. The notochord (hence the name "chordate") is a dorsal

stiffening rod formed from embryonic mesoderm. The nerve cord and later nervous system form from the embryonic ectoderm. Gill slits are essentially channels on each side which connect the exterior of the body with the front part of the alimentary tract, specifically the region behind the mouth, called the *pharynx*. Thus a continuous water channel is established from the mouth to the pharynx and from the pharynx to the outside through the gill slits. Food present in the water taken in by mouth is collected in the pharynx and is passed on into the esophagus. The water returns to the environment via the gill slits past the gills, where oxygen is absorbed into the circulatory system.

The body is segmented in two of the three chordate subphyla, the lancelets and the vertebrates. This

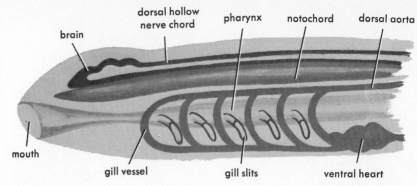

FIG. 11.57 The anterior portion of a hypothetical chordate, to show the basic diagnostic features of the phylum Chordata.

Labels: brain, dorsal hollow nerve chord, pharynx, notochord, dorsal aorta, mouth, gill vessel, gill slits, ventral heart

feature is also characteristic of the annelid-arthropod group of organisms, but it has here evolved independently. A distinct head is present only in vertebrate chordates, and these animals are therefore designated alternatively as *Craniata*. The representatives of the other chordate subphyla, all headless, are collectively called *Acrania* (Table 7).

Subphylum Urochordata

Tunicates, or "sea squirts," are marine. Of the approximately 2,000 known species, most are sessile and many form extensive colonies in the water. The adults are quite unlike typical chordates, but their larvae clearly reveal the chordate character of these animals. A tunicate larva has the general form of a tadpole (Fig. 11.58). It possesses a large muscular tail, a very well developed notochord, and a dorsal hollow nerve cord, expanded anteriorly into a primitive brain. A complete alimentary system is present, as are pharyngeal gill slits.

After a free-swimming existence of some hours, the tunicate larva attaches its anterior end to a rock or other solid object and undergoes a remarkable metamorphosis. In the adult (Fig. 11.59), the tail is resorbed, the notochord has disappeared completely, and the nervous system has become reduced to a single ganglion. The pharynx has enlarged, however, and has developed many additional gill slits. Also, the region of the mouth has shifted so that the alimentary tract is roughly U-shaped. A cellulose-containing covering, the **tunic**, has developed around the whole animal, leaving only two openings, the **incurrent** and the **excurrent siphon.** Water and food enter the animal via the incurrent opening. Food is filtered out in the pharynx and is carried over a ciliated groove into the esophagus. Water passes through the gill slits and leaves via the excurrent siphon. This opening also conducts waste products and reproductive cells to the outside.

Ancestral tunicates probably were the first chordates. They "invented" the unique tadpole larva which swims by means of a muscular tail rather than with cilia, as is typical of the larvae of all other animal phyla. Tadpolelike larval chordates then undoubtedly gave rise to the other chordate subphyla.

TABLE 7
Some diagnostic features of chordates

group	subphylum	head	segmentation	skeleton	paired gills	nervous system	tail
Acrania	Urochordata	−	−	larval notochord	many	larval dorsal nerve cord	larval tail
	Cephalochordata	−	+	permanent notochord	many	permanent dorsal nerve cord	larval and adult tail
Craniata	Vertebrata	+	+	embryonic notochord; vertebral column in adult	few	permanent dorsal nerve cord and brain	larval and adult tail

FIG. 11.58 Photo and diagram of a tunicate tadpole. (Photo, General Biological Supply House, Inc.)

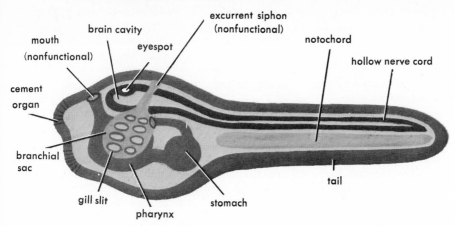

FIG. 11.59 Cutaway model of an adult tunicate. Food-bearing water is drawn into the pharynx through the incurrent opening. Food passes into the U-shaped alimentary tract, and water emerges through the gill slits and the excurrent opening to the outside. (American Museum of Natural History.)

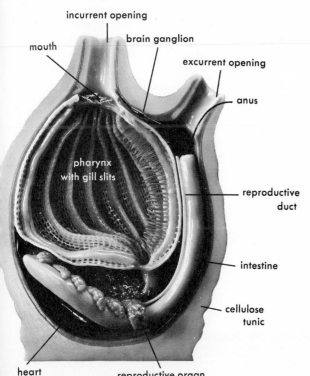

Subphylum Cephalochordata

The lancelets, often better known by the group name *amphioxus*, comprise some 30 species of small, marine sand burrowers. These animals are more or less fish-shaped, slender, and compressed laterally (Fig. 11.60). They possess a notochord which persists throughout life and which extends over the whole length of the body. The nerve cord is dorsal and tubular, but there is no brain and a head is not present. The mouth leads into a ciliated pharynx with 60 or more pairs of gill slits. Water passing through these emerges into an **atrium,** an ectodermal chamber which surrounds the pharynx and opens ventrally, anteriorly to the anus.

Amphioxus is a segmented animal. This is shown most obviously by the musculature, which is formed into segmental bundles, or **somites.** The nerves leading to these muscles and the excretory and reproductive

FIG. 11.60 Amphioxus, the lancelet. The many pharyngeal gill slits are very prominent just behind the mouth. Note also the notochord, the very dark rod just above the gill slits, running from front to back. A head is absent. (Carolina Biological Supply Co.)

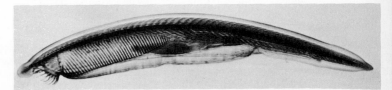

organs similarly are arranged on a segmental pattern. Lancelets therefore are clearly and very closely related to vertebrates. They differ from vertebrates principally in the permanence of the notochord and in the absence of a head. They probably are a marine offshoot of an evolutionary line which has led from ancestral marine tunicates to ancestral freshwater vertebrates. This off-shoot may have been unable to make the transition from ocean to river, and has adapted instead to a life in shallow coastal waters and estuaries.

Subphylum Vertebrata

The vast majority of chordates are vertebrates. All other Metazoa are called, contrastingly, "invertebrates." Vertebrates are so named because, in late embryonic stages, a segmented vertebral column develops in addition to or more generally as a replacement of the notochord. The individual vertebrae are made of cartilage or bone. Segmentation is a general feature of vertebrate structure, but in many groups the segmental patterns become somewhat obscured in adult stages. Vertebrates possess a well-developed head, with brain, brain case, and paired sense organs. The nerve cord is dorsal and tubular, as in other chordates. Pharyngeal gills are present as well. In most groups an outpouching from the pharynx develops into a lung. Gills and lungs rarely occur at the same time, the gills usually forming first, the lungs thereafter. A distinct adult tail is a virtually unique vertebrate characteristic. The base of the tail is marked ventrally by the anus.

Vertebrates are believed to have arisen in fresh water and to have invaded the ocean and the land from there. Aquatic vertebrates, in particular the bony fishes, are still the most numerous representatives of the subphylum. These and all other classes of fishes, including the extinct class of placoderms (see Chap. 30), are sometimes grouped into a superclass *Pisces.* On the other hand, the four classes of four-legged land vertebrates are collectively referred to as the superclass *Tetrapoda.* Some of the identifying characteristics of the seven living classes are as follows (see also Table 8).

Agnatha. These are roughly eel-shaped animals, with smooth, scaleless skin and without paired fins (Fig.

11.61). The anterior end of the body is modified into a funnellike sucker, in the center of which is the mouth. Jaws are absent. The notochord persists throughout life, and the adult in addition possesses a brain case and segmental vertebral elements made of cartilage. There are seven pairs of gills; lungs do not form. The heart is ventral as in all vertebrates, and as in all fishes it consists of two chambers, one auricle and one ventricle. The sense organs include, apart from lateral eyes a functional **pineal eye,** located dorsally along the midline of the head (see also Chap. 20). Lampreys comprise freshwater as well as marine species, but even the latter migrate into rivers for spawning. Fertilization is external (i.e., both sperms and eggs are shed into open water), and the adults die after releasing their reproductive cells. The larvae develop in fresh water. Hagfishes are marine, and they spawn and develop in the sea.

Chondrichthyes. In this and all subsequent vertebrate classes, the notochord is an embryonic structure only and is replaced completely by a vertebral column. In the chondrichthians, this column and all other skeletal parts consist of cartilage. The class includes sharks, skates, and rays, most of them marine, but some living in fresh water (Fig. 11.62). The skin of these animals is studded with tiny, pointed **denticles,** which in structure and development are quite like the teeth of vertebrates generally. Two pairs of fins are present in addition to several unpaired fins, as are upper and lower jaws, characteristic also of subsequent classes. Breathing is by gills, of which there are five to seven pairs. The cartilage fishes are strongly muscled and most are active, open-water predators. Some are plankton feeders. These include the whale sharks, which sometimes reach lengths of approximately 50 ft and are the largest vertebrates after the true whales.

Osteichthyes. At least half the number of all vertebrate species are bony fishes. As indicated by the name of this class, the adult skeleton is made largely of bone, a feature characteristic also of all four-legged vertebrates. Bony fishes typically have scaly skin, paired fins, and gills on each side of the pharynx covered by

FIG. 11.61 Lamprey, lateral view. Note gill slits. (*Carolina Biological Supply Co.*)

TABLE 8
Some diagnostic features of vertebrates

super-class	class	skin	skeleton	append-ages	breath-ing	heart chambers	fertili-zation	develop-ment	other
Pisces	Agnatha	smooth	permanent notochord plus car-tilage skeleton	without paired fins	gills	2	external	in water	without jaws; cold-blooded; without neck; without lungs
	Chondrich-thyes	denticles	embryonic notochord; adult car-tilage skeleton	paired fins	gills	2	external	in water	with jaws; cold-blooded; without neck; without lungs
	Osteich-thyes	scales	embryonic notochord; adult bony skeleton	paired fins	gills; lungs in some	2	external	in water	swim bladder in most; cold-blooded; without neck
Tetrapoda	Amphibia	smooth, glan-dular	embryonic notochord; adult bony skeleton	2 pairs legs	gills and lungs	3	external	in water	cold-blooded; without neck
	Reptilia	scales	embryonic notochord; adult bony skeleton	2 pairs legs	lungs	4	internal	on land	with neck; cold-blooded
	Aves	feathers	embryonic notochord; adult bony skeleton	legs and wings	lungs	4	internal	on land	with neck; warm-blooded
	Mammalia	hair	embryonic notochord; adult bony skeleton	2 pairs legs	lungs	4	internal	mostly within female	warm-blooded; nurse young; nonnucleated red corpuscles

a hinged bony plate, the **operculum** (Fig. 11.63). The animals also develop an internal membranous sac, pouched out ventrally from the pharynx. In most species this sac becomes a swim bladder. In the lungfishes, however, the sac functions partly like a lung. It is probable that in ancestral bony fishes the sac served as a lung primarily and that in most descendant forms it became adapted secondarily as a swim bladder, the breathing function being lost. Lungfishes appear to be one exception to this. Another must have been the so-called lobe-finned fishes, the ancestors of which also included the ancestors of the land vertebrates (Fig. 11.64; also Chap. 30).

Amphibia. The two main groups of this class are, first, the salamanders and newts, in which a tail is present throughout life, and second, the frogs and toads, which are tailless as adults. Frogs and toads may be distinguished by their dentition; frogs possess teeth on their upper jaws, toads do not. All amphibia have smooth, moist, glandular skins without scales and two pairs of legs which are equivalent developmentally and

FIG. 11.62   Left, a skate, member of the class of cartilage fishes. Right, close-up of sharkskin, showing the toothlike denticles. *(Left, Carolina Biological Supply Co.; right, General Biological Supply House, Inc.)*

FIG. 11.63   Anterior portion of a carp, a member of the class of bony fishes. Note scales and also the operculum, a bony plate behind the eyes which covers the gills and lets water out at its rear edge. *(Courtesy of E. P. Haddon, U.S. Fish and Wildlife Service.)*

structurally to the paired fins of fishes. Larval amphibia typically live in fresh water, are fishlike in most respects, and breathe by means of gills and through the skin. The adults of all newts, some salamanders, and some toads are aquatic, and the adults of all others are terrestrial. Virtually all adults have lungs, and the newts and some of the aquatic salamanders in addition retain the gills throughout life. The heart of amphibia is three-chambered and consists of two auricles and one ventricle. In most species, fertilization and embryonic development take place in water, regardless of whether the adults are terrestrial or not.

Reptilia. Many people tend to confuse these true land vertebrates with amphibia. But reptiles are easily identified by their dry, scaly skin, by the presence of a fairly well-defined neck, and by their large shelled eggs, which are always laid on land, even when the adults are aquatic (see Table 8). The living representatives of this class are the turtles and tortoises, the snakes and lizards, the alligators and crocodiles, and the tuatara, or *Sphenodon,* a lizardlike evolutionary relic of past ages found today only in New Zealand. The legs of reptiles typically are five-toed and equipped with claws. But in sea turtles they are modified into flippers, and in snakes and some lizards limbs are not present at all. Gills do not mature but develop only partially as nonfunctional structures in the embryo. Breathing is always by lung. This and a four-chambered heart are characteristic of birds and mammals also.

Reptiles, birds, and mammals are alike, furthermore, in that fertilization is internal; i.e., the process occurs within the body of the female, not in open water. Moreover, after fertilization the shelled land eggs develop specialized internal accessory membranes which permit the embryos to survive in terrestrial environments without drying out. One of these accessory membranes is the so-called **amnion,** a fluid-filled sac in which the embryo grows (see Chap. 26). Because an amnion is present in reptiles, birds, and mammals, these three terrestrial classes of vertebrates are often referred to collectively as *Amniotes,* and all other vertebrate classes are referred to as *Anamniotes.*

Aves. In their internal structure, these feathered vertebrates greatly resemble primitive reptiles. Apart from the presence of feathers, birds are characterized by forelimbs which are modified into wings and by the absence of teeth, the mouth armature being a horn-covered beak or bill. Birds are "warm-blooded"; i.e.,

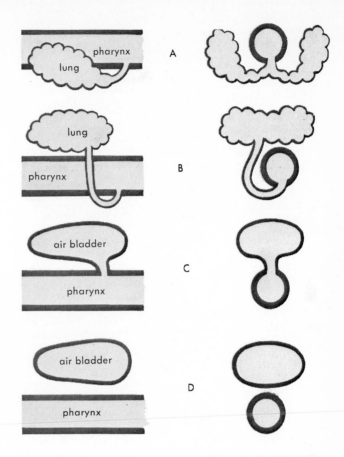

FIG. 11.64 The interrelation of lung, air bladder, and alimentary tract in fishes. Left figures, longitudinal view. Right figures, cross-sectional view. *A,* the pattern in tetrapods and some lungfishes. *B,* the pattern in other lungfishes and probably also in ancestral lobe-fins. *C,* the pattern in some modern bony fishes. *D,* the pattern in all other modern bony fishes. The connecting duct between pharynx and air bladder has disappeared.

they maintain a constant body temperature, like mammals. Undoubtedly because of the aerodynamic requirements of flight, birds are more like one another than the members of any other vertebrate class. We may note, however, that many birds have reduced wings and cannot fly. Ostriches, emus, moas, kiwis, and penguins are among the flightless types. Of the 10,000 or so avian species, more than half belong to a single order, the *passerine,* or perching birds. These include the songbirds and many other familiar bird types.

FIG. 11.65 Top, egg-laying mammals, or Prototheria: left, a spiny anteater; right, a duckbilled platypus. Bottom, an opossum, a pouched or marsupial mammal of the subclass Metatheria. *(Top left, top right, American Museum of Natural History; bottom, Carolina Biological Supply Co.)*

Mammalia. The female members of this class possess milk-producing **mammary glands** and nurse their young. Three other identifying features are the possession of **hair,** the transverse division of the body cavity by a **diaphragm,** and the nonnucleated condition of mature red blood corpuscles. The class comprises some 6,000 species grouped into three subclasses (Fig. 11.65). The subclass *Prototheria* consists of egg-laying types. These are the least progressive mammals, and they still display many of the features of ancestral reptiles from which the class of mammals evolved. Egg-laying mammals today include only the duck-billed platypus and the spiny anteaters. The subclass *Metatheria* comprises the pouched or marsupial mammals. In these, the young are born in a very incompletely developed state and development is completed in an abdominal skin pouch of the female. Opossums and the kangaroos, koala bears, wombats, and other marsupials of Australia belong to this group. The vast majority of mammals are included in the subclass *Eutheria,* the placental mammals. The young of these mammals develop within the body of the female in a womb, or uterus. Among these most familiar of all living creatures, some are aerial (bats), some are aquatic (whales, sea cows, seals), and most are terrestrial. They include carnivores such as dogs and cats, hoofed forms such as cattle, sheep, and pigs, and also elephants, horses, and rabbits. The tiniest mammals are the shrews; the largest are the whales; the most numerous are the rodents; and certainly the brainiest and in all respects by far the most interesting and important are the primates, which include monkeys, apes, and men.

REVIEW QUESTIONS

1. What structural and functional features distinguish most Metazoa from most Metaphyta? What are the chief nutritional patterns among animals? How does alimentation influence the general structural and functional organization of animals?

2. How does the requirement of locomotion influence the general architecture of an animal? Contrast the basic design of moving and nonmoving animals.

3. Which phyla are included among the Radiata, and what diagnostic features distinguish these phyla? Describe the characteristics of sponges.

4. Name the classes of coelenterates and describe the life cycles characteristic of each. Distinguish between polyps and medusae. Which phyla are included among acoelomates? Name the classes of flatworms and describe the main structural features of Turbellaria. Review the life cycles of flukes and tapeworms.

5. Which are the pseudocoelomate phyla and what features characterize the group as a whole? Describe the structure and the life cycle of rotifers. Distinguish between entoprocts and ectoprocts and describe the basic structure of each. Which are the schizocoelomate phyla?

6. What is the fundamental body plan of mollusks? Describe the internal structure of animals within each of the molluscan classes and show what features distinguish each class from the others. Which mollusks develop via (a) trochophores, (b) veligers, (c) neither?

7. Describe the diagnostic features of annelids. Name the annelid classes and describe the internal structure of polychaetes. How do the other classes differ? What evidence relates annelids to mollusks on the one hand and to arthropods on the other? Describe the characteristic features of *Peripatus*.

8. Describe the group characteristics and the basic body organization of arthropods. Name the classes and the distinguishing features of each. Show how segmentation is exploited adaptively in (a) crustacea, (b) insects.

9. How do arachnids, centipedes, and millipedes differ structurally from insects? How is breathing accomplished in the various arthropod classes? Describe the structure of simple and compound eyes and show in which arthropod classes each type of eye is found.

10. Which phyla are included among the enterocoelomates and for what reasons? How do these phyla differ from one another? State the group characteristics of echinoderms and name the various classes. Describe the structure of a starfish.

11. Review the classification of chordates. Contrast the diagnostic features of the three subphyla. Which subphylum is believed to be ancestral to the vertebrates and for what reasons? Describe the basic structure of the various nonvertebrate chordates.

12. Describe the group characteristics of vertebrates. Name the classes and describe the identifying features of each. Which classes are (a) amniotes, (b) anamniotes, (c) tetrapods, (d) jawless, (e) warm-blooded, (f) gill breathers, (g) lung breathers?

SUGGESTED COLLATERAL READINGS

Any of the following books may be consulted for further information on given animals:

Borradaile, L. A., F. A. Potts, L. E. S. Eastham, and J. T. Saunders: "The Invertebrata," Cambridge, New York, 1951.

Buchsbaum, R.: "Animals without Backbones," University of Chicago Press, Chicago, 1948.

Hyman, L.: "The Invertebrates," McGraw-Hill, New York, 1940–1959.

Romer, A. S.: "Man and the Vertebrates," 3d ed., University of Chicago Press, Chicago, 1941.

———: "The Vertebrate Body," Saunders, Philadelphia, 1950.

Storer, T. I., and R. L. Usinger: "General Zoology," 3d ed., McGraw-Hill, New York, 1957.

Young, J. Z.: "The Life of the Vertebrates," Oxford, New York, 1950.

Particular animals and their activities are discussed in the following popular articles:

Griffin, D. R.: The Navigation of Bats, *Sci. American,* vol. 183, 1950.

Ladd, H. J., and J. I. Tracey: The Problem of Coral Reefs, *Sci. Monthly,* vol. 69, 1949.

Lyman, C. P., and P. O. Charfield: Hibernation, *Sci. American,* vol. 183, 1950.

Milne, L. J., and M. J. Milne: Temperature and Life, *Sci. American,* vol. 180, 1949.

Rodbard, S.: Warmbloodedness, *Sci. Monthly,* vol. 77, 1953.

Storer, J. H.: Bird Aerodynamics, *Sci. American,* vol. 186, 1952.

PART 4
METABOLISM

Up to this point, our primary concern has been the "what" of living matter: What are the characteristics of the living world as a whole? What are the structures and functions of the living material, and what kinds of living organisms exist on earth? In the remainder of this book, we shall continue to heed the what, but our primary concern will be the "how": How does the living world come into being and how is it maintained? How are the structures developed and how are the functions carried out? In other words, our preoccupation will be less with the *organizational* and more with the *operational* nature of living material.

The operations of living matter are circumscribed by two words: metabolism and self-perpetuation. In this sequence of chapters, we deal with the first. Metabolism, we recall, may be described roughly as a group of processes which makes the living machinery run, which transforms an otherwise inert system into an active one. Specifically, metabolism includes, first, **nutrition;** second, the production of internal energy, or **respiration,** made possible by some of the nutrients; and third, the **utilization** of raw materials and of energy, always toward chemical activities such as synthesis of new living components, sometimes toward physical activities such as movement.

Nutrition is auxiliary to the remainder of metabolism. This remainder occurs within individual cells and constitutes *cellular metabolism.* It is the main phase of all metabolism, for only if its cellular motors are running can the whole organism be alive.

ENVIRONMENT AND NUTRITION

12

In this chapter we shall examine three correlated topics. The first deals with the general interrelations between the **environment and metabolism;** we inquire here into the direct and indirect ways in which the external environment influences all metabolic processes. The second topic analyzes the various existing **forms of nutrition,** which represent the most common link between the external environment and the metabolism of living organisms. And the third topic outlines the general **processes of nutrition** through which any given organism actually obtains its nourishment.

ENVIRONMENT AND METABOLISM

All of metabolism begins with raw materials, and all basic raw materials ultimately come from the physical environment of the earth. The environment also influences metabolism in other major ways. For example, every metabolic reaction, hence every organism as a whole, is affected greatly by environmental temperature, pressure, the nature of the surrounding medium, in short, by geography and weather generally. In this respect, forces of global dimensions have a direct bearing on forces of molecular dimensions. We may note, therefore, that the environment sets the stage for metabolism principally in two ways: the environment is the ultimate supplier of all raw materials, and it provides the physical and chemical background against which metabolic processes must be carried out.

How does the environment function in these roles?

ENVIRONMENTAL CHARACTERISTICS

The most important general observation we can make about the environment is that it is forever changing, on every scale from the submicroscopic to the global. The physical world is subjected unceasingly to various astrophysical, meteorologic, geologic, and geochemical forces which alter every component of the earth sooner or later, very rapidly in some cases, rather slowly in others. Being part of the earth's substance, living matter too is subjected to these forces and it therefore undergoes unceasing change. As we have seen, the very origin of living matter on earth was itself a result of environmental change. Organisms subsequently became a powerful cause of continued change.

The fundamental reason for uninterrupted environmental change is that the earth as a whole, hence also living matter and every other component, is an **open system.** Such systems exchange materials, energy, or both with their surroundings. By contrast, a **closed system** exchanges nothing with its surroundings (Fig. 12.1). On earth, to be sure, the amounts of material entering from space or leaving into space are negligible. However, *energy* both enters and leaves, and this makes the earth an open system. Most importantly, various forms of solar energy—heat, light, X rays, electric rays, ultraviolet rays, and many others—beam to earth uninterruptedly; and enormous amounts of energy radiate out, principally in the form of heat. As a result, the earth's material substance can never attain static equilibrium; so long as the sun shines and the earth spins, energy flux creates balance-upsetting disturbances. Every imbalance creates new imbalances of its own, and, as a general consequence, the earth's environment is forever changing.

Such changes, being produced primarily by sun and planetary motion, occur predominantly in rhythmic, patterned **cycles.** Daily and seasonal climatic cycles are familiar examples. Other environmental cycles may be less readily discernible, particularly if their scale is too vast or too minute or if they occur too fast or too slowly for direct observation. Living matter is interposed into these cycles; and, as the earth's components circulate, some of these components become raw materials in living metabolism.

Any chemical an organism requires as raw material may be called a **nutrient,** or **metabolite.** Since a living body consists partly of inorganic and partly of organic chemicals and since all life functions are directed toward maintaining and perpetuating this body, it is clear that an organism must supply itself with both inorganic and organic metabolites. We recall that organic metabolites are also called **foods.**

The physical environment is the ultimate source which supplies organisms with all required *inorganic* metabolites. From some of these, the required *organic* metabolites must then be manufactured and distributed within the living world itself. Thus all organisms build up their bodies at the ultimate expense of inorganic materials withdrawn directly from the physical environment. Excretion products formed within organisms return to the environment largely while the organisms live. And when they die, all other materials of their bodies return to the environment as well. As we shall see, **decay** caused by saprotrophic bacteria and fungi gradually retransforms all the returned substances into the same kinds of inorganic materials which were withdrawn from the environment originally (Fig. 12.2).

Living organisms may therefore be envisaged as transient constructions built out of materials "borrowed" temporarily from the environment. One important corollary of this is that, despite its material contribution to the formation of organisms, the physical earth *conserves* all its raw materials on a long-term basis; and this makes possible an indefinitely continued, repeated re-creation of living matter. Therefore, the continuity of life depends on the parallel continuity of death.

A second corollary is that, because of their life and their death, organisms contribute in major ways to the movement of earth substances in cycles. Billions of tons of materials are withdrawn from the environment into billions of organisms all over the world, are made components of living matter, are redistributed among and between organisms, and are finally put back into the environment as they were obtained. Such life-involving cycles become part of and often reinforce and contribute to the physical cycles on earth. As in the purely physical cycles, those in which living matter participates run on energy supplied by the sun. Solar energy is trapped by living organisms via photosynthesis, and

FIG. 12.1 In a closed system, nothing enters or leaves. In an open system, materials or energy or both may enter or leave.

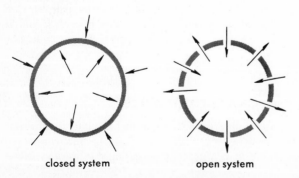

closed system   open system

some of this energy is later spent by organisms in moving parts of the earth through their bodies.

The global environment consists of three main subdivisions. The **hydrosphere** includes all liquid components, i.e., the water in oceans, lakes, rivers, and on land. The **lithosphere** comprises the solid components, i.e., the rocky substance of the continents. And the **atmosphere** is the gaseous mantle which envelops the hydrosphere and the lithosphere. Living organisms require inorganic metabolites from each of these subdivisions. The hydrosphere supplies liquid *water;* the lithosphere supplies all other *minerals;* and the atmosphere supplies *oxygen, nitrogen,* and *carbon dioxide.*

FIG. 12.2 The cyclical interaction between the physical environment and living matter. Raw materials taken by living matter from the physical environment return to the latter through excretion and decay.

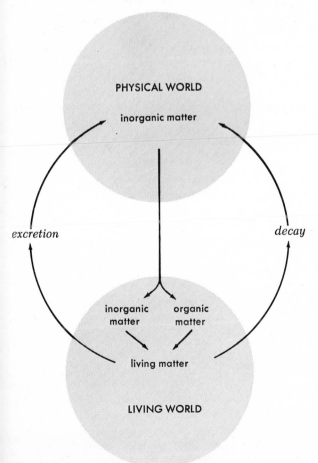

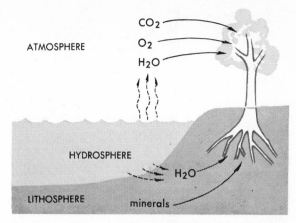

FIG. 12.3 The material contributions of each of the three subdivisions of the environment to the maintenance of living matter.

Together, these inorganic materials provide all the chemical elements needed in the construction and maintenance of living matter (Fig. 12.3). In addition to being sources of supply, the three subdivisions of the environment also affect metabolism in various other specific ways. We shall examine the metabolic contributions of each of the subdivisions in turn.

THE HYDROSPHERE

Water is the most abundant mineral of the planet. It covers some 73 per cent of the earth's surface entirely, and it is a major constituent of the lithosphere and the atmosphere. As shown in Chap. 4, water is also the most abundant component of living matter. It is not surprising, therefore, that it is the major inorganic nutrient required by all living organisms. In metabolism, water is the exclusive source of the element hydrogen and one of several sources of oxygen.

The basic water cycle which moves and conserves water in the environment is quite familiar. Solar energy evaporates water from the hydrosphere into the atmosphere. Subsequent cooling and condensation of the vapor at higher altitudes produces clouds, and precipitation as rain or snow then returns the water to the hydrosphere. This is the most massive process of any kind on earth, consuming more energy and moving more material than any other (Fig. 12.4).

In using water as metabolic raw material, organisms withdraw it principally from the hydrospheric segment of the global cycle. Aquatic organisms absorb

FIG. 12.4 The global water cycle. Evaporated water eventually returns to earth through precipitation.

water directly from their liquid environment; they excrete some of it back while they live; and after death the remainder, still in the form of liquid water, is returned through decay. Terrestrial organisms are interposed more extensively in the global cycle, and indeed they contribute substantially to its continuance. These organisms absorb liquid water from the reservoir present in soil and in bodies of fresh water. Plants and animals move such water through their bodies and in the process they retain required quantities. The remainder is excreted, partly as liquid water but more particularly as water vapor which raises the moisture content of the atmosphere. We may note that a given quantity of environmental water is moved from hydrosphere to atmosphere far faster through the metabolic agency of living organisms than if that water were simply allowed to evaporate directly from the hydrosphere. In other words, the metabolism of terrestrial organisms actively accelerates the global water cycle. Sometimes this may have an effect on the climate. For example, the trees of tropical jungles release so much water vapor that the air over vast areas remains permanently saturated with moisture, cloudbursts occurring virtually every evening. After terrestrial organisms die, any liquid water in their bodies again returns to the hydrosphere through decay.

Water influences metabolism not only through its function as a prime nutrient but also through its effect on virtually all aspects of climate and weather, both in the sea and on land. Very largely, these effects are immediate or distant consequences of the interplay between solar energy, the rotation and revolution of the earth, and the hydrosphere—the same interplay which also produces the global water cycle.

In the ocean, water warmed in the tropics becomes light and rises to the surface, whereas cool polar water sinks. These up-down displacements bring about massive horizontal shifts of water between equator and pole. The rotation of the earth introduces east-west displacements. These effects, reinforced substantially by similarly patterned wind-producing air movements, result in **oceanic currents.** The latter influence climatic conditions not only within the seas, but also in the air and on land (Fig. 12.5).

Another climatic effect is a result of the thermal properties of water. Of all liquids, water is one of the slowest to heat or cool, and it stores a very large amount of thermal energy. The oceans thus become huge reservoirs of solar heat. The result is that sea air chilled by night becomes less cold because of **heat radiation** from water warmed by day. Conversely, sea air warmed by day becomes less hot because of **heat absorption** by water cooled by night. Warm or cool onshore winds then moderate the inland climate in daily patterns. Analogous but more profound effects are produced by heat radiation and absorption in seasonal summer and winter patterns.

Thirdly, global climate over long periods of time is determined by the relative amount of water locked into **polar ice.** Temperature variations averaging only a few degrees over the years, produced by still poorly understood geophysical changes, suffice for major advance or retreat of polar ice. During the last million years, "ice ages" have developed and waned rhythmically, and warm *interglacial* periods, characterized by ice-free poles, have intervened between successive advances of ice. Four glaciation cycles have occurred, each lasting in the order of 60,000 to 200,000 years. At the present time, the earth is slowly emerging from the last ice age, which reached its peak some 50,000 to 20,000 years ago. As polar ice is melting, water levels are now rising and coast lines are gradually being submerged. If trends during the past 50 years are reliable indications, the earth appears to be warming up generally. Deserts are presently expanding; snow lines on mountains are receding to higher altitudes; in given localities, more days of the year are snow-free; and the flora and fauna native to given latitudes are slowly spreading poleward. It is difficult to be sure whether these changes are merely part of a short warm cycle or are really indicative of a long-range trend.

All these various cyclic changes in the hydrosphere have profound impact on metabolism. By influencing

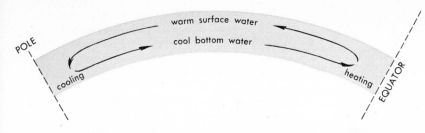

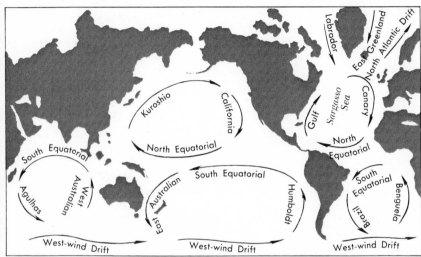

FIG. 12.5 Top, the depth circulation of ocean water. A cross-sectional ocean profile between equator and pole is shown. Water warmed in equatorial regions rises, and water cooled in polar regions sinks. This produces north-south and up-down circulation as indicated. However, this basic equator-to-pole movement is modified by the rotation of the earth, by winds, and by the position of the continents. Bottom, the actual circulation so produced and the names and flow directions of the chief currents shown in surface view.

temperature, humidity, amount of precipitation, winds, waves, currents, and indeed the very presence or absence of water in given localities, they play a major role in determining what kinds and amounts of metabolism are possible in such localities, hence what kinds and amounts of organisms may live there.

THE LITHOSPHERE

This subdivision of the environment plays two vital roles in metabolism. First, as already pointed out above, it is the exclusive source of most **mineral** metabolites for all organisms, terrestrial as well as aquatic; and, second, it forms the bulk component of **soil,** required specifically by terrestrial plants.

Minerals and Cycles

Like the world's water, the rocky substance of the earth's surface moves in a gigantic cycle, but here the rate of circulation is measured in thousands and millions of years. One segment of this global mineral cycle is **diastrophism,** the vertical uprising of large tracts of the earth's crust. Major parts of continents or indeed whole

continents may undergo such diastrophic movements. They occur when a land mass is pushed up from below or is subjected to great lateral pressure, generated in adjacent portions of the earth's crust. Uplifting or up-buckling then follows. Changes of this sort take place exceedingly slowly.

The most striking instance of diastrophism is *mountain building.* Presently the youngest and highest mountain ranges are the Himalayas, the Rockies, the Andes, and the Alps. All of them were thrown up some 75 million years ago, and we may note that the earth's crust in these regions is not completely settled even now.

Quite apart from the tremendous upheaval caused by mountain formation itself, such an event has long-lasting effects on climate, hence on metabolism. A high, massive mountain barrier is likely to interfere drastically with continental air circulation. For example, moisture-laden ocean winds may no longer be able to pass across the barrier. Continual rain will therefore fall on the near side and the region may become lush and fertile. By contrast, the far side will be arid and desert conditions are likely to develop (Fig. 12.6). The following are two good examples: fertile California on

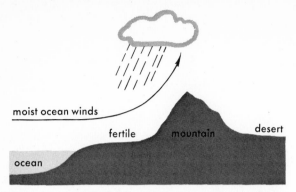

FIG. 12.6 The effect of a mountain on climate. A mountain deflects moisture-rich ocean winds upward and causes rain to remain confined to the slope facing the ocean. That slope will therefore be fertile, but the far slope will become a desert.

the ocean side of the Sierras and the deserts of Arizona and New Mexico on the other side; fertile India on the ocean side of the Himalayas and the belt of deserts north of them. Organisms living on either side of a newly formed mountain range must adapt to the new environmental conditions by evolution. As we shall see, periods of extensive mountain building have always been followed by major evolutionary turnover among organisms (see Chap. 30).

The second segment of the global lithospheric cycle involves **gradation,** the lowering of high land and the leveling of mountains. These changes are brought about in part by actual geologic sinking of land and in part by actions of the hydrosphere and the atmosphere. These actions usually take the form of **erosion** and **dissolution** of rock. Many erosional processes are quite familiar. For example, water and gravity produce shearing, canyon-cutting rivers (Fig. 12.7). Water and high temperatures produce corrosive humidity. Water and low temperatures produce grinding, rock-pulverizing glaciers. And as freezing water expands in rocky crevices, it carves boulders and stones off the face of a mountain. Water, wind, and sun in time so reduce mountain to hill and hill eventually to plain. Together with geologic sinking, these processes often may make land lie so low that substantial parts of it become overrun by the ocean.

Accompanying the physical forces of gradation are chemical forces, and these are of particular importance to metabolism. First, the chemical action of water, and also chemical processes which accompany the decay of dead terrestrial organisms, are major erosional factors. They contribute to breaking large stones into smaller ones and small pebbles into tiny sand grains and microscopic rock fragments. Gradation so plays a principal role in the formation of the rocky components of *soil.*

Second, whenever water is in contact with rock, it dissolves small quantities of it and so acquires a *mineral* content. The dissolved minerals are carried largely in the form of ions. Accordingly, as rain water runs off high land, it becomes progressively laden with minerals. Streams and rivers form, and these irrigate adjacent areas and contribute to the water content of soil. Rain adds to soil water directly. In soil, the water leaches more minerals out of the many rock fragments present and the total supply then serves as the mineral source for terrestrial organisms. After the organisms die and decay, the mineral ions of their bodies return to the soil.

Dissolved soil minerals eventually drain back into rivers, and rivers drain into the ocean. Therefore, as the lithosphere is slowly being denuded of mineral compounds, the hydrosphere fills with them. It was partly by this means that the early seas on earth acquired their original saltiness, and as the global water cycle

FIG. 12.7 The cutting, erosional effect of a river. This canyon was channeled out by the stream flowing through it. (U.S. Department of Agriculture.)

now continues, it makes the oceans even saltier. Organisms in the sea freely use the mineral ions as metabolites.

The death of marine organisms subsequently helps to complete the global mineral cycle. Many plants and animals use mineral nutrients in the construction of protective shells and supporting bones. After these organisms die, their bodies sink down toward the sea floor, in a slow, steady rain (see Chap. 7). All organic and some of the inorganic matter dissolves during the descent, but much of the mineral substance persists in solid form and reaches the sea bottom. So abundant and uninterrupted is this rain that it forms gradually thickening layers of ooze over huge tracts of the sea floor. Various types of Protista contribute particularly to these mineral accumulations. In the course of millennia, the older, deeper layers of the ooze may compress into rock. The global lithospheric cycle then becomes complete when a section of sea bottom or low-lying land generally is subjected to new diastrophic forces. High ground or mountains are thereby regenerated and such parts as were sea floor originally may be thrust up as new land in the process (Fig. 12.8).

The lithospheric cycle supplies many more *types* of minerals than organisms normally require. Those withdrawn and used by most organisms include, for example, ions of nitrates (NO_3^-), phosphates ($PO_4^\equiv$), chlorides (Cl^-), carbonates ($CO_3^=$), and sulfates ($SO_4^=$); and ions of sodium (Na^+), potassium (K^+), calcium (Ca^{++}), manganese (Mn^{++}), magnesium (Mg^{++}), copper (Cu^{++}),

and iron (Fe^{+++}). From the standpoint of quantities, the relatively *least* plentiful mineral circulating in the environment will determine the maximum quantity of living matter that can be supported on earth. Despite the dense cover of life now carpeting the earth, available quantities of most minerals are still well in excess of currently required amounts. However, because of the uninterrupted, global growth of organisms for millions of years, a few key minerals now tend to be in relatively short supply. In particular, phosphates and nitrates have become significant limiting factors. For example, agriculturally used soils may often be burdened with so much vegetation that they may become exhausted unless artificially enriched with fertilizers—largely phosphates and nitrates. Similarly, the amount of plankton life sustainable in the ocean is now determined principally by the amounts of available phosphates and nitrates. As we shall see shortly, however, nitrates are supplied not only by the lithospheric cycle but by an atmospheric cycle as well.

Soil

As noted, the lithosphere plays a special role in the metabolism of land plants in that it contributes importantly to the formation of soil. This complex material serves in plant maintenance in two major ways: it provides mechanical *anchorage* for plants, without hindering growth and aeration of roots, and it holds water and mineral ions, the source from which land plants must obtain supplies of these *inorganic nutrients*.

Before ancestral plants invaded the terrestrial environment, the land was bare of soil. But processes making possible its later formation were already under

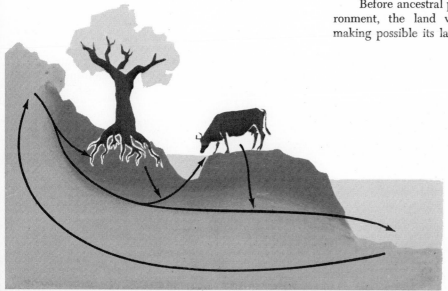

FIG. 12.8 The global mineral cycle. Minerals absorbed by terrestrial plants and animals return to soil by excretion and death. Rivers carry soil minerals into the ocean, where some of them are deposited at the bottom. Portions of sea bottom may then be uplifted geologically, and the new land so formed reintroduces minerals into a global cycle.

way. A profusion of stones and rock chips, produced by the forces of gradation, was steadily fragmented and ground into powder by the milling of rivers, the shear of ice sheets, and the battering impact of coastal surf. Silt was deposited in floodplains and along river and ocean shores. Winds spread the dust farther inland. Small rock grains of rough, jagged texture formed **sand,** and even smaller microscopic and submicroscopic particles formed **clay.** Sand and clay became the hard mineral fraction of soil.

The other major component of soil was contributed by living organisms. Early terrestrial Monera and Protista, organisms which do not require soil themselves shed their excretion products into the sand layers, and upon death their bodies came to be added as well. Saprotrophic bacteria and fungi carried in by air or water found sustenance in this organic material. Decay ensued which transformed the formerly living substance into a variety of complex chemicals, the organic fractions of soil, collectively called **humus.** Acids produced by decay also roughened the surfaces of rock fragments, and so monerans and protists contributed to the formation of sand.

Humus mixed in with sand and clay constituted soil (Fig. 12.9). Formed first in isolated patches, it provided a foothold for small metaphytes. As these died and decayed, more soil was produced, larger plants could root there, and over the centuries continuous soil layers developed in large areas. At the present time, perhaps a foot of soil, on an average, covers the arable land. In barren regions, moreover, new soil may still be developing today by the same processes which were effective earlier. Thus, various monerans and protists may come to inhabit lifeless sandy areas. Subsequent decay and partial dissolution of the sand grains may slowly lead to the enrichment of the area with humus and dissolved minerals. In effect, new soil is so being formed.

Actually, soil is not an essential medium for plant maintenance. For example, floating aquatic plants do very well without it. Moreover, land plants too can be maintained adequately without soil, for example, by immersing them in mineral-rich water. Such procedures are called **hydroponic** cultures. They are used today in many experimental and commercial situations (Fig. 12.10). Evidently, so long as the environment provides water and minerals at all, it does not matter too much through what medium the plant obtains these materials. On land, soil happens to be the usual and the cheapest, hence the most treasured, large-scale supplier. And it has the additional, very essential property of anchoring plants mechanically, without halting the continuous expansion of root systems.

General references to "soil" are usually references to the **topsoil,** the upper, most valuable layer. Topsoils differ widely in color, according to the types of minerals and humus components contained in them. The roots of small plants are embedded entirely in topsoil. Larger plants send their roots into the extensive subjacent layer, the **subsoil.** Here the proportion of clay may be higher than in topsoil and subsoil may therefore be relatively dense. Also, the proportion of humus may be reduced. Subsoil is usually underlain by **loose rock,** and this layer extends down to the continuous **bedrock** of the continent (Fig. 12.11).

The quality of topsoil depends on a wide variety of factors. Where a soil layer is too thin or where soil particles are blown away by wind or washed away by water, plants cannot obtain firm anchorage. Moreover, if the sand particles are too small or if there is too much clay, the soil is likely to be packed tight and root growth will be difficult. But if the sand grains are too

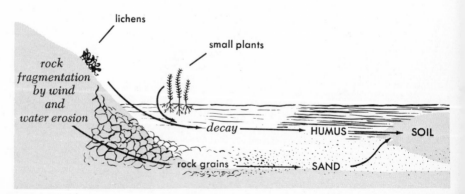

FIG. 12.9 The formation of soil. Chemical and physical decomposition of rock yields humus and sand, respectively, and these two components together form soil.

FIG. 12.10 Hydroponics, the soilless culture of plants. A nutrient solution (bottom) maintains these tobacco plants, which are held mechanically in a box filled with wood shavings. This box normally rests directly on top of the nutrient container. (Paul Popper, Ltd., London.)

FIG. 12.11 Profile of soil. Note dark topsoil, underlain by light-colored layer of subsoil. Streaked layers of clay lie under the subsoil, and the clay merges into rock near the bottom of the photo. (U.S. Department of Agriculture.)

large, roots slip through the free spaces and plant anchorage is insecure. One important determinant of soil quality thus is the *size* of the soil particles. Another is the *shape* of the particles, for smooth round grains leave spaces between them through which water would drain off rapidly. On the other hand, coarse grains with rough, jagged edges still leave sufficient room for aeration and root growth. However, despite such particle shape, water would be lost by drainage. It is the organic matter which aids in endowing soil with its crumbly, spongelike, water-retaining properties. In a good soil, this water-retaining action of humus is augmented by the subsoil, which prevents water from seeping away too rapidly.

From the standpoint of their physical characteristics, therefore, the best soils form layers of considerable thickness, contain rock fragments of appropriate size and shape, and are rich in humus. Moreover, they are protected against water erosion by appreciable amounts of subsoil and against wind erosion by hedges, trees, and plant cover in general. For as the soil holds

the plant, so the plant also holds the soil (Fig. 12.12). In agriculturally important regions, practices designed to conserve the physical values of soil are now widespread. For example, wind and water erosion can be reduced through flood control, through appropriate rain drainage, through contour plowing, and through provision of adequate windbreaks (Fig. 12.13).

The chemical value of a soil depends on its usable

FIG. 12.12 As soil holds the plant, so the plant also holds the soil. Left, eroded land. Sandy gullies are present, which would enlarge gradually. Right, same landscape as above, after planting and about three years of growth. Erosion has been halted. *(U.S. Department of Agriculture.)*

water and mineral content. Soil particles are enveloped by thin films of water. This water is *bound;* i.e., electrochemical forces hold the water molecules tightly against the rock fragments. Even relatively dry soil still retains its films of bound water. If there is much water in soil, some of the fluid is bound, but most of it is beyond the range of soil-particle attraction. Held loosely in the spaces between the hard particles, *unbound* water is the immediate water source for plants (Fig. 12.14).

Dissolved in the water are the mineral ions. We have already discussed three major ways by which these metabolites are replenished: inflow of new mineral-laden water, direct chemical dissolution of soil particles by soil water, and decay of dead plants and animals.

Decay not only returns minerals but also adds new organic substances, and it so raises the humus content of soil. These relatively slow natural processes of replenishment may be augmented by man, through conservation procedures designed to prevent nutritional exhaustion of soil. For example, he may add mineral-rich *fertilizers* to soil. He may let soils *rest* for one or more seasons. He may grow crops and, instead of harvesting them, may plow them right back into the ground. Or he may adopt a program of *crop rotation,* whereby different crops are planted in successive seasons, each crop requiring a different set of minerals from the soil.

Some natural replenishment of soil minerals is

FIG. 12.13 Left, soil leaching and gully erosion by water. Drainage ditches are not available for water runoff from mountainous areas in background. Right, aerial view of contour-plowed region. In contour plowing, plow lines are run at right angles to the slope of the land to reduce wind and water erosion. *(Left, U.S. Department of Agriculture; right, U.S. Soil Conservation Service.)*

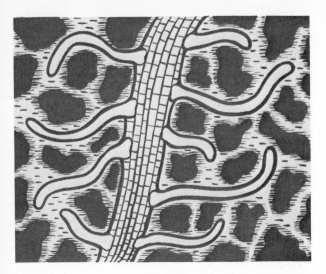

FIG. 12.14 Root hairs and soil. Solid black areas represent soil grains. Halos of densely placed lines surrounding them represent bound water. Root hairs occupy regions filled with unbound water.

basically have the same general pattern as the ocean currents, and the winds of the former strongly reinforce the latter. Also, the motions of air substantially influence climatic conditions, hence metabolism as well.

Of much greater significance to metabolism, however, are the chemical cycles of the atmosphere. Air consists mainly of oxygen, O_2 (about 20 per cent); carbon dioxide, CO_2 (about 0.03 per cent); nitrogen, N_2 (about 79 per cent); water (in varying amounts, depending on climatic conditions); and minute traces of inert gases (helium, neon, krypton, argon, xenon). Excepting the inert gases, all these components of air serve as metabolites and each circulates in a global cycle in which organisms play a conspicuous role. Also, all the gases are dissolved in natural waters, and in this respect the hydrosphere is in equilibrium with the atmosphere. Regardless of whether they are aquatic or terrestrial, therefore, all organisms have access to the aerial gases.

The metabolic role of the water vapor in air has already been discussed, for this vapor represents the atmospheric segment of the global water cycle. The cycles of the other gases are as follows.

accomplished also by certain bacteria, and we shall see in the next section how this occurs (Fig. 12.15).

THE ATMOSPHERE

Like the hydrosphere, the atmosphere as a whole is subjected to physical cycles by the sun and the spin of the earth. Warmed equatorial air rises and cooled polar air sinks, and the axial rotation of the earth shifts air masses laterally. The resulting global air currents

The Oxygen Cycle

Atmospheric oxygen enters the living world as a gas required in respiration (Fig. 12.16). As we shall see later, the function of oxygen in respiration is to collect hydrogen. Respiration unites oxygen with hydrogen, and water forms as a result. This water joins all other water present in living organisms and as such it may undergo three possible fates. Some of it may be excreted immediately and so add to the water content of the environment. Another fraction may be used as a building material in the construction of more living matter, water here being the source of the elements

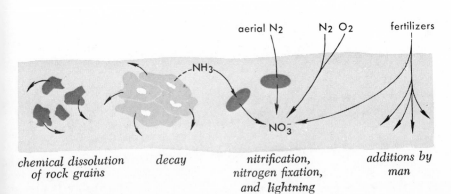

aerial N₂   N₂ O₂   fertilizers

—NH₃—

NO₃⁻

chemical dissolution   decay   nitrification,   additions by
of rock grains   nitrogen fixation,   man
                                        and lightning

FIG. 12.15 The principal ways through which soil minerals are replenished.

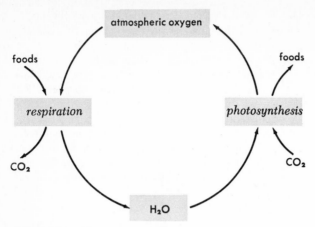

FIG. 12.16   The oxygen cycle.

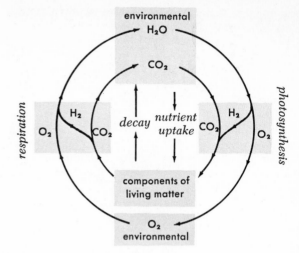

FIG. 12.17   The interrelations of the oxygen, water, and carbon cycles.

hydrogen and oxygen. Such structural oxygen remains within an organism until death, and subsequent decay returns it to the environment. However, the return is not usually in the form of free atmospheric oxygen, but is either in the form of water or in the form of carbon dioxide. Evidently, the global oxygen cycle is closely interlinked with the global water and CO_2 cycles (see also below). A third possible fate of water within organisms is its utilization as a fundamental raw material in photosynthesis. In this process, as we shall see, water is split apart into hydrogen and oxygen, the hydrogen then being used in food manufacture. The oxygen is a byproduct. Such free oxygen may now again be used in respiration, or it may be returned to the environment as molecular atmospheric oxygen, completing the cycle.

In sum, atmospheric oxygen as such *enters* metabolism only through respiration and *leaves* metabolism only through photosynthesis. In intervening steps, the oxygen is incorporated into water and in this form it may interlink with the water cycle or, indirectly, with the carbon cycle. The interrelations of these three cycles are outlined in Fig. 12.17.

We may note here that atmospheric oxygen is the source of the ozone (O_3) layer which envelops the earth at an altitude of some 10 miles. This layer prevents a great deal of the high-energy radiation of the sun (ultraviolet rays, X rays) from reaching the earth's surface, and so it affects metabolism indirectly, by shielding out potentially lethal rays.

The Carbon Cycle

Atmospheric carbon dioxide is virtually the exclusive carbon source and, with water, one of the two major oxygen sources for the construction of living matter. The gas enters the living world through photosynthesis, in which it is a fundamental raw material (Fig. 12.18). Photosynthesis incorporates CO_2 into organic substances, which serve two principal functions. One fraction is used in the construction of more living matter. The carbon and oxygen so supplied by CO_2 remain in living matter until death. Decay subsequently returns CO_2 to the atmosphere, and this completes one possible carbon cycle. Another fraction of the organic substances is used as fuel in respiration. This process releases CO_2 as a byproduct. Such carbon dioxide may

FIG. 12.18   The carbon cycle.

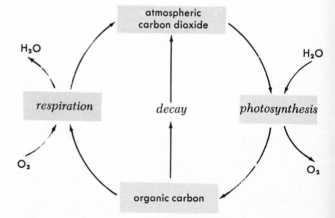

now be used in photosynthesis again, or it may return to the environment and complete a second possible carbon cycle.

The carbon dioxide content of the atmosphere is replenished not only through biological combustion, i.e., respiration, but also through nonliving combustion, i.e., real fires. For example, forest fires and burning of industrial fuels release CO_2 into the air. Such events represent a long-delayed completion of the carbon cycle, for wood, coal, oil, and natural gas all contain combustible organic substances which were manufactured through photosynthesis, in many cases millions of years ago. Aerial CO_2 was then used up, and the gas is returned to the atmosphere only now. The rapid, very voluminous release of CO_2 by man-made combustions today may increasingly affect global climates, for atmospheric CO_2 acts as a heat screen. That is, it permits various solar energies other than heat to reach the earth's surface readily, where some of them are transformed into heat, but it retards the radiation of earth heat into space. Carbon dioxide therefore has a "greenhouse" effect which in some measure probably contributes to the present warming up of the earth. Note, finally, that occasional net additions of CO_2 to the atmosphere are brought about by volcanic eruptions.

The Nitrogen Cycle

Nitrogen is required by organisms in the construction of proteins, nucleic acids, and other nitrogenous compounds. Atmospheric nitrogen serves as the ultimate source (Fig. 12.19). But aerial N_2, the most abundant component of air, is rather inert chemically and it actually cannot be used as such by the majority of organisms. The most common *usable* nitrogen source frequently is the *nitrate* ion, NO_3^-. This ion may be absorbed by plants as a mineral metabolite from the environment and may be converted by them (but not by animals) into amino groups ($-NH_2$) and other nitrogen-containing components of living matter. Some of the environmental sources of nitrate have already been referred to above; e.g., the mineral accumulates through dissolution of rock by water or through addition of soil-fertilizers by man. Small quantities also form in the air when the energy of lightning bolts combines aerial nitrogen and oxygen. Rain then carries such nitrates to the ground. As we shall see presently, another major nitrate source is the global nitrogen cycle.

Nitrogen incorporated into the organic structure of plants stays there until death. Animals must obtain their usable nitrogen from one another and ultimately

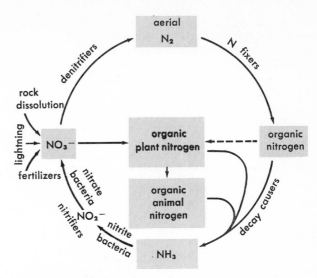

FIG. 12.19 The nitrogen cycle.

by eating plants, and eventually animals die as well. Through subsequent decay, all organic nitrogen of dead plants and animals is ultimately converted into *ammonia*, NH_3. This substance becomes available in the environment, where it forms a nutrient for so-called **nitrifying bacteria.** These are of two types. One type absorbs ammonia and converts it into *nitrite* ions, NO_2^-, which are excreted into the environment. The second type absorbs the nitrite and converts it into *nitrate* ions, NO_3^-, which are similarly excreted. Thus, the combined metabolic activities of the nitrifying bacteria provide environmental nitrates. This is a major source from which plants obtain their nitrogen supplies.

Environmental nitrates are also acted upon by **denitrifying bacteria.** These are of various kinds, and the net result of their combined metabolic activities is that nitrate is converted into molecular, atmospheric nitrogen, N_2. They therefore reduce the available supply of environmental nitrates and increase the nitrogen content of the air. However, still another set of bacteria indirectly compensates for this loss of nitrates. Atmospheric N_2 can be used directly by so-called **nitrogen-fixing** organisms, namely, certain bacteria and blue-green algae which live in water and soil. These absorb aerial nitrogen as a metabolite and are able to incorporate it into their amino acids and proteins. Some nitrogen-fixing bacteria are free-living soil saprotrophs. When they die, the nitrogenous materials of their bodies decay and yield ammonia to the soil, which is then transformed into nitrates by the nitrifiers. Other nitrogen-fixing bacteria are mutualistic symbionts on the roots of leguminous plants such as alfalfa, clover, soybeans, and others. The bacteria here bring about the formation of characteristic root nodules (Fig. 12.20; see also Chap. 7). The nitrogen fixed by the bacteria becomes available to the legumes as *usable* nitrogen. Legumes actually may in some situations acquire most or all of their nitrogen from the N-fixing bacteria in the nodules.

Thus, by converting aerial nitrogen into usable nitrogen, the nitrogen-fixing bacteria complete the global nitrogen cycle. We note that this cycle depends on at least four different sets of bacteria: the decay causers, the nitrifiers, the denitrifiers, and the nitrogen fixers. We may emphasize also that these bacteria act as they do, not because they are aware of the grand plan of the global nitrogen cycle, but because they derive immediate metabolic benefits from their actions. For example, the decay causers are saprotrophs which require dead organisms as their source of food. Ammonia happens to be the waste byproduct of their gathering and processing activities involving nitrogen-containing foods. Analogously, the other bacterial types above utilize one kind of nitrogenous compound as nutrient and excrete an altered kind as waste product. We shall hear more about these metabolic activities below.

So long as the global environment makes available water, mineral ions, and atmospheric gases, and so long as it provides suitable operating conditions generally,

FIG. 12.20   Nodules of nitrogen-fixing bacteria on pea roots. *(R. H. Noailles, Museum of Natural History, Paris.)*

organisms are ready to carry on their metabolism. A first step in this process is **nutrition,** and the next section will show how it is accomplished.

FORMS OF NUTRITION

Various nutritional patterns may be distinguished on the basis of how organisms obtain their required inorganic and organic metabolites.

Organisms do not differ with respect to their procurement of *inorganic* metabolites; all organisms obtain them in finished, prefabricated form from their environment. However, organisms *do* differ with respect to their procurement of *organic* metabolites, or foods. Some organisms manufacture foods from their inorganic supplies and thus are able to subsist in an exclusively inorganic environment. Such organisms are collectively called **autotrophs** (see Chap. 3). Other organisms are unable to create usable foods out of inorganic metabolites; they must obtain from the environment certain minimum amounts and kinds of prefabricated organic metabolites. Such organisms are collectively called **heterotrophs.**

Autotrophic organisms, which manufacture foods from inorganic sources, require not only external sources of appropriate nutrient raw materials but also external sources of energy. In some cases, external energy for food manufacture is obtained from *light,* and such organisms are collectively called **photosynthesizers.** In other cases, some inorganic nutrients serve as raw materials for food manufacture and other inorganic nutrients, i.e., *chemicals,* serve as external energy sources. Such organisms collectively are **chemosynthesizers.** Analogous subgroups of light users and chemical users may be distinguished among heterotrophs.

We may therefore characterize nutrition from the standpoint of food sources, i.e., its autotrophic or heterotrophic nature, and we may also characterize it from the standpoint of external energy sources, i.e., its photosynthetic or chemosynthetic nature. If we characterize it from both standpoints simultaneously, we may identify four categories of organisms, each featuring a distinct form of nutrition:

> **photolithotrophs,** which use inorganic raw materials and light energy to manufacture foods on their own
>
> **chemolithotrophs,** which use inorganic raw materials and chemical energy obtained from some

of the raw materials to manufacture foods on their own

photoorganotrophs, which convert prefabricated organic raw materials into usable foods with the aid of light energy

chemoorganotrophs, which use prefabricated organic raw materials directly as foods

The first two categories include all the autotrophs; the last two, all the heterotrophs. The first and third categories include all the photosynthetic organisms; the second and fourth, all the chemosynthetic organisms. Which specific groups of organisms are in each of these categories is indicated in Fig. 12.21.

AUTOTROPHS

Inasmuch as the simplest organic metabolites, i.e., carbohydrates, contain the elements carbon, hydrogen, and oxygen, it is clear that every autotroph requires an inorganic source of each of these elements. In addition, an external energy source is required to combine the three elements into organic substances.

Autotrophs of all kinds use environmental carbon dioxide as their inorganic carbon and oxygen source. Thus, the manufacture of foods may be symbolized generally as follows:

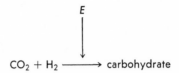

$$CO_2 + H_2 \xrightarrow{E} \text{carbohydrate}$$

In virtually all cases, the carbohydrate formed is a derivative of glucose (see Chap. 13), and from this basic

	FOOD		
	manufactured from inorganic source	*absorbed from prefabricated organic source*	
from light source	PHOTOLITHOTROPHS purple sulfur bacteria green sulfur bacteria blue-green algae algae (except colorless ones) metaphytes	*PHOTOORGANOTROPHS* purple nonsulfur bacteria	*PHOTO-SYNTHETIC TYPES*
PRIMARY ENERGY			
from chemical source	*CHEMOLITHOTROPHS* sulfur bacteria iron bacteria hydrogen bacteria nitrifying bacteria	*CHEMOORGANOTROPHS* saprophytic bacteria (including decay, some N-fixing, some denitrifying types) symbiotic bacteria (including some N-fixing types) fungi slime molds protozoa colorless algae metazoa	*CHEMO-SYNTHETIC TYPES*
	AUTOTROPHIC TYPES	*HETEROTROPHIC TYPES*	

FIG. 12.21 The classification of organisms on the basis of energy sources and methods of food procurement.

food all the other constituents of the organism are then produced.

Autotrophs differ in their energy and hydrogen sources.

Photolithotrophs

As Fig. 12.21 indicates, this large group includes all metaphyta, most algae, blue-green algae, and most pigmented bacteria. In all these photosynthetic autotrophs, the external energy source is *light,* and one or more varieties of *chlorophyll* are present to trap the energy of light. Such organisms are therefore largely green, but in many cases other pigments obscure or completely mask the color of chlorophyll. The hydrogen source of all photolithotrophs except the photolithotrophic bacteria (see below) is environmental *water*. Light energy is used to split the water and free hydrogen is made available in this manner. Thus, for the vast majority of photosynthesizers, the pattern of food production may be symbolized as follows:

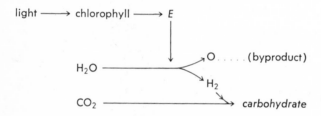

Free oxygen is a byproduct here. This is by far the most important form of photosynthesis, and we shall devote the whole next chapter to a study of the details of this process.

In the photolithotrophic bacteria, the hydrogen source is not water and oxygen is never a byproduct of photosynthesis. Two families of bacteria belong to this group, the *purple sulfur bacteria* and the *green sulfur bacteria,* both members of the Pseudomonadales. The first family possesses a variety of chlorophyll known as **bacteriochlorophyll.** It is green, but its color is masked by red and yellow carotenoids which are also present. Green sulfur bacteria possess a unique chlorophyll which is different from bacteriochlorophyll. Also, its green color is not masked by the additional yellow carotenoids. Both groups of bacteria are adapted to live in sulfur springs and other sulfurous regions, where hydrogen sulfide (H_2S) is normally available. This compound serves as the hydrogen source. For the photolithotrophic bacteria, therefore, the special pattern of photosynthesis becomes:

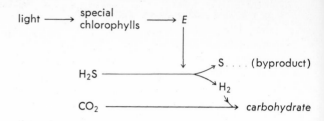

The byproduct here is elemental sulfur. It is stored inside the cells in the purple sulfur bacteria, and it is excreted from the cells in the green sulfur bacteria.

Chemolithotrophs

This second group of autotrophic organisms consists entirely of bacteria. They cannot use light, and their external energy sources in food manufacture are a variety of inorganic metabolites absorbed from the environment. In most cases, these metabolites are combined with oxygen in the cells, resulting in energy and a variety of inorganic byproducts. Water and carbon dioxide are the inorganic raw materials in subsequent food manufacture. The general pattern is

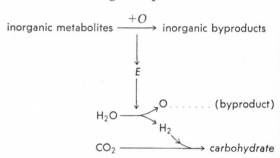

Among the best-known chemolithotrophs are the **sulfur bacteria,** the **iron bacteria,** the **hydrogen bacteria,** and the **nitrifying bacteria.** All are members of the Pseudomonadales. Sulfur bacteria absorb either hydrogen sulfide (H_2S) or molecular sulfur (S_2) from the environment and combine these metabolites with oxygen. The resulting energy is used toward food manufacture, as outlined above, and the byproducts are either S_2 (if H_2S is the original nutrient) or sulfate ions ($SO_4^=$, if S_2 is the original nutrient):

If the byproduct is sulfur, granules of this element are deposited inside or outside the cell; if the byproduct is sulfate, these ions either become part of the mineral content of the cell or are excreted. Note that some of the sulfur bacteria (notably species of *Thiobacillus*) also play an important role in the global nitrogen cycle, by virtue of their *denitrifying* activities; i.e., these sulfur bacteria convert nitrate ions into atmospheric nitrogen.

Iron bacteria are stalked organisms living in fresh and salt water where iron compounds are in solution. The bacteria absorb these compounds and combine them with oxygen, thereby converting them into insoluble substances. Energy is gained in the process:

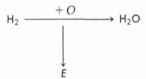

Hydrogen bacteria utilize molecular hydrogen as nutrient. By combining such hydrogen with oxygen, energy is gained and water forms as a byproduct:

$$H_2 \xrightarrow{\ +O\ } H_2O$$
$$\downarrow$$
$$E$$

As noted earlier in this chapter, nitrifying bacteria are of two types, one using ammonia and excreting nitrite ions, the other using nitrite ions and excreting nitrate ions. Both types combine their specific nutrient with oxygen and in each case energy is gained:

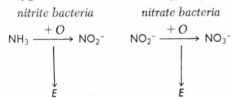

For the bacteria themselves, the important product here is energy, which makes food manufacture possible. For all other living organisms, the important products here are the excreted byproducts, which make the global nitrogen cycle possible.

HETEROTROPHS

Organisms in this group can acquire inorganic metabolites such as H_2O and CO_2 from the environ-

ment but cannot convert them into foods. Heterotrophs must therefore obtain prefabricated organic raw materials from the environment. It follows that the survival of heterotrophs is strictly contingent on the preexistence of autotrophs, for these must be the ultimate sources of the needed organic metabolites. To be sure, it happens frequently that a heterotroph obtains organic materials from another heterotroph, according to a particular food chain (Chap. 7). In such cases, the last heterotroph in the series depends on autotrophs for its organic supplies.

Photoorganotrophs

The identifying feature of this very interesting nutritional type is that the external energy source is light; i.e., the organisms are photosynthesizers. But they require organic raw materials nevertheless. To this group belong mainly the *purple nonsulfur bacteria* (or simply "purple bacteria"), another family of the Pseudomonadales. Like the purple sulfur bacteria, the purple nonsulfur bacteria possess bacteriochlorophyll as well as red and yellow carotenoids which mask the color of the green pigment.

Purple bacteria absorb organic materials from the environment, but these metabolites are not or cannot be used directly as foods. Instead, the metabolites serve as sources of hydrogen. Extracted hydrogen is then combined with carbon dioxide, and the resulting carbohydrates do serve as usable foods:

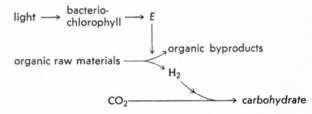

Purple bacteria may manufacture foods in this manner only if light is present and oxygen is *absent*. In some species, a different type of nutrition may also occur in the dark and in the presence of oxygen. Under such conditions, absorbed organic raw materials may be used as foods *directly*. In other words, the organisms then are chemoorganotrophs, i.e., like all other heterotrophs discussed below.

Chemoorganotrophs

The vast majority of heterotrophs belongs to this nutritional category, in which organic raw materials represent prefabricated, directly usable foods. Chemo-organotrophs can only use foods, not produce them.

Three kinds of organisms are included in the group: **holotrophs, saprotrophs,** and **symbionts** of various kinds. Holotrophs are the free-living bulk-feeders, i.e., most Metazoa and many colorless Protista. All have mouths or equivalent ingesting structures, and they digest ingested food and egest any unusable remains. *Alimentation* therefore is the identifying nutritional characteristic of holotrophs.

Saprotrophs comprise the slime molds, most colorless algae, and, above all, very many bacteria and fungi. They all subsist on dead organisms or on nonliving derivatives of organisms: dead plants and animals of all kinds; dung, sewage, and other elimination and excretion products; and derived materials such as milk, bread, and leather. In short, anything and everything nonliving that contains organic components is likely to provide usable food for saprotrophs. These organisms decompose such organic matter chemically and absorb nutrient molecules from the resulting juices. Thus, saprotrophs bring about *decay*. Note that decay occurs *only* if and when saprotrophs are at work.

As a result of their decay-causing nutritional activities, saprotrophs are vital links in global nutrient cycles. The final decomposition products of decaying organic matter are H_2O, CO_2, and N_2, and, as noted earlier in this chapter, these materials return to the environment from which living matter obtained them originally. All the decay-causing organisms which participate in the water, oxygen, and carbon cycles belong to the saprotrophic chemoorganotrophs. And of the various types of organisms which participate in the nitrogen cycle, three are likewise saprotrophic: the decay-causing bacteria and fungi, some of the denitrifying bacteria, and some of the nitrogen-fixing bacteria.

Symbionts include commensalistic, mutualistic, and parasitic types (see Chap. 7). Some organisms within each of these subgroups actually are bulk-feeding holotrophs (e.g., lampreys) or belong to other nutritional categories, but most must absorb inorganic and organic nutrients in prefabricated molecular form directly from their hosts. Specific food requirements vary greatly. For example, one bacterial parasite may have to obtain a given vitamin or amino acid in prefabricated form, but another may be able to manufacture such a nutrient from other organic starting materials. Biochemical differences of this sort are exceedingly numerous, and they are one reason why a symbiont cannot pick hosts at random. Survival is possible only in hosts in which all required types of nutrients are available.

As noted in earlier chapters, a single individual of some species, particularly species of primitive Protista, may be capable of using several alternative methods of nutrition; such an organism correspondingly belongs to at least two of the above four basic nutritional categories at the same time. But most organisms are limited to just one of the four methods, and the vast majority actually are photolithotrophs and chemoorganotrophs.

PROCESSES OF NUTRITION

The ultimate function of any form of nutrition is *cellular* nutrition, i.e., the supply of required metabolites to each cell an organism contains. Nutrition therefore may be defined as all those events through which necessary and directly usable supplies are delivered to, and into, individual cells. Accordingly, two general kinds of nutritional processes may be distinguished: processes of **procurement,** which make nutrients available to an organism, and processes of **internal transport,** which distribute the nutrients within the organism to all cells.

Possibly the most important single component of all nutritional processes is *absorption*. It plays a role in all forms of nutrition; it contributes to most processes of nutrient procurement and nutrient transport; and it is the chief means of cellular nutrition.

ABSORPTION

This process occurs at the *surfaces* of cells, and it involves metabolites of *ionic* and *molecular* form. Absorption may be defined as the transfer of compounds from the environment through a cell surface into the interior of a cell. "Environment" here means both physical and biological surroundings; when a cell obtains nutrients from adjacent cells, or from sap or blood flowing by, that is absorption too.

Absorption is accomplished by at least three kinds of processes: water is absorbed in part by **osmosis;** inorganic and organic materials dissolved in water are absorbed in part by **diffusion;** and water and all dissolved materials are absorbed additionally and most particularly by energy-consuming **chemical work** done by a cell (see Chap. 4). Virtually any cell chosen at random may serve to illustrate these events, for the basic mechanism of absorption is the same regardless of the cell type or the nature of the organism.

Whenever the concentration of dissolved materials is greater within a cell than in its surroundings, the cell will absorb water osmotically. A good example of this is the uptake of soil water by the root-hair cells of vascular plants (Fig. 12.22). Normally, a root-hair cell contains a higher concentration of dissolved particles than soil water. Osmotic pressure therefore pulls soil water into the root hair. However, osmotic force cannot be the only agency responsible for water absorption. If the soil is made to contain a higher concentration of dissolved particles than the root-hair cells, then the plant should *lose* water to the soil. Yet under such conditions the roots still take up water, though less than before.

Clearly, osmotic pull normally contributes some absorptive force, but another agency contributes also. This other agency depends on the *living* condition of the root cell, and it is best described as *active absorptive work* done by the cell. That work is required is known, for water absorption consumes energy and is contingent on continued cellular respiration. When the respiratory machinery of the cells is stopped with poison, then biological water absorption is likewise stopped, though purely physical osmotic absorption

still continues. Thus, in ways which actually are understood only poorly as yet, a living root cell actively *pulls* water into itself through the cell surface (see Fig. 12.22).

An exactly similar combination of physical osmotic forces and living biological forces appears to govern water absorption not only in root-hair cells but in all other cells as well, e.g., when any plant or animal cell absorbs water from another, or from body fluids such as sap or blood, or when a single-celled aquatic organism absorbs water from its external liquid environment.

Minerals and foods dissolved in water may be absorbed into a cell by *diffusion*, but only if the concentration of dissolved particles outside the cell is greater than inside. However, this is actually the case rather rarely, the opposite being far more usual. Consider again a root-hair cell of vascular plants. As just noted above, the concentration of particles within the cell is far greater than the concentration of soil minerals outside the cells. Therefore, if mineral absorption were merely a matter of physical diffusion, the root-hair cell should lose ions to the soil. This does not happen. On the contrary, ions migrate from the soil *into* the root, *against* the prevailing diffusion gradient. Moreover,

FIG. 12.22   Left, osmosis in roots. Particle concentrations are greater in root cells than in soil; hence more water moves into root cells from soil than in the reverse direction. Middle, the effect of "salting" the soil. Even if the particle concentration in soil is made greater than in the root, water still moves into the root (solid arrows), against the osmotic gradient (broken arrows). This indicates that osmosis is not the only agency in water absorption; active absorption by living root cells is of importance as well. Right, diffusion in roots. Because root cells contain a higher concentration of mineral ions than soil, ions should be expected to diffuse out of roots (broken arrows). Yet ions actually migrate from soil into roots (solid arrows), against the diffusion gradient. This indicates that diffusion cannot be responsible for ion absorption. Active absorption by living root cells is involved instead.

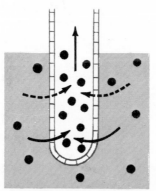   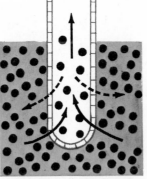   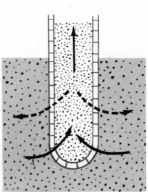

osmosis in normal soil   *osmosis in "salted" soil*   *diffusion in normal soil*

some ions are absorbed readily; others are not (see Fig. 12.22).

In other words, selective, active, energy-consuming absorptive work is again done by the living root cell. Poisoned cells cannot carry out such absorption. And in a living cell, as noted, much of the energy needed for mineral absorption is actually expended in counteracting and overcoming the outwardly directed force of diffusion. The pattern here described for root-hair cells applies equally to *any* cells which absorb materials dissolved in water. Moreover, the pattern holds not only for mineral absorption but also for food absorption.

Indeed, in the case of at least one food something of the detailed chemistry of "living" absorption is known. Specifically, it is now fairly well established that cells do not take up glucose as such, except to the minor extent that purely physical diffusion may occur. Suppose that glucose is about to be absorbed by a saprotrophic bacterium or by a nongreen parenchyma cell in a green vascular plant or by an intestinal mucosa cell in an animal or by any other heterotrophic cell. If the glucose molecule is to be transferred through the cell surface, it must be **phosphorylated;** i.e., it must be combined chemically with a phosphate group. Glucose-phosphate is the result. The chemical reaction which produces glucose-phosphate occurs at, or in, the cell surface, and it consumes energy. This accounts for some of the energy expenditure of a cell doing absorptive work. Phosphorylated glucose enters the cell and becomes available there in metabolism (Fig. 12.23).

FIG. 12.23 The general pattern of glucose absorption by a cell and phosphorylation.

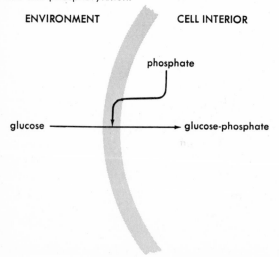

ENVIRONMENT · CELL INTERIOR

phosphate

glucose → glucose-phosphate

Phosphorylation of glucose and of other carbohydrates is of significance not only in cellular nutrition but also in photosynthesis, in respiration, and indeed in most other metabolic processes in which carbohydrates participate. We shall encounter this process repeatedly in subsequent chapters. For future reference, therefore, we may briefly examine some of the chemical aspects of phosphorylation. Phosphate groups are derivatives of the mineral nutrient phosphoric acid, H_3PO_4. The formula of this acid may also be written as $H–O–PO_3H_2$. Here the $–O–PO_3H_2$ is the phosphate group. In it, the $–PO_3H_2$ part may be symbolized in abbreviated form as $–\textcircled{P}$, hence a phosphate group may be written as $–O–\textcircled{P}$. Phosphorylation is a reaction in which such an $–O–\textcircled{P}$ group becomes attached to a carbohydrate. For example, in the case of glucose,

$$C_6H_{12}O_6 \quad + \quad –O–\textcircled{P} \xrightarrow{\ energy\ } C_6H_{11}O_5–O–\textcircled{P} \ + \ –O–H$$

glucose   phosphate   glucose
            group   phosphate

Glucose-phosphate is a phosphorylated carbohydrate. Because $–O–\textcircled{P}$ groups interact with organic molecules, such phosphate groups are often also called "organic phosphates" (to distinguish them from "inorganic phosphates," which are ions of phosphoric acid, such as $PO_4^{\equiv}$). Note from the equation above that an $–O–\textcircled{P}$ group in a phosphorylated carbohydrate occupies the place normally filled by an $–O–H$ group. For example, free glucose contains 12 H and 6 O atoms, but the glucose portion of glucose-phosphate contains only 11 H and 5 O atoms. However, one additional O atom is supplied by $–O–\textcircled{P}$; hence glucose-phosphate may also be written as $C_6H_{11}O_6–\textcircled{P}$. Therefore, whenever a carbohydrate gains a phosphate group, the *net* effect is the addition of one $–\textcircled{P}$ group and the removal of one H atom. Conversely, if a phosphorylated carbohydrate is **dephosphorylated,** the *net* effect is the removal of one $–\textcircled{P}$ group and the addition of one H atom:

$$C_6H_{12}O_6 + –\textcircled{P} \rightleftharpoons C_6H_{11}O_6–\textcircled{P} + –H$$

In all subsequent references to phosphorylation, we shall for simplicity disregard the $–O–$ in $–O–\textcircled{P}$, and shall treat the symbol $–\textcircled{P}$ as an equivalent for a whole phosphate group. In line with this, a $–\textcircled{P}$ or "phosphate" group will simply be regarded as replacing an H atom of a carbohydrate molecule.

Carbohydrates participate in metabolism largely in phosphorylated form. Accordingly, we may note that glucose, possibly the most important single carbohydrate nutrient in all organisms, is itself rather useless metabolically. To be useful to a cell it must be absorbed, and to be absorbed it must be phosphorylated at the cell surface.

Various reactions at the cell surface may also occur in the uptake of metabolites which are not carbohydrates, but in most of these instances the details are not yet fully known. Once a metabolite of any kind has been absorbed into a cell, intracellular distribution is achieved mainly by *diffusion* and *cyclosis*. Through these processes, every part of a cell comes to have access to all nutrients the cell may have acquired only at specific points of its surface.

PROCUREMENT AND TRANSPORT

In unicellular organisms, the procurement aspect of nutrition includes absorption in all cases (Fig. 12.24). If the organism is autotrophic, all inorganic nutrients are procured by absorption. If the unicellular form is heterotrophic and bulk-feeding, most inorganic and all organic nutrients are ingested via gullets or in amoeboid fashion. Yet water and dissolved mineral ions are usually obtained by direct absorption through the cell surface. If the unicelled organism is heterotrophic and not bulk-feeding, then absorption constitutes virtually the whole of its nutrition, for in such cases *all* required inorganic and organic nutrients must be obtained by absorption from the environment. Saprotrophs and symbionts among bacteria and protists provide pertinent examples.

The transport aspect of nutrition is virtually non-existent in unicellular forms. Once present within a cell, nutrients need merely be distributed to all parts of the cell by diffusion and cyclosis.

Both the procurement and the transport processes are far more elaborate in most multicellular organisms. Apart from primitive multicellular types in which each cell accomplishes its own nutrition individually and independently (e.g., many multicellular algae), all other multicellular organisms acquire nutrients only at specialized body regions. For example, metaphytes absorb inorganic materials through roots or rootlike structures and photosynthesize organic materials in leaves or other aerial structures. Analogously, metazoans usually obtain nutrients only via specialized alimentary systems, although some symbiotic types absorb directly through their body surfaces (e.g., tapeworms). Whatever the detailed pattern, nutrient procurement in all such cases is localized, and it involves at least tissues and often whole organ systems which function variously in absorption or in photosynthesis or in alimentation or in combinations of these processes. Consequently, nutrients procured only at specific regions must then be transported to all other cells of the organism. Such internal nutrient transport includes **short-distance conduction** in all cases and **long-distance conduction** in most cases (Fig. 12.25).

Short-distance transport, an exceedingly important nutritional process in all multicellular organisms, means nutrient transfer from one cell to immediately adjacent cells. Such cell-to-cell transfers are achieved by *secretion* of metabolites from one cell and *absorption* by the next. Secretion is more or less the exact reverse of absorption, the same forces working in opposite directions. Thus, water moves out of a cell partly by osmosis, partly by chemical work; dissolved materials leave partly by diffusion, and again partly by chemical work.

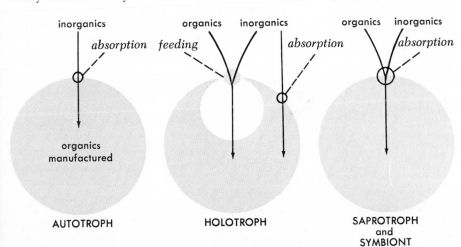

inorganics

absorption

organics manufactured

AUTOTROPH

organics   inorganics

feeding   *absorption*

HOLOTROPH

organics   inorganics

absorption

SAPROTROPH and SYMBIONT

FIG. 12.24 Nutritional patterns in unicellular organisms. In autotrophic cells, inorganic nutrients are absorbed and organic nutrients are manufactured internally. In holotrophs, absorption of some inorganic nutrients (e.g., water) supplements bulk feeding. In saprotrophs and symbionts, all required nutrients usually are absorbed. Thus absorption plays a principal role in the nutrition of all unicellular types.

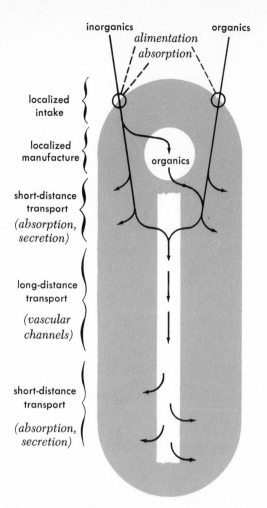

FIG. 12.25 Nutritional patterns in multicellular organisms. After localized intake or manufacture, the nutrients may be partly distributed to cells by short-distance transport. Also, short-distance transport serves as a feeder mechanism which carries nutrients to the long-distance rapid-transit channels (xylem and phloem in plants, blood and lymph in animals). From these channels, nutrients are delivered to cells again by short-distance transport.

The chemical, selective, "living" action of cell membranes is particularly evident here, for a given metabolite which is absorbed by a cell may not necessarily be also secreted. In very many cases, *more* of a particular inorganic or organic metabolite is allowed into a cell than is allowed out, or vice versa. By this means, cell-to-cell transfers of given metabolites may become unidirectional. Also, one and the same cell group may act differently with different metabolites, or indeed with the same metabolite at different times. It is largely impossible to predict beforehand how given cells will transport given metabolites, and only experiment can determine this in each case.

In addition to short-distance conduction, comparatively rapid, highly specialized long-distance nutrient conduction occurs in structurally complex multicellular organisms. This function is performed by the *vascular* tissues: xylem and phloem in plants, blood and lymph vessels in animals. Where the internal structural elaboration of an organism is great, the presence of "rapid-transit" long-distance conductors clearly is an important adaptive advantage. In tracheophytes, the longitudinal extension of the body may be relatively enormous (e.g., Sequoias and Eucalyptus trees may be up to 400 ft high, counting only stem and crown), and long-distance conduction actually occurs only along the vertical axis. In animals, body size often is a less critical factor than internal organizational complexity, and here long-distance conduction via a circulatory system is extensively multidirectional.

But note that, in all cases, rapid-transit long-distance conduction must operate in conjunction with short-distance conduction. In a tracheophyte, for example, cell-to-cell transfers must serve as the "feeder" mechanism which carries inorganic nutrients from root cells and organic nutrients from leaf cells to the rapid-transit channels. In animals, analogously, nutrients procured by alimentation must be brought by short-distance transfers from the intestinal cavity through the gut wall to the circulatory channels. Moreover, at the terminals of the rapid-transit lines in both plants and animals, nutrients must be delivered to the receiver cells by local short-distance conduction. Ultimately, therefore, *cellular* nutrition in all multicellular organisms is basically absorptive; and we may note that although man, for example, possesses an alimentary system, all human cells, including even those of the alimentary system, acquire nutrients by absorption.

With this general outline of nutritional processes as a background, we proceed next to a detailed examination of the two most common sets of nutritional processes, namely, those occurring in photolithotrophic plants and in chemoorganotrophic animals.

REVIEW QUESTIONS

1. Why is the global environment always changing and never stable? What are open and closed physical systems? How do living organisms contribute to cyclic environmental change?

2. Review the global water cycle. What forces maintain it? How do organisms participate in this cycle? In what different ways does the world's water influence climates?

3. What are diastrophism and gradation? How does the formation of mountains influence climates? Cite examples. In what ways is the global lithospheric cycle of nutritional importance?

4. Review the general pattern of mineral cycles. On the basis of this, construct diagrams showing the pattern of global phosphate and calcium cycles.

5. Describe the development of soil. What are the principal components of soil? In what ways does soil serve in the maintenance of plant life? Name the successive soil layers from the surface downward and show how these layers differ in composition.

6. What factors of composition determine the quality of a soil? Against what agencies must soils be protected and by what means can such soil conservation be accomplished? What are hydroponics? Review the ways in which soil minerals are replenished.

7. What is the chemical composition of the atmosphere? Which of these components do not play a role in the maintenance of organisms?

8. Review (a) the oxygen cycle, (b) the carbon cycle. Show how these cycles are interlinked with each other and with the global water cycle.

9. Review the global nitrogen cycle. How many different groups of bacteria aid in the maintenance of this cycle? What is the role of decay in the atmospheric, lithospheric, and hydrospheric cycles?

10. Define nutrition. What are the major nutritional processes of organisms?

11. Define autotroph, heterotroph, photolithotroph, photoorganotroph, chemolithotroph, chemoorganotroph. Which groups of organisms belong to each of these categories?

12. Review the general patterns of food procurement in the various groups of (a) autotrophs, (b) heterotrophs.

13. Review the different nutritional patterns of (a) purple sulfur bacteria, purple nonsulfur bacteria, green sulfur bacteria, and nongreen sulfur bacteria, (b) nitrifying bacteria, denitrifying bacteria, and nitrogen-fixing bacteria.

14. Where and through what processes do different groups of organisms obtain (a) water, (b) other mineral substances, (c) molecular foods, (d) atmospheric gases? What is phosphorylation and what role does it play in nutrition?

15. What processes bring about short-distance transport of nutrients (a) within individual cells, (b) from cell to cell? Name the tissues in plants and animals in which long-distance transport of nutrients occurs.

SUGGESTED COLLATERAL READINGS

References relating to the nutrition of specific organisms will be found at the ends of the next two chapters. The global environment and the influences of its hydrospheric, lithospheric, and atmospheric components on living matter are variously discussed in the following:

Bennett, H. H.: "Elements of Soil Conservation," 2d ed., McGraw-Hill, New York, 1955.

Cole, L. C.: The Ecosphere, Sci. American, vol. 198, 1958.

Dudley, F.: Progress in Soil Science, Am. Scientist, vol. 34, 1946.

Gilbert, F. A.: "Mineral Nutrition and the Balance of Life," University of Oklahoma Press, Norman, Okla., 1957.

Henderson, L. J.: "Fitness of the Environment," Macmillan, New York, 1913.

Kellogg, C. E.: Soil, *Sci. American,* vol. 183, 1950.

Kimble, G. H. T.: The Changing Climate, *Sci. American,* vol. 182, 1950.

Osborn, F.: "Our Plundered Planet," Little, Brown, Boston, 1948.

Plass, G. N.: Carbon Dioxide and Climate, *Sci. American,* vol. 201, 1959.

Swanson, C. L. W.: Soil Conditioners, *Sci. American,* vol. 189, 1953.

Vogt, W.: "Road to Survival," Sloane, New York, 1948.

Von Engeln, O. D., and K. S. Caster: "Geology," McGraw-Hill, New York, 1952.

Wald, G.: Life and Light, *Sci. American,* vol. 201, 1959.

Wallace, F.: Mineral Deficiencies in Plants, *Endeavour,* vol. 5, 1946.

Whaley, W.: Research and the Land. *Am. Scientist,* vol. 38, 1950.

PLANT NUTRITION

13

As outlined in the preceding chapter, processes of nutrient procurement in metaphytes include absorption of preexisting inorganic metabolites from the environment and intracellular manufacture of organic metabolites by photosynthesis. Processes of nutrient transport include cell-to-cell short-distance conduction and, in tracheophytes, also long-distance conduction via xylem and phloem. We shall discuss **absorption and transport** processes in a first section and **photosynthesis** in a second.

ABSORPTION AND TRANSPORT

Atmospheric gases enter a tracheophyte mainly via stomata and are absorbed directly into individual photosynthetic cells. All other inorganic nutrients are absorbed via the root system. Nutrients so obtained include liquid water in which are dissolved soil minerals as well as given amounts of atmospheric gases. Absorption occurs largely in the root-hair cells of the root epidermis, for these cells provide most of the available absorbing surface. After being absorbed, through processes already described in Chap. 12, the nutrients are carried by lateral cell-to-cell transfers to the xylem in the root core. Containing linear series of vertical tracheids and vessels which reach uninterruptedly from root tip to leaf tip, xylem provides the channels for the upward conduction of inorganic metabolites. Accompanying the uptake by roots and the transport by xylem, phloem tissue conducts organic metabolites manufactured in green cells to the stem and the roots. In addition, phloem also transports stored organic metabolites up or down, to all parts of the plant. How are these various processes accomplished?

XYLEM CONDUCTION

When a root-hair cell absorbs water and minerals, the most immediate effect is that the excess water tends to dilute the substance of the cell. Should we not also expect that cell to swell? We should indeed, but this does not happen to any appreciable extent, for most of the absorbed water and the dissolved materials are removed almost as soon as they enter the cell. The fluid is secreted from the root-hair cell and is absorbed by the cortex cells immediately adjacent to the root epidermis. As a result, water which first has been in the soil and then in the epidermis is now in the outermost layer of the root cortex. *These* cells then tend to swell, and their interior tends to become more dilute. However, excessive swelling is prevented by the cell walls and water is therefore transferred again, into the next inner layer of cortex cells (Fig. 13.1).

In this manner, water and minerals are drawn progressively from cell layer to cell layer, toward the core of the root. Some of these nutritional supplies are retained by the cells along the route, but the bulk soon reaches the root endodermis. This tissue (which in some plants includes specialized unsuberized *passage cells*) provides a path into the stele of the root. Water and dissolved materials are moved through the endodermis, through the layers of the pericycle, and from there they are pushed into xylem vessels.

"Pushed" is the right word. The water stream from soil to xylem vessel is continuous and uninterrupted and it is not a stream which trickles lazily by its own weight. Rather, the combined osmotic pressure and the combined absorptive force of all root cells are behind the water, and this generates **root pressure.** It is this pressure which drives water forcefully into the xylem tubes at the root core and which also aids in driving sap upward through the xylem vessels (Fig. 13.2).

FIG. 13.1 The absorption path within a root. Water and dissolved minerals are absorbed by successively deeper layers of cells. In this manner, supplies eventually reach the xylem.

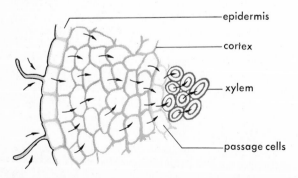

- epidermis
- cortex
- xylem
- passage cells

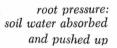

transipration:
water evaporated
and pulled up

root pressure:
soil water absorbed
and pushed up

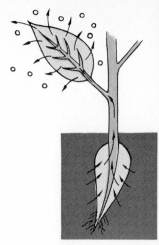

FIG. 13.2 Xylem tubes contain continuous columns of water. Root pressure adds more water at the bottom, and transpiration removes water at the top through evaporation. Hence a water column in xylem moves upward.

In a healthy plant, xylem tubes are never empty of water. Even before a xylem vessel becomes functional, cellular water already fills the interior of the vessel elements. Later, when the cell substance of these elements disintegrates, the water remains. As the plant grows in length, each new vessel element joined to the top of an existing vessel adds a corresponding cylinder of water to the column below. Water thus *grows* up, as the plant grows up. No matter how high the plant, therefore, continuous uninterrupted water columns range from every root-hair membrane, through root cortex, pericycle, and xylem vessels, to every leaf mesophyll membrane.

Upward "transportation" consequently becomes a matter of adding water at the bottom of such columns and withdrawing an equivalent amount from the top, minus the fraction which living tissues incorporate into their substance. As we have seen, absorption by the root adds water at the bottom and generates root pressure. This is one force which pushes the water columns up.

But root pressure is not alone responsible for the lifting of water. A second force, and probably a more important one than root pressure, is pull from above. This force is generated by **transpiration,** i.e., evaporation of water from the leaves (see Fig. 13.2). As water vaporizes from a mesophyll cell, the cell tends to develop a water deficit and so the concentration of cellular particles tends to increase. Osmotic difference therefore draws water in from neighboring cells. *These* cells now tend to develop a water deficit. Osmotic pull is propagated back in this manner, along cell paths leading to xylem terminals. As in roots, osmotic pull is accompanied by active cellular absorption. The combined osmotic and absorptive action of leaf cells pulls water up through the xylem, in quantities commensurate with the amount evaporated. The effectiveness of this pull from above is familiar to everyone. An isolated leaf or a flower with a stub of stem and a few leaves survives for a considerable time when put into a glass of water; as water transpires from exposed plant tissues, fluid is pulled up from below.

We note that the two forces which raise sap against gravity are living cellular *push* from below and living cellular *pull* from above. Continued over a period of time, water which at first stands at the level of the root is gradually shifted up into the leaves. Water or minerals now entering the roots of a high tree therefore may not reach leaves for several hours, and materials now absorbed by mesophyll cells may have entered the roots several hours before.

It should be clear that such a mechanism of transport depends on uninterrupted continuity of the water columns. The condition that the transport fluid is water, rather than another medium, greatly facilitates the maintenance of column continuity, for water possesses a high degree of **cohesion**. Individual molecules attract one another rather strongly, and a column of water therefore "hangs together" with appreciable tenacity.

The mechanism of water conduction is the same where transport is not through vessels but through tracheids. The pit membranes of tracheids are permeable to water and mineral ions and present no barrier to continuous flow. Indeed, the bordered pits along the sidewalls of tracheids permit a measure of *lateral conduction*, as well as equilibration of flow pressure among adjacent columns of water.

The key point in xylem transport is that the power source lies in living roots and leaves. The nonliving xylem tubes as such are passive, in the same way that a pipeline between two pumping stations is passive. Conduction through phloem is different in this respect. In this system the power source appears to be spread out all along the transportation route.

PHLOEM CONDUCTION

Unlike vessels or tracheids, sieve tubes are two-way paths (Fig. 13.3). Downward conduction in sieve

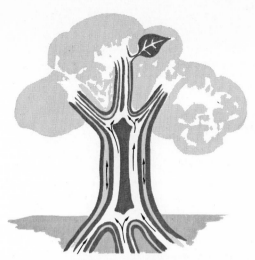

FIG. 13.3 The conduction pathways in a plant. The inner xylem system transports upward; the outer phloem system, both upward and downward.

tubes has long been known to occur: many roots store carbohydrates, which are photosynthesized only in leaf or stem. The occurrence of upward conduction has come to light through grafting experiments. For example, a stem of a tobacco plant grafted to a root of a tomato plant develops normal tobacco leaves, but these are entirely free of nicotine. Conversely, a tomato-plant stem transplanted to a tobacco-plant root produces tomato leaves, but these are full of nicotine. The first graft indicates that only the roots of a tobacco plant synthesize nicotine; the second graft, that the drug is transported upward. And since xylem channels are virtually free of nicotine, upward conduction must occur largely in phloem (Fig. 13.4).

Indeed, most of the organic nutrients of a plant travel in the sieve tubes. Photosynthesized carbohydrates and their derivatives migrate from leaves and stem downward; organic storage products and materials manufactured from them travel from roots and stem upward. Some upward conduction of organic substances also occurs in xylem vessels. For example, small amounts of sugar are generally present in this channel.

The driving force in phloem transport is probably generated by the individual sieve-tube cells, and it probably does not differ from that which brings about internal transport in *any* cell. That is, movement of materials may be accomplished by cyclosis and by diffusion. In a sieve tube, the vertical direction of conduction may be imposed by the anatomic arrangement.

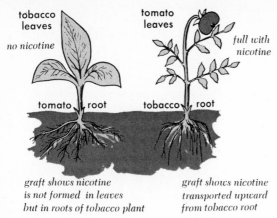

tobacco leaves

no nicotine

tomato   root

tomato leaves

full with nicotine

tobacco   root

graft shows nicotine is not formed in leaves but in roots of tobacco plant

graft shows nicotine transported upward from tobacco root

FIG. 13.4 If tobacco leaves are grafted onto tomato roots (left), nicotine will be absent from the tobacco leaves. If tomato leaves are grafted onto tobacco roots (right), the tomato leaves will eventually contain nicotine. Experiments of this sort show that only tobacco roots manufacture nicotine and that this substance is transported upward by the phloem.

Absorption of organic materials into sieve-tube cytoplasm and secretion out of it may well be accomplished most easily at the top and bottom perforations, where the barriers may be minimal (Fig. 13.5).

The two-way aspect of phloem conduction becomes intelligible on this basis. Mesophyll cells in the leaf photosynthesize; hence they acquire relatively high carbohydrate concentrations. Terminal sieve-tube cells in the vicinity do not photosynthesize; hence their carbohydrate content is lower. Consequently, diffusion tends to equalize the concentrations, and the terminal sieve-tube cells absorb some of the mesophyll-produced carbohydrate. Their own carbohydrate content increases as a result, relative to that of lower sieve-tube cells next in line along the conduction path. These lower sieve-tube cells absorb from units above them, and in this fashion nutrient conduction continues downward (Fig. 13.6). Cells along the way may retain greater or lesser amounts of the carbohydrate. But the bulk will be carried into the roots, step by step from one section of sieve tube to the next, under the influence of the diffusion gradient pointing from the leaves toward the roots.

Alternatively, organic materials may be carried upward if the concentrations of such materials are high in the roots and lower above. This is the case, for example, in winter and early spring, when leaves are absent and photosynthesis does not take place. Organic nutrients

stored in the roots during the preceding summer then travel upward into the food-requiring regions of the stem and the crown.

Like so many other cell membranes, the cellular membranes of phloem exhibit selective activity. If a horizontal disk is cut from a stem and if this disk is allowed to grow back into its original space in an inverted position, then the stem will be intact, but a section of it will have reversed polarity. This will not interfere with xylem conduction. But phloem conduction may be impaired. Substances like glucose may still travel downward through the inverted section of stem; yet materials like auxins, growth hormones manufactured only in apical shoot meristems (see Chap. 19), generally may not. Sieve-tube membranes evidently let some substances through in one direction only.

Phloem conduction, up or down, is slow compared with xylem conduction. In phloem, also, we do not find a distinct flowing sap as in xylem vessels. The transportation medium, namely, sieve-tube cytoplasm, flows and shifts within its cellulose confines only but does not itself flow up or down bodily. Nutrient molecules alone are handed from one unit to the next. Such conduction in phloem is often spoken of as **translocation.**

Absorption of inorganic supplies and all transport by phloem and xylem not only contribute to but also depend on photosynthesis; for it is this most vital nutri-

FIG. 13.5 Conduction in phloem units. All materials in the sieve tubes are kept in circulation by cyclotic streaming. Differentials in concentration determine whether or not a given substance will pass through sieve plates from one phloem unit to another.

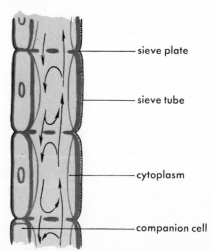

sieve plate

sieve tube

cytoplasm

companion cell

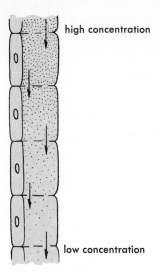

high concentration

low concentration

FIG. 13.6 The role of nutrient concentrations in phloem conduction. If a given nutrient is highly concentrated at one end of a phloem channel and less highly concentrated at the other, as shown, then a diffusion gradient will point from the high to the low concentration. The nutrient thus will be translocated in that direction.

tional activity which produces the very building materials and the energy for the construction of the whole green plant, including roots, leaves, transport tissues, and all other structures it may possess. As we have seen, many photolithotrophs actually are without roots, stems, or leaves, yet photosynthesis is common to all of them. We now turn to a detailed discussion of this food-manufacturing process.

PHOTOSYNTHESIS: BACKGROUND

The fundamental importance of the set of reactions in which CO_2 and H_2O are transformed into carbohydrates and oxygen cannot be overestimated. Carbohydrates produced through photosynthesis constitute the basic raw materials which, directly or indirectly, give rise to all organic components of virtually all plants and animals and to virtually all living energy. The only organisms not dependent on photosynthesis are the chemolithotrophic bacteria (see Chap. 12), which together amount to probably less than 0.0001 per cent of all the living matter on earth.

The global impact of photosynthesis is underscored

by statistical data. Every year, some 200 billion tons of carbon go through the photosynthetic process. This makes it the most massive chemical event and the second most massive event of all kinds on earth. Only the global evaporation-precipitation cycle of water involves more material. Carbon dioxide is used up in photosynthesis in enormous amounts. If the gas were not replenished through plant and animal respiration and other combustion processes, then the CO_2 content of the entire atmosphere would be exhausted in a few months and that of the ocean in about 300 years. Oxygen is released through photosynthesis so voluminously that all the O_2 of the present atmosphere could be generated in about 2,000 years, an incredibly short time from a geologic standpoint. Finally, the solar energy harvested annually through photosynthesis in the form of carbohydrates amounts to fully one-fourth of the total energy available to man from all sources.

This quantitative and qualitative importance of photosynthesis has been appreciated for only a very short time. Research on the nature of the process began in the seventeenth century, when work by Van Helmont implied that plant growth could not be a result of any soil eating by roots, as Aristotle had believed. Van Helmont planted a willow twig in a measured amount of soil, and after caring for this plant for some years, he found that the weight of the soil had decreased by only a few ounces. But the twig had become a young tree weighing many pounds (Fig. 13.7). Van Helmont's

FIG. 13.7 The classical experiment of Van Helmont. This investigator showed that added water, not soil eating by roots, accounted for plant growth.

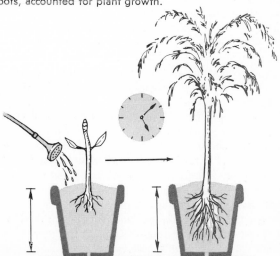

FIG. 13.8 The classical experiment of Priestley. This investigator showed that a plant and an animal, when sealed in separate chambers, could not survive but that they could survive if they were sealed in a chamber together.

work therefore suggested that water added to soil, not soil itself, must serve as nourishment in plant growth.

Around the middle of the eighteenth century, Priestley discovered that an animal and a plant sealed together in a glass chamber could survive, although the animal or the plant alone could not survive (Fig. 13.8). He concluded that the plant changed "fixed air" exhaled by the animal into "good air"; or as we would say today, plants take up CO_2 exhaled by the animal and the animal takes up O_2 released by the plant. Later, Ingenhousz showed that the Priestley effect hinged on the presence of light and of living green tissue. Work during the nineteenth century demonstrated that CO_2 and water absorbed by a green plant yielded O_2 and an *organic* endproduct. This endproduct was subsequently identified as a carbohydrate. Thus, not until almost the beginning of the present century could the over-all photosynthetic equation be written:

$$CO_2 + HO_2 \xrightarrow[chlorophyll]{light} \text{carbohydrate} + O_2$$

We know today that this equation does not describe the actual photosynthetic reaction. Contrary to what the equation suggests, carbohydrates are *not* formed simply by mixing carbon dioxide and water; the product of such mixing would be only carbonic acid. The above is, in fact, merely a vague statement of *input* and *output*. It indicates what kinds of materials go into photosynthesis and what kinds come out, but it does not, for example, give quantitative information concerning these materials. Moreover, it indicates neither the amount nor the kind of light required, and it does not specify the requirement of living cells with intact grana. Above all, the statement does not indicate

the many intermediate processes now known to occur between input and output.

A consideration of these finer details of photosynthesis is now our objective.

LIGHT AND CHLOROPHYLL

Chlorophyll is perceived as a green substance. This elementary observation actually tells a great deal about the role of the chlorophyll molecule in photosynthesis.

The Meaning of Color

Color is not an inherent property of an object. It is a subjective impression, dependent entirely on how the eye-brain complex interprets particular light waves received from the object. When we "see color," the following series of events takes place. An object is illuminated with light waves from a self-luminous source. Depending on the physical and chemical properties of the object, some of the light waves may be **absorbed** into it, some may be **transmitted** through it, and some may be **reflected** from it. If transmitted or reflected waves reach the eye, nerve impulses will travel from the eye to the brain and the brain will then interpret these impulses as "color" (Fig. 13.9).

It follows that an object which *absorbs* all the light falling on it, transmitting or reflecting nothing, would be invisible and would appear as a "hole in space." A black object approaches this theoretical condition most closely. An object which *transmits* all light would be completely transparent and so would also be invisible. And an object which *reflects* all light would appear in the color of the light falling on it (Fig. 13.10).

FIG. 13.9 Light reaching an object may be partly reflected, partly absorbed, and partly transmitted. Light which is absorbed cannot be seen by an external observer.

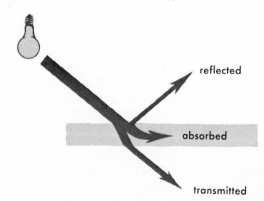

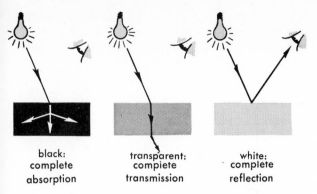

black:
complete
absorption

transparent:
complete
transmission

white:
complete
reflection

FIG. 13.10 Complete light absorption by an object makes that object theoretically invisible or black in practice. Complete light transmission makes an object theoretically invisible, too, or transparent in practice. Complete reflection makes an object appear to be of the same color as the light; i.e., if white light is completely reflected, the object will appear white.

The subjective nature of color is revealed in a number of familiar situations. For example, certain color-blind persons cannot distinguish red and green objects. The trouble here clearly lies not with the objects but with the visual mechanism of the viewers. Most seeing animals do not even possess visual organs capable of distinguishing between different light waves. These animals may perceive form and shape, but to them the world is a pattern in gray.

Evidently, although we commonly say, "chlorophyll is green," we must realize that chlorophyll and pigmented substances generally as such actually have no color of their own. The above phrase, for example, is a shorthand figure of speech for essentially the following: "The properties of the chlorophyll molecule are such that it absorbs certain light waves and reflects and transmits others. If these reflected or transmitted waves reach the eye, most of us will interpret them as 'green.'"

Waves and Energy

Light waves of any kind are forms of energy—radiant, electromagnetic energy. The sun emits many electromagnetic radiations other than light, and, like light, each of them is characterized by a definite **wavelength** and **energy content.** The greater the wavelength, the smaller is the energy content. Electric waves, the longest of the solar radiations, are the least energetic. Progressively shorter and more energetic are radio waves, infrared waves, light waves, ultraviolet waves,

and X rays. So arranged in order of wavelengths, this electromagnetic radiation series forms a continuous **radiation spectrum.**

Just as a radio receiver is sensitive to only a portion of this spectrum, namely, radio waves, so the human eye is sensitive to only a portion, namely, the **visible spectrum,** consisting of light waves. The human eye-brain complex is so constructed that the longest, least energetic light waves are perceived as the color red, and the shortest, most energetic, as the color violet. Light waves of intermediate length and energy content are perceived in the various other colors of the rainbow: orange, yellow, green, and blue. Viewed together, in a properly mixed beam such as sunlight, the whole spectrum of visible waves is interpreted as "white" or "near-white" light.

We may conclude, therefore, that the light waves which chlorophyll reflects and transmits, and which make chlorophyll appear green to us, have intermediate length and energy content and that the light waves which chlorophyll absorbs must be the other components of the visible spectrum, namely, the long red waves and the short blue-violet waves.

Since light is energy, it can be made to do work, potentially at least. But if light is to do actual work, it must be *absorbed* by a suitable working mechanism. A mechanism which merely reflects or transmits light does not trap the energy of that light, and energy which is not trapped cannot supply power for work. Therefore, inasmuch as chlorophyll reflects or transmits "green" waves, we may infer that these *cannot* play a role in photosynthesis. On the other hand, chlorophyll does absorb all except the green light waves to greater or lesser degree. We may therefore infer that any of or all these absorbed waves *do* supply energy for photosynthesis. Indeed, most plants exposed exclusively to green light usually cannot photosynthesize and soon die. But plants grow well when they receive light from any other part of the visible spectrum.

Pigments and Chloroplasts

Earlier chapters have shown that different groups of organisms possess different kinds and combinations of chlorophyll. All kinds of chlorophyll molecules contain a tetrapyrrol skeleton formed into a ring, with an atom of magnesium in the center of the ring (see Chap. 4). Such a ring represents the "head" of a chlorophyll molecule. Attached to it at one point is a "tail," a long chain of linked carbons. Relatively minor variations in the kinds and groupings of other atoms joined to

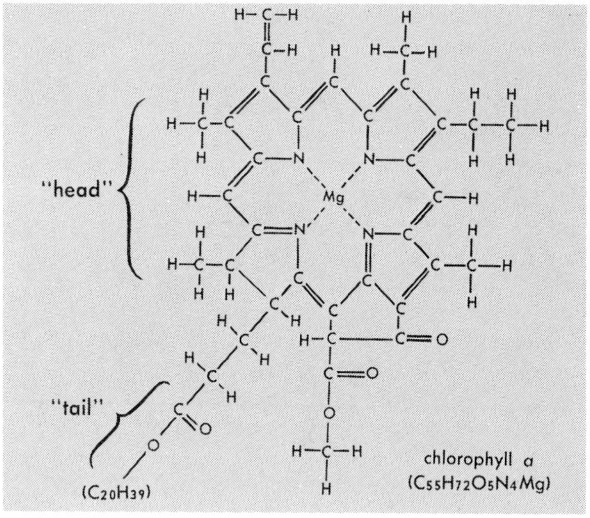

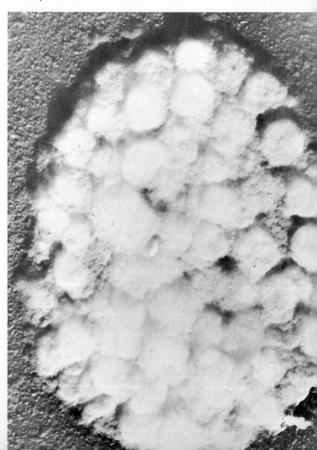

FIG. 13.11 The chemical structure of a molecule of chlorophyll.

this head-and-tail skeleton account for the differences among different kinds of chlorophylls (Fig. 13.11).

Chlorophylls, along with carotenoid and xanthophyll pigments, are concentrated within grana, which in turn may be organized into larger chloroplasts (Fig. 13.12). As noted in Chap. 8, grana and granumlike bodies but not chloroplasts are present in the Monera. All other photosynthetic organisms possess distinct chloroplasts. The electron microscope shows that each granum within a chloroplast consists of a series of protein layers arranged like coins in a stack. Between every two such layers is a double layer consisting of fatty material, chlorophyll, and molecules of other pigments (Fig. 13.13). The fairly orderly arrangement of these molecules in the diagram may depict actual conditions; the pigment molecules are believed to be positioned with a regularity approaching that of a crystal.

In the chloroplasts of different plant groups, the various chlorophylls, carotenoids, and xanthophylls are present in different proportions, hence the various external colors of plants and also the various lighter and deeper shades of green in a landscape.

In flowering plants and in many others, the production and maintenance of chlorophyll within chloroplasts ordinarily require exposure to light. A young shoot, for example, does not turn green until it is well above the soil surface. In a plant grown in a dark chamber, chlorophyll soon breaks down and the plant loses its green color. In the continued absence of light

new chlorophyll is then not synthesized. However, in certain green tissues, chlorophyll may disintegrate even in the presence of light, as a normal process of development. For example, immature fruits are green, and as they ripen, the color of chlorophyll in many cases gives way to the brilliant shades of the carotenoid and other pigments.

Some evidence exists that the manufacture of chlorophyll within cells may be assisted by the carotenoids normally present in chloroplasts. Carotenoids essentially are long chains of carbon atoms, and parts of such chains may form the "tails" of the chlorophyll molecules.

A green cell may possess from a few up to about eighty chloroplasts. In a mature tree, all the chloroplasts together may provide a surface area for light absorption totaling some 150 sq. miles. Chloroplasts contain nucleoproteins, as noted in Chap. 4, and these green bodies reproduce within cells. Thus the chloro-

FIG. 13.12 Electron micrograph of a single chloroplast, showing the grana. (Courtesy of R. W. G. Wyckoff, "Electron Microscopy," Interscience Publishers, Inc., New York, 1949.)

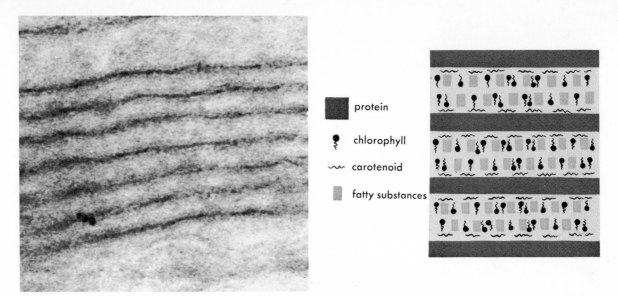

protein

chlorophyll

carotenoid

fatty substances

FIG. 13.13 Photograph, highly magnified electron-micrographic view of the interior of a granum, showing the layered structure. Diagram, the internal structure of a single granum. Note the layered arrangement of the components. *(Photograph, courtesy of Dr. A. J. Hodge, California Institute of Technology, and J. Biophys. Biochem. Cytol., vol. 1, p. 605.)*

plast population may keep pace with the growth of the tissues of which they are constituents.

The materials and the machinery for food production are now assembled. In a vascular plant, far-off roots have supplied the green cell with water, minerals, and a certain amount of dissolved gases (e.g., CO_2). Stomata have admitted most of the gases. Already deployed in the green cell are the chloroplasts and their grana, which contain the pigments, the enzymes, and the whole chemical machinery required for food production. These materials and structures set the scene for photosynthesis. The play begins when sunlight illuminates this scene.

WATER AND CARBON DIOXIDE

The Unit Reaction

Photosynthesis is a series of events in which the elements *carbon, hydrogen,* and *oxygen* are joined in such a way that the result is a *carbohydrate.*

We may symbolize the composition of carbohydrates as (CH_2O), which represents the simplest theoretical unit of carbohydrate structure. For example, if six such units were joined together, we would obtain $6 \times (CH_2O) = C_6H_{12}O_6$, a sugar. (CH_2O) as such actually does not play a role in photosynthesis. As we shall see, the simplest real carbohydrates produced are triplets of (CH_2O), namely, $C_3H_6O_3$. However, many of the chemical aspects of photosynthesis can be simplified considerably if a hypothetical (CH_2O) is regarded as the unit product. If necessary, the equations used may later be multiplied by a factor of 3 to bring them more nearly into line with actual events. With these provisions, and disregarding the slightly different events in photosynthetic bacteria, we may write the following input-output statement for a unit reaction of photosynthesis:

$$CO_2 + H_2O \longrightarrow (CH_2O) + O_2$$

Carbon dioxide and water are the chemical raw materials, and molecular oxygen is a byproduct.

What are the sources of the atoms in (CH_2O)? The equation shows readily that the C must come from CO_2. Also, the source of the hydrogen must be H_2O. But what serves as the oxygen source in the manufacture of (CH_2O)? Is it CO_2, or H_2O, or can it be either one?

The Oxygen Source

The source of oxygen has been discovered experimentally, with the help of an **isotope** of oxygen. Isotopes are variant forms of a chemical element, some found in small quantities in nature, others produced artificially by man. All isotopes of a given element have identical chemical properties but different physical properties. More specifically, the different isotopes of an element differ in mass. Such differences of "weight" make it possible to distinguish one isotope from another. In the case of oxygen, the ordinary form of the element is O^{16}; i.e., the atomic weight is 16. One of the isotopes of oxygen is O^{18}, with an atomic weight of 18. Such isotopic O^{18}, or simply O°, in effect is *labeled* oxygen. By virtue of its heavier atoms, it can be traced through any number of chemical reactions. For example, one may artificially prepare H_2O°, or water containing O° instead of ordinary oxygen. No matter what then happens to this water during chemical reactions, the fate of its labeled, identifiable oxygen can be followed precisely.

Water of this kind has actually been used to determine the oxygen source in the photosynthetic production of (CH_2O). A plant was given H_2O° instead of ordinary water as raw material. The problem was to find out whether the carbohydrate endproduct of photosynthesis then did or did not contain O°. The results (Fig. 13.14) suggested that the O° of H_2O° did *not*

FIG. 13.14 If a plant is given water in which the oxygen is isotopic, then the oxygen released during photosynthesis will be isotopic. This indicates that the oxygen source for the photosynthetic manufacture of carbohydrates is *not* water.

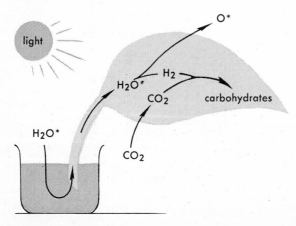

appear in the carbohydrate but appeared in the oxygen byproduct:

$$CO_2 + H_2O^* \longrightarrow (CH_2O) + O_2^*$$

Apparently, the oxygen of water is *not* the oxygen source in carbohydrate manufacture. *That oxygen source, instead, must be* CO_2.

The Fate of Water

In view of this conclusion, the last equation is unbalanced. CO_2 has *two* ordinary oxygens, but only *one* appears in (CH_2O). Moreover, the two O° atoms in the output (O_2°) obviously cannot result from the single O° supplied by H_2O° in the input. Since nature operates only via balanced reactions, the input clearly must be *two* H_2O° for every CO_2. We then obtain

$$CO_2 + H_2O^* + H_2O^* \longrightarrow (CH_2O) + O_2^* + H_2O$$

This must be the general balanced form of the input and output in actual photosynthesis. The fates of the various atoms here may be indicated as follows:

$$CO_2 + H_2O^* + H_2O^* \longrightarrow O_2^* + H_2O + (CH_2O)$$

In other words, of the atoms in (CH_2O), the C and O derive from CO_2 and the H_2 from the water in the input. All remaining atoms of the input form byproducts, namely, molecular oxygen and water. We note that, in normal photosynthesis, water is an output byproduct as well as an input raw material; twice as much water must be supplied as is actually used up (Fig. 13.15).

The conclusion that water supplies only its hydrogen and not its oxygen to carbohydrate manufacture leads to an important inference. Clearly, before water can contribute its hydrogen atoms, these atoms must first be separated from the oxygen. In other words, water must be *split* at some point during photosynthesis:

$$2\, H_2O \longrightarrow [2\, H_2] + O_2$$

$$CO_2 + [2\, H_2] \longrightarrow (CH_2O) + H_2O$$

The agencies at work in the water-splitting process can be identified in broad terms through a now classical type of experiment, the so-called *Hill reaction*. Leaves are dried and powdered, and the chloroplasts in this powder are isolated and cleaned. The pure chloroplast

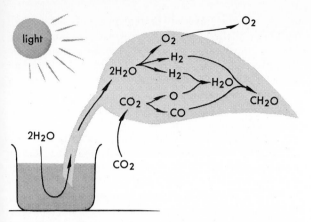

FIG. 13.15 The fate of the atoms of the raw materials required in photosynthesis. Water contributes only its hydrogen, and carbon dioxide contributes both its carbon and half of its oxygen, toward carbohydrate manufacture. The byproducts are molecular oxygen and half as much water as entered the photosynthetic process as raw material. Note that the equations in the diagram are balanced.

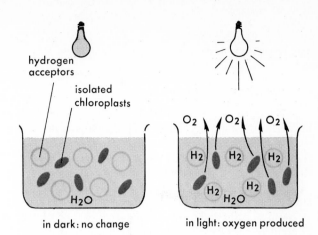

in dark: no change   in light: oxygen produced

FIG. 13.16 The functions of light and chlorophyll. Chloroplasts and hydrogen acceptors are suspended in water. In the dark, no change occurs (left). If the light is turned on, oxygen bubbles form (right). This indicates that water is split into H_2 and O in the chloroplasts, with the aid of light energy. Oxygen escapes (or may be captured by acceptors such as a haemoglobin), and hydrogen is picked up by the hydrogen acceptors.

preparation is then suspended in water to which are added certain iron salts as well as certain amounts of haemoglobin. The whole is now illuminated. The result: as soon and as long as the light is on, the chloroplasts actively release oxygen. Such oxygen combines with the haemoglobin present, forming oxyhaemoglobin. The amounts of oxyhaemoglobin, hence the amounts of oxygen released by the chloroplasts, can be measured (Fig. 13.16).

Since such an experiment does not involve living cells, carbohydrate production cannot be expected to occur and indeed does not occur. But the experiment does involve light, chloroplasts, and water, and this combination evidently remains functioning. The release of oxygen must mean that water is split into hydrogen and oxygen and that light energy and chlorophyll must be specifically associated with the splitting process. The iron salts in the experiment serve merely as acceptors or absorbers of hydrogen, just as haemoglobin serves as acceptor of oxygen.

We may conclude that *the function of light and of chlorophyll in photosynthesis is to promote a splitting of water.*

We may therefore conclude further that photosynthesis must consist of two main phases. The first may be termed **photolysis,** i.e., the splitting of water in the presence of light and chlorophyll. This must be followed by **CO_2 fixation,** i.e., the combining of the hydrogen produced by photolysis with the carbon and oxygen of CO_2 (Fig. 13.17). In chemical terminology, addition of hydrogen to a compound is one form of "reduction"; the second phase of photosynthesis may therefore be categorized specifically as a "reductive CO_2 fixation."

We shall now examine each of these two phases in greater detail.

FIG. 13.17 The general pattern of the two phases of photosynthesis: photolysis and CO_2 fixation. Both phases take place within the grana of chloroplasts.

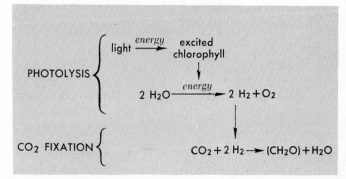

PHOTOLYSIS

IONIZED CHLOROPHYLL

What happens when light strikes a chlorophyll molecule? We already know that the energy of virtually all *but* the green light waves is absorbed. The result of this absorption of red and blue-violet light is that the chlorophyll molecule may *lose an electron.*

This physical event affects the structure of the atoms which make up a chlorophyll molecule. If such an atom absorbs light of sufficient energy, one of the orbital electrons may be displaced from its normal orbit and may fly off, away from the atom. Such an electron may be said to incorporate the energy of the light which the parent atom has absorbed; i.e., the electron is in a highly energetic state. Chlorophyll is so constructed that if it absorbs one *photon,* the smallest energy unit of light, then the molecule becomes *excited* and one electron may subsequently be dislodged from the molecule. Chlorophyll so may serve as an **electron donor.**

If we let the letters "Ch" stand for "chlorophyll," then the molecule minus an electron may be designated as Ch⁺, or *ionized* chlorophyll. The electron itself is e^- (see Chap. 2). Thus:

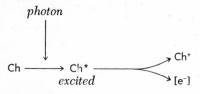

The photons in red light have just sufficient energy to excite and ionize chlorophyll. Blue-violet light is more energetic, but it can be shown that it ionizes chlorophyll to no greater extent than red light does. When blue-violet light is absorbed, some of this energy ionizes chlorophyll and the remainder merely dissipates as heat.

Many materials other than chlorophyll are known to be ionized readily by light. This phenomenon is the basis of the action of photoelectric cells, for example, of wide use in industry. But only excitation of chlorophyll specifically appears to be able to support the process of photosynthesis; another substance would not do. Indeed, if chlorophyll itself is to be useful in photosynthesis, it must be present in very specific states and forms. For example, there is some evidence that the

orderly, neatly layered arrangement of chlorophyll molecules in the grana may be of extreme importance. Efficient functioning of such molecules appears to be uniquely associated with their crystallike array in intact grana. If their internal structure is destroyed, the grana no longer mediate photolysis. Similarly, if chlorophyll is extracted from grana, the pigment is no longer effective as a photolytic agent.

Furthermore, chlorophyll *a* appears to be the specific pigment required for photolytic reactions. Other pigments are known to contribute to photolysis, but only indirectly.

For example, carotenoids absorb blue light (and therefore appear red-orange-yellow to the eye). The energy of this absorbed blue light may be transferred successively to other carotenoid molecules, then to chlorophyll *b,* and may eventually contribute to the excitation of chlorophyll *a.* Similarly, *r*-phycoerythrin of red algae absorbs blue light, and this energy may be transferred to chlorophyll *d* and from there to chlorophyll *a.* In all such serial transfers, chlorophyll *a* is always the last receiver of energy. Moreover, regardless of which other pigments absorb light, *only* excitation of chlorophyll *a* can promote photolysis directly; photosynthesis may occur in the absence of other pigments or other chlorophylls, but it cannot occur in the absence of chlorophyll *a.* Blue-green algae, it will be recalled, possess *only* chlorophyll *a,* and photosynthetic Protista and Metaphyta all possess various chlorophylls *as well as* chlorophyll *a.* This green pigment appears to be the universal key to photolysis. (Note that photosynthetic bacteria do not possess chlorophyll *a,* but they also do not photolyze: their hydrogen source is never water).

After a molecule of chlorophyll *a,* present in intact grana, has become excited by light and has served as an electron donor, it may function as an **electron acceptor;** i.e., ionized chlorophyll may recapture an external electron and once more become electrically neutral. For example, it may almost immediately recapture the same electron it originally lost. If this happens, the energy which the electron brings back to the molecule will be emitted again from chlorophyll, sometimes in the form of *heat,* sometimes even in the form of *light.* Such reradiation of originally absorbed energy is an instance of **fluorescence.** Chlorophyll is known to fluoresce to a very minor extent. It should be clear, however, that this cannot constitute the important photosynthetic function of chlorophyll; fluorescence simply means reversal of the original process of energy absorption, hence dissipation of energy into space without accomplishing useful work.

Rather, the importance of chlorophyll lies in its role as a donor of electrons which most often are *not* recaptured at once by chlorophyll. Nor indeed are these electrons allowed to fly off into free space; if that were to happen, their energy would likewise dissipate uselessly. Instead, the electrons are trapped within the grana of a chloroplast by various electron acceptors *other* than chlorophyll. These acceptors are normal organic constituents of cells generally, and they are known to function in serial succession: one acceptor captures an electron from chlorophyll and transfers it to a second acceptor; the latter then transfers the electron to a third acceptor; etc. In such serial transfers, *metabolic energy becomes available.* This may be envisaged roughly (but not quite correctly) by assuming that the electron is originally energy-rich and that it becomes de-energized progressively as it is transferred via the acceptors. The energy so obtained by electron transfer then becomes available within the chloroplast for the support of useful metabolic work—e.g., photosynthesis.

Thus *the basic role of light in photosynthesis is to supply* **physical** *energy which, via electron transfers away from chlorophyll, is then converted by graded steps into useful* **chemical** *energy.*

More specifically, two separate and alternative pathways of electron transfer away from chlorophyll are now known to exist. One pathway, which we may call *cyclic* electron transfer, leads to the formation of chemical energy only. The other pathway, designated as *noncyclic* transfer, results in the formation of both chemical energy and hydrogen. The latter subsequently enters the process of CO_2 fixation and contributes to food manufacture.

CYCLIC ELECTRON TRANSFER

In this pattern of transfer, an electron dislodged from excited chlorophyll is captured immediately by one of several possible first acceptors. Two vitamins or vitamin derivatives in particular are believed to serve as first acceptors. They are **vitamin K** and **flavin mononucleotide** (**FMN** for short). The latter is a derivative of *riboflavin*, or vitamin B_2. As we shall see in Chap. 16, both substances also play a role in respiration, where they act in essentially similar manner, i.e., in electron transfers. In photosynthesis, either vitamin K or FMN may accept an electron temporarily:

$$\text{light} \longrightarrow \text{Ch} \begin{array}{c} \nearrow [e^-] \\ \searrow \text{Ch}^+ \end{array} \quad \begin{array}{c} \text{vit. K or FMN} \\ \searrow \text{(vit. K or FMN)} \cdot e^- \end{array}$$

Subsequently, the electron may be "handed off" to a second acceptor. This second acceptor is actually a group of substances, collectively known as the **cytochrome system.** All members of this system are variants of a single chemical called *cytochrome.* It is a red, iron-containing tetrapyrrol pigment, structurally related to the haemoglobin of animal blood and to chlorophyll (see Chap. 4). Cytochromes occur in all cells and, like the vitamins above, they too play an electron-transferring role in respiration, as we shall see.

In the transfer of an electron from the first acceptors to the second, the energy of the electron is "stepped down," as it were, and the energy so made available is trapped by certain chemicals which become energy-rich as a result. In this manner, physical energy is converted into chemical energy. The detailed way in which this actually occurs is indistinguishable from the process of energy-trapping in respiration; we shall examine this process fully in Chap. 16. Here we may recall from Chap. 3 that the key energy-trapping reaction in cells involves the transformation of adenosine diphosphate (ADP) into adenosine triphosphate (ATP), according to the equation

$$\text{ADP} + \text{phosphate} + E \longrightarrow \text{ATP}$$

This equation symbolizes the energy-trapping reaction of both respiration and photosynthesis. Thus, in the transfer of one electron from vitamin K or FMN to the cytochromes, some energy becomes available and is incorporated into ADP and phosphate. One molecule of ATP is formed as a result:

$$\begin{array}{ccc} \text{(vit. K or FMN)} \cdot e^- & & \text{vit. K or FMN} \\ & \times & \\ \text{cytochromes} & & \text{cytochromes} \cdot e^- \\ & \downarrow \text{energy} & \\ \text{ADP} + \text{phosphate} & \longrightarrow & \text{ATP} \end{array}$$

The ATP so produced now is available in the chloroplast or the cell generally for the support of any energy-requiring activity. Evidently, sunlight provides cells with usable chemical energy in two ways. One involves complete photosynthesis, i.e., the manufacture of foods. After such foods are produced, they may be burned through respiration and supply energy by this means. The second way is more direct; as outlined above, it leads from sunlight via chlorophyll to the production of usable energy (ATP) before food manufacture is even completed. In this sense, the initial, light-requiring steps of photosynthesis anticipate, and play the same energy-supplying role as, respiration. We reach the important conclusion that *photosynthesis is as much an energy-supplying (i.e., ATP-supplying) process as it is a food-supplying process.*

After the cytochromes have accepted an electron and after ATP has been formed, the electron may be handed off in turn to a third acceptor. This third acceptor is *ionized chlorophyll* itself, which initiated the whole sequence by losing the electron to begin with. Two points may be noted here. First, in electron transfer from the cytochromes to ionized chlorophyll, the physical energy of an electron is stepped down still further and one additional ATP molecule is created:

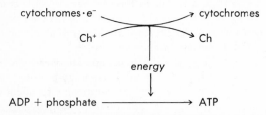

Second, by now regaining the electron it lost originally, the chlorophyll molecule ceases to be ionized and again becomes electrically neutral.

The net result of the whole sequence is that an electron has traveled in a complete cycle, from chlorophyll back to chlorophyll. But the electron which starts on such a cycle may be said to have been made energy-rich by light, and the electron which returns may be said to be energy-poor; the energy difference is incorporated into two molecules of ATP. It is this gain of ATP which makes the cycle metabolically valuable. As noted above, if the electron simply had been recaptured by chlorophyll immediately, chlorophyll would only have fluoresced and the potential available energy of the excited electron would have dissipated into space.

The whole cycle is outlined in Fig. 13.18.

NONCYCLIC ELECTRON TRANSFER

The cyclic pattern just described yields usable energy and so represents a valuable supplement to respi-

ration. But it does not yield the hydrogen essential for photosynthetic food manufacture. Such hydrogen is known to be supplied through a second, alternative pattern of electron transfer away from chlorophyll. This pattern is noncyclic; it differs from the first in that an electron dislodged from chlorophyll does not itself return to chlorophyll. Instead, ionized chlorophyll gains back its lost electron from another, independent source. That source ultimately is *water,* the raw material which also functions as the source of hydrogen in food production. Note that the description to follow is not exact in all details but merely outlines the pattern of events in general terms.

In water, some molecules normally always exist in ionized form, dissociated into hydrogen ions and hydroxyl ions:

$$H_2O \longrightarrow H^+ + OH^-$$

The positive charge on H^+ signifies that a unit of negative charge, namely, an electron (e^-), has been removed from a hydrogen atom. Analogously, the negative charge on OH^- signifies that an electron has been added to an OH group. In other words, for convenience of description we may envisage the ionization of water to involve the formation of three components:

$$H_2O \begin{cases} H \longrightarrow H^+ + e^- \\ OH \end{cases} \quad \text{or} \quad H_2O \begin{cases} [H^+] \\ [OH] \\ [e^-] \end{cases}$$

Each of these three components, viz., $[H^+]$, $[OH]$, and $[e^-]$, participates in the noncyclic pattern of photolysis here under discussion. First, the hydrogen ion $[H^+]$ does not remain "loose" in a chloroplast but becomes attached to a specific *hydrogen acceptor.* This acceptor is a derivative of a nucleotide and is called **triphosphopyridine nucleotide,** or **TPN** for short. All cells possess it, and it too serves in respiration as well, as we shall see. One molecule of TPN becomes associated with two hydrogens, and we may therefore consider that *two* water molecules have been ionized previously. Thus, as shown in Fig. 13.19, TPN becomes associated with two $[H^+]$, and $TPN \cdot [H^+]_2$ is formed.

Second, two $[OH]$ groups, also formed by the ionization of two water molecules, ultimately appear in the form of one molecule of water and one atom of free oxygen (see Fig. 13.19). The water molecule so produced adds to the water content of the cell as a byproduct, and the free oxygen, also a byproduct, may

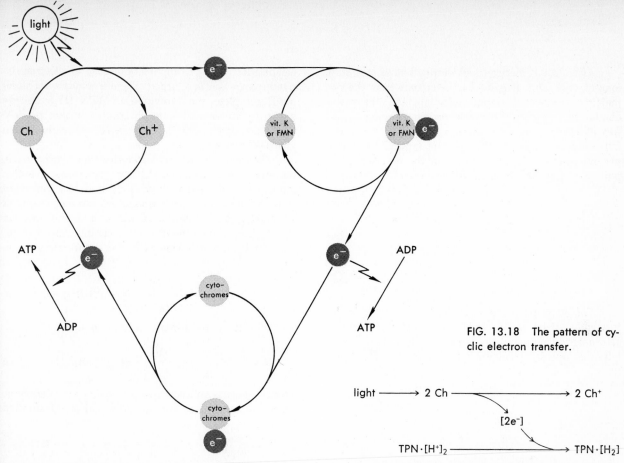

FIG. 13.18   The pattern of cyclic electron transfer.

$$\text{light} \longrightarrow 2\ \text{Ch} \longrightarrow 2\ \text{Ch}^+$$
$$[2e^-]$$
$$\text{TPN} \cdot [\text{H}^+]_2 \longrightarrow \text{TPN} \cdot [\text{H}_2]$$

escape as a gas (in the form of oxygen *molecules*, O_2). This is the source of the free oxygen which has long been known to be liberated in photosynthesis.

Third, the two electrons formed in the ionization of two water molecules do not remain loose either, but are captured by specific electron acceptors. The cytochromes, already encountered above, are again thought to serve in this particular electron-accepting role. As Fig. 13.19 indicates, a cytochrome·$2e^-$ complex is probably formed.

With the ionization products of water so accounted for, we may now consider the role of chlorophyll. As before, if chlorophyll is illuminated, an electron is dislodged from it. Let us assume that two chlorophyll molecules are illuminated simultaneously, each absorbing one photon. Two electrons are then freed. What happens to these electrons and how does ionized chlorophyll get electrons back?

The two excited electrons from chlorophyll are captured by the TPN·$[\text{H}^+]_2$ complex which, formed by ionization of water and being positively charged, may function as electron acceptor:

In other words, the two electrons combine with the two hydrogen ions associated with TPN, and electrically neutral TPN·$[\text{H}_2]$ is formed. *This substance is the hydrogen source for the later manufacture of carbohydrates.*

FIG. 13.19   The ionization products of water and the immediate fate of these products in the grana.

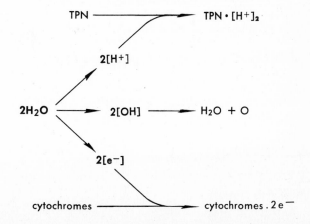

After losing electrons, chlorophyll does not stay ionized very long. It gains back electrons from the remaining product of water ionization, i.e., the cytochrome·$2e^-$ complex. Moreover, as this complex transfers its electrons to chlorophyll, energy becomes available; one molecule of ATP can be formed for every electron transferred, precisely as in the corresponding portion of the cyclic pattern discussed earlier. Thus,

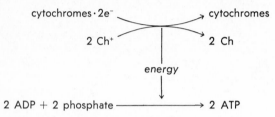

The whole sequence of reactions is now completed; it is summarized in Fig. 13.20. Note that the electrons returning to chlorophyll are not the same as those which left; the process is noncyclic. Note also that, for every

electron lost from chlorophyll originally, an electron derived from water is returned. The electrons from chlorophyll complete the formation of TPN·[H$_2$] already begun by water, and water in addition makes possible the return of electrons to chlorophyll, a reaction which yields ATP as well.

Figure 13.20 also indicates that, apart from ADP, the net input of materials into the whole reaction sequence is one molecule of TPN and two molecules of water; and that, apart from ATP, the net output is TPN·[H$_2$], one molecule of water, and one atom of free oxygen. Hence the entire process may also be summarized by the following balanced input-output statement:

$$2\,H_2O + TPN \xrightarrow[+\ chlorophyll]{+\ light} TPN \cdot [H_2] + O + H_2O$$

or, reduced to the arithmetical minimum,

$$H_2O + TPN \xrightarrow[+\ chlorophyll]{+\ light} TPN \cdot [H_2] + O$$

This in effect is an abbreviated statement of photolysis. Water is supplied as raw material and is transformed

FIG. 13.20 The pattern of noncyclic electron transfer.

into H_2 and free O. Thus water has been "split" under the influence of light and chlorophyll. Note here that water actually splits by ionizing and that the function of light energy, via chlorophyll, is to convert the ionization products into metabolically useful forms.

Inasmuch as electron transfer from chlorophyll may proceed either by the cyclic or by the noncyclic route, we may infer that both routes actually occur in living green cells. Presumably, any given single illuminated chlorophyll molecule may produce now electrons traveling cyclically, now others traveling noncyclically. Accordingly, in a chloroplast as a whole, multitudes of chlorophyll molecules at any given moment support the production of ATP, and other multitudes at the same time support the production of both ATP and $TPN \cdot [H_2]$.

With the formation of $TPN \cdot [H_2]$, the photolytic phase of photosynthesis may be regarded as completed. This product next enters the process of CO_2 fixation.

CO_2 FIXATION

THE PATTERN

Like the photolytic reactions, which are driven by the energy of light, the reactions which join hydrogen and CO_2 to yield carbohydrate do not take place by themselves; energy is required here as well. In CO_2 fixation, as in metabolic reactions of green cells generally, one source of usable energy is photolysis, as noted above. Another and probably the major source is *respiration*, i.e., the burning of foods.

An interesting consideration arises here. Since respiration burns foods and since all foods in a green cell are derived ultimately from the carbohydrates produced through CO_2 fixation, it follows that CO_2 fixation is both a requirement for and a consequence of carbohydrate manufacture (Fig. 13.21). Put another way, a portion of the harvest of photosynthesis, namely,

food, must be funneled back through respiration into the harvesting process itself, to make that process possible at all. Thus, it takes foods to get more foods.

Just as the use of isotopes has uncovered the occurrence of photolysis, so has this method helped to elucidate the mechanics of CO_2 fixation. Photosynthesizing plants were given artificially prepared C^*O_2. The carbon atom here was an isotope of ordinary carbon. The latter is C_{12} and the isotope used was C_{14}, 2 mass units heavier. At successive times during photosynthesis, plants using C^*O_2 as raw material were killed and their cells were analyzed for substances containing the isotope C^*. Since the plants must have manufactured such substances from the C^*O_2 given initially, this procedure could reveal not only the identity of the photosynthetic endproduct but also the sequence of reactions leading to the formation of that endproduct.

This sequence is now known in fairly complete detail. CO_2 fixation turns out to be a *cycle* of reactions, operating somewhat like an endless belt of an assembly line in a factory. As such a belt moves along, a steady stream of raw materials is funneled to it at one point, and these materials are processed by various workers or machines along the way. A stream of finished products then emerges at another point, and the empty portions of the belt return to the starting point, where they pick up new batches of raw materials. The general pattern of such a cycle, as it applies to metabolic events, is as follows:

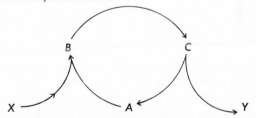

X and Y here are raw material and endproduct, respectively, and A, B, C represent the "endless belt" of chemicals which achieve the transformation of X into Y.

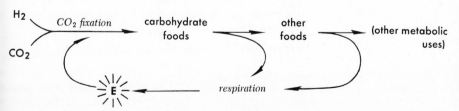

FIG. 13.21 Of the foods produced through CO_2 fixation, some may have to be burned through respiration to provide energy for continued CO_2 fixation and food manufacture. Note that such energy may also be provided by ATP formation in photolysis.

Note that such a cycle could include fewer or more than three reaction steps. Also, more than one raw material could be fed in, at one or at several points, and more than one endproduct could emerge. Note further that C "regenerates" A, an essential requirement if the reaction sequence is to be a continuously running cycle. As we shall see, many vital metabolic transformations occur through such cyclic sequences.

In CO_2 fixation, the reaction cycle consists essentially of three segments, as in the generalized diagram above. CO_2 is fed in between points A and B; hydrogen enters between B and C; and finished carbohydrate emerges between C and A, the segment which also regenerates the starting condition (Fig. 13.22).

Each of these segments consists of not a single reaction but a long series of interconnected reactions. As will be seen presently, energy to run the cycle is required in two of the segments. In all segments, each reaction must be catalyzed by a highly specific enzyme. Note in this connection that all reactions to be discussed below, like metabolic reactions generally, tend to be reversible, at least theoretically. They may proceed in either direction, and the same enzymes are required in each case (see Chap. 2). However, conditions in cells are normally such that, in certain processes, a given reaction proceeds preferentially or more completely in just one direction. This preferred direction will be indicated in the equations below.

The chemicals A, B, and C which form the cycle, all normal constituents of cells, are *phosphorylated carbohydrates*; i.e., they are characterized by the presence of phosphate, or $-\text{\textcircled{P}}$ groups (see Chap. 12).

FIG. 13.22 The general pattern of the CO_2-fixing cycle. In segment AB, CO_2 enters as raw material, and in segment BC, hydrogen enters as raw material. Segment CA yields the carbohydrate endproduct and regenerates the starting point A.

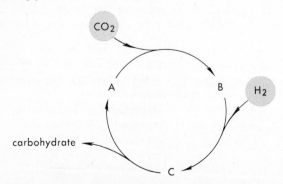

SEGMENT "AB"

The starting substance of the CO_2-fixing cycle is a phosphorylated carbohydrate called **ribulose diphosphate,** $\text{\textcircled{P}}-C_5H_8O_5-\text{\textcircled{P}}$, or **RDP** for short. This compound is a chemical derivative of the 5-carbon sugar *ribulose* $(C_5H_{10}O_5)$. In RDP, each end of the carbon chain carries one of the two $-\text{\textcircled{P}}$ groups:

RDP

As we shall see shortly, the CO_2-fixing cycle must run completely through three consecutive turns before a single molecule of carbohydrate endproduct is obtained. To condense the presentation of these reactions, we may add the three turns together, and instead of starting with one molecule of RDP and running the cycle three times, we may start with three molecules of RDP and run the cycle just once. Keep in mind, however, that a description of events in such terms is an artificial *summation* and does not correspond to the reaction sequence as it is actually believed to take place.

If, then, three molecules of RDP are assumed to be the starting point, the first step is a reaction of these three molecules with three molecules of CO_2, the first of the raw materials:

$$3\ \text{\textcircled{P}}-C_5H_8O_5-\text{\textcircled{P}} + 3\ CO_2 \longrightarrow 3\ \text{\textcircled{P}}-C_6H_8O_7-\text{\textcircled{P}} \quad (1)$$

The endproduct on the right simply incorporates all the atoms present on the left. As a result, the 5-carbon chain of each RDP molecule becomes lengthened into a 6-carbon chain by the addition of CO_2.

The endproduct on the right exists only for an exceedingly short time. It reacts immediately with three molecules of water, borrowed from the general cellular supply. "Borrowed" is the right word here, because the water will be returned in a later reaction, as we shall see. Thus,

$$3\ \text{\textcircled{P}}-C_6H_8O_7-\text{\textcircled{P}} + 3\ H_2O \longrightarrow 3\text{\textcircled{P}}-C_6H_{10}O_8-\text{\textcircled{P}} \quad (2)$$

The new endproduct is again a 6-carbon chain, and it still carries a $-\text{\textcircled{P}}$ group at each end. This substance is extremely unstable. It breaks up into two fragments, by a split through the middle of the 6 linked carbons. Each 6-carbon chain becomes *two* 3-carbon chains in this manner. Since three 6-carbon molecules are being split, six 3-carbon molecules will result:

$$3 \; \textcircled{P}\text{-}C_6H_{10}O_8\text{-}\textcircled{P} \longrightarrow 6 \; C_3H_5O_4\text{-}\textcircled{P} \qquad (3)$$

All the six 3-carbon molecules so formed are mutually identical, and each carries one $-\textcircled{P}$ group at one end of the molecule. This compound is called **phosphoglyceric acid,** or **PGA** for short:

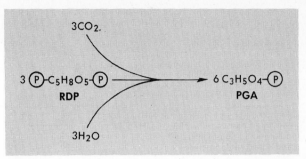

FIG. 13.23   Summary of segment *AB* of the CO_2-fixing cycle.

$-\textcircled{P}$, undergoes a structural simplification in a subsequent reaction in which it loses a molecule of water. Since this happens in six $C_3H_7O_4\text{-}\textcircled{P}$ molecules, six water molecules will appear as byproducts:

$$6 \; C_3H_7O_4\text{-}\textcircled{P} \longrightarrow 6 \; C_3H_5O_3\text{-}\textcircled{P} + 6 \; H_2O \qquad (5)$$

The H_2O so formed returns to the general supply of cellular water. This more than "pays back" the 3 H_2O "borrowed" earlier, in reaction 2 of the cycle. The excess, amounting to 3 H_2O, reduces the net water requirement for reaction 4. As noted above, 6 H_2O must be split in conjunction with photolysis to provide twelve H atoms. Reaction 5 now pays back three of the six water molecules used up in reaction 4, leaving a net water expenditure of 3 H_2O for every three CO_2 molecules fixed photosynthetically.

With the formation of 6 $C_3H_5O_3\text{-}\textcircled{P}$ in reaction 5, the second segment of the cycle is completed. The compound $C_3H_5O_3\text{-}\textcircled{P}$ is **phosphoglyceraldehyde, PGAL** for short. Its molecular structure is

The formation of PGA completes the first segment of the CO_2-fixing cycle. We may summarize the entire segment as in Fig. 13.23. Three molecules of RDP, reacting with three molecules each of CO_2 and water, have become six molecules of PGA; carbon dioxide has been effectively trapped, or "fixed."

SEGMENT "BC"

In a first reaction here, the PGA formed in the previous segment unites with hydrogen, the second raw material in CO_2 fixation. As noted earlier, this hydrogen has been produced by photolysis and is available in the form of $TPN \cdot [H_2]$. Thus it is $TPN \cdot [H_2]$ which actually participates in the reaction. This is also the first point in the cycle where energy is required; the transfer of hydrogen from $TPN \cdot [H_2]$ to PGA necessitates an expenditure of energy. Symbolically,

$$\left[6 \; H_2O + 6 \; TPN \xrightarrow{photolysis} 6 \; TPN \cdot [H_2] + 3 \; O_2 \uparrow \right]$$

$$6 \; C_3H_5O_4\text{-}\textcircled{P} + 6 \; TPN \cdot [H_2] \xrightarrow{energy} 6 \; TPN + 6 \; C_3H_7O_4\text{-}\textcircled{P}$$

$$(4)$$

Twelve hydrogen atoms, produced earlier by splitting of six water molecules in conjunction with photolysis, take part in this reaction. In other words, each of the six PGA molecules adds two hydrogen atoms to its structure.

The principal endproduct of the reaction, $C_3H_7O_4$

It will be noted that PGAL differs from PGA, which begins segment *BC*, only in that PGAL possesses one less oxygen atom. The events of segment *BC* may be summarized as in Fig. 13.24.

SEGMENT "CA"

Of the six molecules of PGAL just formed, *one* represents the net endproduct of photosynthesis as a

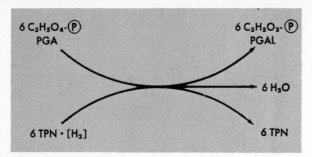

FIG. 13.24 Summary of segment BC of the CO_2-fixing cycle.

whole. Solar energy, grana, chlorophyll, photolysis, CO_2 fixation—all cooperate to yield this final result. A billion years of cellular evolution was needed to make that one molecule of PGAL, and on its foundation rests the whole living world. We shall discuss the fate and function of this molecule in the next section.

What of the remaining five PGALs? These undergo a long and intricate series of reactions in which their atoms become reshuffled extensively. Energy is required in these reorganizations, the second place in the cycle where energy must be expended. Also, one additional phosphate group enters the reactions, and this group displaces one of the hydrogens. The final result is the formation of three identical new molecules. In highly artificial, condensed form, we may summarize this sequence as in Fig. 13.25.

As a check of reaction 1 of the cycle will show, the three molecules of P–$C_5H_8O_5$–P resulting from segment CA are actually not new but are RDP. We note that the starting point of the cycle has been regenerated. In essence, therefore, the function of segment

FIG. 13.25 Summary of segment CA of the CO_2-fixing cycle.

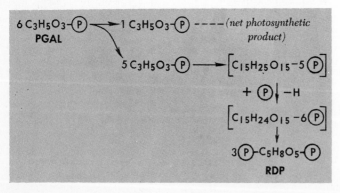

CA is to reorganize five 3-carbon chains (PGAL) into three 5-carbon chains (RDP).

The entire CO_2-fixation cycle is outlined in Fig. 13.26. From this figure, the total input and output may be seen to be

$$3\ CO_2 + 3\ H_2O + 6\ H_2 \xrightarrow[\ [-H]\ ]{[+\,\textcircled{P}\,]} C_3H_5O_3\text{-}\textcircled{P} + 6\ H_2O$$

or *net*

$$3\ CO_2 + 6\ H_2 \xrightarrow[\ [-H]\ ]{[+\,\textcircled{P}\,]} C_3H_5O_3\text{-}\textcircled{P} + 3\ H_2O$$

In other words, the three individual carbon atoms sup-

FIG. 13.26 Summary of CO_2 fixation as a whole. The reaction cycle is shown above, and the total input and output are indicated below.

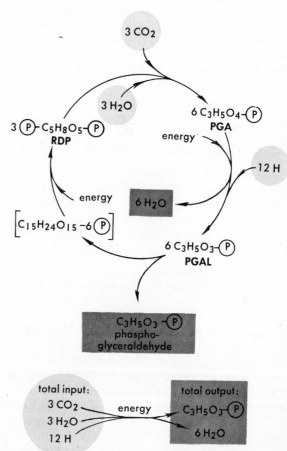

plied as *inorganic* raw material in the form of CO_2 emerge bound into a single *organic* molecule, PGAL.

THE ENDPRODUCTS

The principal endproduct of photosynthesis, PGAL, is a *food*. Indeed, a plant nourished artificially with prefabricated PGAL may survive without photosynthesis and without any other organic supplies.

As PGAL forms in the grana, it does not accumulate to any great extent. It rapidly undergoes one of three main fates: it may be used directly as a **nutrient** in the cell which produced it; it may be "packaged" for **export** to other cells; or it may be packaged for **storage.**

PGAL is usable immediately as a respiratory fuel. It may happen, therefore, that some of the PGAL just manufactured is burned at once to provide the energy for more CO_2 fixation. PGAL is also usable directly as a building material, and it may contribute to the construction of any of the innumerable structural components of plant cells. For example, PGAL just produced could be used to build anew or to repair some of the chemical machinery required for PGAL production itself: chlorophyll, or TPN, or RDP, or any one of the enzymes taking part in CO_2 fixation.

But a green cell generally manufactures much more PGAL than it requires for its own maintenance. The bulk of the photosynthetic product becomes available for export through the phloem, to root cells, stem cells, and nonphotosynthesizing cells in general. However, PGAL is not exported as such. It is probably too reactive a material. In transit from leaf to root, for example, it would react with other substances long before it could reach its destination. A less reactive, "packaged" form of PGAL would clearly be more advantageous. The green cell actually does package PGAL by converting it into sugars such as glucose, fructose, and sucrose.

In the conversion to glucose, for example, two molecules of PGAL are combined into one molecule of glucose. This is a reaction sequence of considerable importance in metabolism, and we shall deal with it in some detail in a later chapter. Here we merely outline it in abbreviated form (Fig. 13.27). We may note generally that, if carbohydrates are to be transported from cell to cell or from tissue to tissue, the vehicles are primarily sugars such as the above. These are less reactive than PGAL, hence they are not so likely to be altered chemically during transit. Since conversion to sugars (particularly sucrose) and export to other cells is

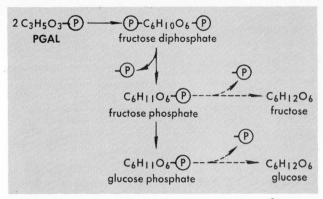

FIG. 13.27 Some of the steps in the metabolic conversion of PGAL to glucose. The detailed reaction sequence is given in Chap. 16, Fig. 16.15.

the fate of most of the photosynthesized carbohydrate, sugar is often, though not quite correctly, regarded as the primary endproduct of photosynthesis.

When sugars are absorbed by nonphotosynthesizing cells, they may first be rephosphorylated (see also Chap. 12) and in this form they may then be used directly in metabolism. Clearly, the green cells of a plant must in daytime manufacture enough PGAL for themselves, and must export enough sugar to all other cells, to suffice for a 24-hr period.

Actually, green cells normally produce so much PGAL that some of it may be stored. Storage occurs largely in roots and stem, but small amounts are generally stored in leaves as well. Like carbohydrate transport, carbohydrate storage does not involve PGAL as such. In any storage problem, two considerations are paramount: first, the stored material should take up as little space as possible, and, second, it should be "out of circulation," i.e., relatively unavailable for participation in persisting activities. Since PGAL reacts readily with cellular components in its vicinity, it would not remain out of circulation for long. Even glucose, though less reactive, would enter metabolic processes fairly rapidly. Moreover, both these carbohydrates take up considerable molecular space.

Plants have developed ways to "condense" PGAL molecules into more compact, sufficiently unreactive packets. This may take the form of **dehydration synthesis,** i.e., the joining together of two or more molecules accompanied by a simultaneous removal of water. For example, the green cell may first produce glucose from PGAL as above. Two glucose molecules may then

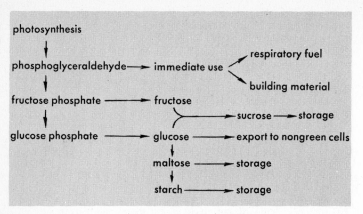

FIG. 13.28   The possible fates of PGAL.

be joined, and one water molecule is removed at the same time:

$$C_6H_{12}O_6 + C_6H_{12}O_6 \longrightarrow C_{12}H_{22}O_{11} + H_2O$$

The resulting 12-carbon carbohydrate is **maltose,** or malt sugar, a disaccharide (see Chap. 4). Maltose may now be stored as such, or pairs of maltose molecules may be combined and condensed further until up to several hundred glucose units have been joined into single large molecules such as *starch*. For example.

$$500\ C_6H_{12}O_6 \longrightarrow (C_6H_{10}O_5) \times 500 + 500\ H_2O$$

This starch molecule is smaller by 500 water molecules than 500 individual glucose molecules, and it is very much less reactive. It is therefore eminently suitable as a storage form of carbohydrates, and it is actually very common among plants. Starches, or, more precisely, **amyloses,** vary somewhat in composition; i.e., they may contain from about 300 to about 1,000 glucose units per molecule. The generalized formula for starch may be written $(C_6H_{10}O_5)_n$, where n is the number of glucose units per molecule. As will be seen in Chap. 16, starch may also be produced from glucose-phosphate directly, without an intermediate free glucose stage.

Maltose and starch are not the only storage forms of the photosynthetic product. Some plants build PGAL into storage fats (e.g., olive oil, castor oil, peanut oil;

also the oils of many algae). Other plants make a variety of storage sugars, fructose and sucrose in particular (see Fig. 13.27). Sugar cane and sugar beets, as well as many kinds of fruits, owe their sweetness to stored fructose and sucrose.

Storage syntheses of this sort occur both in green and in nongreen cells. In the latter, imported sugar is the starting material and nonpigmented plastids often are the sites of storage (see Chap. 4). Whenever a nongreen cell must draw on its stored reserves, the exact reverse of storage synthesis takes place. For example, starch may be converted into glucose by addition of water, or it may be phosphorylated directly and decomposed into glucose-phosphate.

The various possible fates of the photosynthetic endproduct are indicated in Fig. 13.28, and the pattern of photosynthesis as a whole is outlined in Fig. 13.29. Since *two* PGAL molecules are required to manufacture *one* glucose molecule, we arrive at the following overall input-output statement for the production of glucose:

$$6\ CO_2 + 12\ H_2O \longrightarrow C_6H_{12}O_6 + 6\ O_2 + 6\ H_2O$$

or, reduced to the mathematical minimum,

$$6\ CO_2 + 6\ H_2O \longrightarrow C_6H_{12}O_6 + 6\ O_2$$

Photosynthesis is a very efficient process. It has been estimated that, of all the light energy absorbed by chloroplasts, some 50 to 60 per cent is recovered as energy built into glucose. However, in terms of light energy absorbed by plants in a given surface area of the earth, photosynthesis is markedly less efficient. For example, the energy absorbed by a field of wheat represents only about 2 per cent of the total light energy delivered by the sun; chloroplasts are spread rather thinly over the whole field. Yet this 2 per cent of sunlight, produced by thermonuclear reactions 93 million miles away, constitutes the whole power source which, through photosynthesis, keeps living organisms alive.

Together with the other nutritional processes discussed earlier, photosynthesis provides the raw materials with which *individual* plant cells, green or not, carry out their metabolism. The animal equivalent of nutrition in plants will be examined in the next chapter.

FIG. 13.29   Overall summary of photosynthesis as a whole. In the portion of the diagram symbolizing photolysis, only the noncyclic electron-transfer sequence is indicated.

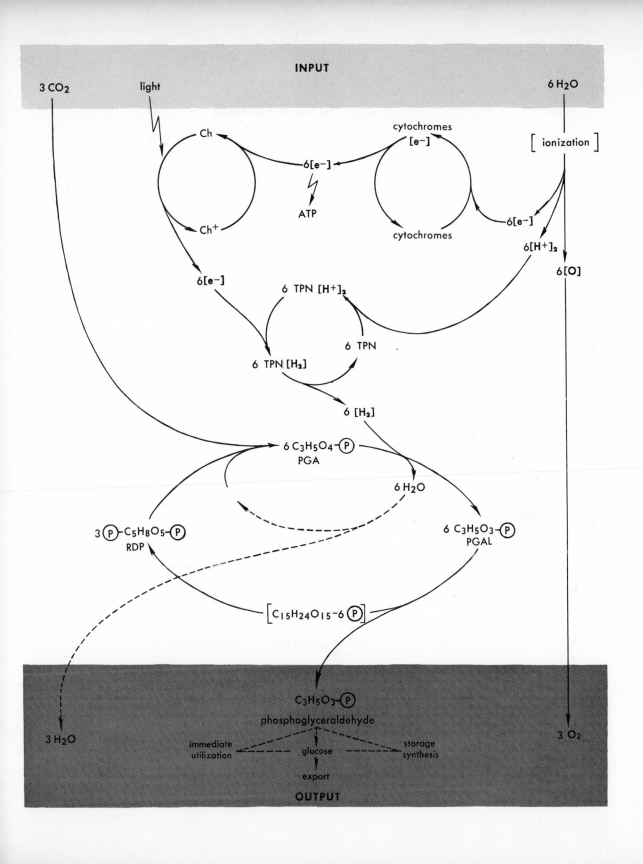

REVIEW QUESTIONS

1. Describe the mechanism of xylem conduction. What kinds of nutrients are transported in xylem and in which direction?

2. What is (a) root pressure, (b) transpiration? How are these forces generated? What roles do they play in xylem conduction? What is the importance of cohesion of water in xylem conduction?

3. What forces bring about phloem conduction? What kinds of nutrients are carried in phloem and in which direction? Describe in detail the processes which would bring about the upward translocation of a given nutrient.

4. If a cut length of stem bearing some leaves were put upside down into a glass of nutrient-rich water, how would (a) xylem conduction and (b) phloem conduction be affected? How has it been proved that phloem may transport in both directions? Can all phloem-transported substances migrate in either direction?

5. Distinguish between absorption, transmission, and reflection of light. What physical processes are implied in the statement "Chlorophyll is green"? What is the solar radiation spectrum and what physical attributes distinguish different portions of it? What is the visible spectrum and how is chlorophyll affected by visible light?

6. What is the general chemical structure of chlorophyll? What are plastids and what kinds are there? What is the internal architecture of chloroplasts?

7. State the general chemical nature and function of photosynthesis as a whole. Review the sources of the carbon, the hydrogen, and the oxygen atoms which compose photosynthesized carbohydrates. What experiments have demonstrated the derivation of the oxygen in such carbohydrates?

8. What are the functions of light and chlorophyll in photosynthesis? What experiments have demonstrated these functions? What are the general events in photolysis and CO_2 fixation?

9. Review the detailed sequence of events in photolysis. How is light energy trapped by chlorophyll and transferred into chemical processes? What is fluorescence? What are the light-trapping functions of carotenoids and of chlorophylls a and b? How is photolytically produced hydrogen transferred into CO_2-fixing reactions? What are the net input and the net output of photolysis?

10. Review the general pattern of CO_2 fixation. What are the major steps? What roles do phosphorylated carbohydrates play? What role does energy play in CO_2 fixation?

11. What are the starting materials and the endproducts of each of the three main phases of the CO_2-fixing cycle? For each phase, review the processes which bring about the conversion of starting material to endproduct. What are the net input and output of CO_2 fixation as a whole?

12. What is the principal net endproduct of photosynthesis as a whole? Review the possible fates of this endproduct. What are the main transportation and storage forms of carbohydrates in plants and how is the photosynthetic endproduct converted into these?

SUGGESTED COLLATERAL READINGS

The history of research on photosynthesis is excellently documented by a series of important original articles reprinted in the following book. Some of the articles describe key experiments referred to in this chapter.

Gabriel, M. L., and S. Fogel: Photosynthesis, in "Great Experiments in Biology," Prentice-Hall, Englewood Cliffs, N.J., 1955.

The following sources may be consulted for additional information on topics relating to plant nutrition:

Bassham, J. A., and M. Calvin: The Path of Carbon in Photosynthesis, in W. Ruhland (ed.), "Encyclopedia of Plant Physiology," vol. V, part 1, Springer, Berlin, 1960.

Calvin, M.: The Photosynthetic Cycle, University of California Research Laboratories, vol. 2924, 1955.

Ferry, J. F., and H. S. Ward: "Fundamentals of Plant Physiology," Macmillan, New York, 1959.

Harrison, K.: "A Guide Book to Biochemistry," Cambridge, New York, 1959.

Hill, R., and C. P. Whittingham: "Photosynthesis," Wiley, New York, 1955.

Meyer, B. S., D. B. Anderson, and R. H. Böhning: "Introduction to Plant Physiology," Van Nostrand, Princeton, N.J., 1960.

Various aspects of plant nutrition are discussed in the following articles:

Arnon, D. I.: The Chloroplast as a Complete Photosynthetic Unit, *Science*, vol. 122, 1955.

————: The Role of Light in Photosynthesis, *Sci. American*, vol. 203, 1960.

Aronoff, S.: Chlorophyll, *Botan. Rev.*, vol. 16, 1950.

Evans, R. M.: Seeing Light and Color, *Sci. American*, vol. 181, 1949.

Fogg, G. E.: Nitrogen Fixation by Blue-Green Algae, *Endeavour*, vol. 6, 1947.

————: Nitrogen Fixation, *New Biol.*, vol. 18, 1955.

Frank, C.: Carotenoids, *Sci. American*, vol. 194, 1956.

Greulach, V. A.: The Rise of Water in Plants, *Sci. American*, vol. 187, 1952.

Hambidge, G.: "Hunger Signs in Crops," American Society of Agronomy, Madison, Wis., 1941.

Hudson, J. P.: Plants and Their Water Supply, *Endeavour*, vol. 16, 1957.

Kamen, M. D.: Discoveries in Nitrogen Fixation, *Sci. American*, vol. 188, 1953.

Milner, H. W.: Some problems in the Large-scale Culture of Algae, *Sci. Monthly*, vol. 80, 1955.

Syrett, P. J.: Transpiration, *New Biol.*, vol. 25, 1958.

Thimann, K. B.: Autumn Colors, *Sci. American*, vol. 183, 1950.

Thomas, J. B.: Chloroplast Structure and Function, *Endeavour*, vol. 17, 1958.

ANIMAL NUTRITION

14

Being a heterotroph, specifically a chemoorganotroph, an animal requires inorganic as well as prefabricated organic nutrients from its environment. We shall be particularly concerned in this chapter with complexly structured holotrophic animals, in which nutrient procurement is accomplished by **alimentation,** and nutrient transport by short-distance conduction as well as by **circulatory systems.** As shown in Chap. 11, alimentation in most cases takes place in a tubular alimentary tract which contains a mouth for ingestion, an intestine and often also other structures for digestion, and an anus for egestion. Usable nutrients obtained by digestion are absorbed through the wall of the intestine into the circulatory system. Nutrient transport in this system may occur indirectly via a **liver,** as in vertebrates and some other metazoan groups; or, where a liver is absent, transport may be direct from intestine to other tissues. These various processes are controlled and coordinated by nerves, by muscles, and in vertebrates, also by hormones.

ALIMENTATION

THE NUTRIENTS

We have found in the preceding chapter that a plant cell may survive if it is given water and minerals and if it is supplied with or is allowed to photosynthesize organic carbon. From these three categories of nutrients, a plant cell is able to construct all the other components of its substance. But if an animal cell is given only these three types of nutrients, it soon dies; for it requires four additional types of nutrients which, unlike the plant cell, it cannot manufacture on its own.

First, water, minerals, and photosynthesized organic carbon do not provide usable organic nitrogen required for the construction of proteins and nucleic acids, for example. In simple form, organic nitrogen may be represented by the amino group, —NH$_2$, and plants are able to make —NH$_2$ out of mineral nitrates (Chap. 12). But even though nitrates are available to them, animals cannot convert these ions into —NH$_2$. Their cells therefore must be supplied with prefabricated —NH$_2$ or other forms of usable organic nitrogen. Plants or other animals which have eaten plants must be the source of supply.

Second, plants can convert phosphoglyceraldehyde (PGAL) or glucose or other forms of organic carbon into all the vitamins they require. Animals cannot do likewise. Most animals do manufacture at least some of the vitamins, although in many cases only in inadequate quantities. Specific abilities here vary with the species, but no species is as self-sufficient in this regard as a green plant. Missing vitamins consequently must be supplied in prefabricated form and plants are again the ultimate source of supply.

Third, unlike plants, animals are unable to convert organic carbon into all two dozen or so kinds of amino acids needed for protein manufacture (see Chap. 4). Depending on the species, eight or ten kinds, so-called "essential" amino acids, must be supplied in prefabricated form, and plants are the ultimate suppliers here as well.

Fourth, again unlike plants, many animals are unable to convert organic carbon into all necessary kinds of fatty acids. Accordingly, various "essential" fatty acids must be obtained ready-made from plants.

The minimum nutrient supplies to an animal cell must therefore include at least seven types of materials: *water, minerals, organic carbon, organic nitrogen, vitamins, essential amino acids,* and *essential fatty acids.* Evidently, animals cannot survive without plants, which provide five of these seven items (Fig. 14.1).

This reduced manufacturing ability of animal cells probably may be explained on an evolutionary basis. Laboratory experiments have shown that the synthesizing capacities of organisms are affected greatly by gene mutations. If such random hereditary changes occur in an animal, certain metabolic reactions may be blocked and the manufacture of given nutrients may then no longer be possible. But the animal may still survive. Being a heterotroph, it may obtain the missing nutrients in prefabricated form from plants or other animals. Thus, in the course of evolution, different animal species may have developed different deficiencies in synthesizing ability, yet could compensate for this by eating plant-derived foods. Plants under analogous circumstances would die out, for if an autotroph can no

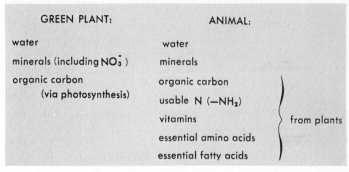

FIG. 14.1 A comparison of minimum nutrient requirements of plants and animals.

longer manufacture a vital nutrient, it has no other means to obtain it. All surviving autotrophs therefore are without synthesizing deficiencies, but surviving heterotrophs are variously characterized by species-specific metabolic inabilities.

If an animal could obtain all the nutrients it requires in the form of pure, immediately usable ions and molecules, it would not need an alimentary system. It could then simply acquire such nutrients from the environment by direct absorption through its cell surfaces. As noted in Chap. 12, this is actually the nutritional pattern in many saprotrophic and symbiotic heterotrophs. But, apart from water and minerals dissolved in water, directly usable nutrients in ionic and molecular form are largely unavailable to free-living holotrophic animals. What a holotroph requires is plant or animal matter in *bulk,* living or dead. And it is the principal function of an alimentary system to separate bulk nutrients into individual ions and molecules directly usable by cells.

This is accomplished by digestion. *Mechanical digestion* first subdivides ingested materials into fine particles suspended in water, and *chemical digestion* then reduces these particles to molecular dimensions. In the process, usable ions and molecules become separated out and more complex molecules are broken up into smaller, usable ones. In this chemical dissolution of bulk foods, *digestive enzymes* secreted by *digestive glands* play important roles, as we shall see.

Digestion produces a food solution in which three groups of substances may be found. First, it includes nutrients which animal cells require but cannot manufacture on their own. These comprise water, minerals, and the five categories of plant-derived substances listed above. Second, it includes nutrients which *can* be manufactured by animal cells but, since eaten food generally supplies them, need not be manufactured. For example, animal cells may manufacture various carbohydrates and fats from organic carbon, but they may not need to do so if carbohydrates and fats are included in eaten food. And third, the food solution usually contains indigestible or otherwise unusable materials. Plant cellulose, for example, is a common indigestible component of bulk foods. Substances in this last category are eliminated or *egested* (Fig. 14.2).

What are the details of these alimentary processes, particularly as they occur in vertebrates such as man and other mammals?

INGESTION: HUNGER

What prompts us to eat *what* we eat? What makes us decide *how much* to eat? As yet, neither question can be answered fully. The first focuses attention on the nature and control of *appetite* and is much more difficult to answer than the second, which raises the problem of the nature and control of *hunger*.

The brain unquestionably plays an important role in appetite control, just as, in mammals, this organ is now known to control the *amount* of food eaten. According to an early popular hypothesis, the stomach was believed to regulate the quantities of food consumed. Muscular contractions of an empty stomach were thought to give rise to sensations of hunger, and a hungry animal was assumed to eat until its stomach

was filled. Such filling then was believed to stop the hunger pangs, hence also food intake. But this hypothesis, still widely quoted among nonbiologists, turned out to be untenable long ago; even after surgical removal of the entire stomach, hunger sensations nevertheless continue to come and go as before. Moreover, a "stomach hypothesis" of hunger control does not account for chronic overeating or undereating.

A better explanation has emerged from experiments which have revealed the existence of special eating-control centers in the mammalian brain. In a brain region known as the *hypothalamus* (see Chap. 22), two such centers have been identified. One is a **hunger center.** When it is stimulated, it sends out nerve impulses to various parts of the body, which cause the animal to eat. The other is a **satiety center** which, when stimulated, makes the animal refuse food. In test rats, tiny electrodes have been used to stimulate one or the other of these centers continuously. The result of such tests has been that the treated animals either overeat and become extremely obese or undereat and starve amidst a plentiful food supply. Evidently, the amount of food a mammal normally eats is determined by the commands the hunger and satiety centers send to the body.

But how do these centers decide whether to send a command "eat" or a command "do not eat"? Experiments have shown that *blood glucose* is the critical agent which stimulates one or the other of the eating-control centers. As we shall soon see, glucose circulat-

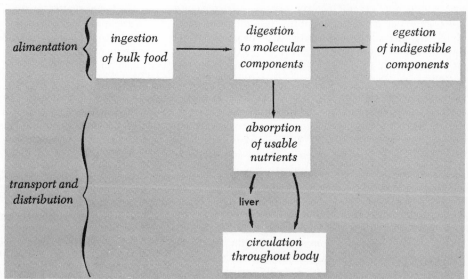

FIG. 14.2 The general pattern of animal nutrition.

ing in the blood is a very sensitive indicator of the hour-by-hour nutritional state of the body. Shortly after a meal, the glucose concentration in the blood tends to rise. Long after a meal, blood-glucose levels tend to fall. If blood reaching the brain contains too much glucose, then the satiety center probably becomes selectively sensitive to this high glucose level and issues the command "do not eat." Conversely, low glucose levels probably stimulate the hunger center selectively, resulting in the command "eat" (Fig. 14.3).

It should be clear that any condition which directly or indirectly influences glucose delivery to the brain, or affects the operation of the brain centers as such, is bound to affect food intake. Dozens of such conditions may actually do so. Proper glucose delivery depends, for example, on normal digestive processes, normal liver function, normal blood circulation, and normal hormone balances. As we shall see, all of these factors affect glucose metabolism profoundly. If, through disturbances in any of these functions, the brain receives consistently false information about the actual glucose supplies in the body, then consistent overeating or undereating may result.

Moreover, the brain centers are themselves subject to faulty operation. And they are influenced by a large variety of psychological factors, by reflexes, and by habits of long standing. They are also influenced by inherited genetic constitution, which, in the final analysis, governs the detailed operation of the body, in all its aspects. Clearly, if the brain centers receive correct information but interpret it incorrectly, or interpret correctly but send out faulty commands, then abnormal food intake may again be the result.

We note that whether or not to eat, a seemingly simple decision, actually is determined by a multitude of interdependent, interacting internal processes. It is therefore not surprising that, as is well known, practically *any* disturbance of *any* body function has an effect on food intake.

Granting that desired kinds and appropriate amounts of food are being ingested, what happens to such food in its passage through the alimentary canal?

DIGESTION: ENZYMES

Digestion in different parts of the alimentary tract is achieved either by *mechanical* means or by *chemical* means or by both. Mechanical digestion, carried out mainly by teeth, tongue, and the muscular grinding action of the stomach, achieves a progressive physical

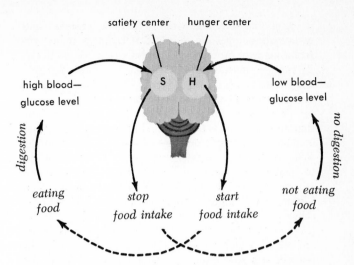

FIG. 14.3   The control of food intake. Desire or lack of desire for food is governed by the satiety (S) and hunger (H) centers of the brain, which in turn respond differentially to the glucose concentration in blood.

breakdown of bulk food. In parallel with this, chemical digestion occurs.

No matter where they occur or what foods are involved, all instances of chemical digestion are reactions of the same common type: **enzymatic hydrolysis.** "Enzymatic" implies that the reaction is accelerated by an enzyme, and "hydrolysis," that the reaction is one of dissolution or decomposition, *water* being the dissolving agent. A generalized digestive reaction may be written

$$\text{food} + \text{H}_2\text{O} \xrightarrow{\;enzyme\;} \text{food components}$$

In most animals, digestive enzymes are *extracellular* enzymes; i.e., they are produced within cells but they are secreted and function outside cells. This puts them into a special category, for virtually all other enzymes in an organism are intracellular and function within cells. Moreover, digestive enzymes are relatively unusual also in that many of them may act on entire categories of chemicals. For example, digestive *lipase* promotes the decomposition of fat into fatty acids and glycerin:

$$\text{fat} + \text{H}_2\text{O} \xrightarrow{\;lipase\;} \text{fatty acids} + \text{glycerin}$$

Here the lipase may be effective with any kind of fat, regardless of which specific types of fatty acids a fat is composed of. Analogously, certain protein- and carbohydrate-digesting enzymes decompose many *different* kinds of proteins and carbohydrates, respectively. By contrast, most other, intracellular enzymes are highly specific and each is effective only in reactions involving one particular type of molecule (see Chap. 2).

The reason for this broader effectiveness of some digestive enzymes is that many different food molecules contain groups of atoms which are arranged in the same way. For example, in a fat, fatty acids are linked to glycerin in a certain fashion (see Chap. 4). The enzyme lipase acts specifically on this type of link. Lipase may therefore aid in the digestion of any substance in which such a link is present, namely, *any* fat (Fig. 14.4). In a protein, similarly, various amino acids are joined together by peptide bonds. Digestive proteinases act specifically on such bonds. Because the bonds occur in all types of proteins, proteinases may aid in the decomposition of all of these. In general, we may say that digestive enzymes, like all other enzymes, act specifically on particular chemical bonds; and because certain kinds of bonds are common within broad categories of food molecules, digestive enzymes are broadly effective.

FIG. 14.4   The group specificity of lipase. This enzyme specifically attacks the bonds between glycerin and fatty acids, regardless of whether the carbon chains of the fatty acids are short, long, or intermediate in length. Hence lipase may digest fats of all kinds. Group specificity of this sort also characterizes several other digestive enzymes.

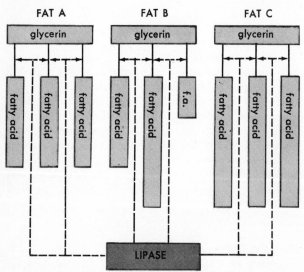

Note, incidentally, that it is never an enzyme itself which accomplishes digestive decomposition. Enzymes only increase the *speed* of digestion or other reactions (see Chap. 2). As just pointed out above, it is *water* which brings about food decomposition and the function of digestive enzymes is to accelerate the process very greatly. Note further that, like all enzymes, digestive ones likewise operate best at particular temperatures and pH. As we shall see, appropriately acid, alkaline, or neutral conditions are maintained in the different portions of the alimentary tract where enzymes are at work.

Note, finally, that digestive breakdown of a food molecule often is the exact reverse of the synthesis of that molecule. For example, the digestion of fat yields fatty acids and glycerin; the synthesis of fat requires the joining of fatty acids and glycerin. In general,

$$X + H_2O \xrightleftharpoons[\substack{(enzymatic\ dehydration) \\ synthesis}]{\substack{decomposition \\ (enzymatic\ hydrolysis)}} \text{parts of } X$$

The same enzyme promotes the reaction in either direction; we already know that an enzyme does not determine the direction of a chemical process (see Chap. 2).

ORAL DIGESTION

In the mouth, tongue and teeth initiate mechanical digestion, and, in man, **saliva** mixed into the food mass initiates chemical digestion.

Saliva is manufactured in three pairs of salivary glands, which connect with the mouth by ducts (Fig. 14.5). Salivary secretion is started reflexly. That is, when food comes into contact with the tongue and the lining of the mouth, nerve endings are stimulated. These transmit nerve impulses to the brain, and the brain in turn sends impulses to the salivary glands. The latter respond by secreting saliva (Fig. 14.6). As is well known, smell, sight, or mere thought of food may start the flow of saliva. This is brought about by *conditioned reflexes* (see Chap. 22); pleasant past experiences with food here have the same effect as actual food in the mouth. It is also well known that emotions may influence salivation.

Saliva contains water, a variety of inorganic ions, mucus proteins, and two digestive enzymes, **salivary amylase** and **salivary maltase** (Fig. 14.7). The whole mixture is chemically neutral or very slightly alkaline

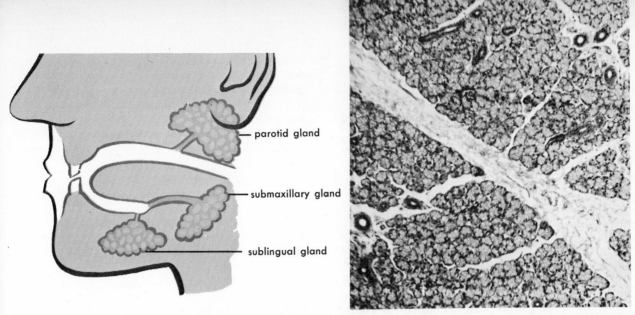

FIG. 14.5 The diagram indicates the location of the salivary glands in man; the photo depicts a section through one of these glands. Note the connective tissue (light areas in photo) which traverses the gland and binds groups of gland cells together. Note also the several small salivary ducts (dark rings). *(Photo courtesy of Dr. B. J. Serber, College of Medicine, New York University.)*

FIG. 14.6 The salivary reflex. Food in the mouth stimulates nerve endings, and sensory impulses travel to the brain. This organ interprets the impulses and sends command impulses to the salivary glands. These then begin to secrete saliva. The diagram illustrates the nature of reflexes generally, and it may be noted here that many other digestive processes are controlled by reflexes of this sort. Nerve impulses are sent to particular brain centers, and command signals then go from there to appropriate responding organs.

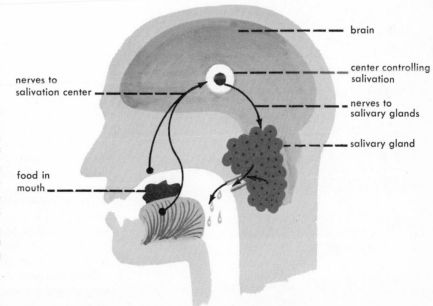

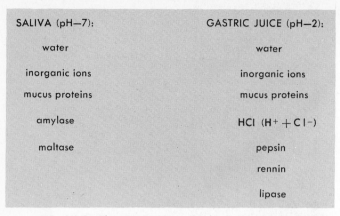

SALIVA (pH—7):	GASTRIC JUICE (pH—2):
water	water
inorganic ions	inorganic ions
mucus proteins	mucus proteins
amylase	HCl (H+ + Cl-)
maltase	pepsin
	rennin
	lipase

FIG. 14.7 The composition of saliva and of gastric juice.

FIG. 14.8 In the pharynx, the food channel crosses the air channel. When a person swallows, the larynx is raised up against the epiglottis. This blocks the air channel into the trachea and normally prevents food from going the wrong way. *(Model designed by Dr. J. F. Mueller, Ward's Natural Science Establishment, Inc.)*

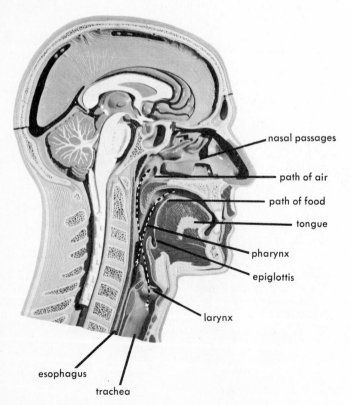

or acid. From a mechanical standpoint, saliva keeps oral membranes moist and lubricates food for easier passage through the throat. From a chemical standpoint, the two enzymes promote the preliminary digestion of eaten carbohydrates. If starch or glycogen or other polysaccharides are eaten, salivary amylase accelerates their conversion into disaccharides or monosaccharides:

$$\text{polysaccharides} + H_2O \xrightarrow{\textit{amylase}} \text{maltose, glucose}$$

If malt sugar is eaten or is produced as above by oral digestion of polysaccharides, then it may be converted to glucose with the aid of salivary maltase:

$$\text{maltose} + H_2O \xrightarrow{\textit{maltase}} \text{glucose}$$

Since food does not remain in the mouth very long, and since brief periods of chewing do not always bring saliva into intimate contact with every part of a bite of food, oral carbohydrate digestion usually takes place only to a superficial degree. But saliva mixed into the masticated food is carried along into the stomach, and it is there that most of the digestive action of saliva occurs. Since only amylase and maltase are present in saliva, this fluid does not initiate digestion of foods other than carbohydrates.

From the mouth proper, food passes into the **pharynx** (Fig. 14.8). This is a cavity where the food channel crosses the air channel which leads from the nasal passages to the windpipe. A slitlike opening into the windpipe, the **glottis**, is formed by a pair of ligaments which may meet along the midline and close up the orifice. Closure is effected during swallowing, when food crosses the air channel—unless one tries to swallow and exercise one's voice at the same time.

The pharynx connects with the **esophagus,** a tube leading to the stomach. A bite of food is moved through the esophagus by the muscles in its walls. When food touches the walls, nerve endings in them are stimulated. Nerve impulses are sent from there to the brain, and returning impulses bring the esophageal muscles into action. These muscles constrict the esophageal tube behind a ball of food, and a wave of constriction then travels toward the stomach, carrying food before it. Such a constriction progressing in wave fashion is called **peristalsis**. The direction of esophageal peristalsis may on some occasions be reversed, as is the case in vomiting.

GASTRIC DIGESTION

The stomach is a highly muscular organ located immediately under the rib cage, slightly on the left side (Fig. 14.9). The esophagus enters roughly at midregion, called the **cardiac** region of the stomach. To the left of this is the pouchlike **fundic** region and to the right, nearest the intestine, is the **pyloric** region.

When balls of food arrive in rapid succession, most of them are pushed into the fundic part, where they are stored temporarily. The cardiac and pyloric portions are the work regions of the stomach; they are kept filled only partially. If too much is eaten at one meal, the cardiac and pyloric parts as well as the fundus fill up, and indigestion may result.

The stomach completes mechanical and continues chemical digestion. **Gastric juice** plays a role in both. Sight, smell, and thought of food, which initiate salivary secretion by conditioned reflex, may at the same time initiate gastric secretion. Moreover, actual food in mouth or esophagus reflexly stimulates the stomach. As a result of these nervous effects, gastric juice is already flowing to some extent even before food has arrived. A more copious flow is produced once food comes into direct contact with the stomach lining. This mechanical stimulation also initiates the production of **gastrin,** a hormone. Stomach cells in contact with food release gastrin, and the hormone is picked up by blood vessels and is distributed throughout the body. When some of the hormone returns to the stomach and reaches the specialized cells capable of manufacturing

FIG. 14.9 The parts of the stomach. Note the peristaltic constriction in the esophagus, pushing food before it.

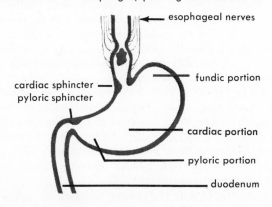

esophageal nerves

cardiac sphincter
pyloric sphincter

fundic portion

cardiac portion

pyloric portion

duodenum

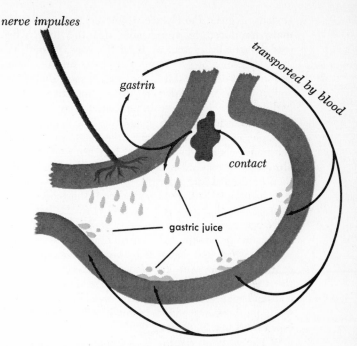

nerve impulses

gastrin

transported by blood

contact

gastric juice

FIG. 14.10 The three processes by which the stomach lining may be stimulated to secrete gastric juice: (1) by mechanical contact with food; (2) by nerve impulses from the brain; and (3) by the hormone gastrin. Released from the stomach lining by contact with food, gastrin returns via the blood stream to other parts of the stomach, stimulating secretory cells there.

gastric juice, these cells are activated. Evidently, gastric secretions may be started and maintained by three types of stimuli, namely, nervous, mechanical, and chemical ones (Fig. 14.10).

Gastric juice is a mixture of water, mineral ions, mucus proteins, *hydrochloric acid* (present in the form of ions, H^+ and Cl^-), and three enzymes, *pepsin, rennin, and lipase* (see Fig. 14.7). By virtue of the presence of HCl, the whole is very strongly acid—pH 2, approximately. Different sets of cells in the stomach lining secrete the acid and the enzymes.

Hydrochloric acid macerates and breaks down food molecules in the same way that any strong acid decomposes substances on which it is spilled. Tough fibrous material in plant and animal food is loosened; the cement between cells is eroded; and the food mass literally falls apart. It may be asked why hydrochloric acid does not act similarly on the stomach wall itself.

It does, if given the chance. However, the acid is normally produced in appreciable quantity only when food is actually present or is on the way. Second, the mucus proteins of gastric juice coat the stomach lining and protect it. And third, the acid is soon diluted by water in food. But despite these protective factors, hydrochloric acid (and gastric enzymes) may sometimes be secreted in excessive quantity. This happens, for example, by continued nervous stimulation of the stomach under chronic emotional stress, when food may not always be present. Portions of the stomach wall may then be eroded and a gastric ulcer may result.

In parallel with acid maceration, the food mass is thoroughly churned and ground by the powerful muscular action of the stomach wall. This action is essentially peristaltic, the constricting waves traveling both forward and backward. Also, strong stationary contractions may cut into food at different levels of the stomach. This rather violent combined action of acid and muscular grinding reduces solid food to fairly small particles suspended in fluid. All further breakdown is chemical.

The enzyme **pepsin** is secreted in the form of *pepsinogen*, an enzymatically inactive molecule. In the presence of hydrogen ions from HCl, pepsinogen is converted to active pepsin. This conversion is thought to be an "unmasking" process, in which pepsinogen splits into active pepsin and a smaller molecular fragment:

$$\text{pepsinogen} \xrightarrow{H^+} \text{pepsin} + \text{fragment}$$

Once some pepsin has so formed, it may itself convert more pepsinogen into pepsin:

$$\text{pepsinogen} \xrightarrow{pepsin} \text{pepsin} + \text{fragment}$$

Secretion of inactive pepsinogen and conversion to active pepsin in the stomach cavity protect the stomach wall; if active pepsin were secreted as such, this strong enzyme might digest the very cells which produce it rather than food.

In the acid medium of the stomach cavity, active pepsin accelerates the breakdown of proteins into free amino acids. But during the relatively short time of stomach digestion, pepsin usually cannot act long enough to reduce all proteins in food to amino acids. Many protein molecules are broken up only partially into variously long polypeptide chains. A good many proteins usually escape peptic digestion altogether, for pepsin may not reach all the food particles present.

Rennin is an enzyme unique to mammals. It acts specifically on *caseinogen*, the protein of milk. Secreted as inactive *prorennin* and converted to the active state by hydrogen ions, rennin splits caseinogen into two smaller proteins, *casein* and *whey*. In the presence of calcium ions (e.g., from milk), casein then coagulates, or *curdles*, and this protein curd subsequently may be digested by pepsin. The entire sequence is

$$\text{prorennin} \xrightarrow{H^+} \text{rennin}$$

$$\text{caseinogen} \longrightarrow \text{casein} + \text{whey}$$

$$\xrightarrow{Ca^{++}}$$

$$\text{curd} \longrightarrow \text{peptic digestion}$$

The presence of a special enzyme aiding the digestion of milk is a useful mammalian adaptation. Milk is the first and for sometime the only food of a young mammal. But milk is a liquid and its proteins are present in dissolved form. Therefore, milk would pass through the stomach as quickly as water and pepsin could not act on it for any length of time. The rennin mechanism, however, coagulates milk, and the now solidified, curdled milk proteins do stay in the stomach long enough to permit appreciable peptic digestion.

Lipase in the stomach digests fats into fatty acids and glycerin. Much of the gastric lipase is not actually produced in the stomach but is regurgitated from the intestine. Gastric fat digestion is particularly superficial. As we shall see presently, thorough breakdown of fats requires bile and an alkaline environment. Neither of these exists in the stomach. Moreover, fats do not mix with water, and lipase, which is present in water, therefore does not readily reach the interior of large drops of fat. Consequently, gastric lipase acts largely on fats which are already divided up into fine colloidal droplets, e.g., the fat in milk or in cheese or in mayonnaise.

Since gastric juice does not contain carbohydrases, the only carbohydrate digestion in the stomach is that brought about by saliva carried down from the mouth. Even this stops fairly soon, for in the highly acid medium of the stomach salivary enzymes cannot long remain active.

By the time food is ready to leave the stomach,

it is a semifluid macerated mass containing some digestion products: a certain amount of glucose, fatty acids, glycerin, and polypeptides. But most carbohydrates, most fats, and a considerable portion of the proteins in food have so far not been digested.

The openings into and out of the stomach are guarded by **sphincters,** ring-shaped muscles which on contraction close off the connecting tubes (see Fig. 14.9). As food comes from the esophagus into the stomach, the *cardiac sphincter* opens reflexly. While gastric digestion proceeds, both the cardiac and the *pyloric sphincter* are closed. But some 20 to 30 min after a meal is eaten, a first lot of the food in the stomach is already digested and may be ready for passage into the intestine. The pyloric sphincter then opens, letting digested food out. Thereafter this sphincter closes until more food is to be expelled into the intestine. In this way, the stomach empties gradually. In man, complete gastric digestion of an average meal may take 3 to 4 hr.

INTESTINAL DIGESTION

The long, much-coiled **small intestine** extends from the stomach to the juncture with the shorter **large intestine,** so called because of its greater diameter (Fig. 14.11).

The uppermost foot or so of the small intestine is the **duodenum** (Fig. 14.12). In this section adjoining the stomach, the most important digestive fluids are mixed with food as it enters. These fluids are **intestinal**

FIG. 14.11 Abdominal dissection, man. A few of the coils of the small intestine are shown in the right portion of the photo; parts of the thicker large intestine are on the left side and just above the small intestine. Note that what appears on the left in the photo is on the right of the body. (Photographic Department, Rhode Island Hospital.)

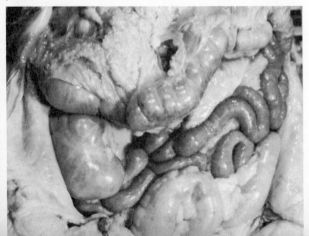

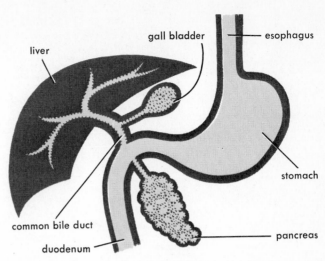

FIG. 14.12 The duodenal region, diagrammatic.

juice, bile, and **pancreatic juice.** As they and food are slowly propelled through the length of the small intestine by peristalsis, chemical digestion is carried to completion.

Intestinal juice is secreted by specialized glands in and just under the lining of the duodenum (Fig. 14.13). Secretion is started by contact of food with this lining. Under the influence of HCl carried over from the stomach, the duodenal wall also manufactures **secretins,** a group of hormones. Picked up by blood, these hormones are distributed through the body. Two organs respond to them: the *liver* and the *pancreas.* Stimulated by secretins, liver cells secrete bile. Excess bile produced at other times may have been stored in the gall bladder, an organ which may contract and expel some of its store. Ducts from both liver and gall bladder join into a *common bile duct* and bile passes through it into the duodenum (see Fig. 14.12). Secretins also stimulate cells in the pancreas. Pancreatic juice flows through a *pancreatic duct* into the duodenum, entering near the opening of the bile duct (Fig. 14.14).

Thus the appearance of food in the duodenum triggers, directly through contact, the secretion of intestinal juice and, indirectly through secretins, the arrival of bile and of pancreatic juice within a short time. All three fluids are alkaline, and, mixed with food, they soon abolish the acidity of the gastric product. All three fluids contain water, inorganic ions, and mucus proteins. In addition, they contribute a number of other agents, as indicated in Fig. 14.15.

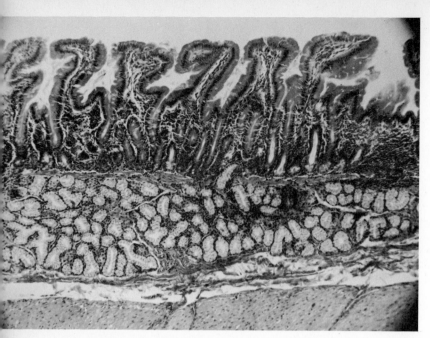
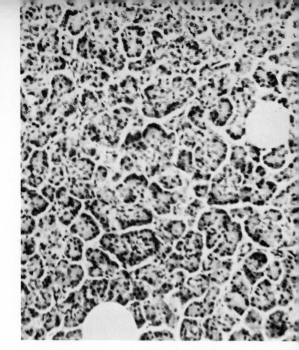

FIG. 14.13   Left, cross section through the wall of the duodenum. The cavity of the gut is toward the top. Underneath the folded inner surface tissues of the gut, note the glandular layer. Its secretion is discharged into the gut cavity and contributes to the composition of intestinal juice. Right, section through the pancreas. The large round spaces in the photo are sections through branches of the pancreatic duct. (Left, General Biological Supply House, Inc.; right, courtesy of Dr. B. J. Serber, College of Medicine, New York University.)

FIG. 14.14   The secretin mechanism. Contact of gastric HCl in food with the lining of the duodenum leads to the secretion of the hormone secretin. This hormone travels via the blood stream to the liver and the pancreas, where it stimulates the secretion of bile and of pancreatic juice, respectively.

FIG. 14.15   The composition of intestinal juice, bile, and pancreatic juice.

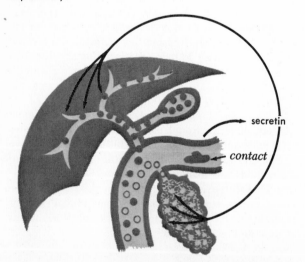

INTESTINAL JUICE	BILE	PANCREATIC JUICE
enterokinase	bile salts	trypsinogen
amino-peptidase	bile pigments	chymotrypsinogen
di-peptidase		carboxy-peptidase
disaccharases		amylase
amylase		lipase
lipase		

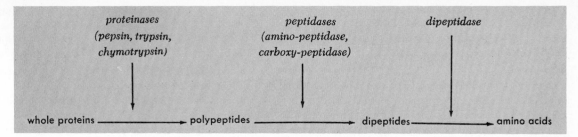

FIG. 14.16   Summary of the pattern of protein digestion.

Protein Digestion

This is accomplished with the aid of *trypsinogen,* *chymotrypsinogen,* and the three *peptidases* listed in Fig. 14.15.

Trypsinogen and chymotrypsinogen are inactive enzymes. Their secretion in inactive form protects the pancreas and the pancreatic duct from being digested. Conversion to the active enzymes takes place in the duodenum. When trypsinogen and chymotrypsinogen arrive in the duodenum, intestinal juice is already flowing and **enterokinase** is therefore available. This substance is an enzyme but not a digestive enzyme. It acts on a few trypsinogen molecules and transforms them into active trypsin. Enterokinase so initiates the formation of trypsin. In turn, trypsin now activates all remaining trypsinogen, producing more trypsin, and acts on chymotrypsinogen, producing active chymotrypsin:

$$\text{trypsinogen} \xrightarrow{\;+\,enterokinase\;} \text{trypsin}$$

$$\text{trypsinogen} \xrightarrow{\;+\,trypsin\;} \text{trypsin}$$

$$\text{chymotrypsinogen} \xrightarrow{\;+\,trypsin\;} \text{chymotrypsin}$$

Active trypsin and chymotrypsin digest whole protein molecules to polypeptides, like pepsin in the stomach. Accordingly, whole proteins which have escaped gastric digestion are now broken up in the intestine.

At this stage, the *amino-peptidase* from the intestinal juice and the *carboxy-peptidase* from the pancreas enter the digestive reactions. These enzymes accelerate the further decomposition of any polypeptides present in the gut. Amino-peptidase attacks one type of bond in amino acid chains; carboxy-peptidase attacks another. The result of their action is the appearance of *dipeptides,* molecules consisting of only two joined amino acids.

Finally, the *dipeptidase* from intestinal juice re-duces all the dipeptides to individual amino acid molecules. Dissolved in the food solution, these are the usable nutrients which the animal body obtains by subjecting eaten whole proteins to step-by-step digestion. The whole sequence of protein digestion is summarized in Fig. 14.16.

Carbohydrate Digestion

Pancreatic and *intestinal amylase* have essentially the same action as salivary amylase. Since food remains longer in the gut and is more finely divided than in the mouth, polysaccharide digestion here is more thorough. Disaccharides form. These, as well as disaccharides eaten as such or produced by salivary digestion, are converted to monosaccharides by the *disaccharases* of intestinal juice. For example, intestinal *maltase* splits malt sugar into two glucose molecules; *sucrase* (also called *invertase*) splits cane sugar into glucose and fructose; *lactase* splits milk sugar into glucose and galactose. Added to whatever glucose has formed by salivary digestion, these and other monosaccharide sugars are the usable nutrients obtained from complex carbohydrates. The whole digestive sequence is outlined in Fig. 14.17.

Note that quite a number of complex carbohydrates cannot be digested by mammals at all. For ex-

FIG. 14.17   Summary of the pattern of carbohydrate digestion.

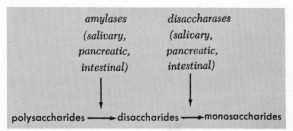

ample, cellulose passes through the alimentary tract unchanged, the molecule being too complex for attack by the amylases. Note also that, unlike the proteinases, the amylases are not secreted in inactive form but are immediately active as produced. Protection of the secreting glands and ducts is evidently not required, probably because animal tissue generally does not contain more than 1 per cent carbohydrate. Moreover, most of this carbohydrate is accumulated in the interior of cells, where it is beyond the reach of the extracellular, amylase-containing juices which flow by along the cell surfaces.

Fat Digestion

This is accomplished efficiently only in the presence of **bile salts.** Like soap, these complex organic salts reduce the surface tension of fat and so produce a fine colloidal emulsion of fat in water. Since fat does not dissolve in water and since fat-splitting lipase *is* dissolved in water, digestion can occur only at the boundary of water and fat. The larger the boundary surface, therefore, the more thorough will be digestion. By producing a colloidal suspension, bile salts increase the available fat-water surface tremendously. Even so, only about one-half of all ingested fat is digested chemically. The remainder stays in the form of finely divided whole fat.

Fat which is digested chemically is split by *intestinal* and *pancreatic lipase* into fatty acids and glycerin. These two types of molecules, produced in part also in the stomach, plus the undigested colloidal whole fat, represent the usable nutrients obtained from eaten fat. Bile salts may combine with fatty acids into complexes which are utilized more readily than fatty acids alone. The sequence of fat digestion is summarized in Fig. 14.18.

Bile pigments do not appear to have any digestive function. They are metabolic wastes produced in the liver as byproducts of the destruction of red blood corpuscles. Brownish green or greenish yellow in color,

FIG. 14.18   Summary of the pattern of fat digestion.

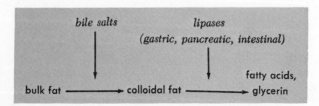

bile pigments enter the gut as components of bile. They are eliminated with the indigestible remains, to which they give their characteristic color. Some quantities of bile pigments do not go through the gut but are picked up from the liver and gall bladder by the blood and are transported to the kidneys. Excreted from there, the pigments are responsible for the characteristic color of urine. When the gall bladder or the bile ducts are blocked by gallstones, bile dams up and cannot reach the intestine. Fat digestion is then impaired. Moreover, bile pigments are absorbed in excessive amounts by the blood and, carried in part into the skin, produce jaundice. In birds, bile pigments may be excreted by being incorporated into the shells of eggs. For example, the blue color of robins' eggs is due to chemically modified bile pigments.

The chemical aspects of digestion as a whole are summarized in Fig. 14.19.

ABSORPTION

As more and more usable nutrients are liberated by intestinal digestion, food becomes increasingly fluid. The resulting solution is kept continuously agitated by two processes.

Peristalsis is one of these. A peristaltic wave may sweep forward for a short distance at some section of the small intestine, then may stop, and another wave may traverse the same or an even longer section. Stationary contractions may occur. Whole loops of the intestine may contract and shift and slide over other loops. Then forward peristalsis may again take place. As these movements proceed all along the gut, they keep food moving and churning and bring it thoroughly into contact with the mucosa, i.e., the tissue lining the interior surface of the gut (see Chap. 5).

The mucosa is the second agency which keeps the food solution in motion. This tissue is greatly folded and is formed into millions of near-microscopic *villi*, fingerlike protrusions which produce a velvety, carpetlike texture. By virtue of the folds and the villi, the surface area of the mucosa is exceedingly large. And the villi move continuously from side to side, stirring the food solution and circulating it thoroughly about the mucosal lining.

Such churning of food by peristalsis and the action of the villi is advantageous for two reasons. First, churning mixes and remixes food with the digestive juices, allowing the chemical breakdown of virtually all potential food substances present. Second, agitation

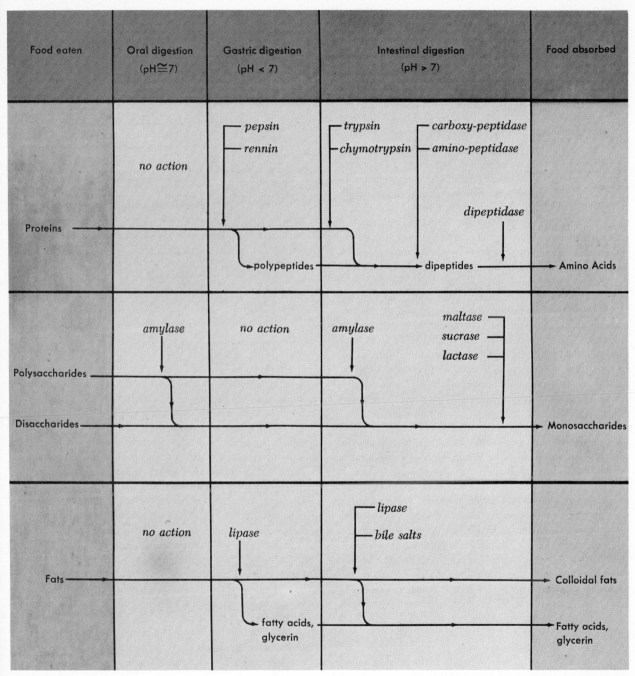

FIG. 14.19 Overall summary of digestion.

brings food into contact with different regions of the intestinal lining, a necessary condition if thorough *absorption* of food is to occur. The large area of the lining clearly facilitates this.

Absorption brings about a transfer of usable nutrients into the transport system, the circulating blood and lymph. A few substances, alcohol, for example, can be absorbed through the stomach wall, but most foods are absorbed through the intestine. Here nutrients must first be transferred from the gut cavity into the cells of the mucosa, and these lining cells then must release the food compounds into the deeper submucosa where blood and lymph vessels are situated.

In line with the pertinent discussion in Chap. 12, absorption of nutrients into the mucosa includes osmosis of water, diffusion of materials dissolved in water, and selective absorptive work by mucosal cells. The selective action of the mucosa is illustrated well by the different rates with which foodstuffs are absorbed. For example, glucose, galactose, and fructose all have the same molecular size and composition, namely, $C_6H_{12}O_6$; yet of these three 6-carbon sugars, galactose is absorbed most rapidly, fructose least rapidly. Moreover, sugar molecules containing only 3, 4, or 5 carbon atoms, though smaller than the 6-carbon molecules, are generally absorbed much more slowly, if at all. Mucosal cells evidently "recognize" and select among the substances present in digested food.

As in sugar absorption elsewhere, uptake of this food at the surfaces of mucosal cells is similarly accompanied by *phosphorylation*. When sugar is subsequently secreted from mucosal cells into the deeper tissues of the gut wall, *dephosphorylation* occurs and free sugar is re-formed. Phosphorylation does not take place in the absorption of other usable nutrients. Water, minerals, amino acids, and vitamins diffuse through the mucosa unchanged. Similarly, colloidal fat droplets, still undigested chemically, as well as fatty acids and glycerin, are passed as such through the mucosa and reappear on the other side. There some of the fatty acids and the glycerin may recombine immediately into whole fats. This increases the amount of colloidal fat transported away from the gut (Fig. 14.20).

During the 4- to 8-hr stay of food in the small intestine, this organ absorbs most of the minerals and the usable organic nutrients—monosaccharides, amino acids, fatty acids, glycerin, colloidal whole fat, and vitamins. The small intestine removes relatively little water from the food solution. On the contrary, by pouring digestive juices into the gut cavity, it actually

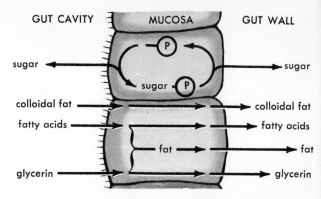

FIG. 14.20 The pattern of absorption of sugars and lipids through the intestinal mucosa. Note that absorption of sugars involves chemical reaction. This is also true for fatty acids, which combine chemically with bile salts during absorption.

adds water to food. Water is absorbed primarily in the large intestine.

EGESTION

Intestinal peristalsis occurs in such a way that, over a period of hours, food is slowly shifted into the lower part of the gut. Most of the water, some of the mineral ions, and all the indigestible and unabsorbable materials eventually move into the large intestine, also called the **colon**. The first portion of this section of the alimentary tract is the **caecum**, a blind pouch which, in man and a number of other mammals, carries a terminal fingerlike extension, the **appendix** (Fig. 14.21). In many herbivorous mammals (e.g., rodents), the caecum is extremely large. It serves as a temporary food-storage pouch and provides additional time for digestion, an advantage in a plant-eating animal. At the far end, the large intestine joins the **rectum**, a short tube opening to the outside through the **anus**.

The large intestine has a dual function. First, it is an *absorbing* and *excreting* organ. During the 10- to 12-hr stay of materials in the colon, the bulk of the water and the remaining inorganic nutrients are absorbed. At the same time, many metabolic wastes, and inorganic substances present in the body to excess, are excreted into the colon cavity. We note that, by differentially absorbing from and adding to the materials in the gut cavity, the large intestine aids in maintaining a properly balanced internal composition of the body. That the colon actually does regulate the internal water balance, for example, is indicated by the familiar upset conditions of diarrhea and constipation.

Second, the large intestine initiates *decay* of indigestible and unabsorbable materials. This is brought about by dense, permanent populations of bacteria, which live in the gut as symbionts. These microorganisms obtain food from many of the materials the host cannot digest or absorb. As a result of the nutritional activities of the bacteria, the substances in the colon undergo rapid decay. Frequently, the bacteria release byproducts of their own metabolism, and some of these byproducts may be nutrients usable by the host. Vitamins are among them. Mammals actually obtain an appreciable fraction of their vitamin supply from the intestinal bacteria.

After passing through the large intestine, what is left of the original eaten food is largely *roughage:* tough fibers, gristle, pieces of cellulose, and unmac-

FIG. 14.21 Abdominal dissection, man. Portions of the large intestine are shown on the left of the photo and toward the top. The rounded termination of the large intestine, near left bottom, is the caecum, a blind pouch. Attached to it is the appendix (white arrow). *(Photographic Department, Rhode Island Hospital.)*

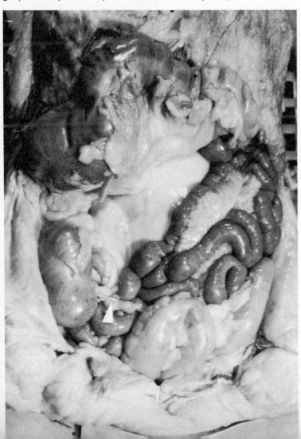

erated plant tissue, all suspended in more or less reduced quantities of water. Mixed with this are bile pigments, colon excretions, bacteria and bacterial products, and whatever else may have been added or left over in the passage of food through the gut. These **feces** ("dregs") are in a more or less advanced state of decay, and they are ultimately egested as semisolid masses.

The first phase of nutrition, alimentation, is now completed. Water, minerals, and the necessary organic nutrients have been absorbed, have been moved through the intestinal mucosa, and are ready to be transported throughout the body.

TRANSPORT AND THE LIVER

TRANSPORT PATHWAYS

In each villus of the intestinal wall are small branches of the two parts of the long-distance transport system of the body: capillaries of the blood-carrying *circulatory* channels and capillaries of the *lymph* channels (Fig. 14.22). Blood is pumped to the intestine through a few large arteries, which then branch out in the gut wall into extensive networks of microscopic capillary vessels (Fig. 14.23). The gut wall thus contains a rich supply of circulatory channels and blood reaches into all intestinal villi, where it comes close to the mucosal cells.

Here blood picks up most of the nutrient compounds already absorbed through the intestinal mucosa: water, minerals, vitamins, monosaccharides, amino acids, and fatty acids and glycerin. Colloidal droplets of whole fat, being enormously larger than molecules, cannot enter the blood capillaries in the villi. As we shall see presently, the fat droplets are transported instead by the lymph system.

In their short-distance transfer into the blood, nutrient compounds must pass from the intestinal tissues through the walls of the blood capillaries. These capillary walls are exceedingly thin, consisting of a single layer of greatly flattened cells. To a great extent, nutrient transfer through such cells is brought about by diffusion, but active absorption by the capillary walls undoubtedly plays a role as well. Within blood, the nutrients are carried as dissolved ions and molecules.

Food-laden blood now leaves the intestine. The capillaries in the gut collect into larger vessels, these join and rejoin, and a single very large channel even-

FIG. 14.22 The villi of the intestine and a detailed diagrammatic representation of a single villus. Of the nutrients absorbed through the layer of mucosal cells, whole fats (open circles) collect in the lacteal of a villus and are transported from there through the lymph system. Other nutrients (black dots) are picked up by the blood stream.

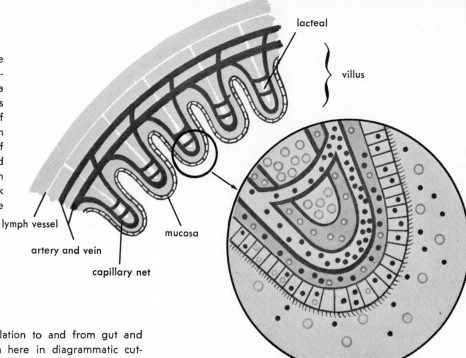

FIG. 14.23 The blood circulation to and from gut and liver. The intestine is shown here in diagrammatic cutaway view to indicate the path of blood. Flow direction of blood is indicated by arrows.

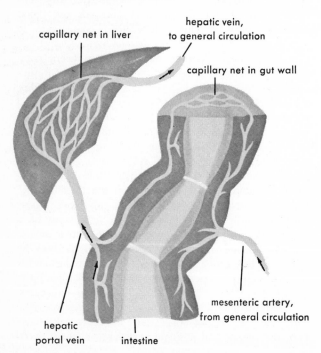

tually emerges from the whole intestine: the **hepatic portal vein.** This vessel leads directly into the liver (see Fig. 14.23).

Whatever nutrients are not or cannot be transported to the liver in this fashion are collected by the lymph system. Among such nutrients are mainly the colloidal whole fats, but also water, minerals, and variable quantities of other substances which may have escaped transport by blood.

The lymph system (Fig. 14.24) compensates for the "leakiness" of the blood circulation. As blood flows in its closed network of vessels, it loses a certain amount of fluid through the thin walls of the capillaries. This escaped fluid, consisting principally of water, mineral ions, and molecular organic nutrients, is lymph. It is responsible for the moist condition of all body tissues. Note here that a leaky blood circulation is not an instance of faulty engineering. On the contrary, fluid escape from capillaries is an adaptive necessity, for this is how the blood ultimately provides the cells of the body with water and all other necessary supplies.

But blood vessels would soon run dry if fluid losses were not made up. This is where the lymph

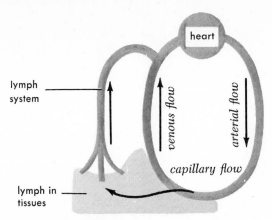

FIG. 14.24 The pattern of the lymph circulation of the body, diagrammatic. Fluid (lymph) escapes from the blood capillaries into the tissues of the body (large arrow at bottom of figure) and returns via lymph vessels into the blood circulation.

system comes into play. Tiny lymph capillaries originate in all parts of the body, intestine included, and they pick up any free fluid in the tissues. Lymph capillaries then join into progressively larger, progressively fewer ducts until a single large channel is formed. This channel empties into a vein in the left shoulder region, and so it returns to the blood all the fluid lost originally.

The lymph capillaries which originate in the intestine are called **lacteals.** One lacteal is situated in each villus (see Fig. 14.22). Also present in a villus is intestinal lymph, fluid which has become mixed with the nutrients supplied by the intestinal mucosa. Most of these nutrients enter the blood stream, as noted. But all others, including chiefly the colloidal whole fats, remain in lymph and so pass into the lacteal. After a heavy meal, the lacteals may become milky white from the large quantities of emulsified fat suspended in them. From the lacteals, nutrients are transported through the larger lymph vessels of the body and eventually into the blood. The whole fats are then carried by the blood into the principal fat-storing regions of the body, as we shall see. Accordingly, the fats largely bypass the liver. But any other nutrients eventually do circulate via the blood into the liver, where they join those already carried in over the more direct route of the hepatic portal vein.

In the liver, the hepatic portal vein breaks up into a very extensive network of capillary channels (see Fig. 14.23). Every liver cell so comes into contact with incoming blood. The cells absorb blood-borne nutrients, process them, and return the finished products to the blood in the capillary channels. The channels ultimately join and form larger vessels, and these finally empty into a single large duct, the **hepatic vein.** Blood in this vein carries all liver-processed foods away from the liver into the general body circulation. In this manner, nutrient supplies reach all parts of the body.

The principal pathways of nutrient transport are summarized diagrammatically in Fig. 14.25. We now inquire what happens to food molecules during their stay in the liver.

THE ROLE OF THE LIVER

Representing the largest gland of the body (Fig. 14.26), the liver has been estimated to carry out some 200 separate functions. Many of these are not concerned directly with nutrient transport, but the many that are make the liver the principal receiving station, processing plant, warehouse, distributing organ, and traffic control center, all rolled into one. Liver cells regulate not only what kinds but also what quantities of nutrients are sent out into body tissues. They carry out numerous chemical transformations of incoming materials, and they serve as storage depots for some of them. Through such quartermastering activities, the liver plays a major role in the maintenance of optimal working conditions throughout the body.

The adaptive advantage of an organ such as the liver is evident. No matter when or at what regular or irregular intervals an animal eats, the liver collects most of the food as it is absorbed from the gut and then releases it into the body at a pace adapted to the particular requirements of the moment. Therefore, whereas the metabolism of other animals reaches peaks just after food has been eaten, the metabolism of animals with livers may remain at a continuously steady level.

We may regard the liver as one side of a vast balance. The other side of the balance is the remainder of the body, and blood serves as carrier, signal mechanism, and general connecting link between the two sides (Fig. 14.27). Nutrients coming or not coming from the gut into the liver may shift the balance one way; nutrients used up or not used up by the body tissues may shift it the opposite way. These balancing processes operate through chemical equilibria. They normally adjust in such a manner that the original balance is maintained or, if upset, reattained.

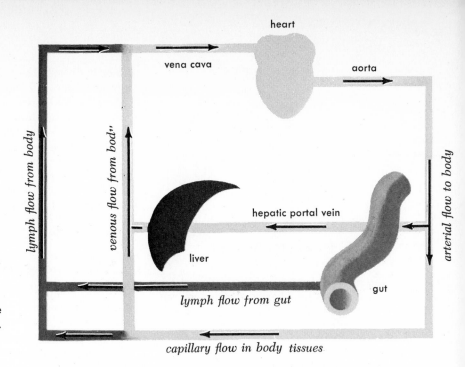

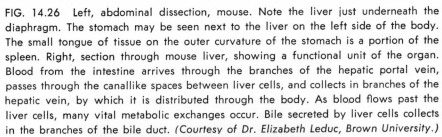

FIG. 14.25 Summary of the pathways of nutrient transport.

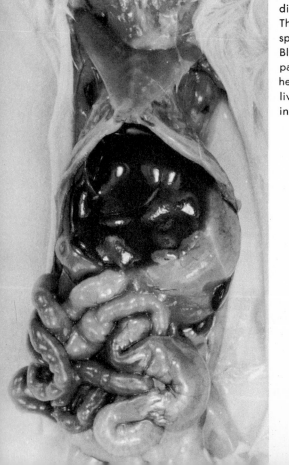

FIG. 14.26 Left, abdominal dissection, mouse. Note the liver just underneath the diaphragm. The stomach may be seen next to the liver on the left side of the body. The small tongue of tissue on the outer curvature of the stomach is a portion of the spleen. Right, section through mouse liver, showing a functional unit of the organ. Blood from the intestine arrives through the branches of the hepatic portal vein, passes through the canallike spaces between liver cells, and collects in branches of the hepatic vein, by which it is distributed through the body. As blood flows past the liver cells, many vital metabolic exchanges occur. Bile secreted by liver cells collects in the branches of the bile duct. (Courtesy of Dr. Elizabeth Leduc, Brown University.)

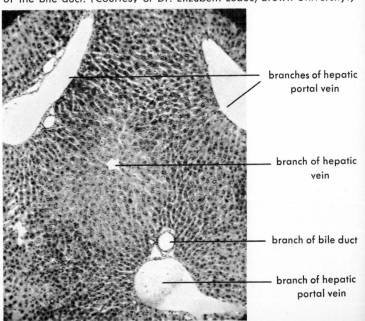

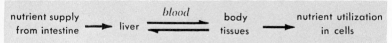

FIG. 14.27 The general pattern of the nutrient balance in the body and the role of the liver in maintaining this balance.

Small fractions of the nutrients from the intestine are likely to be used by liver cells for their own maintenance. What is the fate of the remainder?

CARBOHYDRATE DISTRIBUTION

The body-wide carbohydrate balance may be symbolized as in Fig. 14.28. This figure indicates that, as in plants, *glucose* is the principal compound in carbohydrate *transport*. Glucose is therefore found mainly in the blood. The principal form in which animals *utilize* and *store* carbohydrates is *glycogen*. This polysaccharide is found in all cells, and, insofar as it is stored, it is the functional equivalent of starch in plants. Many animal tissues store more glycogen than is required for immediate use. Muscle and skin hold considerable quantities, but the liver is the principal storage depot.

Blood-sugar Constancy

The carbohydrate balance described above is affected by relative rates of supply and demand. Whenever the rate of carbohydrate supply from the gut exceeds the rate of utilization in the tissues, then a net excess of carbohydrates will accumulate. Such an excess is stored away in the liver as glycogen. Conversely, if intestinal supply does not keep up with tissue utilization, then the liver makes up the deficit by releasing some of its stored glycogen as blood glucose. As a result of such activities, the liver maintains a *constant* blood-glucose concentration, irrespective of the rates of supply and utilization. To be sure, small-scale fluctuations of blood-glucose levels may and do

occur, but such fluctuations normally do not exceed certain fairly narrow limits and are rebalanced quite rapidly. The meaning of "constancy" here is therefore not mathematical but biological; the term implies maintenance of steady conditions within set limits. In this sense, the blood-glucose concentration is one of the most closely regulated constancies in the body (Fig. 14.29).

Just how does the liver carry out this regulating function? In all cells, those of the liver included, blood glucose may be converted into cellular glycogen and vice versa. As we shall see later in greater detail, this important reversible conversion is a two-step process involving *phosphorylated* glucose, i.e., glucose-phosphate.

$$glucose \rightleftharpoons glucose\text{-}phosphate \rightleftharpoons glycogen$$

This reaction sequence is the key to the carbohydrate-regulating activity of the liver. Liver cells contain stored glycogen, and blood flowing through the liver past the cells contains glucose. The two carbohydrates are in chemical equilibrium. If for any reason the glucose concentration in blood should rise, then the chemical equilibrium will be disturbed. By the principle of mass action, the glucose excess in blood will then be converted into liver glycogen, through the reactions above. Conversely, if for some reason the blood-glucose level should fall, then the chemical balance will shift the opposite way and liver glycogen will become blood glucose, until the original equilibrium is reattained (Fig. 14.30). In effect, liver and blood are so coordinated that any change in the glucose $\rightleftharpoons$ glycogen balance is automatically counteracted. The blood-glucose concentration is maintained constant in this manner.

A rise in blood sugar usually occurs after a meal is digested, when blood and lymph transport foods from the gut. Conversely, blood sugar tends to fall during periods of fasting, e.g., during sleep. A fall of blood glucose also tends to occur during strenuous exercise, when muscles and other body tissues use up glycogen at a faster than normal rate. These tissues then become low in glycogen, and, as a result, the blood-glucose $\rightleftharpoons$ tissue-glycogen balance shifts in such a way that blood-glucose levels decrease and tissue-glycogen levels increase. But in this and all similar

FIG. 14.28 The carbohydrate balance of the body.

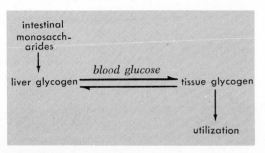

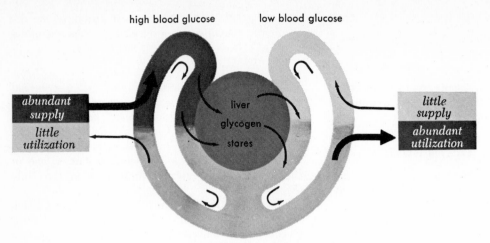

high blood glucose   low blood glucose

abundant supply
little utilization

liver glycogen stores

little supply
abundant utilization

constant normal blood glucose

FIG. 14.29   Blood-glucose balance. If much glucose is supplied to blood from food and little is used, then the blood-glucose concentration will tend to be high (top and left). Under such conditions the liver withdraws glucose and stores it as glycogen, so establishing a normal glucose level (bottom left). On the other hand, if much glucose is used up and little is supplied, then the blood-glucose concentration will tend to be low (top and right). The liver then adds glucose to blood from its glycogen stores, and so reestablishes the normal glucose level (bottom right). Through these actions, the liver maintains a *constant* blood-glucose concentration.

situations, the liver rapidly counteracts any change of blood-glucose levels by either enlarging or reducing its glycogen stores (Fig. 14.31).

Factors in Sugar Balance

In mammals and in vertebrates generally, *hormones* play a significant role in these shifting balances. For example, the hormone **insulin,** secreted by specialized cells in the pancreas, promotes the phosphorylation of glucose. The hormone therefore controls the conversion of glucose into glycogen. If, as in a diabetic animal, insulin production is inadequate, then glucose becomes unusable and the liver and all other tissues cannot manufacture glycogen. Glucose accumulates in the blood, yet the tissues of the body become starved of carbohydrates. Fats and proteins must then make up for the lack of cellular carbohydrates. Much of the unusable blood sugar is excreted in the urine, but the blood-glucose level remains abnormally high nevertheless. Conversely, if too much insulin is produced, glucose will be converted to liver and tissue glycogen to such an extent that the blood-glucose level drops drastically. The brain is particularly dependent on glucose,

and when the glucose supply in blood becomes abnormally low, "insulin shock" and eventual death may ensue.

The hormone **adrenalin,** secreted in the core of the adrenal gland, acts in exactly the opposite fashion. It promotes the dephosphorylation of glucose and therefore accelerates the conversion of glycogen into glucose. Adrenalin is secreted particularly during intense emotional or physical stress. The hormone then causes a large-scale conversion of liver glycogen into blood glucose, appropriately at a time when the body tissues require a great deal of fuel. As we shall see later, many other hormones affect carbohydrate balances as well.

What happens if, in a healthy animal, the liver and all body tissues hold glycogen to capacity, all current carbohydrate needs are satisfied, yet still more sugar is being supplied by the gut? Internal carbohydrate saturation may actually be reached rather rapidly, since even at peak storage the carbohydrate content of the body does not exceed 1 per cent of the total weight. If sugars supplied by food exceed the internal capacity, then a small fraction of the excess

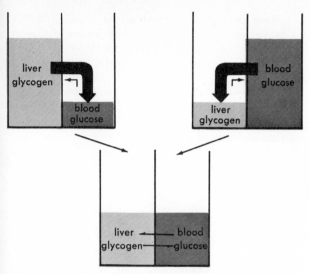

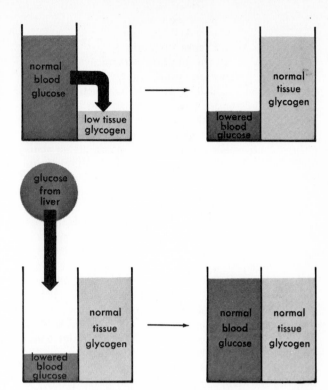

FIG. 14.30 The reaction balance between liver glycogen and blood glucose. If blood-glucose concentrations are low, mass action will bring about more reaction from liver glycogen to blood glucose than the other way round (left), and conversely if blood-glucose concentrations are high (right). As a result, blood glucose and liver glycogen will tend to be maintained in equilibrium (bottom).

FIG. 14.31 Maintenance of glycogen balance in tissues. If concentrations of tissue glycogen are low, blood glucose will restore the normal concentrations (top left). This will lower the concentration of blood glucose (top right), but only temporarily, for glucose supplied by the liver will soon restore the normal concentration in blood (bottom left and right).

may be excreted in urine. This occurs, for example, right after a heavy meal. But the bulk of any carbohydrate excess goes to the liver and some of it from there to other tissues, where it is *converted into fats*. This explains why even a nonfatty diet may produce increased layers of body fat, particularly if over a long period of time more food is eaten than the body requires.

Conversely, if an animal subsists on reduced food intake or undergoes outright starvation, then the internal glycogen stores soon will be greatly diminished. Yet, up to a point, the blood-glucose level and the carbohydrate supply to the tissues may still remain normal. Under such conditions the liver draws on the fat of the body and converts as much of it as required into glycogen and into glucose.

One major function of the liver thus emerges. Through glycogen storage and blood-glucose control and, whenever necessary, through interconversion of carbohydrates and fats, this organ ensures that all cells of the body receive an adequate glucose supply. This supply does not depend on any particular pattern of mealtimes and is geared to the changing requirements of the tissues.

AMINO ACID DISTRIBUTION

A body-wide equilibrium exists, as outlined in Fig. 14.32. Just as for carbohydrates above, if the rate of amino acid supply from the intestine exceeds the rate of utilization in the tissues, then an amino acid excess will develop.

FIG. 14.32 The amino acid balance of the body.

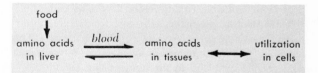

Amino Acid Excess

This is the usual situation. Amino acid requirements are greatest in young, growing animals, in pregnant females, and in animals in which extensive tissue repair is under way, as after disease. In all such cases, protein synthesis and growth proceed at a very high rate and large quantities of amino acids are utilized in the cells. But even then, more amino acids are usually eaten than are required. In healthy adults, where processes of growth and structural replacement occur at a much reduced rate, amino acid requirements are reduced correspondingly.

Unlike carbohydrates, excess amino acids are not stored. Some tissues may accumulate more protein than they require, and such proteins in a sense may be considered to represent amino acid reserves available to the body when food supplies are deficient. But specialized storage of amino acids comparable to the storage of carbohydrates does not occur. What then happens to the usual excesses of these acids? The bulk of them is transformed chemically through reactions taking place in the liver.

The first step in this transformation is **deamination**. As the term implies, the amino group ($-NH_2$) is split away from the remainder of an amino acid molecule. An enzyme, *deaminase*, promotes the reaction:

$$NH_2-RCH-COOH \xrightarrow{\text{deaminase}} -NH_2 + -RCH-COOH$$

amino acid

$$\downarrow$$

$$NH_3$$

ammonia

The separated $-NH_2$ group ultimately appears as free **ammonia** (NH_3). This is a toxic material. In many animals, aquatic ones in particular, ammonia is carried from the liver to the kidneys by blood and is excreted as such in urine. In other animals, free ammonia is first changed into less toxic substances and the latter are then excreted in urine. In insects and birds, for example, ammonia is combined with certain other organic molecules and is made into **uric acid**. This acid is then carried to the kidneys for excretion. Mammals dispose of ammonia in a different way. The compound is combined in the liver with carbon dioxide, abundantly available as a byproduct of respiration. The result of this combination is **urea**. This substance is then carried by blood to the kidneys and excreted.

Urea production by combination of NH_3 and CO_2 in the liver occurs through a cyclical sequence of reactions called the **ornithine cycle**. As indicated in Fig. 14.33, three amino acids normally present in the liver form the "endless belt" of this cycle: *ornithine, citrulline,* and *arginine*. Ornithine first reacts with one molecule of ammonia and one molecule of carbon dioxide, yielding citrulline. This amino acid then combines with another molecule of ammonia, forming arginine. Arginine finally splits into two fragments, in a reaction requiring the enzyme *arginase*. One of these fragments is urea, the other is ornithine, and the starting point of the cycle is thereby regenerated.

The second product of deamination, $-RCH-COOH$, is not excreted but is salvaged; it is converted to *fats* or *carbohydrates* by liver cells. Fats and carbohydrates so formed are treated indistinguishably from all other fats and carbohydrates; they may be stored as liver and tissue glycogen or they may be added to the fat pool of the body. Clearly, an animal may become fat not only by eating too many carbohydrates or fats but also by consuming too many proteins; too much food of any kind will make an animal obese.

Deamination is the fate of most excess amino acids. But some are not deaminated. Instead, they are used in liver cells as starting materials in the production of a number of special compounds. For example,

FIG. 14.33 The ornithine cycle.

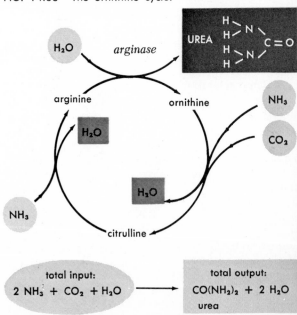

blood normally contains a permanent population of free protein molecules. Some of these blood proteins are enzymes. Others play a role in blood clotting, as we shall see. Still others establish immunity against infectious agents (see Chap. 21). Many of these blood proteins are manufactured in the liver, and the raw materials are whole amino acids.

Amino Acid Deficiency

The assumption so far has been that food provides a net excess of amino acids. What happens when the opposite is the case? Much of the answer is contained in the deamination reaction, which is reversible. Proceeding to the right as above, amino acids are broken up; proceeding to the left, they are synthesized. Under the usual conditions of amino acid excess, mass action operates in such a way that the breakup reaction to the right occurs to a far greater extent than the reverse reaction. But if the protein content of eaten food is so low that a deficiency of amino acids develops, then some of this deficiency may be made up by the liver through the reverse of deamination, i.e., amino acid synthesis by *amination.*

In such a synthesis, some nitrogenous substance may be the source of the required $-NH_2$ groups and eaten or stored carbohydrates and fats may be transformed into $-RCH-COOH$ groups. But note that carbohydrates and fats cannot be converted into all required kinds of $-R-$ portions. Of the two dozen or so types of naturally occurring amino acids, eight or ten, the misnamed "essential" ones, cannot be manufactured by animals. This actually represents an inability of animals to manufacture eight or ten kinds of $-R-$ portions. Unless these are supplied steadily by food, in fully prefabricated form and in appropriate quantities, an animal will die of malnutrition. Clearly, an adequate diet must contain daily doses of foods which supply essential amino acids or at least the corresponding $-R-$ portions. All "nonessential" types of $-R-$ portions *can* be produced in the liver even if food does not provide them, so long as carbohydrates or fats are available as raw materials. Together with $-NH_2$, such $-R-$ portions may be synthesized into "nonessential" amino acids, and these may reduce an existing deficiency.

A second major regulating function of the liver is now in evidence. Through deamination and synthesis, the liver balances the external amino acid supply against the internal demand, and it gears the distribution of these acids to the varying requirements of the tissues. Moreover, through the associated processes of urea production and blood-protein manufacture, the liver also carries out vital protective functions and so contributes significantly to maintaining a steady state in the body.

LIPID DISTRIBUTION

We recall that colloidal droplets of whole fat are absorbed from the gut into the lymph system and, bypassing the liver, are carried from there into the bloodstream. As blood then circulates throughout the body, most colloidal fats are taken up directly by the *fat depots,* i.e., the regions where bulk fats are stored: under the skin, around the heart and the kidneys, and particularly along the membranes which envelop the intestine and the other abdominal organs. Some colloidal fats also enter the liver, reached in this manner by a rather roundabout route. A more direct path to the liver is taken by the fatty acids and the glycerin absorbed from the gut. As we have seen, these digestion products of fat enter the liver via the hepatic portal vein.

The liver is an important fat depot. It not only receives fats, fatty acids, and glycerin but, as noted earlier, also manufactures fats from excess carbohydrates and amino acids. The total fat content of the liver is in balance with that of the other fat depots of the body. If liver fat increases too much, the excess is sent via the blood to the other depots. Conversely, the other depots make up any deficiency in liver fat. In these redistributions, fat is transported either as whole fat or as fatty acid and glycerin.

The tissues of the body are supplied either by the liver or by the other fat stores. Consequently, the overall fat balance of the body is maintained by a three-cornered equilibrium, as shown in Fig. 14.34. The healthy animal generally eats just enough that, over fairly long periods of time, a net increase or decrease of the body fat does not occur.

We already know that an animal could survive if it were fed a carbohydrate-free diet which contained a compensating amount of fat. The liver could then transform fat into the required carbohydrates. What would happen in the converse situation, when an animal is on a fat-free diet but eats a proportionately larger amount of carbohydrates? Such an animal could probably not survive. To be sure, liver and depot fat would be kept at normal levels, through fat manufacture from carbohydrates. The fat requirements of tissue cells would be satisfied similarly. Yet health would be

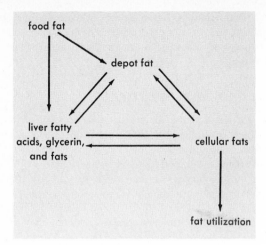

FIG. 14.34   The fat balance of the body.

impaired nevertheless, for certain fatty acids (e.g., *linoleic acid*) cannot be manufactured by many animals. Such essential fatty acids must be supplied by food in fully prefabricated form. In this respect such acids are quite like the essential amino acids and most vitamins.

OTHER NUTRIENTS

Specialized storage of water and of mineral ions does not occur, beyond such quantities of these substances as form part and parcel of the normal working machinery of the body. Some water is synthesized as a secondary product in many metabolic reactions, but much more water is lost by evaporation, egestion, sweating, and urination. Inorganic ions are lost in this manner also. Food must compensate for these losses. Any food eaten is likely to contain considerable quantities of water and at least some of the necessary ions. A diversity of foods generally ensures a balanced ion supply. This distribution of water and inorganic ions absorbed by the gut does not involve the liver in any

special manner. Like all other cells of the body, liver cells merely absorb portions of these substances from the blood and use them for their own maintenance.

But the liver *is* involved especially in the distribution of several vitamins. Some vitamins absorbed from the gut are transported directly to tissue cells. However, others are taken up and collected by the liver and are released as the tissues require them. Vitamins A and D are in this category. The livers of fish store particularly large quantities of these vitamins, hence the nutritive value of, for example, cod liver oil. In certain instances, the liver also manufactures vitamins from nonvitamin precursors. The pigment carotene, present in many plant and animal foods, is not a vitamin. But when carotene reaches the liver, it may be transformed into active vitamin A (see Chap. 20).

In addition to these many storing and food-processing activities, the liver also performs numerous other, not necessarily nutritional, functions. For example, the synthesis of blood proteins has already been mentioned. Also, the liver destroys red blood corpuscles and in the embryo it manufactures them. Other manufacturing processes include bile production and the synthesis of special liver products which, like hormones, are vital for the maintenance of tissue cells but which are not available in food. It may be noted in this connection that the occasional inclusion of liver in the diet has long been known to be beneficial generally and indeed necessary in certain diseases. The main activities of the liver are summarized in Fig. 14.35.

Thus, among the nutrients delivered to individual animal cells are glucose; all different kinds of amino acids; fats, fatty acids, and glycerin; water and mineral ions; vitamins; and various special organic compounds. Being so supplied through the digestive and absorptive agency of the intestine, the regulative agency of the liver, and the transportive agency of blood, the animal cell, like the plant cell, may now see to the main business at hand: *utilization* of nutrients for survival. This means *liberation of energy* on the one hand and *construction of new living matter* on the other.

REVIEW QUESTIONS

1. Review the general nutritional pattern of animals and contrast the nutrient requirements of plants and animals. For which materials are animals dependent on plants and why? What is the basic function of an alimentary system?

2. Review what is known about appetite and

hunger control. What role does the brain play in such control? Discuss the chemical aspects of digestion generally. What roles do enzymes play in digestion and how are digestive enzymes distinct from others? What is the relation between digestion and synthesis?

3. Review the events of oral digestion. What is

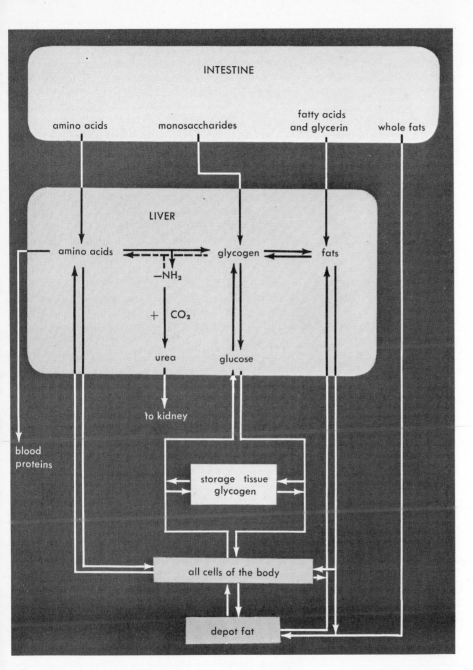

FIG. 14.35 The overall pattern of liver function, food distribution, and nutrient balances with respect to carbohydrates, fats, and proteins.

the composition of saliva and how is salivary secretion initiated? What mechanical and chemical digestive processes occur in the mouth? Through what processes is food transferred into the stomach? What are the anatomical parts of the stomach and what are their functions?

4. What is the composition of gastric juice and by what processes is secretion of this fluid controlled? Review the mechanical and chemical events of gastric digestion. What are the specific functions of HCl, pepsin, and rennin? What are the results of gastric digestion?

5. Which digestive fluids are added to food in the duodenum and what is the composition of these fluids? Where are the fluids manufactured and what processes stimulate their secretion? What is enterokinase and what is its function?

6. Review the specific course of protein, carbohydrate, and fat digestion in the intestine. What enzymes are involved in each case? What are the results of these digestive processes? What are intestinal villi and what are their functions? How and in what form are different categories of food absorbed into the intestinal wall? What tissue is it that accomplishes absorption?

7. What are the functions of the large intestine? What is the role of the intestinal bacteria? Do these symbionts live mutualistically, commensalistically, or parasitically? If pure glucose were eaten, where would it be digested? Why are eaten vitamins or orally administered medicines not digested in the alimentary tract?

8. Describe the blood circulation through the intestine. Which food materials are carried away from the intestine by blood? Describe the pattern of the lymph circulation in the body as a whole. What is the function of this circulation and what is the composition of lymph? What is the arrangement of the lymph vessels in the intestine? Which foods are carried away from the intestine by lymph?

9. By what pathways do foods reach the liver? What is the pathway and destination of colloidal fat? By what pathways do processed foods leave the liver? What is the broad, general function of the liver and what is the adaptive advantage of this organ? What happens to carbohydrates reaching the liver? Discuss fully. What happens if carbohydrate supplies are exceedingly excessive?

10. By what processes is the constancy of the blood-glucose concentration maintained? Discuss several specific situations in which the blood-glucose level tends to change and show how such tendencies are counteracted by the liver.

11. What is deamination? When and where does it occur, and what are the results of this process? In which form do various animals eliminate nitrogenous wastes? Review the ornithine cycle. Can the liver manufacture carbohydrates and fats from derivatives of amino acids? Conversely, can the liver manufacture amino acids from carbohydrates or fats? Discuss fully. Can the liver manufacture essential amino acids?

12. Describe the interplay between liver, fat depots, and body tissues in fat metabolism. Can an animal survive if fats are substituted for carbohydrates in its diet? Can an animal similarly survive in the converse situation? Suppose that an animal were not given any food for a considerable length of time. What specific progressive changes would then occur in the body-wide balances of carbohydrates, fats, and proteins?

SUGGESTED COLLATERAL READINGS

Supplementary information on the topics discussed in this chapter may be obtained from any of the texts cited below.

Carlson, A. J., and V. Johnson: "The Machinery of the Body," 4th ed., University of Chicago Press, Chicago, 1953.
Fulton, J.: "Textbook of Physiology," Saunders, Philadelphia, 1950.
Heilbrunn, L. V.: "An Outline of General Physiology," Saunders, Philadelphia, 1952.
Prosser, C. L., F. A. Brown, D. W. Bishop, T. L. Jahn, and V. J. Wulff: "Comparative Animal Physiology," Saunders, Philadelphia, 1950.

Of great historical interest in the study of animal nutrition are the following two sources. The first is a reprint of the original (1833) book by Beaumont, the father of modern gastric physiology.

Beaumont, W.: "Experiments and Observations on the Gastric Juice and the Physiology of Digestion," Harvard University Press, Cambridge, Mass., 1929.
Bernard, C.: On the Mechanism of Formation of Sugar in the Liver, in M. L. Gabriel and S. Fogel, "Great Experiments in Biology," Prentice-Hall, Englewood Cliffs, N.J., 1955.

Among many popular articles on nutrition, the following are recommended:

Boyd-Orr, I.: The Food Problem, *Sci. American,* vol. 183, 1950.

Mayer, J.: Appetite and Obesity, *Sci. American,* vol. 195, 1956.

Quisenberry, K. S.: The World's Principal Food Plants, *Sci. Monthly,* vol. 79, 1954.

Remington, R. E.: The Social Origins of Dietary Habits, *Sci. Monthly,* vol. 43, 1936.

Weaver, W.: People, Energy, and Food, *Sci. Monthly,* vol. 78, 1954.

GAS EXCHANGE

15

Most organisms are *aerobes;* i.e., their cells require oxygen for respiration. Also, respiration yields the byproduct carbon dioxide and this gas must be eliminated from the organism. Therefore, if a cell is to respire, it must not only be nourished with foods. It must in addition be provided with oxygen and it must be rid of carbon dioxide. The ways in which organisms exchange O_2 and CO_2 form the subject of this chapter.

PATTERNS OF GAS EXCHANGE

A first component of gas exchange is **breathing,** which may be defined as an exchange of respiratory gases between a whole organism and the physical environment. A second component in multicellular organisms often is **gas transport,** into and away from all cells. The ultimate function of all components of gas exchange is to satisfy the gas requirements of each individual cell of an organism. As noted, gases play a role in respiration, and respiration in turn is a chemical process of energy liberation taking place *within a cell.* It should be clear, therefore, that breathing and gas transport are *auxiliary* processes to respiration and that breathing is not the same as respiration. A whole *organism* breathes; in addition, the individual *cells* of an organism also respire.

In organisms in which individual cells are in direct contact with the external environment, exchange of respiratory gases is accomplished readily. Oxygen simply diffuses into each cell and carbon dioxide diffuses out. Such direct cellular exchange is characteristic of all Monera, all Protista, all Metaphyta and some Metazoa, notably the sponges and the radiate and acoelomate phyla.

In all unicellular organisms, breathing as defined above constitutes virtually the whole of gas exchange and a problem of gas transport does not exist. Moreover, even in complexly constructed multicellular organisms such as vascular plants, nearly every living cell is in contact with the external environment. Oxygen may therefore reach individual cells directly, over various routes. Stomata admit air into the leaves, and leaf cells thus have direct access to gaseous oxygen. The gas diffuses through cell surfaces and dissolves in cellular water. Some of this oxygen is carried into the phloem channels along with water, and stem and root tissues may be supplied in this fashion. Oxygen also enters the plant through the roots, dissolved in soil water. Root cells may retain some of the gas and the remainder reaches xylem vessels. Stem and leaf tissues may therefore obtain oxygen over that path. If the stem is green, stomata on its surface provide a third entry point for air. And if the stem is woody, lenticels and any crack in the bark will do similarly. Finally, green tissues produce oxygen as a byproduct of photosynthesis, still another source of this respiratory gas.

Respiratory CO_2 in vascular plants may diffuse straight into the environment from cells exposed directly to soil or air. Deeper-lying cells may release CO_2 into the xylem or phloem, and the stomata may then pass the gas into the atmosphere. In green tissues, respiratory CO_2 may be used as a raw material in photosynthesis (Fig. 15.1).

In effect, exchange of respiratory gases in plants is predominantly direct, much of the living tissue being in immediate contact with the external environment. Gas diffusion to and from deeper cells and a certain amount of transport by xylem and phloem accomplish the rest. Since much of the deeper substance of a vascular plant is nonliving supporting and conducting material, the gas requirement in such regions is zero.

FIG. 15.1 The pattern of gas exchange in plants. The main sources and transport pathways of oxygen and carbon dioxide are indicated in the diagram.

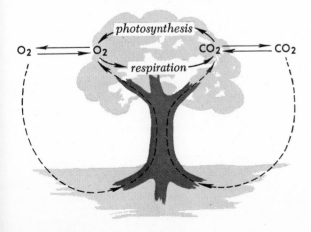

FIG. 15.2 The four principal patterns of animal breathing. From left to right: tracheal tubes (e.g., insects); skin breathing (e.g., earthworms); gill breathing (e.g., fishes); and lung breathing (e.g., man). The surface for gas exchange in all but the insect is indicated in light gray.

In primitive metazoans, analogously, the tissues between the external environment and the alimentary system consist of comparatively few cell layers and the alimentary system communicates with the exterior. Respiratory gases may therefore diffuse directly to and from all cells. However, most animals are constructed so complexly and compactly that most cells are not in contact with the external environment. In such cases, gas exchange is accomplished by specialized breathing and transport *systems*.

Four different types of breathing systems are encountered (Fig. 15.2). One occurs in insects and some other arthropods. These animals possess hollow **tracheal tubes,** which begin at the body surface and lead into the interior. There they branch extensively, microscopic branch terminals reaching into all tissues. In effect, air is piped from the outside to all interior cells and cellular gas exchange then can take place even deeply within the animal (see also Chap. 11).

In all other compactly built animals, gas exchange occurs across thin membranes. These are usually one cell layer thick. They are exposed on one side to external air or water and on the other to blood vessels. Oxygen is absorbed into blood, and carbon dioxide is released from it. Thus the breathing membrane collects and releases gases, and the blood circulation represents the transport system which delivers the gases to and from all cells.

The three principal variants of this pattern are **skin breathing, gill breathing,** and **lung breathing.** Earthworms, for example, breathe exclusively through their thin, moist skins. Frogs use their skins too, but in addition frog tadpoles possess gills; and frog adults, lungs. In fish, crustacea, and many other aquatic animals, external water flows past gills and the gill membranes exchange gases. Many differently constructed gills are found in different aquatic animals, but the principle of operation is the same in all.

Lungs occur chiefly in terrestrial vertebrates. These breathing organs operate like gills, except that they are adapted to function in air instead of water. We shall examine the pattern of lung breathing in some detail, and the specific pattern in man may serve as an illustrative example.

BREATHING

THE BREATHING SYSTEM

Several familiar organs form the air channels of the breathing apparatus: **nose** and **nasal passages**, **pharynx**, **larynx** (or Adam's apple), **trachea** (or windpipe), and **lungs**.

The Upper Tract

The nasal passages are narrow, winding pathways leading past intricately grooved and ridged walls (Fig. 15.3). Along the walls are found a number of

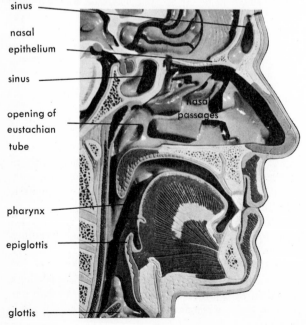

FIG. 15.3 The nasal passages and the upper parts of the breathing system. *(Model designed by Dr. J. F. Mueller; photo, Ward's Natural Science Establishment, Inc.)*

sinus

nasal epithelium

sinus

opening of eustachian tube

nasal passages

pharynx

epiglottis

glottis

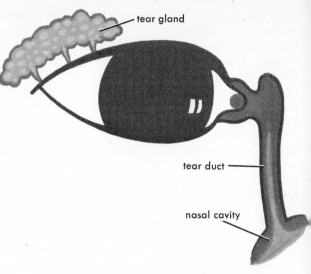

tear gland

tear duct

nasal cavity

FIG. 15.4 The tear apparatus, diagrammatic.

paired openings. Some of these connect with the head **sinuses,** hollow air-filled cavities within some of the skull bones. For example, one large sinus is present in each of the two frontal bones which form the forehead.

Another pair of openings admits the contents of the **tear ducts** into the nasal passages. Tears are secreted continuously by glands in the outer corners of the eyes. The lymphlike fluid flows over, and so moistens the surface of the cornea, then collects in the inner corners of the eyes and runs through the tear ducts into the nose (Fig. 15.4). Near the entry of the nasal passages into the pharynx, another two openings, one on the right, the other on the left, lead into the **eustachian tubes.** These pass into the middle-ear cavities. This connection permits the equilibration of air pressure between the external atmosphere and the middle ear, a space which is closed off from the outside by the eardrum (see Chap. 22).

Nasal passages, head sinuses, tear ducts, and eustachian tubes are lined with a continuous single layer of epithelial cells. Mucus secreted by the cells moistens the exposed surfaces. The epithelial cells in the nasal passages are ciliated, and some of these cells are specialized as odor receptors. Nerves lead from them to the nearby brain, where impulses are interpreted as smell.

Air passing through the narrow spaces of the nasal pathways is warmed and moistened, is freed of dust by the ciliated cells which act as a filtering screen, and is smelled. As everyone is uncomfortably aware, inflammation of the passages as in a cold or in hay fever blocks air transmission to greater or lesser degree. The tissues swell up and obliterate the pathways. Increased secretion of mucus adds to the discomfort. Smelling is impaired. Tears overflow from the eyes, since the fluid cannot easily drain off into the blocked nasal chambers. And in severe cases, the inflammation may spread into the head sinuses, the middle-ear cavities, the throat, and the pathways leading from the throat to the lungs. Breathing by mouth under such conditions introduces relatively unwarmed, dust-laden, and unsmelled air.

As has been noted in Chap. 14, the air and the food channel cross in the pharynx (see Fig. 14.8). The esophagus is more or less collapsed in the absence of food, but some air may pass into it nevertheless. Most of the air enters the larynx through the **glottis,** a slit which can be closed or opened to varying degrees. The larynx consists of a number of cartilages. Held together by membranes and movable relative to one another by muscles, these cartilages enclose a hollow, cylindrical chamber. Attached to the inner surfaces of this chamber is a pair of horizontally placed fibroelastic ligaments, the **vocal cords.** These run from front to back in the laryngeal cavity, leaving an air passage in the mid-plane (Fig. 15.5).

Voice Production

Sound is produced when air is expelled past the vocal cords through the glottis. The shape of the glottal opening and, as in a violin string, the length and tension of the vocal cords determine tone pitch. The shape of the larynx may be changed at will by muscles, and this in turn alters the tension of the cords. Taut ligaments vibrate rapidly and produce a highly pitched

sound. Also, notes are the higher, the shorter and thinner the vocal cords and the narrower the glottal slit. The volume of the sound produced depends on the force of the air blast and on the amplitude with which the cords vibrate.

A third characteristic of voice, tone quality, is influenced by the size and shape of the resonating cavities: chest, pharynx, mouth, and nasal passages. That tone quality changes as the position of lips, tongue, jaws, and cheeks is changed is familiar to everyone. Tone quality is altered also during a cold or when the nose is pinched or when sound is produced on inhalation rather than on exhalation as is normal. During puberty in males, the chest cavity and larynx enlarge and the vocal cords lengthen. The voice "breaks" as the individual learns to control his modified sound equipment. Deeper tones than in females are produced thereafter. The vocal cords may thicken or scar during disease or become encrusted with mucus during a cold; a rasping voice is the result.

Most mammals make sounds of some sort. The giraffe is a notable exception. In birds, the only other vertebrate group with extensive, conspicuous voice capacity, sound is produced not in the larynx but in a **syrinx.** This voice box is located at the lower, not the upper, end of the windpipe.

The Lower Tract

The larynx is continuous with the trachea. This tube is prevented from collapsing by C-shaped rings of cartilage set horizontally into its wall. As in the larynx, the inner lining of the trachea is a ciliated, mucus-secreting layer of cells. The cilia beat upward, carrying mucus, dust, and occasional bits of food which

FIG. 15.5   The vocal cords of man. The view is from above, looking into larynx and trachea. From left to right: sequence of vocal-cord positions during the transition from quiet breathing to voicing. *(Bell Telephone Laboratories, Inc.)*

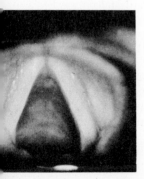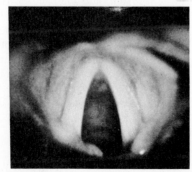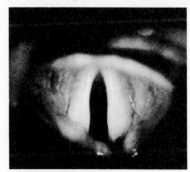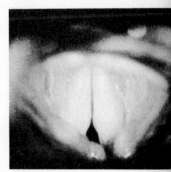

"went the wrong way" into the pharynx. Air forced out as a cough facilitates the process.

At its lower end, the trachea divides into two **bronchi,** tubes having a smaller diameter than the trachea but the same structure otherwise (Fig. 15.6). Each bronchus subdivides after a distance into **bronchioles** and each of the latter in turn branches repeatedly. Cartilage supports are not present in these smaller ducts. Also, their walls become thinner as they branch. Only the inner ciliated lining layer and some connective tissue containing elastic fibers are carried forward into the microscopic terminations of the branch system. Each such terminus is a raspberry-shaped sac made of a single layer of thin flat cells. This is an **alveolus** (Fig. 15.7). The sum of all alveoli constitutes the lung. The alveoli are held together by connective tissue, which carries nerves and a dense network of blood capillaries. The left and right parts of the lung are sculptured into lobes, their number corresponding to the number of main branches arising from the bronchi.

The lung on each side is situated in an **intrathoracic space,** which is bounded by two **pleural membranes.** The outer of these membranes lies against the diaphragm below, against the cavity holding the heart along the mid-plane of the chest, and against the rib cage at the top and along the sides. The inner membrane covers the lung itself. Except for openings which admit the bronchi and the blood vessels to the lungs, the intrathoracic cavities are sealed off from the rest of the body. This feature is essential in breathing.

FIG. 15.6   The lower parts of the breathing system. Note that the intrathoracic cavity is sealed.

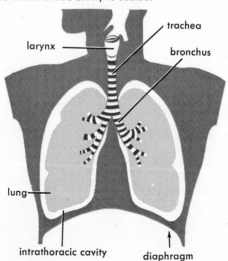

larynx

trachea

bronchus

lung

intrathoracic cavity

diaphragm

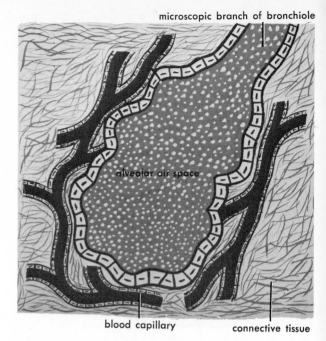

microscopic branch of bronchiole

alveolar air space

blood capillary

connective tissue

FIG. 15.7   An alveolus of the lung, surrounded by capillaries and connective tissue.

THE BREATHING PROCESS

Air is moved through the breathing system by action of the **diaphragm,** the **rib muscles,** or both. The diaphragm participates in *abdominal breathing;* the rib muscles, in *chest breathing.*

The diaphragm separates the chest cavity from the abdominal cavity; stomach and liver lie directly underneath it. In relaxed condition, this thin muscular partition is dome-shaped. When it is contracted, the upward curvature of the dome disappears and the diaphragm flattens out. Such contraction pushes liver, stomach, and intestine downward and outward and so forces the belly out. Hence the designation "abdominal breathing." A flattening out of the diaphragm also enlarges the chest cavity and this is the effective event in *inhalation* (Fig. 15.8). As a result of the enlargement, the pressure in the sealed intrathoracic space falls. This lowered pressure sucks the lung alveoli wide open. Air pressure within the alveoli consequently falls also, but this decrease is rebalanced instantly by air rushing in through the nose or mouth.

When the diaphragm relaxes, it resumes its original dome shape. The belly is pulled back and the chest

ABDOMINAL (DIAPHRAGMATIC) BREATHING   CHEST BREATHING

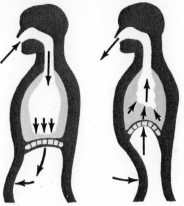

inspiration   *expiration*   *inspiration*   *expiration*

FIG. 15.8 The essential events in abdominal breathing and chest breathing.

cavity, together with the intrathoracic space, reattains its former volume. Pressure within the intrathoracic space is then no longer lowered, and further suction is therefore not exerted on the alveoli. As a result, the elastic fibers which cover the alveoli recoil and air is pressed out from the lungs in an *exhalation.*

Breathing movements carried out by the rib cage have the same effect on the lungs as the above. Ribs are hinged to the vertebral column along the back and to the breastbone, or *sternum,* along the front. Attached between successive ribs are two layers of muscles, which raise or lower the rib cage. When the chest is raised, the thoracic cavity expands and, through suction on the alveoli, inhalation occurs. A lowering of the chest results in exhalation (Fig. 15.9). Chest breathing may enlarge the intrathoracic spaces much more than abdominal breathing; as a result, the former may produce deeper breaths than the latter.

Evidently, the mammalian method of breathing is a pressure mechanism. This knowledge has made possible procedures of "artificial respiration," often employed when injury or disease has incapacitated the automatic internal controls which maintain breathing normally. In artificial respiration by hand or in "iron lungs," the chest is subjected to intermittent external pressure, which forces air into and out of the lungs just as does normal breathing.

In view of the importance of pressure, effective breathing clearly depends on the structural wholeness of the intrathoracic space. If the chest wall is pierced by a wound, external air enters the cavity on that side and the diaphragm or the rib muscles then can no longer exert suction on the lung. The lung consequently stays collapsed. In some diseases (e.g., tuberculosis), it is often desirable to rest one of the lungs. This is done by injecting air into one of the intrathoracic cavities. The lung on that side then collapses and becomes nonfunctional. The procedure may have to be repeated from time to time, for the injected air is gradually absorbed and removed by the blood circulation.

FIG. 15.9 The positions of the rib cage in inhalation (left) and exhalation (right) during chest breathing.

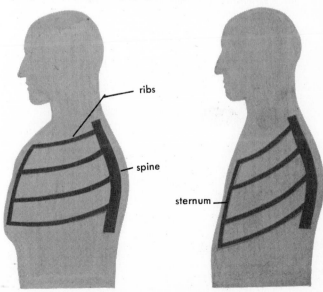

ribs

spine

sternum

THE CONTROL OF BREATHING

What maintains the bellowslike breathing movements year after year, without interruption? And what adjusts these movements in rate and depth to changing requirements? Breathing is maintained and regulated by a **breathing center** in the brain. This center is located in the **medulla oblongata**, the hind portion of the brain near the juncture of skull and neck (see Chap. 22).

The Normal Cycle

The breathing center responds to two kinds of incoming stimuli, one nervous, the other nonnervous. The nonnervous stimulus is *carbon dioxide,* present in blood at all times as a byproduct of cellular respiration. Blood-borne CO_2 accelerates the activity of the breathing center. The higher the CO_2 concentration, the greater the activity, and vice versa. This activity consists in sending nerve impulses to the breathing muscles, i.e., the diaphragm or the rib muscles. Special nerves conduct such impulses. For example, a pair of large **phrenic nerves** innervates the diaphragm. When impulses from the breathing center reach the breathing

FIG. 15.10 The control of inhalation (left) and of exhalation (right). Left, CO_2 in blood stimulates the breathing center to send impulses to the diaphragm, leading to inhalation. Right, impulses from the inflated lung inhibit the breathing center, leading to exhalation.

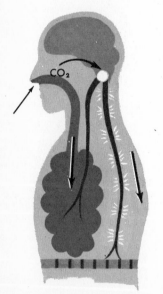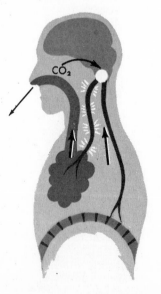

muscles, these contract, the chest cavity enlarges as a result, and the lung alveoli are sucked open. Air is then inhaled (Fig. 15.10).

The very stretching of the alveoli now stimulates special sets of nerves which originate in the alveolar walls. These nerves conduct impulses from the inflated lung to the breathing center. When such impulses arrive there, the center is *inhibited.* That is, the impulses override and suppress the stimulating effect of blood-borne CO_2. Consequently, the center ceases to send signals to the breathing muscles. This prevents inhalation from going too far, for in the absence of signals from the brain, the breathing muscles relax. As they do so, the chest cavity becomes smaller, the lung alveoli recoil to their original state, and air is exhaled.

After the alveoli have recoiled, they are no longer stretched and the nerve endings in their walls therefore are no longer stimulated. Impulses then cease to be sent to the breathing center and the center consequently ceases to be inhibited. In the absence of inhibition, blood-borne CO_2 can again exert its effect. The breathing center now resumes its impulse transmission to the breathing muscles and a new inhalation begins. The whole cycle is outlined schematically in Fig. 15.11.

Blood-borne oxygen also has an effect on the breathing center, but this effect is much less powerful than that of CO_2, and it probably plays only a minor role during normal breathing. We may conclude that a basic breathing rhythm is maintained by alternating, automatically self-renewing effects on the breathing center, produced largely by nervous inhibitions and carbon dioxide stimulations.

Variations in Rhythm

It should follow that, as the inhibitions and stimulations vary, so should the breathing rhythm. This is the case. As is well known, both the rate and depth of breathing can be altered easily. For example, an exercise of will or powerful sensory and emotional experiences may affect breathing greatly. These are nervous influences, relayed to the breathing center over many different and often indirect nerve paths.

Carbon dioxide also produces modifications of the breathing pattern. When the CO_2 concentration in blood is high, the *rate* of breathing is proportionately high, and vice versa. High CO_2 concentrations build up whenever the rate of CO_2 production through respiration is greater than the rate of CO_2 removal via the lungs. This is the case, for example, at the start of strenuous physical work, when intensified energy pro-

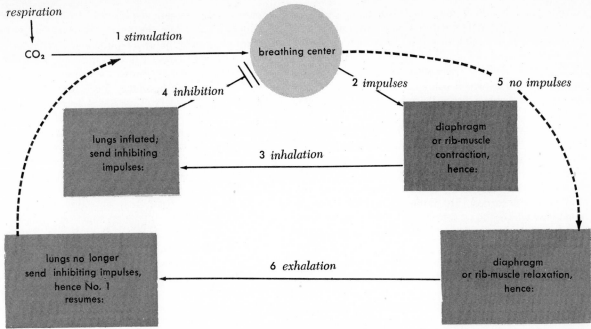

FIG. 15.11 Summary diagram of breathing control. An arrow tipped with a transverse double bar, as in 4, designates inhibition.

duction in cells liberates increasing amounts of CO_2. By speeding up breathing under such conditions, CO_2 hastens its own removal through the lungs. Faster breathing at the same time increases the oxygen supply, just when the tissues require more oxygen. It will be found later that CO_2 also speeds up the heart; more rapid circulation therefore aids additionally in increasing the speed of gas exchange.

The concentration of CO_2 in blood becomes extremely high when breathing is deliberately stopped altogether. But the accumulating gas then soon stimulates the breathing center so strongly that a resumption of breathing is *forced*, even against the most intense will. An animal cannot commit suicide by holding its breath.

Conversely, when the CO_2 concentration in blood is low, the breathing center is stimulated rather weakly and breathing slows down. This is the case during sleep or rest, when respiration and CO_2 production are minimal. The extreme here is the *overventilated* condition, produced, for example, when breathing is intentionally made as deep and as rapid as possible. Carbon dioxide may then be exhaled so fast that abnormally little of the gas reaches the breathing center. A similar lack of CO_2 and of oxygen may develop in the rarefied atmos-

phere at very high altitudes. Under conditions of this sort, the breathing center may temporarily cease to operate altogether and a "blackout" may ensue. Breathing will remain stopped until the CO_2 concentration has again built up to a high enough level to stimulate the center adequately.

Breathing is a means to an end. The most immediate end is the procurement of additional oxygen and the removal of excess carbon dioxide. Fresh atmospheric air as inhaled contains some 20 per cent oxygen and 0.03 per cent carbon dioxide. Exhaled air includes only 16 per cent oxygen, but some 4 per cent carbon dioxide. Evidently, a fifth of the available oxygen has been retained in the body and more than 100 times the amount of carbon dioxide has been expelled. What happens to the one and where does the other come from?

GAS TRANSPORT

THE PATHWAY

Inasmuch as blood is the transport medium of the respiratory gases, an intimate association between circulation and breathing may be inferred. Indeed, the heart is virtually embedded in lung and millions of blood capillaries ramify over the lung alveoli. Blood and air here approach each other very closely. Moreover, as we shall see later, the same region in the medulla oblongata which contains the breathing center also contains centers controlling heartbeat and circulation.

If blood is rich in oxygen, it is called *arterial* blood; if it is rich in CO_2, it is called *venous* blood. An **artery** is a blood vessel leading *away* from the heart; a **vein,** a vessel leading *to* the heart. Note that the designation "artery" or "vein" depends not on the kind of blood carried, but rather on the direction of blood flow within the vessel.

In all body tissues, cellular gas exchange takes place; cells take up oxygen from and add carbon dioxide to the blood. Here, therefore, blood becomes venous. This CO_2-rich blood then travels to the heart,

entering this organ via a vessel called the **vena cava** (Fig. 15.12). From the heart, venous blood is pumped through a pair of short **pulmonary arteries** into the nearby lungs. These arteries branch into extensive networks of capillaries spread over the lung alveoli. Pulmonary gas exchange takes place here; CO_2 leaves the blood and O_2 enters. Thus blood becomes arterial. This O_2-rich blood now collects in a pair of **pulmonary veins,** which lead back to the heart. Redistributed from the heart via the **aorta** throughout the body, blood supplies new oxygen to tissue cells and is ready to carry off new carbon dioxide. That is the general pattern. How is it realized in detail?

THE EXCHANGES

The transfer of oxygen from the lung alveoli into the blood and the reverse transfer of carbon dioxide are governed primarily by diffusion. This is one of the

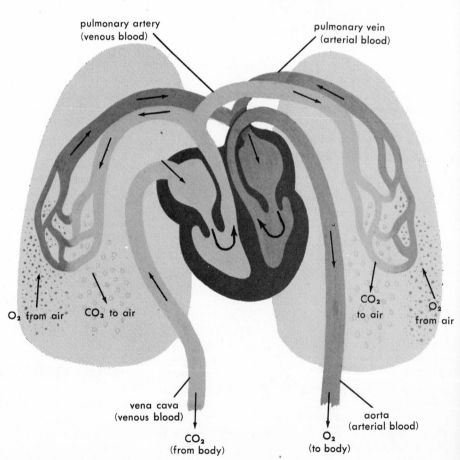

FIG. 15.12 The pulmonary circulation. Arterial blood is shown in dark gray, venous blood in light gray. Note that in this diagram the left side of the body appears on the right, and the right side of the body on the left. Anatomical drawings are usually oriented as if observer and subject were face to face.

pulmonary artery (venous blood)

pulmonary vein (arterial blood)

O_2 from air CO_2 to air

CO_2 to air

O_2 from air

vena cava (venous blood)

aorta (arterial blood)

CO_2 (from body)

O_2 (to body)

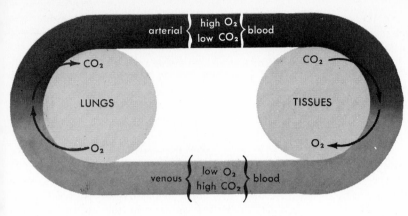

FIG. 15.13 The exchanges of respiratory gases between the lungs and blood and between the body tissues and blood. Oxygen enters the blood in the lungs and leaves in the tissues. Carbon dioxide enters in the tissues and leaves in the lungs.

very few instances when active cellular absorption and secretion do not appear to play a role. The wall of an alveolus consists of a thin, single layer of cells, and the wall of a blood capillary also consists of such a layer (see Fig. 15.7). Neither of these walls offers resistance to the passage of gaseous O_2 and CO_2. Gas exchange may therefore take place much more rapidly than if absorption and secretion were necessary.

The specific direction in which the gases move is determined by the prevailing pressure gradients, or **tension gradients,** between blood and lung. Specifically, atmospheric air in the lungs contains only a little CO_2, but the venous blood which flows into the lungs from the body is virtually saturated with the gas. The pressure, or tension, of CO_2 in blood is therefore greater than that in the alveoli and a tension gradient points *out* of the capillaries. Carbon dioxide consequently moves in that direction, or, better, more CO_2 molecules diffuse out of the blood than into it. As a result, blood ceases to be venous (Fig. 15.13).

The pressure pattern is the reverse with respect to oxygen. Blood flowing into the lungs from the body is oxygen-poor, for the tissues have removed much of the gas. But the air in the alveoli contains a maximal amount of O_2. Accordingly, a tension gradient points *into* the blood and more O_2 molecules diffuse into the capillaries than in the reverse direction. As a result, blood becomes arterial.

These interrelations explain why breathing is inefficient at high altitudes. In rarefied air, the atmospheric oxygen pressure is greatly reduced and the pressure differential between lung and blood is low. Oxygen diffusion consequently does not take place as readily. We may similarly understand why the close atmosphere of an unventilated, overcrowded room makes breathing difficult. The CO_2 tension in the room

is high, approaching that in blood. Hence CO_2 cannot easily leave the blood.

Just as in the lungs, cellular gas exchange in the body tissues is also governed by tension gradients (see Fig. 15.13). Cells continuously use up oxygen in respiration and the tension of this gas in cells is therefore low. The tension in arterial blood is higher, however, and O_2 diffuses from blood into tissue cells. Blood consequently ceases to be arterial. At the same time, since respiratory CO_2 is produced in cells steadily, the CO_2 tension within tissue cells is high. But arterial blood has low CO_2 tensions and the gas therefore diffuses from tissue cells into blood. This makes blood venous.

How are respiratory gases carried in blood?

THE VEHICLE

Oxygen Transport

Transport of respiratory gases requires a medium containing water, a number of inorganic ions, and red blood corpuscles.

The corpuscles owe their red color to **haemoglobin.** This complex pigment, customarily symbolized as Hb, consists of two parts, *haeme* and *globin*. Haeme resembles chlorophyll structurally, but as has been noted in Chap. 4, it contains iron rather than magnesium. Haeme is the active, functionally significant fraction of haemoglobin. Globin is a protein which probably serves mainly as a carrier of haeme.

We may note that, in many animals other than vertebrates, transport of respiratory gases is achieved not by haemoglobin but by various other pigmented compounds. Some of these contain iron, as haemoglobin does, but others contain copper instead. In some cases, particularly among annelids and mollusks, such bloods are green or blue in color. Moreover, the respiratory pigments of some animals are not present in blood cells but are in solution in blood water. It can be shown that vertebrate haemoglobin is the most efficient of all the different gas carriers encountered among animals.

Haemoglobin has the capacity of forming a loose chemical combination with oxygen:

$$Hb + O_2 \rightleftharpoons HbO_2$$

By the principle of mass action, this reversible reaction will shift to the right when O_2 is present in excess. As we have seen, this is the case in the lung capillaries, and HbO_2, or **oxyhaemoglobin**, forms there.

Oxygen is carried in blood largely in the form of HbO_2. A little oxygen also *dissolves* in the water of blood, in the same way that all atmospheric gases dissolve in water. Indeed, blood contains dissolved CO_2 and N_2 as well. When the external air pressure suddenly falls, as during rapid ascents into high altitudes or up from great depths, then the dissolved gases may fizz out of the blood in the form of bubbles. Dangerous

"bends" may result. The effect here is rather like removing the cap of a bottle of soda; gases then fizz out similarly.

When oxyhaemoglobin reaches the tissues, the reaction above shifts to the left. Cells are oxygen-poor relative to the blood, and the conditions of mass action are therefore such that HbO_2 "unloads" its oxygen. Free Hb forms again and the free O_2 is taken up by the tissues (Fig. 15.14).

It may be noted that haemoglobin may transport not only oxygen but also *carbon monoxide*: $Hb + CO \rightleftharpoons HbCO$. This union is achieved much more easily than the union with oxygen. Accordingly, if carbon monoxide is present in the atmosphere, Hb becomes HbCO in preference to HbO_2. This means that little oxygen can be transported to the tissues, which consequently cannot respire. Therein lies the poisonous effect of carbon monoxide.

Carbon Dioxide Transport

Of the CO_2 released from tissue cells, a small fraction dissolves physically in blood water, as already

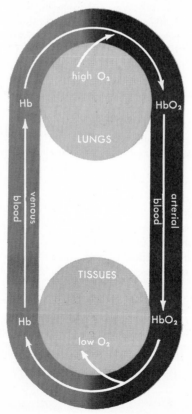 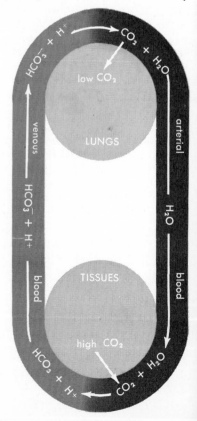

FIG. 15.14 The transport of respiratory gases in blood. Oxygen is carried in the form of oxyhaemoglobin (HbO_2), carbon dioxide in the form of bicarbonate ions (HCO_3^-).

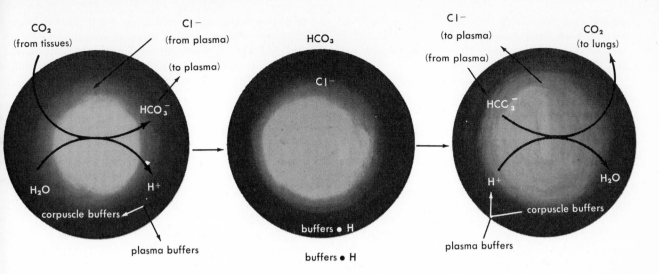

IN TISSUE CAPILLARIES   IN TRANSIT THROUGH VEINS   IN LUNG CAPILLARIES

FIG. 15.15   The chloride shift in red corpuscles. In tissue capillaries (left), CO_2 reacts with water in the corpuscles. Bicarbonate ions appear, and as these diffuse into the plasma, chloride ions diffuse into the corpuscles. Hydrogen ions are also formed, and these are buffered (middle). In the lungs these processes occur in reverse, resulting in the liberation of gaseous CO_2 (right).

noted. Another small fraction combines with haemoglobin and is transported to the lungs in the form of $HbCO_2$. But the bulk reacts with water chemically and forms bicarbonate ions (HCO_3^-):

$$CO_2 + H_2O \rightleftharpoons \underset{\substack{carbonic \\ acid}}{H_2CO_3} \rightleftharpoons \underset{\substack{bicarbonate \\ ion}}{H^+ + HCO_3^-}$$

Inasmuch as tissue cells constantly add CO_2 to blood, this reaction proceeds to the right in the tissues. Most of the CO_2 is therefore transported to the lungs in the form of HCO_3^-. In the lungs, the conditions of mass action are reversed; CO_2 escapes into the alveoli, the reaction consequently shifts to the left, and more free CO_2 is released for exhalation (see Fig. 15.14).

We may note that the *rapid* conversion of CO_2 and H_2O into HCO_3^- and H^+, as above, requires an enzyme, *carbonic anhydrase*. This enzyme occurs only within red blood corpuscles. HCO_3^- is therefore formed mostly in these corpuscles. After they are formed, bicarbonate ions largely diffuse out of the corpuscles and are carried to the lungs in the fluid component of the blood.

Inasmuch as bicarbonate ions are electrically nega-

tive, we might expect that, as they leave the red corpuscles, the corpuscles would not remain electrically neutral. But it has been found that, for every bicarbonate ion which diffuses out from a red corpuscle, a chloride ion (Cl-) diffuses in. Chloride ions are normally present in blood water. This exchange, called the **chloride shift**, preserves the electrical neutrality of the red corpuscles. In the lungs, these processes take place in reverse. Chloride ions move out of red corpuscles and bicarbonate ions move back in. The enzyme carbonic anhydrase then promotes the rapid re-formation of free CO_2, and this gas diffuses from the blood into the lung alveoli (Fig. 15.15).

The reaction between CO_2 and H_2O yields not only bicarbonate ions but also hydrogen ions (H^+). This ion lowers the pH, and blood therefore might be expected to become considerably more acid whenever it transports CO_2. However, this does not happen, since blood is strongly *buffered* (see Chap. 2). Among the substances which act as buffers are various inorganic ions as well as blood proteins, including haemoglobin. These buffers unite with H^+ as it is formed, and the resulting combinations remain more or less nonionized. As a result, the amounts of free H^+ are greatly reduced and pH does not change appreciably. In the lungs, the conditions of mass action are such that the buffers release H⁺, and CO_2 and H_2O are re-formed (see Fig. 15.15).

The processes auxiliary to cellular metabolism are now completed. Every cell of an organism has been supplied with oxygen, has been rid of carbon dioxide, and has already been provided with nutrients; it is ready to produce energy and to synthesize new living matter.

REVIEW QUESTIONS

1. Distinguish between breathing and respiration. How does gas exchange occur among plants? What are the principal patterns of gas exchange among animals?

2. Describe the structural organization of the breathing system in man. How is sound produced and how can sound be varied in pitch, volume, and quality? What is an alveolus and what is its relation to the lung? What chest structures surround the lungs?

3. Describe the pressure changes in the body associated with inhalation and exhalation in (a) abdominal breathing and (b) chest breathing.

4. How are inhalation-exhalation cycles controlled and maintained automatically? Review here the role of CO_2 and that of the brain. Show by what sequence of events inhalation comes to alternate with exhalation.

5. Describe the processes through which breathing rate increases when physical exercise is begun and decreases at the onset of sleep. What is overventilation and what is its effect?

6. Describe the pattern of blood circulation through the body. Where, specifically, does venous blood become arterial and arterial blood become venous? In the circulation through the lungs, which blood vessels contain arterial and which contain venous blood?

7. By what processes does arterial blood become venous and vice versa? Show what factors govern these changes and describe the actual changes in lungs and tissues.

8. How is oxygen carried in blood? What reactions occur in the lungs and in the tissues? Why is carbon monoxide a poison?

9. How is CO_2 carried in blood? What reactions occur in the lungs and in the tissues? What is the role of red blood corpuscles in CO_2 transport? What is the chloride shift? What is the function of carbonic anhydrase and of blood buffers?

10. How are breathing and gas transport affected during ascent to high altitudes? How is nitrogen carried in blood? Why is breathing difficult in an unventilated room? What happens when a person holds his breath for a long time?

SUGGESTED COLLATERAL READINGS

Any of the texts cited at the end of Chap. 14, especially the first, may again be consulted to advantage for additional information on breathing and gas transport. Various comparative aspects of these topics are described in the following sources:

Baldwin, E.: "An Introduction to Comparative Biochemistry," Cambridge, New York, 1949.

Buchsbaum, R.: "Animals without Backbones," University of Chicago Press, Chicago, 1948.
Fox, H. M.: Blood Pigments, Sci. American, vol. 182, 1950.
Williams, C. B.: Insect Breathing, Sci. American, vol. 188, 1953.

RESPIRATION

16

Nutrition and gas exchange make cellular metabolism possible. Cellular metabolism in turn makes possible continued nutrition, gas exchange, and indeed life itself.

Whatever the organism and whatever its pattern of nutrition and gas exchange, the pattern of its cellular metabolism is always the same: with or without the aid of oxygen, and with organic nutrients as fuel, cells respire, i.e., *produce* metabolically usable energy. Such energy may then be *used* within the cell that produced it, toward cellular maintenance and self-perpetuation. Energy production is the subject of this chapter; energy utilization, that of the next.

THE PATTERN OF RESPIRATION

FUEL AND ENERGY

Respiration may be defined as a conversion of the chemical energy of organic molecules into metabolically usable energy within living cells.

The last part of this definition, "within living cells," means largely *mitochondria*. The main phases of respiration take place in these specialized components of the cell cytoplasm. Virtually all complex cellular processes occur in distinct "factory" locations, and we have seen this to be so, for example, in photosynthesis. We may now note it to be the case in respiration also. To the mitochondria present in every cell flow all the necessary raw materials, and from them emerges usable energy. The electron microscope reveals that mitochondria have a complicated fine structure (see Fig. 4.22). Much of the chemical machinery of respiration has been shown to be located along the walls of the internal mitochondrial partitions.

Concerning the remainder of the definition above, we may note that, directly or indirectly, the chemical energy of organic molecules represents

395

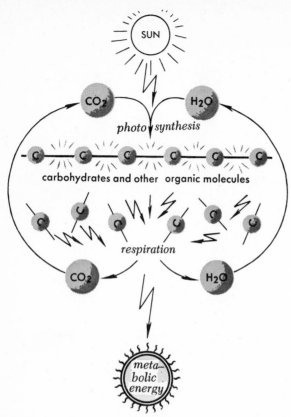

FIG. 16.1 The source of respiratory energy. The ultimate source is the sun, some of whose energy is trapped by photosynthesis into organic molecules. Respiratory energy results from a breakdown of these molecules.

stored solar energy. It is the sun which, through photosynthesis, makes possible the construction of primary organic molecules. All other organic substances are derived secondarily from these. In a sense, therefore, the bonds of organic molecules incorporate solar energy. And if the bonds are broken under appropriate conditions, the locked-in energy becomes available for metabolic work. An essential step of respiration is such a breaking of bonds in organic molecules, particularly the carbon-to-carbon bonds, which store relatively large amounts of energy (Fig. 16.1).

A similar process is very familiar from the non-living world: burning. Fuels burned in a stove are principally wood, coal, oil, or "gas," i.e., organic materials containing stored solar energy. Energy is obtained here also by breaking bonds. The principle involved is precisely the same as in respiration, and respiration, in-

deed, may properly be regarded as a burning. If this is so, why does respiration not produce the high temperatures of a fire?

For two reasons. First, a fire is *uncontrolled* combustion, in the sense that all the bonds within a fuel molecule may be broken simultaneously. A maximum amount of energy may then be released all at once. Such sudden, explosive release generates the high temperatures of a fire. Respiration, on the other hand, is *controlled* combustion. Energy is obtained from one bond at a time. If a fuel is respired completely, the total energy yield is the same as if it were burned in a stove; but in respiration the energy is removed bit by bit, bond by bond. Temperatures therefore stay low. Enzymes exercise the necessary control. Respiration is a series of enzymatic reactions, and biological combustion cannot take place any faster than the controlling enzymes will permit.

Second, the energy produced in a fire is dissipated energy—largely heat and to some extent light. But in respiration only very little of the available energy escapes as heat and practically none as light. Instead, most of it is "packaged" directly into new *chemical* energy. As we shall see, fuel energy creates *new* chemical bonds, and it is in this form that metabolic energy is used in cells. Since chemical bonds are not "hot," temperatures stay low during respiration (Fig. 16.2).

ENERGY CHANGES

Oxidation-Reduction

How is chemical energy removed from a bond? As we shall see, there are several ways. One of the most important, in respiration as in a fire, is *withdrawal of hydrogen* from the fuel, or **dehydrogenation.** This process requires the presence of a hydrogen acceptor. If we let A stand for such an acceptor, then combustion may be symbolized generally as follows:

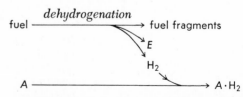

Thus if a hydrogen acceptor is available, hydrogen can be withdrawn from a fuel. The carbon bonds of the fuel may break as a result; bond energy becomes available; and the hydrogen can be collected and held by the acceptor.

organic fuel

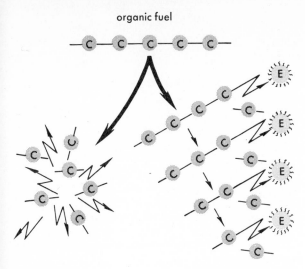

fire:
sudden, free energy

respiration:
gradual, "packaged" energy

FIG. 16.2 Comparison of a fire and respiration. In a fire, organic molecules are decomposed all at once, yielding sudden, free energy (left). In respiration, bonds of organic molecules are broken one at a time, yielding energy gradually. Moreover, this energy does not become free but is "packaged" into other chemicals (right).

Many different substances can and do serve as hydrogen acceptors. One which serves in fires and in a major form of respiration is atmospheric *oxygen.* Combustion in the presence of oxygen thus takes the general form:

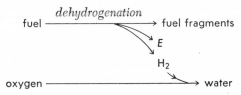

Water is a byproduct.

Note that hydrogen acceptors *do not start* combustion. They merely serve to collect and to remove hydrogen. Note also that dehydrogenation is more or less synonymous with **oxidation,** whether oxygen or any other hydrogen acceptor is involved. In losing hydrogen, a substance is said to become oxidized; in gaining hydrogen, a substance is said to become *reduced.* In combustion, therefore, a fuel molecule may become oxidized by dehydrogenation and a hydrogen acceptor becomes reduced at the same time.

If it is not the hydrogen acceptor that starts combustion, what is? In a fire, the starter is heat. We must supply an initial amount of heat (by friction as in lighting a match, or through an electric spark, for example) to ignite the fuel, that is, to achieve a first dehydrogenation. Pictured crudely, such activation energy applied from the outside may be thought to agitate the atoms of a fuel molecule to such an extent that hydrogen atoms begin to break loose. Enough energy is thereby released in the form of heat to initiate a self-sustaining chain reaction. Adjacent fuel molecules become agitated; *their* hydrogen atoms may be thought to break loose; more energy is thereby released; new fuel molecules become agitated; etc.

In living cells, respiration actually never starts because it never stops. It is always under way, unceasingly. The "fire" of life was lit when life first originated, and since then it has been handed down from parent to offspring, without interruption. The continuing dehydrogenations are maintained not by heat but by enzymatic reactions. Special enzymes promote hydrogen removal from fuels, and special enzymes also act as primary hydrogen acceptors. As we shall see, these reactions themselves require energy. To maintain them, therefore, some of the energy obtained as a result of respiration must be funneled back to sustain the respiration process itself (Fig. 16.3).

The Fuels

What are the organic fuels in cells? The answer is anything that contains breakable carbon bonds, which means *any* organic constituent of cells: carbohydrates, fats, proteins, their various derivatives, vitamins, other special compounds, and indeed all the innumerable substances which together make up a cell. Like a fire, respiration is no respecter of materials. Anything that can burn will burn, and in cells this is the very sub-

FIG. 16.3 Some of the energy resulting from respiration must be funneled back into respiration to sustain that process.

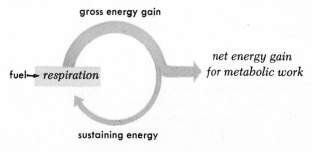

stance of cells itself. Respiration does not distinguish between the expendable and the nonexpendable. For example, an amino acid which is an important structural member of the framework of a cell or is part of an enzyme may be burned just as readily as an amino acid which has been absorbed as a food.

However, if a fire is fed much of one fuel but little of another, more of the first is likely to be burned. Indeed, under normal conditions, a cell receives a steady enough supply of foods to make *them* the primary fuels rather than the structural parts of a cell. Also, some kinds of materials burn more easily than others and some are more accessible to the fire than others. On this basis, foods, carbohydrates and fats in particular, are again favored as fuels and the finished components of a cell tend to be spared. Yet the sparing is relative only. The formed parts of a cell *are* burned gradually, including even those which make up the burning apparatus itself, i.e., the mitochondria.

But if a cell itself burns away, how can it remain intact and functioning? Only by continuous construction of new living components, offsetting the continuous destruction through respiration. Note that these two processes go on side by side, at all times: destructive energy metabolism and constructive synthesis metabolism. One is in balance with the other, and foods serve both as fuel for the one and as building materials for the other. We say that the components of a cell are continuously "turned over," i.e., existing parts are continuously replaced by new ones. Living matter, we note, is never quite the same from instant to instant (Fig. 16.4).

The Energy Gain

What happens to the energy obtained from respiratory fuels? If it were to dissipate freely into the surroundings, it would become more or less useless metabolically. Evidently, an energy-trapping device is required in cells. Such a device exists. We have already encountered it in Chaps. 3 and 13, and it is represented by the reversible reaction which interconverts adenosine diphosphate (ADP) and adenosine triphosphate (ATP):

$$\text{ADP} + \text{phosphate} + \text{energy} \rightleftharpoons \text{ATP}$$

Proceeding to the right, this reaction symbolizes the energy-trapping process of respiration. Energy made available by a fuel molecule becomes incorporated into ADP and phosphate, and ATP is formed. *Hence ATP is the chief endproduct of respiration.*

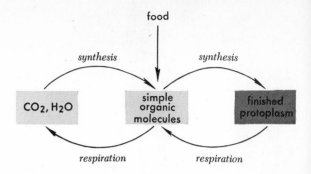

FIG. 16.4 Destruction of cellular materials by respiration is offset by simultaneous construction of cellular materials by synthesis. See Fig. 17.11 for a more comprehensive illustration.

ATP is also the energy vehicle; i.e., it emerges from the mitochondria and diffuses to all locations within a cell where energy must be utilized. In utilization, the above reaction proceeds to the left: ATP breaks down, energy is released and used, and ADP and phosphate reappear.

In summary, therefore, respiration as a whole consists of three correlated events. First, a fuel molecule is oxidized, which means most often that hydrogen is removed from it. The hydrogen becomes attached to an appropriate acceptor, and if the acceptor is oxygen, water forms. This phase of respiration may be termed **hydrogen transfer.**

Second, as a result of oxidation, the carbon-to-carbon bonds of the fuel molecule may be broken. Smaller fuel fragments then form, and these may be oxidized and broken up in turn until the original fuel has been degraded completely into 1-carbon fragments. These always appear in the form of CO_2. This phase of respiration constitutes **fuel breakdown.**

Third, also as a result of oxidation, energy becomes available. A little of this energy escapes as heat, indicating that respiration is not 100 per cent efficient. However, most of the energy does not become free in this manner but is instead harvested by the ADP/ATP system. ATP then forms the main product of respiration. This phase may be called **energy transfer.** We may symbolize these three events as in Fig. 16.5.

The above outlines the general pattern of respiration sufficiently for a preliminary understanding of the process. To carry understanding one step deeper, we now proceed with a more detailed discussion of each of the three main phases of respiration.

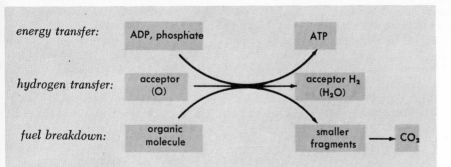

FIG. 16.5 The three main phases of respiration: breakdown of fuel, hydrogen transfer from fuel, and energy transfer from fuel.

ENERGY TRANSFER

OXIDATION

We have just noted that the net result of respiration is a transfer of energy from chemical bonds in fuel into the chemical bonds of ATP. Why, then, respiration to begin with? If fuel energy already exists in the form of chemical bonds, what is the point of respiration if it only creates other chemical bonds?

Some bonds hold more energy than others. We may distinguish between **high-energy bonds** and **low-energy bonds.** To create the former, a relatively large amount of energy must be expended and a correspondingly large amount becomes available when such a bond is broken. However, most bonds in organic fuel molecules are of the *low*-energy type. For example, any of the carbon-to-carbon, carbon-to-hydrogen, carbon-to-nitrogen, or carbon-to-oxygen links we have encountered so far are low-energy bonds. If one of these is broken, only a comparatively small amount of energy becomes available.

A critical dilemma thus arises. On the one hand, organic fuels provide only bond energies of low intensity. But on the other, very concentrated, intense packets of energy are needed for the synthesis of cellular components, for movement, and for metabolic work in general. Fuels, as it were, provide energy of popgun intensity, but metabolic work requires cannons. What is needed, clearly, is an energy-*intensifying* process, one which would pool the many low-energy packets of a fuel molecule into a smaller number of high-energy packets.

Respiration does just that. It first concentrates the low bond energies of fuel and creates within a fuel molecule one or more high-energy bonds. This is the crucial event in oxidation and in respiration as a whole.

Then these high-energy bonds are transferred from fuel into the structure of ATP, a substance which is a high-energy carrier. Clearly, respiration accomplishes more than merely making new bonds out of old ones; it makes high-energy bonds out of low-energy bonds. And through ATP it supplies energy of uniformly high intensity to all points of utilization.

The creation of high-energy bonds from low-energy bonds is achieved essentially by *internal reorganizations* of a fuel molecule. Each such molecule is characterized by a specific pattern of atoms, hence a specific pattern of bonds between the atoms. If a chemical change occurs, some of the atoms may change position, others may be removed, still others may be added. Whatever happens, the arrangement of the atoms will change and the pattern of the bonds will therefore change also. Many changes of this sort do not affect the content or distribution of the bond energies. But some do. And it may then happen that the original bond energies of the molecule become redistributed in such a way that one of the bonds comes to hold a great deal of energy, whereas others hold even less than before. In effect, a high-energy bond will have been created at the expense of several low-energy bonds (Fig. 16.6).

If a molecular reorganization occurs which does redistribute the energy so that a high-energy bond is

FIG. 16.6 Through internal reorganization of the atoms of a molecule, a high-energy bond may be created. Such a reorganization is an oxidative change.

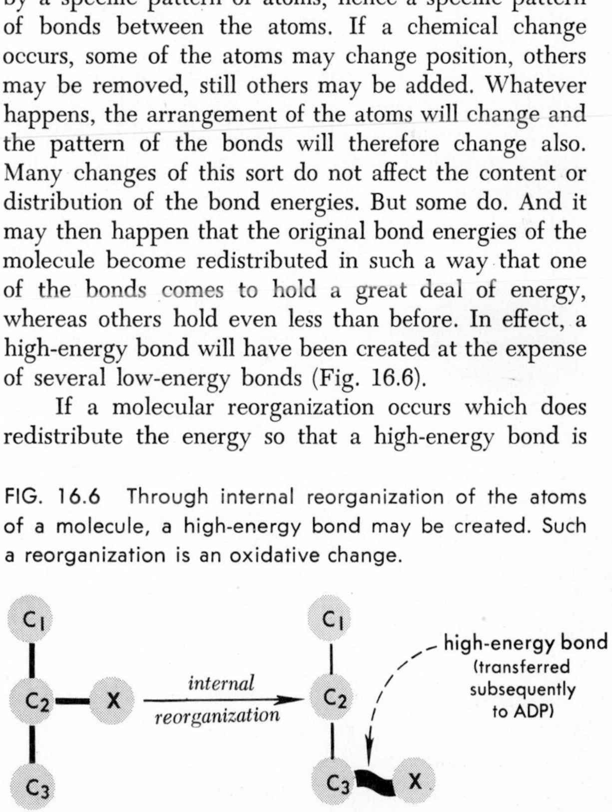

created, then we say that an *oxidation* has taken place. As already noted, one of the important types of oxidative changes is *dehydrogenation,* removal of hydrogen from a fuel. Other chemical changes which can be oxidative include removal of water (*dehydration*), removal of CO_2 (*decarboxylation*), and removal of electrons (a form of *ionization*). The last is particularly significant in respiration and occurs in many instances in conjunction with dehydrogenation, as we shall see. In sum, respiration includes oxidative reactions of the following general type:

fuel with low-energy bonds → *oxidation* → fuel with high-energy bonds

H_2, H_2O, CO_2, e^-

PHOSPHORYLATION

The principal high-energy bond in metabolism is the **phosphate bond,** i.e., the bond which joins a molecule to a phosphate group or, more precisely, to the –Ⓟ portion of a phosphate group (see pertinent discussion in Chap. 12). Note that not all phosphate bonds are of the high-energy variety. For example, glucose-phosphate and many other phosphorylated compounds dealt with previously are low-energy combinations. But, put in terms of a crude approximation, the properties of the phosphate bond are such that it can contain a great deal of energy, much more than is needed simply to hold –Ⓟ to a molecule. In that case, the phosphate bond in effect stores *extra* energy; it is a high-energy bond. To distinguish the high-energy bond, we use the symbol ⌢. Thus, we may have either

or

fuel-Ⓟ   *low-energy phosphate bond*

fuel~Ⓟ   *high-energy phosphate bond*

A low-energy phosphate bond may be converted into a high-energy phosphate bond if more energy becomes concentrated in it. As noted above, such energy enrichment of a bond may be achieved by oxidation. Hence we may have

fuel-Ⓟ → *oxidation* → fuel~Ⓟ

H_2

Clearly, before such a reaction can take place, "fuel–Ⓟ" must be available as a starting material. In other words, the addition of a low-energy –Ⓟ group to a fuel molecule, or *phosphorylation,* will be an important preliminary toward the creation of high-energy bonds. Respiration actually includes such preliminary phosphorylations, and the creation of high-energy bonds proceeds according to the following general sequence of events:

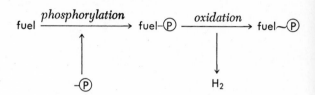

PHOSPHATE TRANSFERS

The phosphorylation of a fuel obviously requires a phosphate donor, i.e., a substance which may contribute –Ⓟ groups. One group of such donors includes phosphoric acid (H_3PO_4) and inorganic ions derived from phosphoric acid. These substances are supplied by the external environment as mineral nutrients; they are the ultimate source of all phosphates in cells. Either phosphoric acid or its ions may phosphorylate an organic molecule. For example, if we rewrite H_3PO_4 as $H-O-PO_3H_2$, we note that phosphoric acid contains $-PO_3H_2$, or a –Ⓟ group. This group may become transferred to an organic molecule by chemical reaction, resulting in phosphorylation.

Once an organic molecule is so phosphorylated, its –Ⓟ may then be transferred in turn to various other organic molecules. In many such cases, a **low-energy transfer** occurs; i.e., the low-energy value of the –Ⓟ bond does not change. For example, if M and N symbolize the main portions of two molecules, then we may have

M–Ⓟ → M·H

N·H → N–Ⓟ

(Note again that the *net* effect of a gain or a loss of –Ⓟ is the loss or the gain of H, but that the actual exchange involves –O–Ⓟ and –O–H.)

In a particularly important series of cases, **high-energy transfers** take place. This occurs between organic molecules which possess ~Ⓟ groups and the ADP/ATP system which harvests respiratory energy.

For example, if a fuel molecule has been phosphorylated and oxidized, it may possess a $\sim$Ⓟ group as a result. Such a group is then transferred to ADP, and this is a high-energy transfer. The pattern is

fuel$\sim$Ⓟ $\longrightarrow$ fuel residue

ADP $\longrightarrow$ ADP$\sim$Ⓟ = ATP

ADP becomes ADP$\sim$Ⓟ (ATP) by accepting $\sim$Ⓟ from fuel. Through this type of transfer, some of the energy of a fuel becomes incorporated into ATP. *This is a main energy-harvesting reaction of respiration.*

We shall see below that $\sim$Ⓟ groups are created in substances other than fuels, through energy derived ultimately from fuels. In all such cases, $\sim$Ⓟ groups may be transferred to ADP as above, resulting in the formation of ATP. Note here that *only* through ATP can energy become available for useful metabolic work within cells. Any other substance possessing $\sim$Ⓟ groups cannot contribute its energy to metabolic work directly; ATP always must be the intermediate energy carrier.

ATP is not only a carrier and potential donor of a high-energy bond but also a carrier and potential donor of a phosphate group. Indeed, like phosphoric acid, ATP is a major phosphorylating agent in cells. It may react with a fuel molecule and donate its third phosphate (as well as energy) to the molecule. ATP thereby becomes ADP again. For example, glucose is normally phosphorylated by ATP:

$C_6H_{12}O_6$
glucose

$C_6H_{11}O_6$-Ⓟ
glucose-phosphate

ADP$\sim$Ⓟ $\longrightarrow$ ADP

Two points should be noted here. First, as above, the fuel which gains a –Ⓟ group loses H. This hydrogen is incorporated into ADP and is usually not specially indicated when ADP is written in symbolic form. Second, the high energy of the transferred phosphate bond is not preserved; $\sim$Ⓟ is detached from ATP but –Ⓟ is attached to the glucose. Like many phosphorylated fuels, glucose-phosphate is a low-energy combination. Yet $\sim$Ⓟ supplies more energy than is needed to produce this combination. In every such case, any excess energy of $\sim$Ⓟ dissipates as heat. Heat losses of this sort are unavoidable. Many phosphorylations, such as that of glucose, can be achieved only by ATP, even though not all the energy supplied by ATP is being used.

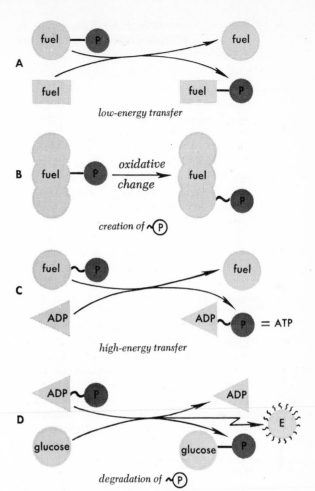

FIG. 16.7   The four ways in which phosphate bonds may be transferred or changed: low-energy transfers, creation of high-energy bonds, high-energy transfers, and degradation of high-energy bonds.

In sum, we note that the bond energies of phosphate groups may be affected in four different ways (see also Fig. 16.7):

1. –Ⓟ to –Ⓟ   *low-energy transfer, as in phosphate exchange by two molecules*
2. –Ⓟ to $\sim$Ⓟ   *creation of high bond energy, as in respiratory oxidation*
3. $\sim$Ⓟ to $\sim$Ⓟ   *high-energy transfer, as in the harvesting of energy by ADP $\longrightarrow$ ATP*

4. $\sim$(P) to $-$(P) *loss of high bond energy, as in phosphorylation of glucose by ATP*

All four types of changes play vital roles in respiration, and respiration may in fact be regarded as a sequence of reactions consisting of these four types of energy changes involving phosphates. Figure 16.8 summarizes this basic pattern of energy transfers in respiration.

Note here that useful energy never becomes "free." Instead, it is conducted from molecule to molecule in discrete packets, in the form of high-energy phosphate bonds. Note also that all transfer reactions are fundamentally reversible. But the steady expenditure of energy during metabolic work imposes a one-way direction, so that fuels continue to be oxidized and ATP continues to be formed. Figure 16.8 shows clearly that ATP produced by respiration must be funneled back into respiration itself, to make more of that process possible. But far more total ATP is formed by respiration than is needed to carry out the initial phosphorylations. Therefore, for every given amount of fuel fed into respiration, a given *net* amount of ATP is gained. It is this net gain which sustains all other metabolic processes in cells.

What happens to the hydrogen removed from fuel–(P) during oxidation? This leads to a consideration of the second of the three phases of respiration.

HYDROGEN TRANSFER

THE PATTERN

As noted above, dehydrogenation is the most common oxidative change which creates high-energy bonds in a fuel. Whenever hydrogen is to be removed from a fuel molecule, two conditions must be fulfilled. First, specific *dehydrogenases* must be present. These enzymes control the extraction of hydrogen, and each different fuel generally requires its own specific dehydrogenase. Second, a specific *hydrogen acceptor* must be present. Atmospheric oxygen is an excellent acceptor. Yet fuels do not deliver H to oxygen directly. Moreover, oxygen may not always be available.

Fuels release hydrogen only to special organic acceptors of complex construction. Indeed, a whole series of such acceptors exists and, as in a bucket brigade, hydrogen from fuel is passed successively from one acceptor to the next, in fixed sequence. When oxygen is available, this gas functions as the last acceptor in the series; H_2O then forms as a byproduct of respiration. If we let *A, B, C* stand for different hydrogen acceptors, then the pattern of H transport to oxygen may be symbolized as follows:

$$[H_2] \diagdown \qquad A \diagup \qquad \diagdown B \cdot [H_2] \qquad C \diagup \qquad \diagdown H_2O$$
$$(from$$
$$fuel) \qquad\qquad\qquad\qquad\qquad\qquad\qquad\qquad\qquad\qquad\qquad$$
$$A \cdot [H_2] \qquad\qquad B \qquad\qquad C \cdot [H_2] \qquad\qquad oxygen$$

We may ask at this point why a succession of carriers is required at all. Could not hydrogen be passed on to oxygen directly? Indeed it could and that this is so can be demonstrated readily in the test tube. When such a test-tube experiment is performed, hydrogen and oxygen are found to combine explosively. We should not conclude, however, that a similarly direct combination in cells would lead to explosion of cells; the quantities of gases involved there at any moment would probably be far too small to cause damage. The important conclusion is, rather, that the combination of hydrogen and oxygen is an *energy-yielding* process. And this undoubtedly explains the adaptive value of the succession of hydrogen carriers in cells. If hydrogen were to combine directly with oxygen, any energy released would appear suddenly, all at once. Most or all of it would then dissipate as heat and would become useless metabolically. But with a succession of carriers, the energy can be freed little by little and this energy becomes useful.

What is the source of the energy in hydrogen transfer? The source may be envisaged to be **electron energy,** and we may note that "hydrogen transfer" in respiration actually includes **electron transfer.** Approximated crudely, we may picture this process by assuming that, at the start of a transfer sequence, hydrogen *ionizes* into two components, $[H^+]$ and $[e^-]$. The electron here may be thought of as a high-energy electron, and it alone rather than a whole hydrogen atom may be assumed to be passed by a succession of carrier molecules to the end of the transfer sequence. In the process, the energy of the electron may be thought to be "stepped down," as it were, and the energy so made available at each step can become useful. Each time a carrier molecule *A* "hands off" the electron to the next carrier *B* in the series, the carrier *A* is oxidized; as noted earlier, removal of an electron is an oxidative change. The energy obtained in such oxidations is again harvested by the ADP/ATP system. Shown symbolically:

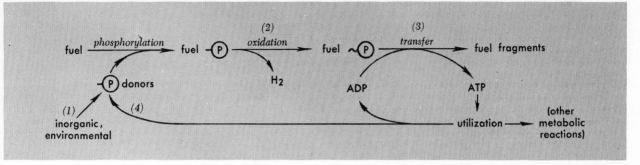

FIG. 16.8   The general sequence of reactions in respiration. The numbered steps here correspond to the categories of phosphate transfer outlined in the text and in Fig. 16.7. Thus, (1)— P to — P , (2) — P to ~ P, (3) ~ P to ~ P, and (4) ~ P to — P .

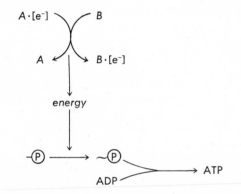

While an electron is carried through the transfer sequence, the hydrogen ion formed at the start of the sequence may be thought to remain free in the reaction medium and essentially passive. However, it rejoins its electron when the latter arrives at the end of the transfer sequence and here the hydrogen ion, the electron, and oxygen combine to form water:

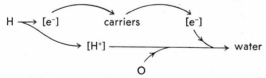

Thus, there are actually *two* sources of ~Ⓟ, hence of ATP, in respiration. One is the oxidation of fuel–Ⓟ into fuel~Ⓟ by dehydrogenation, as outlined earlier. The other is the creation of ~Ⓟ during electron transfer away from fuel. This second source is in principle like the first, for electron carriers too may be regarded as "fuels" which become oxidized as they lose electrons (Fig. 16.9).

Of the two sources of ~Ⓟ, the second is the more important. It can be shown that, for every two electrons (derived from 2 H) transferred through the entire carrier series to oxygen, three ATP molecules are usually formed. A given fuel molecule yields numerous hydrogen pairs, hence numerous electron pairs, and the total ATP gained from their transfer to oxygen is usually far greater than the ATP gained from fuel dehydrogenation itself.

The whole pattern of electron and hydrogen transfer in respiration is clearly reminiscent of the analogous transfer in photosynthesis. As we have seen in Chap. 13, photosynthesis resembles respiration in that ATP is created during electron transfers. Electron carriers here play an important role, and we shall presently find that the carriers in photosynthesis and respiration actually are in part the same substances. Moreover, in photosynthesis, hydrogen is removed from water and is incorporated into organic molecules. During this process,

FIG. 16.9   The two sources of ATP in respiration. One source is oxidation of fuel, and a second is hydrogen transfer from fuel to oxygen.

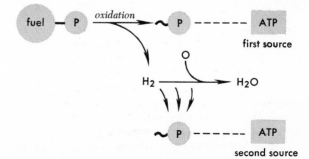

"low-energy" electrons from water become "high-energy" electrons in chlorophyll, and these electrons are then added to the hydrogen which becomes part of organic molecules. Now we note that, in respiration, hydrogen is removed from organic molecules and is formed back into water. At the same time, this hydrogen supplies electrons which during their transfer make energy available. Thus there is a direct continuity in the history of these electrons. They originate in water and are passed successively to chlorophyll, to hydrogen from water, to organic molecules, to hydrogen from these organic molecules, and finally back to water. Also, there is a direct continuity in the history of the energy. The energy originates in the sun and becomes incorporated into chlorophyll. In conjunction with electron transfers the energy then passes through photosynthesis into organic molecules and from there eventually into respiratory processes and finally into ATP. We note once more that the ultimate energy donor of virtually all life is the sun, and we may now add that the ultimate energy transfer is associated with electrons which originate in water and in the end return to water (Fig. 16.10).

What substances are the specific carriers in respiratory electron transfer and how do they function?

AEROBIC TRANSPORT

The Formation of Water

To simplify description in the following, we shall assume that whole hydrogen atoms, not just their electrons, are being transferred from fuel molecules to oxygen. We shall therefore speak of hydrogen carriers or acceptors, realizing, however, that these substances are fundamentally electron carriers.

Two substances serve as the first acceptors when hydrogen is removed from fuel: **diphosphopyridine nucleotide,** or **DPN** for short, and **triphosphopyridine nucleotide,** or **TPN** for short. The TPN here is the very same that also serves as hydrogen carrier in photosynthesis. Evidently, the photosynthetic role of TPN is roughly the reverse of its respiratory role. In one case TPN conducts hydrogen from water to food (via CO_2 fixation), and in the other case it conducts hydrogen from food to water (Fig. 16.11).

Figure 16.11 suggests that, in a superficial way, photosynthesis and respiration are the reverse of each other. One process releases oxygen, uses up CO_2, creates foods, and expends more energy than it yields; the other yields more energy than it expends, destroys

foods, releases CO_2, and uses up oxygen. However, this apparent oppositeness disappears if we consider not simply inputs and outputs, but the actual intermediate reactions. For example, carbohydrates are always the endproduct of photosynthesis, but only sometimes the starting materials of respiration. The steps of respiratory dehydrogenation and the steps of photosynthetic CO_2 fixation are not the reverse of each other. Water is a necessary raw material in photosynthesis; but, as we shall see, if oxygen is not available, water is not a byproduct of respiration. And TPN itself, always a carrier in photosynthesis, is only sometimes a carrier in respiration. Therefore, rather than regarding photosynthesis and respiration as opposites, it is far more correct, in line with the data in Fig. 16.10, to regard them as two consecutive phases in a continuing process of translating solar energy into ATP. In this continuing process, as elsewhere in living matter, the same events may be brought about by the same substances. As a case in point, TPN is a hydrogen and electron carrier, and as such it may function wherever and whenever hydrogen and electrons are to be carried; this happens to include both photosynthesis and respiration. Analogous correspondences will also be encountered in several other instances below.

Some respiratory fuels release hydrogen specifically to TPN; others, specifically to DPN. Indeed, in many reactions we shall discuss, it is DPN, not TPN, which must be available as the hydrogen acceptor. DPN and TPN are closely related. They differ only by one phosphate group, and in cells one may be converted into the other: DPN + -℗ $\rightleftharpoons$ TPN. As their names suggest, both DPN and TPN are manufactured in part from nucleotides, in part from pyridine. The latter is a derivative of one of the B vitamins, namely, **nicotinic acid.** Here is the reason why this vitamin is essential for life and why it must be produced by plants and eaten by animals. Each of their cells requires nicotinic acid as a vital building material in the construction of DPN and TPN.

We may describe the respiratory functions of DPN and TPN as follows:

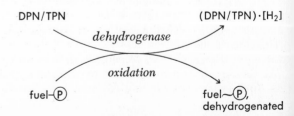

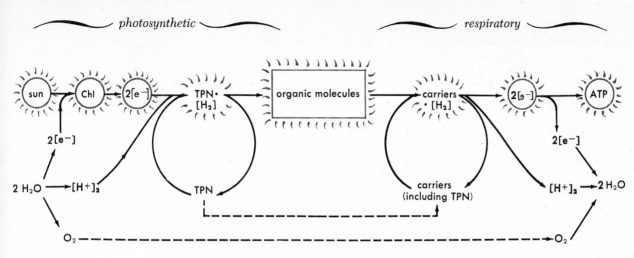

FIG. 16.10   The continuity of energy and electrons in photosynthesis and respiration. Energy originating in the sun is transferred through photosynthesis into organic molecules and from there through respiration into ATP. The electrons associated with this energy transfer originate in water, and ultimately they return to water. Note that the hydrogen carriers in photosynthesis and respiration are partly identical.

The subsequent fate of $DPN \cdot [H_2]$ or $TPN \cdot [H_2]$ depends on whether or not oxygen is available to a cell. Recall that in Chap. 3 we have referred to two forms of respiration: oxygen-dependent **aerobic respiration** and oxygen-independent **anaerobic respiration**, or *fermentation*. Fermentation is the more primitive form, but aerobic respiration is the more common form. We assume for the present that conditions are *aerobic* and that oxygen is in ample supply.

Under such conditions, the carrier required specifically just after DPN or TPN is a derivative of another component of the vitamin B complex: **riboflavin**, or vitamin B_2. Riboflavin is converted in cells into two types of compounds, either one of which may function as a hydrogen acceptor. The two compounds are **flavin adenine dinucleotide**, or **FAD** for short, and **flavin mononucleotide**, or **FMN** for short. The latter will be recognized as an electron carrier serving also in photosynthesis. Note, furthermore, that both FAD and FMN are derivatives not only of riboflavin but also of nucleotides. Thus nucleotides produce, on the one hand, nucleic acids and genes and, on the other, compounds such as ADP/ATP, DPN/TPN, and FAD/FMN, all playing vital roles in energy metabolism. This circumstance strongly underscores again the crucial significance of nucleotides in the origin and maintenance of life.

FIG. 16.11   With respect to the generalized features here shown, respiration tends to be the reverse of photosynthesis. However, the more detailed aspects of these two processes are very largely *not* the reverse of each other. Compare this figure with Fig. 16.10.

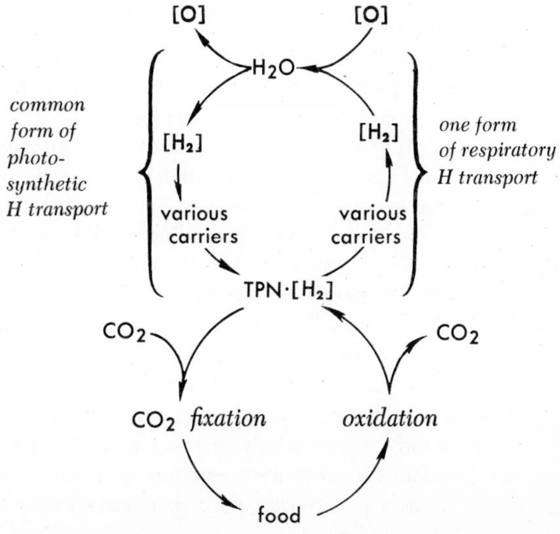

The specific role of FAD and FMN in respiration may be described symbolically as

$$(DPN/TPN) \cdot [H_2] \qquad DPN/TPN$$
$$FAD/FMN \qquad (FAD/FMN) \cdot [H_2]$$

As hydrogen is passed on to FAD or FMN, free DPN or TPN reappear and become available again to accept new hydrogen from fuel.

FAD$\cdot[H_2]$ or FMN$\cdot[H_2]$ in turn "hands off" its hydrogen to a series of carriers which together represent the **cytochrome system,** already encountered as an electron-carrying system in photosynthesis. As pointed out in that context, the iron-containing cytochromes are red tetrapyrrol pigments, and we may now add that the iron is also the specific electron-carrying agent of these pigments. In the equation

$$\underset{\substack{ferric \\ ion}}{Fe^{+++}} + e^- \rightleftharpoons \underset{\substack{ferrous \\ ion}}{Fe^{++}}$$

the reaction to the right symbolizes the electron-accepting process. If we consider it to be part of a more inclusive hydrogen-accepting process, then the respiratory function of the cytochromes may be symbolized as:

$$(FAD/FMN) \cdot [H_2] \qquad FAD/FMN$$
$$cytochromes \qquad cytochromes \cdot [H_2]$$

Free FAD or FMN reappears, available now to accept new hydrogen from DPN$\cdot[H_2]$ or TPN$\cdot[H_2]$.

We may reiterate here the structural similarity of the cytochromes to the chlorophylls on the one hand and to the haemoglobins on the other. All three groups of pigments are tetrapyrrol derivatives and all three function as carriers in energy metabolism. Chlorophylls and cytochromes carry electrons and are direct or indirect participants in ATP formation; haemoglobins carry oxygen via the blood to animal cells, where the oxygen is likewise an (indirect) participant in ATP formation. Thus, like the nucleotides, the tetrapyrrols have come to be adapted during chemical evolution to serve similar, crucially important functions in multiple ways.

Hydrogen-carrying cytochromes are the penultimate compounds in the whole transfer series; the next and last carrier is atmospheric oxygen, whether or not it is brought into a respiring cell by haemoglobin:

$$cytochromes \cdot [H_2] \qquad cytochromes$$
$$oxygen \qquad H_2O$$

As free cytochromes here reappear, the ferrous ions of the cytochromes release electrons and become ferric ions, symbolized by the reaction to the left in the reversible equation two paragraphs earlier.

This pattern of aerobic hydrogen transport as a whole is summarized in Fig. 16.12.

Conditions for H Transport

Several additional observations may be made concerning the transport reactions above. First, as everywhere else in metabolism, each of the reactions here must be catalyzed by a specific enzyme. We may note also that vitamin E and vitamin K are known to be required in the reactions. Vitamin K has already been mentioned as an electron carrier in photosynthesis, where it serves as an alternate to FMN. Possibly vitamins K and E function in similar capacities in respiration.

Second, it is clear that relatively small quantities of the hydrogen carriers suffice to transport comparatively large quantities of hydrogen; each carrier molecule functions cyclically and may be used repeatedly.

Third, if any one of the reactions is stopped, the whole transport system becomes inoperative and the energy it normally supplies cannot be obtained. Reaction blocks may occur in a number of ways. For example, *inhibitor* substances of various kinds may interfere specifically with given transport reactions. Thus, potassium cyanide specifically inhibits the cytochrome system, and this is why cyanide is such a violent poison. Another form of reaction block is produced if one of the carriers is in deficient supply. A consistently riboflavin-deficient nutrition, for example, would soon impair the reactions in which FAD and FMN are participants.

Any such reaction barrier introduced into the transport sequence will act like a roadblock and will lead to an accumulation of hydrogen back of the barrier. For example, if the cytochrome system is blocked, FAD$\cdot[H_2]$ cannot get rid of its hydrogen. All available FAD will then soon hold $[H_2]$ to capacity, and none will be free to accept more $[H_2]$ from DPN$\cdot[H_2]$ or TPN$\cdot[H_2]$. Therefore, DPN$\cdot[H_2]$ and TPN$\cdot[H_2]$ cannot get rid of their own hydrogen and free DPN/TPN will no longer become available to accept more hydrogen from fresh fuel. Respiration will be effectively stopped.

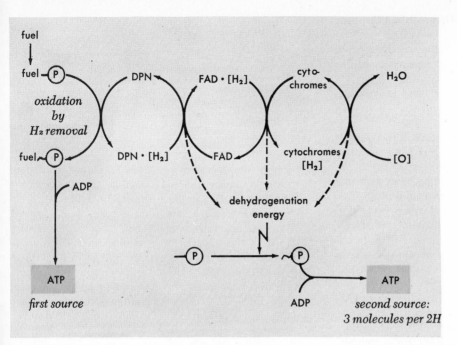

FIG. 16.12 Summary of aerobic hydrogen transfer.

Experimental use of reaction blocks has been one of the principal methods of elucidating the normal pattern of hydrogen transport. For example, after the experimental production of a riboflavin deficiency in a heterotrophic test organism, one would find that the amount of hydrogen-holding cytochrome molecules decreases, whereas the amount of $(DPN/TPN) \cdot [H_2]$ increases. One would conclude, then, that DPN/TPN and the cytochromes are part of the H-transport system and that DPN/TPN must function before FAD/FMN, the cytochromes after. Blocking techniques of this sort are employed quite generally whenever the components of a sequence of metabolic reactions are to be identified.

ANAEROBIC TRANSPORT

The Pattern

Cyanide poisoning and vitamin B deficiencies are not particularly common hazards in the life of an organism, and most organisms on earth would probably survive quite well even without special protective adaptations against such contingencies. But there is one ancient hazard affecting H transport which all living matter has had to cope with ever since it originated. That is the unavailability of atmospheric oxygen. Lack of oxygen is a reaction barrier of the same sort as cyanide poisoning or vitamin deficiencies. The conse-

quence is a damming up of hydrogen all the way back to DPN/TPN, with the further consequence that respiration as a whole becomes blocked.

The earliest organisms lived in an environment which did not provide free oxygen at all (see Chap. 3). Yet these organisms survived. Today, certain Monera, especially bacteria, cannot use oxygen even though the gas may be available. Such organisms are *obligate anaerobes*. Various other Monera and Protista are *facultative anaerobes;* i.e., they may or may not use oxygen and survive either way. The fungus yeast is an example. Most organisms, including many Monera and Protista and all Metaphyta and Metazoa, are *obligate aerobes;* i.e., they must have oxygen if they are to survive. However, such aerobes very frequently may not be able to obtain enough of the gas. For example, during strenuous activity, energy requirements and respiration rates may become so high that even maximum breathing rates cannot meet the oxygen demands of the cells.

Whenever oxygen supplies are inadequate or whenever hydrogen transport to oxygen is otherwise blocked, organisms may respire in a way which does not require oxygen. This is *anaerobic respiration*, or *fermentation*, probably the ancient original form of energy production inherited by all organisms. Under conditions of oxygen deficiency, this anaerobic type of respiration may become a substitute or a subsidiary source of energy.

The principle of anaerobic hydrogen transport is relatively simple: when the exhaust pipe of an engine is stopped up, the engine may still continue to operate if an alternative outlet for the waste gases is available. Oxygen is the normal outlet for hydrogen. If oxygen is unavailable, another final acceptor is used.

This alternative acceptor functions directly after $(DPN/TPN) \cdot [H_2]$. Whenever $DPN \cdot [H_2]$, for example, cannot unload hydrogen to FAD, it unloads to the alternative acceptor. Thus free DPN becomes available again and fuel dehydrogenation can continue.

The alternative hydrogen acceptor is **pyruvic acid** $(C_3H_4O_3)$. As we shall see shortly, this acid is produced normally during the respiratory breakdown of carbohydrates. If oxygen is amply available, pyruvic acid is merely one of the intermediate steps in the combustion of carbohydrates. In other words, it is a fuel which, in the presence of oxygen, may be burned further to CO_2 and H_2O. But pyruvic acid has the property of reacting readily with hydrogen. And if $(DPN/TPN) \cdot H_2$ cannot use its normal hydrogen outlet to FAD/FMN, pyruvic acid is used instead. The acid then ceases to be a fuel and becomes a hydrogen carrier.

When pyruvic acid reacts with hydrogen, the result is the formation of *lactic acid* or of *alcohol* and CO_2:

$$C_3H_4O_3 \xrightarrow{+H_2} C_3H_6O_3$$
pyruvic acid   *lactic acid*

or

$$C_3H_4O_3 \xrightarrow{\qquad} \begin{cases} [C_2H_4O] \xrightarrow{+H_2} C_2H_6O \text{ } alcohol \\ CO_2 \end{cases}$$
pyruvic acid

Different enzymes promote these reactions in different organisms, hence the difference in the endproducts. Some Monera and Protista form lactic acid (e.g., milk-souring bacteria); others form alcohol (e.g., yeasts). Metaphyta generally form alcohol; Metazoa, lactic acid.

With these reactions, anaerobic respiration comes to a halt. The overall pattern is outlined in Fig. 16.13. It should be clear that anaerobic respiration is precisely the same as aerobic respiration up to the point where DPN/TPN accepts hydrogen from fuel. Since only carbohydrates normally yield pyruvic acid directly, fermentation will be most efficient when carbohydrates are available as fuels. Other types of fuel may also be sources of pyruvic acid, but, as we shall see, lengthier reaction sequences are required to produce it and the acid is consequently formed more slowly. Indeed, anaerobic respiration is predominantly carbohydrate dependent.

The Energy Gain

The energy gained anaerobically is far less than that gained aerobically. First, with the path to oxygen blocked, the ATP normally created by H transfer to oxygen cannot be realized. Second, anaerobic combustion stops at the pyruvic acid stage and the potential energy still contained in pyruvic acid therefore remains unused and locked in lactic acid or alcohol. As we shall see, fermentation yields only about 5 per cent of the energy obtainable through aerobic respiration.

Nevertheless, fermentation energy alone does suffice to sustain the life of the obligate or facultative anaerobes among Monera and Protista. The lactic acid or alcohol and CO_2 produced by such organisms are largely excreted into the environment. Through beer and wine, man has known longer about these excreted fermentation products than about the organisms which give rise to them.

In obligate aerobes, on the other hand, the energy gain from fermentation alone is too small to sustain life.

FIG. 16.13 Summary of anaerobic hydrogen transfer.

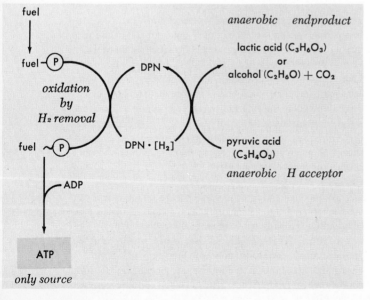

fuel

fuel — (P)

oxidation by H_2 removal

fuel ~ (P)

DPN

DPN · [H₂]

ADP

ATP

only source

anaerobic endproduct

lactic acid $(C_3H_6O_3)$
or
alcohol $(C_2H_6O) + CO_2$

pyruvic acid
$(C_3H_4O_3)$

anaerobic H acceptor

If hydrogen transport to oxygen is blocked completely, cell death will occur quickly even though fermentation is under way. However, fermentation may suffice to *supplement* aerobic respiration when energy demands are high. For example, during intensive physical activity among animals, the oxygen supply to the cells may be insufficient despite faster breathing, and an **oxygen debt** will be incurred. Fermentation then proceeds in parallel with aerobic respiration and more energy becomes available in this manner. Lactic acid will accumulate as a result, particularly in the muscles, which bear the burden of physical work.

Muscular fatigue is associated with increasing accumulation of lactic acid. When the amount of acid becomes very high, fatigue may become so great that intense activity can no longer be maintained. During an ensuing rest period, faster breathing at first continues. The oxygen debt is thereby being repaid and the extra oxygen permits the complete combustion of the accumulated lactic acid. With the gradual disappearance of lactic acid from the muscles, fatigue disappears, breathing slows down, and a normal oxygen-energy balance is then reestablished.

Thus the energy content of lactic acid is not necessarily lost permanently to a fermenting cell, a generalization which holds true for alcohol also. For example, yeast produces alcohol anaerobically and excretes it into the environment. But it may later reabsorb alcohol and burn it aerobically. In short, both lactic acid and alcohol are potential fuels which may be burned completely when oxygen supplies are fully adequate and when fermentation is therefore no longer necessary as a supplement or alternative to aerobic respiration.

These accounts of energy transfer and hydrogen transfer set the stage for a discussion of the third aspect of respiration, namely, the actual combustion of fuels.

FUEL COMBUSTION

THE PATTERN

In the course of reorganizing internally and thereby acquiring high-energy bonds, a fuel molecule becomes changed chemically. Sometimes the change is not great and the basic structure of the molecule is not affected. But sometimes the oxidative change may bring about a splitting of the carbon skeleton of the molecule. High-energy bonds may form regardless of whether a molecule splits or not, but when a split does occur, fragments with shorter carbon chains result. These are still energy-yielding fuels. Sooner or later they in turn may be split into still shorter chains. Eventually, fragments which contain but a single carbon atom each will arise.

This final 1-carbon breakdown product emerges from respiration in the form of CO_2. Carbon dioxide represents the end condition of all metabolic fuels. When a fuel has been degraded this far, all extractable energy has already been extracted. Complete degradation of a fuel to CO_2 can occur only in the presence of oxygen.

If we follow the sequence of fuel breakdown backward, then the next-to-last fuel fragment should consist of *two* linked carbons. This is the case. As we shall see shortly, the fundamental molecule representing the 2-carbon stage in respiration is a derivative of acetic acid called *acetyl*. This atomic grouping does not normally exist by itself but is combined with a carrier molecule, namely, *coenzyme A*, or *CoA* for short. We shall discuss the significance of CoA below; for the present we need note only that the 2-carbon stage in fuel breakdown is represented by the acetyl portion of the complex **acetyl CoA**. In other words, progressive breakdown eventually transforms all fuels to acetyl CoA, and this compound then yields 1-carbon CO_2.

The manner in which the stage of acetyl CoA is reached differs for different types of fuels. For example, many carbohydrates are first broken up into 3-carbon compounds. Carbohydrates often contain whole multiples of 3 carbons. As noted, photosynthesis yields a 3-carbon endproduct, and more complex carbohydrates are built up from such units. This holds for glucose and all other 6-carbon sugars, for 12-carbon disaccharides, and for polysaccharides such as starch and glycogen. As we shall see, when any of these are used as respiratory fuels, the original 3-carbon units reappear in the course of breakdown. Many other organic substances, glycerin, for example, are 3-carbon molecules to begin with. All such C_3 compounds are eventually converted to **pyruvic acid** ($C_3H_4O_3$). This acid is the common representative of the 3-carbon stage in respiration. Pyruvic acid subsequently loses one carbon in the form of CO_2 and becomes acetyl CoA.

Fatty acids and related molecules consist of long, even-numbered carbon chains. These do not break up into 3-carbon units, but become 2-carbon units directly. Other fuels are 2-carbon molecules to begin with, and

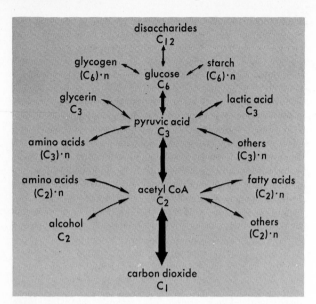

FIG. 16.14 Some of the main pathways in the aerobic combustion of fuels. Pyruvic acid, acetyl CoA, and carbon dioxide form a main sequence which other pathways join, like branches of a tree.

all such C_2 compounds eventually appear as acetyl CoA. Amino acids break down partly to pyruvic acid (which subsequently becomes acetyl CoA), partly to acetyl CoA directly. This holds also for many other organic substances which may happen to be used as fuel.

Thus, the overall pattern of aerobic fuel combustion may be likened to a tree with branches or to a river with tributaries (Fig. 16.14). A broad main channel is represented by the sequence pyruvic acid $\longrightarrow$ acetyl CoA $\longrightarrow$ carbon dioxide. Numerous side channels lead into this sequence, some funneling into the 3-carbon pyruvic acid step, others into the 2-carbon acetyl CoA step. The side channels themselves may be long or short, and each may have smaller side channels of its own. In the end, the flow from the entire system drains out as 1-carbon carbon dioxide.

The various sequences in this pattern are series of metabolic reactions. All are fundamentally reversible, but they proceed in a preferred direction during respiration. Each reaction requires specific enzymes as usual and, among vertebrates, often also specific hormones.

Carbohydrates are among the chief respiratory fuels, and they play a particular role in anaerobic

respiration. Their combustion may advantageously be examined first.

CARBOHYDRATE BREAKDOWN

The general pattern of this sequence, often referred to as **glycolysis**, consists of two phases. In a first series of reactions, complex carbohydrate fuels in cells are degraded into smaller fragments. Preliminary low-energy phosphorylations occur at the same time, and energy is here *expended*. These reactions may be said to represent a *preparatory phase*. In a subsequent series of reactions, high-energy phosphate bonds are created by oxidation, and energy is then *harvested*. More energy is gained here than has been expended earlier. This may be called the *oxidative phase*.

The Preparatory Phase

The starting material in carbohydrate breakdown may be taken to be glucose or glucose derivatives such as starch or glycogen. The first preparatory reaction is the phosphorylation of these carbohydrates to **glucose-phosphate**. ATP in some cases and H–O–(P) in others are the phosphate donors, and one –(P) group is expended for every 6-carbon unit phosphorylated.

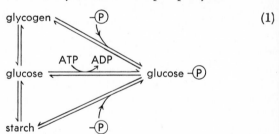

(1)

Note that glycogen and starch may first become glucose before they are converted to glucose-phosphate. Such transformation to free glucose occurs by addition of water (see Chaps. 13, 14). But glycogen and starch may be phosphorylated directly into glucose-phosphate, and the free glucose stage is then bypassed. This is the usual event in respiration. Whatever pathway is followed, it should be remembered that one molecule of either glycogen or starch yields many molecules of glucose-phosphate, at the expense of a corresponding number of phosphate groups.

Equation 1 above illustrates that glucose-phosphate may be an intermediate in the reversible conversion of glycogen into glucose:

glycogen ⇌ glucose-phosphate ⇌ glucose

We have already referred to this in Chap. 14, in connection with the role of the liver in carbohydrate transport throughout the body. The hormones *insulin* and *adrenalin* were then noted to influence this conversion in vertebrates. Specifically, insulin was found to promote the phosphorylation of blood glucose, hence its utilization as tissue glycogen. We may appreciate now how this is so. By being converted into glucose-phosphate, blood glucose may be drawn directly into cellular respiration. Or it may first be stored as cellular glycogen, which may become glucose-phosphate later and serve as fuel then. Note that *estrogen*, a vertebrate sex hormone, promotes the phosphorylation of glucose also and that still other hormones may affect this important reaction as well.

Whatever the source of glucose-phosphate, the respiratory fate of this fuel is always the same. It first undergoes a series of internal rearrangements which transform it into **fructose-phosphate**. This conversion does not change the low energy values of the phosphate bonds:

(2)

$$C_6H_{11}O_6\text{-}\textcircled{P} \xrightarrow{\text{rearrangement}} C_6H_{11}O_6\text{-}\textcircled{P}$$
glucose-   fructose-
phosphate   phosphate

When free fructose is a respiratory fuel, it enters the reaction sequence at this point. With the aid of ATP, fructose may become fructose-phosphate and the latter adds indistinguishably to the fructose-phosphate formed from glucose, starch, or glycogen:

glucose   fructose
starch
glycogen   ⎞ ← ATP
                                         ⎠ ↘ ADP
glucose-⊕ ⇌ fructose-⊕ ⟶ *further respiration*

This scheme also shows how cells may convert fructose into glucose or vice versa.

Fructose-phosphate next becomes **fructose-diphosphate**. The –⊕ group of fructose-phosphate is situated at one end of the carbon chain, and a low-energy phosphate group now becomes attached to the other end of the molecule. ATP is the phosphorylating agent again:

(3)

ATP   ADP
$$C_6H_{11}O_6\text{-}\textcircled{P} \longrightarrow \textcircled{P}\text{-}C_6H_{10}O_6\text{-}\textcircled{P}$$
fructose-   fructose-
phosphate   diphosphate

fructose-
diphosphate

In gaining a second –⊕ group, fructose-phosphate also loses an H atom to ADP.

If an imaginary line is drawn through the fructose-diphosphate molecule between the third and fourth of its six carbons, then the two halves will be noted to contain mirror-image carbon skeletons. This is significant in what happens next. Fructose-diphosphate *splits* between its third and fourth carbons, and *two 3-carbon fragments* are thereby formed. These undergo slight internal rearrangements and become two identical molecules: **phosphoglyceraldehyde**. This transformation still does not change the energy values of the phosphate bonds:

(4)

$$\textcircled{P}\text{-}C_6H_{10}O_6\text{-}\textcircled{P} \xrightarrow[\text{rearrangement}]{\text{splitting}} 2\ C_3H_5O_3\text{-}\textcircled{P}$$
fructose-   PGAL
diphosphate

PGAL

Phosphoglyceraldehyde, PGAL for short, will be recognized as the principal organic endproduct of photosynthesis. We now find it to be an intermediate in the combustion of sugar. PGAL evidently interconnects the reaction sequence of photosynthesis with that of carbohydrate respiration:

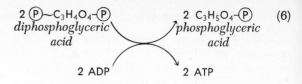

$$
\text{glucose-} \rightleftarrows \text{fructose-} \rightleftarrows \text{fructose-} \rightleftarrows 2 \text{ PGAL}
$$
$$
\text{phosphate} \quad\quad \text{phosphate} \quad\quad \text{diphosphate}
$$

photosynthesis

further respiration

We note that PGAL just photosynthesized may be used at once as fuel, via further respiratory reactions; or it may be converted into fructose, glucose, or starch, via the reactions to the left in the above sequence (see also Fig. 13.27). We conclude that the photosynthetic formation of polysaccharides *from* PGAL is the exact reverse of the respiratory breakdown of polysaccharides *to* PGAL.

The Oxidative Phase

The last step of the preparatory phase and the first step of the oxidative phase occur simultaneously in one reaction. PGAL already possesses one $-\text{P}$ group, attached to one end of the molecule by a low-energy bond. Another preliminary phosphorylation now takes place and a second $-\text{P}$ group is added to the other end of the molecule. The phosphorylating agent in this case is phosphoric acid, H-O-P, drawn from the mineral supply of the cell. The whole H-O-P molecule is added to PGAL. At the same time, an oxidative dehydrogenation occurs. The result is that the $-\text{P}$ group just added acquires a high-energy bond and that two atoms of hydrogen are removed. These are accepted immediately by DPN, which must be present. The simultaneous phosphorylation and oxidation of PGAL may be symbolized as follows:

(5)

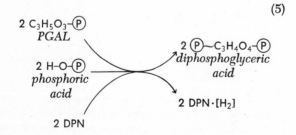

The principal endproduct, **diphosphoglyceric acid,** next transfers its $\sim\text{P}$ to ADP:

(6)

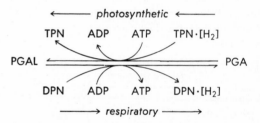

In this reaction, the molecule which loses the $\sim\text{P}$ group gains an H atom from ADP. Two molecules of ATP are created, and these *pay back* the 2 ATP expended earlier, in preparatory reactions 1 and 3. As yet there has been no *net* gain of energy.

The other endproduct, $\text{C}_3\text{H}_5\text{O}_4\text{-P}$, is already familiar. It is **phosphoglyceric acid,** *PGA* for short. In photosynthesis (see Chap. 13), PGA adds hydrogen from $\text{TPN}\cdot[\text{H}_2]$ and energy from ATP and becomes PGAL. In respiration, we now find that PGAL loses hydrogen to DPN and energy to ADP, and so becomes PGA. The two sequences are virtually mirror images. Symbolically:

$$
\overset{\longleftarrow \quad \textit{photosynthetic} \quad \longleftarrow}{\underset{\longrightarrow \quad \textit{respiratory} \quad \longrightarrow}{\text{PGAL} \rightleftharpoons \text{PGA}}}
$$

TPN   ADP   ATP $\text{TPN}\cdot[\text{H}_2]$

DPN   ADP   ATP $\text{DPN}\cdot[\text{H}_2]$

In short, photosynthesis and carbohydrate combustion *share* the reversible sequence PGAL $\rightleftharpoons$ PGA. A PGA molecule may contribute to photosynthetic carbohydrate production by the reaction to the left in the scheme above; or, by the reaction to the right, it may result from respiratory carbohydrate breakdown.

Oxidation now continues; an oxidative *dehydration* occurs, in which PGA loses not hydrogen alone but hydrogen and oxygen in the form of water. A new high-energy bond is created at the same time:

(7)

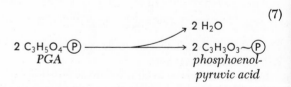

Since water appears rather than hydrogen alone, hydrogen acceptors are not required here. The principal endproduct, $\text{C}_3\text{H}_3\text{O}_3\sim\text{P}$, is called **phosphoenol-pyruvic acid.** This substance next transfers its $\sim\text{P}$ to ADP:

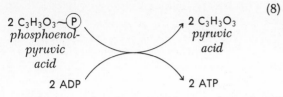

(8)

Two additional molecules of ATP are created and these represent the *net* energy gain of the reaction sequence up to this point. The $\sim$Ⓟ group lost from phosphoenol-pyruvic acid is replaced by a hydrogen from ADP, and $C_3H_4O_3$, **pyruvic acid,** is formed. This compound no longer carries any phosphate groups.

The whole reaction sequence so far is summarized in Fig. 16.15. On balance, if we assume that the sequence started with one molecule of free glucose, then the total input is seen to be (apart from the glucose) four molecules of ADP and two molecules each of phosphoric acid and ATP. The total output consists of two molecules each of DPN·[H_2], pyruvic acid, ADP, and water and four molecules of ATP. The *net* input-output is therefore

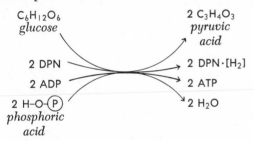

Altogether, four phosphorylations have occurred (reactions 1, 3, and 5). Two of the –Ⓟ groups have been supplied by phosphoric acid, the other two by ATP. Each of these four phosphates sooner or later has acquired a high-energy bond, and four ATP molecules have been formed. Two of these pay back for the ATP expended and two are net gain. The fate of the atoms in glucose may be described by the equation

$$C_6H_{12}O_6 \longrightarrow 2\ C_3H_4O_3 + 2\ [H_2]$$

Thus the net loss of atoms from glucose amounts to 2 [H_2], and these are held by DPN.

If respiration occurs under *anaerobic* conditions,

FIG. 16.15 The conversion of glucose into pyruvic acid. The main steps of the conversion are shown in the reaction sequence, and an input-output summary is given separately.

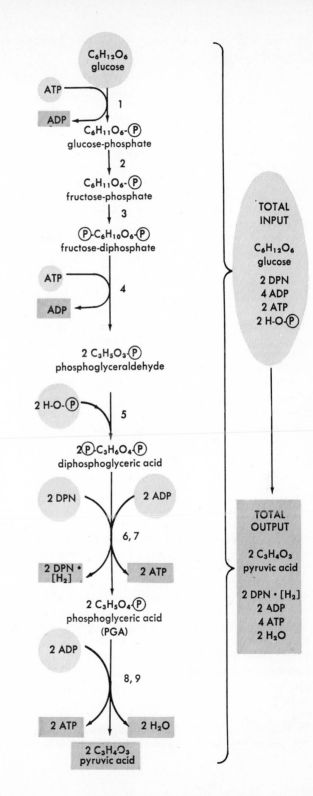

pyruvic acid must now serve as the final hydrogen acceptor:

$$(9a)$$

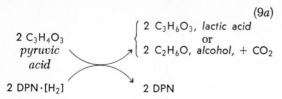

$$2\ C_3H_4O_3 \atop \textit{pyruvic acid} \longrightarrow \begin{cases} 2\ C_3H_6O_3,\ \textit{lactic acid} \\ \text{or} \\ 2\ C_2H_6O,\ \textit{alcohol},\ +\ CO_2 \end{cases}$$

$$2\ DPN \cdot [H_2] \longrightarrow 2\ DPN$$

Carbohydrate combustion in this case stops with the formation of lactic acid or alcohol and CO_2. The two ATP gained represent the net energy yield of the entire process.

But if conditions are aerobic, two desirable consequences supervene. First, the 2 $[H_2]$ held by DPN may be passed on to oxygen. As noted earlier, this transfer yields three additional ATP molecules per $[H_2]$, or 6 ATP total. Second, since pyruvic acid need not serve as a hydrogen carrier, it may be burned further. Most of the energy of the original glucose is actually still untapped. As we shall see, complete combustion of pyruvic acid will supply many more ATP molecules than have formed thus far.

With the production of pyruvic acid, the special sequence of carbohydrate combustion, glycolysis, may be regarded as completed. As has been noted, pyruvic acid is also a key stage in the combustion of many other types of fuels.

C₃ TO C₂

Metabolic Pathways

Like carbohydrates, so also fats, proteins, and most other classes of cellular compounds may contribute to pyruvic acid formation. In each such case a separate breakdown sequence exists, yielding greater or lesser net amounts of energy. We shall not discuss these sequences in as detailed a fashion as that for carbohydrates but shall merely indicate general patterns.

When cellular fats are used as respiratory fuel, they are first degraded to fatty acids and glycerin. The latter, a 3-carbon unit, is then transformed into phosphoglyceraldehyde, PGAL. This compound becomes pyruvic acid via reactions already discussed above for carbohydrates. Fatty acids bypass the pyruvic acid stage and split up directly into 2-carbon units. These then convert to acetyl CoA. The general pattern is outlined in Fig. 16.16. It should be clear that this pat-

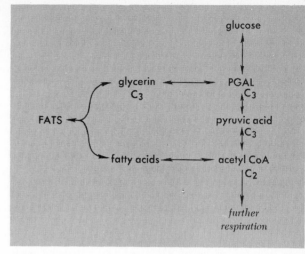

FIG. 16.16 Some of the major pathways in fat metabolism.

tern also describes metabolic pathways by which carbohydrates may be converted into fats and vice versa.

Cellular protein fuels first break down into their amino acid components, and these are subsequently deaminated. This process of $-NH_2$ removal resembles deamination in the liver. Note, however, that in most liver-possessing animals only liver cells can transform $-NH_2$ into urea. In most other cells, plant or animal, $-NH_2$ groups detached from amino acids are attached to various other organic compounds. New amino acids or other nitrogenous substances may be formed in this way. The deaminated remnants of the original amino acids undergo various reactions which convert them either into pyruvic acid or into acetyl CoA. The pattern is outlined in Fig. 16.17. Note that some of the arrows in the degradation of essential amino acids must be unidirectional for animals, as shown.

Cells contain or temporarily possess many other substances which either are 3-carbon units to begin with, such as lactic acid, or may become 3-carbon units by one reaction pathway or another. In all such cases, pyruvic acid is likely to be one stage of the pathway. Similarly, any substances which are or can become 2-carbon units, e.g., fatty acids, are likely to be metabolized to acetyl CoA. One of the most important substances which can become acetyl CoA is pyruvic acid, and this is the pathway by which 3-carbon compounds are degraded to 2-carbon compounds during respiration (Fig. 16.18).

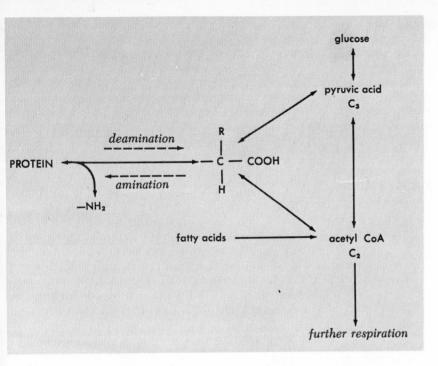

FIG. 16.17 Some of the major pathways in protein metabolism.

Formation of Acetyl CoA

This degradation is an oxidative, energy-yielding process. The oxidative change which creates a high-energy bond in pyruvic acid is a combined *dehydrogenation* and *decarboxylation:* both hydrogen and CO_2 are extracted. Several consecutive reactions occur, and they require a whole battery of acceptors and carriers. DPN must be present to accept hydrogen. Another temporary hydrogen acceptor required is so-called **lipoic acid.** Extraction of CO_2 from pyruvic acid requires the presence of a derivative of *thiamine,* or vitamin B_1. This vitamin is a building material with which cells construct **thiamine pyrophosphate,** the substance needed in the removal of CO_2 from pyruvic acid. Another ingredient necessary for this removal is magnesium ion, Mg^{++}.

Finally, formation of acetyl CoA can occur only in the presence of **CoA,** or **coenzyme A.** Coenzymes are substances which function like enzymes, i.e., they speed up given reactions; but they are not proteins like true enzymes. Moreover, coenzymes appear to function only in conjunction with true enzymes. We have already encountered a number of coenzymes, though under different names. For example, DPN is often called coenzyme I, or CoI. TPN similarly is CoII.

FIG. 16.18 Some of the main pathways leading to the formation of acetyl CoA.

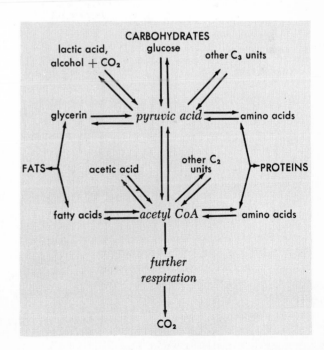

Thiamine pyrophosphate, just mentioned above, is known alternatively as *cocarboxylase*. Coenzyme A has no other name. It too is a derivative of the vitamin B complex, more specifically, the B vitamin *pantothenic acid*. This acid is combined in cells with other constituents, including a sulfur-containing –S–H group. Thus coenzyme A may also be represented as CoA–S–H. It is an important carrier in the respiratory transformation of pyruvic acid to acetyl CoA.

The actual transformation consists of a series of reactions which may be symbolized as a condensed three-step sequence. In a first step, pyruvic acid loses CO_2 in the presence of magnesium ions and thiamine pyrophosphate (cocarboxylase):

(1)
[9b]

$$C_3H_4O_3 \xrightarrow[\text{Mg}^{++}]{\text{cocarboxylase}} C_2H_4O + CO_2$$
pyruvic acid ⟶ acetaldehyde

The carbon dioxide escapes as a byproduct, and the remaining acetaldehyde molecule reacts further. Specifically, it enters reactions with lipoic acid and with CoA:

(2)

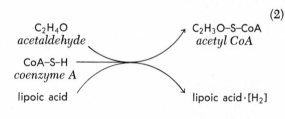

C_2H_4O
acetaldehyde

CoA–S–H
coenzyme A

lipoic acid

C_2H_3O–S–CoA
acetyl CoA

lipoic acid·[H_2]

As shown here, acetaldehyde becomes joined to CoA, resulting in acetyl CoA. At the same time, one hydrogen atom each is removed from acetaldehyde and CoA, and the [H_2] is accepted by lipoic acid. Phosphate groups are not involved here, hence high-energy bonds are not created. However, the dehydrogenations are energy-yielding nevertheless, for the [H_2] is transferred from lipoic acid to DPN and from there later to oxygen, with a resulting energy gain. Thus,

(3)

lipoic acid·[H_2] ⟶ lipoic acid
DPN ⟶ DPN·[H_2]

Free lipoic acid so becomes available again, and it may participate once more in reaction 2.

The entire conversion of pyruvic acid to acetyl CoA is summarized in Fig. 16.19. An arithmetical summary of the fate of the atoms in pyruvic acid may be represented as

$$C_3H_4O_3 + CoA–S–H \longrightarrow C_2H_3O–S–CoA + CO_2 + H_2$$
pyruvic acid ⟶ CoA ⟶ acetyl CoA

C₂ TO C₁

As noted earlier, acetyl CoA represents the next-to-last stage in fuel breakdown. By one pathway or another, directly or indirectly, any given fuel is eventually degraded to the 2-carbon acetyl of acetyl CoA, and acetyl in turn is finally degraded to 1-carbon CO_2.

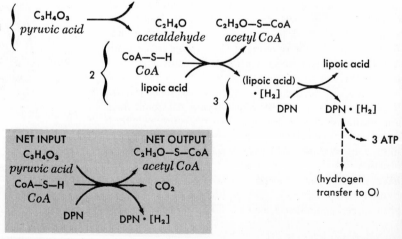

FIG. 16.19 Summary of the conversion of pyruvic acid to acetyl CoA. Numbered steps correspond to the reactions discussed in the text.

Evidently, in this segment of breakdown there are no longer various different fuels, but only the single common fuel acetyl CoA, regardless of what the original starting fuel may have been.

The respiratory breakdown of acetyl CoA has the form of a *cycle* of reactions. Acetyl CoA is funneled in at one point of the cycle; two carbons emerge at other points as CO_2; and the starting condition is eventually regenerated. The whole sequence is known as the **citric acid cycle**, a name taken from one of the participating substances.

The energy harvested in this cycle is far greater than that gained in all previous reactions together. Per molecule of acetyl CoA, about one dozen new ATP molecules arise, partly through oxidative decarboxylations and dehydrogenations. However, most of the new energy derives from hydrogen transfers to oxygen, as outlined earlier in this chapter. In the reactions below, we shall indicate in parentheses the net total ATP yield, formed both by fuel oxidation and by hydrogen transfers.

The complete cycle consists of nine steps. DPN is required at certain of these, TPN at others. Water is sometimes a raw material, sometimes an endproduct; with each turn of the cycle, a net total of two water molecules is expended. In much abbreviated form, the reaction sequence is as follows (see also Fig. 16.20).

The starting material is a 4-carbon compound called **oxaloacetic acid**, a normal constituent of cells. It reacts with acetyl CoA and water and yields **citric acid**. This is a 6-carbon compound familiar as the acid component of lemon juice:

(1)

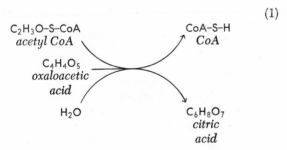

Free CoA here reappears, available to participate once more in the reactions which convert pyruvic acid to acetyl CoA. The other endproduct, citric acid, next undergoes four successive reactions which include a dehydrogenation and a decarboxylation. The final result is energy, CO_2, hydrogen held by TPN, and a 5-carbon compound called **ketoglutaric acid**. In summary,

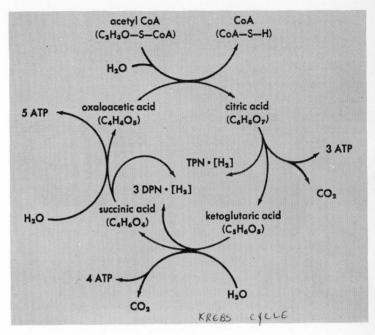

FIG. 16.20   Some of the main steps of the citric acid cycle.

(2–5)

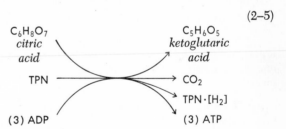

Dehydrogenation and decarboxylation now occur again, yielding more energy, more CO_2, more hydrogen (here held by DPN), and a 4-carbon compound called **succinic acid**. Water is a raw material in this sequence:

(6)

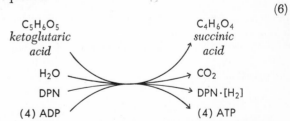

Succinic acid finally undergoes three reactions which include two successive dehydrogenations. More energy is obtained, and oxaloacetic acid is regenerated. Water is again required. In summary,

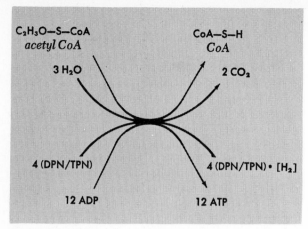

FIG. 16.21   Input-output summary of the citric acid cycle.

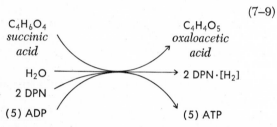

(7–9)

The net total input and output of the entire cycle are shown in Fig. 16.21. And the arithmetical summary of the fate of acetyl CoA is given by the statement:

$$C_2H_3O-S-CoA + 3\ H_2O \longrightarrow 2\ CO_2 + 4\ H_2 + CoA-S-H$$
$$\textit{acetyl CoA} \qquad\qquad\qquad\qquad\qquad\qquad\textit{CoA}$$

THE ENDPRODUCT

With the complete conversion of fuel to CO_2, combustion has reached its endpoint. What is the overall tally? We may illustrate by considering glucose as the starting fuel and by tracing the fate of its carbons, hydrogens, and oxygens.

As we have seen, the net conversion of one molecule of free glucose to pyruvic acid is described by the equation

$$C_6H_{12}O_6 \longrightarrow 2\ C_3H_4O_3 + 2\ H_2$$

(see page 413)

Two ATP, net, are obtained from glucose breakdown as such, and since each H_2 transported to oxygen yields three ATP, the total *aerobic* energy gain up to the pyruvic acid stage is eight ATP.

Next, *two* pyruvic acid molecules are transformed into acetyl CoA, according to the equation

$$2\ C_3H_4O_3 + 2\ CoA-S-H \longrightarrow$$
$$2\ C_2H_3O-S-CoA + 2\ H_2 + 2\ CO_2$$

(see page 416)

The energy yield here is six ATP, from the transport of 2 H_2 to oxygen.

Finally, in *two* turns of the citric acid cycle, one for each of the two acetyl CoA molecules,

$$2\ C_2H_3O-S-CoA + 6\ H_2O \longrightarrow$$
$$4\ CO_2 + 8\ H_2 + 2\ CoA-S-H$$

(see this page)

Here the net energy yield from both fuel oxidation and hydrogen transport is 12 ATP per turn of the cycle, or 24 ATP for two turns.

If we now add the three equations above, we obtain

$$C_6H_{12}O_6 + 6\ H_2O \longrightarrow 6\ CO_2 + 12\ H_2$$

The 12 H_2 has been transferred to atmospheric oxygen, yielding water. Twelve oxygen atoms are required to accept 12 H_2, and 12 H_2O then form. Hence we have

$$C_6H_{12}O_6 + 6\ H_2O + 6\ O_2 \longrightarrow 6\ CO_2 + 12\ H_2O$$

or, reduced to the arithmetical minimum,

$$C_6H_{12}O_6 + 6\ O_2 \longrightarrow 6\ CO_2 + 6\ H_2O$$

This is the familiar input-output statement for the complete combustion of glucose. But it should be amply clear that this statement does not symbolize an actual reaction, for glucose does not react directly with oxygen at all. A lump of sugar exposed to the oxygen of air merely remains sugar and does not change into CO_2 and water. The statement also does not indicate the major endproduct, namely, the energy yield of 38 molecules of ATP for each molecule of glucose burned aerobically. This contrasts sharply with the yield of only two ATP when glucose is burned anaerobically.

If a fuel other than glucose is used, different quantities of oxygen are likely to be required and different amounts of CO_2, water, and ATP will be produced. Whatever the fuel, more ATP is always gained than expended, and it is this net gain which makes the long and complicated reaction sequences of vital adaptive value.

The entire pattern of respiration is outlined in Fig. 16.22. In cells, these metabolic processes take place exceedingly fast. For example, a glucose molecule

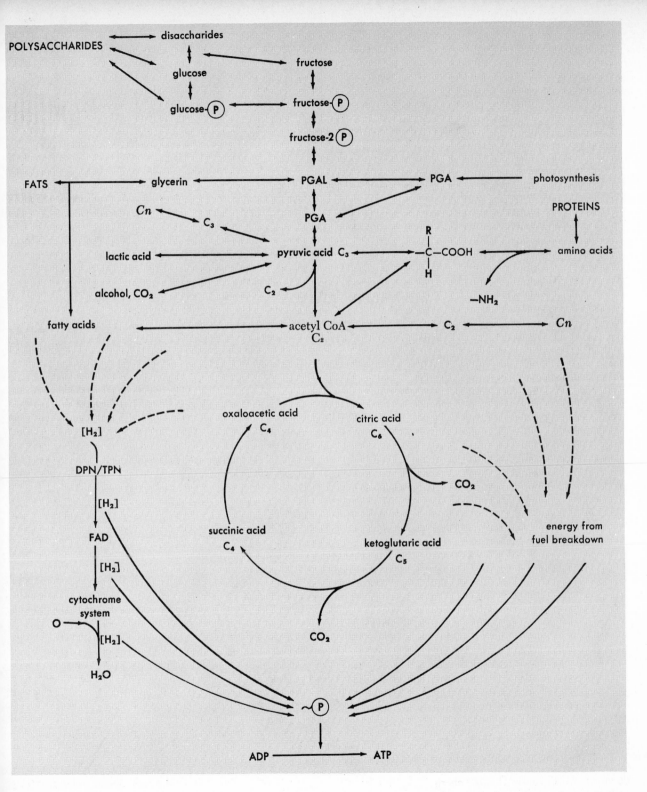

FIG. 16.22 Overall summary of the metabolic pathways in respiration.

is estimated to be burned completely within a single second. Considering the number of reactions, reactants, enzymes, carriers, and the like, such speed is truly impressive. In mammals, moreover, respiratory rates are greatly influenced by the thyroid hormone *thyroxine*. This hormone accelerates respiration in proportion to its concentration. How this effect is achieved and what particular reactions are influenced is still more or less completely unknown. Most organisms are not mammals, and their respiration is not under thyroxine control. Nevertheless, respiratory breakdowns still occur extremely rapidly. Very efficient enzyme action is probably one condition which makes speed possible. Another condition undoubtedly is the close, ordered proximity of all required ingredients in the submicroscopic recesses of the mitochondria. Just as a well-arranged industrial assembly line turns out products at a great rate, so do the even better-arranged mitochondria.

The fate and function of their chief product, ATP, is our next subject.

REVIEW QUESTIONS

1. Compare and contrast a fire with respiration. What do they have in common? What is different? Which materials are fuels in respiration? What three general types of events occur in respiration?

2. What is oxidation? What happens to the atomic pattern of a molecule during oxidation? What is the result of oxidation in terms of bond energies? What different kinds of oxidative changes occur in respiration?

3. Describe fully the role of phosphates in respiration. What is the ADP/ATP system and how does it function? What different kinds of energy changes may occur in phosphate bonds and what role does each play in respiration?

4. What is dehydrogenation? Where does it occur and what role does it play in respiration? In what general way is hydrogen transferred to oxygen? Review the pattern of ATP formation during this transfer. To which specific carriers is hydrogen first transferred from fuel?

5. Distinguish between aerobic and anaerobic respiration. In which organisms and under what conditions does either occur?

6. Review the specific sequence of carriers in (a) aerobic H transfer and (b) anaerobic H transfer. How and where may transfer in (a) become blocked and what happens then? What endproducts are formed in (b) and what are the subsequent fates of these?

7. What is the general significance of pyruvic acid, acetyl CoA, and CO_2 in the respiratory breakdown of fuels? Review the chief steps in the breakdown of carbohydrates to pyruvic acid. (*Note:* Chemical formulas need not be memorized; the important thing is to *understand* what kinds of changes occur, how one step leads to the next, and what, in *words*, these steps are.)

8. What happens to pyruvic acid if conditions are (a) aerobic and (b) anaerobic? How much ATP is gained in either case during the conversion of glucose into pyruvic acid, including energy harvested during H transfer?

9. Which classes of foods break down to pyruvic acid during respiration and which to acetyl CoA? Describe the steps of these breakdowns.

10. What ingredients must be present if pyruvic acid is to be converted to acetyl CoA? What are coenzymes? What are coenzyme A and cocarboxylase and what are their specific functions? From what materials are these two coenzymes manufactured in cells?

11. Review the reaction sequence in the conversion of pyruvic acid to acetyl CoA and describe the total input and output. How much ATP is gained, including energy harvested during H transfer to oxygen?

12. Review the steps of the citric acid cycle. What is the total input and output of this cycle? How much ATP is gained and what are the sources of this gain?

13. Review and summarize the overall fate of one molecule of glucose during complete respiratory combustion. What is the total net input and what is the total net output? What happens to the individual atoms of glucose? What is the total ATP gain and how much is gained during each of the main steps of breakdown?

14. Review the general and the specific interrela-

tions of respiration and photosynthesis. In what sense are the two processes the reverse of each other? What reversible reactions are shared in common? Make a large flow diagram which interconnects the chemical events of respiration and photosynthesis.

15. Where in cells does respiration occur? What factors probably contribute to the speed of respiration? Inasmuch as respiratory reactions are reversible, how does it happen that energy continues to be produced?

SUGGESTED COLLATERAL READINGS

The following are popularly written articles dealing with various aspects of respiration:

Green, D. E.: Enzymes in Teams, *Sci. American,* vol. 181, 1949.

————: The Metabolism of Fats, *Sci. American,* vol. 190, 1954.

————: Biological Oxidation, *Sci. American,* vol. 199, 1958.

Siekevitz, P.: Powerhouse of the Cell, *Sci. American,* vol. 197, 1957.

Stumpf, P. K.: ATP, *Sci. American,* vol. 188, 1953.

Three reprints of important original articles, all found in M. L. Gabriel and S. Fogel, "Great Experiments in Biology," Prentice-Hall, Englewood Cliffs, N.J., 1955:

Buchner, E.: Alcoholic Fermentation without Yeast Cells.

Keilin, D.: On Cytochrome, a Respiratory Pigment Common to Animals, Yeast, and Higher Plants.

Warburg, O.: The Enzyme Problem and Biological Oxidations.

In addition to the physiology texts listed in Chaps. 13 and 14, the following books give excellent accounts of the chemistry of respiration:

Baldwin, E. B.: "Dynamic Aspects of Biochemistry," 3d ed., Cambridge, New York, 1957.

Gerard, R. W.: "Unresting Cells," chaps. 5–7, Harper, New York, 1949.

Harrison, K.: "A Guide Book to Biochemistry," Cambridge, New York, 1959.

ENERGY UTILIZATION

17

In what cellular processes must energy be expended? The answer is, in all processes which contribute to the maintenance and self-perpetuation of a cell.

Such processes include physical as well as chemical ones. The most important physical roles of energy are to produce *heat*, to some extent also to produce *light* and *electricity*, and above all, to produce *movement* of cells and cell parts. The chief chemical roles of energy are maintenance of respiration itself and, most particularly, maintenance of activities associated with the *synthesis* of new cellular components. Such components must be manufactured to offset the combustion and the wear and tear of existing ones, to make possible cellular repairs after injury, to maintain growth, and to permit reproduction. In all these processes of synthesis, energy is one requirement, structural building blocks in the form of nutrients are another. Under the heading of energy utilization, therefore, two major subtopics are the **physical uses** and **chemical uses** of energy.

How much energy must be expended by a cell for physical and chemical activities? The answer here varies, according to the varying intensities of cellular activity. But while a cell lives, its activities are never zero. Accordingly, if life is to continue, at least a basic minimum quantity of energy is required under all conditions. Clearly, a discussion of energy **requirements** forms a third major subtopic. We shall deal with it first.

THE ENERGY REQUIREMENT

CALORIES, ATP, AND OXYGEN

Every energy requirement of living organisms must be met by respiration: demand must be balanced by supply. So far, the supply of energy has been measured in terms of ATP molecules. Utilization, on the other hand, is measured in terms of mechanical work, chemical work, and many other forms of activity. Evidently, before comparative statements can be made about supply and demand, a common yardstick should be available.

Such a yardstick is *heat*. This is the cheapest and most usual form of energy. All other forms of energy can be converted into heat, and any energy quantity may therefore be expressed as a **heat equivalent.** Two or more of these equivalents may then be compared directly. The unit of measurement here is the **Calorie.** One Calorie (or Cal) is defined as that quantity of heat which would raise the temperature of one liter of water by one degree centigrade. For example, to raise the temperature of a liter of water from the freezing point to the boiling point would require 100 Cal.

What is the energy content of a metabolic fuel expressed in heat equivalents? To determine this, one simply burns the fuel in a laboratory furnace and measures the total heat given off. By such means, it is found that, for example, 1 g of glucose or of carbohydrates generally contains 3.8 Cal. A gram of protein liberates roughly the same amount of heat, namely, 4 Cal; and a gram of fat yields about 9 Cal. Table 9 lists the heat equivalents or "caloric values" of some common foods.

From such values, one may calculate how much energy is *potentially* available in given quantities of fuel. In cells, does all this energy become *actually*

available in the form of ATP? In other words, how efficient is respiration? How much of the energy content of fuels can be harvested as useful chemical energy? We know from the preceding chapter that cellular combustion of, for example, 1 molecule of glucose yields about 40 molecules of ATP. It can be shown that when all the molecules in 1 g of glucose are burned in cells, the total amount of energy trapped as ATP is equivalent to 2.5 Cal. Since 1 g of glucose contains an energy potential of 3.8 Cal, as noted, the efficiency of respiration is 2.5/3.8, or 67 per cent (Fig. 17.1).

This is a most remarkable efficiency level. The very best man-made machines can use barely 40 per cent of the energy potential of fuel. In respiration, the 33 per cent of fuel energy not stored as ATP represents unavoidable energy loss through heat dissipation. But even this energy is not entirely wasted, for heat benefits a cell in many ways (see also below).

We note that if an organism is supplied with 100 Cal—for example, if a man eats a slice of bread— then ATP energy equivalent to about 67 Cal will become available for cellular metabolism. How far does such an amount of energy go toward support of life? To answer this, we must know the rate of energy expenditure of an organism under specified conditions.

To assess this expenditure, could one not simply determine the energy content of all the food obtained by an organism during a stated period? No, because

TABLE 9

Caloric values of some common foods

1 glass of milk	200
1 tablespoon mayonnaise	100
1 boiled egg	75
1 doughnut	200
1 slice of bread	100
1 plain cookie	50
1 teaspoon sugar	20
1 frankfurter	100
1 broiled lamb chop	100
1 small slice roast beef	100
1 strip crisp bacon	30
1 average serving navy beans	300
1 boiled medium potato	100
1 average serving peas	50
1 average serving plain lettuce	10
1 banana	100
1 small apple	50
1 medium tomato	20
1 cherry	10

FIG. 17.1 The efficiency of respiration, contrasted with the energy gained when fuel (glucose) is burned in a fire.

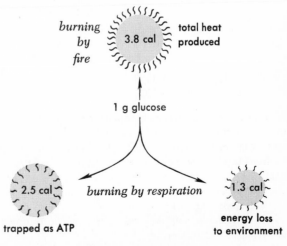

(efficiency: 2.5/3.8 = 67%)

all this food is normally not used toward energy production. An indeterminable fraction may be stored; another fraction may be used in synthesis rather than in respiration; and some food may also be eliminated unused. Moreover, an organism very often acquires more food or less food than actually needed. Clearly then, the amount of energy potentially supplied by food is not a reliable measure of actual energy requirements.

A much better measure is *oxygen consumption*. Atmospheric oxygen is not stored; it is used specifically in respiration only; and it is taken into an organism in amounts geared precisely to actual requirements. As we have seen in Chap. 12, rates of gas exchange are proportional to respiration rates. Furthermore, one can easily determine how much fuel may be burned with the aid of a given quantity of oxygen. For example, 1 l of oxygen will support complete combustion of 1.25 g of glucose.

Therefore, to determine the energy requirement of an organism, it is necessary to specify, first, the activity of the organism and environmental conditions such as temperature, humidity, and other physical factors; second, the period of time during which the energy requirement is to be measured; and third, the amount of oxygen consumed during this period.

If one measures not only oxygen consumption but at the same time also carbon dioxide output, then it is possible to determine what *kinds* of foods an organism burns to meet its energy requirement. The ratio of CO_2 released to O_2 consumed, known as the **respiratory quotient** (RQ), is quite characteristic for each of the main food classes. For example, when glucose is respired aerobically, the quantitative relation between the two respiratory gases is given by the statement:

input	output
$C_6H_{12}O_6$	6 H_2O
6 O_2	6 CO_2

In other words, for every six molecules of oxygen consumed, six molecules of CO_2 are obtained. The respiratory quotient therefore is $CO_2/O_2 = 1.0$. Such an RQ is characteristic for carbohydrates generally. Accordingly, whenever measurement shows that RQ = 1.0, this indicates that the organism burns carbohydrates.

Different RQs are obtained for other food materials. For example, complete respiration of the common fat *tristearin* is described by

input	output
2 $C_{57}H_{110}O_6$	110 H_2O
163 O_2	114 CO_2

Here RQ = 114/163 = 0.7, which is characteristic for fats generally. Thus, when a measured RQ is about 0.7, the organism undoubtedly respires fats. In analogous manner, it can be shown that an RQ of about 0.8 characterizes the combustion of proteins; and if a mixture of carbohydrates, fats, and proteins is used as fuel, the RQ will usually fall somewhere between 0.8 and 0.9.

BASAL METABOLISM

Most actual measurements of energy requirements have been made on man, but the same procedures apply in principle to any organism, plant or animal. The conditions chosen are often those of *basal* metabolism, i.e., when body activity is reduced to a minimum. The test subject is at complete physical and mental rest, as during quiet sleep, and the digestive system is empty. Oxygen consumption and CO_2 output are then measured over a given period of time. Under such conditions, the energy expended by the test subject represents his **basal metabolic rate, BMR** for short. It indicates the energy necessary *just* to remain alive during complete rest or sleep: the energy required to maintain minimum breathing and heartbeat; minimum activity of brain, liver, kidneys, and all other vital organs; and minimum respiration and other chemical activities in all cells.

Tests have shown that under basal conditions a human adult consumes on an average about 14 l of oxygen per hour. Since 1 l burns 1.25 g of glucose and since 1 g of glucose yields 3.8 Cal, the energy expenditure will be $14 \times 1.25 \times 3.8$, or 66.5 Cal. In other words, a slice of bread of 100 Cal will supply just enough effective energy to keep an adult alive during 1 hr of sleep.

BMR values vary widely. A growing child expends more energy per pound of tissue than a nongrowing adult. A male metabolizes slightly more intensely than a female. If the temperature of the environment is low, more energy is expended toward maintenance of constant body temperature. A short, thin person possesses a large skin area in proportion to his volume, and he uses more energy to offset the greater heat loss through surface radiation and evaporation. Because of such variables, actual BMR determinations are quite complicated in practice and require control and measurement of numerous factors.

Indeed, BMR varies not only with age, sex, weight, height, season, and climate but also with race and, above all, state of health. During disease, BMR values may become abnormally low or high, and this may sometimes be a clue to the nature of the disease. An abnormal BMR usually indicates that the utilization or the combustion of foods is somehow defective. This is the case in diabetes, for example, where insulin production is inadequate and glucose utilization is impaired. Or respiration within cells could be impaired as a result of vitamin or thyroid deficiencies. BMR measurements are made frequently when diseases of this sort are suspected.

Conditions are not basal when the body is active. Energy requirements then are greater in proportion to the intensity or the amount of activity. Thinking, speaking, sitting, eating, walking, chopping wood, or merely keeping one's eyes open, all raise the energy requirement beyond BMR levels. Table 10 lists the requirements of various kinds of activities. It will be noted that profound thinking (sedentary work) comes cheap in terms of energy. This does not mean that brainwork is valued low in the scheme of nature. On the contrary, animals have become so adapted that cerebration, like heartbeat and other essential processes, is guaranteed even if only a minimum of energy is available.

From the figures in Table 10, *daily* energy requirements may be calculated. For example,

	college student	lumberjack
8 hr sleep, at 70 Cal per hr	560	560
12 hr sedentary work, at 100 Cal	1200	
2 hr walking and light work, at 200 Cal	400	
2 hr athletics, at 500 Cal	1000	
8 hr heavy work, at 500 Cal		4000
8 hr sedentary occupation, at 100 Cal		800
daily total	3160 Cal	5360 Cal

The requirement of the college student could be satisfied by a little over 1 lb of butter a day; 1 lb butter = 454 g fat ⟶ about 4100 Cal; and at 67 per cent

TABLE 10

Caloric requirements during various activities, performed continuously for 1 hr

basal activity (sleep)	70
sitting at rest	100
walking (leisurely)	200
moderately active work (carpentry)	250
walking down stairs	350
sawing wood	450
swimming	500
very fast running	600
walking up stairs	1100

efficiency, 4100 Cal provides about 2750 Cal. But it should be clear that such an intake would not represent an adequate diet. Additional food is needed for cellular synthesis, and this, as well as respiration itself, requires a wide *variety* of foods. The caloric value of a diet is only *one* aspect of adequate nutrition.

The energy expended daily by an organism sustains both the physical and the chemical activities of all cells. What are these activities and how does the energy of ATP support them?

PHYSICAL ROLES OF ATP

Probably the most abundant physical use of ATP is made in mechanical cell functions. Of these, the most readily discernible are those which produce movement, in the form of either locomotion of whole organisms or internal motion of parts of organisms. We shall first examine the basis of one major type of movement, namely, the contraction of specialized animal muscle cells.

MUSCULAR MOVEMENT

The characteristic activity of muscle cells ranks among the most important activities carried out by animal cells generally, for few animal functions exist that do not include muscular contraction. Moreover, muscles are quantitatively the most abundant tissue of an animal, particularly a vertebrate. A proportionately large amount of all available energy must be expended to keep muscles contracting. Even during "inactive" periods like sleep, for example, the muscular system maintains not only posture and shape but also vital functions such as breathing, heartbeat, and blood pressure. Mainly because of muscular movement, the energy requirements of animals are far greater pound for pound than of any other kind of organism.

The Contractile Units

The functional units of all kinds of muscles are long, thin, intracellular filaments called **myofibrils.** Each muscle cell or muscle fiber contains many such myofibrils aligned in parallel and extending in the same direction as the long axis of the whole cell or fiber (Fig. 17.2). In striated muscles (see Chap. 5), the myofibrils exhibit alternate dark and light crossbands visible under the microscope. When such a muscle contracts, only the dark bands become shorter. The total contraction is the sum of all the individual contractions of the dark bands.

The electron microscope shows that each myofibril is actually a bundle of many long, ultrathin, parallel filaments. These are composed principally of five kinds of materials: water, inorganic ions, ATP, and two proteins called **actin** and **myosin.** Together, these form the basic contraction apparatus.

That this is so has been demonstrated dramatically by experiment. With appropriate procedures, actin and myosin can be extracted from muscle, and it can be shown that neither actin nor myosin alone is able to contract. But by mixing actin and myosin together, artificial fibers of **actomyosin** can be made. To these fibers may be added water, inorganic ions, and ATP. When this is done, it is found that as soon as ATP reaches an actomyosin fiber the latter contracts violently. Such contracting fibers may lift up to 1,000 times their own weight, just as a living muscle may do. And it is also found that, in a contracted fiber, ATP is no longer present but low-energy phosphates are present instead.

Experiments of this sort provide clues how contraction might be brought about in a living muscle. The process is far from being fully understood, but some of the main events are known. Muscle activity is at least a two-step cycle involving alternate *contraction* and *extension*. Energy is used up at some point or points in such a cycle. One view is that the energy makes possible the contraction of a muscle, like compressing a spring. Subsequent extension then is thought to be essentially an automatic recoil, like releasing a compressed spring. According to an alternative view, energy must be expended to extend a muscle, as in stretching a rubber band. Contraction would then be automatic, like releasing an extended rubber band. A good deal of evidence appears to favor this second hypothesis, but the first cannot be ruled out; indeed there are indications that muscle may require energy for both contraction and extension. Muscle is shorter

FIG. 17.2   The structure of skeletal muscle. A whole muscle fiber is shown at left. Note here the cross striations, the internal longitudinal myofibrils, and the many nuclei, which appear as dark patches. Right, an electron micrograph of a few individual myofibrils. Note that each myofibril in turn consists of bundles of still finer filaments. These latter are the functional units of the contraction apparatus. Note again the prominent cross striations. *(Left, General Biological Supply House, Inc.; right, courtesy of Dr. K. R. Porter, Rockefeller Institute.)*

and thicker when contracted, longer and thinner when extended.

The Energy Cycle

The energy donor in muscle activity is ATP which, together with actin and myosin, forms an actomyosin-ATP complex. The ATP here appears to be not only the energy donor but also a necessary *structural* part of the contraction apparatus; ATP makes actomyosin supple and elastic and able to contract at all. When ATP disappears or separates from actomyosin—for example, in extreme fatigue or during rigor mortis after death—muscle becomes rigid and stiff.

During a contraction-extension cycle, the ATP of actomyosin-ATP yields up its energy. To prepare a muscle for a new contraction-extension cycle, new energy must be supplied from the outside. Respiration is the ultimate source of this energy, but it is not the immediate source. Fast though combustion of muscle glycogen is, it is far too slow to supply the ATP required by an active muscle. A glycogen molecule in muscle may burn within a second, but in that second the wing muscle of an insect may contract up to 100 times and use up energy far faster than could be supplied directly by fuel combustion.

Unlike most other cells, muscles are able to *store* large amounts of energy. Cells other than muscles usually may store energy only in the form of ATP. The amounts of ADP available for conversion to ATP are limited, and in such cells energy utilization can occur only as rapidly as ATP can be formed and re-formed by respiration. But some cells, most notably muscles, are alternately highly active or virtually inactive. During periods of intense activity, therefore, more ATP may be required in a muscle than respiration may be able to create. Conversely, during rest, fuel oxidation in muscles may produce more $\sim$℗ than the entire ADP/ATP system can hold. Muscles and a few other animal tissues are able to cope with such excess supplies or demands. They possess a device which can store high-energy phosphate bonds beyond the storage capacity of ATP.

This device operates through either of two compounds. One of them is **creatine,** a nitrogen-containing organic substance found largely in the muscles of vertebrates. The other is **arginine,** an amino acid already encountered in the earlier discussion of urea production in the liver (see Chap. 14). Apart from its other functions, this acid plays the same role in the muscles of most invertebrates as creatine plays in vertebrates.

We may describe this role as follows:

in most vertebrate muscles

in most invertebrate muscles

ATP ADP
arginine ⟷ arginine~℗

In other words, creatine or arginine may accept $\sim$℗ from ATP and so become creatine-phosphate and arginine-phosphate, respectively. These last two compounds are collectively referred to as **phosphagens.** Conversely, a phosphagen may donate $\sim$℗ to ADP and so revert to creatine or arginine.

The adaptive value of these reactions in muscle is clear. If, during rest, fuels supply more $\sim$℗ than can be harvested as ATP, then the reactions above proceed to the right; ATP unloads $\sim$℗ into phosphagen and becomes ADP. This ADP is now free to collect more $\sim$℗ from fuel. Phosphagen stores accumulate in this manner in far greater quantities than ATP could accumulate. When a muscle subsequently becomes active, the energy of the ATP in actomyosin-ATP is used up, as noted earlier. If then the muscle is to be reenergized, new actomyosin-ATP must be formed. The immediate energy sources for such "recharging" of muscles are the phosphagens. They transfer their $\sim$℗ groups into the contraction apparatus, and later they are themselves reenergized by respiration. Thus, respiratory ATP slowly and continuously replenishes the phosphagen stores and these ample stores rapidly and repeatedly re-create actomyosin-ATP while a muscle is active. Figure 17.3 summarizes these energy relations.

Muscular activity clearly can continue only as long as the energy stores of phosphagen last. If these stores become exhausted, actomyosin-ATP cannot be regenerated and muscle becomes fatigued. As noted in Chap. 16, fatigue is associated with comparative oxygen lack, fermentation, and lactic acid accumulation. Muscle *can* contract in the complete absence of oxygen so long as fermentation alone can maintain the phosphagen stores and so long as lactic acid concentrations are not excessive. Indeed, muscle normally probably respires anaerobically as well as aerobically, and any lactic acid formed can be carried off by blood as fast as it appears. Lactic acid tends to accumulate only dur-

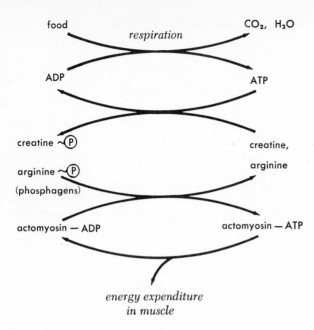

food

respiration

CO₂, H₂O

ADP

ATP

creatine ~Ⓟ

creatine,

arginine ~Ⓟ

arginine

(phosphagens)

actomyosin — ADP

actomyosin — ATP

*energy expenditure
in muscle*

FIG. 17.3 The energy relations in muscle activity. Respiration supplies energy for muscles via the phosphagen stores.

ing intense activity, and increasing fatigue then brings the activity to a halt sooner or later. Thereafter, aerobic combustion of muscle glycogen continues at a rapid pace and depleted phosphagen stores are replenished. At the same time, lactic acid slowly diffuses into the blood, becomes liver glycogen, and returns to muscle and other tissues as blood glucose.

The Action Cycle

What is the detailed mechanism of muscle contraction and extension? This aspect of muscle activity is just beginning to be clarified, and complete answers are not yet available. It is generally believed that, in an actomyosin-ATP complex, the actin and myosin components are arranged as parallel fibrils which may be joined side by side, perhaps by temporary chemical cross-linkages. According to one view, contraction of such a unit might be brought about by an accordion-like folding or pleating of the originally stretched out actin and myosin components. More recent findings suggest that the parallel actin and myosin fibrils might maintain an extended shape at all times but might slide over one another. If actin and myosin were to

slide farther apart, a muscle would extend; in the opposite case, it would contract (Fig. 17.4).

At least three groups of data must be taken into account in any hypothesis designed to explain how either a pleating or a sliding would be initiated and controlled. First, it is known that the specific trigger for the contraction of a muscle is a nerve impulse. Second, it is known that inorganic ions, notably Mg^{++} and Ca^{++}, are associated with or attached to the actomyosin-ATP complex. By virtue of such positive charges, the complex may possess an electric potential over its surface; one of the known effects of nerve impulses is to bring about a reduction of electric potentials (see Chap. 22). Third, it is known that muscles, like several other tissues, contain ATPases, i.e., enzymes which promote the conversion of ATP into ADP. The specific ATPase of muscle either is identical with myosin itself or is so closely linked with myosin that available techniques are unable to separate the two. Evidently, the actomyosin-ATP complex possesses not only built-in potential energy in the form of ATP but also the necessary built-in enzyme which may make this energy available. The action of the enzyme is believed to remain inhibited in some unknown way prior to arrival of a nerve impulse; directly or indirectly, the impulse appears to be the necessary stimulus for ATPase activation.

The following events might then take place during muscle action (Fig. 17.5). Initially, the actin and myosin components of actomyosin-ATP would be stretched apart and the muscle would be extended. Such a condition might be maintained by the electric charges; since like charges repel one another, any contraction of the actomyosin-ATP complex would be pre-

FIG. 17.4 Actin and myosin filaments are represented by horizontal lines (top). According to one hypothesis, muscle contraction would occur when actin and myosin become pleated or folded (bottom left). According to a newer hypothesis, actin and myosin may slide relative to each other and account in this manner for extension-contraction cycles of muscle (bottom right).

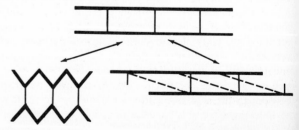

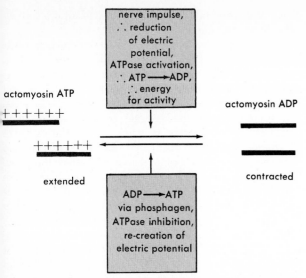

actomyosin ATP

++++++

++++++

extended

nerve impulse,
∴ reduction
of electric
potential,
ATPase activation,
∴ ATP ——ADP,
∴ energy
for activity

actomyosin ADP

contracted

ADP ——ATP
via phosphagen,
ATPase inhibition,
re-creation of
electric potential

FIG. 17.5 Summary of probable events during a unit cycle of muscle activity. Known events correlated with contraction are listed in the box above the reversible arrows; events correlated with extension, in the box below the arrows.

vented by electric repulsion of the actin and myosin components (regardless of whether such contraction would be achieved by pleating or sliding). However, when a nerve impulse arrives, it may reduce the electric potentials and thus might remove the obstacle to contraction. The nerve impulse would also activate the ATPase, ATP would be split, and the potential energy of actomyosin-ATP would become actual. As noted, it is still not quite clear whether this energy brings about the actual contraction of the actomyosin complex or a reextension after the complex has contracted. In either event, the energy might promote the formation of new cross-linkages between actin and myosin. After the energy is spent, new potential energy is supplied by phosphagen. Muscle extension and recovery must also be accompanied by an inhibition of ATPase activity, by rebuilding of electric potentials, and by an unpleating or sliding apart of the actin and myosin components.

Whatever the actual details of the fundamental action cycle in muscle may prove to be, cycles of this sort clearly take place fast enough to propel a cheetah, for example, at speeds of 50 miles per hr; and they are powerful enough to permit many animals, man included, to lift objects weighing more than the animals themselves.

NONMUSCULAR MOVEMENT

In animals as well as other organisms, nonmuscular locomotion is very common. Numerous animal larvae move by means of cilia, and in many cases the adults may move by both cilia and muscles (e.g., flatworms). Flagellary and amoeboid propulsion is widespread among Protista and the sperm cells of Metaphyta, as we have seen, and various other, less readily definable types of locomotion occur among Monera such as spirochetes, beggiatoas, blue-green algae, and slime molds.

In all these cases, ATP appears to be the common energy source. However, it is virtually unknown how the chemical energy of ATP is translated into the mechanical energy of motion. In the case of flagella, the locomotor apparatus is at least identifiable and some evidence suggests that the beat of a flagellum might be produced by alternate contraction and relaxation of ultrafine protein filaments within the fibrils of the flagellum. If so, a machinery somewhat like that in animal muscles may conceivably be involved. In the various other forms of locomotion, distinct cell structures specialized to produce movement do not appear to exist. The machinery for locomotion here undoubtedly resides diffusely in all or most parts of the cell cytoplasm. Our understanding of these locomotor processes is at present limited to the elementary and rather unenlightening observation that if energy is unavailable to a cell, propulsion cannot occur.

Not all motion is locomotion. Regardless of whether or not an organism as a whole moves, its parts move. Some of these motions occur universally. For example, all cells move nutrients through their boundaries, both in absorption and secretion. We have already spoken of the requirement of respiratory energy in some of these processes, e.g., in the absorptive work required during water and mineral uptake and in phosphorylation during glucose uptake. All cells move compounds also within their substance, partly through diffusion, partly through cyclosis. The role of ATP is less clear here, but that it plays *some* role, even if very indirectly, seems almost certain. For example, localized heat production by ATP may create convection currents which might contribute to cyclotic streaming of cytoplasm. Moreover, cyclosis stops if respiration stops. Among other intracellular movements are the precise migrations of chromosomes during cell division (see Chap. 23). The mechanism of these motions is again unknown. Some preliminary evidence suggests that contractile protein filaments energized by ATP might play a role here just as in flagellary and muscular motion.

In addition to such intracellular movements, groups of cells and indeed whole tissues and organs undergo numerous types of motions associated with growth, development, and the maintenance of steady states. We shall discuss some of these movements in later contexts and note here only that all of them are undoubtedly ATP-dependent too; if the ATP supply of an organism is stopped, the various movements also stop.

But the energizing of *mechanical* cell functions is not the only physical role of ATP. Production of *heat*, of *light*, and of *electricity* is an additional household task of many a cell type, and ATP is again the energy donor.

HEAT PRODUCTION

One source of internal heat has already been referred to in the last chapter; if the high-energy phosphate of ATP is used in low-energy phosphorylations, then any excess energy of $\sim\text{\textcircled{P}}$ becomes heat. Another internal heat source is ATP-energized movement; for friction of moving parts generates heat. Moreover, ATP is not used with 100 per cent efficiency in the production of movement. Conversion of the chemical energy of ATP into the mechanical energy of motion is accompanied by a loss of energy; this energy dissipates into the substance of a cell in the form of heat.

Added to whatever heat is supplied by the external environment, ATP-derived heat maintains the temperature of an organism and offsets heat lost to the environment by evaporation and radiation, creates tiny convection currents within cells and so assists in diffusion and cyclosis, and, above all, provides adequate operating temperatures for enzymes and all other functional parts of cells.

As noted in Chap. 11, heat production in birds and mammals is balanced dynamically against heat loss, and a constant body temperature is thereby maintained. In all other organisms, proper internal operating temperatures are maintained ultimately by the external environment, and the internal temperature of such organisms by and large matches that of the external. If, therefore, the environment is either too cold or too hot, the organisms cannot survive. Within these extremes, however, ATP may create internal heat which to some extent counteracts low environmental temperatures; just as the cooling effect of evaporation may reduce internal heat which to some extent counteracts high environmental temperatures.

Clearly then, heat is an essential requirement of every organism, and if ATP served in no other function than heat production, it would still be among the most vitally necessary components of cells (Fig. 17.6).

BIOLUMINESCENCE

"Living" light is emitted by virtually all major groups of organisms. Monera, Protista, and virtually all metazoan phyla include marine or terrestrial representatives which are bioluminescent. Evidently, the capacity to produce light has independently developed several times during evolution. Yet the essentials of the light-generating mechanism appear to be alike in all cases.

This mechanism consists of at least six components: water, inorganic ions, oxygen, ATP, and two groups of substances called, respectively, **luciferin** and **luciferase.** These last differ in composition in different species. Luciferin and the enzyme luciferase are the principal light-generating elements. They can be ex-

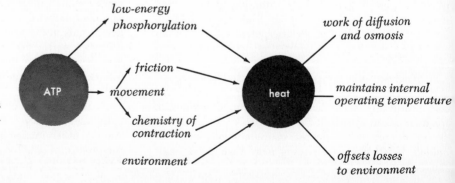

FIG. 17.6 The principal sources and functions of heat in organisms.

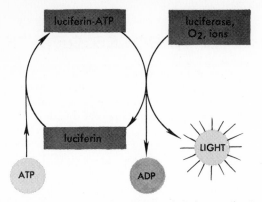

FIG. 17.7 The general pattern of light production in bioluminescent organisms.

tracted from light-producing cells, and they are non-luminous on their own. If ATP is added to luciferin, a luciferin-ATP complex is formed. If, in the presence of ions and oxygen, a solution of luciferase is now added, the mixture emits light. At the same time, oxygen is used up and ATP becomes ADP. If, after the light disappears, more oxygen and more ATP are added, light is generated again. Light production evidently is an oxygen-requiring, ATP-dependent process (Fig. 17.7).

Bioluminescent organisms may stay lit up for appreciable periods or may produce brief flashes (Fig. 17.8). In bioluminescent animals, light emission depends on nervous stimulation of specialized cells in light-producing organs (see Fig. 7.26). The light emitted by different organisms may be of any wavelength in the visible spectrum; i.e., to the human eye it may be red, yellow, green, or blue. Little or no nonvisible radiation is generated. The actual wavelength of the emission is probably determined by the particular chemical makeup of luciferin. In some cases, two or more kinds of luciferin may occur in a single organism, and such an organism then may light up in several colors. In all cases, the available energy is spent very efficiently, for little heat is lost during light production. Hence the frequent designation of living light as "cold" light. Also, the unit intensity of the light is remarkably great. It compares favorably with that of modern fluorescent lamps.

BIOELECTRICITY

Bioelectricity is a byproduct of all cellular processes in which ions play a part. In other words, elec-tricity is as common throughout the living world as table salt. However, certain eels and rays are highly specialized in their capacity to produce electricity. These fish possess **electric organs** composed mainly of modified muscles. The component cells are disk-shaped and noncontractile, and they are piled into stacks. Assemblies of this sort have an appearance and a function reminiscent of storage batteries connected in series.

The details of operation here are understood less well than those of light production. However, it is known that the generation of electricity depends on ATP and a substance called **acetylcholine**. This chemical will be encountered again later, for it functions widely as a key agent in the transmission of nerve impulses. It also functions in the generation of bio-electricity. This event is apparently accompanied by a splitting of acetylcholine into separate acetyl and cho-

FIG. 17.8 Bioluminescence of dinoflagellates passing through the pores of a laboratory filtering device. See also Fig. 8.9. (Courtesy of Dr. F. T. Haxo, Scripps Institute of Oceanography.)

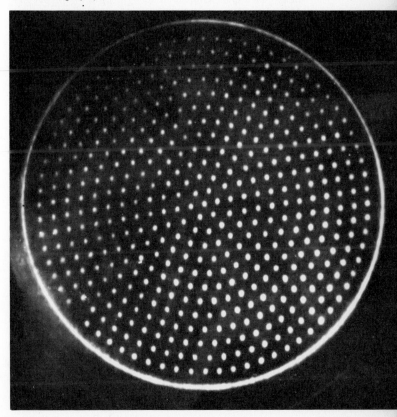

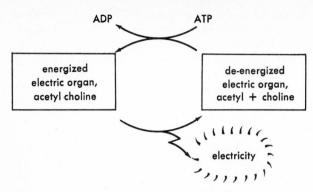

FIG. 17.9 The general pattern of the production of bioelectricity.

line fractions. The two are then recombined into acetylcholine, with energy from ATP (Fig. 17.9).

As in light production, the efficiency of energy utilization is remarkably great. So also is the intensity of the electricity generated. An electric eel may deliver a shock of up to 400 volts, enough to kill another fish or to jolt a man severely or to light up a row of electric bulbs wired to a tank into which such an eel is put. Nervous stimulation of the electric organ triggers the production of electricity.

It is still unknown just how the chemical energy of ATP is actually converted into light energy or electric energy. But that ATP is the key is clearly established, and this versatile compound emerges as the source of all forms of living physical energy, usual or unusual (Fig. 17.10). Indeed, ATP is even more versatile, for it is also the source of all living *chemical* energy.

FIG. 17.10 General summary of the functions of ATP.

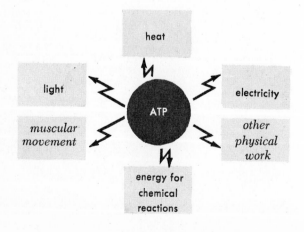

CHEMICAL ROLES OF ATP

The energizing of **synthesis** reactions represents the chief chemical role of ATP. A cyclical interrelation is therefore in evidence. On the one hand, breakdown of organic compounds leads to a net buildup of ATP through respiration. On the other hand, breakdown of ATP leads either to physical activity as discussed above or to a net buildup of organic compounds through chemical synthesis. Figure 17.11 outlines this basic cycle of energy and materials which governs the overall metabolism of all cells.

Synthesis of cellular components and breakdown occur simultaneously, all the time. As already noted in the last chapter, breakdown may affect any cellular constituent regardless of composition or age. A protein just synthesized through long reaction sequences and at great expense of energy is as likely to be destroyed as a glucose molecule already present for days. A certain *percentage* of all cellular constituents is decomposed every second. Which constituents actually make up this percentage is largely a matter of chance.

Such randomness applies also to synthesis. Regardless of the source of materials, a certain percentage of available molecular components is synthesized every second into finished cell substance. If synthesis and breakdown are exactly balanced, the net characteristics of a cell may remain unchanged. But continuous *turnover* of energy and materials occurs nevertheless, and every brick in the building is sooner or later replaced by a new one. Thus the house always remains "fresh."

Synthesis and breakdown cannot sustain each other in a self-contained, self-sufficient cycle, even when the two processes are exactly balanced; for energy dissipates irretrievably through physical activities and through heat losses in chemical reactions, and materials dissipate through elimination, evaporation, and friction. Just to maintain a steady state, therefore, a cell must be supplied continuously with energy and raw materials: solar energy, CO_2, and water in the case of photosynthesizing cells, and in the case of all other cells, condensed packages of these three, namely, organic nutrients. Very often, moreover, the rate of supply of such materials must exceed the rate required for mere maintenance, for net synthesis may exceed net breakdown. This is the case, for example, in growth, in repair after injury, and in cells which manufacture secretion products.

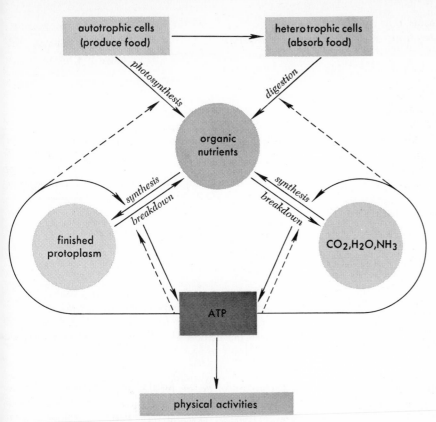

FIG. 17.11 The fundamental metabolic balance of cellular energy and materials. A less comprehensive version of the above is given in Fig. 16.4.

Two broad classes of synthesis reactions may be distinguished: *maintenance synthesis,* in which the reaction products stay within the producing cell and usually contribute to the survival of that cell, and *export synthesis,* in which the reaction products leave the producing cell and often contribute to the survival of other cells.

MAINTENANCE SYNTHESIS

The overall function of maintenance synthesis is the manufacture of all those cellular constituents which a cell does not obtain directly as prefabricated nutrients or secretions from other cells. Such missing constituents include most of the critically necessary compounds for cellular survival: nucleic acids, structural and enzymatic proteins, polysaccharides, fats, and numerous other groups of complex organic substances.

Many of these compounds are manufactured by reactions which are the exact reverse of breakdown reactions. For example, the synthesis of polysaccharides and fats in effect has already been discussed: read in reverse, the respiratory and digestive reactions outlined in preceding chapters describe such syntheses adequately. Moreover, the same enzymes, vitamins, and other reaction aids function at the same steps in the reversed sequences. Acetyl CoA often represents a fundamental starting compound, and from it may be produced fatty acids as well as pyruvic acid, glycerin, and glucose. Polymerization of 6-carbon units accompanied by removal of water then yields polysaccharides; combination of fatty acids and glycerin, similarly accompanied by dehydration, yields fats.

The purely chemical aspects of the synthesis of nucleic acids and proteins are likewise the reverse of breakdown reactions. In the case of proteins, a cell first obtains or manufactures $-NH_2$ and $-RCH-COOH$ groups. These are then combined into amino acids, and the latter are subsequently polymerized by dehydration and formation of peptide bonds. Intracellular proteinases called **cathepsins,** very similar in function to the extracellular pepsins and trypsins of animal digestive tracts, catalyze such linking together of amino acids. The resulting polypeptide chains represent the structural units of proteins. Analogously, nitrogen bases, pentoses, and phosphates are joined to form nucleotides, and these are subsequently polymerized into nucleic acids (see Chaps. 4, 14, 16).

However, the synthesis of nucleic acids and proteins also has vital biological aspects which make it not simply the reverse of chemical breakdown. First, unlike most other compounds, which are produced diffusely in various cellular regions, nucleic acids and proteins are synthesized only in special "factory" locations. Nucleic acids originate in the *chromosomes* of the nucleus; proteins, in the *ribosomes* of the cytoplasm. Second, again unlike other compounds, both nucleic acids and proteins are specific; i.e., each cell must manufacture very particular, unique sets of each of these compounds. If a cell contains glycogen, for example, all such glycogen molecules are alike; but all nucleic acid molecules and all protein molecules are decidedly not alike. We have already discussed this condition of specificity in Chap. 4. Because of the specificity requirement, more is needed for nucleic acid and protein synthesis than simply appropriate raw materials, enzymes, and ATP. What is needed in addition is *specificity control*, i.e., regulation of the particular sequence in which given nucleotides are linked into a specific nucleic acid and in which given amino acids are linked into a specific protein.

The crucial specificity control is exercised by the nucleic acids themselves, notably by the chromosomal deoxyribose nucleic acids (DNA) which form the genes. As already pointed out in Chap. 3, genes carry chemically coded building instructions, and these specify the exact makeup of all the DNA, all the RNA, and all the proteins to be synthesized in a cell. We shall see in Chap. 18 just how the genetic code is believed to influence actual synthesis. It is this immediate genetic control which makes nucleic acid and protein synthesis critically different from all other syntheses. Direct gene control is not essential in carbohydrate synthesis, for example. Precursor molecules such as glucose are all alike, and regardless of which two glucose molecules are joined by synthesis, the result will always be the same maltose. All nucleotides or all amino acids are not alike, however, and it makes a great difference which particular two nucleotides or which particular two amino acids are joined. Hence the requirement of direct genetic control in such cases (Fig. 17.12). Note, incidentally, that *breakdown* of any compound, nucleic acids and proteins included, can occur without the immediate

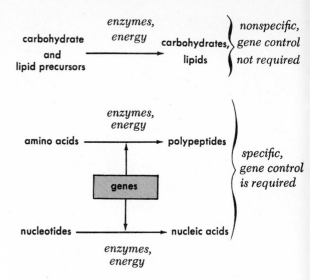

FIG. 17.12 The requirement of specificity control in protein and nucleic acid synthesis. Without gene control, the structural pattern of new proteins and nucleic acids would not match the pattern of preexisting proteins and nucleic acids.

participation of genes; for the precise pattern of breakdown is relatively unimportant so long as breakdown is accomplished in *some* way. Pattern becomes important only in building. Note also that even where direct gene control is not required, indirect control occurs in any case: enzymes catalyze metabolic reactions, and genes govern the synthesis of enzyme proteins.

Newly synthesized compounds contribute to the maintenance of a cell according to structural and functional patterns already outlined in Chap. 4. For example, new nucleic acids become part of chromosomes and other cell structures in which these compounds are normally present. Analogously, newly formed proteins add to and replace parts of numerous cellular components. For example, by virtue of their particular specificities, proteins might become incorporated into various fibrils, membranes, mitochondria, chloroplasts, or indeed any other cellular structure. Alternatively, the properties of a newly manufactured protein might be such that it may come to function as a specific enzyme or as a raw material in the synthesis of protein-containing complexes. Like proteins, fats and carbohydrates become part of the structural and functional makeup of cells. In addition, as we have seen, they serve importantly as storage materials.

Apart from these main categories of cellular constituents, cells also contain large numbers of other components, many of them derivatives of the main categories. Manufactured through special reaction sequences, such substances include, for example, ATP, DPN, cytochrome, and others we have already encountered in various contexts. Some types of synthesis reactions are restricted to specific, variously specialized cell types. A good example of this is the production of chlorophyll and of pigments generally in particular cell types only. Characteristic synthesis products of certain tissues, plant tissues especially, have often proved to be useful to man—rubber, quinine, caffeine, nicotine, to mention only a few. It is still largely unknown what functions, if any, such substances might have in the very cells in which they are manufactured. Inasmuch as such compounds are not formed universally in all cells, they cannot be of general significance in metabolism. In some cases at least, constituents of this type probably represent unique waste products, permanently retained in the cells of organisms which do not possess specialized excretory systems.

EXPORT SYNTHESIS

Every cell is an exporting cell to some extent; for at the very least it exports metabolic wastes such as CO_2 and often water. The term **excretion** is generally used to refer to exported wastes, although what is waste in one cell may often be an essential metabolite in another cell (e.g., H_2O). Specially synthesized products which are exported from cells and are clearly not wastes are given the general designation **secretion.**

Secretions may have a variety of roles: **nutritive** (e.g., glucose secreted by photosynthesizing cells); **digestive** (e.g., enzymes poured into the gut); **excretory** (e.g., urea secretion by liver cells); **regulative** (e.g., hormones secreted by given plant and animal cells); **supportive** (e.g., secretion of cellulose in plants, bone substance in animals); **reproductive** (e.g., aromatic scents secreted by plants and animals); or variously **protective** (e.g., secretion of irritants and poisons by plant and animal cells, including the secretions of antibiotics by soil organisms). Indeed there are few functions in any organism that do not require cellular secretions of some sort.

In multicellular organisms, single cells and more particularly groups of cells which are specialized for the manufacture of given secretions are known as **glands.** Among plants, for example, the digestive juices produced by leaves of carnivorous species are manufactured in glands. Many vascular plants of saline soils possess root glands which secrete salt. Young leaves in the buds of many woody plants develop temporary glandular hairs which secrete a gummy substance covering the entire bud and protecting the bud during the winter. Glands are sometimes involved also in the phenomenon of **guttation,** i.e., the occasional exudation of water droplets from the surfaces of leaves. So-called **hydathodes** are responsible for guttation. Some hydathodes are merely cell paths which offer little resistance to water coming from xylem. In these cases, water is forced out by root pressure, through modified stomata incapable of closing. But in other cases, hydathodes are distinct glands which discharge water from the interior of a leaf to the surface. Guttation is a means of eliminating water when the roots absorb more than the leaves can transpire, e.g., under conditions of high environmental humidity (Fig. 17.13).

Among animals, glands are broadly of two types. So-called **endocrine** glands are ductless, and they secrete into the blood. *Hormones* are the characteristic products of endocrine glands; we shall discuss their nature and function in Chap. 20. All other secretions are manufactured in **exocrine** glands, which empty their products into free spaces or into ducts. Among glands of this type are digestive glands (e.g., liver, pancreas, salivary glands), skin glands (e.g., sweat glands, various oil- and wax-secreting glands), and numerous glands associated with the reproductive, circulatory, and other systems. Many exocrine glands have already been encountered in earlier chapters; many others will be referred to in later contexts (Fig. 17.14).

Added to materials synthesized and used *within* a given cell, secretions received from *other* cells complete the list of ingredients required for the formation of new cellular substance. This total multitude of chemicals, built up at the expense of ATP, then maintains and perpetuates the body of a cell. But it must not be imagined that newly constructed compounds just happen to arrange themselves into new living material. If the proteins, fats, and other components were merely mixed together in water, the result would be a complex but lifeless soup. As already noted in Chap. 4, *omnis cellula e cellula*—all cells arise from preexisting cells; all life arises from preexisting life. New cellular constituents become living matter only if older living matter provides the framework; the house may be added to and its parts may be replaced or modified,

FIG. 17.13 Glandular structures in plants. Top left, a pitcher plant, showing glandular hairs on inner surface of leaf modified for trapping insects. Top right, glandular hairs on a modified leaf of an insect-catching plant. Bottom left, glandular hair from the stem of a geranium plant. Bottom right, section through a hydathode. Note columns of cells forming a water-conducting vascular canal. Arrow points to permanently open stoma of hydathode. *(Top left and right, Jean Carel, Paris; bottom right, reprinted with permission from K. Esau, "Plant Anatomy," John Wiley & Sons, Inc., New York, 1953.)*

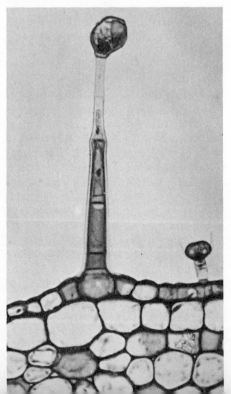
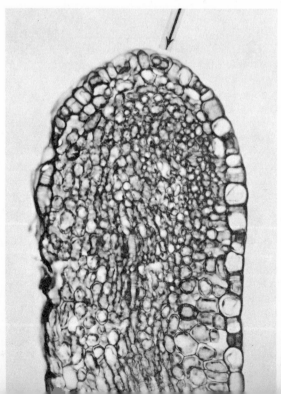

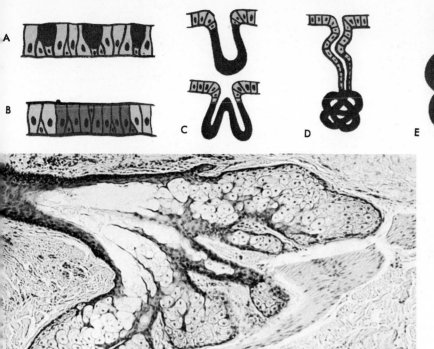

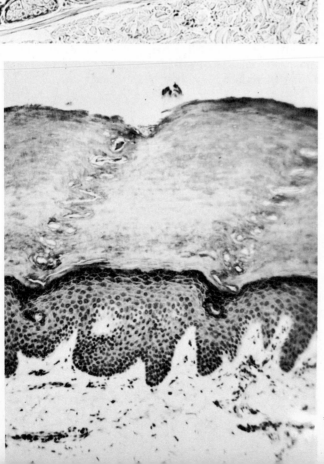

FIG. 17.14 Glandular structures in animals; exocrine glands. Diagram: A, solitary secreting cells, as in lower gut; B, sheet of secreting cells, as in nasal epithelium; C and D, glandular pockets, D as in sweat glands; E, pouched glands, as in sebaceous skin glands; F, the duct system and secretory terminals in mammary glands. Photos: sections through skin. One photo shows the meandering duct of a sweat gland; the other, the secreting pouches of a sebaceous gland. These glands produce an oily secretion, which keeps hair soft and pliable. (Photos courtesy of Dr. William Montagna, Brown University.)

but an altogether new house cannot be built. That apparently occurred only once during the history of the earth.

We have completed the discussion of metabolism. Viewed from afar, this whole complex of functions rides on a powerful energy beam emanating from the sun. Our ultimate energy donor plays via photosynthesis into all the organic matter of plants, radiates into ATP through respiration, and, still strong, so energizes life's process.

Viewed close up, metabolism is a staggering multitude of reactions and shifting chemical equilibria, of matter conversions and energy conversions, of spinning atoms and vibrating molecules. Yet when all is done, the outcome, unfailingly in each of billions of organisms and trillions of cells, is far from random. Rather, it is a highly ordered, efficient set of processes, oriented toward continued nutrition on the one hand and toward continued production of energy and new living matter on the other (Fig. 17.15).

What creates this remarkable orientation and what maintains it? The specific answer is processes of *control;* and the general answer, processes of *self-perpetuation.* Metabolism is one half of life; self-perpetuation is the other. The system which only metabolizes is but an inanimate machine and an uncoordinated machine at that. To ensure internal coordination, to allow it to meet the impact of the external environment, and therefore to make it a *living* system, it must perform

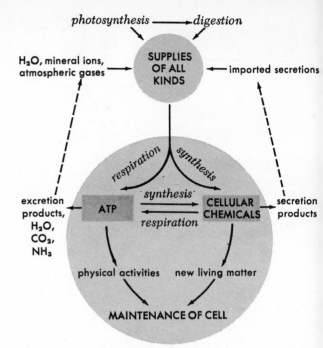

FIG. 17.15 The overall pattern of metabolism and its chief component processes.

the processes of self-perpetuation. These make orderly metabolism possible—but they are themselves made possible by this metabolism.

REVIEW QUESTIONS

1. Define Calorie, heat equivalent, BMR. Why are energy requirements and expenditures of organisms often expressed in Calories? What is the "caloric value" of a given food? How much of the energy of a food is trapped by respiration and what happens to the rest?

2. What is the relation between measurement of oxygen consumption and measurements of BMR? What is the actual rate of oxygen consumption in man? What variables affect BMR? How would you measure the BMR of a plant?

3. What is a respiratory quotient? How is such a quotient measured and how does it vary with the kind of food an organism burns?

4. Describe the internal fine structure of a muscle. What and where is actomyosin? What are the roles of ATP in muscle? In what specific ways is the ATP supply maintained? Describe the energetic aspects of a unit cycle of muscle activity.

5. Describe the nervous, chemical, mechanical, and electrical events which, according to current hypotheses, may conceivably occur during a unit cycle of muscle activity.

6. What different kinds of movements occur in organisms and their cells? What is known about the role of energy in these movements?

7. In what ways does an organism obtain and

produce heat? What are the functions of heat in metabolism?

8. How do organisms produce bioluminescence? Which groups of organisms are bioluminescent? How do the properties of living light compare with those of nonliving light? How and by what organisms is bioelectricity produced?

9. Describe the basic balance of synthesis and breakdown in living organisms. How does protein specificity influence the ingredients required for protein synthesis? What are the ingredients? By what general sequence of processes does protein synthesis occur, and where?

10. Describe the specific sequence of reactions through which acetyl CoA in cells could be synthesized into (*a*) fats and (*b*) glycogen or starch. If necessary, consult Chap. 16. What are the various possible functions of proteins, fats, and carbohydrates synthesized in cells?

11. What are export syntheses? What are some of their metabolic and self-perpetuative functions? What is a gland? Define guttation and hydathode. Name and describe the function of various glands in animals.

12. Review and summarize the broad components of metabolism as a whole, and review again the general relation between metabolism and self-perpetuation.

SUGGESTED COLLATERAL READINGS

The texts listed at the end of Chaps. 13 and 14 contain accounts of various topics dealt with here. These texts may profitably be consulted for additional information on, for example, energy requirements and cellular synthesis. On synthesis, see also the book by Baldwin cited at the end of Chap. 16. Of the readings suggested below, the one by Lavoisier is a reprint of a famous classical paper.

Fowden, L.: A Biochemical Enigma: the Mechanism of Protein Synthesis, *New Biol.*, vol. 23, 1957.

Gale, E. F.: Experiments in Protein Synthesis, *Sci. American*, vol. 194, 1956.

Green, D. E.: The Metabolism of Fats, *Sci. American*, vol. 190, 1954.

Harvey, E. N.: The Luminescence of Living Things, *Sci. American*, vol. 179, 1948.

————: Luminescent Organisms, *Am. Scientist*, vol. 40, 1952.

Hayashi, T., and G. A. W. Boehm: Artificial Muscle, *Sci. American*, vol. 187, 1952.

Hoagland, M.: Nucleic Acids and Proteins, *Sci. American*, vol. 201, 1959.

Johnson, F. H.: Heat and Life, *Sci. American*, vol. 180, 1949.

Katchalsky, A., and S. Lifson: Muscle as a Machine, *Sci. American*, vol. 190, 1954.

Lavoisier, A., and P. Laplace: Memoir on Heat, in M. L. Gabriel and S. Fogel, "Great Experiments in Biology," Prentice-Hall, Englewood Cliffs, N.J., 1955.

Szent-Gyorgyi, A.: Muscle Research, *Sci. American*, vol. 180, 1949.

PART 5
SELF-PERPETUATION:
THE STEADY STATE

We recall that self-perpetuation comprises three groups of processes: first, those which maintain the **steady state** of living units and adjust and coordinate their internal operations; second, processes of **reproduction,** which extend the operations of living units in space and in time; and third, processes of **adaptation,** which mold and fit the long-term characteristics of living units to the characteristics of specific environments. Through self-perpetuation, living matter in the global aggregate becomes potentially indestructible.

Adaptation depends on reproduction, and reproduction depends on steady-state control. All three components of self-perpetuation operate on all levels of the living organization, and cellular self-perpetuation is prerequisite for the persistence of all higher levels. Consequently, maintenance of steady states within cells becomes the foundation of self-perpetuation as a whole.

Our plan of procedure for this first series of chapters is therefore clear. We shall begin with a discussion of processes on which all steady states in living matter are ultimately based, namely, **gene functions** specifically and **control functions** generally. With this background we shall then concentrate on the various aspects of cellular and higher-level steady-state control. Thus we shall inquire into the nature of **growth factors** such as vitamins and hormones and into their controlling influence on cells and whole plants and animals. And we shall also deal with specialized animal control functions without counterparts in plants, namely, various functions of the **circulatory,** the **excretory,** and the **nervous systems.**

GENES AND
CONTROL PATTERNS

18

The control of molecular steady states in living matter ultimately traces to gene action; genes form the foundation of all control on all levels of the living hierarchy. Through this, as we shall see, genes also govern reproduction and adaptation, and genes thereby become the basis of all self-perpetuation. It is therefore proper to discuss **gene function** first. In performing their functions, genes and all other control devices produce optimal operating conditions within living matter. Moreover, they adjust living processes in such a way that the optimal conditions tend to be maintained despite changes in the environment. Different types of control devices accomplish this in different characteristic ways, yet in all cases the underlying principles of operation are the same. This common **pattern of control** will be the subject of the second part of this chapter.

GENE FUNCTION

Life began after the first nucleic acids had been formed. Creation of original life took billions of years, for it had to occur by physical and chemical chance; there was no blueprint to follow. But after nucleic acids were on the scene, creation of new life could become a very rapid process. Today it takes only 20 minutes to create a new bacterium, only 22 months to create a new elephant. This great acceleration is made possible by nucleic acids, more specifically, by genes, the modern descendants of the first nucleic acids. Present in every cell, genes do provide a blueprint, a recipe, for the creation of life and also for its controlled maintenance. Through genes, creation and maintenance cease to be matters of chance but become matters of controlled planning.

GENE CHARACTERISTICS

We already know that genes are located in **chromosomes** and that these filamentous bodies are typically present within a nucleus. Also present in a nucleus are one or more spherical **nucleoli.** Both chromosomes and nucleoli are

443

suspended in a semifluid nuclear sap (see Chap. 4). We recall, furthermore, that the number of chromosomes per nucleus is an inherited trait and is constant for each species. Human cells, for example, typically contain 46 chromosomes each.

That the nucleus is vital for cytoplasmic survival has been known for a long time. The first pertinent experiments, now classical, were done on amoebae. These large-celled protozoa are readily cut into halves, so that one half is with nucleus, the other without. The results show that a nucleated half carries on in every respect like a normal amoeba. But a nonnucleated half invariably dies. An amoeba without nucleus may persist for as long as a month and at first it may even move and feed. However, it never grows, it never reproduces, and soon it cannot digest or metabolize food. Evidently, nuclear effects are fundamentally long-range effects, a conclusion confirmed by other experiments.

Just as survival of the cytoplasm depends on the nucleus, so does survival of the nucleus depend on the cytoplasm; a naked isolated nucleus dies sooner or later. Inasmuch as the cytoplasm is the site of food management, respiration, and synthesis, a nucleus freed of cytoplasm undoubtedly succumbs from lack of energy and raw materials.

Gene function therefore must be viewed against a background of cyclical interactions between nucleus and cytoplasm. The nucleus, its genes comparable to a policy-making board of directors, supervises the long-range activities of the cytoplasm. The cytoplasm in turn executes nuclear directives, and this includes feeding and caring for the nucleus.

Is there a special director gene for every single cytoplasmic function to be carried out? This is not likely on general grounds. A nucleus is estimated to contain in the order of a few thousand genes. But the cytoplasm most likely performs in the vicinity of tens or hundreds of thousands of separate chemical and physical activities. Consequently, a single gene probably has control over numerous cytoplasmic processes.

What is a "single gene"? In a chromosome, individual genes certainly cannot be seen. Although chromosomes usually have a banded appearance in stained preparations (Fig. 18.1), such microscopic bands do not mark the positions of discrete single genes, which are of molecular dimensions and thus vastly smaller. Indeed, even if objects of molecular size were visible, genes would still not be marked off from one another

and the whole molecular structure of a chromosome would appear as an undivided continuum. The point is that individual genes are identifiable only through their biological effects.

This conclusion is underscored by the way in which "gene" is defined. If we say, quite justifiably, that *a gene is a unit of length within a chromosome*, we find that at least three different, more or less equally acceptable definitions of "unit" are possible. A gene may be (1) that minimum part of a chromosome which controls a single metabolic reaction in a cell, or (2) that minimum part of a chromosome which, when it mutates, i.e., changes structurally in some permanent way, alters just one trait of a cell, or (3) that minimum part of a chromosome which, in the nucleus of a reproductive cell, can transfer, or "cross over," to a neighboring chromosome. The significance of the events here referred to, especially the last, will become clearer in Chap. 28. For the present we merely note that a "gene" may be defined either as a *unit of biochemical action* or as a *unit of mutation* or as a *unit of crossing over*.

And these units usually are not identical. Any one of them may be shorter or longer than any other, and this itself may vary for different genes. Evidently, the

FIG. 18.1 Chromosomes. In this stained preparation of insect chromosomes, characteristic crossbands are clearly visible. Such banding is found in all chromosomes studied. *(From D. F. Poulson and C. W. Metz, J. Morphol., vol. 63, 1938.)*

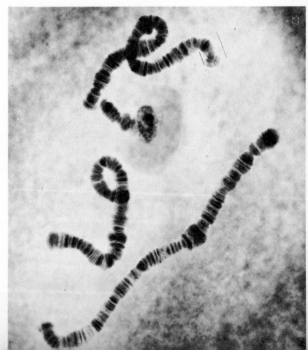

term "gene" does not refer to any specific, fixed piece of a chromosome but rather to an *operational concept*. Just as the unit of physical length varies according to whether we define it in inches or in centimeters or in ells, so does the genetic chromosome unit vary according to the experimental methods we use to measure it. Henceforth, when we refer to a "gene" without further qualifications, we must keep in mind that we are making a rather vague reference to *some* section of a chromosome.

Notwithstanding this multiplicity of operational definitions, the chemical definition of a gene can be more specific. A chromosome or section of a chromosome consists of DNA, RNA, and several types of proteins, all these components forming so-called *nucleoprotein* complexes. And it is clearly established that the material of the genes is the DNA fraction of nucleoprotein. That this is so is shown most convincingly by two classical lines of evidence, both obtained through work on bacteria.

It is possible to extract nucleoproteins from one strain of bacteria and to separate this extract chemically into DNA and protein. If then the DNA is put into a medium in which another strain of bacteria is present, these organisms will absorb some of the foreign DNA. As a result, the recipient bacteria acquire some of the genetic traits of the original DNA donors. However, if similar experiments are performed with the protein fraction of the original nucleoprotein, genetic changes do not occur in the recipient organisms. Evidently, the **bacterial transformation** is brought about specifically by DNA, and DNA therefore must be the substance of genes (Fig. 18.2).

Substantially the same conclusion is warranted by the phenomenon of **transduction**. In it, genetic material from one bacterium is transferred to another bacterium through the agency of particular viruses. These viruses are *bacteriophages;* i.e., they parasitize bacteria (see Chap. 7). Such a virus infects a bacterium and reproduces within the bacterial cell at the expense of the host. The host then dies and the offspring viruses are released, free to infect more bacteria. It happens on occasion that bits of the genetic material of a host bacterium become incorporated into newly forming offspring viruses. When the latter subsequently infect new bacterial hosts, they carry the genetic material of the old hosts into the new. In this way the new hosts acquire additional hereditary agents and may develop changed or new traits as a result (Fig. 18.3). The important point here is that the genetic material so

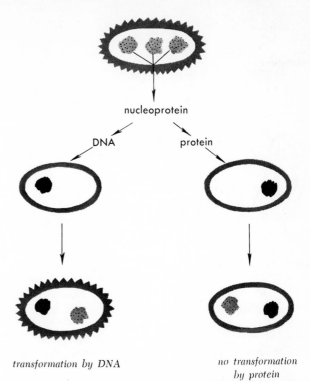

transformation by DNA   *no transformation by protein*

FIG. 18.2 Bacterial transformation. The nucleoprotein of a rough-coated bacterial type is extracted, and separate DNA and protein fractions are prepared. If a smooth-coated bacterial type is allowed to absorb the DNA fraction, it will change into a rough-coated type. But it will remain smooth-coated if it absorbs only the protein fraction. Experiments of this sort show that the nucleic acid part, not the protein part, of nucleoproteins is of genetic importance.

transferred by viruses is DNA. Incidentally, recall from Chap. 3 that whenever a virus infects a cell, only the virus DNA enters the cell and takes over control of the metabolism of the host cell; the protein portion of the virus remains outside the host cell. Clearly, virus genes are equivalent to virus DNA.

There is little question, therefore, that gene function must be interpreted on the basis of DNA structure. This structure has already been outlined in Chap. 4, and we know that it is symbolized by the Watson-Crick model. DNA thus may be regarded as a spiraled double chain, each chain being a nucleotide polymer containing deoxyribose sugars. Two such chains are held together by pairs of purine and pyrimidine components, four different types of such pairs being pres-

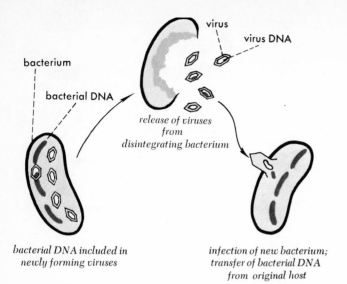

release of viruses from disintegrating bacterium

bacterium

bacterial DNA

virus

virus DNA

bacterial DNA included in newly forming viruses

infection of new bacterium; transfer of bacterial DNA from original host

FIG. 18.3 The principle of transduction. Newly forming bacteriophage viruses may incorporate into their own structure pieces of the genetic material of the host bacterium. When such viruses infect new bacterial hosts, these hosts acquire additional bacterial genes.

ent: adenine-thymine and the reverse ($A \cdot T$, $T \cdot A$), and guanine-cytosine and the reverse ($G \cdot C$, $C \cdot G$). These four pairs may occur any number of times and in any sequence, establishing the particular specificity of a given type of DNA (Fig. 4.9). It is known that, in a chromosome, only some of the DNA present is genetically active, the remainder being genetically inert. Different specificities of DNA probably account for such functional differences. Apparently, only certain purine-pyrimidine sequences happen to make DNA effective and useful as genes, just as only certain amino acid sequences make proteins effective and useful as enzymes. In so far then as DNA does have genetic activity, how can this activity be explained in terms of the molecular structure?

THE GENETIC CODE

It appears that genes perform their crucial controlling functions by, surprisingly, doing virtually nothing. As is characteristic of controlling agents generally, genes turn out to be, essentially, stable and more or less passive containers of information. The information in each case consists of a particular, specific sequence of purine-pyrimidine pairs. And all that genes appear to do or allow to be done to them is to have their

specific information *copied* by other kinds of information carriers. We are led to regard genes somewhat like important original "texts," carefully protected and preserved in the "library" of the nucleus. They are available as permanent, authoritative "master documents" from which duplicates may be prepared.

The specific information contained within genes represents a set of building instructions, like the instructions given by a blueprint. The genetic instructions supply the chemical machinery of a cell with "orders" for just two kinds of building jobs: how to make *new genes* exactly like the originals and how to join amino acids together to make *specific proteins*. In other words, each gene is a guardian of a specific chemical code and gene function consists of transfers of such codes. How are code transfers accomplished and how does this actually lead to control of cellular activities?

Code Transfer: DNA to DNA

The first of the two construction activities referred to above, namely, the synthesis of new genes exactly like original genes, occurs in the nucleus every time a cell or a nucleus divides. Just before cell division, the entire set of genes present in a cell is duplicated precisely. One set is subsequently incorporated into each of the two new cells formed by the division of the original mother cell (see Chap. 23). The production of two gene sets out of one requires manufacture of new DNA; and since the two resulting gene sets are identical, an exact code transfer from original DNA to newly manufactured DNA must occur. The Watson-Crick model suggests how new specific DNA may be made from old. For example, consider the DNA model illustrated in Fig. 18.4. The specific coded information contained in this model is represented by the particular sequence of the purine-pyrimidine pairs. Duplication of

FIG. 18.4 This and Fig. 18.5 illustrate the process of DNA duplication as envisaged on the basis of the Watson-Crick model. In this diagram, a portion of a sample DNA molecule is shown. It is to be duplicated with preservation of specificity. *P*, phosphate; *D*, deoxyribose; *A*, adenine; *T*, thymine; *G*, guanine; *C*, cytosine.

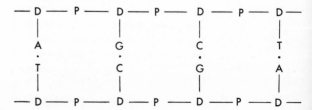

such a sequence with simultaneous preservation of code specificity is envisaged to occur in three steps.

First, the purine-pyrimidine pairs which hold an original DNA double chain together somehow become disengaged and the double chain so "unzips" into two separate single chains (Fig. 18.5a).

Next, each pyrimidine and purine, now free of its former association with a purine or pyrimidine partner, may reassociate with a new identical partner drawn from the pool of raw materials supplied by the cytoplasm. For example, every adenine (A) in a nucleotide chain may attach to its free bond a new thymine mole-

cule (T) if such a molecule is available as raw material. Analogously, every thymine, guanine, or cytosine projecting from a nucleotide chain may reexpress its particular chemical affinity for a given partner and combine with A, C, or G, respectively, from the raw material supply (Fig. 18.5b).

Newly attached purines and pyrimidines in turn are capable of combining with deoxyribose sugar (D), and this sugar has affinity for phosphate (P). If, therefore, D and P are similarly available as raw materials, new nucleotides may be built up progressively, in "correct" association with each preexisting nucleotide

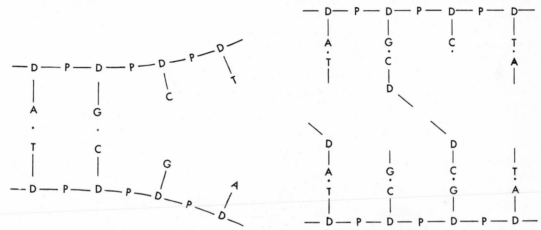

FIG. 18.5 Simplified representation of how DNA duplication may occur. Top left, the double DNA chain "unzips" into two single chains. Top right, each single chain attaches to itself appropriate purines and pyrimidines, drawn from the available supply of raw materials. Bottom left, each chain ultimately has attached complete and appropriate nucleotides. Bottom right, final pair of double chains.

chain. This process need not necessarily occur stepwise. For example, if the available raw materials should include the whole nucleotide *P–D–T* in prefabricated condition, then this nucleotide may attach as a finished complex to an *A* projecting from a nucleotide chain. Other preformed blocks of components may be similarly available as raw materials, and these too may attach as wholes (Fig. 18.5c).

FIG. 18.6 Experiment showing that newly produced DNA contains both preexisting and newly manufactured nucleotide chains. A cell about to divide is provided with radio-labeled raw materials for DNA synthesis (top). During division each chromosome duplicates, and both offspring cells are then found to contain radio-labeled DNA (center). The diagram shows that, in *each* of these offspring cells, only *one* of the two nucleotide chains is radio-labeled. This one has been newly manufactured; the other has preexisted in the parent cell. That such an interpretation is valid is proved if the offspring cells are allowed to divide again (bottom). For when one of the radio-labeled chains now duplicates, it synthesizes a new, *unlabeled* chain as its partner. Hence in the DNA so formed, one chain (radio-labeled) has again preexisted; the other chain (unlabeled) has been newly formed. When an originally unlabeled chain duplicates, neither of the two resulting chains carries a label.

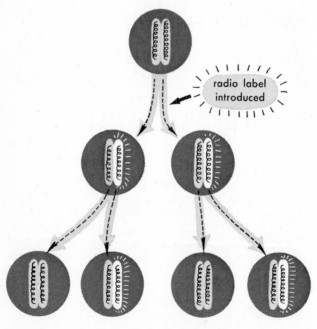

radio label introduced

In this manner, new nucleotides may be built up gradually wherever free bonds are available on a preexisting chain. The third and final step then requires only a linking up of the newly attached nucleotides, to form new chains (Fig. 18.5d).

The overall result is that *one* DNA double chain has given rise to *two* double chains. These are identical to each other as well as to the original "mother" chain. DNA thus has reproduced and the specific information code has been preserved. Note that all DNA always incorporates the old and the new. One of its two nucleotide chains preexists; the other is newly manufactured.

That this is actually so has been demonstrated experimentally. A cell about to divide has been supplied with radio-labeled raw materials needed in the manufacture of DNA. After cell division, the chromosomes of *both* offspring cells contain radio-labeled DNA. This suggests that each newly manufactured DNA double chain contains one radio-labeled, newly produced nucleotide chain and one unlabeled, preexisting nucleotide chain. If now such an offspring cell is allowed to divide again (without further additions of radio-labeled raw materials), then only one of the resulting cells contains labeled chromosomes; the other contains unlabeled chromosomes. This is as expected on the basis of the postulated duplication mechanism of DNA (Fig. 18.6).

Note that this duplication process is itself as much a hypothetical model as the Watson-Crick structure. To what extent it describes the real mechanism of gene duplication is quite unknown. But because it does show how gene duplication *might* occur, and because a better model is not available, it is widely accepted as a reasonable approximation of actual events. It should be remembered here that, according to Watson and Crick, DNA is normally spiraled (see Fig. 4.10). Therefore, duplication of a spiral would produce two intertwined spirals, and these would have to unwind before they could separate. This may or may not happen in actuality.

The basic idea underlying this duplication process is often referred to as the **template hypothesis.** Each single nucleotide chain of DNA serves as a *template* or blueprint or master pattern according to which a new, *matching* nucleotide chain is manufactured. It is in this sense that genetic DNA may be regarded as passive, simply permitting its particular information to be copied and to be transferred to new DNA.

Code Transfer: DNA to Protein

Granting that the specific information of DNA is preserved through successive cell generations, what is the functional value of this information in the life of a cell? The value lies in the second kind of copying process referred to earlier: the genetic information of DNA instructs the cell how to build specific proteins. In this, a template principle is probably involved again. Through code transfer from DNA to protein, genes ensure that any new proteins manufactured in a cell contain particular, specific sequences of amino acids and so have particular, specific architectural configurations. We may therefore understand why gene control is long-range control: when genes are removed, specific proteins built earlier still persist in a cell; and as long as the supply lasts, life may continue.

Protein synthesis takes place on the cytoplasmic granules called *ribosomes*. But genes are in the nucleus. Clearly, some kind of functional connecting link between nucleus and cytoplasm must exist. Ribosomes happen to be especially rich in *ribose* nucleic acid, RNA. The presence of this substance in these particular granules and its chemical similarity to the DNA found in genes suggest the striking possibility that the connecting link between genes and ribosomes might be RNA. Indeed, RNA occurs not only in the ribosomes, but also in the chromosomes and in the nucleoli of a cell nucleus. Accordingly, to test whether or not RNA is the link between DNA and proteins, it would be necessary to show that RNA actually originates in the nucleus and that RNA is indeed intimately associated with protein synthesis in the ribosomes.

Ample evidence for these hypotheses is now available. For example, it can be shown that chromosomal DNA contributes part of its own substance toward the manufacture of cytoplasmic RNA. Two amoebae may be used to demonstrate this (Fig. 18.7). One amoeba is put into a medium containing radioactive phosphate. Some of this phosphate will be absorbed and will be used as a raw material in the construction of the numerous phosphate-containing chemicals in the amoeba. DNA is among them. In a radioactive amoeba, therefore, the nucleus will eventually contain DNA in which at least some of the phosphate is radioactive. The second amoeba is not made radioactive, but, through delicate surgical operations, its nucleus is removed. The experiment now consists in transplanting the radioactive nucleus of the first amoeba into the nonradio-

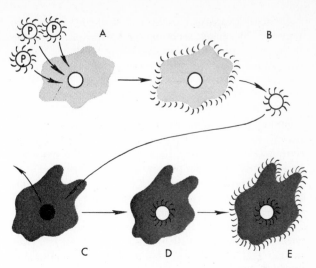

FIG. 18.7 An amoeba is made radioactive with phosphates *(A, B)*, and the nucleus is used to substitute for the nucleus of an untreated amoeba *(C)*. The radioactivity of the implanted nucleus then spreads into the cytoplasm *(D, E)*, indicating that radioactive phosphate passes from the nucleus into cytoplasm. Since RNA is the principal phosphate-containing derivative of the nucleus, the experiment suggests the nuclear origin of cytoplasmic RNA.

active, nonnucleated second amoeba. One then obtains an organism in which no component except the transplanted nucleus is radioactive.

But it soon becomes apparent that this radioactivity does not remain confined to the transplanted nucleus. It spreads into the originally nonradioactive cytoplasm, and analysis shows that it is particularly the phosphate of cytoplasmic RNA which becomes radioactive. Evidently, nuclear DNA contributes phosphate to cytoplasmic RNA. This is a good indication that RNA has a nuclear origin.

Other important evidence revolves around the *nucleolus*. As noted earlier, each nucleus contains at least one of these round, fluid-filled bodies. Three kinds of data have been assembled about them. First, nucleoli can be shown to be direct products of chromosomes. At certain times, certain chromosomes bud off material which collects into nucleoli (see Chap. 23). Second, as mentioned, nucleoli contain large amounts of RNA and indeed these bodies may be regarded as specialized storage sites for RNA. And third, at certain times nucleoli discharge their contents into the cytoplasm. Furthermore, it is now substantiated convincingly that cytoplasmic RNA and protein synthesis go together. In many secreting cells, for example, the secretion products are proteins. It can be shown readily that when secretion synthesis occurs at a rapid pace, the RNA content of the ribosomes is high. Conversely, RNA decreases when secretion synthesis does. Analogous evidence has been obtained from experiments on nonnucleated amoebae. As noted, such individuals may persist for considerable periods. Analysis shows that during this time the protein content of the amoebae slowly decreases; new proteins are apparently not synthesized. In parallel with this decline, the RNA content declines also. These two changes are here related directly to the absence of a nucleus.

Above all, evidence of the most direct and conclusive kind is now available also. Ribosomes, still containing their RNA, can be extracted from cells, and purified ribosomal preparations may be suspended in water to which amino-acid raw materials and ATP have been added. If such a system is examined later, some of the amino acids have disappeared, but whole proteins are present instead. Evidently, ribosomal RNA has promoted the synthesis of proteins in the test tube (Fig. 18.8). Moreover, such test tube syntheses can now be made to yield not just any protein but a *specific* protein like an enzyme. Bacterial cells known to manufacture given internal enzymes may be used as the source of nucleic acid extracts. These extracts may then promote the test-tube synthesis of proteins which exhibit the same specific enzymatic activity as the enzymes in the living bacteria.

Thus there can be relatively little doubt that genes control protein synthesis according to the following general scheme. First, RNA appears to be manufactured in the chromosomes. In this process, the DNA of the genes probably serves as a template and the specific information of the different DNA molecules is copied and incorporated into RNA molecules under construction. How this might occur in detail is still unknown. In any event, the RNAs would be specific and they would now carry the exact code information of the DNAs. Second, variously specific RNA molecules then accumulate in the nucleoli. And third, specific RNAs from the nucleoli eventually reach the ribosomes in the cytoplasm. Here the RNA molecules probably function as templates in their own turn. The particular sequence of the different purine-pyrimidine pairings in RNA appears to function somewhat like a series of differently shaped "pigeon holes," each capable of attracting and holding an amino acid of a

FIG. 18.8 The requirement of RNA in specific protein synthesis. A, RNA is known to be manufactured in chromosomes, to be stored in the nucleoli, and to be discharged into the cytoplasm; B, left, secretion of much protein (rods) by a cell is correlated with a high RNA content (circles); right, low protein content and low RNA content similarly go together. C, in an enucleated cell such as an isolated half of an amoeba, a gradual decrease in protein content (rods) is accompanied by a corresponding decrease in RNA content (circles). D, in test-tube experiments, RNA extracted from cells is found to promote the conversion of amino acids (black circles) into specific proteins (rods).

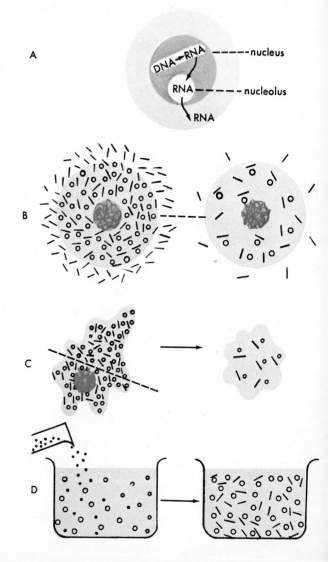

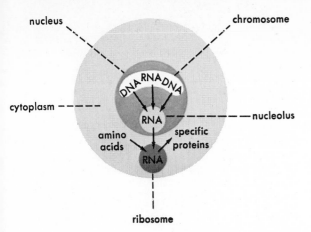

nucleus

chromosome

cytoplasm

nucleolus

DNA RNA DNA

RNA

amino acids

specific proteins

RNA

ribosome

FIG. 18.9 The functional connection between DNA and RNA, and the transport pathway of RNA from nucleus to cytoplasm. The genetic code is transferred over this pathway from DNA to proteins.

particular chemical type. When these amino acids are then linked together in the specific sequence imposed by RNA, the resulting protein will have a specificity which matches that of RNA. And since that specificity has been determined by the genes, genes ultimately control the kinds of proteins a cell can manufacture (Fig. 18.9).

The way in which ribosomal RNA actually arranges different amino acids into a specific sequence is being learned rapidly. Moreover, the real code is now in process of being solved. There are some two dozen different types of amino acid, and for each there must be a unique purine-pyrimidine code. That is, a certain short sequence of purine-pyrimidine pairs must specify one type of amino acid, another sequence of pairs must specify a second type, etc. Current investigations are revealing which actual sequence of purine-pyrimidine pairs specifies which actual type of amino acid.

In the process of lining up of amino acids in given specified sequences, RNA probably is essentially passive, just as genes are passive. Genes merely allow their specific information to be copied by RNA, which in turn allows that information to be used in protein manufacture. The advantage of such indirect functioning of genes is clear. Genes remain protected within the nucleus as in a vault and are therefore less subject to destruction by the respiratory metabolism of the cytoplasm. Whenever genetic information is required in the cytoplasm, genes do not move to the place of

action themselves but send expendable copies of themselves in the form of nongenetic RNA. In this sense genes may be likened to a policy-making board of directors and RNA to the foreman who actually executes the directives of the managing board.

As noted, many important details in these code transfers are still obscure, but a finer conception of the function of genes emerges in any case (Fig. 18.10). A whole chromosome may be regarded as a single supermolecule consisting fundamentally of a very long and perhaps completely continuous DNA double chain. Coded information along this chain varies as the sequences of purine-pyrimidine pairs vary. Just before cell reproduction, the entire chain serves as a supertemplate and two identical chromosomes are formed from the one. At other times, shorter sections of the chain function as subtemplates and correspondingly short RNAs are built with matching codes. The actual length of such subtemplates would vary. Moreover, a given section of the DNA chain serving as subtemplate in one case could partially overlap with a section serving as subtemplate in another case. As noted earlier, various experimental techniques enable us to mark and identify certain sections along a chromosome, and we

FIG. 18.10 The two kinds of specificity transfers: A, transfer from DNA to new DNA, at the time of chromosome duplication; B, transfer from DNA to RNA and protein.

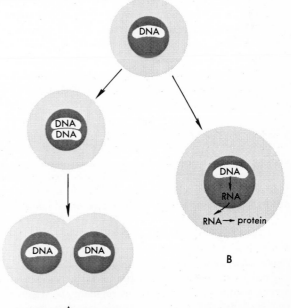

DNA

DNA
DNA

DNA

DNA

DNA

RNA

RNA → protein

A

B

call such sections "genes." But we do not know how many subtemplates may be included wholly or partially within one of our "genes," hence our difficulty of defining "gene" uniquely in a functional sense. Hence also the conclusion that a "single gene" controls numerous cytoplasmic processes.

RESULTS OF GENE ACTION

Because the existence of genes was historically first suspected through studies of heredity (see Chap. 28), many people unacquainted with the results of modern research still regard genes to be important only as agents of heredity. But it is now quite clear that gene transmission from parent to offspring constitutes just one of the many processes in which these agents participate. Moreover, hereditary gene transmission is of not much greater importance than the simultaneous parent-to-offspring transmission of cell membranes or ribosomes or mitochondria. As we shall see, adequate heredity requires transmission of at least one *whole cell* with all its parts, genes included. Therefore, the crucial significance of genes is not simply that they are inherited, but rather that they carry out controlling functions during the entire life of a cell or an organism. And by governing the synthesis of new genes and of specific proteins, genes play so strategic a role that they ultimately control the whole nature and the very life of every cell in every organism (Fig. 18.11).

First, since proteins make up more of the formed organic framework of cells than any other constituents, genes determine the basic *architecture* of every cell. This means, too, that every normal architectural change during the life cycle of a cell, and every architectural difference among the cells of one or of different organisms, is ultimately gene-determined.

Second, by controlling the nature of proteins, genes control the nature of enzymes, all of which are proteins. Since virtually every metabolic reaction in a cell requires at least one enzyme, genes so determine what kinds of *metabolic processes* are possible in a cell. Nutritional reactions, respiratory reactions, motion-producing reactions, synthesis reactions of all kinds—all are enzyme-dependent, hence gene-dependent.

Third, by so governing the whole metabolic character of a cell, genes are the ultimate maintainers of *steady state*. For genes control not only themselves (by governing gene duplication) but also all other control agents within cells. Thus, genes regulate the nature of enzymes, as already noted. Genes regulate hormone

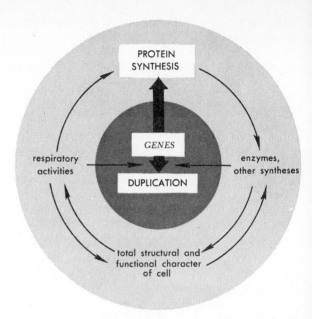

FIG. 18.11   The controlling role of genes in metabolism and steady-state maintenance. The principal action of genes is control of their own duplication and control of protein synthesis, via RNA. Through this, genes exert secondary and tertiary effects, as shown.

action first by determining which cells are to manufacture which hormones, and second by determining which hormones and what quantities of them are to be admitted into every cell through the plasma membrane. Genes regulate vitamin action by controlling the manufacture of these substances within cells and, again, by regulating surface absorption in cells which do not synthesize vitamins on their own. Control of surface absorption also accounts for gene control over the inorganic constituents of cells. We note that whereas enzymes, vitamins, inorganic substances, and all other growth factors control metabolic reactions directly, genes control them indirectly, by exercising control over the other controllers.

Fourth, by governing synthesis in general and production of new genes in particular, genes direct growth, development, and the *reproduction* of cells. By being exchanged among cells and pooled within cells, as we shall see, genes become the basis of *sex*. By duplicating and being transmitted to offspring cells, genes become the basis of *heredity*. Moreover, through one final property, genes become the key to *evolution*.

This final property is **mutability**, the capacity to

mutate. As already noted in Chap. 3, genetic nucleic acids are among the most stable of all organic compounds. Indeed, unless an information carrier were relatively stable, it would cease to be useful as a repository of important information. In addition to the inherent chemical stability of genes, several safeguards exist which ensure that the specific genetic messages are not lost or altered.

One such device is the nucleus itself. We may actually regard the evolutionary "invention" of distinct nuclei by the early Protista as adaptations useful primarily in shielding genes from destructive metabolism of the cytoplasm. Another safeguard is *redundancy;* when one wishes to ensure that a message is not lost or altered, one makes it redundant, i.e., one repeats it several times. Indeed, the genetic messages are stored in more than one place. Each cell of most organisms ordinarily contains two complete sets of genes, one set having been inherited originally from the egg-producing parent and the other from the sperm-producing parent, hence the even number of chromosomes in most species. Moreover, each cell type is usually represented by many like cells. Even if some cells die, therefore, the genes of the remaining cells still possess the specific information characteristic of that cell type.

Yet despite inherent stability, protected existence, and redundancy, structural change is bound to occur; genes are no more exempt from the modifying impact of the environment than any other component of the earth. As we shall see later, a variety of physical and chemical agents may affect and alter gene structure and therefore gene specificity. Such new specificities will be stable and will be passed on into all subsequent gene duplicates. Protein synthesis will be affected accordingly, and, as a result, cell traits will become changed. *Mutations* of this sort may probably arise also during the process of gene duplication, for, like any other process, gene duplication is probably not error-free. If an occasional error occurs during the formation of new nucleotide chains, then an imperfect copy will in effect be a mutated copy (Fig. 18.12).

Whatever the cause, gene mutations bring about stable changes in cellular characteristics (see also Chap. 28). Unless such changes produce lethal effects at once, they will be preserved and transmitted to offspring cells. Mutations in reproductive cells therefore may lead to offspring organisms exhibiting altered traits. As we shall see in a later chapter, this is the basis of evolution.

In summary, therefore, we find that genes serve in

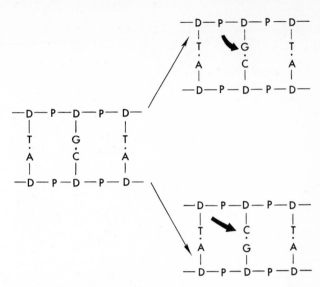

FIG. 18.12   It is possible that errors may occur on occasion when DNA molecules reproduce (e.g., lower right, inverted position of C·G pair). Imperfect copies so formed would be stable mutated copies, and mutations would be transmitted to subsequent molecule generations.

just one primary role: they allow their specificities to be copied. Three indirect secondary roles emerge from this: genes control protein specificities; genes control the specificities of new genes; and, to the extent that gene stability is imperfect, genes may change their specificities. Through these three secondary activities, genes indirectly carry out tertiary functions which encompass every aspect of living. For by controlling all metabolism and all self-perpetuation, genes govern cell structure, cell function, and cell development. And by controlling cells, genes govern the life of all organisms, hence the survival of the whole living world. Genes started life, genes still continue it, and, by their failure or absence, genes ultimately end it (Fig. 18.13).

It may be pointed out in this context that modern experiments dealing with gene function on a molecular level have already contributed much toward an eventual test tube synthesis of living matter. As indicated above, specific proteins can now be synthesized artificially with the aid of nucleic acid extracts, and the actual genetic code of nucleic acids is being cracked. Moreover, simple nucleotide polymers of known composition can be prepared by laboratory synthesis from individual nucleotide precursors. Before long, therefore, it will probably be possible to create a test tube system in which nucleotides give rise to nucleic acid chains

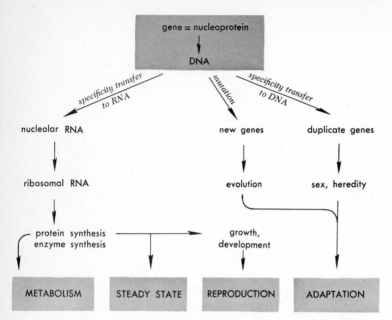

FIG. 18.13 Overall summary of the pattern of gene action. Through their fundamental action of transferring their specificities, genes control cellular metabolism and all phases of cellular self-perpetuation.

carrying specific information, in which such chains promote transformation of amino acids into specific proteins, and in which these proteins function enzymatically and catalyze specific chemical reactions. To be sure, such a system would still be far from being alive; for example, it would not self-perpetuate. Nevertheless, inasmuch as it would metabolize in precisely the same way as a living system metabolizes, the test tube system would represent a major element of a living unit. Recall, furthermore, that starting materials like amino acids and sugars can be produced artifically from simple materials such as ammonia, methane, and water (see Chap. 3). Thus there does not appear to be any theoretical obstacle to the experimental production, within possibly a decade or two, of a lifelike metabolizing system from the simplest inorganic precursors. And perhaps within one or two human generations, artificial metabolizing systems may even have been perfected to such an extent that their nucleic acids might self-duplicate and so initiate self-perpetuation of a whole system. Living units created in this way probably would have roughly viruslike characteristics. Experimental creation of complete living cells, however, is

undoubtedly still very far in the future. In any event, it is worth noting generally that research is now being widely pursued which, usually as an incidental by-product, provides important data for a possible future laboratory synthesis of life. (And it should be quite clear that such synthesis obviously will not mean creation of "little men in test tubes.")

Genes are the most fundamental control agents of organisms, but they are not the only ones. All such agents are components of **control systems,** and these systems maintain steady states at the various levels of the living hierarchy. Just what is the broad meaning of "control" and what is the general nature of a control system? Further, what controllers other than genes are there and what are the actual control systems of which genes and other controllers are a part? The next section will deal with these questions.

PATTERNS OF CONTROL

To define "control," we first define **stress:** any external or internal condition which tends to upset the normal, smooth operations of a system may be regarded as a stress. In a living organism, *external* stresses are often produced by the environment: by enemies, injurious agents, lack of food, change of temperature, and innumerable other physical, chemical, and biological conditions. *Internal* stresses arise continuously as a result of the very processes of life: fuels are used up, concentrations change, parts age and wear out, waste products accumulate, etc. In so far as any external or internal change, usual or unusual, affects living matter, it also becomes a more or less significant stress. Actually, the living system is under stress all the time.

The problem of maintaining a steady state, therefore, is to counteract or to relieve stress. The requirement for this is, first, ability to *recognize* stress when and where it exists, and second, ability to *react* to such stress in self-preserving fashion. What is needed, in other words, is ability to recognize a **stimulus** and ability to carry out an appropriate **response** to that stimulus. So long as a system recognizes stimuli and reacts to them with fitting responses, it exercises **control.** And it may then remain intact and functioning, despite stresses which would otherwise upset its internal coordination. *Thus the net result of control in living matter is steady state, and the net result of steady state is maintenance of life for the longest possible time.*

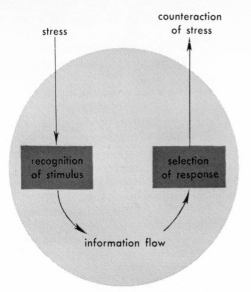

FIG. 18.14 The general pattern of maintenance and control of steady state.

CONTROL SYSTEMS

In a system composed of many parts acting cooperatively, as in living matter, steady state will be preserved if the parts may continue to act in harmony despite stress. If a stimulus should change the action of one part, then, in response, the action of all other parts should change correspondingly in such a way that the total action of the system still remains integrated and coordinated.

To achieve such persisting internal coordination, a first fundamental requirement is continuous and rapid *flow of information* among the parts of the system. Each part must be kept informed of what other parts are doing, so that, if a stimulus affects one part, other parts may receive notice of it. Moreover, if the system is capable of responding to a stimulus in more than one way, a second fundamental requirement is ability to make *selections*. A simple system designed to give always the same response is not required to select. But where several response possibilities exist, ability to

decide among them clearly is crucial; choice of inappropriate responses leads to unsteady, not steady, states (Fig. 18.14).

Thus "control" ultimately becomes a matter of information and of selection. These terms imply messages or signals of some sort, message carriers, senders, receivers, transmission pathways, relays, switches, channel selectors—in short, all the components of a communications system. Indeed, in one form or another, communications systems are found wherever steady states are maintained. In living matter we find them within cells and between cells, within organisms and between organisms, on all levels of organization. Such systems are control systems.

System Organization

All living control systems operate on a common pattern. An initial stimulus irritates, or *excites,* a receiving device, called a **receptor.** Excitation of this receptor causes the emission of a signal, which is transmitted over a **sensory pathway** to an interpreting and response-selecting device. The latter may be referred to generally as the **modulator.** This component sends out an appropriately chosen command signal over an appropriately chosen **motor pathway.** The signal leads to an **effector,** a device which executes the commands. This is the response which counteracts the original stimulus (Fig. 18.15).

We may illustrate the operation of such a system by means of a mechanical model. Suppose that the water level of a flow tank, as in Fig. 18.16, is to be maintained in steady state. That is, despite possible variations of inflow or outflow (e.g., if an obstruction develops in one of the pipes, or if someone resets the speed of inflow or outflow), the water level is to stay at a predetermined height. Such a system is an *open system,* since materials are continuously entering and leaving; and the problem is to maintain a *dynamic equilibrium.* In these respects the model corresponds closely to living entities, which also are open systems maintained in dynamic balance (see Chap. 12). By contrast, in a closed system nothing enters or leaves, and balance is a static equilibrium.

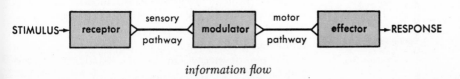

information flow

FIG. 18.15 The pattern of the control components in living matter.

OPEN SYSTEM   CLOSED SYSTEM

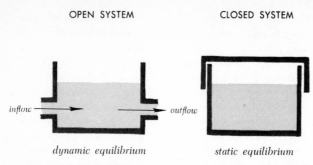

dynamic equilibrium   *static equilibrium*

FIG. 18.16   The difference between an open and a closed system. Continuous flow characterizes the open system, and if a balanced condition is attained, the equilibrium is dynamic. Nothing enters or leaves the closed system, and if an equilibrium is attained, it is static.

To establish a dynamic equilibrium in our model, we must install an automatic control device. Without help from external agencies, such a mechanism ought to be able to "sense" any change in water flow, and, by means of valves, it should so readjust the inflow and the outflow that the water level in the tank remains relatively constant.

We have equipped our tank with automatic controls in Fig. 18.17. An air-filled float R functions as receptor. Inasmuch as it moves up or down with the water, it senses changes of water level. Any up or down motion of R is communicated via a rod *sp*, the sensory

FIG. 18.17   Model of a steady-state—maintaining device. R, receptor; M, modulator; E, effector; *sp*, sensory pathway; *mp*, motor pathway. If the system is adjusted as described in the text, then any change of inflow or outflow will bring about signals through R→*sp*→M→*mp*→E. Valve positions will then be adjusted in such a way that the change of inflow or outflow will be counteracted and an original water level in the tank will be reestablished.

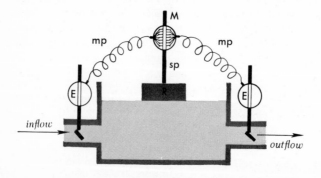

pathway, to the modulator M. Here the sensory message—up or down motion of *sp*—is interpreted and appropriate commands for response are sent out. Imagine M to be a simple electrical trigger mechanism. It might be so built that any upward motion of *sp* trips a switch which makes an electric current of certain strength and duration flow through the wires *mp*. Similarly, any downward motion of *sp* would reverse the switch position and another electrical impulse, of different strength and duration, would be produced. Indeed, possible switch positions might be more numerous and each might cause the flow of a current of unique characteristics. These electrical impulses are the command signals, transmitted over the motor pathways *mp* to the two effectors E. The effectors are engines which operate the valves at the inflow and the outflow. They are so built that each different command signal received makes them move the valves into different positions.

Imagine now that for some external reason the inflow decreases. The outflow is still as before; hence the water level will begin to drop. But at once the modulator M will be informed of this change via R and *sp*. Appropriate electric signals will now go to the effectors and the inflow valve will open more, the outflow valve close more. As a result, before the water level can drop very far, the net inflow will increase and the water will rise back to normal. This new change of level will again be communicated to the modulator; new signals will go out to the effectors; and the valves will be returned to their original position.

If at this point the inflow is still reduced, the control device will go into action once more, precisely as above. Clearly, by readjusting as often as necessary, the device is capable of maintaining a steady state despite changes in the "environment."

System Properties

Our model illustrates a number of features common to control systems, living ones included.

First, internal *operating energy* is needed to make the system work. In the model, energy is required for the transmission of electric signals and for the motors which move the valves. Signal transmission itself can be accomplished on little energy. Indeed, the sensitivity of the whole device can be made desirably great if the float and the rod *sp* are built very light, so that they move easily, and if the modulator sends signals on a minimum of energy. On the other hand, the effectors will be the more useful, the more powerful they are, i.e., the faster and the more forcefully they can respond even against the push of the flowing water. The effectors therefore should have available an ample supply of energy—certainly more than they receive from the modulator in the form of signal energy. Consequently, an **amplifier** should be built into the effector to increase the power of the incoming signal energy to a level sufficient to move the valves. Controls within cells are designed on just this principle. That is, receptors, modulators and connecting pathways are highly sensitive and operate on a minimum of energy supplied by ATP. And the effectors work on amplifier energy supplied by comparatively large amounts of ATP.

A second common feature of control devices is that response to a stimulus is not a sudden, single event, but a stepwise, repeated one. In our model, a small, initial change in valve position will produce a small initial change in water level. The receptor immediately signals to the modulator that a certain adjustment has been carried out. Accordingly, the modulator then cues the effectors to continue, to stop, or to reverse

FIG. 18.18 The general pattern of a control cycle and the role of feedback in such a cycle.

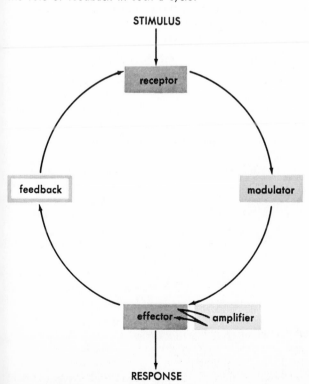

STIMULUS

receptor

feedback

modulator

effector amplifier

RESPONSE

operations. The resulting effector action is essentially a new stimulus, which is again communicated back via the receptor to the modulator. Continuous information thus passes from sensory to motor component and from motor back to sensory component. Many such cyclical passages of information, each contributing a small effector action, are usually required before a total response to a stimulus can be achieved. Indeed, the control device is not at rest even then. For in the absence of environmental stimuli, the receptor in effect signals "no change" to the modulator, the modulator sends "no adjustment required" to the effector, and the effector then informs the receptor of "no operation."

In such unceasing cyclical passages of information, we note that a response is "fed back" into the sensory end of the regulating device as a new stimulus, informing of the degree of counteraction already accomplished. The new stimulus in turn, fed into the modulator, informs of the degree of counteraction yet to be carried out. **Feedback** is to the motor-sensory segment of the cycle what modulation is to the sensory-motor segment. Both feedback and modulation control the direction, the amount, and the duration of adjustment. In living matter, as elsewhere, control activity becomes *effective* control only if appropriate feedbacks are operative. Without feedback, the modulator would never become aware of what the effector has been doing; hence it would never be able to send out "correct" new commands. The general pattern of the control cycle is outlined in Fig. 18.18.

Feedbacks and continuous cycles of information account for a third common property of control systems: they function essentially by **trial and error,** by "hunting" for the correct equilibrium condition. Refer again to our model in Fig. 18.17. Suppose that the inflow changes so as to cause an initial drop in water level. Depending on the sensitivity of the apparatus, a given number of seconds may elapse before the valves are brought into corrective positions. By that time, the water level may be down 1 in., say. Now the water begins to rise, but again there will be a time lag of some seconds before the effectors receive the new command to return the valves to normal. By that time the water may already have risen somewhat *above* the correct level. Fresh signals to reverse valve positions a bit will now be forthcoming, and by the time that action is executed, the water may again be down *below* the appropriate level.

Most controls *overshoot* in this fashion, and they undergo hunting oscillations to either side of the equilibrium state. Clearly, it will be important that such oscillations either become smaller and smaller till they subside or else continue at constant amplitude. Poorly adjusted control devices often produce ever-increasing hunting oscillations, in which case "steady" state of course will not be maintained.

The seemingly erratic motion of a unicellular flagellate protist is a good example of the trial-and-error nature of control operations. If such an organism moves from a region of darkness to one of light, for example, it does not normally follow a straight, beeline course. Instead, it moves forward and a little to the left, then it "tacks" and moves right, then perhaps it changes course upward, or downward, etc. In other words, the internal controls of the cell make it "hunt" for regions of ever-increasing brightness in trial-and-error fashion. In the process the cell often overshoots the "correct" path. Each such overshoot leads to a more or less rapid feedback via the eyespot, which signals the internal controls that light intensity is decreasing, not increasing as it should. Reversal of direction or change to a new direction is then initiated. Another good example of overshoots is the zigzagging locomotion of a drunk walking toward a stated object. Under the influence of alcohol, nervous control over locomotion becomes loose and imprecise and increased hunting oscillations occur. Normally, such oscillations are so small and subside so rapidly that straight-line locomotion is possible.

A fourth common property of control systems is that they have inherent limits of efficiency. If they are overloaded, i.e., if they must work too fast or too hard, they may become "neurotic." They may make **errors** in sensing stimuli or in interpreting signals or in selecting and executing responses. Extreme overloading may cause internal structural breakdowns, which may make the device inoperative altogether. In living organisms, functional or structural failures of control systems result in *disease*. Disease itself is a stress stimulus to other, still intact regulating devices and repair or circumvention of the diseased condition may ensue.

What kinds of control systems are actually found in living organisms? The regulating devices of living matter are organized into a hierarchy which parallels the hierarchy of structural levels. Cells contain complete internal control systems made up of molecules. Tissues contain control systems made up of cells. Organs contain control systems made up of tissues. In such an order, the response of one level may be a component of the regulating activity on the next higher

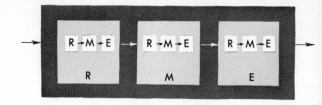

R or M or E

FIG. 18.19 The hierarchy of control systems in living matter. *R*, receptor; *M*, modulator; *E*, effector. The entire control apparatus of one level (within a rectangular box) is a component of the control apparatus on the next higher level.

level. For example, the effector activity of a cell may serve in tissue control. Or the cell as a whole may function as receptor, in which case its response represents a sensory signal on the tissue level. Or the cell may function as modulator, which makes its response a motor signal on the tissue level. Or the cell may function as effector, and its response then constitutes a feedback signal on the tissue level. In like manner, effector activity of a whole tissue may serve in organ control. These interrelations are generalized in Fig. 18.19.

It follows that controls among cellular molecules are the foundations of all controls on higher levels.

MOLECULAR CONTROL

Regardless of how a cell is stressed, the stress stimulus usually affects one or more *metabolic* processes. For example, changes in nutrient supplies, waste accumulation, injury, pH change, temperature change, sol-gel transformations, or indeed any other physical or chemical stimuli are likely to influence a cell either by *accelerating* or by *decelerating* particular metabolic reactions. Also, regardless of how a cell responds, the response ultimately is produced by metabolic processes. For whatever the effector action of a cell may be, acceleration or deceleration of respiration or of chemical activities such as synthesis or of physical activities such as movement is likely to be involved.

Steady-state maintenance in a cell therefore becomes largely a matter of controlling cellular metabolism. The duration, speed, and amount of every reaction must be suitably geared to the duration, speed, and amount of every other reaction. To maintain such coordination, every accelerated reaction must eventually be decelerated back to normal and every decelerated reaction must be accelerated back to normal.

Acceleration

A metabolic reaction is itself the simplest and most basic kind of control system. Molecules function as receptors, modulators, and effectors. The water in which a reaction takes place serves as sensory and motor pathway. For example, consider the reaction

$$\text{glucose} \xrightleftharpoons{\textit{enzymes}} \text{polysaccharide}$$

When this reversible reaction is in chemical equilibrium, it is also in dynamic equilibrium or steady state; a net change does not occur. The totality of glucose molecules in a cell, called a *glucose pool*, may now function as receptor. For example, if additional glucose arrives in the cell as food, this will be a stimulus "sensed" by the glucose pool as an increase in concentration. By mass action, the reaction to the right will now outbalance that to the left and more polysaccharide will be formed. The polysaccharide pool is then the effector, and increase of polysaccharide concentration is the response. For as polysaccharide accumulates at the expense of glucose, the glucose pool decreases back to normal; and the original stimulus is thereby removed. The extra polysaccharide in turn may represent a new stimulus in the cell, initiating other reactions and new responses.

Note that the designations "receptor" and "effector" are not fixed. If a cell were to acquire additional polysaccharide rather than glucose, then the *polysaccharide pool* would be the receptor and the glucose pool the effector. Note further that, in either case, the function of the modulator is performed by the *enzymes*. Mass action notwithstanding, it takes a specific enzyme to "interpret" a specific stimulus and to direct the specific response. Because it is specific for a particular reaction, an enzyme cannot interpret various different stimuli, but only one. And it cannot select among several possible responses, but must promote the same response every time. Yet inasmuch as it functions like a "clearing center" for incoming and outgoing chemical information, every enzyme is a fundamental modulator in reaction control.

Several other kinds of reaction modulators occur in cells, the most essential of all being the nucleic acids, including *genes* as well as *RNA*. Through their control over enzyme synthesis, nucleic acids are the *ultimate* modulators of metabolic reactions. Enzymes may be regarded as the *immediate* modulators. Thus the molecular control system governing the glucose-polysaccharide reaction above may be symbolized as:

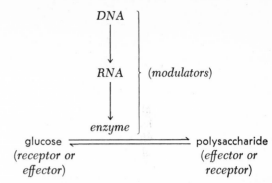

In addition to nucleic acids and enzymes, molecular modulators in cells include various *growth factors,* among them hormones, mineral substances, vitamins, and other classes of compounds (see Chap. 19). These too accelerate metabolic reactions. For example, we have seen in Chap. 16 that the conversion sequence from polysaccharide to acetyl CoA or vice versa requires, apart from numerous enzymes, several coenzymes manufactured from B vitamins, magnesium ions, and also, in vertebrates, hormones such as insulin, adrenalin, and thyroxin. This is by no means an unusual circumstance, for virtually all metabolic reactions appear to require enzymes *plus* various other agents. Most reactions analyzed closely have been found to depend on a whole battery of accelerators, including enzymes, vitamin derivatives, often also hormones and inorganic ions, and, ultimately, DNA and RNA.

All these agents are functionally similar: they are essentially enzyme*like* in action. They are specifically necessary for specific reactions; small quantities of them suffice; and they do not become part of the endproduct but are recoverable intact and unchanged after the reaction. In short, they all function more or less like *catalysts*. And in the language of control systems, they function as information relays, or as modulators. They share with enzymes the property of being differentially sensitive to single sensory messages only and of promoting the same reaction responses every time, without freedom of choice. The pattern of a complete molecular control system may be symbolized as in Fig. 18.20.

Being active in the manner of catalysts, the molecular modulators all tend to *accelerate* reactions. How, then, are reactions decelerated or inhibited? Steady-state maintenance clearly requires both.

Deceleration

Deceleration occurs in four major ways. One way is based on the **reversibility** of most metabolic reac-

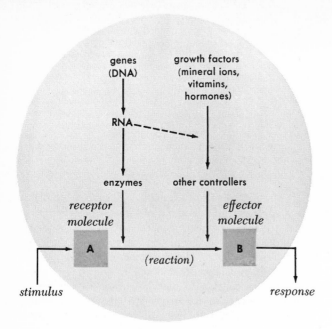

FIG. 18.20 The molecular modulators within cells and the pattern of their control over steady-state–maintaining metabolic reactions.

tions. For example, glucose ⇌ polysaccharide. It should be clear, therefore, that a reaction in one direction can be inhibited by accelerating the opposite reaction. This principle actually holds not only on the molecular level but also in steady-state control on any other level. Brakes and accelerators are present together and hold one another in mutual check. The net

FIG. 18.21 Adaptive enzymes. The shaded bodies within the containers represent bacteria. As the available external nutrients vary in abundance, so the internal enzymes capable of acting on these nutrients come to vary in abundance too.

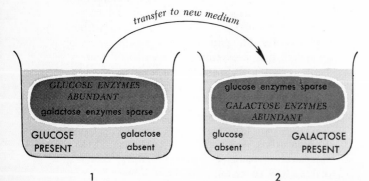

reaction they allow to occur is a restrained compromise between excitation and inhibition. Any change in the concentrations of the reactants or in the quantities of the modulators will change the balance between excitation and inhibition. And the reaction will then speed up in one direction, hence slow down in the other.

It happens in certain cases that an acceleration of one reaction inhibits not only the opposite reaction but also some quite different reaction as well. This second method of decelerating a metabolic process is referred to most often as **adaptive enzyme formation**. It has been studied most extensively in bacteria. For example, if a bacterium is given glucose as its nutritional source of carbon, then it manufactures large amounts of the specific enzymes necessary to metabolize glucose. Reactions involving glucose thus occur abundantly and rapidly. At the same time, enzymes catalyzing other carbon sources are produced in very small amounts only, and a food such as galactose, for example, is metabolized extremely slowly. However, if now glucose is withdrawn and galactose alone is made the carbon source, then the pattern of enzyme manufacture soon changes. Specifically, glucose-metabolizing enzymes decrease in amount and galactose-metabolizing enzymes become exceedingly abundant. As a result, originally rapid glucose reactions slow down but originally slow galactose reactions speed up. In this manner, the quantity of a given enzyme is always "adapted" to the actual quantity of the reactant metabolized by that enzyme. Correspondingly, this means that reactions are accelerated or inhibited as the amounts of reactants increase or decrease (Fig. 18.21).

A third deceleration method is based on **competition among modulators** for reactants. For example, we know that glucose can become either polysaccharide or pyruvic acid. Either step requires specific modulators (M_1, M_2):

$$\text{pyruvic acid} \xleftarrow{\quad M_1 \quad} \text{glucose} \xrightarrow{\quad M_2 \quad} \text{polysaccharide}$$

M_1 and M_2 in this case compete for available glucose. If M_1 has a competitive advantage—e.g., by combining more easily with glucose or by being present in larger amount—then polysaccharide synthesis will be decelerated and pyruvic acid formation will be speeded up. Here again the modulators hold one another in check and the net reactions are quickly adjusted when any part of the balance shifts.

A fourth method of deceleration depends on **competition among reactants** for modulators, the converse of the above. This may occur where given cellular reactions are so alike that the same modulator may promote them. For example, the same lipase could transform different fatty acids along with glycerin into either fat *A* or fat *B*:

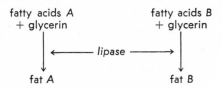

The reactants of the *A* side here compete with those on the *B* side for the required enzyme. Accordingly, whenever concentrations or other conditions favor one reaction, the other will be inhibited. We may therefore appreciate how competition for a limited quantity of modulator in a cell may crowd out one reaction at the expense of another.

We may note here in passing that chemical competition is often the cause as well as the cure of disease. For example, disease may be caused by a poison, which competes either with a normal modulator or a normal reactant and so crowds out an essential reaction. Cure may then be effected by reversing the abnormal competition, i.e., by supplying normal modulators or normal reactants in sufficient quantities to crowd out the disease reaction (see Fig. 2.11).

Modulator Interaction

Control of molecular metabolism may now be envisaged as follows (consult Fig. 18.22). In a given sequence of reactions, each separate reaction is influenced by several modulators of various types—genes and enzymes always, vitamins and vitamin-derived coenzymes often, and inorganic ions and hormones in many cases. Some of these modulators promote a given reaction in one direction (M_1, M_2, M_3), and others promote it in the opposite direction (M_4, M_5). Some modulators compete for reactants (M_4, M_6) and such modulators act *antagonistically*. Similarly, some reactants compete for modulators, e.g., *B* and *B'* compete for M_7. Other modulators are mutually reinforcing in their activity (M_4, M_5) and these are said to act *synergistically*.

Depending on the specific balances between all modulators and all reactants at any moment, the whole sequence or parts of it will proceed one way or the other for certain lengths of time, in certain amounts, and at certain rates. The overall result of such multiple

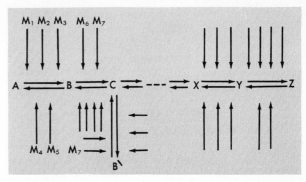

FIG. 18.22 The general pattern of control of molecular metabolism. *A, B, C, . . . , X, Y, Z* symbolize molecular reactants, and M_1, M_2, etc., symbolize molecular modulators. Some of these modulators act synergistically and reinforce each other in their action. Others act antagonistically. Also, just as modulators may compete for reactants, so reactants may compete for modulators. Each step of a reaction sequence is controlled by a battery of modulators, and the net reaction is a resultant of the various modulator effects.

excitations and inhibitions is a steady state, a dynamic equilibrium. When, now, a stimulus affects any part of the sequence, the balance between the excitations and inhibitions shifts automatically; and so, like ripples in a pond traveling away from a center of disturbance, the reaction sequence will undergo "hunting oscillations" until a steady state is reattained.

We may ask here why multiple controls for each reaction are required to begin with. Would not a single modulator suffice? Possibly it might, but there is safety in numbers. As already noted earlier for genes, multiple controls provide redundancy. This reduces the chance of error, and even if one of the many modulators becomes inoperative, the reaction will probably not be stopped completely.

SUPRAMOLECULAR CONTROL

All other living controls are based on the molecular controls of metabolism. In the cell, molecules are variously aggregated into comparatively large formed structures. By virtue of the control functions of their component molecules, the larger structures carry out specific higher-level control functions of their own.

Cellular Controls

Many molecular aggregates within cells, visible under the microscope, serve as receptors. For example, pigmented granules absorb light and form excellent photoreceptors (e.g., eyespots, chloroplasts). Long filaments are sensitive to displacement, to pressure, to touch, and they may therefore serve as receptors of mechanical stimuli (e.g., sensory hairs, fibrils). Other formed microscopic structures may be sensitive to particular classes of chemicals, and they may function as chemoreceptors (e.g., mitochondria, storage granules).

Formed bodies also function as modulators. Of these, the cell nucleus with its chromosomes and genes is the most complex. Analogously, complex cellular modulators also include, for example, the ribosomes, the kinetosomes, the chloroplasts, and other bodies. Their specific control functions have already been discussed. Complex cellular effectors are equally varied. Many contribute to the numerous physical and chemical responses necessary in the internal maintenance of a cell. Others link a cell to its external environment. For example, some bring about cell movement (e.g., kinetosomes, flagella), and some absorb or secrete various substances through the cell surface (e.g., Golgi bodies).

It should be noted, however, that not all molecular control systems within a cell are necessarily grouped into formed bodies like the above. On the contrary, most molecules, hence the controls in which they participate, are free in cellular water, and only specific kinds of molecules are organized into microscopically visible controlling agents. Furthermore, virtually every microscopic formed body present in a cell contributes to *multiple* control functions. It may serve as receptor in one instance, as modulator in another, as effector in yet a third. For example, the cell surface is a receptor when it "recognizes" a glucose molecule, but it is an effector when it allows that molecule to pass through. The cell nucleus has been referred to above as a modulator, which indeed it often is. But it may also serve as receptor—it receives many stimuli from the cytoplasm; or it may be an effector—it executes many responses. Similarly, kinetosomes, chloroplasts, and most other microscopic bodies may each function variously as receptors, modulators, or effectors. Clearly, functional labels are not fixed. How one designates a structure participating in several control processes depends largely on which of these processes one wishes to emphasize. Such multiplicity of function is evident not only in cellular controls but in all supracellular ones as well.

Moreover, the cellular level is the lowest on which we encounter modulators capable of distinguishing between various sensory messages and of *selecting* among various response possibilities. For example, the cell surface is *selectively* permeable. Functioning as a modulator, it may interpret the chemical nature of different kinds of molecules in contact with it and it may "decide" how fast and to what extent each such molecule is to be passed through. Similar selectivity is displayed by other complex control components within a cell and also by all supracellular control systems.

How does this crucial capacity of making decisions arise? The answer is not yet clear. But note that a complex cellular modulator contains within it many and different molecular control systems, each capable of a single response. It is therefore likely that the number of decisions a complex modulator may make is correlated with the number of different molecular unit systems of which it is composed.

Supracellular Controls

The response of a cell as a whole may be propagated to adjacent cells by direct contract, or it may be transmitted more widely by the internal transport systems—xylem and phloem in plants, blood circulation in animals. If one cell stimulates others in the manner of a chain reaction, a whole tissue or organ or organism may eventually be drawn into a larger response. Steady-state regulation of this kind is still essentially cellular. Although more than one cell is involved, receptors, modulators, and effectors beyond those present in the individual cell do not exist.

This form of functional control constitutes the highest pattern found among plants. Even in the most complexly constructed vascular plant, steady state of the whole organism is achieved by cell- and tissue-level controls and there are no tissues which are specialized primarily or exclusively for control functions only. As we shall see, for example, shoot tips play an important controlling role but the tissues here serve in many metabolic and developmental functions also. Similarly in all other cases; given cells or tissues carry out many functions and, to a greater or lesser degree, control is generally one of them.

In this respect plants differ from animals, most of which possess organs and organ systems specialized more or less exclusively for control functions. In this category are nervous systems and, where present, also endocrine systems. Possession of such systems is an adaptation to the characteristically animal way of life. Most animals move, largely by means of complexly organized muscle systems, and such motions require correspondingly complex control. Furthermore, fast locomotion brings animals into new external environments in rapid succession, hence such animals must make correspondingly rapid adjustments of their internal environments. The nervous and endocrine systems contribute importantly to such internal regulation and coordination. In nervous control, sense organs on the body surface and within the body are receptors. A brain is the chief modulator; muscles and glands are effectors; and nerves serve as sensory and motor connecting paths. Transmission of information through such a sequence of specialized neural structures constitutes a *reflex*, the basis of nervous steady-state control. Two examples of reflexes are given in Fig. 18.23. The endocrine system produces hormones, in different amounts

at different times, and these substances contribute to *chemoregulation*, i.e., adjustment of the whole internal chemical environment of the body.

To be sure, nervous and endocrine systems alone do not achieve all necessary control in animals. Indeed, as in a plant, *each* body part of an animal contributes to organismic control, even though in most cases other functions are performed as well. For example, the liver is more than a digestive gland; its vital role in chemoregulation has already been discussed (Chap. 14). Similarly, the body circulation is more than a transport system. As will be shown in Chap. 21, blood and blood vessels also serve importantly in body defense, in chemoregulation, and in numerous additional regulatory roles. Chemoregulation is also a chief function of

FIG. 18.23 Examples of organismic steady-state controls in animals. Left, sugar balance controlled via blood and hormones; right, two correlated control sequences modulated by the brain, one voluntary, the other involuntary and likely to accompany this particular voluntary sequence.

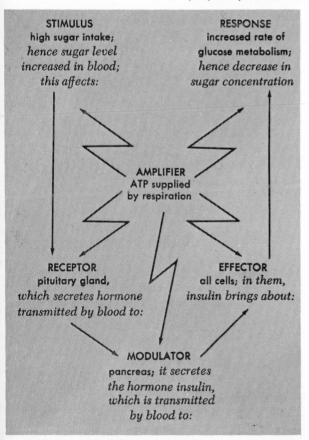
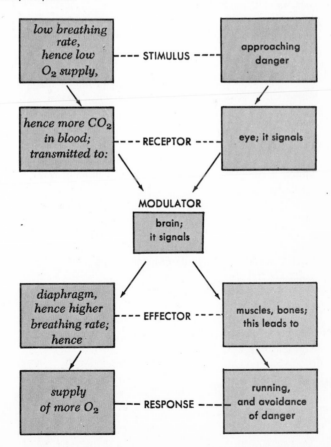

the kidneys, which are not just disposers of waste. Analogously for most other organs and systems; they perform controlling functions in addition to others.

Note, moreover, that any given regulatory activity requires simultaneous and *cooperative* functioning of most or all organs and systems. For example, on the basis of information presented in various chapters, it should not be too difficult to verify that control of constant body temperature in birds and mammals is a cooperative effort of all organ systems, the reproductive system perhaps excepted. Actually it is not surprising that steady-state maintenance on the level of the whole organism should require functional contributions of every part of the organism.

Clearly, inasmuch as every part of living matter is controlled *by* all other parts and at the same time contributes *to* the control of all other parts, "controlling" becomes a very major component of "living." Recognizing the stimuli of the environment and actively responding to them is even more characteristic of "being alive" than metabolizing. Without control, life becomes nonlife. Conversely, nonlife became life when the first control mechanism came into existence. That, as we have seen, was the nucleic acid molecule, the gene. All evolution ever since may be looked upon as a progressive development of more varied and more efficient control mechanisms. These were capable of counteracting more environmental stresses, hence they permitted the extension of life in any given environment for longer periods. The controls developed in man are one culmination of this. Through exquisitely sensitive receptors such as eyes and ears, through refined modulation such as learning and thinking, and through versatile responses such as speaking, writing, and using tools for building and manufacturing, the human organism has become one of the best controlled, remarkably able to resist the stresses of the most varied environments.

A more detailed examination of specific controls in plants and animals will be the subject of the next four chapters.

REVIEW QUESTIONS

1. In what different ways may one define "gene"? Why does a single definition not suffice? Where in a cell do (a) DNA and (b) RNA occur? Review the Watson-Crick model of DNA structure. How do DNA and RNA differ chemically?

2. What experimental evidence indicates that the nucleus and the cytoplasm of a cell cannot survive in isolation but must interact cyclically? What evidence indicates that genes are actually DNA? What is the template hypothesis and what is it designed to explain?

3. Describe the possible mechanism of code transfer from DNA to DNA, based on the Watson-Crick model. Similarly describe the possible mechanism of code transfer from DNA to RNA.

4. Describe experimental evidence indicating (a) that RNA is manufactured in the nucleus, (b) that nuclear RNA is transferred into the cytoplasm, and (c) that cytoplasmic RNA plays a role in the control of protein synthesis.

5. Review the pattern of processes by which genes control (a) cellular metabolism, (b) other cellular controllers, including other genes, and (c) all aspects of self-perpetuation.

6. How is the stability of genes safeguarded? What is the importance of gene stability? What is the effect of alterations in gene structure?

7. Review the pattern of gene function as a whole. Which function may be regarded as primary? Which indirect secondary functions derive from this and which tertiary functions result in turn from the secondary ones?

8. In general terms, what kinds of processes take place in the execution of control activities? What general function do such controls serve in the maintenance of life? What is the role of information flow in the maintenance of steady states?

9. What are the structural components of every control system in living matter? What specific role does each component play in the maintenance of dynamic equilibria? Review the functional properties of control systems. How is the energy requirement distributed among control components? What is feedback, and what is its significance in control activities?

10. What is the significance of trial and error in control activities? What happens when control systems are overloaded? Interpret the temperature-regulating

action of a home thermostat in terms of a control system and indicate the specific roles of feedback and of trial and error.

11. In what sense does a molecular reaction constitute a control system? What kinds of substances may serve as molecular modulators? What functional characteristics do these have in common? What is the relation of genes to control systems?

12. Review the ways in which molecular reactions may be decelerated. Give examples. Distinguish between antagonistic and synergistic control components. What is the significance of redundancy in control activities?

13. For each microscopic body usually present in cells, describe a cellular activity in which that body functions as (*a*) receptor, (*b*) modulator, (*c*) effector, and (*d*) sensory or motor pathway.

14. Review the general pattern of steady-state control on supracellular levels. How do plants and animals differ in this respect? Which parts of an organism do not participate in control activities?

15. Interpret the automatic alternation of inhalation and exhalation in breathing, as outlined in Chap. 15, in terms of control activity. What parts of the breathing system serve as receptors, modulators, effectors, and transmission paths, and what are the stimulus, the feedback, and the response? How does the breathing system respond to external stress and what is the result of overstress?

SUGGESTED COLLATERAL READINGS

The following are excellent popular articles on various aspects of gene structure and function:

Beadle, G. W.: The Genes of Men and Molds, *Sci. American,* vol. 179, 1948.

Crick, F. H. C.: The Structure of the Hereditary Material, *Sci. American,* vol. 191, 1954.

Danielli, J. F.: On Transplanting Nuclei, *Sci. American,* vol. 186, 1952.

Gale, E. F.: Experiments in Protein Synthesis, *Sci. American,* vol. 194, 1956.

Gamow, G.: Information Transfer in the Living Cell, *Sci. American,* vol. 193, 1955.

Horowitz, N. H.: The Gene, *Sci. American,* vol. 195, 1956.

Ingram, V. M.: How Do Genes Act? *Sci. American,* vol. 198, 1958.

Mirsky, A. E.: The Chemistry of Heredity, *Sci. American,* vol. 188, 1953.

Taylor, J. H.: The Duplication of Chromosomes, *Sci. American,* vol. 198, 1958.

The following are annotated reprints of important original papers, all collected in M. L. Gabriel and S. Fogel, "Great Experiments in Biology," Prentice-Hall, Englewood Cliffs, N.J., 1955.

Avery, O. T., C. M. McLeod, and M. McCarthy: Studies on the Chemical Nature of the Substance Inducing Transformation of Pneumococcal Types.

Beadle, G. W., and E. L. Tatum: Genetic Control of Biochemical Reactions in *Neurospora.*

Horowitz, N. H.: On the Evolution of Biochemical Synthesis.

Muller, H. J.: Artificial Transmutation of the Gene.

A well-documented account of material related to this chapter can be found in the following book:

Anfinsen, C. B.: "The Molecular Basis of Evolution," Wiley, New York, 1959.

The articles listed below provide useful background information on control operations in living systems:

Brown, F. A.: Biological Clocks and the Fiddler Crab, *Sci. American,* vol. 190, 1954.

Brown, G. S., and D. P. Campbell: Control Systems, *Sci. American,* vol. 187, 1952.

Gerard, R. W.: The Dynamics of Inhibition, *Sci. American,* vol. 179, 1948.

King, G.: What Is Information? *Sci. American,* vol. 187, 1952.

Nagel, E.: Self-regulation, *Sci. American,* vol. 187, 1952.

Tustin, A.: Feedback, *Sci. American,* vol. 187, 1952.

Walter, W. G.: An Imitation of Life, *Sci. American,* vol. 182, 1950.

CONTROL
IN PLANTS

19

As noted in the preceding chapter, regulatory activities in a whole plant are carried out by cells and tissues which are not specialized for control particularly but perform other functions as well. Even so, a plant may respond in quite varied ways to virtually all environmental changes which might affect it. For example, a plant may recognize and respond appropriately to gravity; to changing light intensities and light directions and to different wavelengths of light; to varying durations of illumination, which implies the existence of a highly developed time sense; to changing temperatures and humidities; to wind and water flow; to changing seasons; to chemical changes in the environment; and to injurious agents, animals included.

Consequently, plants display overt behavior. To a large extent such behavior is produced by **growth factors,** i.e., various modulators of the intracellular control systems of plants. We shall first discuss the nature and action of these growth factors and shall then consider the resulting forms of plant **behavior.**

GROWTH FACTORS

Genes and enzymes are produced directly in the cell in which they exert controlling functions. By contrast, other intracellular controllers sometimes or always originate outside the cells in which they function. Because these imported controllers often reveal their activities through specific effects on growth and development, they are frequently referred to as *growth factors* or *growth substances*. Strictly speaking, of course, genes and enzymes qualify as "growth factors" also. However, as defined customarily, growth factors are controlling agents which a cell requires for its maintenance but which that cell cannot manufacture on its own. Such agents must therefore be imported into a cell. Depending on where they are imported from, two general categories of growth factors may be distinguished. If a controlling agent is obtained not from within the organism but from the external environment, then the growth factor is referred to as a **growth regulator**. But if a controller is produced in a given body part of an organism and is transported to cells which cannot manufacture it, then that growth factor is a **hormone**.

The principal classes of growth regulators are **vitamins** and **minerals**. In animals, both must be obtained in prefabricated form from the environment. But in the autotrophic plants, all vitamins are manufactured within the plant body and in most cases directly within each cell in which these substances must be used. In green plants, therefore, vitamins belong to the same self-manufactured group of compounds as genes and enzymes, and only in heterotrophs are vitamins distinctly identifiable as growth regulators. In view of this we shall defer a detailed discussion of vitamins until the next chapter. Green plants do require minerals from the external environment, and we may note that these substances evidently serve in two general capacities: in part they are nutrients used as structural components of cells and in part they are growth regulators used in reaction control. In some cases, the same mineral may serve in both capacities. For example, magnesium is both a structural component (e.g., in chlorophyll) and a controlling agent (e.g., in respiratory reactions; see Chap. 16).

Plant hormones comprise largely three groups of substances: **auxins, gibberellins,** and **kinins**. Other groups probably exist (see below), but the three listed are best known and have been studied most. In some cases, certain vitamins function as hormones in plants. For example, root tissues usually do not produce enough thiamine (vitamin B_1) on their own, but they obtain additional supplies of this vitamin from stem and leaf tissues. In this instance thiamine is a hormone. Note, moreover, that hormones may be extracted from plant tissues and may then be introduced into other plants, as in various experimental and commercial procedures (see below). In such cases, hormonal substances are used as growth regulators, i.e., as controlling agents derived from external sources.

The normal control functions of a particular growth factor are usually investigated by deliberately making an organism deficient in that factor or by supplying an organism with an excess of it. In either case, abnormal *unsteady* states are induced, and these often give clues about the normal controlling roles of the growth factor. For example, much has been learned about the regulating functions of given mineral sub-

stances by withholding such substances from a plant and by then analyzing the resulting abnormalities. Plant hormones have similarly been studied by experimental production of excesses or deficiencies. Some of the principal data obtained are outlined in the following sections.

AUXINS

These growth factors of plants were the first to be identified definitely as hormones. The effects of auxins had already been observed in the nineteenth century by the eminent biologist Charles Darwin. He noted that, as young grass seedlings elongated, they curved toward the light source. Using lightproof caps, Darwin was able to show that the light-sensitive region was the apical tip of a seedling, not the region farther back which underwent the actual bending (Fig. 19.1).

Later work by other investigators on grass and also oat seedlings showed that a material diffusible substance must be moving from the apical tip of a seedling to the elongating cells farther back. It was found that if the tip of a seedling was cut off and then returned, but with a layer of gelatin between the cut surfaces, then the bending toward light still occurred. This result indicated that the diffusible substance was water-soluble and could move through the aqueous gelatin. By contrast, a layer composed of fatty materials or a nonporous barrier of mica would not let the substance through. In other experiments the tip of a seedling was cut off in the dark and was then replaced along one side of the cut surface of the seedling stump. Under such dark conditions, the seedling still curved as it grew. Moreover, the direction of bending was always

FIG. 19.1 Darwin's experiments with grass seedlings. If the tip of a seedling is capped (B), bending toward a light source will not occur.

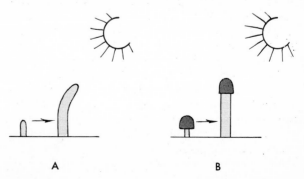

A   B

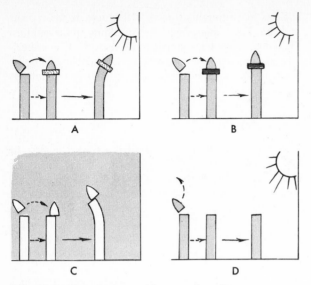

FIG. 19.2   Experiments with oat coleoptiles.

toward the side opposite to that of the attached tip. Thus, curving growth was apparently caused by an uneven distribution of the growth-promoting substance: the side of the seedling receiving more of the substance grew faster than the opposite side, hence the bending. If the seedling tip was cut off and not replaced at all, the seedling ceased to elongate altogether. All these data suggested strongly that the growth-promoting substance functioned rather like a hormone (Fig. 19.2).

The hormone was isolated in 1928 and was named **auxin.** Many seedling tips were placed on an agar block, and this block was shown to collect all the auxin diffusing out of the tips. For if the tips were discarded and the block was placed on the stump of a decapitated seedling, the auxin in the agar was effective in promoting various growth phenomena, including elongation and bending of the seedling (Fig. 19.3). Following these isolation studies, the chemical nature of auxin was identified. It is *indole acetic acid, IAA* for short ($C_{10}H_9O_2N$).

Also called *heteroauxin,* IAA is but one of a group of similarly acting substances. Two others, for example, are naphthalene acetic acid ($C_{12}H_{10}O_2$) and 2,4-dichlorophenoxyacetic acid, or 2,4-D for short ($C_8H_6O_3Cl_2$). Still other auxins exist and many can be synthesized in the laboratory. Indeed, it is often possible to predict whether a given new compound will be an auxin in plants. The characteristic effect of an auxin is its ability to promote bending of a seedling, and this effect

appears to be correlated with the presence of particular atomic groupings in an auxin molecule. For example, such a molecule is likely to possess an unsaturated carbon ring, an acid side chain, and a certain spatial arrangement of the ring and the side chain (Fig. 19.4). Notwithstanding such usually common structural features, auxins differ in their biological potency and also in their specificity.

IAA is known to occur in many Monera, Protista, and Metaphyta. Chemical derivatives of it, without hormonal effects, are also found in Metazoa. In a plant, IAA is manufactured in various body parts. Generally, actively growing and developing regions produce the largest amounts. For example, particularly auxin-rich regions are meristems of all kinds (including shoot tips, root tips, and cambia), and also young leaves, developing flower parts, fruits, and plant tumors during their active growth phases. How does IAA actually affect a plant cell? Available data indicate that auxins promote the *elongation* of individual cells apparently by influencing cell-wall metabolism. The effect is such that more primary wall material is produced and is deposited at the two ends of a cell. In addition, the structural framework of the cell becomes loosened, permitting the actual deposition of more cell-wall material.

Thus, in normal plant development, the apical tip of a shoot (or a root) produces IAA and this substance diffuses to cells farther back where it brings about cell elongation. If the cross-sectional distribution of IAA is roughly even, the shoot will elongate straight up. The growth-promoting effect of auxin is known to be somehow reduced by light, hence an illuminated shoot does not grow as fast as if it were kept in darkness. Under normal field conditions, therefore, plant growth is a compromise between (1) stimulation by

FIG. 19.3   Experiments on auxin isolation.

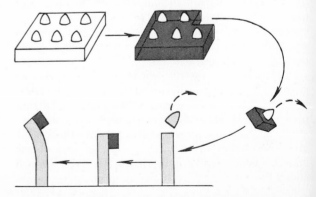

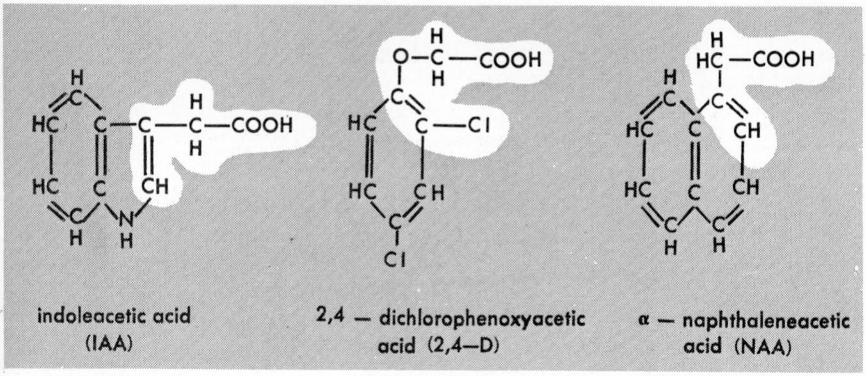

FIG. 19.4 The chemical structure of various auxins. Shaded portions emphasize the similar atomic groupings often present in auxins.

indoleacetic acid (IAA)

2,4 — dichlorophenoxyacetic acid (2,4—D)

α — naphthaleneacetic acid (NAA)

light via photosynthesis and food production and (2) inhibition by light via reduced auxin effects. If a shoot is illuminated predominantly from one side, auxin will be less effective on that side than on the other. The shoot will then curve toward the light source as it elongates. These basic effects of IAA and of auxins generally have numerous secondary consequences which influence the steady-state maintenance of the whole plant. We shall see below what these important additional effects are.

GIBBERELLINS, KININS

In the so-called "foolish seedling" disease in rice, a fungus of the genus *Gibberella* infects a young rice plant and this plant then grows extremely tall, projecting well above neighboring plants in a field. Extracts of the fungus similarly can increase the size of the rice plants, and from such extracts pure gibberrellins have been isolated. Gibberellins are now known to occur not only in fungi but also in vascular plants, where they are normal constituents qualifying as hormones. Four different but closely related compounds are included in the group, gibberellic acid being the most potent.

Gibberellins affect stem length. In young stems particularly, the hormones increase the length of all the internodes without affecting the number of nodes. The results of this can be very striking. For example, by applying gibberellic acid to dwarf peas, such plants can be made to grow to the size of normal peas. Similarly, dwarf varieties of corn will grow to normal height if a little gibberellic acid is placed on the leaves. Many biennial plants can be induced to complete their whole life cycle in a single year by treatment with gibberellins. And if gibberellic acid is applied to cabbage, nor-

mally a low head with closely associated leaves, then the plant can be induced to become vinelike (Fig. 19.5).

These profound growth-promoting effects appear to be a result of increases in the rates of cell division. Just how gibberellins actually accelerate cell divisions

FIG. 19.5 The effects of gibberellins. Left, untreated cabbage and cabbage after gibberellin treatment. Right, untreated dwarf pea and dwarf pea after gibberellin treatment. (Courtesy of Dr. S. H. Wittwer and Dr. M. J. Bukovac, Michigan State University, and Econ. Botany, vol. 12, p. 213.)

is not clearly understood as yet. Unlike auxins, gibberellins do not cause bending of a seedling and they affect the whole stem, not only the region behind the apical tip. Also, gibberellins do not exert control over buds, roots, and leaves in the same manner as auxins (see below).

The discovery of gibberellins has shown clearly that cellular steady-state control in plants is far more complex than had been thought when only minerals and auxins were known to play regulatory roles. And the complexity increases even more as additional categories of hormones and growth regulators are being discovered. A case in point are the *kinins* which, like gibberellins, promote cell division. Kinins are degradation products of purines and nucleic acids. They may be normally present in plants as hormones, but to date their action has been studied mainly by application of man-made kinin preparations.

Through their control of cellular activities, growth factors of all kinds govern the behavior of a whole plant, as noted. Explicit behavior may be regarded as the response to the various stimuli which affect a plant. The stimuli may be external or may arise internally as a result of metabolic and self-perpetuative processes. Given cells and tissues function variously as receptors of stimuli and as effectors of responses. Growth factors, through their control of cell and tissue activity, are the basic modulators in a plant as a whole. The behavioral responses of plants to different stimuli manifest themselves principally in two ways, namely, as responses of *movement* and as responses of *development*. We shall examine each of these in turn.

RESPONSES OF MOVEMENT

These responses involve greater or lesser portions of a fixed plant and they are of two types: **growth movements** and **turgor movements**.

GROWTH MOVEMENTS

Growth movements are responses to both *internal* and *external* stimuli. In so far as the stimuli are internal, their exact nature in most cases cannot be pinpointed as yet and the specific role of growth factors in given responses is also not yet clear. Apart from growth as such, which is the principal type of growth response to internal stimuli, three other, special kinds of growth responses to internal stimuli are known (Fig. 19.6).

One of these is **nutational** movement. This is a back-and-forth rocking or nodding motion of the apical shoot tips of certain species caused by alternately changing growth rates on opposite sides of the apical tip. Such motions, of course, occur too slowly to be observable directly, but time-lapse movies show them clearly. This is generally true of all kinds of growth movements. A second type of response includes **spiral** motions of various sorts. These are characterized by rotational growth of an elongating shoot around its long axis. One form of spiral motion is *twining*, in which rotational growth of the shoot tip produces a spirally curving stem. External stimuli, gravity in particular, may be partly responsible for twining growth. External

FIG. 19.6 Some growth movements of plants in response to internal stimuli.

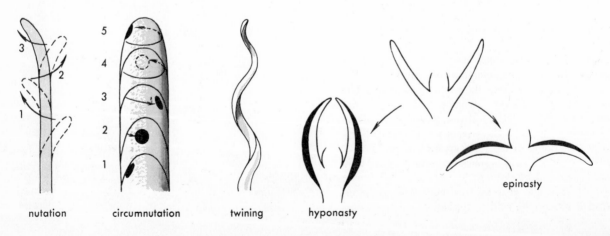

nutation   circumnutation   twining   hyponasty   epinasty

FIG. 19.7 Tropic movements. Top left, normal tomato plant. Top right, the effect of toxic aerial gases—chemotropic response. Bottom left, the effect of gravity—geotropic response. Bottom right, the effect of light—phototropic response. At bottom right, the plant is illuminated from the left. *(Courtesy of Boyce Thompson Institute for Plant Research.)*

stimuli such as temperature and light are probably also partly involved in a third type of response, so-called **nastic** movements. These occur in leaves, petals, and other flattened parts of plants when one surface of such an organ grows faster than the other. Nastic motions thus may result either in an opening and folding out of a body part, as in the opening of maturing buds, or in a closing and folding in.

Growth movements brought about wholly by external stimuli are called **tropisms**. The stimuli producing such tropic responses are clearly identifiable, and the specific role of growth factors is also known, at least in many cases. Several kinds of tropisms are distinguished on the basis of the various growth-inducing stimuli: light-induced **phototropism**, gravity-induced **geotropism**, contact-induced **thigmotropism**, chemical-induced **chemotropism**, and others (Fig. 19.7). A given tropic response may be either *positive* or *negative;* i.e., a plant or plant part may grow toward or away from the stimulus. For example, leaves and stems are positively phototrophic and negatively geotropic; they grow toward light and away from the gravitational center of the earth. Roots, on the contrary, are positively geotropic and negatively phototropic. Pollen tubes are positively chemotropic, growing toward chemical agents produced within a flower ovary. And the shoot tips and tendrils of climbing plants are positively thigmotropic, growing along objects on which they can become attached. Most tropic responses are adaptively advantageous in fairly obvious, and to the plant often very important, ways.

Of all responses of plants, phototropism and geotropism are among the best understood. These move-

ments, and possibly other tropisms as well, are under the control of auxins. As already noted, unilateral illumination of a growing stem reduces the auxin effect on the side facing the light source. This makes cells on the opposite side elongate more extensively, and the stem then curves toward the light. The net result is the observed positive phototropism of stems. How can the negative phototropism of roots be explained?

It has been found that the optimum IAA concentration for elongation of root cells is about 100,000 times less than the optimum for elongation of stem cells. In other words, an IAA concentration which stimulates stem growth *inhibits* root growth. Conversely, an IAA concentration which stimulates root growth is so low that it inhibits stem growth, or at any rate does not promote it (Fig. 19.8). Therefore, if a stem-root system (in water rather than soil) is illuminated from one side, the stem tip will curve toward the light. But any auxin diffusing into the root on the side away from the light will be sufficiently concentrated to inhibit root elongation on that side. As a result, the side facing the light will grow faster and the root tip will curve away from the light stimulus; hence the negative phototropism of roots (Fig. 19.9).

The negative geotropism of stems and the positive geotropism of roots can be explained by migration of auxin under the influence of gravity. It is well known that if a plant is placed horizontally, the stem tip grows upward, the root tip downward. These responses take place even in the dark; they are gravity-dependent, not light-dependent. In a horizontal plant, it can be shown that as much as two-thirds of all the auxin in a shoot tip is present on the lower side of this tip. As auxin moves back to cells capable of elongating, most of the hormone therefore reaches cells located on the lower side of the stem. These cells consequently elongate more than cells on the upper side and the stem tip curves upward as a result. When auxin reaches root cells, the concentration of the hormone is still highest on the lower side, which means that the cells on that side will be inhibited most. Root cells on the upper side then elongate to a comparatively greater extent. The root tip therefore curves downward, in the direction of the center of the earth (Fig. 19.10).

Changes in hormone distribution and differential effects of given hormone concentrations on different plant parts probably play a role in other tropisms as well. In most of these cases, however, it is still not quite clear how the external stimulus actually elicits particular hormone activities.

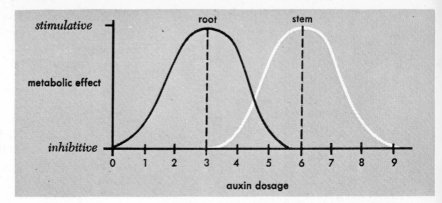

FIG. 19.8 The effect of auxin, at different concentrations, on plant root and stem.

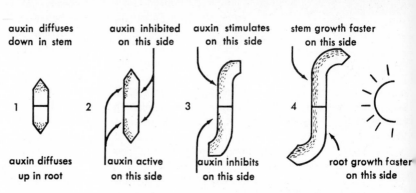

FIG. 19.9 The interaction of light and auxin in the control of stem and root growth.

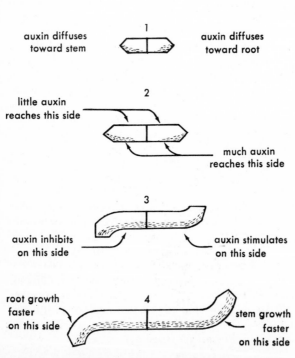

FIG. 19.10 The interaction of gravity and auxin in the control of stem and root growth.

TURGOR MOVEMENTS

These responses of plant parts are initiated largely by external stimuli. The movements result from changes in the turgor (i.e., water pressure) of given cells or cell groups. Unlike growth movements, which are slow and produce more or less permanent results, turgor movements are rapid, often exceedingly so, and they are transient and repeatable. In some cases at least, auxins again appear to be the chief controlling agents. The most important and most widespread turgor movements are the opening and closing movements of the epidermal *guard cells* in leaves and stems. Other turgor movements include the *contact movements* of leaves in sensitive and carnivorous plants and the *sleep movements* of leaves in certain plants.

Guard-cell Movements

A pair of green, crescent-shaped guard cells possesses walls which are thickest and stiffest on the inner

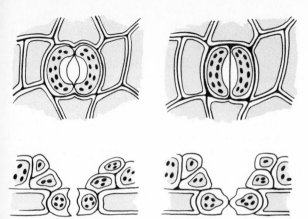

FIG. 19.11 Diagram of leaf epidermis, showing a pair of guard cells. Upper figures, surface view; lower figures, cross-sectional view; left figures, stoma open; right figures, stoma closed.

sides, where they form the stomatal pore (Fig. 19.11). By virtue of this, a stoma can open or close when turgor increases or decreases within the guard cells. Turgor increases when additional water enters the cells. As they then become more turgid they swell, and their thin outer sidewalls curve out farther under the increased water pressure. This pulls the inner thicker portions of the walls apart and the stoma so opens. Conversely, when water leaves the guard cells, they become less turgid. Their elastic walls then revert to their original position and the stoma closes.

The turgor of guard cells can become increased through two interconnected processes (Fig. 19.12). Since guard cells are photosynthetic, they may produce carbohydrates. This raises the concentration of the particles in the cells. As a result, water is drawn osmotically into the guard cells from surrounding epidermal cells and turgor increases. Under illumination, therefore, and if other conditions are optimal, stomata will open and will permit photosynthesis to occur in the leaf mesophyll; CO_2 may enter the air spaces of the leaf and O_2 may depart. Conversely, in darkness the stomata will close.

The second process leading to an increase in guard-cell turgor is initiated when the stomata are closed and when photosynthesis does not occur. At night, for example, respiratory CO_2 accumulates in the guard cells. The gas is present in chemical combination with water, in the form of carbonic acid, H_2CO_3 (more precisely, in the form of bicarbonate and hydrogen ions; the equation governing this is $H_2O + CO_2 \rightleftharpoons$

$H_2CO_3 \rightleftharpoons H^+ + HCO_3^-$). When guard-cell photosynthesis resumes the following morning, the carbonic acid reverts to water and free CO_2, for CO_2 is used up in photosynthesis and this changes the direction of the reaction above to the left, by mass action. As carbonic *acid* disappears, the interior of the guard cells becomes more alkaline. But alkaline conditions are known to promote the enzymatic conversion of storage starch into glucose. Therefore, since one starch molecule yields many glucose molecules, this increase in the concentration of particles leads to an osmotic intake of additional water, hence to increase in turgor and an opening of the stoma. Leaf pores so reopen with the reappearance of the morning sun, permitting photosynthesis to occur again in the mesophyll (see Fig. 19.12).

Could not permanently open leaf pores without guard cells serve just as well? Gases would then enter or leave freely and photosynthesis would or would not occur inside the leaf depending on illumination. But

FIG. 19.12 The control of guard-cell movements.

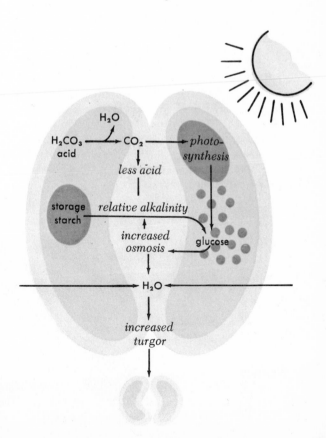

lighting is not the only factor controlling the turgor movements of guard cells. Humidity, temperature, and possibly other environmental conditions appear to play a role as well, and it is in connection with such factors that guard cells display perhaps their most important adaptive function. For example, on a very dry, hot summer day the stomata may be almost fully closed, despite the ample illumination. The rate of photosynthesis in a leaf is then reduced, inasmuch as not enough CO_2 can enter. But the evaporation of internal water, a problem of more immediate concern, is held down at the same time. Besides, if leaf pores were permanently open, they would permit unnecessary evaporation of water during the night.

Other Turgor Movements

A second category of turgor movements is elicited by contact stimuli. Probably the most dramatic instance of such **contact movements** is encountered in the legume *Mimosa*, the "sensitive plant." It has long been known that the leaves of this plant are exceedingly sensitive to touch and also to sudden increases in temperature; the leaves drop down from an erect position almost instantaneously after being stimulated, as if they possessed nervous reflexes. But the mechanism is again movement of water into and out of cells.

At the base of each leaf petiole of *Mimosa* (and of several other legumes) is a so-called **pulvinus,** a swelling containing large cells with many spaces between them (Fig. 19.13). When a *Mimosa* leaf is erect, all the cells of the pulvinus are turgid; it is the mechanical rigidity maintained by this turgor which keeps the leaf erect. But any touch or heat stimulus applied to some part of the leaf quickly leads to the transmission of a signal through the leaf to the pulvinus. A diffusible chemical agent is known to bring about this transmission; some evidence indicates that it may be an auxin. The signal affects the cells on the lower side of the pulvinus in such a way that they lose water rapidly. This water moves into the surrounding intercellular spaces and into other, neighboring cells. As a result of the suddenly reduced turgor in the lower portion of the pulvinus, the leaf as whole drops down. The time elapsed between external stimulus and leaf response is less than $1/10$ sec. However, it takes about 10 min for the recovery of the turgid condition.

Reversible turgor movements may also play a role in the insect-trapping action of the leaves of carnivorous plants such as Venus flytrap. The trapping mechanism in this plant is triggered off by touch-sensitive hairs on the inner leaf surfaces. Subsequent events are not yet fully understood. Some still unidentified diffusible chemical agent again appears to transmit the excitation from the stimulated receptor hairs to the effector cells (Fig. 19.14).

Variously different contact movements are known in several other plants. In some, for example, the stamens of flowers snap to altered positions when an insect touches them and pollen is thereby powdered over the insects. In other flowers, the stigma of a pistil

FIG. 19.13   Diagram, lengthwise section of a pulvinus. Photographs are of *Mimosa*, before and after stimulation of leaflets and leaves. *(Photographs courtesy of Dr. M. S. Fuller, Brown University.)*

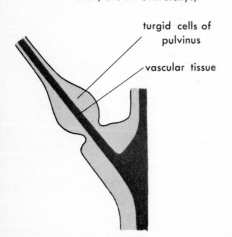

turgid cells of pulvinus

vascular tissue

FIG. 19.14 Venus flytrap. Left, whole plant with traps in various states of closure. Middle and right, a fly enters a trap and is caught. *(Left, Carolina Biological Supply Co.; middle, right, General Biological Supply House, Inc.)*

forms two joined lobes which snap together when pollen grains touch them, so trapping the pollen. Turgor changes and signal transmission by diffusible chemical agents appear to be involved in all such cases. Beyond this, details of the action mechanisms are still unknown.

Changes in light intensity are the specific stimuli for so-called **sleep movements** in many plants, legumes in particular. In such turgor-produced motions, the leaves assume one position during the day and another during the night. The day position is usually horizontal, the night position usually vertical, either upright or hanging. Here again the mechanism of action is not understood as yet, nor is the possible functional significance of these particular movements.

RESPONSES OF DEVELOPMENT

Numerous developmental responses of plants have been shown to be under auxin control and to be initiated normally by internal stimuli. Some of these responses can also be produced by artificial external stimulation through the use of auxin preparations applied from the outside as growth regulators. Many other important developmental responses are elicited normally and naturally by the external environment. Various physical, chemical, and biological agents are the effective stimuli.

THE EFFECTS OF AUXINS

Normal internal stimuli lead to one action of auxin which effects **bud development.** As noted in Chap. 10, lateral stem buds form in the axils of leaves. Buds near the stem tip usually remain dormant, but those farther back along the stem may break dormancy and develop into branch stems. It can be shown that this evident dominance of the main apical tip is due to auxin. IAA produced by the dominant tip moves back toward the axillary buds. However, the optimum IAA concentration for bud growth is only about $\frac{1}{1000}$ of the optimum concentration for cell elongation. Therefore, as high IAA concentrations reach them, buds near the tip are inhibited from breaking dormancy. The apical dominance extends backward for considerable distances until auxin becomes sufficiently dilute to stimulate rather than inhibit bud development. Clearly, these differential sensitivities account for the usual tapering growth pattern of the branch system of a plant (Fig. 19.15). One question remains to be answered: Why is the development of the dominant bud not inhibited by the bud's very high auxin concentration?

Auxins exert developmental control over **meristems** such as cambia. It has been suggested that, in woody plants, auxins produced in the spring by actively growing shoots diffuse to the cambia, where they may activate those tissues and stimulate them to form that season's wood and bark. The effects of auxin on meristem development are evident also in the formation of **callus** tissue. If the stem of a bean plant is cut off and the cut surface is smeared with a paste which contains large amounts of IAA, then this external stimulus will lead to the development of a callus, a tumorous mass of cells which includes meristematic regions (Fig. 19.16). Such a callus may be cut off in turn and may

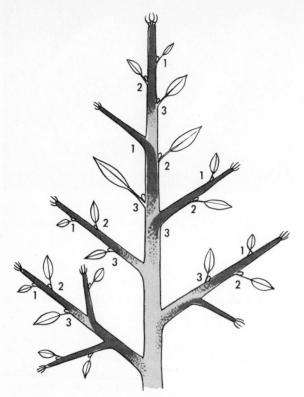

FIG. 19.15 The effect of auxin on bud development. In this diagram, the assumption is made that auxin released from a terminal bud is concentrated enough to inhibit the development of the first three branch buds behind the terminal bud. Branch buds farther back receive less than an inhibitory concentration of auxin and thus may break dormancy.

be kept growing indefinitely in tissue culture, provided IAA is continually added to the medium.

Calluslike tissues are also formed in plant tumors known as **crown galls,** which are encountered in many species, e.g., sunflowers, marigolds, tomatoes, beans (Fig. 19.17). Production of a crown gall is initiated by an external biological stimulus, namely, by parasitic bacteria of a particular kind. These organisms infect plant tissues, and the latter respond by excessive growth and crown gall formation. Bacteria-free portions of such a tumor may be isolated and grown in tissue culture. Once they have been produced, crown gall tissues manufacture large amounts of auxin on their own. This maintains their meristematic characteristics and their persistent growth without any further external bacterial or hormonal stimulation. In their inde-

pendent, autonomous growth, crown galls evidently resemble the malignant tumors of animals. In the latter, however, auxin is never responsible for maintenance of autonomous growth.

Another important developmental function of auxins is their control of leaf fall and fruit drop. Leaves and fruits separate from a plant at an **abscission layer,** a region of special cells formed where a leaf petiole or a fruit stalk joins the stem (Fig. 19.18). In such a layer, the cement between adjacent cells dissolves, cell-wall permeability is lost, and the weakened cells finally die. Abscission of the leaf or the fruit is the consequence. It has been shown that such separations are governed by the relative auxin concentrations on either side of the abscission area. So long as IAA concentrations in a leaf or a fruit are higher than in the stem, abscission normally does not occur. This is the case while leaf or fruit growth is under way, i.e., while these organs actively produce auxins of their own. But when auxin manufacture ceases, at full maturity, for example, or when cold autumn weather slows growth rates, then IAA concentrations in a leaf or a fruit decrease relative to the concentrations in the stem. Abscission is then likely to take place.

Fruit growers make practical use of these relationships. In spring they may spray stems with auxins, a procedure which raises the hormone concentrations

FIG. 19.16 Callus formation on a cut stem of a bean plant after application of high concentrations of IAA.

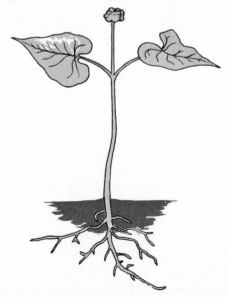

FIG. 19.17 Crown gall on the stem of a sunflower. (Courtesy of Dr. A. Braun, Rockefeller Institute.)

of the stems relative to those of flowers or young fruits. The result will be many premature abscissions and a consequent thinning of the fruits on a tree. The fewer remaining fruits may then become larger and better, since more food will be available to them. Later in the year, auxin spray may be applied to the fruits, which will delay abscission and permit longer tree-ripening of the fruits.

Auxins play an important role in controlling the development of adventitious roots. As is well known, if a terminal piece of stem with an apical bud and some leaves is cut away from a plant and is put into soil or water, then adventitious roots will form from the base

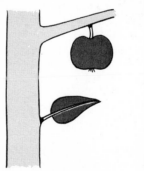

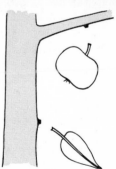

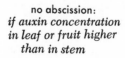

no abscission:
if auxin concentration in leaf or fruit higher than in stem

abscission:
if auxin concentration in leaf or fruit decreased relative to that of stem

FIG. 19.18 Top, junction of leaf and stem, showing abscission layer (dark transverse cell layer) across leaf base. Bottom, the effects of relative auxin concentrations on abscission. (Top, reprinted with permission from K. Esau, "Plant Anatomy," John Wiley & Sons, Inc., New York, 1953.)

of the stem piece. Such **cuttings** are a means of propagating mature plants, and this method of making new individuals is used widely in horticulture. In early attempts to explain root formation in cuttings, it was postulated that some substance moved from the terminal regions of the shoot to the vascular regions of the stem base, where it stimulated development of root tissues. It was found later that such a substance actually exists, and it was demonstrated to be IAA. Weak solutions of IAA are now frequently used to promote root formation in stem cuttings (Fig. 19.19).

Auxins not only aid in making new plants but also in killing old ones. When auxins are applied externally to certain plants, at much higher concentrations than those which normally promote growth, then the growth factors interfere drastically with the metabolism and development of the plants. Dicotyledonous weeds are particularly sensitive to very high auxin levels, and plant death is a frequent consequence. Just how auxins exert this lethal effect is not clearly understood, but the effect itself has become extremely important in weed control. Monocotyledonous crop plants such as corn and grain-formers are hardly affected by auxin concentrations which kill dicotyledonous weeds.

Evidently, auxins perform vital controlling functions in a multiplicity of developmental processes. A basic stimulation or inhibition of cell elongation accounts for many of these functions, but many others cannot be explained in this way alone. Future research must show what effect or effects of auxins are most fundamental in cells and just how the known effects on growth and development emerge as secondary or even more remote consequences.

THE EFFECTS OF LIGHT

In view of the absolute nutritional dependence of green plants on light, it is not surprising that this form of energy should have become one of the most profound external stimuli in the life of plants. Some responses to light have been outlined above. Certain of these, such as the auxin-mediated phototropic responses, are clearly adaptive in plant nutrition; they bring the photosynthetic organs into optimum positions relative to the light source. Similarly adaptive in plant metabolism are the response of guard cells to light and the light-dependence of chlorophyll synthesis and chlorophyll maintenance in flowering plants. However, many other responses to light are more directly of developmental, not of metabolic, significance. A different set of developmental responses is produced by each of the three main attributes of light: *light intensity*, *light quality*, and *light duration*.

Light Intensity

Some responses to varying light intensities are auxin-mediated, and they result from the reduced effectiveness of auxin in bright light. For example, plants grown in darkness or in dim light develop taller stems with longer internodes and larger, more succulent leaves than plants grown in bright light. Even within the same plant, outer leaves which receive the full light of the sun remain smaller than inner, more shaded leaves. Where leaf size is of commercial importance, as in tobacco, for example, plants are often shielded by light screens or nets. Such reduction of intensity of illumination may promote development of larger leaves.

Extended maintenance of plants in darkness or in exceedingly dim light usually leads to the pathological condition known as **etiolation**: stems are excessively long and without sufficient supporting fiber tissue, and leaves are whitish, without adequate amounts of chlorophyll. If light intensity does not increase, death ultimately follows. Conversely, long exposure to excessively bright light stunts plant development abnormally and may also lead to death.

FIG. 19.19 The effect of auxin on root development. After auxin application, the cut stems on left develop roots as on right. (*Courtesy of Boyce Thompson Institute for Plant Research.*)

white light:	red light:	far-red light:
leaf and stem	leaf growth stimulated,	leaf growth retarded,
growth normal	stem growth retarded	stem growth stimulated

FIG. 19.20   The effects of red and far-red light on leaf and stem growth.

Within an adequate range of light intensities, different species of plants develop best at different intensity levels. Some plants, e.g., tomatoes and grasses, require bright, direct light for optimum development. In such plants, the synthesis of living matter increases in roughly direct proportion with increasing light intensities (up to a maximum corresponding to somewhat less than the full light of the summer sun). On the other hand, plants such as violets and ferns develop optimally in dim, diffuse light and are stunted by the direct sun. Still other plants, e.g., roses, do well both in bright and in diffuse light, although growth and flowering may be retarded or may cease if the light intensity is too low.

Light Quality

At any given light intensity, the different wavelengths of light exert considerable effect on plant development. For example, it has been shown that brief exposure to red light often retards stem elongation in plants such as oats, peas, beans, or barley. However, these retardations can subsequently be reversed and stem growth can be stimulated by exposing the plants to light which is close to the limit of visibility, in the far-red region of the spectrum. In leaves, red–far-red treatment produces opposite effects; far-red light retards leaf development, red light reverses the retardation (Fig. 19.20).

Such red–far-red effects on stem and leaf development may be induced repeatedly within the same plant. The nature of the stimulus receptors and the functional significance of these responses to different light qualities are not yet known.

Light Duration

Developmental responses of plants to varying light durations are described by the term **photoperiodism**. Flower development is particularly affected by different day lengths, or *photoperiods*. On the basis of the photoperiod required for flowering, three groups of plants may be distinguished (Fig. 19.21). In so-called **short-day plants**, flowers develop only if the plants are illuminated for less than 12 hr daily. Violets, asters, cockleburs, strawberries, chrysanthemums, and rice are among many plants in this group. In **long-day plants**, flowers develop only if the daily photoperiod is more than 12 hr. This group includes, for example, wheat, clover, beets, and lettuce. A third group of plants is not limited in its illumination requirements, and such **indeterminate plants** produce flowers regardless of the length of the daily photoperiods. Tomatoes, cucumbers, cotton, sunflowers, and dandelions are representative members of this group.

Short-day plants fail to flower or their flowering is

FIG. 19.21   The day-length requirements for flowering of three categories of plants.

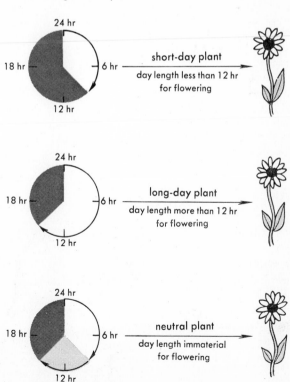

greatly retarded if they are exposed to long photo-periods only. Conversely, long-day plants flower late or not at all if they are grown under short photoperiods. Often, only a brief exposure to appropriate day lengths is needed to induce flowering. For example, if the short-day cocklebur plant is grown under long photo-periods, it will not flower. But if it is exposed to only one single short day and one long night, it will flower, even if the long photoperiods are continued thereafter. Different species exhibit different requirements in this respect.

Some of the factors involved in eliciting photo-periodic responses are known. First, it has been shown that the receptor organs specifically sensitive to light durations are the leaves. Defoliated plants cannot be induced to flower even with proper light treatment. The light sensitivity of leaves differs at different stages of development. Very young leaves are generally insen-sitive, but as they age they become progressively more sensitive until, in many species, sensitivity is again lost at very old stages. Even a portion of a sensitive leaf may be an adequate receptor.

Second, it can be demonstrated that the red por-tion of the spectrum is more effective as a flower-inducing stimulus than the blue portion. The middle green portion is generally ineffective. Also, the amount of flowering can be shown to vary in direct proportion to the total amount of light energy received by the leaves. For example, if two plants are illuminated for the same period but one receives light of greater in-tensity, then that plant is likely to flower faster or more extensively (Fig. 19.22).

Third, it has been found for short-day plants that the length of the *night* is just as important as the length of the day. If the dark periods are of less than a certain critical length, then flowering will not occur even if the light periods are of appropriate length. Moreover, if an appropriately long dark period is interrupted by even a single brief flash of light, then flowering will again be suppressed. The suppression is most pronounced if the light interruption takes place at or near the middle of the dark period. Evidently, short-day plants may justifiably be also called "long-night plants" (Fig. 19.23).

Fourth, aerial CO_2 is required to induce flowering.

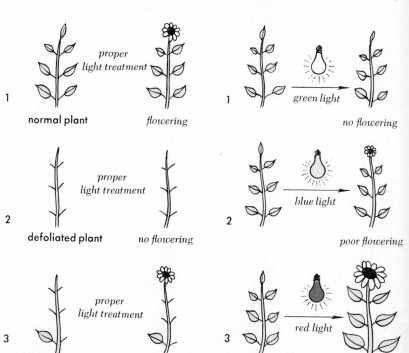

FIG. 19.22 *A,* experiments showing that leaves are the stimulus receptors in photoperiodic responses. *B,* experi-ments showing that red light produces the most pronounced photoperiodic re-sponses.

1   normal plant   proper light treatment   *flowering*

2   defoliated plant   proper light treatment   *no flowering*

3   plant with simple leaf   proper light treatment   *flowering*

A

1   *green light*   *no flowering*

2   *blue light*   *poor flowering*

3   *red light*   *best flowering*

B

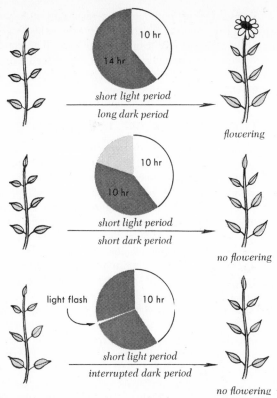

FIG. 19.23 Experiments illustrating the importance of night length and of the continuity of the dark period in photoperiodism in short-day plants.

The role of the gas here is apparently not nutritional, for even a plant with ample food supplies cannot be induced to flower if CO_2 is not present. It has been suggested that CO_2 may be necessary in leaves as a raw material in the manufacture of a special compound required for flower induction. Such a compound A may be synthesized from CO_2 during the light period. During the ensuing dark period, A may be converted into another necessary compound B. Therefore, if the dark period is too short or is made too short by a light interruption, there may not be enough time available for the production of sufficient amounts of B. Flowering will then not occur. Moreover, the more light energy the leaves receive the more A can be formed, hence also the more B.

Fifth, compounds A and B probably cannot be the only substances required for flower induction. A and B are produced in the leaves, but flowers are formed near the shoot tips. It becomes necessary, therefore, to

postulate the existence of a hormone C. This hormone must be manufactured in the leaves from compound B and must then migrate to a shoot tip where it initiates flowering (Fig. 19.24). The actual existence of such a flowering hormone, or **florigen,** can be demonstrated experimentally. In short-day cocklebur plants, for example, one individual may be grown under short photoperiods, which leads to flowering. Another individual may be kept under long photoperiods, which suppresses flowering. If then the two plants are grafted together and if their earlier photoperiods are maintained, it is found that the previously nonflowering plant now begins to flower too. Evidently, a diffusible florigen has moved from one plant into the other and has induced the latter to flower. Indeed, if a wet filter paper is interposed in the graft area between the two plants, the florigen still penetrates through this barrier (Fig. 19.25).

All attempts to isolate florigens (or the postulated compounds A and B) have so far been without success. But the flower-inducing mechanism suggested by the experiments does account for the difference between short-day and long-day plants. In short-day plants, long days would make the nights too short for adequate conversion of compound A into B. Florigen would then be formed in insufficient quantity and flowering could not occur. In long-day plants, short days would not provide adequate illumination for the formation of enough A, again leading to insufficient amounts of florigen and a suppression of flowering. Indeterminate plants would be able to form enough A, B, and florigen under any

FIG. 19.24 Hypothetical sequence of events leading to a photoperiodic response.

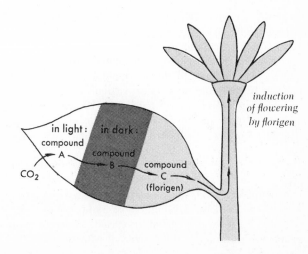

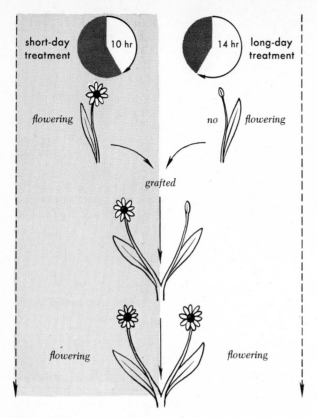

short-day treatment 10 hr

14 hr long-day treatment

flowering

no flowering

grafted

flowering

flowering

FIG. 19.25 Experiment showing that the flowering stimulus resulting from appropriate light treatment may pass from one plant to a grafted partner. Both graft partners are short-day plants. One (top left) has received proper short-day treatment; the other (top right) has received improper long-day treatment.

naturally occurring photoperiods. Evidently, the photoperiodic differences among plants appear to be quantitative rather than qualitative.

As might be expected, the global distribution of plants reflects their photoperiodic nature. Thus, the days in tropical and subtropical regions are fairly uniformly short (rarely more than 12 or 13 hr), and the plants in these regions are largely short-day species. The temperate zone supports both short-day and long-day plants. The former flower mainly during the short-day seasons of spring and autumn, the latter during the long-day season of summer. In higher latitudes beyond the temperate zone, most plants are long-day species adapted to the long days and short nights which characterize most of the growing season. Indeterminate plants are distributed widely over all climatic zones.

Knowledge of photoperiodic responses has been turned to horticultural advantage. By artificially lengthening or shortening day lengths under controlled conditions, given commercially important plants can be induced to flower at virtually any season of the year or may be inhibited from developing flowers.

THE EFFECTS OF TEMPERATURE

Among physical stimuli other than light, temperature is probably the most important. Different plants are adapted to live within different temperature ranges, a range of 70 to 90°F being optimal for most species of the temperate zone. Tropical plants are generally adjusted to higher temperature levels. They may thrive even at 100°F, but they are injured or killed if the temperature drops much below 60°F. By contrast, north-temperate and subarctic plants readily withstand temperatures below 0°F. As noted in Chap. 11, many plants have evolved special adaptations which permit them to cope with extremes in their usual temperature range.

The basic effects of temperature are metabolic; within limits, the rate of chemical processes increases in direct proportion with increasing temperature (see Chap. 2). But temperature also elicits other, developmental responses, and these probably are not due merely to quantitative changes in metabolic rates. The most striking developmental results of temperature treatment, or **vernalization,** again are flowering responses, like those produced by given photoperiods.

Whether or not flowering will occur in mature annual plants can be shown to depend on the temperatures to which the germinating seeds of these plants were exposed. Different species here exhibit different temperature requirements. For example, seeds of temperate-zone annuals like winter wheat must be exposed to low temperatures if flowering is to occur later in the mature plants. Such seeds are normally sown in the fall, and the ensuing winter provides the required low temperature. If the seeds are not vernalized in this manner, flowers will later not be formed. By contrast, seeds of tropical annuals such as rice must be vernalized at high temperatures (80°F or more) if later flowering is to take place (Fig. 19.26).

The receptor of the temperature stimulus in a seed is the embryo. The suggestion has been made that vernalization may permit manufacture of a special hormonal substance which persists as the plant matures and which eventually induces flowering. The name

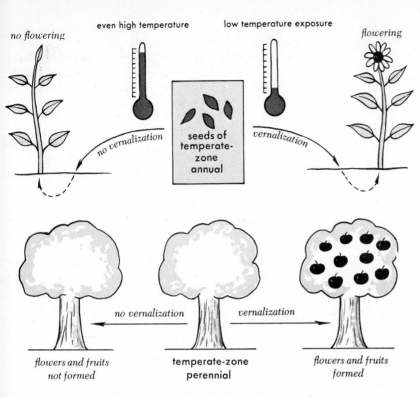

no flowering　　even high temperature　　low temperature exposure　　*flowering*

seeds of temperate-zone annual

no vernalization　　　　　*vernalization*

flowers and fruits not formed　　temperate-zone perennial　　*flowers and fruits formed*

no vernalization　　*vernalization*

FIG. 19.26　Vernalization. Top, vernalization at the seed stage. Bottom, vernalization at the adult stage.

vernalin has been proposed for this hormone, but attempts to extract it have so far not been successful. In any event, experiments show that a plant must be vernalized first before it will respond to photoperiodic stimuli. Conceivably, vernalin produced early in development may be a prerequisite for the later manufacture of florigen.

In nature, annual plants are normally vernalized in the seed stage, as just described. Biennial and perennial plants usually become vernalized at a later stage, during vegetative growth. Biennials such as celery, beets, and henbane grow vegetatively during a first season and the ensuing winter effects the vernalization. Flowering then occurs during the following season. The cycle may be speeded up by early vernalization in the laboratory. For example, if a young first-year henbane plant is cold-treated early during the year, it may be induced to flower during the same year. Perennials such as apples or peaches are normally vernalized in the mature vegetative condition by each successive winter. It follows that if apple or peach trees or temperate-zone perennials in general are grown in tropical or otherwise uniformly warm climates, then they will continue to develop vegetatively but will not

flower. Conversely, if tropical perennials are grown at very high latitudes, then they too will not become vernalized and will not flower.

Whenever vernalization occurs in mature plants, the receptors of the temperature stimulus are the apical buds. That this is so can be demonstrated by grafting experiments. For example, a vernalized apical bud of one plant may induce flower formation in a nonvernalized apical bud of another plant if the two are grafted together. The transmitted signal is apparently quite unspecific, for flower induction occurs even when the graft partners are of different species (Fig. 19.27).

Data such as the foregoing warrant the conclusion that the importance of flowering in the life of plants is fully matched by the complexity of its control. We already know that the process is governed by temperature, by light, and by hormones; and many other partly suspected and partly unsuspected stimuli undoubtedly play additional roles. All the external stimuli affect a plant simultaneously, and, eliciting varied internal responses, the ultimate outcome is the development or nondevelopment of a flower. In all probability, the adaptive value of such a multiplicity of control factors is that they save energy and materials; a flower is nor-

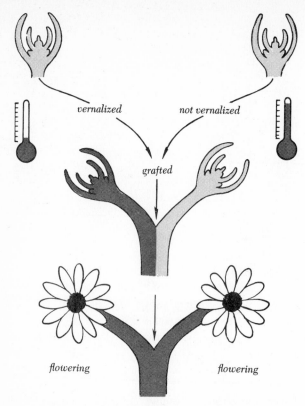

FIG. 19.27 Experiment showing that the flowering stimulus resulting from appropriate vernalization may pass from one plant to a grafted unvernalized partner.

mally formed only under the best possible environmental conditions, when the reproductive effort is most likely to succeed.

THE EFFECTS OF OTHER STIMULI

In addition to light and temperature, **mechanical** stimuli are among other physical factors which often affect plant development. For example, the pressure of rocks around roots makes root shape conform to the available space. Wind pressure from a constant angle makes stems and branches lean away from the wind. Contact with various inert objects makes plants twine around them or attach to them. In their own turn, plants resist pressure and generate growth pressure themselves, as when growing roots split rocks and crack pavement.

Numerous **chemical** stimuli in soil, water, and air also influence plant development. Some of them are more or less beneficial and, like the auxins applied by man, may act in the manner of growth stimulants. Others are variously toxic and poisonous, and they stunt growth or retard development and flowering. Soil decomposition products of given plants often tend to be toxic to later individuals of the same species. This may result in a gradual decline of vigor in successive generations. Crop rotation is beneficial partly for this reason. In heavily industrialized regions, noxious fumes in air and chemical wastes in water also have variously toxic effects on plants. The rapid disappearance of vegetation from such areas is probably due as much to these harmful chemical stimuli as to restrictions of space.

Reference to the main **biological** stimuli has already been made in the earlier account on symbiosis (Chap. 7). As noted in that context, mutualism, commensalism, and parasitism may affect plant growth and development in a beneficial, a neutral, or a harmful manner. One of the frequent developmental responses of plants to biological agents is overgrowth of given tissues, as in the case of bacteria-induced root nodules and crown galls.

Thus, by virtue of the built-in hierarchy of its control systems, a plant is eminently able to become "aware" of the multitude of stimuli continuously impinging on it and to respond to most of them in adequately self-preserving fashion. As a result, the whole plant and all its parts may be maintained in steady state. And as a further result, the plant may attain an actual life span which approaches that potentially inherent in it. The next chapters will show how equivalent control is achieved in animals.

REVIEW QUESTIONS

1. Define growth factor, growth regulator. Review the role of mineral substances in the activities of organisms. Cite specific examples. What are vitamins? How are they distinguished from (*a*) nutrients, (*b*) other classes of growth substances? What are hormones?

2. Describe the chemical nature of auxins and review the experiments which have led to their discovery. What is the effect of auxins on cells? Review in detail all the known effects of auxins on (*a*) growth, (*b*) development, and show how these substances con-

tribute to the control of steady-state maintenance in plants.

3. What are kinins? What are gibberellins? Discuss how gibberellins were discovered and describe their effects on plants and plant cells. What is the effect of kinins on plant cells? Distinguish all known categories of growth factors on the basis of either their chemical nature or their function.

4. Define the nature of different types of growth movements.

5. Describe various tropistic responses of plants and review once more the role of auxins in producing such responses. Show how differential auxin sensitivities are of importance.

6. Define the nature of different types of turgor movements. Review the mechanism of the opening and closing movements of guard cells. Describe the nature of the responses of sensitive plants to touch.

7. Review again the role of auxins in controlling developmental responses of plants. What is an abscission layer? How can fruit or leaf abscission be promoted or inhibited by artificial means? Review all nondevelopmental effects of light on plants.

8. Describe the developmental responses of plants to (a) light intensity, (b) light quality, (c) light duration. What is etiolation? What is a photoperiod? Define short-day, long-day, and indeterminate plants.

9. Describe experiments which demonstrate the existence of (a) florigen, (b) vernalin. Show how the photoperiodic characteristics of given plants are reflected in the global distribution of the plants. What factors play a role in the production of a photoperiodic response and what sort of hypothesis may account for the significance of these factors?

10. Describe the nondevelopmental and the developmental effects of temperature on plants. What is vernalization and what is its practical importance? Show how vernalization requirements differ for (a) annual and perennial plants, (b) temperate-zone and tropical plants. Review the effects of other physical and also of chemical and biological stimuli on plants.

SUGGESTED COLLATERAL READINGS

Classical original papers by famous biologists are reprinted and annotated in the sections on auxins, vitamins, and hormones in M. L. Gabriel and S. Fogel, "Great Experiments in Biology," Prentice-Hall, Englewood Cliffs, N.J., 1955. In addition to the plant physiology texts given at the conclusion of Chap. 13, the following additional articles are strongly recommended for further information on steady-state control in plants.

Audus, L. J.: Growth Substances and Plant Development, *Endeavour*, vol. 14, 1955.

Biale, J. B.: The Ripening of Fruit, *Sci. American*, vol. 190, 1954.

Braun, A. C.: Plant Cancer, *Sci. American*, vol. 186, 1952.

Greulach, V. A.: Plant Movements, *Sci. American*, vol. 192, 1955.

Jacobs, W. P.: What Makes Leaves Fall, *Sci. American*, vol. 193, 1955.

Koller, D.: Germination, *Sci. American*, vol. 200, 1959.

Kraus, E. J.: The Significance of Growth Regulators in Agricultural Practice, *Am. Scientist*, vol. 42, 1954.

Naylor, A. W.: The Control of Flowering, *Sci. American*, vol. 186, 1952.

Salisbury, F. B.: The Flowering Process, *Sci. American*, vol. 198, 1958.

———: Plant Growth Substances, *Sci. American*, vol. 196, 1957.

Schocken, V.: Plant Hormones, *Sci. American*, vol. 180, 1949.

Stowe, B. B., and T. Yamaki: Gibberellins: Stimulants of Plant Growth, *Science*, vol. 129, 1959.

Thimann, K. V.: The Physiology of Growth in Plant Tissues, *Am. Scientist*, vol. 42, 1954.

Van der Veen, R., and G. Meyer: "Light and Plant Growth," Macmillan, New York, 1959.

CONTROL IN ANIMALS: GROWTH FACTORS

20

As pointed out in Chap. 18, steady-state regulation in animals is achieved as in plants on cellular and intracellular levels, but, unlike plants, most animals in addition possess organs and organ systems which contribute importantly to control of the whole body.

Like plants, animals require growth factors, including growth regulators obtained from the external environment and hormones produced within the body. Mineral substances represent one group of growth regulators, and animals by and large require virtually the same kinds as plants—the fundamental reactions in which minerals play a role are basically the same in all organisms. Vitamins represent a second group of animal growth regulators, and these are again largely chemical as in plants. As noted, however, plants manufacture vitamins on their own, whereas animals must procure many of these compounds from the environment. Hormones are produced in most animals as in plants by cells which are not specialized for control functions particularly but perform other functions as well. In such cases, actually, animal hormone activities have been investigated very little as yet. Most attention has been focused on those hormones which are produced in the specialized endocrine systems present in some animals, vertebrates in particular.

Again as in plants, much of the existing knowledge about growth factors in animals has been obtained by the experimental production of excesses and deficiencies in test organisms. This chapter outlines some of this knowledge, specifically as it relates to animal **vitamins** and **hormones.**

VITAMINS

Most animal cell types do synthesize at least some vitamins, but animal cells generally do not manufacture enough or all necessary kinds. Insects, for example, may synthesize all except the B vitamins. A few rodents, apes, and man cannot manufacture their own vitamin C, but other animals can. Man happens to be a particularly poor vitamin synthesizer, being unable to produce sufficient quantities of any of these growth factors except vitamin D.

These differences between various animal species are undoubtedly a result of mutation and evolution. The earliest animals probably were able to produce all vitamins on their own, as plants still do today. In the course of time, random mutations must have blocked different vitamin-synthesizing reactions in different animals, leading to the present diversity in synthesizing ability. Animals with given genetically determined deficiencies survive nevertheless, for, as heterotrophs, they can obtain the missing vitamins as growth regulators from plants. Green plants with such genetic deficiencies could not survive. That mutations may indeed destroy vitamin-synthesizing capacity can be demonstrated experimentally.

More than 30 compounds are known to possess the properties of vitamins. That is, they are required in very small amounts and their prolonged absence from a cell impairs metabolic processes and produces unsteady or diseased states. In this connection, careful distinction should be made between the *biological* and the *clinical* effects of a deficiency. *All* cells of an animal require *all* vitamins; if a vitamin deficiency exists, some metabolic or self-perpetuative process in all cells will be impaired. This is a biological effect. For example, we already know that thiamine is a B vitamin required in all cells for the conversion of pyruvic acid to acetyl CoA. If thiamine is in deficient supply, respiratory reactions in all cells will be affected. Superimposed on such biological effects are clinical ones. That is, the cells of given tissues or organs may be more sensitive to a deficiency than other cells and such body parts will then exhibit symptoms of disease sooner or more pronouncedly than other body parts. For example, thiamine deficiency in man has long been known to lead to the clinical disease *beriberi*, characterized in severe cases by nervous and muscular paralysis. By themselves, clinical data alone would imply that thiamine is required specifically by nerve and muscle tissues. Actually, however, clinical results represent only the large-scale secondary consequences of the deeper biological effects of deficiency which influence all cells. Thus, clinical results can be a beginning of vitamin studies, but they must not be mistaken for the end.

When they were first investigated, vitamins were given letter designations. Later, virtually every vitamin so labeled was found to consist of not one but of several, often related substances. Letters with subscripts then came into use. Today, the tendency is to refer to a new vitamin by its chemical name only. Many vitamins therefore do not have a letter designation, and some have both letter and chemical labels (see Table 11).

Vitamins are partly fat-soluble and partly water-soluble. The first group includes vitamins A, D, E, and K; the latter, vitamins B and C. Water-soluble vitamins frequently pass into cooking water and into the water surrounding canned food. Such juices therefore should not be thrown away.

FAT-SOLUBLE GROUPS

Vitamin A Group

The several closely related substances so designated are derivatives of the *carotene* pigments synthesized by plants. As noted in Chap. 4, carotenes are present in the chloroplasts and chromoplasts of plant cells. Carotenes may therefore be found in leaves, and particularly rich sources are red-orange-yellow plant parts such as carrots, tomatoes, squash, sweet potatoes. Egg yolk, butter, and cream are among animal products rich in carotene. Spinach contains more carotene than an equal weight of egg yolk. In yellow foods, depth of color is an index of comparative carotene content.

Carotene becomes vitamin A by enzymatic hydrolysis; one molecule of carotene splits into two molecules of vitamin A in the presence of water:

$$\underset{carotene}{C_{40}H_{56}} + 2\ H_2O \longrightarrow \underset{vitamin\ A}{2\ C_{20}H_{30}O}$$

The vitamin is stored in the liver to a considerable extent. Fish livers and their oils are particularly rich sources of the finished vitamin. Fish obtain carotene through food chains originating with algae.

One specific cellular function of vitamin A is known; the compound plays an essential part in the chemistry of vision (see Chap. 22). Unavailability of the vitamin leads to night blindness. The following are among its other, less clearly understood functions: it controls proper growth of bones, of tooth enamel, and of nerve tissue; and it prevents drying and cracking of exposed, normally moist membranes, such as the membranes in the eyes, the breathing system, the alimentary tract, and the urogenital tract. Probably through this action, it reduces the incidence of infectious diseases. Indeed, vitamin A is sometimes called the "anti-infection vitamin," but such a designation might apply equally well to many another vitamin.

TABLE 11

The principal vitamins and their functions

name	food sources	chief cellular functions	effects of deficiency
vitamin A	leaves, yellow foods, liver	chemistry of vision; membrane integrity	night blindness; infectious diseases; bone, nerve abnormalities
thiamine (B_1)		cocarboxylase precursor	beriberi
riboflavin (B_2)		FMN and FAD precursor	hair loss; growth failure
nicotinic acid		DPN precursor	pellagra
pantothenic acid		coenzyme A precursor	
folic acid	grain products, yeast, beans, nuts, liver, eggs, meat	nucleic acid metabolism	anemia; growth failure; hemorrhages; bone disorders; nerve, skin disorders; infectious diseases
vitamin B_{12}			
biotin (H)		fat synthesis, CO_2 metabolism	
choline		fat and protein metabolism, amino group transfers	
pyridoxine (B_6)			
vitamin C	citrus fruits, tomatoes, cabbage	aerobic H transfer; synthesis of cell cement	scurvy
vitamin D	liver, fish oils	Ca and P regulation	rickets
vitamin E	most foods	aerobic H transfer	sterility; eye abnormalities; nerve, muscle disorders
vitamin K			failure of blood clotting

Vitamin D Group

Some ten related compounds are included in this group. Two of these, D_2 and D_3, are particularly potent. Chemically, the D vitamins are derivatives of sterols, compounds containing rings of carbon in a particular pattern (see Chap. 4). In man, precursors of the D vitamins are present in skin. As noted, these vitamins are the only ones that man can manufacture on his own in sufficient quantity. The precursors are converted into active vitamins by irradiation with ultraviolet light, hence the designation of the D vitamins as "sunshine vitamins." The active vitamins may be stored in the liver. Good external sources of D vitamins are fish-liver oils and dairy foods. In general, foods rich in vitamin A are also rich in vitamin D.

The specific mode of action of these growth factors is obscure, but their area of action is fairly well established. They regulate reactions involving calcium and phosphorus, particularly in the complex processes of bone formation and bone maintenance. In the cells of the gut, these vitamins probably balance calcium and phosphorus absorption against excretion of these elements into the gut cavity. The vitamins thus maintain an optimum supply of Ca and P within the body, and they subsequently regulate the deposition of these raw materials as bone and tooth substance.

Deficiency of the D vitamins leads to *rickets*.

Among the clinical symptoms of this disease are softening and bending of bones, beading of ribs, erosion of teeth, and elimination of calcium and phosphorus in large quantities. Conversely, continued overdoses of vitamin D may produce abnormal thickening of bones and some calcification of soft tissues.

The D vitamins so far appear to be uniquely animal growth factors; in plants, their functions, if any, are unknown as yet.

Vitamin E Group

Several very closely related compounds are in this category. The vitamins are relatively unstable, but they are so widely distributed in both plant and animal foods that a deficiency is not likely to arise on any normal diet. The chemical nature of the E vitamins is known.

These growth regulators are often called "antisterility vitamins"; deficiency can be shown to lead to permanent infertility in male rats and to death of embryos or to premature births in pregnant female rats. Experiments have indicated that vitamin E is required during human pregnancy at a particular stage of embryonic development, namely, at a time when eyes are formed. Vitamin-E-deficient embryos often exhibit a characteristic abnormality in eye development. Among other clinical results of vitamin E deficiency are injury to the nervous system and muscular atrophy.

The fundamental biological function of the E vitamins within cells has already been discussed; they participate in hydrogen-transfer reactions, for example, during aerobic respiration (Chaps. 13 and 16).

Vitamin K Group

A few related compounds of known structure are so classified. They occur widely in food and are synthesized by intestinal bacteria.

Clinically, the vitamins are known best for their role in blood clotting; i.e., deficiency leads to failure of the clotting mechanism (see Chap. 21). For this reason, vitamin K is often given before surgery, particularly surgery on bile ducts blocked by gallstones. Since vitamin K is dissolved in the fatty portions of food, bile is required for its proper absorption from the gut cavity. Therefore, if the bile duct is blocked, an individual is likely to be vitamin-K deficient and his blood-clotting mechanism will be impaired as a result. Ingestion of the vitamin (along with bile salts) before an operation may forestall severe surgical hemorrhage.

The cellular biological function of K vitamins corresponds to that of vitamin E; for example, K vitamins participate in hydrogen-transfer reactions.

WATER-SOLUBLE GROUPS

Vitamin B Group

Included here are **thiamine** (B_1), **riboflavin** (B_2), **nicotinic acid** ("niacin"), **pyridoxine** (B_6), **biotin** (H), **vitamin B_{12}, pantothenic acid, folic acid,** and **choline.** These vitamins are not particularly related in chemical structure or in biological function. They are grouped together largely because they tend to occur together in plant and animal foods. Most of these vitamins have been identified chemically, and many can be synthesized in the laboratory. The B vitamins are present in natural foods of all types, particularly rich sources being whole-grain products, yeast, peas, beans, and nuts among plant foods, and liver, egg yolks, and meat among animal foods. Intestinal bacteria synthesize many of the B vitamins.

Several B vitamins function in cells as precursors of coenzymes or other participants in respiratory reactions. We have found this to be the case, for example, for thiamine, riboflavin, nicotinic acid, and pantothenic acid (see Chap. 16). The metabolic roles of pyridoxine and choline are understood in general terms. Pyridoxine contributes to the formation of an enzyme required in amino acid metabolism, and choline is a source of a particular group of atoms ($-CH_3$, the "methyl" group) in chemical transformations. Biotin is required in fat metabolism and in the formation and utilization of carbon dioxide. Folic acid and vitamin B_{12} participate in the metabolism of nucleotides.

A more or less well-defined clinical disease is associated with lack of each of the B vitamins. Mild thiamine deficiency, for example, produces fatigue, weakness, and lassitude. More severe thiamine starvation over a period of weeks may result in beriberi, as noted. Riboflavin deficiency leads to loss of hair, growth failure, and eye disorders (Fig. 20.1); niacin deficiency, to *pellagra*, a disease of the skin and the nervous system; vitamin B_{12} and folic acid deficiencies, to anemia; choline deficiency, to bone deformities (in chickens) and internal hemorrhages; and pyridoxine and pantothenic acid deficiencies, to growth failure, anemia, lowered resistance to infections, and nerve and skin disorders. In all these cases, administration of the appropriate vitamin usually relieves the disease.

FIG. 20.1 Some effects of riboflavin deficiency. Top, riboflavin-deficient rat. Pronounced loss of hair, sickly appearance. Weight 63 g. Bottom, same rat as above, 6 weeks later, after riboflavin-rich diet. Recovery complete. Weight 169 g. *(Bureau of Human Nutrition and Home Economics.)*

Vitamin C

This compound is **ascorbic acid,** chemically related to monosaccharide sugars. It is widely synthesized in plants, particularly rich sources being citrus fruit, cabbage, and tomatoes. Most animals—but not man—manufacture it, as has been noted. Ascorbic acid is one of the least stable vitamins. Cooking destroys it, and in fresh and canned foods much of the vitamin diffuses out into the food juices.

That vitamin C participates in aerobic hydrogen transfer is known, but it is not yet known which specific reaction the vitamin affects. Like other vitamins which participate in respiratory reactions, ascorbic acid is generally found in the mitochondria of cells. Vitamin C additionally controls a phase of synthesis metabolism, and its absence here leads to the best-known deficiency symptoms. The vitamin apparently regulates the manufacture of the cement which binds cells together. When this function is impaired, *scurvy* results. Blood vessels begin to "leak" unduly and hemorrhages may occur in any part of the body. Connective tissues no longer bind efficiently, and teeth, for example, loosen from their sockets. In more advanced stages, bones may weaken, muscles degenerate, and death ultimately supervenes. Mild deficiencies of vitamin C may not lead to an outright scorbutic condition, but they may nevertheless impair energy metabolism sufficiently to produce lassitude and to cause fleeting rheumatismlike pains in limb joints.

The names, food sources, and cellular functions of vitamins, as well as the clinical effects of deficiency, are summarized in Table 11.

HORMONES

Two animal groups are known to possess specialized endocrine glands, the insects and the vertebrates. The hormones manufactured and secreted by these glands vary greatly in chemical composition. Some are proteins, a few are amino acids, others are sterols, and the rest are various other simple or complex kinds of compounds. A few can be synthesized in the laboratory, a few have known chemical structure, and the remainder are known only through the effects of hormone deficiency (e.g., undersecretion, excision of the secreting cells) and of hormone excess (e.g., oversecretion, injection of hormone).

Like the auxins of plants, insect hormones are essentially growth promoters. They play particularly important roles during insect development. Produced in special glands located in the brain and the thorax, insect hormones control the development of larvae, the transformation of larvae into pupae, and the final transformation of either larvae or pupae into adults. Beyond these very basic developmental functions, little is known about the cellular, metabolic roles of the hormones. By contrast, the cellular functions of vertebrate hormones may be circumscribed rather well, although the precise reactions in which the hormones participate cannot yet be pinpointed as well as for many vitamins. For example, there is no doubt that the thyroid hormone promotes respiration, but what specific reaction or reactions are affected is still obscure. The account below will be limited to a discussion of vertebrate hormones (Fig. 20.2).

Just as cells probably require all vitamins, so also do all cells probably require all hormones. The term "sex hormone," for example, is somewhat misleading. True, sex hormones are manufactured in sex organs and the hormones contribute to the proper functioning of these organs. As we now know, however, sex hormones also contribute to the functioning of virtually every other organ in the body. It happens that the effect of deficiency or excess of a given hormone may reveal itself first or most obviously in a particular body part. For convenience we may then name the hormone according to this body part, but we cannot conclude that the hormone functions only there.

Apart from their other controlling roles in cells, many hormones perform an additional special function: they control the manufacture and secretion of one another. For example, many endocrine glands cannot secrete their hormones unless they are stimulated to do so by other hormones, secreted in other endocrine glands. As a group, such glands in effect function like a board of directors, in which the members hold one another in close mutual check. The output of each gland is controlled wholly or partially by the output of one or more other glands. As a result, the overall output by all glands is carefully balanced. This is essential, for whereas one hormone may accelerate a given cellular process, another hormone may inhibit the same process. Therefore, unless the amounts of hormones are continuously readjusted relative to one another and relative to the requirements of the moment, flexible control over cellular processes would not be possible.

PITUITARY HORMONES

Situated approximately in the center of the head, the pituitary gland is made up of three parts: the *anterior lobe,* the *intermediate lobe,* and the *posterior lobe* (Fig. 20.3). Each of these is a complete, functionally distinct endocrine gland secreting its own hormones. A short stalk of tissue from the posterior lobe attaches the whole gland to the underside of the brain.

The Anterior Lobe

This part of the pituitary exercises control over several other endocrine glands; the anterior lobe secretes a set of **tropic hormones** required specifically to activate other endocrine organs. For example, the rate of manufacture of thyroid hormone depends on the supply of *thyrotropic hormone (TTH)* from the pituitary. Analogously, production of sex hormones in the gonads (testes and ovaries) is controlled by *gonadotropic hormones (GTH)*. Another tropic pituitary hormone is *adrenocorticotropic hormone (ACTH)*, which controls the hormone output of the outer cortex layers of the adrenal glands.

In exercising such tropic effects, the anterior lobe does not act autonomously but is itself governed by the very glands it stimulates. This is a good illustration of the mutual checking process referred to above which balances the output of various endocrine glands. For example, as more and more TTH is secreted by the anterior lobe, more and more thyroid hormone will be released by the thyroid gland. But once the concentra-

tion of thyroid hormone has reached a certain level in the blood, that hormone has an *inhibitive* effect on the anterior lobe. It stops or reduces further secretion of TTH. But by this very action, further production of thyroid hormone is reduced or stopped and the concentration of thyroid hormone consequently does not rise further. Conversely, if the blood concentration of thyroid hormone is low, the anterior lobe will be inhibited rather weakly and correspondingly much TTH will be secreted. The thyroid gland will therefore be stimulated strongly and more thyroid hormone will be produced. We note that the two glands and their two hormones form an automatic, organ-level control system with built-in feedback. Sex hormones and adrenocortical hormones control their own secretion rates analogously (Fig. 20.4).

In addition to producing the tropic hormones, the anterior lobe also manufactures other hormones (Fig. 20.5). These do not have any demonstrable function as endocrine stimulators but act primarily as metabolic regulators. In this category are the **lactogenic hor-**

FIG. 20.2 The endocrine system.

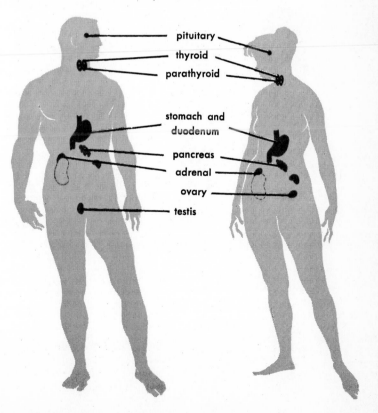

pituitary

thyroid

parathyroid

stomach and duodenum

pancreas

adrenal

ovary

testis

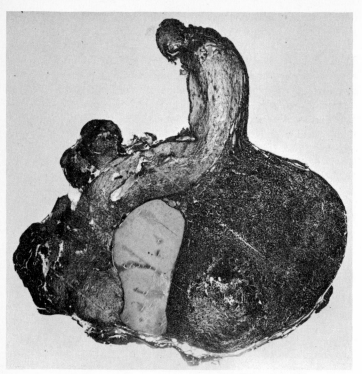

FIG. 20.3   Longitudinal section through a human pituitary gland. The right side of the photo points in the direction of the face; the left side, in the direction of the back of the head. Note the anterior lobe in the right part of the gland and the intermediate and posterior lobes in the left part. The posterior lobe continues dorsally as a stalk which joins the whole gland to the brain. *(Courtesy of Dr. B. J. Serber, College of Medicine, New York University.)*

mones, which participate in the control of milk production in mammals. Injection of these hormones stimulates mammary secretions, and hormone deficiency reduces them. Note, however, that removal of milk by suckling young is at least as essential for continued lactation as the presence of the hormones. Either hormone deficiency or milk accumulation may alone lead to cessation of milk flow.

Another anterior-lobe secretion is a **growth hormone.** In the young, this hormone maintains growth rates of cells generally. *Gigantism* and *dwarfism* are the results of hormone excess and deficiency, respectively. Most circus giants and dwarfs are of this "pituitary" type; i.e, their growth has been accelerated or retarded abnormally during early youth, sometimes as a result

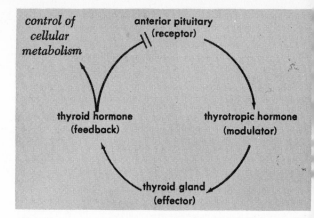

FIG. 20.4   The action of certain pituitary hormones and their feedback control. Pituitary-thyroid interaction is shown as an example. Pointed arrows symbolize stimulation, and the arrow tipped with a transverse double bar symbolizes inhibition. Through this control cycle, the output of thyrotropic hormone is automatically self-adjusting.

of pituitary tumors. When the growth hormone reaches excessive concentrations in the adult, tissues which still can grow are stimulated to do so. Characteristic overgrowths are then produced, particularly in parts of the skeleton. The coarse-featured condition known as *acromegaly* is a result.

FIG. 20.5   Summary of the secretions of the anterior lobe of the pituitary. Arrows tipped with transverse double bars symbolize known inhibitory feedbacks by which the secretion rate of pituitary tropic hormones is adjusted.

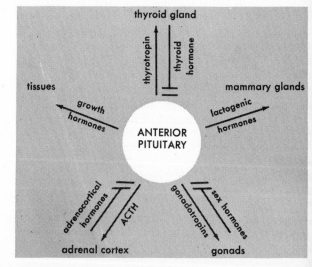

The anterior lobe exerts very definite, demonstrable effects on carbohydrate, protein, and fat metabolism in cells. Some of these effects are direct, produced by specific pituitary hormones such as the growth hormone. Others are indirect, produced via tropic hormones and stimulation of other endocrines. We shall refer to some of these relationships below.

All the hormones of the anterior lobe are proteins. Active but crude pituitary extracts have long been used in research and medicine, and purified, crystalline hormones are now also available. Most vertebrates manufacture very similar hormone proteins, and those of one species are effective when injected into another. Whenever they must be administered for medical reasons, protein hormones cannot be taken by mouth, since such compounds would be digested in the intestine. Cattle, sheep, and pigs are the sources of most commercial hormone preparations, those of the anterior lobe included.

The Intermediate and Posterior Lobes

The intermediate part of the pituitary gland secretes **intermedin,** a hormone functioning most conspicuously in vertebrates which possess adjustable skin pigmentation. In a frog, for example, the hormone brings about an expansion of pigment cells and consequent dispersal of their pigment granules. This lightens skin color. Intermediate-lobe extracts from any mammal exert the same effect when injected into a frog. Mammals evidently possess intermedin, but, in the absence of adjustable pigment cells, the hormone is probably without function. This example illustrates that a control agent can be inherited from early ancestors even though the target of control is not inherited.

The posterior lobe secretes several hormones having distinct functions. Some regulate the excretion of water, a function which adrenal hormones also perform (see below). Water balance in the body is therefore controlled by at least two different groups of hormones, and the two are integrated in their actions. Other hormones of the posterior lobe stimulate the contraction of smooth muscles, particularly those in the blood vessels and in the uterus. Through its effect on blood vessels and on water balance, the posterior lobe influences blood pressure decisively. The effect on the smooth muscles of the uterus may play a particular role during the process of childbirth, when strong labor contractions expel the offspring from the womb. Posterior-lobe hormones are sometimes used by obstetricians to facilitate births.

THYROID HORMONES

The thyroid gland lies along the trachea, just underneath the larynx. Secreting cells are arranged into single-layered hollow spheres, which are held together by connective tissue (Fig. 20.6). The space within the spheres is a storage depot for thyroid secretion.

This secretion, called **thyroglobulin,** consists of globulin, a protein which probably serves as a carrier, and of **thyroxin,** the functionally active hormone. Thyroxin ($C_{15}H_{11}O_4I_4N$) is one of the naturally occurring amino acids. Its potency as a hormone is in some way associated with its four iodine atoms. If two of them are removed or substituted by other atoms, potency is sharply reduced. If all four iodine atoms are removed, potency disappears altogether. Being an amino acid, thyroxin is not digested in the gut, and it can therefore be taken by mouth.

FIG. 20.6 Section through a thyroid gland. The round spaces filled in part with dark material are the regions where thyroid hormone accumulates before being transported away by blood. (Ward's Natural Science Establishment, Inc.)

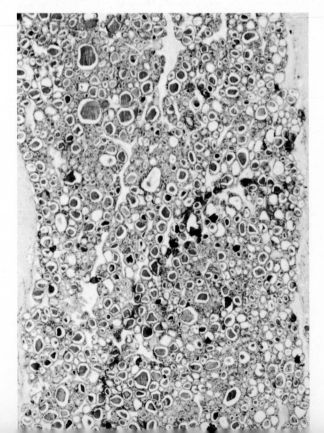

As already noted on several occasions, the cellular function of thyroxin (or of thyroglobulin) is known in general terms: the hormone accelerates respiration. But what particular reaction or reactions are affected is not established as yet.

The clinical effects of thyroxin probably are secondary consequences of its respiratory role. When the iodine content of the diet is low or when the cells of the thyroid gland are defective, a thyroxin deficiency is likely to develop. If this occurs during early youth, *cretinism* may be the result. In this disease, growth is stunted even though the pituitary growth hormone may be secreted normally; mental development is retarded severely; sexual development is delayed or does not take place at all; and body weight increases, since little food is burned in cells but much is stored as fat. In the adult, thyroxin deficiency leads to *myxedema*. This condition is characterized by reduction of mental and bodily vigor, loss of sex drive, loss of hair, and abnormal thickening of the skin, as if much water had accumulated in it (i.e., "edema").

Thyroxin deficiency may be accompanied by thyroid enlargement, or *goiter*. Here the number of thyroid cells increases and more hormone may then be secreted by the enlarged gland. This may or may not suffice to compensate for an original hormone deficiency. If it does, body functions will be normal but a *simple goiter* will be in evidence. If the deficiency is not compensated for, then cretinism in the young and myxedema in the adult may develop in spite of and in addition to the goiter. Goiter, cretinism, and myxedema may all be relieved by the administration of adequate amounts of thyroxin from an external source.

The thyroid gland may enlarge also when hormone production is originally normal. This may happen, for example, through a tumor. Goiter of this type does not compensate for deficiency. On the contrary, it leads to the manufacture of excess hormone over and above normal requirements. As might be expected, the effects of thyroxin excess are virtually the reverse of those of deficiency. Greatly accelerated cellular respiration liberates so much heat that the affected individual feels hot all the time. Despite voluminous consumption of food, so much is burned that body weight may decrease. Whereas the myxedemic individual is sluggish, the hyperthyroid individual is under constant nervous tension, is highly irritable by stimuli, yet is unable to perform sustained work because of lack of fuel reserves.

Apart from carrying out metabolic functions, the thyroid hormone also controls developmental processes, at least in amphibia. In these vertebrates the hormone is specifically required in metamorphosis, the transformation of the tadpole into the adult. If thyroid function in an embryo or a young tadpole is in some way inhibited (e.g., by excising the thyroid gland), then the animal remains a tadpole permanently. Conversely, if a young tadpole is given an excess of thyroxin, then the larva metamorphoses prematurely into a tiny froglet. Metamorphosis takes place normally when the thyroid gland has developed to maturity and produces appropriate amounts of hormone. Under the influence of the hormone, different larval tissues rapidly undergo different kinds of developmental changes and a tadpole so becomes an adult. The developmental role of the thyroid hormone here resembles the role of the insect hormones.

PARATHYROID HORMONES

The parathyroid glands are tiny paired organs either located near but outside the thyroids (e.g., rabbit) or embedded within the thyroids (e.g., dog, man; Fig. 20.7). Removal of the thyroids in dogs and rabbits therefore produces partly different results. This has been the clue which has led to the discovery of the parathyroids.

The hormone of these glands is called **parathormone**, and it is a protein. The basic function of para-

FIG. 20.7 Diagram of the structural relation of the thyroid and parathyroid glands in man. Parathyroid tissue is shown embedded within thyroid tissue.

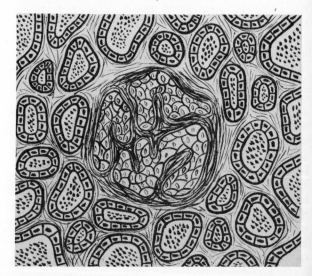

thormone is control of calcium metabolism in cells and, as a corollary, maintenance of a constant calcium level in the blood. If the hormone is in abnormally low supply, even if vitamin D is amply available, blood calcium may be deposited in abnormally large quantities in bones. This leads to a lowering of blood calcium concentrations, to a thickening of bones, and to calcification of joints. Low blood calcium has another drastic effect. Lack of these ions makes muscles and nerves hyperirritable; the slightest stimulus may throw the whole body into convulsive twitching. Such attacks are completely exhausting and lead to death very quickly.

Symptoms are reversed when parathormone is present in excess. Calcium is then withdrawn from bones and the skeleton weakens. Blood calcium rises and the ions may be excreted in abnormally large quantities. Moreover, nerves and muscles become hypoirritable and an individual becomes unresponsive to stimuli.

ADRENAL HORMONES

As their name indicates, "adrenal" organs are situated "at the kidneys." In man, one organ lies directly on top of each kidney. An adrenal organ consists of two structurally distinct parts, namely, an outer *cortex* and an inner *medulla*. Each part is a separate endocrine gland and produces its own distinct hormones (Fig. 20.8).

The Adrenal Cortex

More than 100 different compounds are known to be produced by this structure. All these cortical hormones are closely related sterol compounds. One of the best known is **cortisone.** Secretion of cortical hormones is under the control of ACTH from the pituitary, as noted above.

Insufficiency of the cortical hormones results in *Addison's disease.* Its most conspicuous symptoms include a characteristic bronzing of the skin, muscular weakness, low blood pressure, and digestive disturbances. These abnormalities have been traced to a wide range of upsets in metabolic processes within cells, involving most particularly water, inorganic ions, and carbohydrates.

Kidney cells appear to be particularly sensitive to the cortical hormones, and one of the primary actions of these compounds is control of kidney function. For example, the cortical hormones regulate the water balance of the body, a function carried out jointly with hormones from the posterior lobe of the pituitary, as

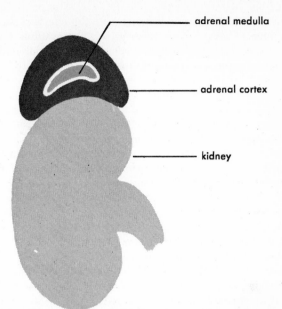

FIG. 20.8 Diagram indicating the position and general internal structure of the adrenal gland.

noted. Cortical hormones also promote the retention of sodium and chloride ions and the excretion of potassium ions. Hormonal insufficiency therefore leads to a lowering of sodium and chloride and to a rise of potassium in the blood. Moreover, the cortical hormones regulate the excretion of metabolic wastes such as urea. Hormone deficiency may therefore lead to an accumulation of urea and other wastes in the blood.

Another primary action of cortical hormones is control of carbohydrate metabolism. For example, the hormones promote the conversion of glycogen into glucose. As noted earlier, insulin directly and thyroxin indirectly have a contrary effect. Evidently, blood-glucose levels and carbohydrate metabolism generally are held in steady state by sets of antagonistic hormones. Inasmuch as the pituitary controls the adrenal cortex via ACTH and the thyroid gland via TTH, the pituitary has an important effect on carbohydrate metabolism.

The adrenal cortex, in addition, influences the sex organs and is in turn influenced by them. Like the cortical hormones, the sex hormones are sterols. Indeed, the chemical differences between the two groups are slight. As a result, abnormal hormone production in the adrenal cortex often amounts to abnormal production of sex hormones and vice versa. Even under normal conditions the adrenal cortex actually produces compounds which more or less duplicate the effects of sex hormones. Long before puberty, i.e., before adult sex hormones are produced, a male is already different from a female, not only in the nature of the sex organs as such but also in characteristics associated with sex generally. Such differences are produced and maintained by adrenal hormones. After puberty, sex hormones secreted by the gonads intensify the sexual differences and the production of adrenal sex hormones declines. Adrenal tumors sometimes lead to a resumption of cortical sex-hormone production, with abnormal intensification of sexual characteristics.

The cortical hormones have still other effects, e.g., on membranes in joints, eyes, and skin and on other body parts. Most of these effects are consequences of cortical control over water, ion, and carbohydrate metabolism and of the influence of the adrenal cortex on other endocrine organs. By virtue of these widely divergent functions, the adrenal cortex constitutes one of the most crucial regulators in the body.

The Adrenal Medulla

The hormone produced by this gland is **adrenalin,** a relatively simple compound which can be synthesized in the laboratory. The adrenal medulla is largely under control of the nervous system. Indeed, the connection between this gland and the nervous system goes even deeper. The gland develops from the same embryonic tissue from which the nervous system develops; and certain nerves regulate cellular functions by releasing adrenalin (see Chap. 22).

When injected into the body or released normally by the adrenal medulla, adrenalin raises blood pressure; increases heart rate; promotes conversion of liver glycogen to blood glucose; inhibits the peristaltic movements of the gut; stimulates the tiny muscles which attach to hairs and feathers, appendages which are raised as a consequence (producing "goose flesh" in man); dilates the pupils of the eye; increases muscular power and resistance to fatigue; promotes faster coagulation of blood; and generally promotes faster and sharper responses to external stimuli.

Together, most or all of these effects are sometimes called the *alarm reaction.* It comes into play during danger or emergency, when an animal is under great emotional or physical stress, as, for example, in doing battle with an adversary. In such situations, adrenalin is released in increased quantity from the adrenal medulla and the hormone then spurs the animal to increased effort. If the action of adrenalin is some-how inhibited, a vertebrate cannot adjust rapidly to emergencies.

SEX HORMONES

As already noted, these are produced in matured ovaries and testes under the stimulus of pituitary gonadotropic hormones. Several male and several female sex hormones are manufactured and, just as in the adrenal cortex, all are sterols. We may refer to male hormones collectively as **androgens,** i.e., "male-producing," and to female hormones as **estrogens,** i.e., "estrus- (menstrual cycle) producing." The most potent androgen is **testosterone;** the most potent estrogen, **estradiol.** The secretion patterns and the specialized functions of sex hormones will be discussed in Chap. 26. Here we may examine the general role of these compounds.

First, the hormones maintain the *primary sex characteristics,* i.e., the structural and functional integrity of the male and female reproductive systems. Second, the hormones maintain *secondary sex characteristics,* i.e., all the features other than sex organs which differentiate male from female. Such secondary male-female differences include different patterns of growth and distribution of hair; voice differences; differences in physical strength, endurance, and muscular development; skeletal differences, as in the hip region; differences in the amount of fat under the skin; marked differences in the degree of mammary development; and differences in skin coloration and plumage among fish, birds, and other vertebrates (Fig. 20.9). In addition, sex hormones maintain sex urge, decisively influence mental vigor and mental development, and stimulate blood circulation. Evidently, they affect the body as a whole.

All these effects are reduced or abolished and the reproductive system atrophies if sex hormones are in deficient supply, e.g., as a result of pituitary insufficiency or direct castration. Injection of androgens into males and of estrogens into females intensifies the sexual characteristics of the animal. Conversely, continued injection of androgens into females and of estrogens into males tends to reverse sexual characteristics in the direction of the opposite sex. In a few vertebrates, a functional male can be converted in this manner into a functional female. Sperm-producing testes then become egg-producing ovaries and other parts of the reproductive system change correspondingly, and vice versa. But in most vertebrates, man included, injection of the opposite hormone merely

FIG. 20.9 Secondary sex characteristics of vertebrates and their differences in males and females. Left, bobwhites. Male at left, female at right. Note differences in color pattern of plumage. Right, pintail ducks. Drake at left, hen at right. Note differences of body size and of plumage pattern. See also Fig. 6.6 for another example. All such sex differences are controlled and maintained by hormones, and they are instances of polymorphism, more specifically, of sexual dimorphism. *(Left and right, courtesy of E. P. Haddon, R. G. Schmidt, U.S. Fish and Wildlife Service.)*

deemphasizes the original sexual traits. For example, an estrogen-injected human male would acquire a more highly pitched voice, would accumulate increased quantities of subcutaneous fat, would develop broader hips, and would perhaps change toward other secondary sexual traits characteristic of females. Yet the sex organs would remain testes, though they would atrophy and become nonfunctional. In many ways, the results here duplicate those of castration.

Both sexes normally produce *both* androgens and estrogens. The compounds are only slightly different chemically, and both are probably manufactured in testes as well as in ovaries. In an extreme case, mares actually secrete very much more androgen than estrogen, yet the horses are females. These observations illustrate the general principle that it is the relative quantitative ratio of hormones, not their absolute amount, which is of importance. Thus, so long as a definite ratio of male and female hormones is present, regardless of which is more abundant in absolute terms, the cells of a female will respond differentially to female hormone, the cells of a male, to male hormone. When this quantitative balance is upset, cellular processes will swing more toward maleness or toward femaleness. Normal sex-hormone balances actually differ slightly for different individuals, and this probably accounts for the various degrees of masculinity and femininity widely in evidence.

OTHER HORMONES

Various other endocrine secretions have been discussed in earlier contexts. For example, the roles of the hormones **gastrin** and **secretin** have been described in the account on digestion (Chap. 14).

We have also dealt with **insulin,** the protein hormone manufactured in the pancreas in groups of endocrine cells embedded within the exocrine tissue which produces pancreatic juice (Fig. 20.10). Unlike pancreatic juice, insulin does not have access to the pancreatic duct; blood is its only exit path. As noted in Chap. 14, the result of insulin deficiency is *diabetes,* a condition in which utilization of blood glucose is impaired. Insulin excess, on the other hand, produces so much liver and muscle glycogen at the expense of glucose that blood-glucose levels fall abnormally.

The kidneys produce a hormone called **renin,** which regulates blood pressure. Two other organs at one time were thought to have endocrine functions: the *pineal* body and the *thymus* body. The pineal is situated on a stalk between the two halves of the brain. In some vertebrates, for example, lampreys and tuataras

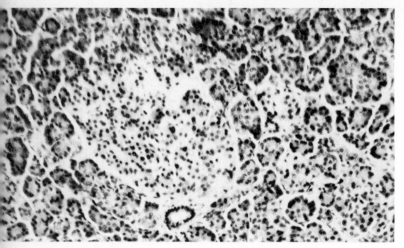

FIG. 20.10 Section through the pancreas. The round, lighter-colored tissue area, somewhat off center in the photo, is an insulin-secreting islet of Langerhans. (Courtesy of Dr. B. J. Serber, College of Medicine, New York University.)

(see Chap. 11), the pineal is quite large. Here it is located directly under the dorsal skin of the head, and the skin at that point is transparent. In these animals the pineal is actually a third functional eye situated on top of the head. In most vertebrates, optic functions of the pineal are not in evidence and the organ is small. Removal of this body has no demonstrable effect whatsoever. An endocrine function may therefore be ruled out.

The thymus body lies in the neck and the upper chest regions. In many mammals it persists throughout life, but in man and some other mammals the organ gradually decreases in size during youth and disappears altogether at the time of puberty. Removal of the organ at any stage of life does not produce any obvious effects. As in the case of the pineal, therefore, an endocrine function of the thymus is unlikely. And what other role the organ might have is also not clearly established.

The functions of the principal hormones are summarized in Table 12.

Many of the vertebrate hormones discussed in this chapter are known to occur also in animals which do not possess endocrine systems and indeed in plants as well. In such organisms, however, the compounds do not always *function* as specific hormones (just as auxins do not function as hormones in the many animals in which such compounds are present). Wide occurrence of certain chemicals indicates that they are fairly usual products of metabolism, and we may infer that, during the evolution of given organisms, many of such already existing chemicals happened to prove useful as control agents in newly evolved processes. In plants and most animals, chemicals which became control agents in this manner continued to be manufactured by cells performing various other functions as well. But in insects and vertebrates, manufacture came to be the specialized function of elaborate endocrine glands. It happens that, to date, only the hormone chemicals produced in plants and in endocrine glands have been studied to any extent.

As noted earlier, steady-state regulation in most animals is achieved not only by cellular growth factors such as hormones and vitamins, but also by various tissue- and organ-level control systems which do not have counterparts in plants. We shall deal with these uniquely animal controls in the next chapters.

REVIEW QUESTIONS

1. Review the chemical nature and the cellular functions of all vitamins, as far as known. How do autotrophs and heterotrophs differ in their vitamin requirements? How, and why, do different heterotrophs differ in their vitamin requirements?

2. Distinguish between clinical and biological effects of vitamin or hormone deficiencies. Which vitamins are fat-soluble and which are water-soluble?

3. Review the food sources and the chemical nature of the principal vitamins. What are the clinical effects of deficiencies of these vitamins?

4. How do given endocrine glands control the activity of other endocrine glands? Show how the activity of the adrenal cortex is regulated by the pituitary, and vice versa.

5. Review the general chemical nature of the principal hormones. What determines whether a medicinal hormone preparation must be injected or may be taken orally?

6. What are the specific hormones produced by the various endocrine glands? As far as is known, what are the primary cellular functions of each of these hor-

TABLE 12
The principal vertebrate endocrine glands and their hormones

gland	hormones	chief functions	effects of deficiency or excess
pituitary, anterior lobe	TTH GTH ACTH lactogenic growth	stimulates thyroid stimulates gonads stimulates adrenal cortex stimulates milk secretion promotes cell metabolism	dwarfism; gigantism; acromegaly
pituitary, mid-lobe	intermedin	controls adjustable skin-pigment cells (e.g., frogs)	
pituitary, posterior lobe	at least five distinct fractions	controls water metabolism, blood pressure, kidney function, smooth-muscle action	increased or reduced water excretion
thyroid	thyroxin	stimulates respiration; inhibits TTH secretion	goiter; cretinism; myxedema
parathyroid	parathormone	controls Ca metabolism	nerve, muscle abnormalities; bone thickening or weakening
adrenal cortex	cortisone, other sterol hormones	controls metabolism of water, minerals, carbohydrates; controls kidney function; inhibits ACTH secretion; duplicates sex-hormone functions	Addison's disease
adrenal medulla	adrenalin	alarm reaction, e.g., raises blood pressure, heart rate	inability to cope with stress
pancreas	insulin	glucose → glycogen	diabetes
testis	testosterone, other androgens	} promote cell respiration, blood circulation; maintain primary and secondary sex characteristics, sex urge; inhibit GTH secretions	atrophy of reproductive system; decline of secondary sex characteristics
ovary	estradiol, other estrogens		

mones? In each case, what are the clinical effects of (a) hormone deficiency and (b) hormone excess?

7. Inasmuch as both sexes produce both male and female sex hormones, how can the sexes remain distinct? What is the effect of injecting male hormone into a female, and vice versa? Distinguish between primary and secondary sex characteristics. What specific features are grouped into the latter category?

8. By three specific examples involving vitamins and hormones, illustrate the high degree of redundancy of control processes within cells. In what respect are hormones both cell-level and tissue- and organ-level controllers?

SUGGESTED COLLATERAL READINGS

Classical original papers by famous biologists are reprinted and annotated in the sections on vitamins and hormones in M. L. Gabriel and S. Fogel, "Great Experiments in Biology," Prentice-Hall, Englewood Cliffs, N.J., 1955. The following additional articles are recommended for further information on hormones:

Beach, F. A.: "Hormones and Behavior," Hoeber, New York, 1947.

Constantinides, P. C., and N. Carey: The Alarm Reaction, *Sci. American*, vol. 180, 1949.

Funkenstern, D. H.: The Physiology of Fear and Anger, *Sci. American*, vol. 192, 1955.

Heilbrunn, L. V.: Calcium and Life, *Sci. American*, vol. 184, 1951.

Levine, R., and M. S. Goldstein: The Action of Insulin, *Sci. American*, vol. 198, 1958.

Li, C. H.: The Pituitary, *Sci. American*, vol. 183, 1950.

Milne, L. J., and M. J. Milne: How Animals Change Color, *Sci. American*, vol. 186, 1952.

Williams, C. B.: The Metamorphosis of Insects, *Sci. American*, vol. 182, 1950.

Zuckerman, S.: Hormones, *Sci. American*, vol. 196, 1957.

CONTROL IN ANIMALS: THE BODY FLUIDS

21

Cells are in steady state relative to their environments. Within an animal, this environment consists of other cells and, in most instances, of body fluids, namely, **blood** and **lymph**. Lymph fills all the spaces between cells and cell layers, and, as noted in Chap. 14, this fluid originates in the bloodstream. Blood itself comes close to most cells, for tiny blood capillaries ramify through virtually all tissues.

The body fluids are major controllers of steady states within tissues and organs. Tissues reflect the conditions prevailing in blood and lymph, and vice versa. In their turn, the body fluids are controlled by two organ systems, the **circulatory system** and the **excretory system**. The first, unlike the transport system of plants, is more than a network of channels. It also regulates the *physical* attributes of the fluids it carries, such as pressure, distribution, and rate of flow. Likewise, the excretory system is more than an eliminating apparatus. It is made up of many screening stations which regulate the *chemical* attributes of the body fluids; the system continuously checks and adjusts the composition of the fluids circulating through it.

BLOOD AND LYMPH

Blood is a tissue. It is composed of loose **cells** and of **plasma,** a fluid in which the cells are suspended. Approximately half of the blood of a vertebrate is cellular, the other half plasma. All body tissues affect the momentary composition of blood by adding wastes and withdrawing nutrients. Four structures in particular regulate the long-term composition: the liver, the marrow of long bones, and the lymph nodes, all of which control the cellular content; and the intestine, the liver, the kidneys, and probably also the lymph nodes, all of which control the composition of plasma.

BLOOD PLASMA

This fluid contains two groups of substances. One group consists of compounds which fluctuate more or less widely in concentration, depending on body activity. In this category are a number of foods in transit, urea and other waste products in transit, hormones in transit, and many other classes of materials that are present occasionally. The second group includes substances normally maintained at *constant* concentrations. In this category are water, many of the mineral ions, plasma proteins, and other compounds which are either nutrients in transit to tissue cells or waste products in transit to the excretory organs.

Constancy of such plasma components is achieved by a balance between supply and removal. Supply of a given component may take the form of absorption from the gut or release by tissue cells or manufacture and release by the liver. Removal may involve liver storage, elimination via the excretory system, or absorption by tissue cells. In each case, too high or too low a concentration of a given substance in the blood is the critical stimulus for its own removal or replenishment. As we have seen, for example, a moderately high blood-glucose level stimulates liver cells to lower it by storing the excess as glycogen. A still higher level stimulates storage not only in liver but also in muscle and skin, for example. And a very high concentration leads to glucose excretion from the kidneys. We note that the differential sensitivity of these control organs to actual supply and demand of a given compound brings about a steady state in blood.

Inorganic Components

The main constituent of blood plasma is *water*. Its source is food and metabolic water excreted by cells into the body fluids. The supply of body water from these sources is carefully counterbalanced by controlled loss of water via the excretory system. Within narrow limits, therefore, the total water content of the body, hence also blood volume, remains constant. Recall here the regulating functions performed by pituitary and adrenocortical hormones (Fig. 21.1).

Blood water has many functions. This store supplies all cells with the water they require. Oozing out from capillaries as the main constituent of lymph, blood water envelops all tissues of most animals, in the same way that ocean water enveloped the cells of their

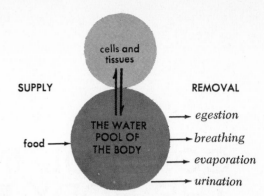

FIG. 21.1   The water balance of the body. Under normal conditions, supply and removal are adjusted for maintenance of a constant water content within the body.

primitive ancestors. By its very presence in a certain quantity within a closed channel system, blood water contributes importantly to blood pressure. After extensive blood loss through wounds, one of the foremost requirements is restoration of blood volume, that is, restoration of water.

Blood water functions as the *transport vehicle* for all other plasma components, for respiratory gases, and for blood cells. The cells are suspended; all other constituents are largely dissolved. One important group of dissolved materials comprises *mineral substances*, present mainly in the form of ions. These are balanced through mineral supply in food, through turnover in tissue cells, and through excretion. As noted in the preceding chapter, growth factors such as vitamin D, parathormone, and adrenocortical hormones contribute to maintenance of mineral balance.

Apart from their function as nutrients and cellular control agents, mineral ions are essential maintainers of the *osmotic pressure* of blood. This pressure is adjusted to the osmotic pressure within tissues. When either blood or the tissues acquire greater concentrations of minerals, then water is pulled osmotically one way or the other. For example, if through intake of much salt water the mineral concentration of blood should rise, then the tissues would become dehydrated. Conversely, if through intake of too much tap water the ion concentration should fall, then the tissues would become overly hydrated. Short-term fluctuations of this sort occur frequently as a consequence of normal metabolism.

Another crucial regulating function of the minerals

in plasma is *pH control* and pH balance between blood and tissues. Any small change of pH is readjusted to normal by the buffering action of the mineral ions (see Chap. 2). Most important in this respect are the positively charged sodium (Na^+), potassium (K^+), calcium (Ca^{++}), and magnesium (Mg^{++}) ions and the negatively charged phosphate ($H_2PO_4^-$, $HPO_4^=$, $PO_4^\equiv$), chloride (Cl^-), bicarbonate (HCO_3^-), carbonate ($CO_3^=$), and sulfate ($SO_4^=$) ions. Over half of the total mineral content of blood represents sodium chloride, common table salt.

Ion pairs like $HPO_4^=/H_2PO_4^-$ and $CO_3^=/HCO_3^-$ are particularly significant buffers in blood. For example, if H^+ ions should accumulate in abnormally large quantities, then carbonate ions ($CO_3^=$) could combine with H^+, forming HCO_3^-. Carbonate concentrations would thereby decrease, bicarbonate concentrations would increase, and the free H^+ ions would have been "taken out of circulation." Analogously, $HPO_4^=$ could combine with H^+ and become $H_2PO_4^-$. The reverse reactions would occur if blood should tend to become too alkaline. Original ion balances may subsequently be restored by the kidneys through excretion of those ions which are present in relative excess.

Mineral ions exert important additional effects. For example, we have noted that calcium ions regulate the sensitivity of nerves and muscles. Calcium also influences the sol-gel states within cells, and it is a component of the cementing substance between cells. Since all cells are in contact with blood or lymph, the concentration of blood calcium evidently is of enormous significance. Earlier contexts have also referred to specific biological actions of most other inorganic ions in the body, and those that are in the body are also in plasma.

Plasma Proteins and Immune Reactions

Plasma proteins endow blood with some of its most important regulating functions, including the function of chemical body defense. These proteins are not primarily nutrients; they represent a permanent population of control agents maintained at constant concentrations. Some of the proteins are known to be manufactured and destroyed in the liver. Others are believed to be formed in the lymph nodes and still others possibly in the lungs. Since all plasma proteins are particles and since most of them are ionized, they play a major role in maintaining osmotic balance and pH balance, like mineral ions. In addition, they perform other functions.

One type of blood protein, **fibrinogen,** has long been known as an essential ingredient in the clotting reaction of blood. We shall discuss this process below. Another group of blood proteins includes a large variety of enzymatically active agents. Some of these, for example, **prothrombin,** are similarly essential in blood clotting. Others are enzymes such as are found also in tissue cells generally and even in the intestine. For example, trypsin is usually present in plasma. The functions of such enzymes in blood are still largely obscure. A third type of blood protein is called **albumin,** because it resembles egg albumen chemically. Of unknown function, albumin is excreted in certain kidney diseases.

A fourth group of plasma proteins, the **globulin** fraction, plays a major role in so-called *immunological* reactions. These include reactions resulting from **blood-type** differences and reactions involving **antigens** and **antibodies.**

That bloods of different individuals may differ in type has been known for some time. Where type differences exist, the blood corpuscles of one individual act as foreign bodies when introduced into another individual, and the plasma globulins of the host may cause the foreign corpuscles to *clump.* Clumped blood cells clog narrow blood capillaries and may cause death. Therefore, before a blood transfusion is made, it is essential to establish blood compatibility. Type differences evidently are of major clinical significance. Biologically, they are merely one further expression of the general phenomenon of protein specificity, i.e., of protein differences among all organisms.

The antigen-antibody reactions referred to above are similarly an expression of protein specificity. An antigen is usually a foreign protein (in some cases it is a polysaccharide) which enters the body fluids of an animal as part of an infectious agent. For example, antigens may be introduced into an animal by viruses, bacteria, plant pollen, or any other protein-containing cell part or tissue part of a foreign organism. An antibody is a blood protein, specifically a globulin, which may make an infected animal *immune* to a foreign antigen. Thus, antibodies function importantly in body defense and in organismic steady-state control.

What does "making immune" mean? It means the combining of an antibody with an invading antigen. Such a union abolishes the free mobility of the antigen and so prevents the antigen from acting in a damaging manner. The combining process is thought to be a "lock-and-key" reaction, quite like the combining of an enzyme with a reactant. The molecular configuration of the antibody protein apparently is such that it "fits" into the configuration of the foreign antigen. In other words, antigen-antibody reactions are specific and any given antigen requires a particular kind of antibody if immunity is to be established (Fig. 21.2).

However, animals do not normally possess pre-existing antibodies for all types of antigens which might possibly invade the blood. This means that an appropriate type of antibody must be manufactured after a given antigen has invaded; and the more rapidly and abundantly such antibodies are formed, the less damage will the animal sustain. The fine details of specific antibody production are not yet clear, but the general pattern of response can be outlined. Among the organs which produce antibodies appear to be the lymph nodes, the liver, and possibly others. The cells of these organs probably absorb samples of invading antigens and then synthesize large quantities of appropriate globulin antibodies. The formation of such globulins, able to react with antigens like lock and key, strongly resembles the process of adaptive enzyme formation. In the latter, as we have seen in Chap. 18, specific

FIG. 21.2   The action of specific antibodies. A foreign protein introduced into an organism is an antigen. It elicits the formation of antibodies, which "fit" precisely the surface configuration of the antigen. These specific antibodies may then combine with the antigens, making the latter harmless.

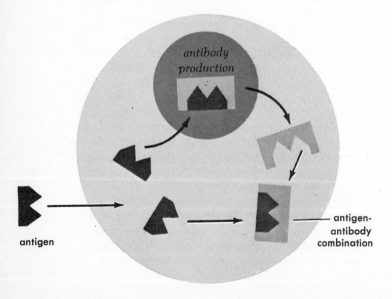

antigen

antigen-
antibody
combination

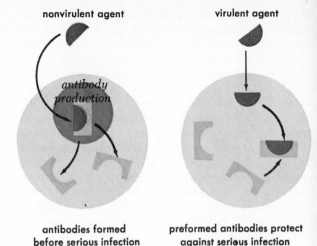

FIG. 21.3   The principle of active immunization. Left, nonvirulent agents are introduced into an organism, and specific antibodies are formed. Right, if virulent forms of the foreign agents should later infect the organism, specific antibodies are already present to combat the infection.

enzyme proteins are formed to fit particular metabolites. Inasmuch as globulin synthesis is protein synthesis, genes should be expected to participate directly in antibody production. That this is actually the case can be demonstrated. For example, certain gene mutations are known to alter the antibody-response capacities of animals. A great deal of research is currently being done in this area of "immunogenetics."

Medical immunization procedures are based on specific antibody production. In vaccination, for example, an individual is injected with nonvirulent strains of disease-producing bacteria or viruses or with killed microorganisms of virulent strains. In either case, disease does not result from the injection; yet antigens of a particular type are introduced nevertheless. The body responds by manufacturing specific antibodies against these injected antigens. Virulent living strains of the microorganisms have the same antigens. Therefore, if at some later time such potentially harmful microorganisms should infect the individual, protective antibodies are already present and the disease will be expressed only in mild form or not at all. Vaccinations so establish **active immunity** for periods up to several years or often throughout life (Fig. 21.3).

In many cases active immunity arises without vaccination. Infectious agents which produce disease in extremely mild and hardly noticeable form invade the body continually and induce the development of antibodies against them. Such virtually nonvirulent agents thus have the same effect as vaccinations and build up immunity. If later their more virulent relatives should invade the body, the protective antibodies are already deployed.

When an individual does suffer from an infectious disease, the effects of the disease can often be reduced by providing **passive immunity.** Here the individual is injected with specific antibodies from an external source. Such prefabricated antibodies are obtained from rabbits, sheep, horses, guinea pigs, and other mammals. The mammal is exposed to a given infectious agent, and globulins manufactured by the mammal against the agent are withdrawn and are used to immunize man (Fig. 21.4). Diphtheria antitoxin is an example of an "immune globulin" which confers passive immunity.

An important consequence of specific antibody production is the rejection of tissues or organs transplanted into an animal from a foreign source. If a part of one animal is grafted to another, the proteins in the graft will be antigens which will induce the production of specific antibodies against them. The graft therefore will not heal in and will be cast off after a few days. This is true even if donor and recipient belong to the same species or indeed to the same family. Successful grafts can be made, however, if tissue from one animal is transplanted to another location in the same animal; the proteins of a given individual do not act as their own antigens. Analogously, grafts can be successful when a foreign tissue is transplanted to a location which does not contain blood vessels. This is the case, for example, in corneal transplants; the cornea is not vascularized. In the absence of blood, an antibody response cannot develop even though an antigen stimulus may be present.

Research in recent years has shown that the usual rejection of foreign grafts can be prevented under special circumstances. In an embryo, the antibody-forming mechanism is not fully developed as yet. Therefore, if an embryo is given tissue from a donor animal, the cells of the embryo will accept the foreign protein as if it were their own. After the embryo has become an adult, this adult may be given a graft from the original donor animal. Such a graft now does not induce antibody production against it, apparently because the

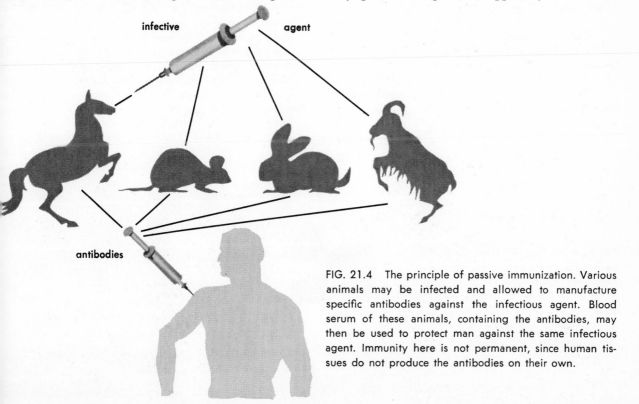

infective agent

antibodies

FIG. 21.4 The principle of passive immunization. Various animals may be infected and allowed to manufacture specific antibodies against the infectious agent. Blood serum of these animals, containing the antibodies, may then be used to protect man against the same infectious agent. Immunity here is not permanent, since human tissues do not produce the antibodies on their own.

adult cells still "remember" to accept the foreign protein as their own. Some day it may perhaps be possible to make practical use of this sort of "training" for graft acceptance.

Through its globulins and all other constituents, blood plasma clearly plays a vital role in steady-state maintenance. Plasma constitutes a sensory and motor path interconnecting all cells of an animal. It represents a modulator contributing to the constancy of chemical and physical conditions in all tissues. And it is a receptor of infectious stimuli and a defensive effector against them. All this is in addition to the purely transportive functions of plasma, namely, delivering nutrients and collecting wastes, and in addition also to the function of plasma as lymph, through which it provides a proper operating environment for all cells. The main constituents and functions of plasma are summarized in Table 13.

BLOOD CELLS

Three kinds of cellular components are found in vertebrate blood: **red corpuscles, white blood cells,** and **blood platelets** (Fig. 21.5).

Red Corpuscles

The major function of these blood constituents is the transporting of respiratory gases (see Chap. 15). In the adult, red corpuscles are manufactured in the red marrow present at the ends of long bones (e.g., ribs, arms, legs). Liver and spleen are the production sites in the embryo, before bones mature. After the skeleton is fully formed and blood-cell production is initiated in it, the spleen becomes principally a blood-storing organ. It may contract like a sponge and squeeze reserve blood into the circulation. The liver becomes the organ where red corpuscles are destroyed.

Production in bone marrow is geared to destruction in the liver. The controlling signal is the amount of oxygen carried by blood (Fig. 21.6). Low oxygen content stimulates bone marrow to produce red corpuscles at a faster rate. At the same time, the liver is inhibited from destroying corpuscles at too fast a rate. Accordingly, when inhaled air contains too little oxygen for extended periods, as at high altitudes, then more blood corpuscles are manufactured. An adequate quantity of gas thus may still be delivered to the tissues by this greater number of corpuscles. A persistently high oxygen concentration in blood has the opposite effect on liver and bone marrow. Through this mechanism, the number of red corpuscles is adjusted to oxygen requirements. Since such requirements and the composition of the atmosphere normally remain fairly constant, the number of corpuscles is constant also.

When the number of corpuscles or their haemoglobin content or both are reduced significantly, the result is *anemia.* This may be brought about by excessive corpuscle destruction in an abnormal liver or by extensive blood loss through wounding. In the latter case, production in bone marrow soon makes up the loss. Anemia may also arise as a result of inadequate production of corpuscles as, for example, when marrow

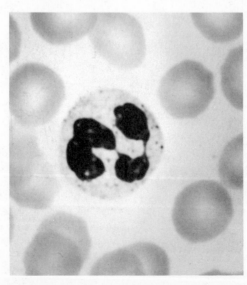
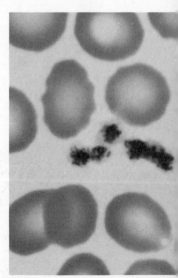

FIG. 21.5 Human red blood corpuscles are shown in both photos. Note absence of nuclei. A white blood cell (nucleated) is shown in center of left photo, and a few blood platelets in center of right photo. *(General Biological Supply House, Inc.)*

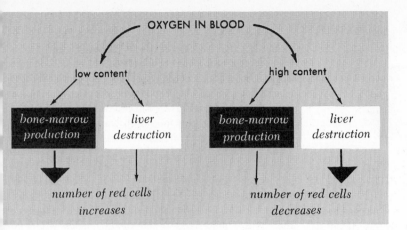

FIG. 21.6 Control of red corpuscle number. Production in bone marrow and destruction in liver are geared to each other by the oxygen content of blood.

TABLE 13

*The principal constituents and functions of blood plasma**

components	functions
1. water	maintains blood volume and pressure; forms lymph; water supply of cells; provides vehicle for other constituents
2. mineral ions	maintain osmotic balance, pH balance; buffer capacity; varied effects on tissue cells
3. plasma proteins	all maintain osmotic and pH balance
fibrinogen	participates in blood clotting
prothrombin	participates in blood clotting
albumins, enzymes	functions obscure
globulins	basis of blood types; act as antibodies
4. glucose, other organic metabolites	in transit to and from cells
5. urea, CO_2, O_2, various foods, hormones, vitamins, and others	in transit to and from cells

* Categories 1 to 4 are maintained at constant concentrations; materials in category 5 occur in variable concentrations.

cells are defective or when the iron content of the diet is low.

In man, each cubic millimeter of blood, roughly the volume of a pinhead, contains over 5 million red corpuscles. It has been estimated that every *second* some 10,000 corpuscles are manufactured and just as many are destroyed. In mammals, but not in other vertebrates, maturation of a red corpuscle in bone marrow includes the disintegration of the cell nucleus. Corpuscles in the mammalian blood stream consequently are enucleated and not "cells" in the strict sense.

Destruction of corpuscles in the liver is random and nonselective, i.e., it affects young corpuscles as well as old ones. The iron of disintegrated haemoglobin becomes generally available in metabolism and may be used, for example, in the synthesis of cytochrome or of new haemoglobin. The tetrapyrrol fraction of destroyed haemoglobin is largely excreted in bile and urine (see Chap. 14).

White Blood Cells

These colorless constituents of blood are complete cells with nuclei. They normally do not divide. Whereas red corpuscles are quite uniform in size and appearance, white blood cells are not. Two groups may be distinguished, **leucocytes** and **lymphocytes**, each including a number of subgroups. These various types are distinguished on the basis of cell structure, size, origin, and function (Fig. 21.7).

Leucocytes are manufactured in red bone marrow, probably by the same generating tissue which gives rise to red corpuscles. Lymphocytes are formed in lymphatic tissue, principally in the lymph nodes found

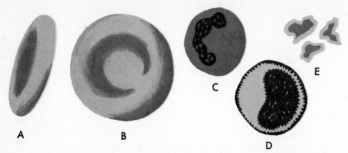

A   B   C   D   E

FIG. 21.7 The cellular components of blood. *A, B*, red blood corpuscle, side and face views; *C*, leucocyte; *D*, lymphocyte; *E*, platelets. See also Fig. 21.5.

along the path of the lymph vessels. Lymphocytes reach the blood stream via the lymph channels. Altogether, white blood cells are much less abundant than red corpuscles. A cubic millimeter of human blood contains about 8,000 white cells. This is a fairly constant number under normal conditions. It is not known where white cells are destroyed or by what mechanism the rates of production and destruction are controlled.

Cancer of the bone marrow, *leukemia*, is characterized by uncontrolled, abnormally rapid formation of white cells. Other diseases similarly may raise the white-cell count excessively or may lower it to abnormal levels. The number of white cells increases temporarily during infectious diseases, and this points up the function of these cells.

To greater or lesser degree all white cells, but leucocytes particularly, are capable of amoeboid locomotion. Like an amoeba, a leucocyte may extend pseudopods into which the rest of the cell then flows. In this way, leucocytes may squeeze in between adjacent cells in the walls of blood capillaries and leave the blood stream (Fig. 21.8). Once they are out in the tissues, the leucocytes migrate toward sites of infection. There they engulf in amoeboid fashion infectious agents such as bacteria. How are white cells guided toward an infected region? Every such region contains many dead cells and disintegration products of cells. Numerous waste materials thus diffuse away from an infection site. Presumably, white cells are sensitive to such waste materials. When blood carries white cells past infected regions, the cells probably are stimulated to migrate to the places where the wastes originate. Accumulations of white cells, cellular disintegration products, and bacteria in infected areas collectively constitute **pus.**

Lymphocytes also serve in body defense. These cells contribute importantly to scar-tissue formation after internal or external injury and in this manner facilitate wound healing. Moreover, they aid in sealing off a surface wound against new infections. Numerous lymphocytes are normally present in the lymph nodes, where the cells act as lymph-purifying agents (Fig. 21.9). For example, microscopic particles of dust, smoke, and other materials present in the atmosphere frequently

FIG. 21.8 Diagram: a white blood cell migrating through a capillary wall. Photos: the migration of blood cells through capillary walls. In each photo, a blood-filled capillary is in upper-right portion. In photo at left, two white blood cells have just penetrated through the capillary wall into surrounding tissues and a red corpuscle is about to penetrate through the wall. In photo at right, the white cells have migrated farther into the tissue and the red corpuscle is halfway through the capillary wall. *(Photos courtesy of Dr. Robert Brenner, Brown University.)*

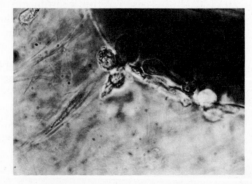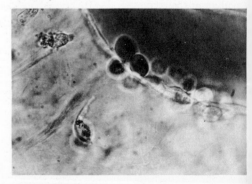

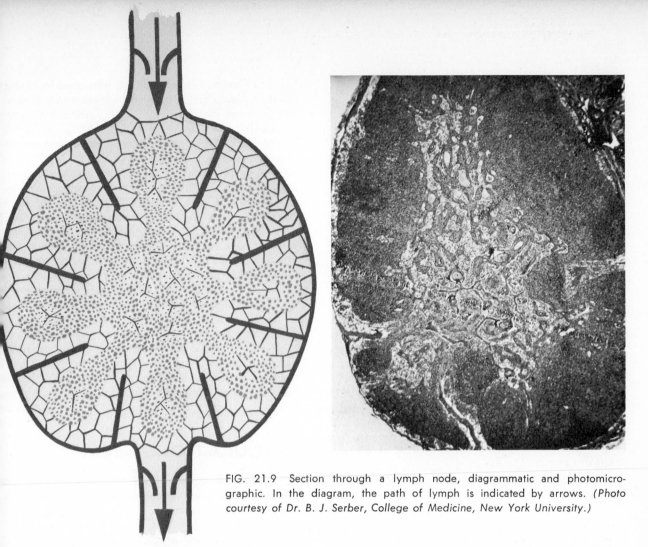

FIG. 21.9 Section through a lymph node, diagrammatic and photomicrographic. In the diagram, the path of lymph is indicated by arrows. *(Photo courtesy of Dr. B. J. Serber, College of Medicine, New York University.)*

get into the lungs and may become embedded in lung tissue. Lymph then usually carries such particles to the lymph nodes. The lymphocytes there engulf the particles and retain them permanently.

Platelets

These are not whole cells but cell fragments often without nuclei (see Figs. 21.5 and 21.7). A plasma membrane covers each platelet. About one-quarter million of these bodies are found in each cubic millimeter of human blood. The origin of platelets is obscure, as is the control system which keeps their number constant. They are probably manufactured predominantly in red bone marrow. A certain fraction is believed to be formed in the connective tissue which binds the lung alveoli together.

Platelets are essential in blood clotting. This self-sealing mechanism of the circulatory system is brought into action whenever platelets encounter obstructions and rupture. In most cases, such obstructions are the rough edges of torn blood vessels. External clotting then occurs. But air bubbles in blood (e.g., when dissolved gases effervesce) or roughness of the inner surfaces of blood vessels (e.g., as produced by solid deposits in hardened arteries) may suffice for the rupturing of platelets. An internal blood clot may then form.

The clotting process is exceedingly complex, far more so than the following simplified and abbreviated outline (Fig. 21.10). Among the materials oozing out from ruptured platelets is an enzymatically active substance, **thrombokinase**, also called **thromboplastin.** This substance interacts with two components of blood plasma, namely, calcium ions and the plasma protein prothrombin. This protein is an inactive precursor of the catalyst **thrombin**. In the presence of calcium ions and thrombokinase, prothrombin becomes converted to

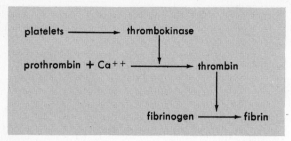

FIG. 21.10   The main features of the clotting reaction.

thrombin. Subsequently, thrombin reacts with fibrinogen, another of the plasma proteins. As a result of the reaction, fibrinogen becomes **fibrin,** an insoluble coagulated protein. Fibrin constitutes the blood clot. It is a yellowish-white meshwork of fibers in which blood corpuscles are trapped, hence the redness of the clot. As noted in Chap. 20, vitamin K is required at some step in the clotting reaction.

Moderate heat speeds clotting time; cold slows it. Clotting can be prevented when any of the ingredients are missing or are made inoperative. For example, fibrinogen can be withdrawn fairly easily from whole blood or plasma. This procedure is often used in storing blood or plasma for transfusions. Plasma minus fibrinogen is called *blood serum.* Clotting can also be prevented by precipitating out the calcium of blood. Leeches, fleas, bedbugs, and other blood feeders secrete *hirudin* and mix it with ingested blood. Hirudin is a clotting inhibitor enabling leeches, for example, to store uncoagulated blood in their digestive tracts for as long as 6 months. Finally, clotting will be impossible when blood platelets are defective. In one type of (hereditary) disease, platelets are missing altogether. In another, platelets have thickened membranes which do not rupture on contact with obstructions. In either of these *bleeder's diseases,* the slightest wound can be fatal.

The functions of the cellular components of blood are summarized in Table 14. We note that, through antibodies, through white cells, and through clotting, blood forms the first line of internal defense. However, this control function of blood and its other functions in transport and tissue maintenance can be exercised only if blood *circulates.* Consequently, as the activities of body tissues are dependent on blood, so the activities of blood in turn are dependent on transport channels.

CIRCULATION

The component organs of the circulatory system are the heart, the blood vessels, and the lymph vessels. Together they represent more than a pumping station and a system of pipes, for, as noted earlier, they also regulate the physical attributes of the moving fluids, viz., the speed and force of motion and the internal distribution of blood and lymph.

From the standpoint of individual tissue cells, the important parts of the circulatory system are the microscopic *capillary vessels.* It is through them and only through them that circulating body fluids and tissue cells exchange life-sustaining materials and information. But to make such capillary exchanges possible, structures like heart and large blood vessels become necessary prerequisites.

THE PATHWAY

In mammals, the heart lies in the mid-plane of the chest, directly underneath the breastbone. But it is tilted somewhat, the lower tip projecting over to the left. This is where the beat of the heart is most readily discernible (Fig. 21.11).

TABLE 14

The cellular constituents of blood and their functions

component	origin	number per cubic millimeter	functions
red corpuscles	red marrow (adults) liver, spleen (embryo)	5 million	transport of O_2, CO_2
white cells leucocytes	red marrow	8,000	engulf bacteria, foreign bodies; aid in wound healing
lymphocytes	lymph nodes		engulf bacteria, foreign bodies; aid in wound healing
platelets	red marrow, lungs	250,000	release thrombokinase, aid in blood clotting

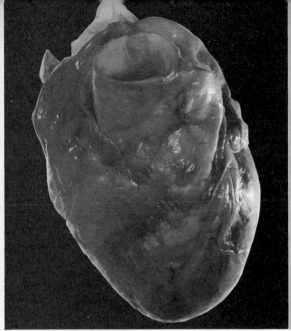 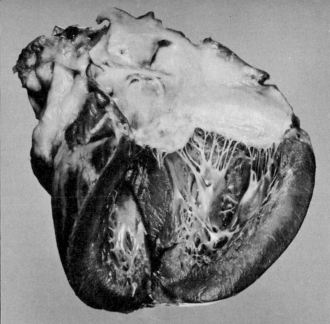

FIG. 21.11 Left, the human heart. The large blood-vessel stump is the aorta. The auricles are partly hidden by the aorta. The size of your fist is very nearly the actual size of your heart. Right, the heart cut open to show the interior of the left ventricle. Note the strands of tissue attached to the two flaps of the bicuspid valve. These strands prevent the valve from opening into the auricle (white area above the ventricle). *(Photographic Department, Rhode Island Hospital.)*

The mammalian heart consists of four chambers, the right and left **auricle** and the right and left **ventricle**. Typically, one large blood vessel is connected to each (Fig. 21.12). The **aorta** leaves the left ventricle and the branches of this vessel supply all parts of the body with arterial (i.e., oxygen-rich) blood. Venous (i.e., oxygen-poor) blood collects from all body regions and returns through the **vena cava** into the right auricle.

The right auricle connects with the right ventricle through the **tricuspid valve**, an opening equipped with three flaps. This valve lets blood through from auricle to ventricle but not in the reverse direction. Venous blood collected in the right ventricle leaves this chamber via the **pulmonary artery**, a vessel leading to the lungs. Here blood is oxygenated, and arterial blood returns through the **pulmonary vein** into the left auricle (see also Fig. 15.12).

A **bicuspid** or **mitral** valve, equipped with two flaps, separates the left auricle from the left ventricle. Like the tricuspid on the right, the mitral valve also opens into the ventricle only. The flaps of both the bicuspid and tricuspid valves are prevented from letting blood pass in the wrong direction by strands of tissue resembling parachute strings. These are attached to the free edges of the valve flaps on one end and to the

ventricle walls on the other (see Fig. 21.11). The bicuspid and tricuspid valves together may be referred to as the auriculo-ventricular valves, or **A-V valves**. Smaller valves are situated where the aorta and the pulmonary artery leave the left and right ventricle, respectively. These valves open away from the heart and close toward it.

Note that the left chambers of the heart are not connected directly with the right chambers. The left carry arterial blood only; the right, venous blood only. Inasmuch as the auricles pump blood only as far as the ventricles, relatively thin muscular walls suffice. But the ventricles, the left one in particular, pump blood into the farthest parts of the body. These chambers possess proportionately thick walls.

The heart and the entire vessel system are lined with a single continuous layer of smooth flat cells. In blood and lymph capillaries no other cells are present (Fig. 21.13). But in the larger channels, muscle and fibroelastic connective tissue envelop the lining layer. The wider a vessel, the sturdier and thicker is its wall. Arteries, which bear the brunt of internal fluid pressure, are particularly thick in comparison with veins or lymph vessels. Large veins and lymph vessels are equipped with internal valve flaps at more or less

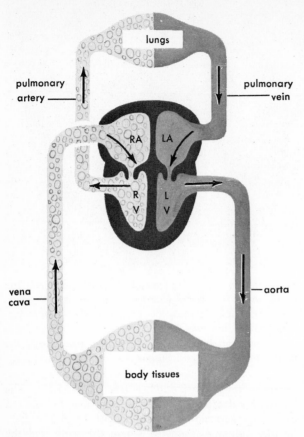

FIG. 21.12 Diagram of the course of blood circulation through the body. Arterial blood is in the left side of the circulatory system (right side of the diagram), venous blood in the right side (left side of the diagram).

FIG. 21.13 Diagram: cross section (top) and surface view (bottom) of blood capillaries. In the cross section, note how few cells are needed to form a tube. In the surface view, note the characteristic wavy outlines of the capillary cells. Photo: section through an artery and two veins. Note the thicker wall of the artery and the presence of many elastic fibers (dark wavy lines) in this wall. *(Photograph, courtesy of Dr. B. J. Serber, College of Medicine, New York University.)*

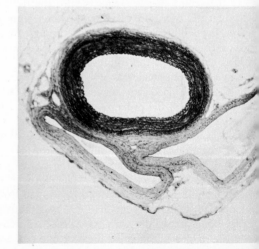

regular intervals. These flaps open toward the heart and close away from it. Body fluids in these vessels are normally under low forward pressure, and the valve flaps prevent the fluids from flowing backward (Fig. 21.14).

THE PROCESS

The heart is a pressure pump. It generates pumping force on contraction, here called **systole,** and it rests during muscular relaxation, or **diastole.** A complete heartbeat consists of one systole and one diastole, the whole beat lasting about 0.8 sec in a normal human adult at rest. On an average, therefore, 72 beats take place per minute.

A heartbeat starts with the contraction of the auricles (Fig. 21.15). These chambers gradually distend as blood returns via vena cava and pulmonary vein. When the auricles are fully distended, their muscular walls contract. The ventricles are relaxed at that time. As the auricles contract, blood cannot flow backward because incoming blood presses steadily *into* the auricles. Therefore, the only path open to auricular blood is through the A-V valves, which lead into the ventricles. These chambers now distend as the auricles empty. The auricular phase of the heartbeat lasts about 0.1 sec. The auricles then relax for the remaining 0.7 sec of the cycle, slowly redistending during this interval in preparation for the next beat (Fig. 21.16).

As soon as the auricles have relaxed, the ventricles, by this time fully distended, contract in their turn. Their thick walls generate much more pressure than the walls of the auricles. Also, ventricular systole lasts

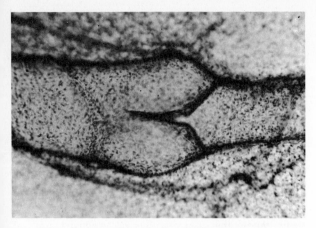

FIG. 21.14 Longitudinal section through a lymph vessel, showing an internal valve. Such valves prevent backflow. Valves very much like this are present also in the larger veins. *(General Biological Supply House, Inc.)*

longer, namely, some 0.3 sec. As the contraction peak is reached, blood is forced against all ventricular openings, including the A-V valves. But as blood slaps against the A-V flaps, these snap shut and prevent backflow into the auricles (see Fig. 21.15). The impact of blood against the valve flaps produces the **first heart sound,** which can be felt or heard as "the" heartbeat.

The only way blood can leave the ventricles is via the aorta on the left and the pulmonary artery on the right. The exit valves into these vessels open as blood presses against them with great force. The sudden quantity of fluid now rushing out dilates portions of the exit arteries adjacent to the heart. But the arterial walls are elastic and snap back into position, thereby adding to the pressure of blood. Most of the blood is thus forced forward, where the open paths lead to the lungs and to all body tissues. But some blood tends to press back into the ventricles. This back pressure snaps the exit valves shut and blood then cannot flow in this direction (see Fig. 21.15). The impact of blood in

FIG. 21.15 The pumping action of the heart. In the left figure, the auricles are shown contracting, forcing blood into the relaxed ventricles. The A-V valves are open, but the pressure of blood closes all others. In the right figure, the ventricles contract, forcing blood into the pulmonary artery and the aorta. The auricles are relaxed at the same time, filling with blood in preparation for the next beat.

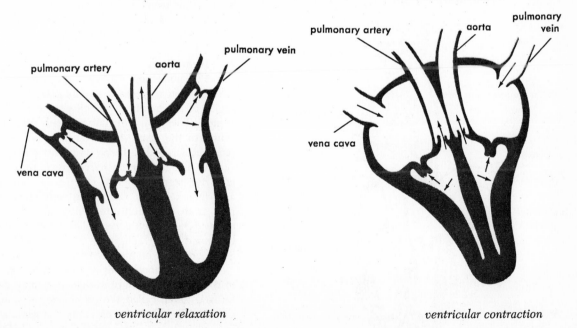

auricular contraction

auricular relaxation

pulmonary artery
aorta
pulmonary vein
vena cava

pulmonary artery
aorta
pulmonary vein
vena cava

ventricular relaxation

ventricular contraction

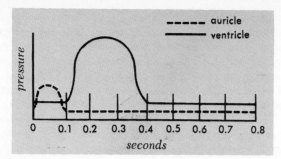

FIG. 21.16 The time relationship between auricular and ventricular beats. Note that the auricles contract and generate pressure when the ventricles are relaxed, and vice versa. Note also that the whole heart is relaxed for half the time of a beat.

closing the exit valves generates the **second heart sound,** fainter than the first.

Note that even the ventricles rest more than half the time. Note also that all heart chambers are always completely full with blood. The quantity of blood in different chambers does vary, however, and such blood

FIG. 21.17 The motor innervation of the heart. Impulses through both inhibitor and accelerator nerves may affect the pacemaker. Impulses from there then stimulate the auricles, as well as the A-V node, which in turn sends signals to the ventricles through the bundle of His.

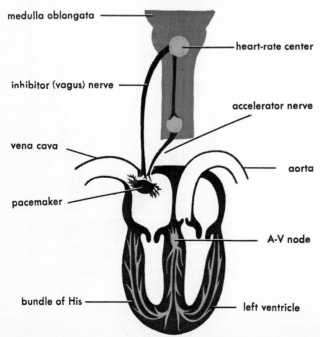

is also under greater or lesser pressure. This differential pressure alone determines the position of the heart valves, hence the course in which blood can flow.

Arterial blood "flows" in rhythmic spurts, according to the rhythm of the heart. As each spurt of fluid impinges on the walls of arteries, it gives rise to **pulse** vibrations. With increasing distance from the heart, arterial spurts become less and less forceful. By the time blood is through capillary vessels and has reached veins, it no longer spurts but flows in a continuous, even stream. The heart here produces very little direct push. Venous blood keeps moving slowly by the push of blood from behind and by contraction of skeletal muscles which squeeze the veins. The valves in the veins impose the right direction on venous return.

The pressure of lymph is even lower than that of blood. Here again, push of lymph from behind and muscular activity provide the major forces which return lymph to the blood circulation.

How are heartbeat and circulation as a whole maintained?

THE CONTROL

Heart muscle possesses inherent contractility. When isolated in an artificial nutrient medium, a piece of heart muscle may for a time contract and relax in a slow rhythm. In the body, this inherent rhythm of the heart is adjusted in strength and in rate by control systems. Some of these operate on a nervous, some on a chemical and physical basis.

Heart Rate

The main nervous regulating center of heart rate is located in the **medulla oblongata,** the same general region of the hindbrain which also houses the breathing center. Two pairs of nerves lead from a **heart-rate center** to the heart (Fig. 21.17). Impulses through one pair accelerate heartbeat; impulses through the other slow it. The accelerator nerves travel through the spinal cord for some distance, emerge in the chest region, and innervate the heart. The inhibitory nerve fibers pass from the heart-rate center into the large **vagus nerves.** One vagus nerve on each side leaves the hindbrain and runs through the neck alongside the trachea. Some branches of the vagus then lead to the heart.

Both the accelerator and inhibitor nerves terminate in the wall of the right auricle at a small patch of specialized tissue called the **pacemaker** or **sinus node** (see Fig. 21.17). When the pacemaker is stimulated, a wave of contraction spreads out from it through both auricles. Auricular contraction in turn stimulates a second patch of tissue, the **A-V node,** situated in the partition which divides the left and right sides of the heart. At the A-V node originates a bundle of modified heart muscle, the **bundle of His,** specialized for impulse conduction. The strands of this bundle radiate through the walls of both ventricles. Thus, auricular contraction stimulates the A-V node, and impulses transmitted from there through the conductive strands initiate ventricular contraction. The time which is required for stimulus transmission from pacemaker to A-V node ensures that the ventricles contract a fraction of a second *after* the auricles.

The pacemaker is the immediate regulator of heart rate, and the heart-rate center in turn controls the action of the pacemaker. Like other processes, the rate of heartbeat is a restrained compromise between acceleration and deceleration. Experiments show that inhibitory signals via the vagus nerves allow a more flexible adjustment of heart rate than accelerator signals. For example, it can be demonstrated that an acceleration of the heart is brought about specifically by a *decrease* of impulse frequency through the vagus nerves; the heart beats faster primarily because of reduced braking action, not because acceleration has been stepped up. Similarly, a slowing of the heart is primarily a result of increased braking via the vagus nerves, not a result of decreased acceleration.

The heart-rate center sends out brake or accelerator signals in response to specific sensory nerve impulses which affect it. Such impulses may reach it from anywhere in the body. As is well known, heart rate can be influenced greatly by external environmental changes, via vision, hearing, and other senses. Moreover, virtually all emotions affect heart rate, and so do internal body activities. In all such cases, sensory impulses are transmitted into specific parts of the brain, and interconnected impulse pathways from there then relay signals to many other parts of the brain, the heart-rate center usually included. Depending on the kind of signal the heart-rate center receives, it accelerates or decelerates the heart.

Among the sensory messages transmitted to the heart-rate center, many originate in the circulatory system itself. For example, sensory nerves lead to the heart-rate center from the walls of the vena cava and the aorta. When these blood vessels become distended by large quantities of blood, their walls stretch and this stimulates the endings of the sensory nerves. If the heart-rate center receives impulses from the vena cava, the center *accelerates* the heart. By contrast, impulses to the center from the aorta bring about a *slowing* of the heart (Fig. 21.18).

Suppose that strenuous work is started. The active body muscles now compress many veins vigorously, and much blood returns to the heart as a result. This distends the vena cava pronouncedly and initiates a *stretch reflex,* as described. Heart rate will increase, therefore, just when the tissues require more fuel and oxygen. Also, a heart beating more rapidly can handle the larger quantities of incoming blood by pumping them out faster. But the increased outflow dilates the walls of the aorta. Stretch reflexes now originate in this

FIG. 21.18 The sensory innervation of the heart. The heart-rate center receives messages through sensory nerves which originate in the vena cava and the aorta. In response to such messages, the center then may send appropriate command signals to the pacemaker, as per Fig. 21.17.

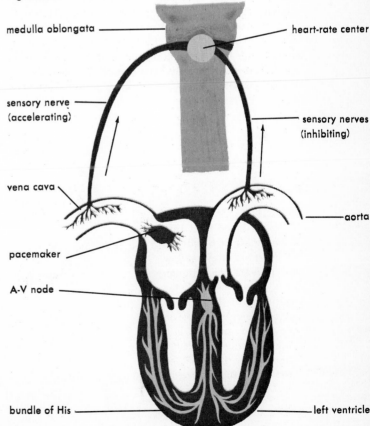

vessel and these *slow* the heart; i.e., they prevent it from beating *too* rapidly (Fig. 21.19).

Through these controls and the built-in feedbacks, heart rate is automatically self-adjusted to the volume of blood which the heart must handle. Moreover, any excessive speedup produces signals forcing a slowdown. Similarly, if the heart should slow down, the aortic walls would be stretched less, reflex inhibition of the heart would decrease, and heart rate would increase back to normal.

In addition to nervous controls like the above, heart rate is regulated decisively by many nonnervous agencies. Most of these act directly on the heart muscle or on the pacemaker specifically. Like any other metabolic process, heartbeat is affected by temperature. High temperature accelerates, low temperate decelerates. The effect of pH is equally pronounced. Relative acidity accelerates the heart, relative alkalinity decelerates it. Since carbon dioxide lowers the pH of blood, this compound increases the rate of the heart when it is present in high concentrations. High CO_2 concentrations also speed up breathing, as noted in Chap. 15. Consequently, fast breathing and a fast heart usually go together. The mineral ions in blood and also hormones have pronounced effects on heart rate. For example, the action of adrenalin under conditions of severe stress has already been mentioned. Analogously, thyroxin, insulin, sex hormones, pituitary hormones, and others all influence heart rate directly or indirectly. At any given moment, therefore, the actual rate of the heart is a net result of many simultaneous nervous and nonnervous effects.

Pressure and Distribution of Blood

If blood pressure became too high, thin blood vessels and the thin-walled auricles of the heart might burst. And if blood pressure became too low, blood would not possess sufficient momentum to circulate.

Even in the absence of a pumping mechanism, a quantity of fluid filling a confined space is under a certain pressure. The larger the volume of fluid and the smaller the available space, the greater will be the pressure. Blood pressure therefore depends on three main factors: blood *volume*, blood *vessel space*, and in addition also the *force* of the heartbeat.

Blood volume is adjusted to some extent through contractions of the spleen, which bring stored blood into circulation, and to a major extent through regulation of fluid intake and fluid loss. Adjustments of blood pressures by such means are comparatively slow. However, virtually instant adjustments may be brought about by alterations in the force of the heartbeat and in the space within blood vessels.

The main determinant of the force of heartbeats is the *amount* of blood received and pumped out in a given span of time. This is a curious but little-

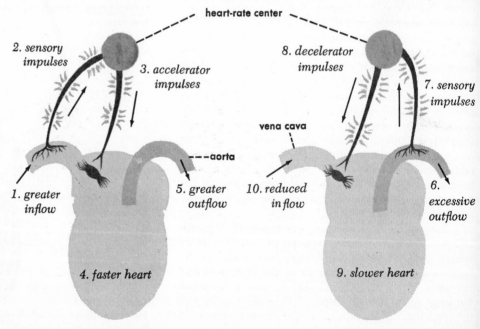

FIG. 21.19 Stretch-reflex control of blood flow. Left, if the inflow of blood into the heart increases, outflow will increase too, through reflex acceleration of the heart (1 to 5). Right, if the outflow rate is excessive, inflow and outflow will quickly be reduced, through reflex deceleration of the heart (6 to 10).

understood phenomenon characteristic of all muscle. Within certain limits, the greater the work load of a muscle and the more it is thereby stretched, the stronger is its contraction. For example, when the heart receives small quantities of blood in each beat and distends only a little, then its contraction will be weak. But when much blood distends the ventricles fully, then the pumping action will be powerful and blood pressure will increase correspondingly.

The heart distends with much blood when venous return is great. As we have just seen above, a stretch reflex originates under such conditions from the wall of the vena cava and heart rate is raised. Venous return evidently affects both the rate and the force of the heart, a circumstance of considerable adaptive value. During exercise, for example, a heart which has a fast but shallow beat could not supply the tissues with extra fuel and oxygen. However, a beat which is both fast and forceful does put the necessary drive behind blood to service the tissues adequately.

The space available within blood vessels is adjusted by contraction and relaxation of the muscles in the vessel walls. **Vasoconstriction** reduces the diameter of blood vessels; **vasodilation** increases it. Vasoconstriction and vasodilation together are referred to as **vasomotion**. These muscular activities are controlled by a **vasomotor center** in the brain, located again in the medulla oblongata, close to the breathing and heart-rate centers. Nerves lead from the vasomotor center to all blood vessels except the capillaries, which do not possess muscles. Experiments show that changes in the caliber of a blood vessel are brought about primarily by variations in the activity of constrictor muscles. Dilator muscles play a lesser role. Consequently, a vessel ordinarily narrows as a result of more impulses from the vasomotor center to constrictor muscles. A vessel widens when fewer impulses reach these muscles (Fig. 21.20).

Vasoconstriction in all parts of the body raises overall blood pressure; vasodilation lowers it. Vasomotion may also occur in limited regions of the body, leading to localized changes in blood pressure. Actual events are controlled by the vasomotor center, which, like the heart-rate center, acts in response to nervous and chemical cues.

Nervous cues to the vasomotor center are as numerous as those which affect heart rate. Virtually any nervous signal transmitted into the brain is likely to have an effect on the vasomotor center as well. For example, pain, emotions, and stresses generally all tend

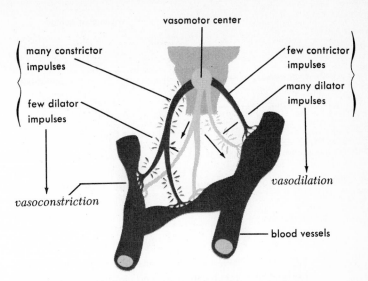

FIG. 21.20   The pattern of vasomotion. Vasoconstriction occurs when a blood vessel receives many constrictor impulses from the vasomotor center and few dilator impulses. Vasodilation occurs when constrictor impulses are few and dilator impulses many.

to increase blood pressure, through body-wide vasoconstriction. At the same time, in specific parts of the body in which stresses are to be counteracted, the local blood pressure often falls through regional vasodilation. For example, if an animal sustains a wound, overall blood pressure rises but the wounded area swells through local vasodilation. The adaptive advantage of this is clear. A rise of overall blood pressure produces a state of readiness which enables the animal to respond to stress more effectively. And a local vasodilation in the stressed region itself permits more blood to flow into that region. More nutrients and oxygen become available there as a result (Fig. 21.21).

Like heart rate, blood pressure is normally prevented from varying excessively by stretch reflexes. Some sensory nerve fibers from the aorta lead into the vasomotor center. When the aorta is greatly distended by blood spurting out from the heart, i.e., when blood pressure is high, a stretch reflex via the vasomotor center brings about body-wide vasodilation. In this manner, a high blood pressure is reduced to normal. Conversely, when the aorta distends very little or not at all, a stretch reflex leads to increased vasoconstriction and a rise of blood pressure.

The chief chemical cue to which the vasomotor

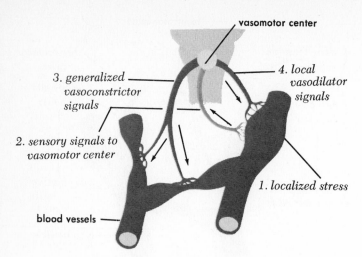

FIG. 21.21 The vasomotor effects of localized stress. Generalized vasoconstriction and localized vasodilation follow through the numbered events shown. Sensory nerves in light gray, motor nerves in black.

center responds is carbon dioxide in the blood, as in the case of the breathing and heart-rate centers. If blood reaching the vasomotor center carries a high concentration of CO_2, then the center transmits constrictor signals throughout the body and blood pressure will rise. Conversely, low CO_2 concentrations result in a generalized fall of blood pressure. We already know that CO_2 also affects heart rate and breathing rate.

Evidently, intensive CO_2 production by highly active tissues neatly stimulates the whole circulatory and breathing machinery to increased efforts, just when such efforts are actually required to sustain tissue activity.

Apart from its effects on the vasomotor center, CO_2 also has a direct, local effect on vasomotion. In tissues in which much CO_2 is produced, the gas acts directly on the blood vessels in the vicinity and dilates them. Thus, active tissues control their own increased blood supply through the local effects of the CO_2 they produce. At the same time, they also promote general vasoconstriction elsewhere in the body, through the effects of their CO_2 on the vasomotor center (Fig. 21.22). Changes of this sort occur after a meal, for example, when the whole alimentary system becomes active and produces large amounts of CO_2. As a result of local vasodilation, blood may then flow freely through intestine and liver, where it is particularly needed at the time. But less blood will flow through the peripheral parts of the body, including the skeletal muscles and the head. An animal therefore tends to be sluggish after a meal and will be disinclined to undertake physical activities. Conversely, an empty digestive system facilitates blood flow through the skeletal muscles and the brain (this is why athletes do not eat immediately before exerting themselves physically).

We note that vasomotor control, both nervous and chemical, regulates not only blood pressure as such but also the *distribution* of blood. The nervous and chemical effects tend to reinforce each other, and the results

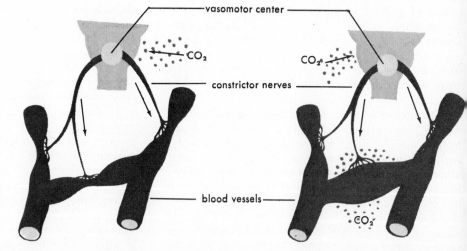

FIG. 21.22 Vasomotor control by carbon dioxide. A, generalized vasoconstriction as a result of stimulation of the vasomotor center by CO_2. B, CO_2 produced locally overrides the general vasoconstriction ordered by the vasomotor center and brings about a local vasodilation.

A

B

are adaptive, being geared to the relative activity or inactivity of body tissues. Moreover, the tissues themselves initiate the distributional changes, through automatic self-regulation via control systems with feedbacks. We may note, furthermore, that the controls of blood pressure and of blood distribution operate in concert with the controls of heart rate and of breathing rate, the net result being that all long-distance transport functions of the body are carried out in interlocking and interdependent fashion. A change in heart rate, for example, may produce changes in blood pressure, in venous return, in the force of the heart, in breathing rate, in the distribution of blood, and eventually in heart rate itself. If one condition of circulation is altered, all others are altered also. Circulatory adjustments illustrate once again that the action of control systems is such as to produce a "right" response to a given stimulus and that built-in feedbacks impose restraints which prevent responses from going too far in direction, strength, and duration.

Control of the physical motion of blood is one requirement if blood is to service the tissues adequately. A second requirement is control of proper chemical conditions in blood, despite changes produced continuously by actively metabolizing tissues. This requirement is met by the excretory system.

EXCRETION

As the body fluids regulate steady-state maintenance in tissues, so the excretory system regulates steady-state maintenance in the body fluids. The excretory system controls the water content and the blood volume of the body, the pH and the osmotic pressure of blood, and, above all, the chemical composition of blood and the body fluids in general. Moreover, through its water-balancing activities, it is also a major regulator of body temperature.

The organs composing the mammalian excretory system are shown in Fig. 21.23. We have discussed the excretory action of many of these in various earlier contexts. For example, the lungs contribute to the elimination of excess water and carbon dioxide. The sweat glands aid in regulating water balance and also mineral balance. The large intestine makes a further contribution to mineral balance. The liver excretes many diverse materials via bile. And various excretory functions are performed also by the nasal epithelium and by the salivary and the other digestive glands—

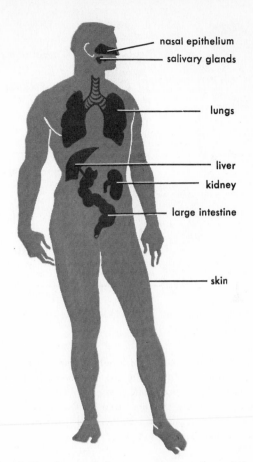

FIG. 21.23 Some of the component organs of the excretory system.

in short, by all the organs with access to the exterior of the body either directly or via the alimentary tract.

But the kidneys exercise the major excretory control. When the kidneys are inoperative, all the above organs together are inadequate to prevent death from excretory failure. As noted earlier, several hormones control the proper functioning of kidney cells.

KIDNEY STRUCTURE

The structure of the mammalian kidney is complex in detail but relatively simple in principle. Each kidney consists of an outer **renal cortex** and an inner **renal medulla** (Fig. 21.24). Located partly in the cortex and partly in the medulla are many thousands of **nephrons,** the operational units of the kidney (Fig. 21.25).

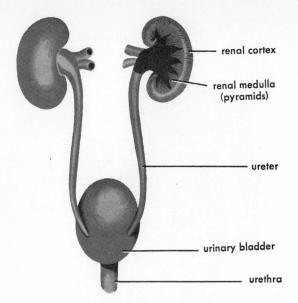

renal cortex

renal medulla (pyramids)

ureter

urinary bladder

urethra

FIG. 21.24   The renal system. Kidney on right is shown in section.

FIG. 21.25   The structure of a nephron and its blood circulation. The portions above the horizontal broken line form part of the renal cortex (see also Fig. 21.24); and the portions below the line, part of the renal medulla. Flow of urine is indicated by feathered arrows; flow of blood, by plain arrows.

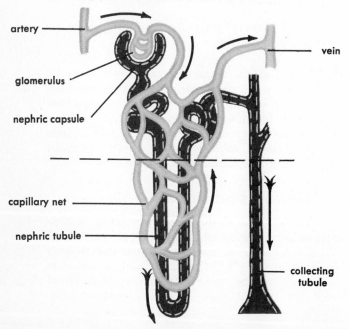

artery

vein

glomerulus

nephric capsule

capillary net

nephric tubule

collecting tubule

The most conspicuous component of a nephron is a tube, called the **nephric tubule.** At one end this tubule enlarges in a **nephric capsule,** a structure resembling a double-layered cup. At the other end the nephric tubule leads into a **collecting duct,** which receives the output of many neighboring nephric tubules. The numerous collecting ducts in a kidney eventually join and form a wide vessel, the **ureter** (see Fig. 21.24). This channel carries urine into the **urinary bladder.** A final duct, the **urethra,** connects the bladder with the outside.

Between the nephric capsule and the entrance into the collecting duct, the nephric tubule is variously coiled and looped. As might be expected, a nephron is in extensive contact with the blood circulation. A large **renal artery** enters the kidney in the region where the ureter leaves, and it branches out repeatedly into many smaller arteries. One of these smaller arteries leads to each nephron (see Fig. 21.25). Dipping into the hollow of the nephric capsule, the small artery breaks up into a dense ball of capillaries called a **glomerulus.** The capillaries then rejoin into a single vessel which leaves the capsule and passes into the tubular portion of the nephron. Here this blood vessel branches out once more into a dense capillary net. This net envelops all parts of the nephric tubule. Near the collecting duct, the capillaries lead into a small vein and many such veins from neighboring nephrons join into larger vessels. All these eventually form a single channel, the **renal vein,** which leaves the kidney where the renal artery enters.

KIDNEY FUNCTION

Two basic processes occur in a mammalian kidney (and indeed in any excretory organ of any animal): **filtration** and **reabsorption.** In filtration, all blood constituents which can pass through the walls of capillaries are taken out from the blood stream. In reabsorption, all those constituents which are waste or are present in excess are eliminated as urine; all other constituents are returned into the blood stream. We note that a kidney functions as an "inspector" of blood; it determines which materials should and which should not be retained in the body.

Filtration takes place in the capsule of each nephron. The filters are the walls of the glomerular capillaries and the adjacent wall of the capsule (Fig. 21.26). Blood pressure supplies the force necessary for filtration. Pushed by this pressure, every blood component which can go through the glomerular and capsular walls will pass into the upper cavity of the nephric tubule. Only two groups of blood constituents normally can *not* pass through the filters, namely, blood cells and plasma proteins. All other components do pass through without change of concentration. Present within the cavity of the nephric capsule is therefore blood minus cells and proteins—*lymph,* or, as lymph in this space is commonly called, **capsular urine.**

Capsular urine next passes into the tubular portion of the nephron, and here reabsorption takes place. This process is carried out by the cells which compose the nephric tubule. On their inner surfaces such cells absorb from passing capsular urine a picked group of substances. And on their outer surfaces the cells secrete these substances back into the blood stream, through the adjacent walls of blood capillaries (see Fig. 21.26). Whatever is not returned into the blood in this manner constitutes urine, specifically **bladder urine,** since it is carried through the collecting ducts and the ureters into the bladder. The wall of the bladder stretches as urine accumulates, and at a certain stage of stretching, sensory nerve endings in the wall are stimulated. A reflex initiates contraction of the muscles in the bladder wall and the organ then empties to the outside.

Of the substances filtered out from blood and subsequently returned to blood in the kidneys, the most abundant is water. In man, blood contains about 5 to 6 qt of water and this amount is filtered through the kidneys roughly once every 45 min. In a 24-hr period, therefore, the kidneys filter about 150 qt of liquid. Yet in the same period, only about 1½ qt of urine, on an average, is actually excreted by the normal adult. This means that tubule cells reabsorb 99 per cent of the water in capsular urine and leave only 1 per cent as urine. As might be expected, more urine is excreted when the fluid intake is large, less when it is small.

Another substance always reabsorbed by the tubule cells and returned to blood is glucose. Capsular urine contains glucose in the same concentration as in blood. Under normal conditions, all the glucose in capsular urine is reabsorbed into the blood and none escapes into bladder urine. As noted in earlier contexts, however, glucose *is* excreted in bladder urine when the compound is present in excessive quantities. Under such conditions, tubule cells probably cannot absorb this carbohydrate fast enough and some of it is then excreted in urine. Glucose is said to be a **high-**

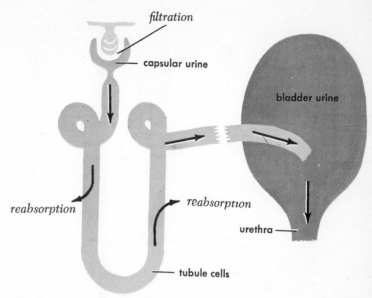

FIG. 21.26   The operation of a nephron. Through filtration of blood, capsular urine is formed, and through reabsorption of various components present in capsular urine, bladder urine is formed.

threshold substance; a high concentration must be present in blood and capsular urine before it will be excreted in bladder urine. Among other high-threshold materials are amino acids, fatty acids, glycerin, vitamins, hormones—in short, essential nutrients and other required metabolites in transit to tissue cells.

On the other hand, some substances in capsular urine are always left in urine and are not reabsorbed by the tubule cells. Among such substances are urea, pigmented blood-breakdown products, and other outright wastes. Inasmuch as materials of this type are excreted even when they are present in very low concentrations, they are referred to as **low-threshold substances.** They become highly concentrated as water is withdrawn from capsular urine. For example, bladder urine contains some seventy times more urea than an equal volume of capsular urine.

Included in a third group are so-called **intermediate-threshold substances.** Tubule cells do or do not reabsorb a given material in this group depending on whether the material is or is not in proper balance in blood. Most mineral ions and many organic substances belong to this category. For example, high salt intake will be followed by excretion of sodium and chloride

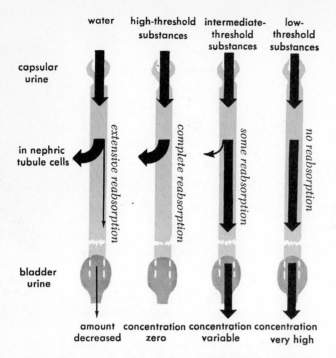

water   high-threshold   intermediate-   low-
         substances   threshold   threshold
                           substances   substances

capsular
urine

extensive reabsorption   *complete reabsorption*   *some reabsorption*   *no reabsorption*

in nephric
tubule cells

bladder
urine

amount   concentration   concentration   concentration
decreased   zero   variable   very high

FIG. 21.27   The selective action of the cells of a nephric tubule. Water is reabsorbed to a very large extent; high-threshold substances like glucose are reabsorbed more or less completely; low-threshold substances like urea are not reabsorbed at all; and intermediate-threshold substances like many mineral ions are reabsorbed in part, depending on the amount already present in blood.

ions if the supply of these ions in blood is already adequate. But if the supply is low to begin with, the tubule cells will reabsorb sodium and chloride and thus raise the salt concentration in blood. Note that water

itself qualifies as an intermediate-threshold substance (Fig. 21.27).

Note too that, as urine becomes more concentrated by withdrawal of water from urine back to blood, the osmotic pull of urine becomes greater. But despite this force, which tends to draw water *from* blood *into* urine, tubule cells nevertheless continue to transport more water from *urine* to *blood*.

Like all other absorbing cells, tubule cells evidently possess exquisite discriminatory powers. They are not only capable of distinguishing one type of compound from another but they are also sensitive to concentrations of materials in blood and are able to readjust these concentrations. By now rejecting, now reabsorbing given substances, they are the final arbiters of the chemical composition, the pH, and the osmotic properties of the body fluids. The overall result is that the excretory system is much more than an expeller of waste. Indeed, what is or is not "waste" is determined from moment to moment principally by the excretory system. In such determinations, the function of *retention* is at least as significant as that of excretion, and the excretory organs could justifiably be said to constitute a "retention system." Moreover, it may be appreciated why examination of urine will reveal not only how well the kidneys function, but also how well steady state is maintained in the body as a whole.

Growth factors and body fluids serve primarily in the internal chemoregulation of the animal body. Through this they also have secondary effects on behavior control. But a far more obvious contributor to the behavior control of animals is the nervous system. Most clearly and most uniquely specialized for functions of steady-state maintenance, the nervous system will be the subject of the next chapter.

REVIEW QUESTIONS

1. Review the composition of blood plasma and the functions of each group of components. How, specifically, may ions in plasma act as buffers? Give examples.

2. What are antibodies? When, where, and how are they produced? Distinguish between active and passive immunity. Why does passive immunity not give as lasting protection as active immunity?

3. What cellular components occur in blood and what are the functions of each? By what processes is the number of red corpuscles maintained relatively constant? What role do lymph nodes play in internal steady-state control? Review the reaction pattern of blood clotting.

4. Name the principal parts of the heart and the principal blood vessels, and review the general course

of blood circulation. What structural features distinguish arteries, veins, lymph vessels, and capillaries?

5. Review the events during a complete heartbeat, with attention to durations, pressure patterns, valve positions, direction of blood flow, and heart sounds. How is blood moved through veins and lymph vessels?

6. Describe the nervous controls of the heart. How are control signals transmitted through the heart itself? Which motor signals accelerate the heart and which decelerate it? Describe stretch reflexes which (a) accelerate and (b) decelerate the heart. Through what specific processes is the heart (a) speeded up when physical exercise is begun and (b) slowed down during rest or sleep? What nonnervous agencies affect heart rate?

7. What three major factors control blood pressure and what governs each of these factors? Describe the action of the vasomotor center. What nervous and chemical agencies affect this center and how?

8. What is the interrelation between vasomotion, heart rate, and breathing rate? Suppose that physical exercise is begun; describe the specific processes leading simultaneously to (a) increased heart rate, (b) increased breathing rate, (c) increased blood pressure, and (d) redistribution of blood within the body.

9. What are the overall functions of the excretory system? What organs compose this system and what is the excretory function of each? Describe the general structure of the kidney and its associated ducts and the specific structure of a nephron.

10. Review in detail the process of urine formation. What are the roles of filtration and reabsorption and where and how does each occur? What are high-threshold substances? Give examples. Construct a table showing how bladder urine differs from blood and capsular urine with respect to (a) the kinds of substances present and (b) the concentrations of substances present.

SUGGESTED COLLATERAL READINGS

Any of the texts listed at the end of Chap. 14 provide background information on topics covered in this chapter. The following readings are recommended in addition:

Boyden, A. A.: The Blood Relationships of Animals, *Sci. American*, vol. 185, 1951.

Burnet, M.: How Antibodies Are Made, *Sci. American*, vol. 191, 1954.

Fox, H. M.: Blood Pigments, *Sci. American*, vol. 182, 1950.

Harvey, W.: On the Motion of the Heart and Blood, translation of original (1616) Latin in T. S. Hall, "A Source Book in Animal Biology," McGraw-Hill, New York, 1951.

Kilgour, F. G.: William Harvey, *Sci. American*, vol. 186, 1952.

McKusick, V. A.: Heart Sounds, *Sci. American*, vol. 194, 1956.

Page, I. H.: High Blood Pressure, *Sci. American*, vol. 179, 1948.

Ponder, E.: The Red Blood Cell, *Sci. American*, vol. 196, 1957.

Smith, H. W.: The Kidney, *Sci. American*, vol. 190, 1954.

Surgenor, D. M.: Blood, *Sci. American*, vol. 190, 1954.

Wiener, A. S.: Parentage and Blood Groups, *Sci. American*, vol. 191, 1954.

Wood, W. B.: White Blood Cells vs. Bacteria, *Sci. American*, vol. 184, 1951.

CONTROL IN ANIMALS: NEURAL COORDINATION

22

Nervous activity is based on *reflexes,* the functional units of the nervous system. A reflex is routed through a *reflex arc,* which, like any other control apparatus, consists of five components: receptor, sensory pathway, modulator, motor pathway, and effector.

The neural receptors are specialized *sensory cells* which may or may not be housed in elaborate organs such as eyes or ears. Receptors translate the energy of incoming stimuli into nerve impulses. These are transmitted over *sensory nerve fibers* to the modulators, namely, *brain* and *spinal cord.* Their activity produces nerve impulses which travel over *motor nerve fibers* to the effectors, i.e., *muscles* and *glands.* Such effectors translate the motor impulses they receive into explicit responses.

The effector functions of muscles and glands have already been discussed in various earlier contexts. In this chapter, therefore, we concentrate primarily on the **neural pathways,** the **neural receptors,** and the **neural centers.**

THE NEURAL PATHWAYS

The mammalian nervous system consists of two subdivisions, the **central nervous system (c.n.s.)** and the **autonomic nervous system (a.n.s.).** Brain and spinal cord house the neural centers of both. The c.n.s. controls largely voluntary, conscious activities, and the a.n.s., involuntary, unconscious ones. But the c.n.s. and a.n.s. are highly interdependent. As we shall see, they form a unified, intimately coordinated functional complex.

Regardless of whether reflex activity occurs in the c.n.s. or the a.n.s., the internal working material of the entire nervous system is always the same: nerve cells, which produce and transmit nerve impulses. These properly demand our first attention.

NERVE CELLS

A nerve cell, or **neuron**, typically consists of a nucleus-containing **cell body** and of one or more **nerve fibers**, which are filamentous outgrowths extending away from the cell body (Fig. 22.1). Nerve impulses normally originate at the terminal of one of the fibers, travel toward the cell body, traverse it, then lead away from the cell body through another of its fibers. Nerve fibers in which impulses travel toward the cell body are termed **dendrites**; those carrying impulses away from the cell body are called **axons**. A neuron characteristically possesses only a single axon, but it may have one or several dendrites. By and large, neurons are comparatively huge cells. Dendrites and axons may be as much as a yard or more long, or they may be relatively short.

Long nerve fibers, but not the cell bodies or the shorter fibers, are enveloped by one or by two sheaths. Most of the long fibers of the central nervous system are surrounded directly by a layer of secreted fatty material, the **myelin sheath**. This sheath in turn is en-veloped by the **Schwann sheath,** which is made up of a single layer of thin flat cells. In most nerve fibers of the autonomic nervous system, only a Schwann sheath surrounds the axon; myelin sheaths are absent here.

Myelin sheaths probably increase the speed of nerve-impulse transmission. It can be shown that myelinated fibers of the c.n.s. may conduct impulses at speeds of about 100 yd per sec, whereas nonmyelinated a.n.s. fibers conduct at about 25 yd per sec at most. The suggestion has been made that the accelerating effect of the fatty myelin layer results from an insulating action; a myelin envelope would be to a nerve fiber what a rubber envelope is to an electricity-conducting metal wire.

The Schwann sheath maintains the continued existence of the nerve fiber it envelops. It is known to supply nutritive materials to the fiber, and it also plays a critical role in fiber regeneration. For example, if an axon is cut, the part which is disconnected from the cell body degenerates (Fig. 22.2). However, if the cut ends of the Schwann sheath are allowed to heal together, then the intact axon stump slowly grows out into the reconnected Schwann tube. A complete new

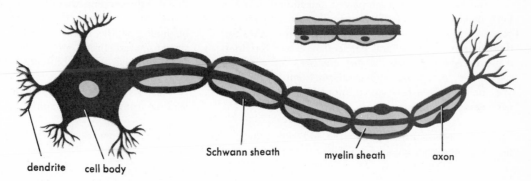

dendrite   cell body   Schwann sheath   myelin sheath   axon

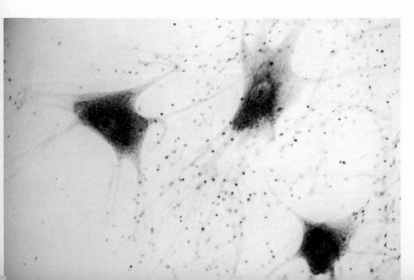

FIG. 22.1 The structure of a neuron. Dendrites may be proportionately longer than shown in the diagram. Upper inset: a length of nonmyelinated axon. The photomicrograph shows fixed and stained cell bodies. *(Photo, General Biological Supply House, Inc.)*

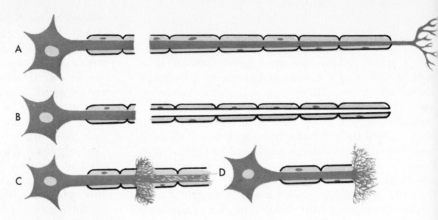

FIG. 22.2 The role of the Schwann sheath in neuron regeneration. *A,* cut axon. *B,* axon on far side of cut has degenerated. *C,* if a Schwann sheath is present, a new axon grows into it. *D,* if a Schwann sheath is not present, new axon growth is random and disoriented.

axon eventually regenerates, replacing the degenerated portion. This is not the case when the cut ends of the Schwann tube do not or cannot heal together. For example, if a section of nerve fiber is destroyed entirely and the sheath ends consequently are too far apart, then the axon stump still grows out. But this may occur in an uncontrolled, randomly oriented manner and the axon may never reach the tissue it should have innervated.

Individual neurons are placed end to end, forming long neural pathways. The axon fiber of one neuron connects functionally with a dendrite of the next. But there is never a structural connection. Fiber terminals come exceedingly close to one another, yet a microscopic gap, a **synapse,** still separates them (Fig. 22.3). We shall soon see how nerve impulses are transmitted across such synapses.

REFLEX ARCS

The minimum number of neurons in a reflex arc is two: one **sensory neuron,** which transmits impulses from a receptor to either brain or spinal cord, and one **motor neuron,** which relays the impulses sent out by brain or spinal cord to an effector. Most reflex arcs consist of more than two neurons. One or more additional **interneurons** may be located within brain or spinal cord, between the end of the sensory and the beginning of the motor neuron. In the entire nervous system, interneurons are actually the most abundant, for they make up the bulk of the brain and the spinal cord (Fig. 22.4).

Sensory neurons leading to and motor neurons leading from brain and spinal cord are collected into

FIG. 22.3 Neurons arranged end to end form extensive neural paths. A synapse, or gap, separates one neuron from the next structurally, but not functionally.

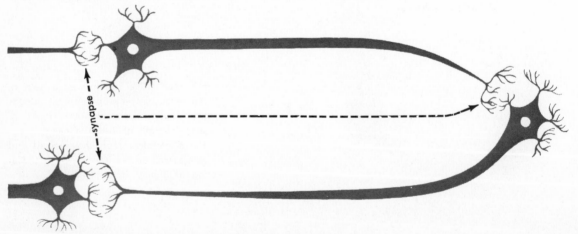

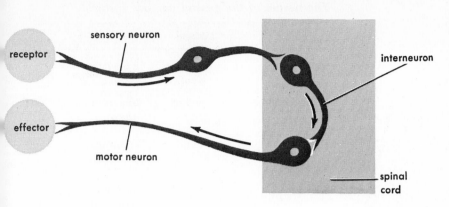

FIG. 22.4 The pattern and the components of a reflex arc. Note that neurons are not joined anatomically, but make functional connection across microscopic spaces called synapses. Note also that the cell body of the sensory neuron lies outside the spinal cord, in a so-called ganglion; that the entire interneuron lies within the spinal cord; and that the cell body of the motor neuron also lies within the spinal cord. Sensory fibers always enter the spinal cord dorsally; motor fibers always leave the cord ventrally.

discrete bundles. Traversing the body like the cables of telephone trunk lines, such bundles of neuron fibers are called **nerves.** In a so-called **mixed nerve,** both sensory and motor fibers are present. In certain nerves only sensory fibers are present, and these are called **sensory nerves.** Analogously, some nerves contain motor fibers only, and they are referred to as **motor nerves.** Nerves are also classified as **cranial** or **spinal,** according to whether they connect with the brain or the spinal cord.

The c.n.s. and the a.n.s. possess their own sets of nerves. Each set connects with distinct c.n.s. or a.n.s. centers in brain and spinal cord. Thus each of the two subdivisions of the nervous system possesses its own reflex pathways.

C.N.S. Pathways

In the c.n.s. of man, 12 pairs of cranial and 31 pairs of spinal nerves carry information to and from brain and spinal cord. These nerves are named and described in Fig. 22.5.

Note that spinal nerves are all mixed nerves and that each divides into two fiber bundles just outside the spinal cord (Fig. 22.6). One bundle attaches to the cord dorsally; this bundle contains fibers of all the sensory neurons of the nerve. The other bundle attaches ventrally; it contains the fibers of all the motor neurons of the spinal nerve. Along the dorsal bundle, close to its attachment to the spinal cord, is a thickened region. Present within it are the cell bodies of the sensory neurons which make up the dorsal bundle. Each of these sensory neurons possesses two fibers; a long dendrite carries impulses from a receptor to the cell body in the thickened region, and a shorter axon

carries impulses from the cell body into the spinal cord. Any collected group of cell bodies found outside the brain or the spinal cord is referred to as a **ganglion.** The thickened region in the dorsal bundle of a spinal nerve is therefore called a **spinal ganglion** (Fig. 22.7). Inasmuch as there are 31 pairs of spinal nerves, each with a dorsal bundle, there are, correspondingly, 31 pairs of spinal ganglia. The ventral bundles of the spinal nerves are without ganglia. The cell bodies and dendrites of the motor neurons are embedded directly within the spinal cord, and only the long axon fibers project to the outside via the ventral bundles (see Fig. 22.6).

The spinal nerves innervate mainly the skeletal muscles in the chest, the abdomen, and the limbs, and they provide the pathways for numerous c.n.s. reflexes. In the familiar knee-jerk reflex, for example, an external mechanical stimulus first affects receptors in the knee-cap tendon (Fig. 22.8). Sensory impulses from there then travel into the spinal cord in the hip region, via sensory neurons in a spinal nerve. The spinal cord (like the brain) may be envisaged as a dense meshwork of neurons, interlinked by synapses (Fig. 22.9). Any impulse coming into the spinal cord thus can be relayed up, even as far as the brain, down, or laterally. However, among the hundreds of possible pathways available, a given incoming impulse is relayed into only a limited, selected number of pathways. Such path selection constitutes the principal control activity of the spinal cord. In the case of impulses from the knee-cap tendon, two principal paths are selected. One leads up into the brain, and impulses over that path produce conscious awareness of the mechanical stimulus

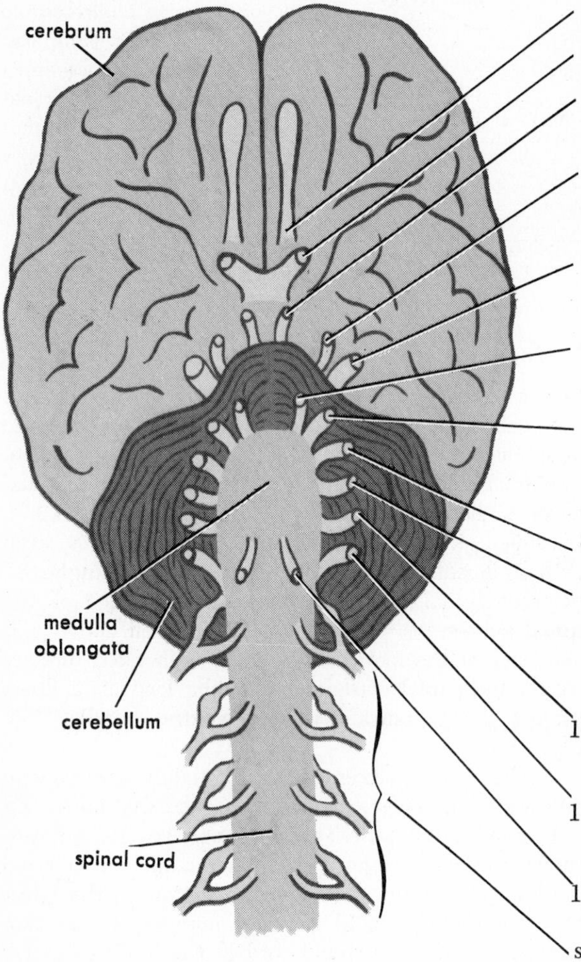

The nerves of the central nervous system

name	type	innervation
cerebrum		
1. olfactory	sensory	from nose
2. optic	sensory	from eye
3. oculomotor	motor	to muscles of eyeball
4. trochlear	motor	to muscles of eyeball
5. trigeminal	mixed	from and to face, teeth
6. abducens	motor	to muscles of eyeball
7. facial	mixed	from taste buds to salivary glands and facial muscles
8. auditory	sensory	from ear
9. glossopharyngeal	mixed	from and to pharynx, from taste buds to salivary glands
10. vagus	mixed	from and to chest and abdomen
11. spinal accessory	motor	to shoulder muscles
12. hypoglossal	motor	to tongue
spinal nerves (31 pairs)	mixed	from and to muscles in arms, legs, and trunk

Diagram labels: cerebrum, medulla oblongata, cerebellum, spinal cord

FIG. 22.5 Diagram of the underside of brain and anterior part of spinal cord, showing the origin of the cranial nerves and a few of the spinal nerves. The names and functions of these nerves are given in the accompanying tabulation.

affecting the knee. Simultaneously, impulses are channeled laterally to motor neurons close by at hip level. These neurons send motor impulses through spinal nerves which innervate the muscles of the leg. In response to the motor impulses, the muscles in the front part of the thigh contract and those in the hind part relax. As a result, the leg kicks out (see Fig. 22.8).

Note that this leg response is accompanied by, but does not depend on, awareness of the knee-tapping stimulus. The leg would kick out even during sleep or

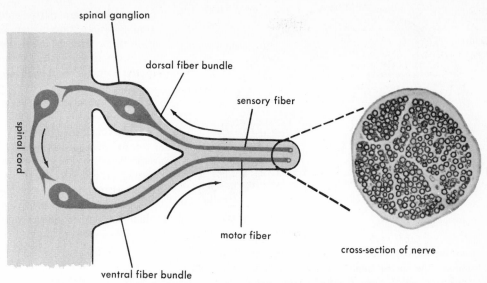

spinal ganglion

dorsal fiber bundle

sensory fiber

spinal cord

motor fiber

ventral fiber bundle

cross-section of nerve

FIG. 22.6   The structure of a spinal nerve. Many fibers, sensory, motor, or both, traveling together constitute a nerve. The photo inset shows what such a nerve looks like in cross section. In this particular section, note that each nerve fiber is enveloped by a myelin sheath (the dark rings). The arrows in the diagram indicate the direction of the nerve impulses. *(Photo courtesy of Dr. Mac V. Edds, Brown University.)*

FIG. 22.7   Enlarged view of a section through a spinal ganglion. Note the many nerve fibers, some seen in cross section, some in longitudinal section. *(Ward's Natural Science Establishment, Inc.)*

FIG. 22.8   A reflex arc in the central nervous system. The knee-jerk reflex is illustrated.

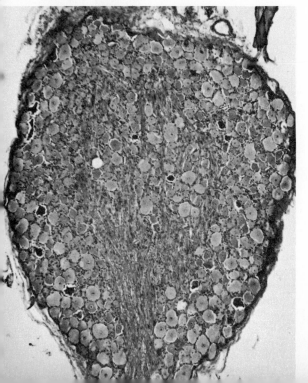

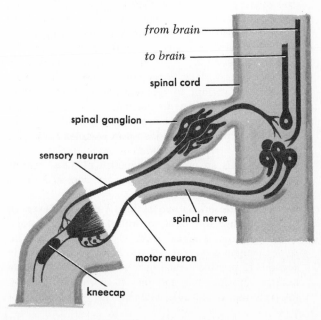

from brain

to brain

spinal cord

spinal ganglion

sensory neuron

spinal nerve

motor neuron

kneecap

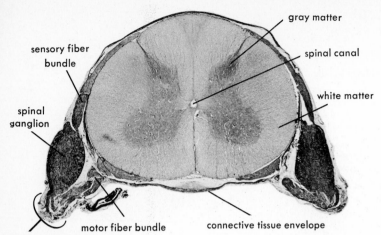

FIG. 22.9   Cross section through mammalian spinal cord. Note the spinal nerves, each dividing into two fiber bundles. The motor bundle connects with the cord ventrally, and the sensory bundle passes through a spinal ganglion and connects with the cord dorsally. The spinal cord itself is a dense meshwork of neurons, the cell bodies of which are aggregated around the center, forming so-called gray matter. The axons and dendrites of these neurons are collected around the gray matter, forming white matter. The central spinal canal contains lymphlike spinal fluid. *(Ward's Natural Science Establishment, Inc.)*

if the brain were destroyed. It is a general characteristic of c.n.s. reflexes that they become conscious, but consciousness is not a necessary condition for their completion. However, consciousness may bring about additional responses superimposed on a primary response. For example, if the knee should be tapped too violently, one is likely to cry out, get up, or run away, or one may attempt to suppress any such expressions of pain or annoyance. In general, consciousness may initiate new reflexes which modify the original response. The total response then adds up to complex subjective *behavior*, different for different individuals. Reflex modification is an important function of c.n.s. centers in the brain, and varied conscious behavior is a direct result.

The knee jerk is one of many **spinal reflexes,** so called because the basic neural path leads through spinal nerves and spinal cord. C.n.s. activity also includes numerous **cranial reflexes,** executed by the brain and the 12 pairs of cranial nerves. Such reflexes usually become conscious too, and they likewise control skeletal, voluntarily movable muscles. Large numbers of

c.n.s. reflexes are partly cranial, partly spinal. For example, visual stimuli may lead to muscular responses in arms or legs. In such cases the sensory portions of the reflexes are cranial, via the optic nerves, and the motor portions are spinal, via spinal nerves. Conversely, in other reflexes the sensory portions may be spinal and the motor portions may be cranial.

A.N.S. Pathways

Reflexes in the a.n.s. generally do not become conscious, regardless of whether they are routed through the brain or the spinal cord. And they regulate the functioning of body parts which are not under voluntary control: smooth muscles, the heart, and most glands and other internal organs.

Some *sensory* pathways of the a.n.s. have already been described in earlier contexts. For example, the

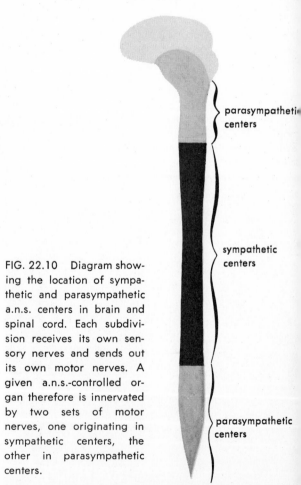

FIG. 22.10   Diagram showing the location of sympathetic and parasympathetic a.n.s. centers in brain and spinal cord. Each subdivision receives its own sensory nerves and sends out its own motor nerves. A given a.n.s.-controlled organ therefore is innervated by two sets of motor nerves, one originating in sympathetic centers, the other in parasympathetic centers.

stretch reflexes which regulate heart function involve sensory neurons from the vena cava and the aorta to the heart-rate center in the brain (see Chap. 21). Heart control is a purely autonomic, involuntary function; the heart-rate center, together with the nerve fibers to and from it, are part of the a.n.s. Similarly, every other internal organ which is not controllable by force of will is innervated by sensory a.n.s. fibers leading to a.n.s. centers in brain or spinal cord. Like the sensory neurons of the c.n.s., those of the a.n.s. similarly pass through ganglia. Indeed, the cell bodies of a.n.s. sensory neurons lie in the same 31 pairs of spinal ganglia which also contain the cell bodies of c.n.s. sensory neurons (see Fig. 22.12).

In brain and spinal cord, the centers of the a.n.s. are organized into two separate sets (Fig. 22.10). One set, located in the middle part of the spinal cord, represents the so-called **sympathetic** portion of the a.n.s. The other set, called the **parasympathetic** portion, is located both above and below the sympathetic portion. The upper parasympathetic centers thus reach into the brain, and we may note that all a.n.s. centers present in the brain belong to the parasympathetic system.

A given internal organ controlled by the a.n.s. receives motor fibers from some part of the sympathetic system *and* from some part of the parasympathetic system. Therefore, the *motor pathways* to every a.n.s.-controlled organ are double and come from two parts in brain or spinal cord. One of these two motor fibers stimulates the organ, the other inhibits it. In some cases, the stimulating fiber originates in the sympathetic system; in other cases, it originates in the parasympathetic system. For example, the fibers which accelerate the heart are sympathetic, and the fibers which slow the heart are parasympathetic. Analogously, the vasomotor fibers which constrict blood vessels come from the sympathetic system and the fibers which vasodilate come from the parasympathetic system. Such dual motor innervation of a.n.s.-controlled organs permits efficient adjustment of steady state; the net activity of an organ is a resultant of a given degree of stimulation or acceleration by one set of motor nerves and a given degree of inhibition or deceleration by another set of motor nerves. The a.n.s. motor controls of a number of other organs are illustrated in Fig. 22.11.

Note also that each motor path in the a.n.s. usually

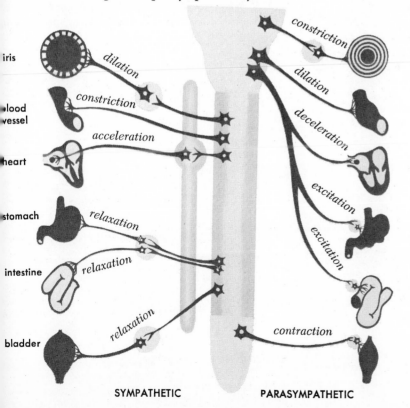

FIG. 22.11 Some of the motor pathways of the autonomic nervous system. The column left of the spinal cord represents sympathetic chain ganglia. Each neural path shown occurs pairwise, one on the left and one on the right of the body. Similarly, sympathetic chain ganglia occur to both the left and the right of the spinal cord. For simplicity, however, only one side is indicated in each case.

SYMPATHETIC   PARASYMPATHETIC

consists of at least two neurons, one following the other. These two neurons synapse in a ganglion located somewhere along the path to a given organ. The first motor neuron, which leads from spinal cord or brain to the ganglion, is called a **preganglionic fiber;** the second motor neuron, from ganglion to the organ, is called a **postganglionic fiber.** In the *sympathetic* system, preganglionic fibers in many cases terminate just outside the spinal cord in the so-called **sympathetic chain ganglia.** These a.n.s. ganglia form two interconnected chains, one along each side of the spinal cord (see Fig. 22.11). In such chain ganglia, terminating preganglionic fibers synapse with postganglionic fibers. The latter then innervate given organs (e.g., the sympathetic motor path to the heart). In other cases, sympathetic preganglionic fibers do not terminate in the chain ganglia but extend farther, to other a.n.s. ganglia located in various parts of the body. Postganglionic fibers then originate there (e.g., the sympathetic paths to stomach and intestine). Note that, in the vicinity of the spinal cord, sympathetic motor fibers (and indeed also sensory fibers) travel together with the fibers of the mixed spinal nerves of the c.n.s. The anatomical interrelations are indicated in Fig. 22.12.

The motor paths of the *parasympathetic* system do not lead through the sympathetic chains. Neverthe-

less, such paths consist analogously of preganglionic and postganglionic portions, specific ganglia being located along the way to given organs (see Fig. 22.11). Moreover, parasympathetic fibers too may run together with c.n.s. nerves. For example, the parasympathetic inhibitory fibers to the heart utilize the pathway of the vagus nerve (see Chap. 21), which otherwise contains c.n.s. fibers and is actually listed as a cranial nerve of the c.n.s.

C.N.S.–A.N.S. Interrelations

Reference has been made in several instances above to the close anatomical interconnection between the c.n.s. and the a.n.s. Thus, brain and spinal cord contain the centers of both c.n.s. and a.n.s.; spinal ganglia contain cell bodies of both c.n.s. and a.n.s. sensory neurons; and given mixed nerves may contain both c.n.s. and a.n.s. fibers. In addition to such structural interrelations, intimate functional interrelations are in evidence. For example, c.n.s.-controlled visual experiences may affect a.n.s.-controlled blood circulation. A frightening sight may initiate a c.n.s. reflex from the eyes to the visual center in the brain and from there to the muscles of the legs. This might lead to running and to deliberate, conscious avoidance of the frightening sight. At the same time, heart rate increases

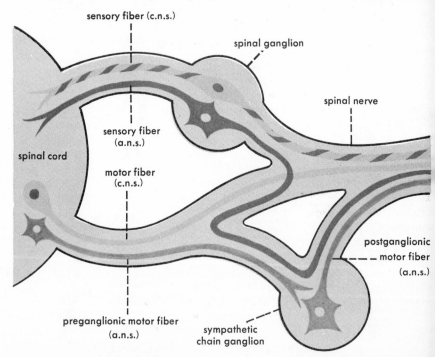

FIG. 22.12 The anatomical interrelations of spinal c.n.s. and sympathetic a.n.s. nerve fibers. Note that a given fiber bundle or nerve connecting with the spinal cord contains sensory fibers of both c.n.s. and sympathetic a.n.s., motor fibers of both c.n.s. and sympathetic a.n.s., or both sensory and motor fibers of both c.n.s. and sympathetic a.n.s. Sensory fibers of all kinds always enter the spinal cord dorsally, and motor fibers of all kinds always leave the cord ventrally.

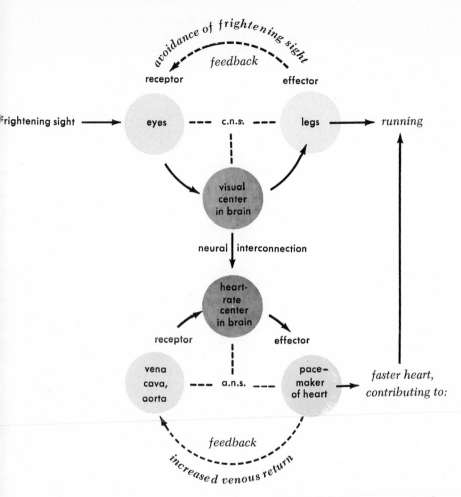

FIG. 22.13 The functional interconnection between the c.n.s. and a.n.s. In the example shown here, a sense perception registered via the c.n.s. leads to coordinated responses controlled by both the c.n.s. and the a.n.s. Note the effect of the a.n.s.-controlled heart on the c.n.s.-controlled running.

and blood pressure rises. Evidently, impulses coming into the visual center from the eyes are relayed also via interneurons to the heart-rate and vasomotor centers. Only such information relays between c.n.s. and a.n.s. can produce an adaptive total response, for voluntary running could not be long sustained without an appropriate involuntary adjustment of the body circulation (Fig. 22.13).

Indeed, a frightening sight is likely to bring into play many additional a.n.s. reflexes as well; breathing will be affected, adrenalin output will increase, sweat glands will be activated, the alimentary system will be inhibited—in short, the whole body will tend to rally into a state of emergency. We may note generally that a.n.s. and c.n.s. are geared together so intimately that any reflex in one system is likely to initiate one or more concurrent reflexes in the other.

Thus are outlined the structural arrangements of the neural pathways. How do these pathways function? What is a nerve impulse, and how is it transmitted?

NERVE IMPULSES

The precise nature of a nerve impulse is still unknown. We may say, in general, that an impulse is a sequence of metabolic reactions propagated along a nerve fiber. After an impulse has passed, the reaction balance returns to the original state, readying the fiber for a new impulse. These processes consume oxygen and energy.

Accompanying the chemical changes are electrical phenomena. Indeed, the intriguing resemblance of the nervous system to a meshwork of electrical wires conducting electrical currents has been the basis of many attempts to explain nervous activity. Moreover, just as one can measure currents in wires by galvanometers, voltmeters, ammeters, and the like, so this same electrical equipment can be used on nerves. But nerve impulses are not simply electrical impulses. The latter travel some 100,000 miles per sec in a wire, the former about 100 yd per sec in a nerve fiber. Nerve impulses are neither purely electrical nor purely chemical, and at present they may best be described as *electro-chemical* events.

Fiber Transmission

Before a nerve fiber can transmit an impulse, it must be stimulated *adequately*. Whereas any environmental change may represent a stimulus, not every such change represents an adequate stimulus. To be adequate, a stimulus must be at least of minimum strength, or *threshold intensity;* it must reach this threshold intensity fast enough, at an appropriately high *rate of change;* and it must last long enough and thus have appropriate *duration*. When a neuron is stimulated adequately, it will "fire," i.e., transmit an impulse from the point of stimulation over its fibers. Under normal conditions within the body, stimulation occurs at a dendrite terminal and an impulse then travels through or past the cell body to an axon terminal.

Whatever else an impulse may be, it is known that it is a *wave of electrical depolarization* sweeping along a nerve fiber. It can be shown that a resting, nonstimulated neuron is electrically positive along the outer side of its surface membrane and electrically negative along the inner side (Fig. 22.14). These electric charges are carried by mineral ions attached to the two sides of the neuron membrane. As a result, an *electrical potential* is maintained across the cell membrane, and the membrane is said to be *polarized* electrically. In some ways this resembles the polarization believed to be maintained in the actomyosin units of muscles (see Chap. 17).

FIG. 22.14   The polarization of an inactive resting neuron. The positive charges on the outside and the negative charges on the inside produce an electric potential across the cell membrane.

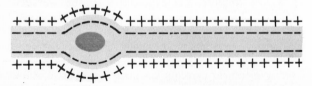

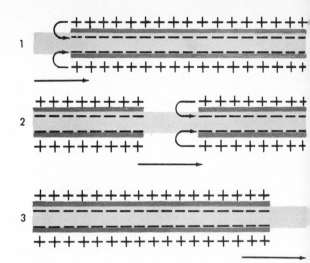

FIG. 22.15   The passage of an impulse through a nerve fiber produces a local depolarization and destruction of the permeability properties of the fiber membrane, propagated in a wavelike manner through successive portions of the fiber. After an impulse has passed a given region, the original polarization and membrane characteristics reappear.

Polarization, as well as the integrity of a neuron membrane, appears to depend on *semipermeability*. The membrane is so constructed that it prevents the positive and negative ions from coming together. If semipermeability were destroyed, the membrane would depolarize; i.e., the positive and negative ions *would* join. Conversely, if depolarization were to occur, membrane semipermeability would be abolished.

When a nerve impulse sweeps along a nerve fiber, local depolarization and simultaneous destruction of semipermeability actually do occur at successive points of the fiber membrane. As this happens at any one point, an avenue is created through which positive and negative ions of an adjacent point may meet (Fig. 22.15). In other words, the impulse itself produces the necessary conditions which allow it to advance farther. In this manner, it travels wavelike along a fiber. Some short time after an impulse has passed a given point, the membrane at that point recovers; both the polarization and the semipermeability are restored.

These electrical aspects of transmission may be demonstrated experimentally. For example, it is possible to expose a nerve of a test animal and to connect a galvanometer to this nerve with fine wires (Fig. 22.16). When the nerve is then stimulated, the needle of the galvanometer is deflected in one direction as the impulse passes the first wire contact and in the opposite direction as it passes the second. This indicates that electrical changes occur during impulse transmission. Moreover, the test reveals that the particular portion of the fiber which carries the impulse at any given moment is electrically less positive on the surface than the remainder of the fiber. This is what should be expected if an impulse were to cause local depolarization, i.e., reduction or removal of the outer positive charge. The current flow accompanying impulse transmission is called the action current, or the **action potential**, of a nerve fiber. By measuring the action potentials of different nerves, one may determine many of the characteristics of the impulses these nerves carry, e.g., speeds, frequencies, and strengths. In some nerve fibers, impulses are fired continuously and in fairly rapid succession. This is the case, for example, in the motor fibers from the heart-rate center to the heart. Adjustment of heart rate is brought about by "frequency modulation"; heart rate changes when the frequency of the impulses changes. In other cases, a fiber is normally at rest and carries impulses only when an effector response is to be brought about. For example, in fibers to many glands, impulses are sent only as long as the glands are to secrete. Each type of fiber has its own characteristic pattern of impulse transmission.

What happens when an impulse reaches an axon terminal? How does it jump across the gap of the synapse to the dendrite terminal of a neighboring neuron?

Synaptic Transmission

Synapses appear to be bridged by chemical processes. In certain cases it can be shown that, when an impulse reaches an axon terminal, the terminal acts like a miniature endocrine gland; it secretes minute amounts of a hormone. This hormone diffuses through the synaptic gap; some of it eventually reaches dendrite terminals of adjacent neurons, and the hormone there affects a dendrite in such a way that a new impulse is initiated in it (Fig. 22.17).

Two different hormones are known to play a role in synaptic transmission. One is *adrenalin* or a substance very similar to adrenalin in chemical structure and biological effect. This hormone is secreted by the axon terminals of the postganglionic fibers of the sympathetic a.n.s. Because they produce adrenalin, these fibers are said to be **adrenergic**.

The preganglionic fibers of the sympathetic sys-

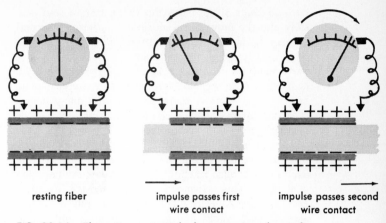

resting fiber · impulse passes first wire contact · impulse passes second wire contact

FIG. 22.16   The action potential of a nerve impulse. Left, resting fiber, connected to galvanometer by wire contacts. Middle, impulse passes first wire contact, which becomes electronegative relative to second contact. Hence current flows through galvanometer from right to left, as indicated by deflected galvanometer needle. Right, impulse passes second wire contact. Current now flows in opposite direction, the second contact being electronegative relative to the first. Current flow accompanying an impulse represents the action potential of that impulse.

FIG. 22.17   Diagram of a neural synapse, showing the release and local spreading of hormones from the axon terminal of one fiber to the dendrite terminal of another. Impulses are transmitted across synapses by such chemical means.

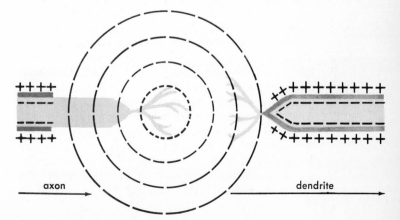

axon · dendrite

tem, all fibers of the parasympathetic system, and possibly also the nerve fibers of the c.n.s. secrete a second type of hormone, namely, *acetylcholine*. We have already encountered this substance in Chap. 17 as a participant in the generation of bioelectricity in specialized electric organs. More commonly, acetylcholine brings about impulse transmission across many neural synapses. Acetylcholine-secreting fibers are said to be **cholinergic.**

In synapses formed by cholinergic fibers, an enzyme is present which splits acetylcholine into separate acetyl and choline fractions and so makes the hormone ineffective. This enzyme is *choline esterase*. Its presence is advantageous adaptively. If it did not exist, acetylcholine would linger in the synapse and would stimulate dendrites repeatedly. If, therefore, two impulses came into a synapse in rapid succession, acetylcholine produced by the first would still be effective when the second produced more hormone. The impulses would then merge into each other and the result would be one long drawn-out response, not two sharply distinct responses. Choline esterase prevents the merging of impulses. There is just time for acetylcholine to stimulate dendrites once or a few times and the hormone is destroyed immediately thereafter.

An equivalent enzyme cannot be demonstrated in the synapses formed by adrenergic fibers; adrenalin does have a lingering effect. This circumstance contributes to the comparative slowness and sustained quality of responses produced by the sympathetic part of the a.n.s.

The consequences of synaptic impulse transmission by chemicals are far-reaching. For example, diffusion takes much longer than impulse conduction within a fiber. A complete reflex, which usually passes through many synapses, consequently lasts longer than would be expected on the basis of impulse speeds within fibers alone. Being "slow on the uptake" is largely a result of delays at synapses. Moreover, nerve fibers as such rarely fatigue but synapses get "tired" fairly easily. During intensive activity, axon terminals may temporarily exhaust their hormone-secreting capacity and synaptic transmission then slows even more or stops altogether for the time being.

Note that the synaptic hormones impose a one-way direction on neural pathways. A nerve fiber can be stimulated artificially at either end or in the middle, and impulses then travel backward, forward, or in both directions. But only axon terminals are specialized to secrete hormones and only dendrite terminals are sensitive to these hormones. As a result, the conduction of impulses is unidirectional.

The *first* nerve impulse in a reflex arc is normally produced by a sensory receptor. Such structures start all nervous activity, and on their functioning depend all subsequent neural events. How are receptors constructed and how do they work?

THE NEURAL RECEPTORS

Eyes do not see, ears do not hear; sensory receptors of any sort only translate incoming stimuli into nerve impulses. Such impulses must then be transmitted to appropriate neural centers, and there the impulses must be interpreted. We may therefore note that seeing, hearing, or "sensing" of any other kind depends on a cooperative functioning of a sensory receptor *and a* sensory nerve path *and* a neural center.

Mammals possess many more than the familiar five senses of vision, hearing, smell, taste, and touch. They also sense pain, pressure, heat, and cold. They sense the position of their limbs and the mechanical equilibrium and the motion of their bodies, all without looking. They possess a genital sense, and they experience distinct sensations when tickled, when a limb "falls asleep," when the skin "stings" or "burns," and when they are hungry, thirsty, or sleepy. These are only some of the numerous senses which penetrate into the conscious. In at least as many other senses conscious awareness is lacking. For example, when a blood vessel dilates under pressure, sensing occurs even though it is unconscious.

A separate type of receptor structure probably does not exist for each of these senses. Only about a dozen different kinds of receptors are demonstrable. They mediate different sensations when they are stimulated singly and when a varied group of them is stimulated together. Receptors are often classified as **exteroceptors** and **interoceptors,** i.e., structures receiving information either about the outside world or about the interior of the body. Some types of receptors occur in large numbers, and each such type is distributed widely throughout the body. Other receptor types are represented in greatly limited numbers, and these are found in circumscribed body regions only, principally in the head. We shall discuss the abundant receptors first.

DISPERSED RECEPTORS

Structural Types

The simplest type of neural receptor is a free nerve ending (Fig. 22.18). In many cases, the hairlike dendrite terminals of sensory neurons also carry a series of nodular thickenings or are bunched together like balls of twine. Other parts are not present, however. Relatively simply constructed sensory endings of this sort are probably the most widespread, and they relay a.n.s. signals from many internal organs as well as a large variety of c.n.s. signals. For example, plain or variously nodulated and coiled sensory endings mediate the sense of pain and also muscle and tendon sense (which inform about the position of body parts).

Moreover, comparatively simple nerve endings represent one type of receptor for touch stimuli. Each hair in the skin is surrounded at its base by a network of sensory fiber terminals. When a hair is bent, the position of the hair base changes slightly and this stimulates the fiber terminals. The resulting nerve impulses are interpreted as touch sensations.

Touch stimuli are received additionally by true sense *organs* located in the skin. These are tiny structures made up of many specialized cells (not neurons), and they are innervated by sensory fiber terminals (see Fig. 22.18). In these instances it is the organ, not the fiber terminal, which translates stimulus energies into nerve impulses. Touch organs may be clustered together relatively densely, as in fingertips, palms, and lips, or they may occur sparsely, as on the back.

In addition to touch organs, the skin also contains tiny organs sensitive to heat, to cold, and to pressure. Together with the numerous touch organs and pain fibers in the skin, these make up the so-called **cutaneous receptors**. They vary in relative distribution and in number. It is estimated that the human skin contains some 4 million pain receptors, half a million pressure receptors, 150,000 cold receptors, and 16,000 heat receptors.

Functional Properties

Very little is known about the mechanism by which specific stimuli, affecting either the tiny sense organs or the free sensory nerve endings, actually pro-

FIG. 22.18   Some types of neural receptors in the skin. *A*, free nerve ending (pain). *B*, nerve net surrounding hair (touch). *C*, Pacinian corpuscle (pressure). *D*, organ of Ruffini (pressure). *E*, organ of Krause (cold). *F*, end organ of Ruffini (warmth). *G*, Meissner's corpuscle (touch).

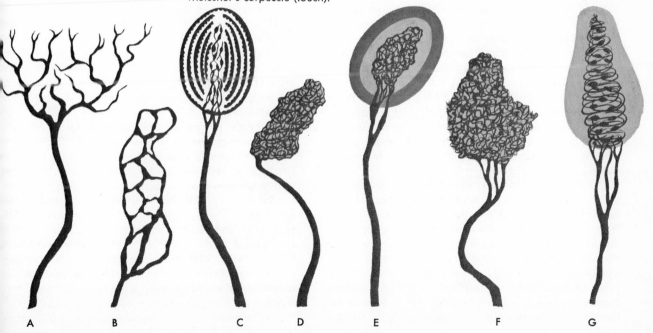

A   B   C   D   E   F   G

duce nerve impulses. Environmental change as such is known to be an important factor, for when a given stimulus persists unchanged for a time, a sense dulls or "adapts." For example, we soon become relatively insensitive to the pressure of clothes, to a persistent odor, or to a taste. Ease of adaptation varies considerably. Pain is most difficult to adapt to, but odor perception dulls very easily. We cannot judge our own body odors, for example. We live with them constantly and we are continuously adapted to them.

Sensations depend on stimulation of *appropriate* receptors. Thus, a feeling of pressure can be produced only by impulses from pressure receptors; pressure stimuli cannot register in heat receptors, for example. However, given stimuli may affect more than one kind of receptor simultaneously, in which case a composite sensation is perceived. For example, simultaneous impulses from heat and pain receptors may give rise to a burning sensation. In a hot shower, both hot and cold receptors may be affected and one may feel hot and cold at the same time. Ice on the skin may produce sensations of burning, through simultaneous stimulation of cold, heat, and pain points.

It can be shown dramatically that the different kinds of sense perceptions depend not so much on impulse differences as on the different *central connections* of nerve fibers. For example, suppose that a fiber from a heat receptor and a fiber from a cold receptor were cut and that the cut ends were allowed to reinnervate the sense organs in switched order. The fiber from the heat receptor would then terminate in the cold center of the brain and the fiber from the cold receptor would terminate in the heat center. Under such conditions, the animal would feel hot every time the cold receptor was stimulated and cold every time the heat receptor was stimulated. Evidently, the quality of a sensation is determined not by the receptor nor by the type of nerve impulse sent by the receptor, but by the neural centers. The sensation depends on which of various centers receives signals.

Furthermore, correct *localization* of a stimulus similarly depends on the central connections. If pain fibers from hand and foot were switched as above, then a needle prick on the foot would prompt immediate examination of the hand for blood, and vice versa. We may note that the anatomical distribution of receptors throughout the body is matched virtually point for point in the anatomical distribution of neural centers. Each receptor has its neural center, and so long as the structural relationships are preserved, impulses will be correctly interpreted as coming from particular body regions and particular receptors.

This generalization should be qualified in one respect. It is fairly common experience that pain which originates in an internal organ is often sensed as if it originated at some remote skin area or at another distant internal region. For example, pain stimuli actually affecting the liver may be felt as pain in the shoulder region. Pain in the uterus may be erroneously thought to originate in forehead, chest, and palm of hand. Similarly, an ache in one tooth is often thought to come from the whole side of the head. In all such cases of **referred pain,** pain fibers originating in different body regions lead into the same general area in the brain or spinal cord. Impulses arriving through one of the fibers may stimulate a greater or lesser portion of that area, as if impulses actually arrived over more than one pain fiber. As a result, pain sensations may be diffuse and may be referred to numerous body regions.

We proceed now to a discussion of the sense organs of the tongue, the nose, the eye, and the ear. These localized receptors are the most familiar, the most elaborate both structurally and functionally, and in all animals also the most important.

TASTE AND SMELL

The Tongue

Our reduced tasting ability when the nose is blocked with a cold reveals that smell is an integral component of "taste." The receptors on the tongue are affected by chemicals in *solution*, whereas the receptors in the nasal epithelium are affected by *vapors* of chemicals. Our sensory judgment about a substance is keenest when impulses from both tongue and nose reach neural centers.

Clusters of elongated ciliated cells, set into depressions in the tongue, form **taste buds** (Fig. 22.19). Sensory fiber terminals from each of the bud cells lead into the brain. Taste buds are distributed all over the upper tongue surface. Structural differences among buds cannot be demonstrated, but well-known functional differences exist; the four primary taste sensations, *sweet, sour, salty,* and *bitter,* arise through stimulation of buds at different regions of the tongue. Bitter substances primarily affect buds located at the back of the tongue; sweet substances, buds in the forward part of the tongue; and sour and salty materials are tasted predominantly along the tongue edges (Fig. 22.20).

Like other sense perceptions, tasting too depends

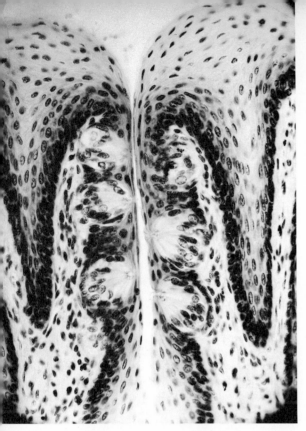

FIG. 22.19 Portion of a section through the tongue, showing taste buds. The buds are located along a deep narrow channel leading into the tongue from the surface. (General Biological Supply House, Inc.)

on the central connections. Certain chemicals produce a sweet sensation when applied to the tongue tip but a bitter sensation when applied at the back of the tongue. Evidently, chemicals possess not "inherent" taste but only the property of stimulating or not stimulating this or that taste bud. And depending on which of the tongue areas sends impulses to its unique brain connections, a given subjective taste sensation will be registered.

Therefore, to say that "sugar is sweet" erroneously implies an objective property of sugar. Sweetness is a subjective sensation; the only pertinent objective property of sugar is its capacity to stimulate certain taste buds. In different individuals, one and the same sugar may produce qualitatively and quantitatively different sensations of sweetness. There is at least one known substance (*phenylthiocarbamide*) which one person may not taste at all, but which might taste sweet to another, bitter to a third, salty to a fourth, and sour to a fifth. Individual differences of this sort trace back to differences in heredity.

Taste buds are highly sensitive receptors. Quinine, for example, a substance normally producing a bitter taste, generally can be sensed in concentrations as low as 1 part in 2 or 3 million parts of water.

Numerous composite tastes are built up from different combinations and intensities of the four basic tastes, from smell, and from other sense perceptions initiated in the mouth. For example, both a hot meal and a cold meal affect the same taste buds if the two meals are alike chemically. But the hot meal vaporizes more and therefore smells more, and it also stimulates heat receptors in the lining of the mouth and on the tongue. The hot and the cold meals consequently taste different.

The Nose

Varied as taste sensations are, odor perceptions are even more diversified. Attempts to establish basic odors from which all others can be derived have met with relatively little success. A fairly adequate scheme can be constructed on the basis of four primary odors, *rancid, vinegary, fragrant,* and *burnt,* each classified in various intensities.

Part of the ciliated lining in the upper nasal passages is the receptor tissue for the sense of smell in vertebrates. Sensory fibers lead into the **olfactory lobe** of the brain, relatively small in man but large in other vertebrates. Man is a comparatively poor smeller, but in most other vertebrates the sense of smell is as well developed and has the same outstanding importance as vision in man.

As among taste buds, structural differences among the cells of the nasal epithelium cannot be detected. Moreover, it is virtually impossible to determine which receptor cells in the nose mediate perception of what odors. Are there as many functionally different types of receptor cells and central fiber connections as there

FIG. 22.20 Diagrams of the tongue, showing the distribution of taste buds for the four taste sensations.

sweet   sour   salty   bitter

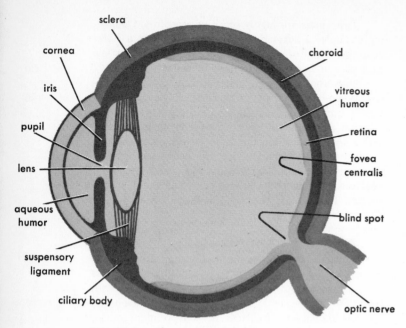

FIG. 22.21   The structure of the eye.

FIG. 22.22   Focusing in camera and in eye. Upper figures, images fall short of photographic film and retina. Lower figures, camera is focused by changing the lens-film distance, and eye is focused by changing the curvature of the lens.

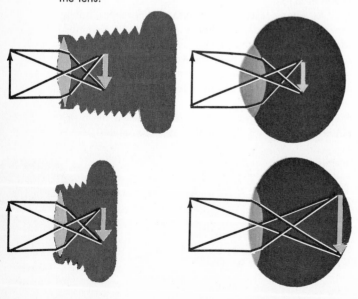

are different odors? Probably not. Is each **receptor cell** capable of emitting as many different types of impulses as there are different odors? Again, probably not. When the perception of one odor dulls by adaptation, perception of other odors is usually not dulled. This suggests that at least some measure of functional distinction among receptor cells and central connections probably does exist. Each receptor cell may perhaps be able to emit a different type of impulse pattern for each of a small group of different odors. Paradoxically, our understanding of smelling mechanisms is much less satisfactory than that of the more complex visual and auditory mechanisms.

VISION

The human eye is among the most efficient light receptors developed during evolution. Insect eyes possibly are better adapted for the detection of motion, and many vertebrates have a larger visual field without moving their heads than man. But the human visual apparatus probably registers color more clearly than that of any other animal, and human eyes are virtually as light-sensitive as eyes can possibly get.

The Eye

The eye is made up of three coats (Fig. 22.21): an outer **sclera,** fibrous in man, cartilaginous in many other mammals; a middle **choroid,** a layer which is pigmented black and carries blood vessels to and from the eye; and an inner **retina,** the actual light-receptor tissue. In many mammals, a thin film of white-green crystalline material coats the choroid layer. This material reflects light and makes the eyes of these animals shine and glow in the dark.

In the front part of the eye, the three coats are modified structurally. The sclera merges into the transparent **cornea.** The choroid coat continues as the sometimes pigmented **iris,** which encloses the **pupil.** Just behind the iris is a ring-shaped muscle, the **ciliary body,** to which the **lens** is attached by ligaments. The spaces between lens and cornea are filled with the fluid, lymphlike **aqueous humor;** and the space between lens and retina contains a glassy, jellylike material, the **vitreous humor.**

Functionally, the eye resembles a photographic camera. But whereas a camera is focused by varying the distance between lens and film, the eye is focused by adjustment of the curvature of the lens; the distance between lens and retina remains fixed (Fig. 22.22). A beam of light passes through the cornea and through the pupil into the lens. The pupillary opening corresponds to the diaphragm of a camera; it enlarges or becomes smaller and so regulates the amount of light admitted into the eye. This control mechanism is set into operation by light itself. Intense light initiates a reflex via retina, the autonomic nervous system, and a set of circularly arranged muscles in the iris. These muscles contract and the pupil becomes smaller. Conversely, low light intensity results in reflex signals to a set of iris muscles arranged like the spokes of a wheel. When these muscles contract, the pupil of the eye enlarges (see Fig. 22.11).

The lens focuses an object onto the retina. When a far-off object is viewed and when the eye is at rest, the lens is fairly flat. As an object moves nearer, the lens curves out increasingly (Fig. 22.23). Lens shape is controlled by the ciliary body. When this muscular ring is relaxed, the ligaments holding the lens are taut and the lens is flat. Conversely, when the ciliary muscle contracts, the lens ligaments relax and the lens, an elastic structure, is then allowed to curve out. The ciliary muscle is under reflex control. A blurred image on the retina elicits reflex impulses to the ciliary body. These impulses produce contraction or relaxation of the ciliary body until the image is no longer blurred. The adjustment reflex then ceases and a focused image so reaches the retina. Note that the image of an object is projected on the retina in an inverted position, just as an image is inverted on the film of a camera.

FIG. 22.23 Focusing when object changes distance. Left, far object, flat lens. Right, near object, curved lens. Lens curves out when the muscles of the ciliary body contract.

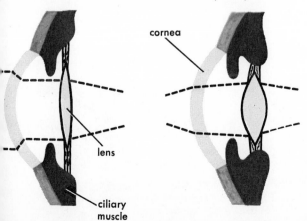

cornea

lens

ciliary muscle

The Retina

This tissue is made up of several layers of neurons and of one layer of **rods** and **cones**. These are the receptor cells which translate light energy into nerve impulses (Fig. 22.24). The rod and cone layer is adjacent to the choroid coat; light must therefore pass through the neuron layers before it reaches the rods and cones. The light-sensitive cells connect functionally with the neurons of the retina, and the neurons in turn synapse among one another in intricate ways. Nerve fibers from the whole inner surface of the retina eventually collect in one region and form the **optic nerve** to the brain. Where this nerve leaves the eye, somewhat off-center, it interrupts the continuity of the rod and cone layer and of the choroid and sclera. This area of discontinuity is the **blind spot,** so called since visual images cannot be formed in it (Fig. 22.25).

Cones are responsible for color vision and for the perception of sharp, bright images. The greatest concentration of cone cells is found in the **fovea centralis,** a tiny depression in the center of the retina. Only cones are present in this area; rods are absent. Also absent are overlying neurons, and the cones are therefore exposed to light directly. By virtue of its dense accumulation of cones, the fovea permits the most acute vision. The concentration of cone cells decreases with increasing distance from the fovea, and at the retinal periphery cones do not occur at all. Rods, on the other hand, are particularly abundant there. Rod cells are sensitive to dim light, and they serve importantly in black-and-white vision and in the detection of motion, particularly motion along the lateral edges of the visual field. Rods are distributed more sparsely away from the retinal periphery and are absent altogether in the fovea.

Some of the chemical aspects of light reception are known for rods. These cells contain **rhodopsin,** a photosensitive pigment also called "visual purple." Rhodopsin consists of two linked fractions, namely, a **retinene** part, which is a derivative of vitamin A, and an **opsin** part, which is a protein. When light strikes rhodopsin, the molecule splits into separate retinene and opsin components and a nerve impulse is produced at the same time. In the dark and with the aid of respiratory energy, retinene and opsin are recombined and visual purple is regenerated in this manner (Fig. 22.26). In very intense light, visual purple may be split faster than it can be regenerated. Vision may then become impaired (e.g., snow blindness). A similar re-

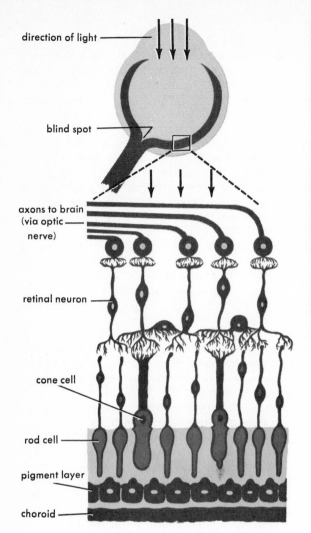

direction of light

blind spot

axons to brain
(via optic
nerve)

retinal neuron

cone cell

rod cell

pigment layer

choroid

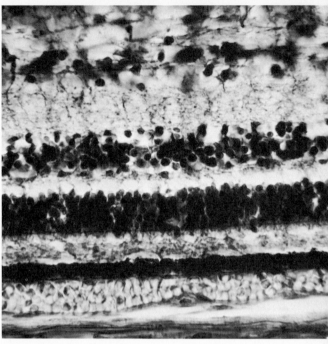

FIG. 22.24 The diagram illustrates the retina in section, greatly simplified. Note that the neuron layers of the retina are toward the inside of the eye and that light must pass through these layers before it reaches the photosensitive rods and cones. The photo shows a cross section through a portion of the human retina. The layered structure is clearly in evidence. Dark round bodies are cell nuclei. *(Photo courtesy of Dr. B. J. Serber, College of Medicine, New York University.)*

FIG. 22.25 Section through the blind spot. The retina is toward the top of the photo. Note the neuron layers at the surface of the retina and the merging of the neuron fibers at the depression of the blind spot, forming the optic nerve. This thick nerve leads downward in the photo. *(Ward's Natural Science Establishment, Inc.)*

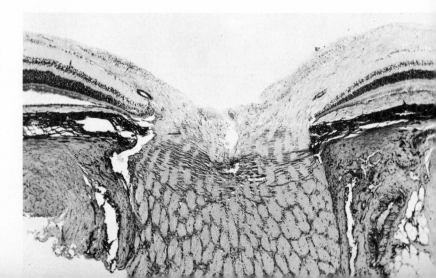

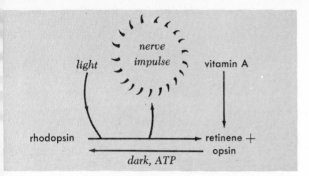

FIG. 22.26 The pattern of the chemistry of rod vision. Note that vitamin A may replenish the supply of retinene and thus indirectly the supply of visual purple (rhodopsin).

sult would follow if vitamin A were in deficient supply, for retinene could not be synthesized.

Light-initiated chemical reactions which produce nerve impulses occur in cone cells also, but the details of these processes are still very poorly known. Are there different cones for each color? Probably not. Any color, including white, can be produced from various combinations and intensities of three primary colors, namely, red, yellow, and blue. Most theories of color vision presuppose that three functionally different cone types exist, one for each primary color. Color television is based on an analogous principle.

Impulse Interpretation

An external object is "pictured" on the retina as a series of points, like the points of a newspaper photograph. Each point corresponds to a rod or a cone. Impulses from these points are transmitted into the brain according to the following pattern.

All fibers from the left sides of *both* eyes lead into the left half of the brain; all fibers from the right sides of both eyes lead into the right half of the brain (Fig. 22.27). In each brain hemisphere the fibers from the eyes lead to an **optic lobe** which contains the visual centers. It can be shown that for each group of rods and cones there exists a corresponding group of interpreter neurons in the visual centers. In other words, the "point picture" of an object on the retina is duplicated more or less faithfully in the optic lobes, by impulses from specific rods and cones to their correlated interpreter neurons. In these neurons the impulses register as vision.

It should be clear that the left half of every external field of vision produces images in the right halves of both eyes. Similarly, the right half of what can be seen is focused onto the left halves of both retinas (see Fig. 22.27). Therefore, in view of the fiber patterns from the eyes to the brain, the right half of a field of vision registers in the left half of the brain and the left half of a vision field registers in the right half of the brain. The left and right optic lobes are not directly continuous. Yet interpreter activity normally is such that the "left" picture of the external world is superimposed smoothly on the "right" picture. Moreover, both halves of the picture are sensed right side up, even though the retinas receive inverted images. Left and right pictures sometimes fail to superimpose smoothly (e.g., under the influence of alcohol), in which case one "sees double."

Why is an inverted retinal image not also "seen"

FIG. 22.27 The nerve fiber tracts from eye to brain. An object in the left field of vision registers on the right halves of both retinas, and impulses are transmitted into the right half of the brain.

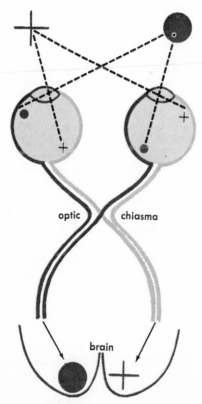

optic   chiasma

brain

as an inverted picture? The answer is that the optic centers in the brain have learned to give visual experiences correct orientations. Recognition of up and down and of space orientation generally is based ultimately on sensing the direction of gravitational pull. Muscles and ears play an important role in this, as the next section will show. Therefore, even if retinal images actually arrived in the optic lobes in an inverted position, gravity perception would teach one, soon after birth, to associate the bottom part of a picture with the idea of "up" and the upper part with the idea of "down." Without gravity (as in outer space), the frame of reference for space orientation is lacking and the notion of "right-side-upness" becomes meaningless.

How do impulses coming into the vision centers actually produce a conscious sensation of light? How indeed does any other sense become conscious? Answers to such questions cannot be given as yet. However, it is known that immense numbers of neural paths lead from the vision centers to virtually all other centers in the brain and spinal cord. Consequently, a tremendous number of reflexes can be initiated through the receptor cells in the eyes. It is this which makes the sense of vision so important to most animals.

THE EAR

In mammals, this organ houses receptors for three different senses: the sense of **static body balance,** the sense of **dynamic body balance,** and the sense of **hearing.**

The **outer ear** carries sound to the **eardrum,** a membrane which separates the cavity of the **middle ear** from the outside (Fig. 22.28). The connection of this cavity with the mouth, via the eustachian tube, has already been referred to in Chap. 15. Three tiny middle-ear bones, **hammer, anvil,** and **stirrup,** moved by the smallest muscles in the body, form an adjustable bridge from the eardrum across the middle-ear cavity to the **inner ear.** The latter is closed off from the middle ear by two membranes. One is stretched across a so-called **round window** and the other across an **oval window.** The stirrup bone of the middle ear is anchored to the membrane of the oval window.

The inner ear is an intricate system of interconnected canals and spaces, all surrounded by bone and filled with a lymphlike fluid. Three main subdivisions may be distinguished: a chamber consisting of two parts, the **utricle** and the **saccule;** the **semicircular canals;** and the **cochlea,** a structure coiled like a snail

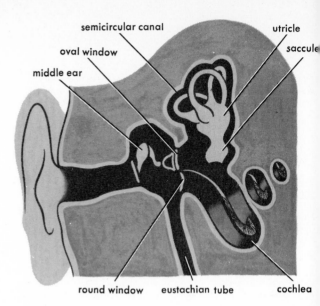

FIG. 22.28 The gross structure of the ear. Note ear bones in the middle-ear cavity and attachment of semicircular canals to utricle.

shell. Each of these subdivisions contains the receptor structures for one of the three senses listed above.

Static Balance

The receptors for this sense are located in the *utricle* and the *saccule*. At several places along the walls of these chambers, clusters of specialized cells are found. Sensory nerve fibers lead off from one side of such cells and ciliumlike hairs project from the other side. The tips of the hairs of a cell cluster attach to a tiny **ear stone,** a calcium-containing body (Fig. 22.29). When the stone is in a certain position, it pulls on some of the hairs more than on others and this stimulates the cells to which the hairs are connected. Nerve impulses from the hair cells to the brain register the particular position of the ear stone. When the head is tilted or when the balance of the body as a whole is changed, then gravity acts on all the ear stones and shifts them in a given manner. Such a change in the position of the stones produces pull on different sets of hair cells. Correspondingly different sets of impulses to the brain then inform of the change in balance. Reflex signals from the brain to appropriate muscles subsequently ensure that equilibrium is not lost.

This sense permits recognition of up, down, side, front, and back, even when visual stimuli and sensory impulses from muscles fail to provide such recognition. A blindfolded mammal with inoperative ear-stone receptors has difficulty in remaining upright. And when its position is abnormal, it does little to correct this position.

Dynamic Balance

The sense of movement and of dynamic body balance is mediated by the *semicircular canals*. Three such canals are present in each ear, and they loop from the utricle back to the utricle. The canals are placed at right angles to one another in the three planes of space (see Fig. 22.28). At one end of each canal is an enlarged portion in which is found a cluster of hair cells, rather similar to those described above. However, an ear stone is not present and the hairs are longer.

When the head is moved, the semicircular canals move with the head. But the fluid in the canals "stays behind" temporarily as a result of its inertia and "catches up" with the head only after the head has stopped moving. This delayed fluid motion bends the hairs of the receptor cells and produces nerve impulses. Different impulse patterns are transmitted to the brain according to the direction and intensity of fluid motion in the three pairs of canals. Every straight-line motion or rotation of the head or of the body as a whole produces a distinct impulse pattern, hence a distinct sense perception (Fig. 22.30).

Mammals pursue a more or less two-dimensional way of life and are relatively unaccustomed to up-and-down motion. When such motion occurs in man, it initiates reflexes via the semicircular canals leading to well-known symptoms of dizziness, nausea, and gastric upsets. Seasickness is produced in this way, as is the discomfort experienced when one rides in an elevator. Lying flat on a ship or bending one's head in an elevator reduces the upsetting sensations, since the head is then in the same relative position to the direction of motion as in walking. The sense of balance may also be affected by rapid temperature change in the environment; uneven cooling or warming of the fluid in the semicircular canals may produce currents which may stimulate the receptor cells. Sensations of motion or of dizziness may therefore be experienced even if the head does not move.

Hearing

The cochlea is the receptor organ for the sense of hearing (Fig. 22.31). The internal space of the cochlea is partitioned into canals by membranes which run the

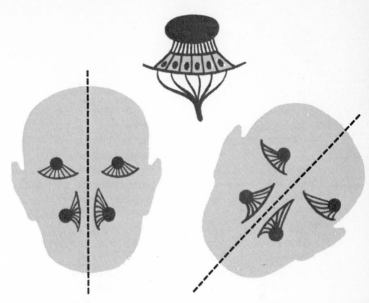

FIG. 22.29 Upper figure, a receptor organ for static balance, showing hair cells and ear stone (diagrammatic). Lower figures, position of the receptor organs in relation to the head, and the effect of tilting the head.

length of the cochlear coils. One of the membranes, the **basilar membrane,** supports rows of hair cells. These are the actual receptors; nerve fibers lead from them to the brain. The hairs make contact with the **tectorial membrane,** a fold of tissue which overhangs the receptor cells. Basilar membrane, hair cells, and tectorial membrane together constitute the **organ of Corti.**

Sound waves produce vibrations in the eardrum. This motion is communicated via the middle-ear bones to the oval window. As the membrane at this window now vibrates, it sets the fluid of the inner ear into motion. Since fluid is practically incompressible, the membrane over the round window bulges outward every time the membrane over the oval window bulges inward; and vice versa. In other words, the round window permits the fluid of the inner ear to vibrate in harmony with the oval window and thus in harmony with external sound waves (Fig. 22.32).

Fluid motion in the inner ear next affects the basilar membrane. The membrane contains strands of tough connective tissue fibers stretched transversely across the cochlear tube. These fibers are shortest at the base of the cochlear coil and longest at the tip of the coil. They may vibrate at different rates or frequencies according to their different lengths. In this

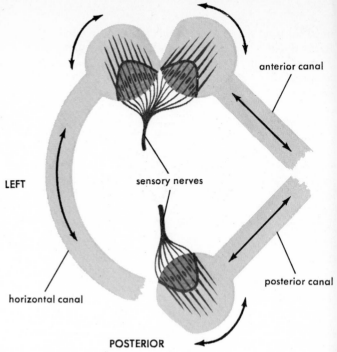

FIG. 22.30 The semicircular canals of the left ear. The top of the diagram is anterior, and the right side is toward the mid-plane of the head. The three canals are set at right angles to one another, and therefore only the horizontal canal reveals its curvature in such a view. Both ends of each canal open into the utricle. One end of each canal is enlarged into a chamber, and in it are present the hair cells which function as receptors for the sense of dynamic balance. Arrows indicate motion of internal fluid when the head is moved.

LEFT

anterior canal

sensory nerves

posterior canal

horizontal canal

POSTERIOR

FIG. 22.31 The cochlea. The diagram shows the coils of the cochlea and a cochlear cross section with the parts of the organ of Corti. A section through this organ is illustrated also in the photo. The tectorial and basilar membranes, and the hair cells, are clearly visible. *(Photo, Ward's Natural Science Establishment, Inc.)*

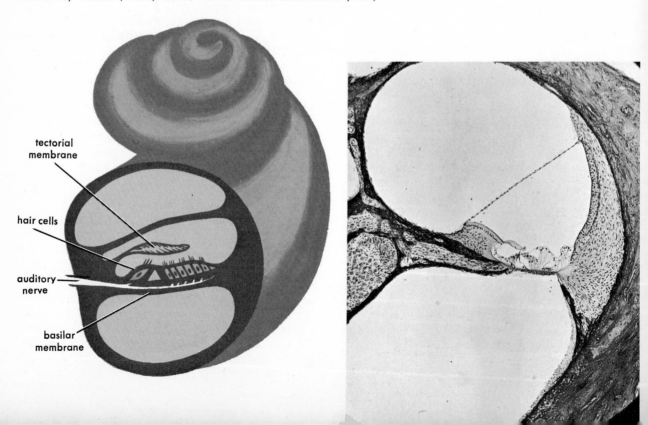

tectorial membrane

hair cells

auditory nerve

basilar membrane

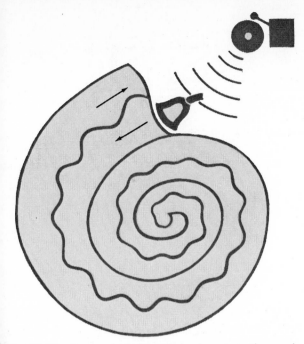

FIG. 22.32 Pressure of the stirrup bone on the oval window sets the basilar membrane into vibration (serpentine line). The round window bulges out, compensating for the inward pressure of the oval window.

respect the fibers resemble the tone strings of a piano. Thus, as the cochlear fluid vibrates at a given frequency under the impact of external sound waves, it sets into motion those basilar fibers which can vibrate at the same frequency. This is a selective *resonance* effect. In a similar way, a string of a piano may be set into resonating vibrations if a corresponding sound is produced nearby with a tuning fork, for example, or by striking an appropriate key on another piano.

In the ear, therefore, different external sound patterns first produce different vibration patterns in the cochlear fluid. Such vibrations in turn then produce corresponding vibrations in particular sets of basilar fibers. As a result, the hair cells attached to the vibrating basilar fibers move up and down. And as these cells touch against the overhanging tectorial membrane, their hairs are bent and nerve impulses are initiated. Each different sound pattern gives rise in this manner to a different pattern of nerve impulses. Such impulses are transmitted via the auditory nerves into the **temporal lobes** of the brain, where the hearing centers are located. In the centers, a given incoming impulse pattern is interpreted as a sound of a particular pitch. If

portions of the hearing centers are injured, selective deafness to high sounds or low sounds may result.

Although mammals such as dogs hear a wider range of sounds and are probably more sensitive to sound than man, the ear of man is unsurpassed in distinguishing tones of only slightly different pitch and tones of widely different quality. As an interpretive sense and as an important adjuster of speech, hearing has acquired a human importance second only to vision.

That the neural centers are as essential in sense perception as the neural receptors has become clear in this section. The centers of brain and spinal cord also are essential in producing effector responses. What is known about the ways in which the brain and the spinal cord carry out their modulating functions?

THE NEURAL CENTERS

STRUCTURAL FEATURES

The normal roles of many parts of the brain and the spinal cord have been discovered by observing the effects of accidental or experimental damage to such parts. In a more precise method, selected points in the brain or the spinal cord of a test animal may be stimulated electrically with needle electrodes. The resulting responses of the animal may then provide clues to the control functions of the stimulated areas. By such means, distinct subdivisions have been identified in the brain and the spinal cord and the location of a large number of neural centers has been pinpointed.

In the brain (Fig. 22.33), the deep central **midbrain** and the posterior **medulla oblongata** contain most of the cranial a.n.s. centers. Situated dorsal to the medulla oblongata is the **cerebellum,** which is the chief motor coordinator. It integrates, for example, the many muscular motions involved in walking, speaking, and other complex activities. The outer portions of the brain, along the top and the sides, constitute the **cerebrum.** This brain part is very large in mammals, and it is divided conspicuously into a right and a left hemisphere. The cerebrum contains c.n.s. control centers; the locations of some of them are indicated in Fig. 22.33. Anteriorly is a large *frontal lobe,* which is the seat of the so-called higher mental capacities, i.e., those associated with consciousness, memory, intelligence, and personality. However, one cannot pinpoint a distinct memory locus, for example, or an intelligence center. Rather, the control of higher capacities appears

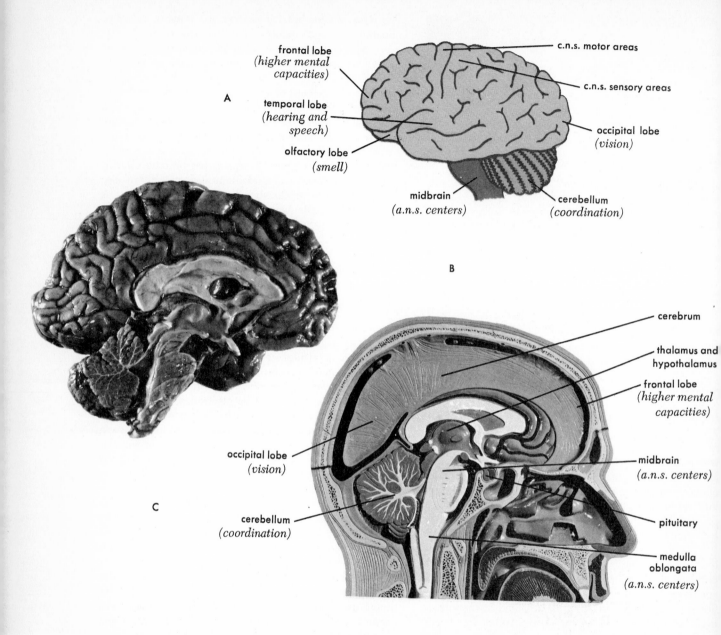

FIG. 22.33   *A*, the left half of the brain, viewed from the outside. The functions of the various labeled parts are indicated in parentheses. *B*, the left half of the brain, viewed from the inner cut side. The various parts and their functions are indicated in the model shown in *C. (B, Photographic Department, Rhode Island Hospital; C, Detail of model designed by Dr. J. F. Mueller, Ward's Natural Science Establishment, Inc.)*

o be delegated diffusely to all the neurons in the frontal lobe. Such diffuseness of control is indicated also by the observation that, if one part of a frontal lobe is damaged, another part may after a long relearning process take over the lost functions.

The highly grooved surface layers of the cerebrum form the **cerebral cortex** (Fig. 22.34). It is composed predominantly of the cell bodies of neurons. The axons and dendrites of these neurons project into the deeper portions of the cerebrum. Inasmuch as the cell bodies do not and the fibers do contain white-colored myelin sheaths, the cerebral cortex is said to consist of **gray matter** and the deeper parts of the cerebrum of **white matter**. The arrangement is reversed in the spinal cord (see Fig. 22.9). In it, the gray matter formed by non-myelinated cell bodies is in the core and the white matter formed by myelinated fibers is on the outside.

FUNCTIONAL FEATURES

The functions of the brain and the spinal cord, most of them already referred to briefly in earlier contexts, may be classified broadly into four major categories.

FIG. 22.34   The cerebral cortex of the human brain, seen from the top. Note that the left cerebral hemisphere is slightly larger than the right. This is usual in right-handed persons. (*Photographic Department, Rhode Island Hospital.*)

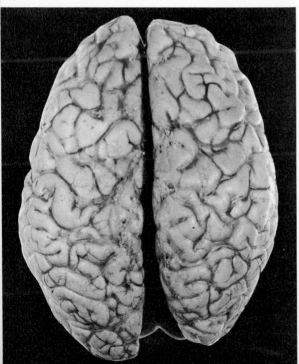

First, brain and spinal cord serve in **pathway selection**. Neural centers receive sensory impulses from receptors and then *select* among thousands of possible motor pathways going out to effectors. Signals are sent only to *some* effectors and only to *appropriate* effectors. As a result, the effector response of an animal to a given stimulus can be adaptively useful and can actually aid in steady-state maintenance. In all probability, the spinal cord carries out such "switchboard" activities only and none of the functions below.

Second, in addition to its role as pathway selector, the brain also serves as **reflex modifier**. It may *suppress* or *exaggerate* responses to incoming information, as when we decide not to cry out under pain or to cry out more than is necessary. It may *store* incoming information as memory and may thereby *delay* the completion of a reflex for shorter or longer periods. On occasion its modifying action may be unduly intensified, as in various mental diseases. Variously inappropriate effector responses are then produced.

Third, the brain is the principal **coordinating center**. It integrates into composite, unified sense perceptions the impulses arriving from many different receptors. And it gears together into smoothly coordinated actions the motor responses of many different effectors.

Fourth, the brain is the controller of such **higher mental capacities** as an animal possesses. The significance of these capacities to mammals in general and to man in particular is well appreciated.

Of these control functions, pathway selection probably is the most fundamental, and all others may be based on it. As yet, very little is known about the mechanism of pathway selection. Among several tentative suggestions and speculations, one is the idea of **pathway facilitation**. This notion emerges from the observation that nerve impulses often may travel more easily over some neural pathways than over others. For example, it is easier to perform a familiar activity than an unfamiliar one. The hypothesis of pathway facilitation suggests that the more frequently impulses travel over given neural circuits, the less resistance this circuit may offer to subsequent impulses. Wherever a choice of circuits exists, therefore, the often used, *facilitated* circuits may be selected in preference to the previously little used, unfacilitated ones. To be sure, it is far from clear just how a circuit in brain or spinal cord might become different structurally or functionally or both when it becomes facilitated.

Nevertheless, a hypothesis of facilitation could

account in general terms for phenomena such as *habit* formation and *learning* by repetition and by trial and error. In a young animal, for example, few brain pathways are as yet firmly established by facilitation. Incoming impulses are transmitted more or less in all directions and behavior is relatively uncoordinated and random. But among the random impulse paths, some will bring about advantageous effector results. The same pathway pattern may then be tried time and again, and a facilitated neural route so may be established eventually.

Learning by experience and forming habits may therefore be a matter of accumulating well-facilitated neural pathways. Actually, numerous neural routes are already fully facilitated at or before birth, and they are responsible for inherited, instinctive behavior. Most animals depend almost entirely on such inborn neural circuits. Later learning and habit formation are of more than incidental significance only in mammals.

Facilitation may also be at the root of learning by association, as in **conditioned reflexes.** Such reflexes were first studied by the Russian biologist Pavlov in experiments on dogs. When a hungry dog sights food, his saliva and gastric juice begin to flow reflexly. If on many successive occasions a bell is sounded every time food is presented, then the flow of the digestive juices can eventually be initiated by sounding the bell alone, without giving food. Evidently, the dog learns to associate a ringing bell with food. Instead of one facilitated pathway to the digestive glands, two now exist; one is mediated via the eyes as before and another has been newly established via the ears. Either one alone or both together may initiate digestive secretions (Fig. 22.35). Neural conditioning of this sort plays a considerable role in behavior development not only in dogs but in mammals generally, man included.

Moreover, making associations between originally separate neural circuits may account for much of intelligence, for insight, for "getting the idea." Suppose that each of two well-facilitated pathways represents one item of information. "Seeing the connection" between such seemingly unrelated bits of information might mean a transmission of impulses over a third neural pathway interlinking the two. The extent to which such neural correlations can be made may depend partly on inherited intelligence, partly on conscious, deliberate efforts of "using one's brain."

The net result of neural activities of all kinds is control of *muscular movement* and of *glandular secretion.* But is it not really more than this, particularly for

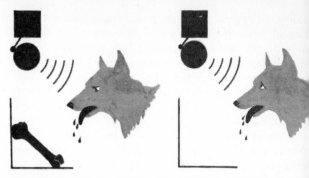

FIG. 22.35 The principle of conditioned reflexes. Left, two simultaneous stimuli (sight of food, sound of bell) produce a response (salivation). Right, if the procedure is repeated often, then a single stimulus alone may eventually produce the characteristic response.

man? Conscious, contemplative thinking, reasoning, reading, aesthetic appreciations, higher mental functions in general—are they not more than mere reflex control of muscles and glands? Actually not. For *all* mental activity aims toward some *action,* potential or actual, present or future. On the one hand, we see, hear, learn, experience, store and correlate information—in short, we *think.* And on the other hand, we speak, walk, build, vote—in short, we *do.* All this doing requires and is directly brought about by muscular and glandular activity. In the final analysis, therefore, thinking sets the stage for moving muscles and better thinking implies more judicious and more diversified use of muscles. Because muscular control contributes powerfully to the maintenance of steady states, nervous systems have become vital components of animals.

Throughout these chapters on steady state, the central running theme has been that built-in control systems endow a living unit with a life span of maximum duration. When the controls fail for any external or internal reason, disease occurs. Intact controls may then be able to restore steady state. However, in time even the best-controlled system goes out of control. As the component parts age and wear out, functional and structural breakdowns occur so often and in so many different places at once that not enough controls remain intact to make the necessary repairs. Irreversible unsteady states and death must be the eventual outcome. But, as pointed out in Chap. 5, living systems here reveal their superiority of design over any nonliving system. Before final disintegration supervenes, the living controls may call into action another self-perpetuating device which circumvents even death: *reproduction.*

REVIEW QUESTIONS

1. Describe the structure of a neuron. How do nuerons in the c.n.s. and a.n.s. differ structurally and functionally? Describe the components and structural arrangement of a reflex arc. Distinguish between nerve fibers and nerves. What different kinds of each are known?

2. Describe the organization of the c.n.s., its nerves, and its centers. Review the detailed course of a c.n.s. reflex arc. What is a ganglion? Distinguish between a cranial and a spinal reflex.

3. Describe the organization of the a.n.s., its nerves, and its centers. What are the (a) structural and (b) functional differences between the sympathetic and the parasympathetic systems? What are sympathetic chain ganglia?

4. What are preganglionic and postganglionic fibers? Describe the detailed course of an a.n.s. reflex arc. Review the innervation of the heart. How are c.n.s. and a.n.s. interconnected (a) structurally and (b) functionally?

5. What is a nerve impulse? How is an impulse transmitted through a nerve fiber? What electrical phenomena take place during impulse transmission? What is an action potential of a nerve fiber? How is an impulse transmitted across a synapse? Distinguish between a cholinergic and an adrenergic nerve fiber. Where does each kind occur? What is choline esterase and what is its function?

6. What is the basic function of all sensory receptors? Describe the location and general structure of receptors for pain, touch, pressure, heat, and cold stimuli. How can it be proved that the kind and localization of a sensory experience depend on neural centers? Describe the location and structure of the taste and smell receptors. What are the primary taste sensations? Are tastes and smells inherent in given substances? Discuss.

7. Describe the structure of the eye. What components form the focusing mechanism and how is the function of focusing carried out? What is the distribution pattern of rods and cones in the retina? What eye structures does light traverse before it reaches the rods and cones? Review the chemical changes leading to impulse production in rods. Describe the pattern of the neural pathways between the eyes and the brain.

8. Describe the structure of the ear. What components form the receptors for (a) static body balance and (b) dynamic body balance? How do these receptors function? Describe the internal structure of the cochlea and the organ of Corti. Show how different sounds produce corresponding sensations of hearing.

9. What are the general functions of neural centers? Review the structural organization of the brain. What is the specific function of each major part or region? What is meant by pathway facilitation?

10. What are conditioned reflexes? Show how such reflexes might be established by pathway facilitation. How do conditioned reflexes contribute to learning, habit formation, and behavior development?

SUGGESTED COLLATERAL READINGS

The following sources are recommended as supplements to most topics of this chapter:

Allen, F.: The Visual Apparatus as an Optical Instrument, *Sci. Monthly*, vol. 72, 1951.

Babkin, B. P.: "Pavlov," University of Chicago Press, Chicago, 1949.

Beidler, L. M.: Our Taste Receptors, *Sci. Monthly*, vol. 75, 1952.

Carlson, A. J., and V. Johnson: "The Machinery of the Body," 4th ed., University of Chicago Press, Chicago, 1953.

Evans, R. M.: Seeing Light and Color, *Sci. American*, vol. 181, 1949.

Haagen-Smit, A. J.: Smell and Taste, *Sci. American*, vol. 186, 1952.

Halstead, W. C.: "Brain and Intelligence," University of Chicago Press, Chicago, 1947.

Kalmus, H.: Inherited Sense Defects, *Sci. American*, vol. 186, 1952.

Katz, B.: The Nerve Impulse, *Sci. American,* vol. 187, 1952.

Liddell, H. S.: Conditioning and the Emotions, *Sci. American,* vol. 190, 1954.

Munn, N. L.: The Evolution of Mind, *Sci. American,* vol. 196, 1957.

Pavlov, I. P.: Conditioned Reflexes, in T. S. Hall, "A Source Book in Animal Biology," McGraw-Hill, New York, 1951.

Sperry, R. W.: The Eye and the Brain, *Sci. American,* vol. 194, 1956.

Wald, G.: Eye and Camera, *Sci. American,* vol. 183, 1950.

———: The Molecular Basis of Visual Excitation, *Am. Scientist,* vol. 42, 1954.

Walter, W. G.: The Electrical Activity of the Brain, *Sci. American,* vol. 190, 1954.

PART 6
SELF-PERPETUATION:
REPRODUCTION

Of all living functions, reproduction happens to be among the most noticeable to the casual human observer. Metabolism occurs largely on an invisible, molecular scale. Control functions result in steady state, i.e., in unchanged, even conditions. Adaptation and evolution occur on a scale so vast that man does not perceive them directly or obviously. But reproduction does take place on a directly perceivable, obvious scale. Moreover, reproductive processes are universal and very dramatic: now there is one, then there are two. This accounts for the selection of reproduction particularly as a certain criterion of life.

To be sure, the deep significance of reproduction lies not in its dramatic nature but in its results. We recall that we have assigned "living" properties to the first of the ancient nucleic acids largely because they possessed *reproductive* properties. These properties have been handed down in an unbroken succession from the first genes to all present genes, and they still form the basis of all reproductive events today.

Just as an organism maintains steady states from its molecules up, so it also reproduces from its molecules up; molecular reproduction is the foundation of all reproduction. In this series of chapters, therefore, we examine first the **patterns of reproduction** among molecules, cells, and whole organisms. Following this, we proceed with a systematic study of specific **reproductive processes** encountered in all main categories of organisms. Lastly, we discuss processes of **development,** the essential events through which reproduced offspring are transformed into adult wholes.

THE PATTERN
OF REPRODUCTION

23

If we define reproduction broadly as extension of living matter in space and in time, then its fundamental importance as a self-perpetuative device is readily apparent: the formation of new living units makes possible *replacement* and *addition* at every level of organization. Among molecules or cells, among organisms or species, replacement offsets death from normal wear and tear and death from accident or disease. *Healing* and *regeneration* are two aspects of replacement. Above and beyond this purely restorative function of reproduction, addition of extra units at any level results in four-dimensional *growth*, i.e., increase in the net amount of existing living matter.

Any new living unit resembles the old, and reproduction therefore implies exact duplication. To create new units, raw materials are required. Indeed, reproduction at any level depends on ample nutrition specifically and on properly controlled metabolism generally. It is also clear that duplication of a large unit implies prior or simultaneous duplication of all constituent smaller ones. Reproduction must therefore occur on the molecular level before it can occur on any higher level. The patterns of reproduction on the principal levels of living organization are the specific topics of this chapter.

MOLECULES AND CELLS

MOLECULAR REPRODUCTION

The multiplication of molecules may take four different forms, according to the nature of the molecule to be multiplied. We are already familiar with all four (Fig. 23.1).

If water or another inorganic substance is to be reproduced within a cell, additional molecules or ions of such substances must be supplied ready-made by nutrition. Evidently, **accumulation** is the simplest form of molecular "reproduction."

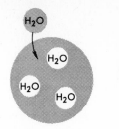

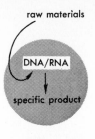
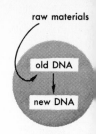

FIG. 23.1 The four forms of molecular reproduction.

accumulation   *enzymatic synthesis*   *template-dependent synthesis*   *self-duplication*

If a carbohydrate, a fat, or any of their numerous derivatives is to be duplicated, it may have to be synthesized from accumulated simpler raw materials with the aid of appropriate enzymes. So long as the enzymes of a cell remain the same, most newly synthesized organic molecules will automatically be exact duplicates of molecules synthesized earlier. Thus, the second form of molecular reproduction is **enzymatic synthesis.** It includes the first form, accumulation, as a component phase.

If a protein molecule is to be duplicated, we know that enzymes are required to link amino acids into a new protein. We also know that proteins are specific. If, therefore, the new protein is to be an exact copy of a preexisting protein, genes and RNA must provide the specific information, the template, for the joining of particular amino acids in particular sequences. Clearly, the third form of molecular reproduction includes the first two forms but is additionally characterized as **template-dependent synthesis.**

Lastly, if a genetic nucleoprotein is to be duplicated, it must serve as its own template and control its own replication (see Chap. 18). All three other forms of molecular reproduction play a part here. Phosphate must be accumulated; sugars, purines, pyrimidines must be synthesized enzymatically; and protein must be synthesized with the aid of both enzymes and genetic templates. But in addition, duplication of genetic nucleoproteins hinges on specific **self-duplication,** and this is the fourth form of molecular reproduction.

In viruses, where the structural organization does not exceed the level of the molecular aggregate, molecular reproduction is equivalent to reproduction of the whole unit. In all truly living systems, accumulation, enzymatic and template-dependent synthesis, and self-duplication contribute either to normal molecular replacement within cells or to molecular additions to cells. The result is *cell growth.* The rate of these proc-

esses depends on the supply of nutrients. If the parts of the cellular framework wear down faster than they can be replaced, then a cell may actually decrease in size and undergo negative growth, or degrowth. Positive growth demands a rate of molecular reproduction which exceeds the rate of molecular destruction.

CELLULAR REPRODUCTION

Molecular duplication, resulting in increase of cell size, may be followed by reproduction of a cell as a whole. This reproductive process is **cell division or fission.**

Few biological events are as central to life and as universally characteristic of it as cell division. It is the sole means by which unicellular organisms multiply. It creates reproductive cells and transforms them into multicellular adults. It replaces dead cells in the adult and thereby offsets normal wear and tear. It heals wounds and regenerates body parts lost or destroyed. And cell division sometimes goes wild and produces tumors, cancers, and other abnormal overgrowths. Indeed, the life histories of organisms may be well described as changing dynamic equilibria between cell division and cell death.

In many cases among Protista, a mother cell may divide into *several* daughter cells, a phenomenon known as **multiple fission.** In the vast majority of cases, however, **binary fission** or division of one cell into two is the rule. Binary fission in most organisms produces two daughter cells of roughly equal size. In some instances, as in yeasts, distinctly unequal cells may result, a form of cell division called **budding.** In all cases, daughter cells enlarge by molecular reproduction, and they may subsequently divide in their turn. The period between two succeeding cell divisions represents a cell generation (Fig. 23.2).

In Protista, Metaphyta, and Metazoa, cell division

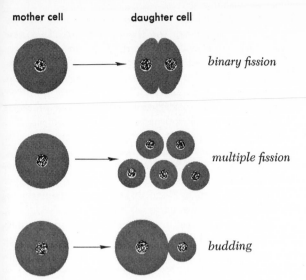

mother cell   daughter cell

binary fission

multiple fission

budding

FIG. 23.2   The principal forms of fission.

consists of at least two separate processes: *cleavage of the cytoplasm* into two parts and *duplication of the nucleus*. These two events normally take place more or less concurrently, but they may become ungeared from each other. In many cell types, for example, nuclear duplication often occurs without cytoplasmic cleavage and a binucleate or multinucleate cell then results. The reverse is encountered as well, i.e., a binucleate or multinucleate cell may cleave without nuclear duplication. Such events may also be induced by experimental

FIG. 23.3   Cytoplasmic and nuclear division of a cell usually occur at the same time (left). But on occasion the nucleus may divide without cytoplasmic division, the result being a binucleate cell (center); or the cytoplasm of a binucleate cell may divide without nuclear division, the result being two uninucleate cells (right).

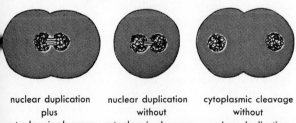

nuclear duplication   nuclear duplication   cytoplasmic cleavage
plus   without   without
cytoplasmic cleavage   cytoplasmic cleavage   nuclear duplication

(normal cell division)   *(binucleate cell   *(binucleate cell forms
                             forms)*   two normal cells)*

means. It is unknown how, in a uninucleate cell, the normal gearing of nuclear and cytoplasmic duplications is accomplished. Since the nucleus usually begins to duplicate somewhat earlier than the cytoplasm, nuclear reproduction probably triggers cytoplasmic reproduction (Fig. 23.3).

Nuclear duplication includes a mathematically precise doubling of the chromosomes and their genes. One of the two chromosome sets so formed becomes incorporated into one of the daughter nuclei, and the second chromosome set, into the other daughter nucleus. This form of nuclear duplication is known as **mitosis,** and the type of cell division in which it may be included is referred to as **mitotic division**. Note therefore that "mitosis" is not simply another word for cell division, but designates a particular kind of *nuclear* division.

Monera do not possess nuclei or chromosomes like other organisms. Cell division in Monera does include gene duplication but does not include mitosis.

MITOTIC CELL DIVISION

THE PATTERN

All living cells probably possess the machinery for division, but whether or not and with what frequency that machinery can become effective depends on a number of factors. As noted earlier, one factor is the state of cellular nutrition. Being a process of duplication, cell division consumes energy and raw materials, and, like other reproductive events, it is therefore contingent on adequate metabolism. Another factor is the state of cellular specialization. Relatively unspecialized cells may divide at more or less regular intervals. By contrast, highly specialized cells such as nerve cells or cells which have lost their nuclei (e.g., red corpuscles, sieve-tube cells) or their entire interior substance (e.g., sclerenchyma) may not divide at all.

The immediate stimulus necessary to initiate division is still unknown. Many cells divide when they have grown to double their original volume. However, attainment of such a volume is probably not a specific stimulus, for cells can be made to divide at any time before their volume has doubled. Moreover, they may be prevented from dividing altogether and may be allowed to grow into giant cells many times larger than twice the original. Several chemicals are known to inhibit division and several to promote it (e.g., various growth hormones). How do such chemicals act? Similarly, physical agents such as X rays may inhibit or promote division, depending on conditions. Although experimental procedures employing such agents have gone far toward controlling cell division, it is still not known how such control actually operates. And it is equally unknown what normal conditions within a cell or outside it so stimulate it that it begins to divide.

Among the Protista, mitotic division takes several different forms in different groups (Fig. 23.4). For example, mitosis may be **intranuclear** or **extranuclear.** In the intranuclear type, all events of mitosis occur right within the nucleus, which persists with its membrane intact till near the end of fission. Then the nucleus divides along with the cytoplasm. In extranuclear mitosis, the nuclear membrane dissolves soon after mitosis starts. Subsequent events take place throughout

FIG. 23.4   The patterns of mitosis. The arrows show that, in extranuclear mitosis, for example, the pattern may be centric or acentric; and in centric mitosis, for example, the pattern may be astral or anastral. Other combinations of patterns are encountered as well.

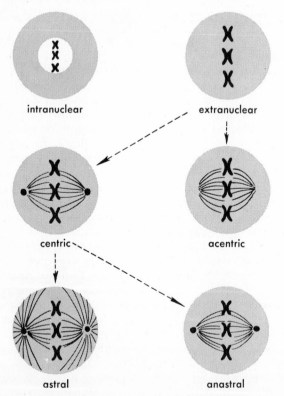

the whole cell, which ceases to be differentiated into nucleus and cytoplasm for the time being. Two new nuclei with new membranes form at the end of mitosis, when the cell cleaves into two.

Mitosis may also be **centric** or **acentric.** In the first case, a centriole is present, and it participates in mitosis in a manner to be described below. In some protistan groups the centriole is situated inside the nucleus, and in such cases mitosis is centric and intranuclear. In other groups the centriole is located just outside the nucleus, and mitosis here is centric and extranuclear. Acentric mitosis occurs in species which do not possess centrioles. Division in these instances may similarly be intranuclear or extranuclear.

Protistan mitoses may be classified further into **astral** and **anastral** types. These terms refer to the presence or absence of an **aster,** a set of temporary fibrils which during mitosis radiate like a sunburst from a centriole. If centrioles are present, asters may or may not form. Thus centric mitoses may be astral or anastral. Acentric mitoses are always anastral.

Each protistan group is characterized by its own type of mitosis, and the distribution of particular mitotic types does not appear to follow any obvious evolutionary pattern. Two species within a given protistan phylum may feature different mitotic types, whereas two species of different phyla may feature the same mitotic type. In one large descendant group of the Protista, namely, the Metaphyta, mitosis is characteristically *extranuclear, acentric,* and *anastral.* In the other large descendant group, the Metazoa, mitosis is *extranuclear, centric,* and *astral.* In what follows we shall concentrate particularly on these two mitotic types.

The first demonstrable event of mitotic division is a chemical event which occurs well before microscopically visible changes can be detected: the DNA content of the cell nucleus doubles. Rapid synthesis undoubtedly occurs at this stage, and the genes of a cell reproduce as outlined in Chap. 18. Gene duplication probably marks the time when the entire collection of chromosomes is doubled. At this stage, however, such doubling is not yet visible microscopically.

A certain amount of time elapses before the visible phases of division begin. During this period, numerous biochemical preparations are probably made throughout a cell for the actual execution of the reproductive process. The visible phases of mitotic division consist of four successive, arbitrarily defined stages: *prophase, metaphase, anaphase,* and *telophase.* One stage merges gradually into the next and it is imposible to fix sharp lines of transition. Nuclear division, i.e., mitosis proper, encompasses all four stages; cytoplasmic division takes place in the last stage.

THE PROCESS

In the extranuclear, centric, astral mitosis of Metazoa, one of the first events of **prophase** is the division of the centriole (Fig. 23.5). As soon as daughter centrioles have formed, the two granules behave as if they repelled each other, i.e., they migrate toward opposite sides of the cell nucleus. Concurrently, portions of the cytoplasm transform into fine gel fibrils. Some of these radiate away from each centriole like the spokes of a wheel and form **asters.** Other gel fibrils develop between the two centrioles. Looping from one centriole to the other in flat curves, these fibrils con-

stitute a **spindle.** The centriole at each end marks a *spindle pole*. As the centrioles move farther and farther apart, the fibrils of the spindle and the asters lengthen and increase in number. Centrioles are not present and asters do not form in the acentric, anastral mitoses of Metaphyta. Spindles do develop, however.

During these stages of prophase, the nuclear membrane dissolves, the nucleoli disintegrate, and nuclear and cytoplasmic substances mix freely. Moreover, distinct chromosomes become visible. Close examination reveals that each chromosome is a *double* filament (Fig. 23.6). As noted, each chromosome has manufactured a mathematically exact duplicate some time before prophase. Such twin chromosomes lie closely parallel and are joined to each other only at a single point, the so-called **centromere.** The location of the centromere varies for different chromosome pairs. Two

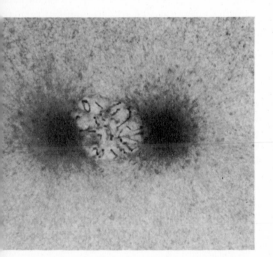

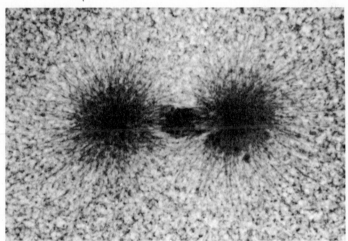

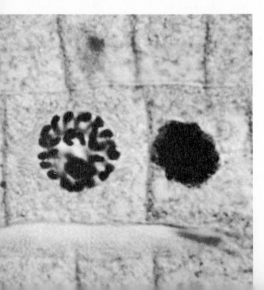

FIG. 23.5   Top left and right, early and late prophase in animal mitosis. In top left, the nuclear membrane is just dissolving and chromosomes are already visible. To either side of the nuclear region is a darkly stained centriole area. These areas develop after a single centriole has divided and the two daughter centrioles have migrated to opposite sides of the nucleus. From each centriole area fine fibrils are beginning to radiate out, i.e., asters are beginning to form. In top right, asters are already conspicuous, and spindle fibrils have formed between asters and chromosomes. The chromosomes are migrating into a metaphase plate. Left, prophase in plant mitosis. Distinct chromosomes are clearly visible, and the nuclear membrane has just dissolved. A spindle is not yet sharply marked in this photo. *(Top left and right, General Biological Supply House, Inc.; left, courtesy of Dr. M. S. Fuller, Brown University.)*

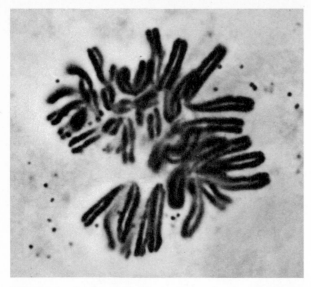

FIG. 23.6 At the time of prophase, chromosomes have already duplicated, and doubled chromosomes, each known as a chromatid, are therefore present. The members of each pair of chromatids are still held together at one point, the centromere. (General Biological Supply House, Inc.)

spindle fibrils become anchored to each centromere, one from each pole of the spindle. In this way, the chromosomes become linked to the spindle. At this general period, prophase comes to a close and **metaphase** begins.

Early during metaphase the chromosome pairs are still scattered randomly through the central portion of the cell, but later they begin to migrate. If we draw an imaginary line from one spindle pole to the other, we mark out a spindle axis. Chromosomes migrate into a plane set at right angles to the spindle axis, midway along it. Specifically, it is the centromere of each chromosome pair which comes to occupy a station precisely within this plane. During the migration, the chromosomes trail behind their centromeres like streamers. Lined up in one plane, the centromeres are said to form a *metaphase plate* (Fig. 23.7).

The lengthwise separation of the chromosome pairs now becomes complete. Each centromere divides and entirely independent chromosomes are produced in this manner. A small gel fibril arises at once between the centromeres of formerly joined chromosomes, and such chromosomes begin to move apart. Once they are completely separated, the members of a pair of chromosomes behave as if they repelled each other. Thus, one set of chromosomes migrates away from the metaphase plate toward one spindle pole and an identical twin set migrates in the opposite direction, toward the other spindle pole. The centromeres again lead and the arms of the chromosomes trail. Also, the gel fibrils between twin centromeres lengthen and fibrils between the centromeres and the spindle poles shorten. This period of poleward migration of chromosomes represents the **anaphase** of mitotic division (Fig. 23.8).

The beginning of **telophase** is marked by the appearance of a *cleavage furrow* in animal cells and a *division plate* in plant cells. Both furrow and plate form in the plane of the earlier metaphase plate. The cleavage furrow at first is a shallow groove circling the surface of a cell. This groove gradually deepens, cuts through the spindle fibrils, and eventually constricts the

FIG. 23.7 Left, metaphase in animal mitosis. Note asters, spindle, and the metaphase plate, halfway along and at right angles to the spindle axis. Note also the fibrils which join the chromosomes lined up in the metaphase plate with the spindle poles. Right, metaphase in plant mitosis. Note the spindle and the metaphase plate, at right angles to the spindle axis. (General Biological Supply House, Inc.)

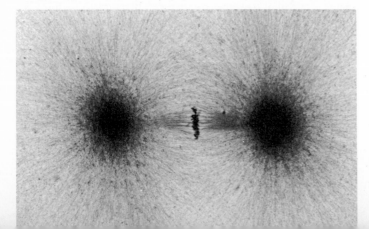
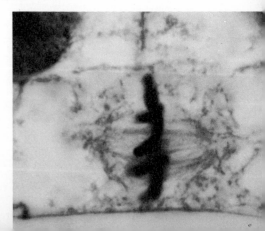

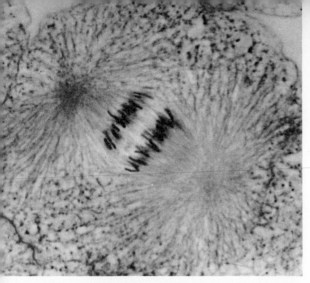

FIG. 23.8 Top left, mid-anaphase in animal mitosis. Chromosome sets are migrating toward spindle poles. Top right and bottom left, early and late anaphase in plant mitosis. In top right, note chromosomes migrating toward spindle poles. At bottom left, chromosomes have arrived at spindle poles and are beginning to aggregate, foreshadowing the formation of nuclei. *(General Biological Supply House, Inc.)*

cell into two daughter cells. The division plate of plant cells is a partition of cellulose which is laid down more or less simultaneously at all points of the plane of cleavage (Fig. 23.9).

While cytoplasmic division is in progress, the chromosomes within each prospective daughter cell aggregate near the spindle pole. Spindle fibrils subside; i.e., the gel composing them reverts to a sol state. A new nuclear membrane forms at each spindle pole, and this membrane surrounds the chromosomes. Concurrently, the chromosomes in each newly forming nucleus manufacture new nucleoli in numbers characteristic of the particular cell type. These nuclear processes terminate roughly when cytoplasmic cleavage nears completion, and mitotic division then has reached its endpoint. The events of this form of cellular reproduction are summarized in Fig. 23.10.

What are the mechanical forces involved in divi-

sion? Specifically, how do chromosomes move? The behavior of the spindle fibrils is highly suggestive. Do these fibrils, like guy ropes, pull and push chromosomes first into the metaphase plate and later toward the spindle poles? This possibility has been tested in experiments (with amoebae) in which spindle fibers have been cut through with needles. Under such conditions, the chromosomes still migrate in normal fashion. In certain insects, moreover, have been found cells in which demonstrable spindle fibrils from pole to chromosome are not formed. Yet here the chromosomes migrate nevertheless. Accordingly, the gelated fibrils would not seem to be responsible for chromosome movements.

However, other lines of evidence indicate the opposite. It happens sometimes that pieces break off from chromosomes. Indeed, this can be induced by exposing cells to X rays or to ultrasonic vibrations. In such cases, the main portion of a chromosome which is attached

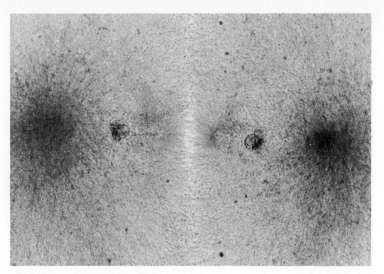
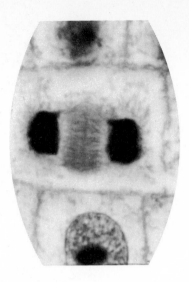

FIG. 23.9   Left, early telophase in animal mitosis. Asters are subsiding, nuclei are re-forming, chromosome threads have become indistinct, and cytoplasmic cleavage is under way, in the same plane as the earlier metaphase plate. Right, telophase in plant mitosis. Two daughter nuclei are in process of formation. Note also the faint indications of a division plate, just beginning to form midway between the daughter nuclei and at right angles to the former spindle axis. *(General Biological Supply House, Inc.)*

FIG. 23.10   Mitosis summary. The assumption here is that cytoplasmic cleavage accompanies mitosis. Note that a "resting" cell is resting only from the standpoint of reproductive activity. In all other respects it is exceedingly active.

to a spindle fibril unfailingly moves toward a pole. But a piece which has broken off and is unattached invariably stays behind and clearly is unable to migrate. In certain animal cells, furthermore, it can be shown that aster fibrils attach to the inner surface of the cell membrane. As these fibrils shorten, the cell membrane is pulled inward, and this produces the constricting groove which eventually divides the cell.

In these instances, spindle fibrils do seem to exert a positive pull. Some investigators have suggested that the fibrils contain myosin, the same protein that makes muscles contract. We note that, on the whole, existing evidence is still conflicting, and for the present we must conclude that the forces responsible for mitotic movements have not yet been identified.

THE RESULT

The net result of cell division is the cleavage of one cell into two cells containing *precisely* identical gene sets, incorporated in identical chromosome sets, and *approximately* equal quantities of all other cellular constituents. Consequently, the structural and functional potential of both daughter cells is the same as

1   2   3
"resting" stage   prophase   metaphase

anaphase   telophase   "resting" stage
4   5   6

that of the original mother cell. In unicellular organisms, cell division is equivalent to reproduction of the whole organism. Daughter cells generally separate, but in some forms they remain sticking together and, as we have seen, form *colonies.*

In multicellular organisms, cell division either contributes to *cell replacement,* as in regeneration or wound healing, or adds to *cell number.* This leads to growth of tissues and organs. The growth of an organism, we note, may be a result either of molecular reproduction and increase in cell *size* or of cellular reproduction and increase in cell *number,* or of both. If the rate of cell division more than balances the rate of cell death, continued net growth occurs. In the opposite case, degrowth will take place.

The rates of cellular reproduction vary greatly. Among multicellular organisms, the most intense rates of cell division occur in embryonic stages, the least intense in old age. Cells which form membranous sheet-like tissues retain a fairly rapid but steadily decreasing rate of division throughout the life of an organism. By contrast, liver or muscle cells, for example, divide only rarely in the adult. And after being formed in the embryo nerve cells do not divide at all. Nerve cells may grow, but only by increase in cell size. Destroyed neurons cannnot be replaced. In general, the more highly specialized a cell, the less frequently it divides, and vice versa (see Chap. 5).

Why does tissue and organ growth slow down with increasing age? With few exceptions, cellular reproductive capacity in the adult remains *potentially* as great as in the embryo. This is shown, for example, by the high rates of cell division in wound healing, in regeneration, in cancers and other tumors, and in **tissue cultures.** Such cultures are prepared by separating groups of cells from an organism and growing them in artificial nutrient solutions (see Chap. 27). Under isolated conditions of this sort, cells are found to reproduce faster than if they had remained within an organism. Moreover, if newly formed cells in a tissue culture are cut away from time to time, the original bit of tissue may live almost indefinitely long, certainly far longer than it would have lived within an organism. Through tissue culture, for example, a piece of the heart muscle of a chicken embryo has been maintained alive for over 30 years, which exceeds the life span of the whole chicken several times.

It is conceivable, therefore, that cell reproduction in intact organisms may slow down mainly because the cells are *not* isolated as in a tissue culture. Instead, cells are integrated very finely into a larger organization. Just as, in the human population, economic, social, and other checks hold the reproduction of the individual to less than maximum rates, so evidently is the rate of cell division held down by metabolic checks in the healthy cell population. Similarly, the slower expansion of an older, established society, compared with that of a new pioneer group, provides a close parallel to comparative growth rates in adult and embryo.

Although growth slows down with increasing age, in most organisms it does not cease entirely. All plants and many animals continue to grow somewhat even in old age. The general range of body size is a genetically determined trait of the species, but within this range wide variations are possible. Trees, for example, are well known to be able to grow for hundreds of years. Some of them, particularly giant redwoods and *Eucalyptus* trees, have attained heights of about 400 ft—the largest organisms ever to exist. Here, as in whales, elephants, and other large animals, bulk arises primarily through continuing cell divisions and increase in cell number, not increase in cell size. Among animals, fish and numerous other types are known to grow throughout life. But in another series of forms, as in man, net growth stops altogether at a certain stage.

ORGANISMIC REPRODUCTION

After periods of growth by molecular and cellular reproduction, the whole multicellular organism may reproduce. The general pattern consists of two phases. First, a **reproductive unit** separates from the parent organism. Second, a duplicate organism forms from the reproductive unit through **development** (Fig. 23.11).

VEGETATIVE REPRODUCTION

In many cases, the reproductive unit consists of the whole or a substantial portion of the parent organism. For example, in Monera and unicellular Protista, the whole body of the adult cell is the reproductive unit and reproduction is accomplished by cell division. In multicellular organisms, a reproductive unit may frequently be formed by less than the whole body but by more than a single cell. A multicellular portion of tissue may separate out from the parent and, under appropriate environmental conditions, may grow directly into a new adult.

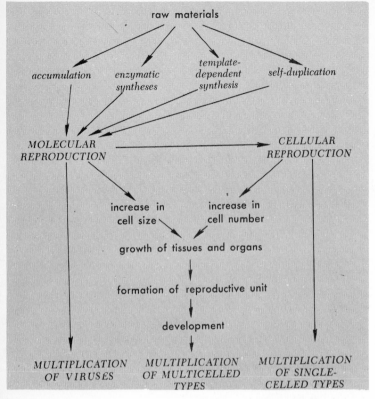

FIG. 23.11 The overall pattern of reproduction.

Such processes of multiplication are highly developed among many Protista, Metaphyta, and Metazoa. For example, in dichotomously branching algae and liverworts, two organisms may arise from one by **posterior decay,** i.e., the main portion of the body dies off, leaving two branch portions as separate individuals. Bryophytes may reproduce also by means of **gemmae,** variously shaped groups of cells which grow out from a plant as reproductive units. These are capable on their own of developing directly into new adults. Similar processes occur in tracheophytes. In the angiosperm *Kalanchoë,* for example, multicellular reproductive units may form along the margins of leaves and develop into whole new adults. Among animals, analogously, certain flatworms, sea anemones, and other types may on occasion divide into two or more portions. Each portion then regenerates the missing body parts (Fig. 23.12).

This general type of multiplication is called **vegetative reproduction.** Its characteristics are that the reproductive unit is either the whole organism or a substantial portion of the organism and that the parent cells which form the reproductive unit are not specialized primarily for reproduction. Virtually *any* portion of the parent may cease its adult function and become part of a vegetative reproductive unit.

Closely allied to vegetative reproduction and representing in fact a special form of it is *regenerative reproduction.* Here the reproductive units arise fortuitously, as a result of injury to the parent by external agents. For example, many organisms may be cut into several pieces and each piece may then grow into a new, whole individual. Almost any piece of a plant, a few segments of an earthworm, an arm of a starfish, a chunk of tissue from a hydra or a sponge—each is an effective reproductive unit. The parent organisms which lose such sections of their bodies usually regenerate the missing parts (Fig. 23.13).

In all these cases, the size and composition of the reproductive unit obviously vary with the nature and extent of damage to the parent. It is clear, also, that regeneration may become reproduction only where the capacity of regeneration is extensive, as in the examples just cited. Regenerative capacity varies with the species, and in many organisms it is highly limited. Salamanders may regenerate a whole limb, but a limb cannot regenerate a whole salamander. In vertebrates generally, the regeneration potential is not even as great as in salamanders but, as in man, is limited to the healing of relatively small wounds.

REPRODUCTIVE CELLS

On theoretical grounds, a reproductive unit of a multicellular organism should not have to be as large a portion of the parent organism as it is in vegetative reproduction. The smallest unit which possesses the genetic information and the operating equipment representative of an entire multicellular organism is a *single cell.* Accordingly, the minimum unit for the construction of such an organism should be one cell. This is actually the universal case. Regardless of whether or not it may also reproduce vegetatively, every multicellular organism is capable of reproducing through single **reproductive cells.** All such cells are more or less specialized for reproduction, and they are formed in more or less specialized reproductive tissues or organs of the parent.

According to the manner of their formation and their later fate, two general classes of reproductive cells may be distinguished. One includes cells which may

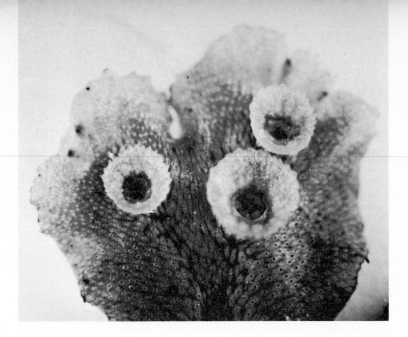

FIG. 23.12 Vegetative reproduction. Top left, a sea anemone is splitting lengthwise into two offspring organisms. Top right, gemmae on a thallus of *Marchantia*. Left, leaf of *Kalanchoë*, showing small, vegetatively formed plants developing along the leaf margin. (*Top left, courtesy of D. P. Wilson, Marine Biological Laboratory, Plymouth, England; top right, left, courtesy of Dr. M. S. Fuller, Brown University.*)

develop into adults *directly*. Such cells are very common in plants and are called **spores**. Among animals, cells of this type are rarer. They are given a variety of names, the designation **bud** cell probably being the most frequent.

Reproductive cells in the second general class can *not* develop directly. Instead, they must first undergo a *sexual process*, in which two reproductive cells fuse. Such cells are called **sex cells**, or **gametes**. Male gametes are *sperms*, female gametes are *eggs*. A *mating* process makes possible the pairwise fusion of gametes. This fusion is **fertilization**, and the fusion product is called a **zygote**. Development of gametes into adults cannot occur until fertilization has taken place. In other words, if sex occurs, it is interpolated between the two basic phases of the reproductive sequence, namely, between the formation of reproductive cells and the development of these cells into adults.

FIG. 23.13 Regenerative reproduction. Left, an arm of a starfish regenerates all missing parts and becomes a whole animal. Right, a starfish which has lost parts of each arm at least once regenerates into a whole animal. Note the lighter shading of the regenerated portions in each arm. The arm at top center has regenerated twice. *(Courtesy of D. P. Wilson, Marine Biological Laboratory, Plymouth, England.)*

FIG. 23.14 The three principal patterns of organismic reproduction.

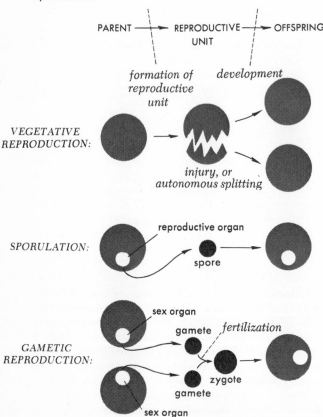

THE TRIPLE PATTERN

We conclude that an organism may reproduce in one or more of three general ways (Fig. 23.14):

1. through **vegetative reproduction,** i.e., by means of relatively large reproductive units variously produced and not specialized primarily for reproduction.

2. through **sporulative reproduction,** i.e., by means of spores or similar specialized reproductive cells which develop directly.

3. through **gametic reproduction,** i.e., by means of gametes, specialized reproductive cells which develop only after a sexual process.

Note that, in a strict sense, the often used terms "asexual reproduction" and "sexual reproduction" are meaningless. In all forms of multiplication, the essential "reproductive" event is the formation of *reproductive units.* The rest is *development.* And it is this developmental phase which may or may not require sexual triggering. Reproduction as such, namely, the formation of reproductive units, is always "asexual."

Each of the three basic methods of reproduction has an adaptive advantage which the other two methods lack. The chief advantage of vegetative reproduction is speed of propagation. Huge numbers of offspring may be produced by this method within a very short time, particularly in unicellular organisms, where vegetative propagation is achieved simply by cell division. In multicellular organisms, vegetative reproduction is not as speedy and the numbers of offspring produced by this method are actually exceeded very often by sporulation. Nevertheless, vegetative reproduction is still far more effective in a numerical sense than gametic reproduction. Moreover, it requires little tissue or cell specialization and it also offers obvious advantages to an organism in the form of regenerative reproduction. As a result, vegetative reproduction has persisted as a method of propagation in all Monera, Protista, and Metaphyta and in all but the most complex Metazoa.

The chief advantage of sporulation is that it represents an excellent device for geographic dispersal. In water, a spore cell may be equipped with flagella and may swim to new territories, even far away from the parent. On land, spores may be encapsulated and protected against desiccation and may be distributed widely by wind and animals. In any environment, moreover, spores can be produced in very large numbers. As might be expected, therefore, spores or equivalent types of reproductive cells typically are formed by organisms which cannot disperse by locomotion: some Monera, sessile Protista, all Metaphyta (which are uniformly sessile), and some sessile Metazoa such as sponges. Most sessile Metazoa, sponges included, may disperse geographically by means of motile embryos or larvae, but, with the exception of sponges and a few other forms, such animals do not produce sporelike cells. Analogously, sporelike cells are absent when the adult animals are capable of locomotion.

Gametic reproduction entails a number of serious disadvantages. For example, this method of propagation depends on chance, for gametes must meet and very often they simply do not. Much of the reproductive effort of the parent organisms is then wasted. Gametic reproduction also depends on locomotion; for if gametes are to meet, they either must move themselves or must be brought together by locomotion of the parent organisms. Yet eggs in all cases and parent organisms in many cases are incapable of locomotion. Above all, gametic reproduction invariably requires an *aquatic* medium. In air, gametes would dry out quickly unless they possessed evaporation-resistant outer shells. But if two cells were so encapsulated, they could then not fuse together. As we shall see, terrestrial organisms actually can circumvent this dilemma only by means of special adaptations.

However, all these various disadvantages are relatively minor compared to the one vital advantage offered by gametes. This advantage is sex. Monera appear to be able to derive the same advantage by other means, as we shall see, but in all other groups sex occurs nearly universally. Sexual processes may or may not take place in conjunction with reproductive processes. Where sex and reproduction are not associated, as in many Protista, the organisms reproduce vegetatively or by spores and sex occurs separately at some stage of the life cycle. Where sex and reproduction do take place together, as in most organisms, gametic reproduction is the result. Such organisms may or may not reproduce additionally by vegetative means or by spores. What is the crucial significance of sex?

SEXUALITY

THE FUNCTION OF SEX

The role of sex is revealed most clearly in those Protista in which sexual processes do not occur together with reproduction. A good example is *Spirogyra*, a filamentous green alga forming dense growths in freshwater ponds. Throughout spring, summer, and early fall, the cells reproduce vegetatively by mitotic division and add to the length of the filament. Pieces of the alga may break off and settle elsewhere, starting new individuals. Later in the fall, two cells from two filaments lying side by side may **conjugate:** a bridge forms which interconnects the two cells. The contents of one cell then pass in amoeboid fashion through the bridge into the other cell and the two cells fuse (Fig. 23.15).

That is a sexual process. What initiates its occurrence, characteristically at that season of the year? Subsequent events provide the clue. All nonconjugated cells soon die as a result of falling autumn temperatures. But the fused double cell, the zygote, is able to secrete a heavy wall around itself. The *cyst*, or *zygospore*, so formed is then able to live through the winter. In the following spring, as surface ice disappears from the pond and temperatures begin to rise, the cyst wall breaks open and a new *Spirogyra* filament develops from the surviving zygote.

A similar sexual process occurs in many other protists. In the ciliate protozoon *Paramecium*, for example, reproduction is achieved as in *Spirogyra* by vegetative cell division. Sex takes place separately through conjugation. In *Paramecium*, however, the sexual process does not involve *fusion* of whole cells, but *exchange of* nuclei and thus of *gene sets* (Fig. 23.16.) Thus, whereas the gametes of *Spirogyra* are whole cells, the gametes of *Paramecium* are nuclei only.

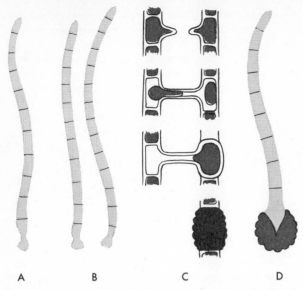

FIG. 23.15 Sexuality in *Spirogyra*. *A*, colony of cells. *B*, two filaments side by side prior to conjugation. *C*, bridge between opposite cells (top); migration of contents of one cell into the other cell (center); formation of cyst or zygospore (bottom). *D*, growth of new filament from opened zygospore.

Note, first, that the sexual process is fundamentally quite distinct from reproduction. *Spirogyra* and *Paramecium* do not "multiply" by sex—if anything, quite the contrary. In *Spirogyra*, two cells form one; in *Paramecium*, two cells enter the process and two cells again emerge. In all other organisms, sex and reproduction are equally distinct, even though in most cases the two processes do occur together.

Note further that in *Spirogyra*, in *Paramecium*, and in virtually all other organisms, man not excepted, sexual activity is particularly evident during periods of persistent *stress*. Sexuality may be brought out or inten-

sified by unfavorable climates, by widespread food shortages, by overpopulation, or by other conditions which cannot be quickly responded to through steady-state control or reproduction. Indeed, most plants and animals living in temperate climates manifest sexual activity typically in the fall or in the spring. Initial unfavorable changes in the fall environment bring forth sexual responses as though anticipating the worse conditions of winter, and sexual activity during spring anticipates the stress conditions of summer heat and dryness.

Just how is sexuality effective against conditions of stress? Events in *Spirogyra* and *Paramecium* supply the general answer: every cell resulting from the sexual process possesses the genes of *both* cells which entered the process. Stripped to its barest essentials, sex may be defined as the accumulation within a single cell of genes derived from two relatively unrelated cells. One method of achieving this is cell fusion, as in *Spirogyra;* another is direct exchange of duplicate nuclei, hence of duplicate gene sets, as in *Paramecium*.

Sex therefore counteracts stress conditions on the principle of "two are better than one." If the self-perpetuating powers of two relatively unrelated parent organisms are joined, through union of their genes, then the resulting offspring organism may acquire a survival potential which is greater than that of either parent alone. If parent *A* survives in environment *a* and parent *B* in environment *b*, then the organism *AB* formed after sexual union may survive in environments *a* or *b* or in both (Fig. 23.17).

Moreover, a still poorly understood *rejuvenation*, on the biochemical, metabolic level, accompanies the sexual process. In certain protozoa and fungi, for example, if sex is experimentally prevented during an indefinite number of successive vegetative generations, then the vigor of the line eventually declines. The organisms ultimately die, even under optimal environmental conditions. Internal stresses apparently appear

FIG. 23.16 Sexuality in *Paramecium*. *A*, original partners. *B*, mating. *C*, nuclear division. *D*, gene exchange. *E*, result. *F*, nuclear fusion and separation of partners. Note that sexuality in *Spirogyra* involves fusion of two entire cells; in *Paramecium*, only exchanged nuclei fuse.

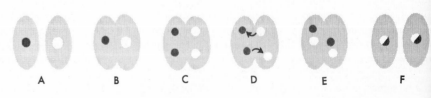

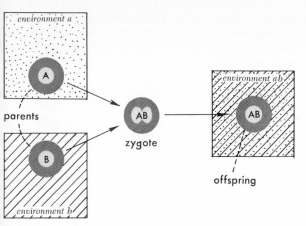

FIG. 23.17 The role of sex in combating stress. a and b
represent two different environments in which live two
genetically different prospective parents; A and B symbolize their genes. Through sex, the offspring acquires
the genes of both parents, hence also the ability to live
in either environment a or b. Sex combines the adaptation potential of the parents and so endows the offspring with increased adaptation potential.

in aged generations, and only a "rejuvenation" through
sex may then save the reproductive succession and
prevent the line from dying out.

We may say that reproduction is a "conservative"
process. Parental characteristics are passed on faithfully
by reproduction from generation to generation, and so
long as the external and internal environment remains
favorable, succeeding generations survive as well as

preceding ones. Sex, on the other hand, is a "liberal-
izing" process. It may offer survival under new or
changed conditions. By combining the genes of two
parents, sex introduces *genetic change* into the resulting organisms. And to the extent that such change may
be advantageous for survival in new environments or
under new conditions, sex had adaptive value. That is
the key point; *sex is one of the chief processes of
adaptation*. It is worth repeating that sex is *not* a process of reproduction.

Since the sexual process involves single cells, it
must be carried out at a stage when an organism consists of but a single cell. In unicellular organisms,
therefore, sex may occur at any stage of the life cycle
regardless of when reproduction occurs, and it may be
dissociated completely from reproduction. By contrast,
if in the life cycle of a multicellular organism sex is to
take place at all, it *must* take place at a unicellular
reproductive stage. Hence, "gametic reproduction": sex
occurs *after* the formation of reproductive cells and
before the development of such cells into multicellular
adults (Fig. 23.18).

MALE, FEMALE,
AND HERMAPHRODITE

In *Spirogyra*, the gamete cells are not visibly distinguishable as being of two different types; before an
actual process of conjugation, one cannot tell which
cell will move across the bridge and which will not.
Moreover, even after this functional difference is established, structural differences between the cells still can-

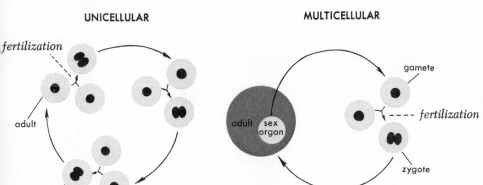

UNICELLULAR

fertilization

adult

zygote

sex possible at any time during
life cycle

MULTICELLULAR

gamete

adult sex organ

fertilization

zygote

sex possible only at gamete stage
of life cycle

FIG. 23.18 The relation
of sex to life cycle. Since
sex is a process involving
single cells, it may occur at
any stage in unicellular organisms but only at the
gamete stage in multicellular organisms.

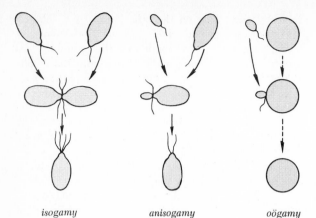

isogamy　　　　*anisogamy*　　　　*oögamy*

FIG. 23.19 The three patterns of fertilization, distinguished on the basis of gamete types. Gametes may be of the same size and motility (isogamy), of different sizes but the same motility (anisogamy), or of different sizes and different motilities (oögamy).

not be detected. Such likeness of the two gamete types is referred to as **isogamy,** a condition encountered quite frequently among Protista. In many Protista, however, the two gamete types do differ visibly. In numerous cases, for example, both types are flagellate but one is distinctly smaller than the other. Such organisms are said to exhibit **anisogamy;** i.e., sexual processes involve gametes of unequal appearance. Still other Protista, and all Metaphyta and Metazoa, exhibit a special form of anisogamy, namely, **oögamy.** Here one gamete type is always motile and usually small and the other gamete type is always nonmotile and usually large. The small type is called a *sperm,* the large type, an *egg.* (Fig. 23.19).

In many organisms, any one individual produces one gamete type only and another individual produces the other type only. The sexes here are said to be **separate.** Such a functional specialization of individuals occurs in man and indeed in most animals and also in numerous plants and many protists. Note, however, that if such organisms exhibit isogamy or anisogamy, the terms "male" and "female" are not strictly applicable. For example, there is little justification for regarding individuals of *Spirogyra* as either males or females. Instead, the two sex types, or **mating types,** are customarily identified by distinguishing symbols such as + and − (Fig. 23.20). True male and female sexes are recognized only in cases of oögamy, i.e., wherever distinct sperms and eggs are produced. In

such organisms, males and females are often distinguished also in other ways. In Metaphyta and Metazoa, for example, sperms and eggs are produced in differently constructed sex organs. Among plants, **antheridia** form sperms, **archegonia** form eggs; among animals, **testes** form sperms, **ovaries** form eggs. Moreover, the sex organs of males and females may be components of differently constructed reproductive systems, and numerous secondary sex characteristics may provide additional distinctions. We note that where the sexes are separate, the degrees of sex distinction may vary considerably. At one extreme are the isogamous protists,

FIG. 23.20 Zygospores of *Spirogyra.* Note that all cells within a given filament have the same sexual properties: they may be either migrating sexual partners or stationary partners which receive cells from a neighboring filament. All cells of a given filament are the same *mating type,* and this accounts for their uniform sexual behavior. *(General Biological Supply House, Inc.)*

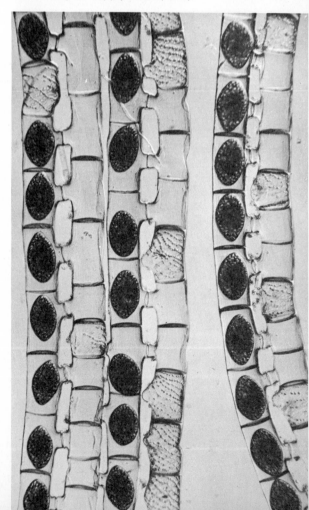

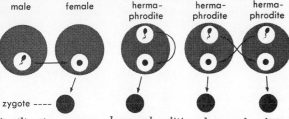

FIG. 23.21   Self- and cross-fertilization. Left, the pattern of fertilization among nonhermaphrodites. Center and right, the patterns of self- and cross-fertilization among hermaphrodites.

where visible differences between sex types are zero. At the other extreme are the advanced Metaphyta and, particularly, the advanced Metazoa, in which virtually every part of the organism may exhibit characteristics of maleness or femaleness.

In numerous organisms, both gamete types are produced within the same individual. Known as **hermaphroditism,** this condition is particularly common among sessile organisms and also among sluggish, slowly moving forms. For example, hermaphroditic organisms include some species of *Spirogyra, Paramecium* and all other ciliate protozoa, and considerable numbers of other Protista. Many, possibly most, Metaphyta are hermaphroditic. Among Metazoa, the phenomenon occurs in flatworms, clams, earthworms, and many other forms, and it is sometimes encountered as an abnormality in vertebrates, man included.

Hermaphroditism is a direct adaptation to the slow or sessile way of life. Since a normal hermaphrodite functions both as a "male" and as a "female," its gametes may not need to search each other out: **self-fertilization** may take place. In such cases, the gametes of one sex type are genetically compatible with the gametes of the other sex type produced in the same individual. Self-fertilizing hermaphrodites of this sort are said to be **homothallic** (particularly in Protista and especially fungi, where this condition is quite common). Other hermaphrodites must carry out **cross-fertilization;** i.e., a gamete of one sex type produced by one individual must fertilize a gamete of the other sex type produced by another individual (Fig. 23.21). Here, evidently, the gametes of one type are *not* compatible with those of the other type formed in the same individual; they are compatible only with gametes of the

other type formed by another individual. In many of such cases, so-called "compatibility genes" are known to make self-fertilization impossible. Cross-fertilizing hermaphrodites are said to be **heterothallic** (the term again being applicable most particularly to Protista).

The fertilization pattern in heterothallic forms is the same as in cases where the sexes are separate, but an adaptive advantage is apparent nevertheless; i.e., fewer reproductive cells are wasted here than in species with separate sexes. Thus if a given species is cross-fertilizing and hermaphroditic, sperms from one individual may meet eggs in *any* other individual, for every hermaphrodite contains eggs. In species with separate sexes, by contrast, many sperms are wasted through chance misdistribution to the wrong sex. Similarly, if cross-fertilizing hermaphrodites are capable of some locomotion, like earthworms, for example, then fertilization becomes possible whenever *any* two individuals meet. Since sluggish individuals are not likely to meet very frequently to begin with, and since every such meeting may result in fertilization, the adaptive value of hermaphroditism is clear (Fig. 23.22).

In any organism, separately sexed or hermaphroditic, it happens often that given gametes fail to find compatible partners. Most of such unsuccessful gametes disintegrate very soon, but in exceptional cases this does not occur. Instead, single gametes may begin to *develop* and form normal adult organisms. This phenomenon is known as **parthenogenesis,** "virginal development" of a gamete *without* fertilization. In certain isogamous and anisogamous species, either gamete type may sometimes develop parthenogenetically. In oögamous species, only the eggs are known in some cases to develop by natural parthenogenesis without being fertilized (e.g., rotifers, social insects; cf. Chap. 11); sperms always disintegrate if they do not find an egg. In selected instances, *artificial* parthenogenesis may be induced by experimental means. For example, a frog egg can be made to develop before it has been fertilized by pricking its surface with a needle. The puncture simulates the entrance of a sperm and development then begins. But a sexual process has not taken place. Note that a parthenogenetic gamete is functionally indistinguishable from a *spore:* both are single reproductive cells which develop directly (Fig. 23.23).

One consequence of every sexual process is that a zygote formed from two gametes possesses twice the usual number of chromosomes. Organisms counteract this increase by a series of special nuclear divisions known as **meiosis.** In many cases meiosis is accom-

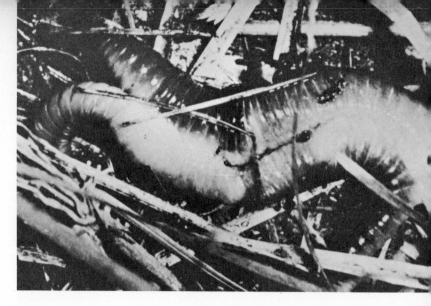

FIG. 23.22 Copulating earthworms. These animals are cross-fertilizing hermaphrodites; hence whenever *any* two of them meet, each may be fertilized by the other. *(General Biological Supply House, Inc.)*

panied by cytoplasmic divisions, and both events are then referred to collectively as meiotic cell divisions.

MEIOTIC CELL DIVISION

THE PATTERN

As noted in Chap. 4, the number of chromosomes per cell is a fixed, genetically determined trait of every organism. However, whenever a sexual process takes place, the gene sets of two sex cells fuse together. In a zygote or fertilized egg, therefore, the chromosome number is doubled. An adult organism developing from such a zygote would consist of cells which would all

FIG. 23.23 Parthenogenesis. If gametes produced by adults (center) fuse and produce new adults via zygotes, then the pattern is regularly bisexual (left). But if a gamete develops into an adult without sexual fusion with another gamete, then the pattern is parthenogenetic (right).

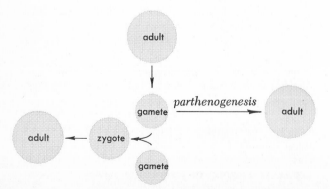

have a doubled chromosome number. If the next generation is again produced sexually, the chromosome number would then quadruple, and this process of progressive doubling would continue indefinitely through successive sexual generations.

This does not happen in actuality. Chromosome numbers do stay constant from one life cycle to the next, and the constancy is brought about by meiosis. *It is the function of meiosis to counteract the chromosome-doubling effect of fertilization by reducing a doubled chromosome number to half.* The unreduced doubled chromosome number, before meiosis, is called the **diploid** number, and it is symbolized as **2n;** the reduced number, after meiosis, is the **haploid** number, and it is symbolized as **n** (Fig. 23.24).

Meiosis occurs in every life cycle which includes a sexual process — in other words, more or less universally. As we shall see in the next section, organisms differ according to *when* and *where* meiosis occurs in the life cycle. In many Protista, including the unicellular alga *Chlamydomonas*, for example, meiosis takes place in the zygote, as a first step in the further development of that zygote. Thus, fertilization produces a zygote with a diploid chromosome number and meiosis then restores the haploid condition. In such a life cycle, evidently, the only diploid stage is the zygote. The pattern is substantially different in many other Protista and in all Metaphyta and Metazoa.

For the present, the essential point is only that meiosis occurs at *some* stage during every life cycle which includes sex, as a counterbalance to the chromosome-doubling effect of fertilization. For purposes of illustration, we shall here continue to discuss the *Chlamydomonas* pattern specifically.

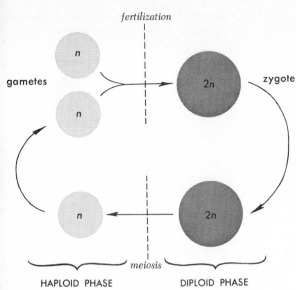

FIG. 23.24   The relation of meiosis to life cycle.

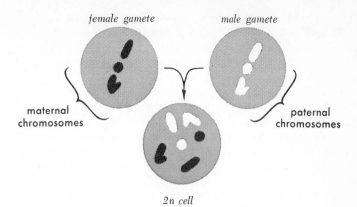

FIG. 23.25   Each diploid cell contains two like sets of chromosomes, representing maternal-paternal pairs. The maternal set originated in the female gamete; the paternal set, in the male gamete.

THE PROCESS

A zygote does not contain a $2n$ collection of mutually different chromosomes, but instead contains a collection of n mutually different *pairs* of chromosomes. For a zygote receives one haploid, n, set of chromosomes via the male sex cell, and a like haploid set via the female sex cell. Therefore, like shoes, the chromosomes of any diploid cell come in pairs. One of each pair is paternal in origin, the other maternal (Fig. 23.25). During meiosis in such a diploid cell, chromosome reduction occurs in such a way that any resulting haploid cell contains *one of each maternal-paternal pair* of chromosomes. In this haploid cell, it is entirely a matter of chance which and how many chromosomes will be maternal and which and how many will be paternal. For example, after meiosis in one species of *Chlamydomonas*, eight chromosomes make up a complete haploid set. Of these eight, a chance-determined number will be paternal, the remainder maternal (Fig. 23.26).

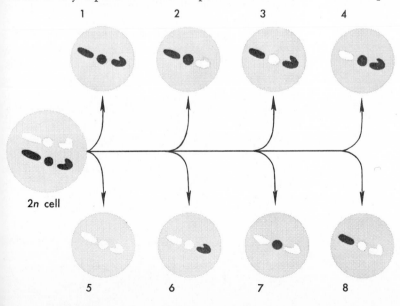

FIG. 23.26   When the chromosome number of a diploid cell is halved by meiosis, a resulting haploid cell contains a single set of chromosomes consisting of a chance-determined number of paternal and maternal chromosomes. The diagram shows the various possible paternal-maternal combinations if $n = 3$.

The phrase "chromosome reduction" might imply that in a diploid cell one of each pair of chromosomes is destroyed or otherwise lost. This is not the case. Instead, the diploid chromosome number is reduced to half by two **meiotic cell divisions.** The general pattern of these divisions is as follows. A diploid cell undergoes two successive cytoplasmic cleavages, which transform the one original cell into four cells. During or before these cleavages, the chromosomes of the diploid cell duplicate *once.* As a result, $2n$ becomes $4n$. And of these $4n$ chromosomes, one n is incorporated into each of the four cells formed. In sum, *one diploid* cell becomes *four haploid* cells (Fig. 23.27).

In *Chlamydomonas,* for example, a zygote contains 16 chromosomes. During meiosis the number doubles to 32 and at the same time the cytoplasm of the zygote divides twice in succession. Four cells result which share the 32 chromosomes equally. Hence each mature cell of *Chlamydomonas* contains eight chromosomes, a complete haploid set.

The two meiotic divisions have many features in common with mitotic divisions. For example, each meiotic division passes through prophase, metaphase, anaphase, and telophase, as in mitosis. Moreover, spindles form and other nonchromosomal events are as in mitotic divisions.

The critical difference between mitosis and the *first* meiotic division lies in their metaphases. In mitosis, we recall, all chromosomes, each of them already duplicated, migrate into the metaphase plate, where all the centromeres line up in the same plane. In the first meiotic division, the $2n$ chromosomes similarly duplicate during or before prophase. These $2n$ pairs, the members of each pair again joined at the centromere, also migrate into the metaphase plate. But now only n pairs assemble in one plane. The other n pairs migrate into a plane of their own, a plane which is closely parallel to the first. Moreover, every pair in one plane comes to lie next to the corresponding type of chromosome pair in the other plane. The metaphase plate is therefore made up of *paired chromosome pairs,* or **tetrads** of like chromosomes lying side by side. And there are n of these tetrads in the whole plate (Fig. 23.28).

During the ensuing anaphase, two chromosomes of each tetrad migrate to one spindle pole, two to the other. At the end of the first meiotic division, therefore, there are two cells, each with n pairs of chromosomes. In the metaphase of the subsequent second meiotic division, the n pairs of chromosomes line up in the same plane and n single chromosomes eventually migrate to each of the poles during anaphase. At the termination of meiosis as a whole, therefore, four cells are present, each with n single chromosomes, a complete haploid set.

In unicellular forms such as *Chlamydomonas,* the four haploid cells resulting from meiosis are four new adult organisms. In many other organisms, as noted, meiosis occurs not in the zygote but at different stages of the life cycle. What are these stages and indeed what is the nature of a life cycle?

FIG. 23.27 The general pattern of events during meiosis, on the assumption that $2n = 2$.

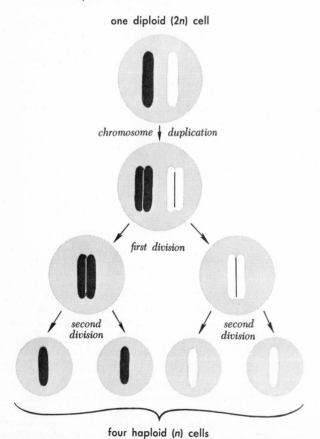

one diploid (2n) cell

chromosome ↓ *duplication*

first division

*second
division*　　　*second
division*

four haploid (n) cells

LIFE CYCLES

THE HAPLONTIC PATTERN

As just pointed out above, *Chlamydomonas* is haploid as an adult. All available evidence suggests

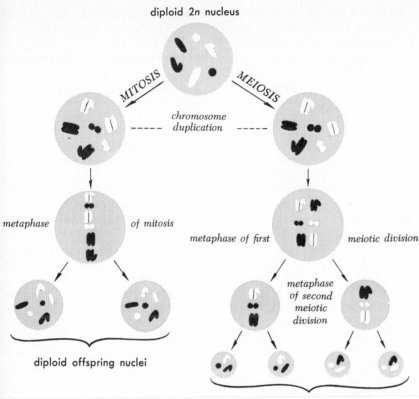

diploid 2n nucleus

MITOSIS   MEIOSIS

chromosome
duplication

metaphase   *of mitosis*

metaphase of first   *meiotic division*

metaphase
of second
meiotic
division

diploid offspring nuclei

haploid offspring nuclei

FIG. 23.28   A comparison of mitosis
and meiosis, on the assumption that
$2n = 6$. Note that the key difference
between the two processes is the
way the chromosomes line up in
metaphase.

that this is a primitive condition, inherited unchanged
from the very first protists and probably even from the
very first living organisms of any kind. It is reasonable
to suppose that a very early ancestral cell possessed
only a single complete set of genes, i.e., that it was
haploid, and that its life cycle consisted simply of a
succession of vegetative generations, each connected to
the next by cell division. In due course sporulation was
"invented," such that any vegetative generation could
produce through a series of rapid cell divisions numerous haploid spore cells. In due course, also, sex was
invented and this introduced a diploid zygote stage as
a result of fertilization. Meiosis in the zygote, or **zygotic
meiosis,** must then have been a corollary invention.
The chromosome-doubling process of fertilization undoubtedly was the stimulus to which the chromosome-
reducing process of meiosis was the rapidly following
response.

A life cycle characterized in this way by zygotic
meiosis and haploid adults is known as a **haplontic** life
cycle (Fig. 23.29). It occurs in all Monera (insofar as

sex is known in this category and insofar as genetic
reduction here can be called "meiosis"; see Chap. 24);
in all primitive and many advanced groups among
green, yellow-brown, and several other types of algae;
and in many fungi. The list suggests clearly and the

FIG. 23.29   The haplontic life-cycle pattern.

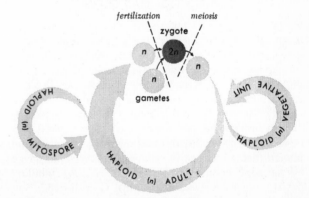

fertilization   *meiosis*

zygote

n $2n$ n

n

gametes

HAPLOID (n)
MITOSPORE

HAPLOID (n) VEGETATIVE UNIT

HAPLOID (n) ADULT

next chapter will show in more specific detail that the haplontic life cycle is basic in the Monera and the Protista. Where sporulation occurs in these haplontic groups, spores are produced at some point in the life cycle between one fertilization and the next. The method of spore production is mitotic division and, like the adults which produce them, the spores are haploid. We may therefore refer to them as **haploid mitospores.**

Evidently, in an organism with a haplontic life cycle, one individual may carry out any of the three basic methods of reproduction, the choice being dictated by the environment. Thus, if environmental conditions are favorable, a given individual may reproduce vegetatively or sporulatively or both. Or, if conditions are unfavorable, the same individual could produce gametes (see Fig. 23.29).

Haplontic patterns have probably given rise to all other types of life cycles. With regard to the timing of meiosis, we may readily guess at which points the process possibly *could* occur. Like sex, meiosis is a cellular process, and it can therefore take place only at a stage when the life cycle passes through a unicellular phase. The zygote does represent such a phase even in multicellular organisms, and as we have just seen, the haplontic life cycle is based on this.

But a multicellular organism may pass through unicellular stages on two other occasions, namely, at the stage of the *gamete* and at the stage of the *spore.* Conceivably, therefore, meiosis could occur at either of these points. As noted earlier, it is not important *when* meiosis takes place so long as it takes place at all within every life cycle which includes sex. In actuality, meiosis does occur at the gamete stage in many organisms and at the spore stage in many others.

THE DIPLONTIC PATTERN

In man, meiosis takes place during the formation of gametes. Within the sex organs of the adult, diploid gamete-producing cells mature into sperms and eggs. As part of this maturation, meiosis takes place in these diploid cells. Mature gametes consequently are haploid. Accordingly, we may speak here of **gametogenic meiosis.**

The mature haploid gametes subsequently participate in fertilization, and the zygote is then diploid. But now, as the zygote divides and develops into a mature human being, the cells *remain diploid.* The whole human adult becomes diploid in this fashion, including the sex organs it eventually forms. Gamete-producing

cells consequently are diploid as well. And meiosis occurs again during the maturation of gametes.

Such a life cycle, characterized by gametogenic meiosis and diploid adults, is called a **diplontic life cycle** (Fig. 23.30). In it, the only haploid stage is the gamete itself, all other stages being diploid. We note that this is almost completely the reverse of a haplontic cycle. Diplontic cycles are very abundant. They are encountered not only in man but in all Metazoa, and among Protista such cycles occur in various advanced groups of algae (e.g., *Acetabularia,* diatoms, *Fucus*), in some fungi, and in most protozoa. The list suggests strongly that diplontic cycles are not primitive but must have been derived from haplontic cycles.

We may readily guess how the evolutionary transition from haplontic to diplontic cycles must have been achieved. In the ancestral haplontic type, meiosis occurs in the zygote, at the very start of the life cycle. In diplontic types, meiosis is *postponed* to the time of gamete formation, i.e., to the very end of the life cycle. Thus, sooner or later during the evolution of Protista, some groups evidently delayed the timing of meiosis as long as it could be delayed.

There is an additional reason for regarding diplontic cycles as advanced. If we consider the time relation of fertilization and meiosis in, for example, man, the superficial impression is gained that the response *precedes* the stimulus: chromosome reduction during gamete formation here appears to be quickly followed by chromosome doubling during fertilization. However, it is quite unlikely that responses anticipate stimuli. In the same measure it is very likely that a diplontic cycle is not original but derived. Gametogenic meiosis can be reasonably interpreted only if it is assumed that it represents a much-postponed chromo-

FIG. 23.30   The diplontic life-cycle pattern.

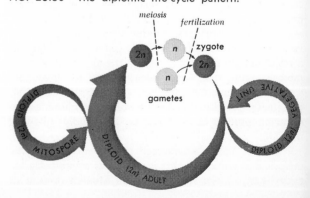

some reduction. Then, properly, fertilization is the chromosome-doubling stimulus and gametogenic meiosis is the greatly delayed response (see Fig. 23.32).

A powerful adaptive advantage results from postponing meiosis. As noted, one consequence is that the adults, and indeed all stages except the gametes, are diploid. This means that each gene in each adult cell is represented twice rather than just once. One gene of a given pair has a maternal ancestry, the other a paternal ancestry. The advantage of double genes is that they increase the redundancy of the genetic information (cf. Chap. 18). Therefore, even if one gene of a pair changes in some way, e.g., by mutation, then the other gene still preserves the original message. In short, the diploid state increases the genetic stability of the individual. Evidently, this has been adaptively sufficiently important to make diplontic life cycles highly popular among organisms.

If an organism with a diplontic life cycle produces spores, such cells are manufactured by a diploid adult. The method of spore formation is again mitotic division and the spores consequently are diploid too. We may therefore speak here of **diploid mitospores.** They are formed by many diplontic Protista and by Metazoa such as sponges (where cells of this type are not usually called "spores," as noted earlier).

THE DIPLOHAPLONTIC PATTERN

The third possible time of meiosis is the stage of spore production. In this case we may speak of **sporogenic meiosis.** The aquatic phycomycetous fungus *Allomyces* illustrates the pattern well. Fertilization produces a diploid zygote, and the developing adult fungus remains diploid. In due course it produces a spore-forming structure called a sporangium. In it, diploid spore-producing cells give rise to spores. Meiosis occurs during this transformation of spore-producing cells into spores. Such spores therefore are haploid, and since their production includes meiosis, we may refer to them as **meiospores.**

A haploid meiospore subsequently germinates and develops into a new, *haploid* fungus. This adult later manufactures haploid gametes, and these subsequently participate in fertilization. A new life cycle then begins with the resulting diploid zygote.

We note that, because meiosis occurs during sporulation, such a life cycle is split up into two generations, each represented by a separate adult. The diploid zygote gives rise to a diploid adult; and since this adult

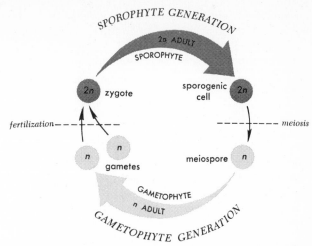

FIG. 23.31 The main aspects of the diplohaplontic life-cycle pattern. Haploid phases are shown in light gray, diploid phases in dark gray.

later produces meiospores, it is called the **sporophyte generation.** The haploid meiospore gives rise to a haploid adult; and since this adult later produces gametes, it is called the **gametophyte generation.**

Cycles of this sort, characterized by **sporogenic meiosis** and **alternation of generations,** are known as **diplohaplontic life cycles** (Fig. 23.31). They are exceedingly widespread, occurring in numerous algae, many fungi, all slime molds, and in all Metaphyta. Such cycles are again derived from the haplontic type by a postponement of meiosis, in this case from the zygote stage to the spore-producing stage (Fig. 23.32).

Diplohaplontic cycles combine the adaptive advantages of both haplontic and diplontic ones. Diploid sporophytes are relatively stable genetically and their characteristics cannot be easily varied. On the other hand, the haploid gametophytes are genetically less stable and their characteristics can be varied more readily. This permits faster adaptation to changing environments, hence faster evolution. Diplohaplontic types evidently combine a measure of evolutionary conservatism with a measure of evolutionary plasticity.

Note that a single individual of a diplohaplontic organism is not capable of reproducing by any one of the three basic methods. For example, a sporophytic individual cannot reproduce via gametes; it must reproduce either vegetatively or sporulatively. The meiospore is its characteristic reproductive product and in most cases it is the *only* such product. However, some sporo-

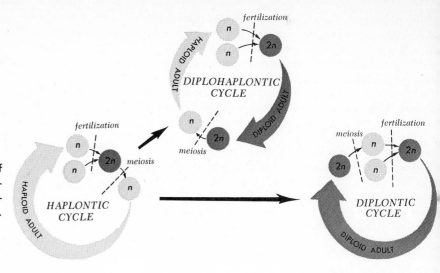

FIG. 23.32 The probable origin of the diplohaplontic and diplontic patterns from the haplontic by postponement of the time of meiosis.

FIG. 23.33 The complete diplohaplontic life-cycle pattern, indicating the nature of the various types of vegetative and sporulative repeating generations.

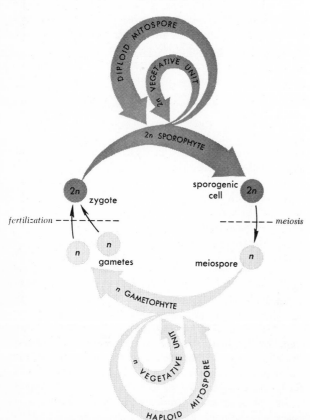

phytic adults have the additional capacity to manufacture another kind of spore. Such spores are produced by mitotic division and are therefore diploid, like the sporophytes manufacturing them. In effect, spores of this kind are diploid mitospores, like those produced by organisms with purely diplontic life cycles. When the diploid mitospores develop, they give rise to new diploid sporophytes. A whole series of successive sporophyte individuals may be produced in this manner via diploid mitospores, and the series ends only with the manufacture of haploid meiospores. This pattern is exemplified in the fungus *Allomyces,* for example. Diploid sporophytes here propagate in series through diploid mitospores, and the diploid phase of the life cycle terminates only when haploid meiospores are formed. These develop into haploid gametophytes (Fig. 23.33).

Analogously, among the gametophytes of various species, *most* may reproduce only vegetatively or via gametes. But in some species the gametophytes may also produce spores by mitotic divisions. Since the parent gametophytes are haploid, the spores formed are haploid mitospores like those produced by organisms with purely haplontic life cycles. For example, certain species of the brown alga *Ectocarpus* exhibit the complete diplohaplontic life cycle with all types of spores. Diploid sporophytes produce more of themselves through diploid mitospores. Then these sporophytes manufacture haploid meiospores which give rise to haploid gametophytes. Then these gametophytes in turn produce more of themselves through haploid mitospores. The life cycle finally ends with the production of haploid gametes and subsequent fertilization (see Fig. 23.33).

With this account of general reproductive patterns as a background, we proceed in the next chapters with a discussion of the specific reproductive processes of given groups of organisms.

REVIEW QUESTIONS

1. How does reproduction contribute to steady-state maintenance? To self-perpetuation in general? Review the forms of molecular reproduction and the nature of each. How does molecular reproduction contribute to organismic reproduction?

2. Define binary fission, multiple fission, budding. What basic events occur in all forms of cell division? What is mitosis? How does cell division contribute to organismic reproduction? What different forms of mitotic division are known? Define spindle, aster, centriole, centromere. How does mitotic division differ in plant and animal cells?

3. What molecular events within cells precede the microscopically visible phases of division? Describe the processes characteristic of prophase and metaphase. What is the metaphase plate and where is it located? What are the events of anaphase?

4. Describe the processes characteristic of telophase. Review the history of the nucleoli during mitotic division. What is the net result of mitotic division? What is known about the mechanical forces which bring about chromosome movements during mitosis? Review some of the experiments and observations which may have a bearing on this.

5. What is a tissue culture? What have experiments with tissue cultures shown about rates of cell division? When and where in an organism are fission rates highest? Lowest?

6. Distinguish between reproduction and development. What is vegetative reproduction? Under what circumstances and in which forms does vegetative reproduction occur? What is sporulation? What is gametic reproduction? How is vegetative reproduction different from sporulation? How is sporulation different from gametic reproduction?

7. What are the most basic events of every sexual process? Under what conditions does sex tend to occur? In what way is sex of adaptive value? Illustrate by the example of *Spirogyra*. Define mating, fertilization, zygote, gamete, spore, isogamy, oögamy, and parthenogenesis.

8. What are the limitations of and the environmental conditions required for (a) gametic reproduction and (b) sporulation? Contrast in detail. What is hermaphroditism? What is its adaptive value? Distinguish between self-fertilization and cross-fertilization.

9. What is the basic function of meiosis, and what makes such a process necessary? Where does meiosis occur? Define haploid, diploid. How many *pairs* of chromosomes are found in a diploid cell? Of these, which and how many are maternal and which and how many are paternal?

10. How many chromosome duplications and how many cell duplications occur during meiosis? In what respects are mitosis and meiosis alike? What is the essential difference between the metaphase of mitosis and the metaphase of the first meiotic division? Describe the complete sequence of events during both divisions of meiosis.

11. Describe the nature of a haplontic life cycle. Name organisms in which such a cycle occurs. Do similarly for diplontic and diplohaplontic life cycles.

12. Which type of life cycle is probably primitive and how may it have given rise to the other types? Define mitospore, meiospore, gametophyte, sporophyte, alternation of generations.

SUGGESTED COLLATERAL READINGS

The selections listed below cover various aspects of cellular and organismic reproduction:

Berrill, N. F.: "Sex and the Nature of Things," Dodd, Mead, New York, 1953.

Loeb, J.: On the Nature of the Process of Fertilization, etc., in M. L. Gabriel and S. Fogel, "Great Experiments in Biology," Prentice-Hall, Englewood Cliffs, N.J., 1955.

Mazia, D.: Cell Division, *Sci. American*, vol. 189, 1953.

————: The Life History of the Cell, *Am. Scientist,* vol. 44, 1956.

Raper, J. R.: Some Problems of Specificity in the Sexuality of Plants, in "Biological Specificity and Growth," Princeton University Press, Princeton, N.J., 1955.

Schrader, F.: "Mitosis," Columbia University Press, New York, 1952.

Stone, A.: The Control of Fertility, *Sci. American,* vol. 190, 1954.

Wenrich, D. H. (ed.): "Sex in Microorganisms," American Association for the Advancement of Science, Washington, D. C., 1954.

Wilson, E. B.: "The Cell in Development and Heredity," 3d ed., Macmillan, New York, reprinted, 1947

Zahl, P. A.: The Evolution of Sex, *Sci. American,* vol. 180, 1949.

REPRODUCTION: MONERA AND PROTISTA

24

All three basic reproductive methods are encountered in these organisms. Very frequently, notably among Protista, a given organism is capable of reproducing by any of the three methods at different times, specific environmental conditions usually determining the particular method. In aquatic forms, spores and gametes most often are flagellate and swimming. Inasmuch as the water supply is abundant, gametic reproduction can be accomplished readily. In terrestrial forms, spores are usually encapsulated but gametes cannot be, as noted in the preceding chapter. Nevertheless, despite the absence of abundant free water, gametic reproduction is made possible by special evolutionary adaptations.

MONERA

Among bacteria, the main reproductive process is rapid vegetative binary fission. Indeed, this form of propagation is so characteristic of the group that it has become part of the phylum name, viz., "fission plants." Inasmuch as microscopically identifiable chromosomes are absent, cell division is not mitotic. It is unknown just how the genetic material of a bacteria is duplicated exactly and distributed equally to the two daughter cells, but that some such process takes place is clear. It is similarly unknown how a dividing wall is laid down through the middle of a bacterial cell undergoing fission. In this respect, however, our ignorance is not limited to bacteria.

Cells divide transversely in most bacteria (see Fig. 5.23), but longitudinal fission as well as budding is known to occur in one group, the *Hyphomicrobiales*, or "budding bacteria." Many cells here may be joined end to end by filamentous secreted strands of cell-wall material. When one cell divides longitudinally, a branch strand may be initiated. A terminal cell in such a strand may then bud, i.e., form a smaller cell by unequal division. The bud cell may subsequently grow to normal size (Fig. 24.1).

FIG. 24.1 Budding in Hyphomicrobiales. Note the branch strand with small terminal bud cell. *(Courtesy of Dr. E. A. Duchow and Dr. H. C. Douglas, University of Washington, and J. Bacteriol., vol. 58, p. 411.)*

Many bacteria form endospores (see Fig. 8.8). Despite the implications of the name, such endospores are not reproductive units but are encapsulated dormant resting stages. The same single cell which encysts in the capsule eventually excysts again, still single. Similarly nonreproductive despite the name are the "fruiting bodies" typically produced by the *Myxobacteriales* (see Chap. 8). The cells composing such bodies form only dormant resting stages; the resemblance to the true fruiting bodies of slime molds is purely superficial.

However, some bacteria do produce true reproductive spores—indeed, several types of them (Fig. 24.2).

FIG. 24.2 The three types of spores formed in Actinomycetales.

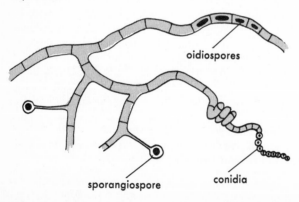

oidiospores

sporangiospore

conidia

This occurs in the *Actinomycetales,* or "branching bacteria," in which the vegetative cells are organized into branched, multicellular, funguslike "hyphae" and "mycelia." At the ends of certain hyphae, round spore cells may be cut off either singly or in linear series. Spores formed in this manner are called **conidia**. This is a characteristic method of reproduction in the antibiotic producer *Streptomyces,* for example. In other cases, the interior substance of a hypha may break up transversely into numerous spores. Reproductive units so produced are known as **oidiospores**. Thirdly, some branching bacteria may develop true sporangia at the tips of certain hyphae. The interior substance of a sporangium may then subdivide into numerous **sporangiospores**. These are remarkable instances of parallel evolution, for all three forms of sporulation are encountered also among the fungi (see below).

Sex is now known to occur in bacteria—in certain bacteria—as a laboratory phenomenon, and then only in very rare instances. Whether or not sex also takes place in nature is still unknown. The sexual process is conjugative, i.e., cells join pairwise and exchange portions of their genetic material. The partners then separate. Considering the extremely small size of bacteria and the virtual impossibility of identifying a mating pair visually among millions of closely packed cells in a culture dish, it is not surprising that bacterial sex remained undiscovered until quite recently. Indeed, when mating finally was discovered, the techniques employed at first were genetic, not direct observation.

The classical experiment was carried out with two different strains of the eubacterium *Escherichia coli.* One strain could use lactose as a fuel in anaerobic respiration (L+) and was also sensitive to the antibiotic streptomycin (S−). These traits were inherited genetically and were stable. Analogously, the other genetically stable strain could not ferment lactose (L−), but was resistant to streptomycin (S+). When L+S− and L−S+ strains were cultured together, the vegetative offspring cells contained many bacteria with traits exactly like the parental strains. But very occasionally bacteria were found which were L+S+; i.e., they could ferment lactose and at the same time were streptomycin resistant. Other individuals were L−S−; i.e., they could not use lactose and were streptomycin sensitive as well. Such traits evidently are combinations of parental traits. The occurrence of combinations indicates the occurrence of mating and of sexual exchange of genes. Methods were later devised to reveal mating pairs visually (Fig. 24.3).

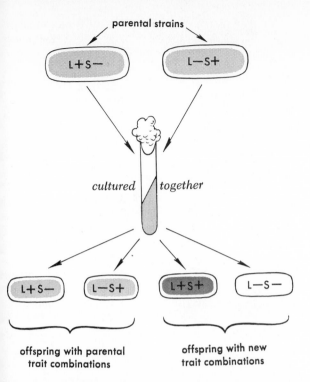

parental strains

L+S—   L—S+

cultured | *together*

L+S—   L—S+   L+S+   L—S—

offspring with parental
trait combinations

offspring with new
trait combinations

FIG. 24.3 Experiment showing gene exchange in bacteria. L+ symbolizes lactose-utilizing capacity, and S+ symbolizes streptomycin resistance.

Experiments of this sort have also established that vegetative bacteria are *haploid* and that some (still unknown) kind of gene-reduction process equivalent to meiosis takes place immediately after conjugation. In other words, insofar as sex occurs in them, bacterial life cycles are haplontic.

If sex is at best rare and is perhaps completely absent in many or most bacteria, how do these organisms adapt to their changing environments? They may do so without sex, by their extremely rapid vegetative multiplication. Rapid reproduction means rapid evolution, through mutations. Bacteria are haploid, which means that every mutational gene change will immediately produce a change in a trait. Therefore, even if millions or billions of bacteria succumb to one environment, a single survivor with appropriate mutations may within a few hours produce new millions or billions of readapted organisms. Bacteria evidently rely on safety through numbers, and they can do very well without sex.

Whereas sex is rare in bacteria, it is totally unknown in blue-green algae. Conceivably, biochemical

and genetic methods similar to those used in bacteria might some day show that sex can occur in the cyanophytes. Even in such an event, however, it would still be true that cyanophytes, like the bacteria, normally adapt by rapid vegetative division and mutation.

In addition to vegetative fission, which occurs in all cyanophytes, many blue-green algae may also reproduce by sporulation (e.g., the Chamaesiphonales, see Chap. 8). In some instances, the contents of a cell subdivide into numerous spore cells. In other instances, spores are cut off in series at one end of a cell. Spores are formed also in some of the Hormogonales, the filamentous cyanophytes. As already noted in Chap. 8, this group of blue-green algae additionally produces **hormogones.** These are vegetative reproductive units. Each is a multicellular section of a filament, enclosed within a common wall and located between transparent, double-walled **heterocysts.** The latter may facilitate breaks in the algal filament, and a separated hormogone may then grow into a new filament in another location.

ALGAE

CHLOROPHYTA

Vegetative multiplication by binary division occurs in all green algae except those belonging to the coccoid line of evolution (see Chap. 9). In unicellular forms (e.g., *Chlamydomonas*, Fig. 24.4), a cell divides vegetatively within its wall and produces usually two new organisms out of one. In multicellular types (e.g., *Ulothrix*, Fig. 24.5), vegetative divisions increase the size of the organism. Another type of vegetative reproduction is fragmentation of a multicellular alga, either accidentally or, in some cases, as a regular reproductive process. Each such fragment grows into a whole new individual.

Sporulation occurs in all chlorophytes. Virtually any vegetative cell may come to function as a *sporangium.* Sometimes the entire content of a sporangial cell may be liberated as a single spore, but more usually a sporangial cell subdivides through successive fissions and gives rise to numerous spores, each with its own wall. Spores are released either through a pore developed in the wall of the sporangial cell or through dissolution of the entire wall. In most species the spores are swimming **zoospores.** Some species living in damp soils produce nonmotile spores called **aplanospores.**

All chlorophyte groups are sexual. In each of the

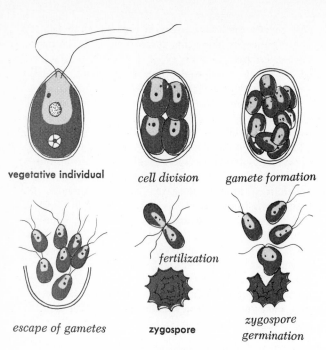

vegetative individual   *cell division*   *gamete formation*

escape of gametes   **zygospore**   *zygospore germination*

fertilization

FIG. 24.4   Reproduction in *Chlamydomonas*.

flagellate, tetrasporine, and coccoid lines, there has been a general progression from isogamy in primitive types to anisogamy in more advanced types to oögamy in very advanced types. In the flagellate line, for example, most species of the unicellular *Chlamydomonas* are isogamous, simple colonial forms are anisogamous, and the complexly colonial *Volvox* is oögamous (Fig. 24.6). The other lines are similar. The pattern is not too rigorous, however. For example, *Chlamydomonas* also includes anisogamous and oögamous species despite its generally primitive character.

In most green algae, typically any vegetative cell may produce gametes and thus may function as a **gametangium.** The formation of gametes tends to be indistinguishable from sporulation. A cell may produce just a single gamete (e.g., *Spirogyra*), or it may subdivide repeatedly and produce numerous gametes of either sex (e.g., *Ulothrix*). Some chlorophytes are separately sexed, others are hermaphroditic. Even closely related species may differ in this respect. For example, certain species of *Spirogyra* exhibit separate sexes; others, hermaphroditism.

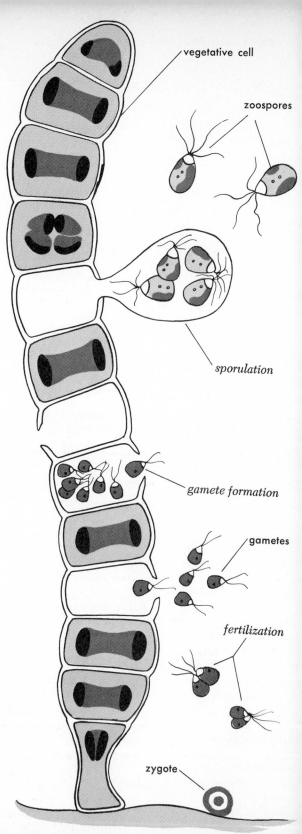

vegetative cell

zoospores

sporulation

gamete formation

gametes

fertilization

zygote

FIG. 24.5   Reproduction in *Ulothrix*.

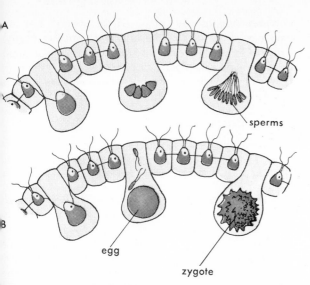

FIG. 24.6 A, sperm formation in Volvox. B, egg production and fertilization in Volvox.

All three types of life cycles are encountered in the green algae. The flagellate evolutionary line (*Chlamydomonas, Volvox*) is typically haplontic. The tetrasporine line is haplontic in its more primitive members (*Ulothrix, Spirogyra*) but diplohaplontic in its advanced members (*Cladophora, Ulva*). The coccoid line is largely diplontic (*Acetabularia, Bryopsis*).

In the haplontic forms (Fig. 24.7), the zygotes usually encyst as in *Spirogyra* and are then known as **zygospores** (even though the designation "-spore" is misleading here). When a zygospore germinates, the first two divisions of the zygote are meiotic, resulting in four haploid cells. In most cases these four are flagellate; and if the alga is unicellular, such cells are four whole adults (e.g., *Chlamydomonas*). If the alga is multicellular, the four cells swim about for some time and then settle and grow into four new multicellular adults (e.g., *Ulothrix*). In effect, the four cells are spores, more specifically, *meiospores*. Since there are four of them, the term "tetraspores" is applicable; hence also the term "tetrasporine" for the algal line in which such spores are characteristic. In some cases (e.g., *Spirogyra*), the four meiospores are not flagellate but remain sessile in the zygospore. Three of the four cells usually degenerate, and the remaining one grows directly into a new adult. If the sexes of the algal species are separate, two of the four meiospores are of one sex type, two of the other.

In the diplohaplontic green algae (e.g., *Ulva,*

Fig. 24.8), the diploid zygote formed by fusion of biflagellate gametes is quadriflagellate, and it does not encyst but remains motile. After swimming about for some time, it settles and proliferates mitotically into a diploid sporophyte adult. This organism eventually sporulates, meiosis occurring during that process. Thus one diploid cell gives rise to four haploid meiospores. Virtually any cell of the adult sporophyte may undergo meiosis and produce spores. The swimming meiospores eventually settle and grow into haploid gametophyte adults. Sporophytes and gametophytes are structurally identical in these groups. Adult gametophytes eventually form haploid gametes, any cell again being a potential gamete producer.

In diplontic green algae (e.g., the multinucleate coccoid *Bryopsis*), a diploid zygote is similarly motile (Fig. 24.9). After it settles, its nucleus repeatedly divides by mitosis, but the cell as a whole enlarges without division. The adult is therefore highly multinucleate and each of its nuclei is diploid. If such an adult sporulates, the spores are diploid mitospores.

FIG. 24.7 The haplontic life cycle typical of many algae.

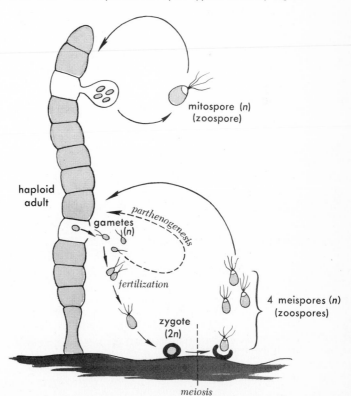

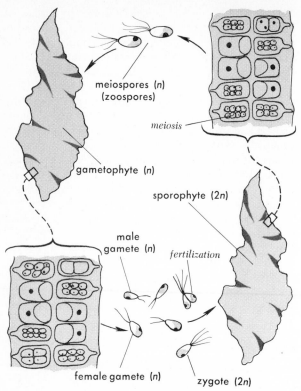

meiospores (n)
(zoospores)

meiosis

gametophyte (n)

sporophyte (2n)

male
gamete (n)

fertilization

female gamete (n)   zygote (2n)

FIG. 24.8   The life cycle of *Ulva*, a typical diplohaplontic alga.

FIG. 24.9   The life cycle of *Bryopsis*, a typical diplontic alga. *A*, whole plant; *B*, detail of terminal branches. See also Fig. 9.7.

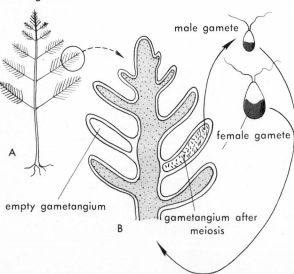

male gamete

female gamete

empty gametangium

A

B

gametangium after
meiosis

Gametes are usually produced in special terminal branches of an adult. The nuclei in such a branch increase in number, the divisions now being meiotic. Each resulting haploid nucleus together with some surrounding cytoplasm then becomes enveloped by a cell wall of its own and flagella develop. Mature gametes ultimately escape through a pore in the wall of the algal branch.

CHAROPHYTA, EUGLENOPHYTA, PYRROPHYTA

The charophytes may multiply vegetatively through regularly produced fragmentation bodies. The algae do not sporulate, and gametic reproduction is always oögamous. Gamete-forming structures develop on the leaflike branches, and they are true *organs*, structurally more complex than those of any other Protista. In the interior of a male sex organ, so-called **antheridial filaments** are present. The content of each cell in such a filament matures into a single sperm. It escapes through a pore in the wall of a antheridial cell. A female sex organ contains a single large egg in the interior. When the organ is mature, spirally elongated cells on the outside separate from one another at their upper ends. The organ so opens out and a path is formed for a sperm (Fig. 24.10).

As noted in Chap. 7, multicellular sex organs with sterile external tissue layers are exceptional for Protista and are encountered otherwise only in Metaphyta and Metazoa. But note that the life cycle of stoneworts is haplontic, a primitive trait not exhibited by any of the Metaphyta or Metazoa.

In euglenophytes and pyrrophytes, groups comprising mainly unicellular flagellate algae, the basic reproductive process is longitudinal vegetative cell division. Sex is virtually unknown and, with the exception of multicellular sessile pyrrophytes, the organisms largely do not form spores.

CHRYSOPHYTA

The reproductive repertoire in this phylum is essentially the same as in the green algae. Vegetative reproduction occurs by cell division (coccoid types excepted) and by fragmentation of multicellular forms. Encapsulated resting endospores called **statospores** are characteristic of the phylum. In the classes Chrysophyceae and Xanthophyceae, sporulation occurs largely as in green algae. Sex is virtually unknown in the yellow-

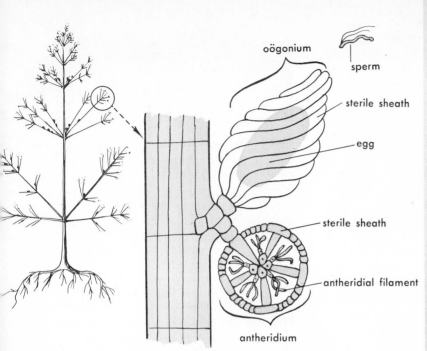

oögonium

sperm

sterile sheath

egg

sterile sheath

antheridial filament

antheridium

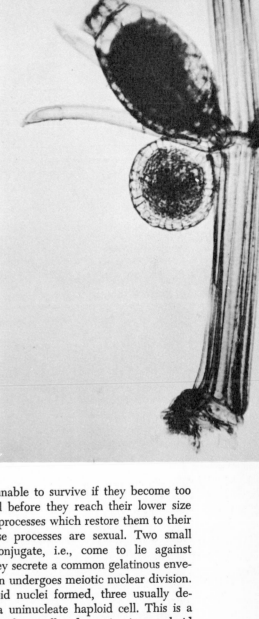

FIG. 24.10 Sex organs of the stonewort *Chara*. Diagram: left, position of sex organs in whole organism; right, the structure of an oögonium and an antheridium. Photograph: external view of an oögonium and an antheridium. *(Photograph courtesy of Dr. M. S. Fuller, Brown University.)*

brown types and is known definitely in only a few of the yellow-green types (e.g., *Vaucheria*, Fig. 24.11).

From the standpoint of reproduction, the most interesting chrysophytes are the diatoms. In these predominantly unicellular organisms, successive cell divisions may give rise to progressively smaller vegetative generations (Fig. 24.12). As noted in Chap. 9, diatoms are characterized by sculptured silicaceous walls which are in two halves, one half fitting snugly over the other. The larger "lid" is an **epitheca**; the smaller "box," a **hypotheca**. After division, one daughter cell inherits the epitheca, the other the hypotheca. In either case, a daughter cell secretes a new wall over its exposed half and this new half-wall is always formed *within* the old half-wall. The old wall consequently is always an epitheca, regardless of what it was originally. The new wall is always a hypotheca. This means that some diatoms in a population may decrease in size progressively as divisions continue. (However, this is not always the case in all species, for hypothecae may stretch to some extent.)

Diatoms are unable to survive if they become too small. Usually well before they reach their lower size limit, they initiate processes which restore them to their original size. These processes are sexual. Two small vegetative cells conjugate, i.e., come to lie against each other, and they secrete a common gelatinous envelope. Each cell then undergoes meiotic nuclear division. Of the four haploid nuclei formed, three usually degenerate, leaving a uninucleate haploid cell. This is a gamete. It slips out of its wall and, moving in amoeboid fashion, fuses with the other similarly formed gamete within the gelatinous envelope. The resulting zygote is known as an **auxospore** (see Fig. 24.12). Undoubtedly under the rejuvenating stimulus of sex, the auxospore photosynthesizes extensively and grows rapidly into a very large cell. Then it develops a new epitheca

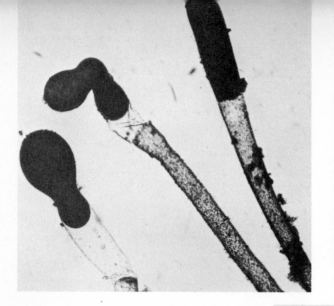

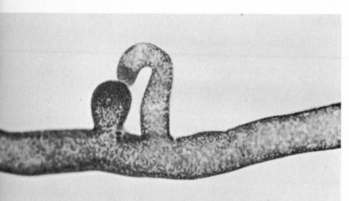
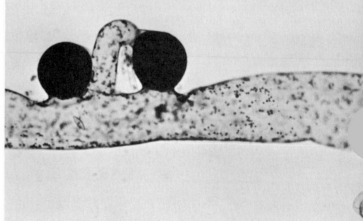

FIG. 24.11   Reproduction in *Vaucheria*. Top left, formation and escape of zoospores. Top right, the multiflagellate surface of a zoospore. Bottom left, a filament with male and female branches. The female branch is the shorter, rounded one. Bottom right, a filament with zygospores. *(Top left and right, courtesy of Dr. W. Koch, University of North Carolina, and J. Elisha Mitchell Sci. Soc., vol. 67, p. 123; bottom left and right, courtesy of Dr. M. S. Fuller, Brown University.)*

and hypotheca. Vegetative divisions thereafter soon restore the normal cell size characteristic of the species. Inasmuch as meiosis is gametogenic, adult diatoms are diploid and the life cycle is diplontic.

PHAEOPHYTA

All methods of reproduction are highly developed in this phylum. There are no unicellular members;

hence vegetative divisions only increase the size of a brown alga. However, vegetative reproduction through fragmentation bodies and through detachment of portions of an alga is known to occur. In *Sargassum*, for example, vegetative reproduction occurs regularly by *posterior decay*, i.e., branches may be liberated as separate organisms if the regions at and behind the branch juncture die off.

The nature of the life cycle defines three classes

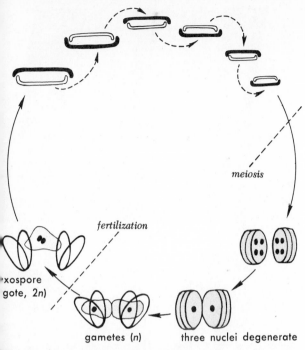

Sargassum and *Fucus*. These diplontic types are always oögamous, separately sexed or hermaphroditic, and they do not form spores. In the rockweed *Fucus* (Fig. 24.15), tips of thallus branches accumulate gelatinous substances internally, and such swollen tips are then known as **receptacles**. Within a receptacle, numerous cavities called **conceptacles** contain gamete-forming structures. Meiosis takes place during the maturation of sperms and eggs. In many species, the receptacles shrink when an outgoing tide exposes the algae to air and the con-

FIG. 24.13   The life cycles of the three classes of brown algae.

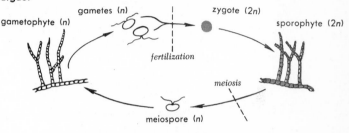

ISOGENERATAE: n and 2n generations alike

FIG. 24.12   Reproduction in diatoms. Top row, left to right, successive vegetative generations. Bottom row, right to left, meiosis, gametes, and fertilization.

of brown algae (Fig. 24.13). In one class, the *Isogeneratae*, the life cycle is diplohaplontic and the sporophyte and gametophyte generations are structurally alike. In the *Heterogeneratae*, the life cycle is again diplohaplontic but the two generations are structurally not alike. In the *Cyclosporae*, the life cycle is diplontic.

   To the Isogeneratae belongs *Ectocarpus*, which is representative of the class as a whole. The life cycle follows the basic diplohaplontic pattern outlined in Chap. 23 (Fig. 23.33). As noted in that context, the sporophyte of *Ectocarpus* may form diploid mitospores and haploid meiospores; the gametophyte may produce haploid mitospores or haploid gametes. Both the sporophytes and the gametophytes of *Ectocarpus* are filamentous algae, with prostrate and erect portions.

   In the Heterogeneratae, the sporophyte is always the larger and dominant generation. The gametophyte is dissimilar in structure and is microscopic. Sporophytes form mitospores and meiospores as above, and the gametophytes produce gametes. The pattern is exemplified by *Laminaria* (Fig. 24.14).

   The Cyclosporae include brown algae such as

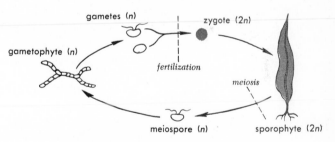

HETEROGENERATAE: n and 2n generations dissimilar

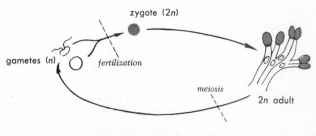

CYCLOSPORAE: diplontic cycle

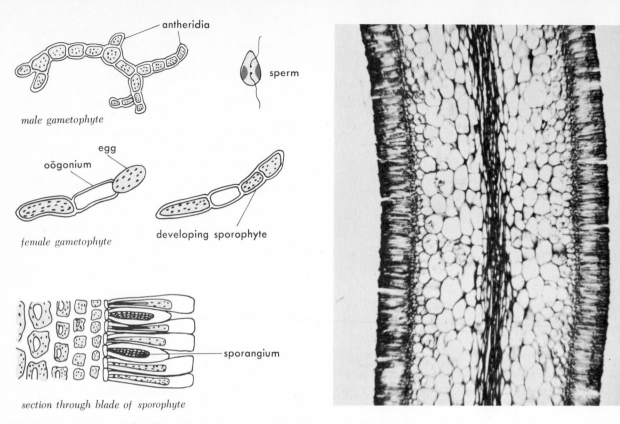

antheridia

sperm

male gametophyte

egg

oögonium

female gametophyte

developing sporophyte

sporangium

section through blade of sporophyte

FIG. 24.14 Stages of the life cycle in *Laminaria*. The photograph shows a section through the blade of a sporophyte, revealing the sporangial layer along the surfaces. *(Photograph courtesy of Dr. M. S. Fuller, Brown University.)*

FIG. 24.15 Conceptacles of *Fucus*. Left, conceptacle with a lining layer bearing antheridial branches. Note the sterile hairs, or paraphyses, projecting through the opening of the conceptacle. Right, conceptacle with conspicuous oögonia. Each mature oögonium contains eight eggs. *(Courtesy of Dr. M. S. Fuller, Brown University.)*

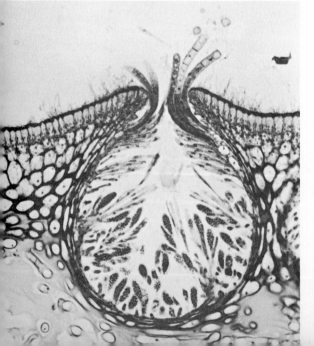

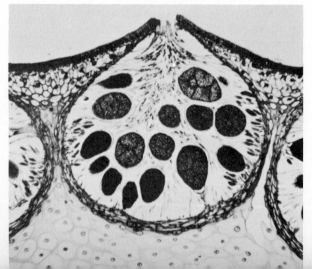

ents of the conceptacles are thereby loosened. The returning tide later reswells the receptacles, and the gametes in the conceptacles are thereby squeezed out into the sea. Fertilization then takes place in open water. The zygote encysts, settles on a rock, and eventually germinates into a new diploid adult.

RHODOPHYTA

The life histories of the red algae are in many ways very unusual and complex. As judged from exist-

ing types, reproductive evolution in the phylum appears to have started with typical haplontic life cycles, meiosis occurring in the zygote. Later stages were characterized by progressive postponement of meiosis, leading ultimately to a life cycle consisting of *three* successive generations: a diploid **carposporophyte,** a diploid **tetrasporophyte,** and a haploid **gametophyte.** This pattern is illustrated well by the genus *Polysiphonia* (Fig. 24.16).

In a haploid gametophyte, a male sex structure is known as a **spermatangium.** In it, a single cell may give

FIG. 24.16 Diagram: *A,* the sexual structures of red algae: (1) whole organism, (2) male branch, (3) female branch during fertilization. *B,* the life cycle of *Polysiphonia. C:* (1) portion of gametophyte at time of fertilization, (2) carposphorophyte borne on gametophyte, (3) tetrasporophyte. The photograph shows a carposphorophyte attached to a gametophyte branch. *(Photograph, General Biological Supply House, Inc.)*

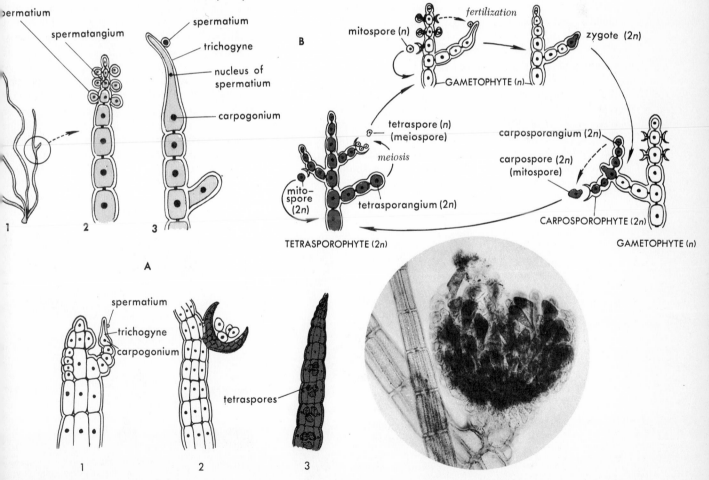

rise mitotically to numerous male gametes, each called a **spermatium.** A female sex structure is a unicellular **carpogonium,** one end of which is elongated into a projection called a **trichogyne.** If a spermatium is carried by sea water to a trichogyne, it may penetrate into the trichogyne. The spermatium nucleus then fuses with the nucleus of the carpogonium, and this fertilization converts the carpogonial cell into the diploid zygote.

In *Polysiphonia* the zygote gives rise to a series of compacted filaments which remain attached to the gametophyte and constitute the diploid *carposporophyte.* Some of the cells of the carposporophyte later form single diploid **carpospores** (mitospores). Each such spore eventually escapes the carposporophyte by amoeboid motion and develops into an independent, free-living *tetrasporophyte.* This adult is diploid and quite like the gametophyte in external appearance. Certain cells of the tetrasporophyte subsequently undergo meiosis, and each such cell so gives rise to four haploid amoeboid cells. These are **tetraspores** (meiospores). They ultimately complete the life cycle by developing into new independent gametophytes.

Apart from the spore types which contribute to this main progression of the life cycle, additional spore types are frequently formed by one or more of the three generations. For example, gametophytes may produce haploid mitospores ("monospores") which repeat the gametophyte generation. Analogously, tetrasporophytes may produce diploid mitospores ("paraspores") which repeat the tetrasporophyte generation.

SLIME MOLDS, PROTOZOA

The life cycle of slime molds, already outlined in Chap. 9, is fundamentally diplohaplontic. However, the haploid phase does not develop into a multicellular body. The adult plasmodium or pseudoplasmodium represents the diploid sporophyte generation. Sporangia, fruiting bodies develop, and meiosis occurs during spore production. The unicellular swarmers formed through spore germination are haploid. Successive vegetative generations of such swarmers represent the gametophyte generation, which thus consists of a *population* of separate single cells. Eventually such cells function as gametes and fertilization reestablishes the diploid condition. Diploid zygotic cells subsequently grow or aggregate into plasmodial sporophytes (Fig. 24.17).

Among protozoa (Fig. 24.18), the usual method of vegetative reproduction is binary fission. Division is longitudinal in all zooflagellates and some ciliates (e.g., *Vorticella*) and is transverse in all other ciliates. Budding occurs in some protozoa (e.g., Suctoria). As pointed out in Chap. 9, each ciliate protozoan possesses two kinds of nuclei. In the micronuclei distinct chromosomes are present. In the macronuclei, however, the genetic material is not organized into microscopically identifiable chromosomes (as in bacteria). During fission, the micronuclei divide mitotically but the macronuclei do not. Instead, a macronucleus merely constricts into two approximately equal parts.

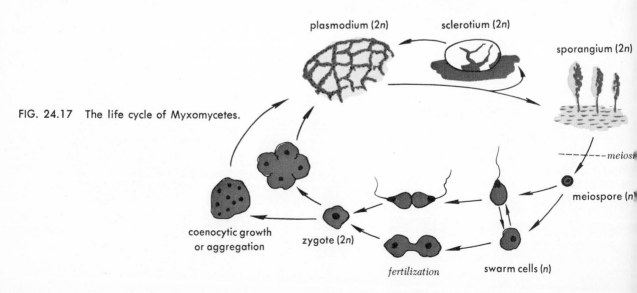

plasmodium (2n)   sclerotium (2n)   sporangium (2n)

FIG. 24.17   The life cycle of Myxomycetes.

----*meiosis*

meiospore (n)

coenocytic growth or aggregation   zygote (2n)   swarm cells (n)

fertilization

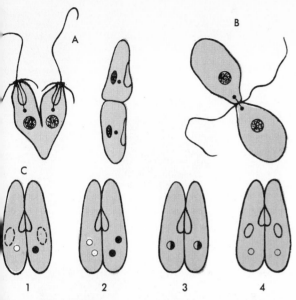

FIG. 24.18 Patterns of reproduction and sex in protozoa, diagrammatic. *A*, longitudinal fission as in zooflagellates and transverse fission as in ciliates. *B*, syngamy, as in zooflagellates. *C*, conjugation, as in ciliates: (1) macronuclear degeneration; (2) micronuclear division (after meiosis), resulting in "male" and "female" gamete nuclei in each individual; (3) nuclear exchange and fusion, resulting in diploid zygote nucleus in each individual (if the male and female nucleus within a single individual were to fuse, the process would be autogamy, or self-fertilization); (4) division of the zygote nuclei, resulting in new micronuclei and macronuclei in each individual.

Numerous protozoan species may encapsulate and become dormant temporarily within protective cysts. Sporulation is known to occur in Foraminifera, Radiolaria, and Sporozoa. In these organisms, a vegetative cell first becomes multinucleate and then undergoes multiple cytoplasmic fission. The cellular products, each containing one nucleus, represent spores. Such cells have been given different names in different sporulating forms.

Gametic reproduction occurs universally among all protozoan groups but some individual types are without sex (e.g., *Amoeba*). Fertilization is achieved either by *syngamy* (cell fusion) as in zooflagellates or by *conjugation* and exchange and fusion of gamete nuclei as in ciliates. In the latter, the macronuclei degenerate during conjugation and only the micronuclei produce

gamete nuclei. After nuclear exchange and nuclear fusion, new micronuclei and macronuclei form from the zygote nuclei. Most protozoan life cycles are diplontic, but haplontic cycles occur in some of the Sporozoa and diplohaplontic cycles in some of the Foraminifera.

Sexual processes have been studied most in *Paramecium*, which has become one of the best known organisms of all kinds. Like ciliates generally, *Paramecium* is hermaphroditic, each organism producing both "male" and "female" gamete nuclei. Ordinarily, exchange of such nuclei during conjugation leads to cross-fertilization. Under certain circumstances, however, single organisms may be self-fertilized; i.e., the two gamete nuclei within a given individual fuse together. One species, *Paramecium aurelia*, has been shown to consist of 16 distinct (but structurally indistinguishable) sexual varieties. Each variety in turn consists of two mating types, and conjugation requires one partner from each of these two types. Analogous sexual specializations are known to exist in other species of *Paramecium* and indeed in several other types of ciliates. Evidently, like any other living process, that of sexuality appears to become the more complex the more it is studied, and even unicellular organisms clearly are very far from being "simple."

FUNGI

PHYCOMYCETES

The reproductive processes of this group of fungi are on the whole rather like those of coccoid, tubular, multinucleate algae. Vegetative nuclear divisions and cytoplasmic growth increase the extent of hyphae and mycelia. Mycelial fragmentation and dispersion may lead directly to an increase in the number of organisms. All Phycomycetes produce spores, either directly from the vegetative body or from special hyphae. Flagellate swimming spores are characteristic of aquatic types; nonmotile and encapsulated spores, of terrestrial types. All groups of the Phycomycetes are also sexual, with largely haplontic but sometimes diplohaplontic life cycles (e.g., the diplohaplontic cycle of *Allomyces*, referred to in Chap. 23). Aquatic Phycomycetes are variously isogamous, anisogamous, and oögamous, and terrestrial types are largely isogamous with nonmotile gametes.

The reproductive repertoire of terrestrial forms is illustrated by bread molds such as the haplontic

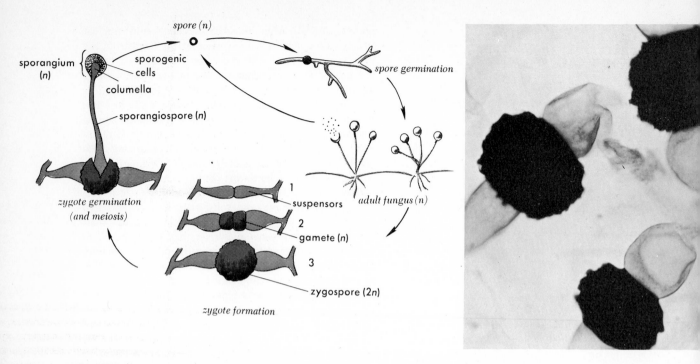

FIG. 24.19   Diagram, the life cycle of *Rhizopus*. Photograph, zygospores of *Rhizopus*. (Photograph, Ward's Natural Science Establishment, Inc.)

Rhizopus nigricans (Fig. 24.19). The vegetative mycelium of this mold is haploid. From it in places grow upright branch hyphae with expanded tips. These tips are sporangia in which spores are produced. Such spores are formed mitotically, i.e., they are haploid mitospores. Each spore is encapsulated within a wall which turns black as the spore matures. Dispersal and later germination of the spores repeats the haploid vegetative generation.

Rhizopus nigricans is a cross-fertilizing hermaphrodite. If two mycelia live in close proximity, each may develop a short **suspensor** hypha, one growing toward the other. The tip of each such hypha becomes walled off as a multinucleate gametelike cell. When the two gametes meet, they fuse and a cyst wall is then secreted around the fusion mass. In the interior, the nuclei pair off, one from one gamete joining one from the other. Such nuclear pairs fuse, forming diploid zygote nuclei. Unpaired nuclei degenerate. When the cyst germinates, its contents grow directly into an upright hypha with a terminal sporangium. The zygote nuclei divide in the process, and the first two divisions are meiotic. Numerous haploid nuclei are thereby formed, and these participate in spore formation in the sporangia. Mature spores grow into new vegetative mycelia as above, completing the sexual life cycle.

ASCOMYCETES

Most ascomycete fungi produce mitospores in the form of *conidia*, i.e., they are budded off in linear series from the tips of branch hyphae. But as noted in Chap. 9, this class of terrestrial fungi is distinguished primarily by the production of **ascospores** within **asci**. Ascospores are essentially meiospores; i.e., meiosis occurs during their formation. Analogously, an ascus is essentially a meiosporangium.

Yeasts exhibit ascosporulation in the simplest form (Fig. 24.20). Brewer's yeast, *Saccharomyces cerevisiae*, exists in haploid and diploid states, and the life cycle is diplohaplontic. Both generations may reproduce vegetatively by budding. If two haploid cells of opposite sex type are brought together, they fuse and form a diploid zygotic cell. Repeated fissions then produce a population of diploid sporophytic cells. Such a cell may later function as a meiosporangium, i.e., as an ascus.

The diploid nucleus undergoes meiosis and the four resulting haploid nuclei are centers around which four ascospores are formed. Of these four, two are of one sex type and two are of the other. They germinate into four haploid, separately sexed, yeast cells which may divide and give rise to a population of haploid gametophytic cells.

Not all yeasts are diplohaplontic and not all produce four ascospores. For example, in other genera the life cycle is haplontic and eight ascospores are formed. Here the zygote functions as an ascus immediately. Its nucleus undergoes three divisions, the first two being meiotic. Such a haplontic cycle with eight ascospores is typical for Ascomycetes generally.

In most Ascomycetes, the basic sexual process is rather different from that encountered in yeasts and in virtually all other living organisms (Fig. 24.21). A vegetative ascomycete mycelium with haploid nuclei produces special, usually multinucleate, sexual branch hyphae. "Female" ones are called **ascogonia;** "male" ones, **spermogonia.** If mating is to take place, two sexually different hyphae must be near each other and parts of their cytoplasm must become fused. The method by which fusion may be effected is shown rather clearly in some of the cup fungi. An ascogonium here develops a fingerlike outgrowth, a **trichogyne,** which curves toward and eventually fuses with the spermogonium. Nuclei from the spermogonium subsequently migrate through the trichogyne into the ascogonium. But the two types of nuclei now present *do not fuse* pairwise at this stage. They remain separate, and indeed they may increase in number by mitosis. Thus, mating, or **plasmogamy,** has occurred, but fertilization has not occurred as yet.

The mated ascogonium of cup fungi, still projecting as a branch from the vegetative mycelium, now develops a radial array of branch hyphae of its own. Each of these branches contains nuclei of the two different sex types. By a series of special processes, the tip of each branch may then become walled off as a cell with just two nuclei of opposite sex type. Such a terminal cell is a young ascus. Its two nuclei now fuse, effecting fertilization. Nuclear fusion is also known as **karyogamy.**

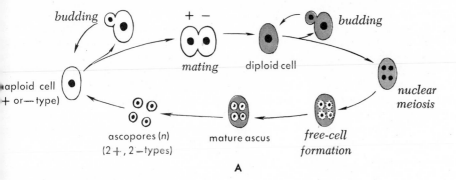

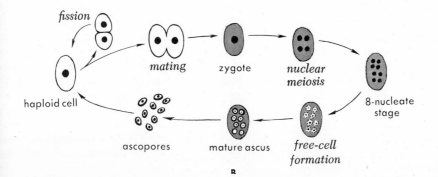

FIG. 24.20 The life cycle of yeasts. A, diplohaplontic species. B, haplontic species.

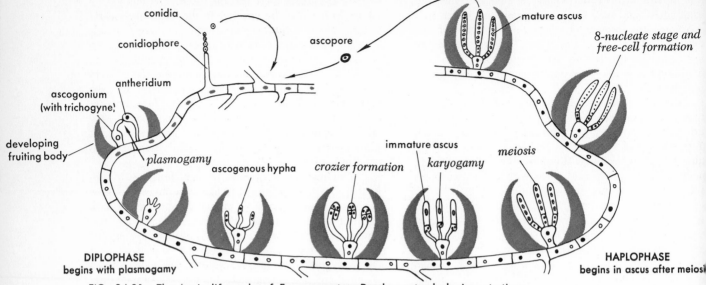

FIG. 24.21   The basic life cycle of Euascomycetes. Read counterclockwise, starting
at top center. See also Figs. 9.37 and 9.39.

We may note, therefore, that in most Ascomycetes the sexual process has become separated into two sub-processes, i.e., plasmogamy, or mating, and karyogamy, or nuclear fusion. In other organisms both occur more or less simultaneously, but in Ascomycetes a substantial time interval elapses between the first and the second. During this time interval, the ascogonium and its branch hyphae are said to be in **diplophase,** i.e., they contain two different sets of nuclei. By contrast, the vegetative hyphae continue to be in **haplophase,** with only one set of nuclei.

The zygotic fusion nucleus in the young ascus is diploid. It undergoes three divisions, the first two of which are meiotic. The resulting eight haploid nuclei become centers around which eight ascospores are produced. These eventually escape and germinate into new haplophasic mycelia. While ascus formation is under way after plasmogamy, vegetative hyphae may have grown up around the ascogonium and its branches, forming a fruiting body. The different types of fruiting bodies in different groups have already been described in Chap. 9.

Thus, distinct gametes are not formed in the Ascomycetes. Also, a single mating produces not just a single zygote but many. Not only may there by numer-

ous asci, each with its own zygote nucleus, but after one ascus has performed its function, further asci may arise successively in the same location: the ascogonium and its branches contain a large store of nuclei of the two sex types. Through such continual ascus formation after a single mating, the diplophasic state may be maintained almost indefinitely. For organisms which cannot move to find mates, this is a highly efficient adaptation to terrestrial life.

BASIDIOMYCETES

As just noted above, Ascomycetes are character ized by an essentially "haplontic" life cycle, with a dominant vegetative haplophase and a diplophase re stricted to special sex-associated and ascus-producing hyphae. Basidiomycetes similarly have developed haplophasic and diplophasic states, again by a separa tion of plasmogamy from karyogamy. Moreover, the diplophasic state may become much more extensive and in some cases even dominant. Consequently, the life cycles of some Basidiomycetes somewhat resemble haplontic ones, others resemble diplohaplontic ones and still others compare with diplontic ones. In furthe contrast to the Ascomycetes, Basidiomycetes never develop any special sexual hyphae.

The basic life cycle may be considered to start with a vegetative haplophase (Fig. 24.22). A haploid nucleus is present in each cellular compartment of the hyphae. Mating or plasmogamy occurs when a hyphal cell produces a lateral outgrowth which fuses with a similar outgrowth from another cell. The fused cell now contains two nuclei, and these remain distinct. Such a cell undergoes repeated divisions and produces the diplophase of the life cycle. The diplophase may grow to become a whole mycelium itself, either still connected with the haplophasic mycelium or separated. Later, the diplophase is terminated by karyogamy, meiosis, and the formation of meiospores. These processes occur in somewhat different ways in the two subclasses of Basidiomycetes, the Homobasidiomycetes and the Heterobasidiomycetes.

In the Homobasidiomycetes, terminals of hyphae each cut off a club-shaped binucleate cell, the **basidium** (see Fig. 9.42). This is a meiosporangium equivalent to an ascus of the Ascomycetes. In a basidium, karyogamy and meiosis occur and the four resulting haploid nuclei become incorporated into four **basidiospores**. As noted in Chap. 9, such spores are budded off on the outside of a basidium. After being dispersed, the basidiospores germinate into new haplophasic mycelia.

In the Heterobasidiomycetes, basidia are not formed directly from diplophasic hyphae. Instead, hyphal cells become transformed into special thick-walled binucleate spores, named differently in different cases. Within such spores karyogamy takes place. Meiosis occurs either before or after germination, but in any event the result of germination is a basidium. In these fungi the basidium consists of four haploid uninucleate cells which are joined end to end. Each cell buds off one basidiospore (see Fig. 9.42).

The diplophase of Homobasidiomycetes often forms distinct fruiting bodies, e.g., mushrooms, in which the basidium-forming hyphae are aggregated. The Heterobasidiomycetes, which include smuts and rusts, do not form fruiting bodies. Among these fungi are types with extreme reductions of either vegetative phase. In certain smuts, for example, the entire haplophase is limited to the four-celled basidia: plasmogamy occurs between these two pairs of cells. The whole subsequent cycle is therefore diplophasic. In certain rusts, by contrast, the entire diplophase is the binucleate cell resulting from plasmogamy: the cell immediately becomes the basidium-producing spore in which karyogamy and meiosis take place. Thus with the exception of that cell, the whole remaining cycle is haplophasic. These instances are close approaches to purely "diplontic" and "haplontic" life cycles. Most other basidiomycete life cycles are somewhere between these extremes; i.e., they are diplohaplontic, with either the haplophase or the diplophase being variously dominant.

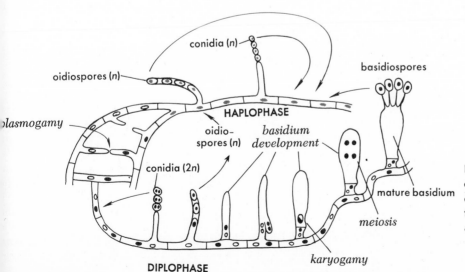

FIG. 24.22 The basic life cycle of Basidiomycetes. Read counterclockwise, starting at top center. See also Figs. 9.42 and 9.44.

REVIEW QUESTIONS

1. Review the reproductive repertoire of bacteria. What are conidia, oidiospores, sporangiospores? Which bacteria produce them? Describe experiments through which bacterial sex has been discovered.

2. What are endospores? How do Cyanophyta reproduce? How can these organisms adapt without sexuality?

3. Describe reproductive processes among green algae. Which groups of these organisms exhibit which type of life cycle? What is a zygospore?

4. Review the reproduction of charophytes, euglenophytes, and pyrrophytes. In what respects is charophyte reproduction atypical for Protista? What are statospores? Which organisms produce them?

5. Describe the reproductive processes of *Vaucheria*. Outline the life cycle of (*a*) diatoms, (*b*) *Ecto-*

carpus, (*c*) *Fucus.* What kinds of life cycles are characteristic of brown algae?

6. Review the life-cycle pattern of red algae. Define spermatium, carpogonium, trichogyne, carpospore, tetraspore.

7. Describe the life cycle of slime molds. Review the reproductive repertoire of protozoa.

8. What reproductive processes occur in Phycomycetes?

9. Through what sequence of processes are ascospores produced? Describe the life cycle of (*a*) diplohaplontic yeasts, (*b*) haplontic yeasts. Define plasmogamy, karyogamy, diplophase, haplophase.

10. Review the life cycle of Ascomycetes and contrast it with that of Basidiomycetes. What are basidia and how are they formed?

SUGGESTED COLLATERAL READINGS

Popular accounts of reproduction in the Monera may be found in the articles cited below. Information on the reproduction of Monera and Protista may also be found in the references listed at the conclusions of Chaps. 8 and 9.

Delbruck, M., and M. Delbruck: Bacterial Viruses and Sex, *Sci. American,* vol. 179, 1948.

Haldane, J. B. S.: Some Alternatives to Sex, *New Biol.* vol. 19, 1955.

Wollman, E. L., and F. Jacob: Sexuality in Bacteria, *Sci. American,* vol. 195, 1956.

Zinder, N. D.: Transduction in Bacteria, *Sci. American,* vol. 199, 1958.

REPRODUCTION: METAPHYTA

25

The reproduction of all Metaphyta is characterized by diplohaplontic life cycles with dissimilar gametophyte and sporophyte generations; vegetative reproduction by fragmentation and bud formation, developed to various degrees in different groups; multicellular sex organs; oögamy, with distinct eggs and sperms or sperm nuclei; development of zygotes into distinct sporophytic embryos; multicellular sporangia with sterile external sheaths; and production of meiospores *only*, no other types of spores being formed.

The gametophyte generation is dominant in the bryophytes, the sporophyte generation in the tracheophytes. The entire reproductive evolution of the Metaphyta has been oriented by an attempt to develop a land-adapted life cycle out of the originally water-adapted diplohaplontic cycle probably inherited from green algal ancestors.

BRYOPHYTA

Vegetative reproduction is particularly highly developed in this phylum. As noted in Chap. 23, fragmentation bodies may be formed in many thallose bryophytes, e.g., by posterior decay of a thallus and consequent liberation of branches as separate plants. The liverwort Marchantia forms **gemma cups** from surface cells of the thallus (see Fig. 23.12). The floor of such a cup continuously develops vegetative buds, or *gemmae,* each an upright spindle-shaped body attached by a tiny stalk. Gemmae are readily dislodged by rain drops; and if the gemmae are splashed to suitable ground, they develop into new plants. Similar buds are formed by many other bryophytes.

As described in Chap. 10, the sex organs develop in different regions in different groups of bryophytes. A sperm-producing antheridium is more or less spherical and consists of an external single-layered **jacket** and of **spermatogenous cells** in the interior. Each such interior cell matures into a biflagellate, spirally coiled sperm. An archegonium is roughly flask-shaped. The expanded

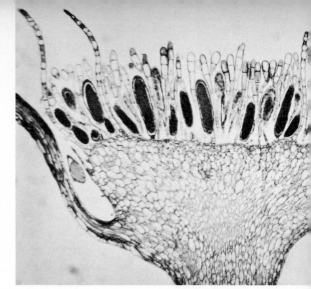

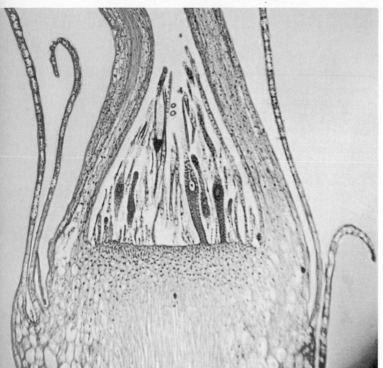

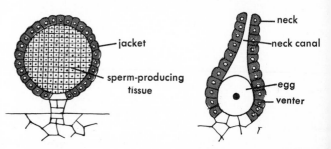

jacket

sperm-producing tissue

neck

neck canal

egg

venter

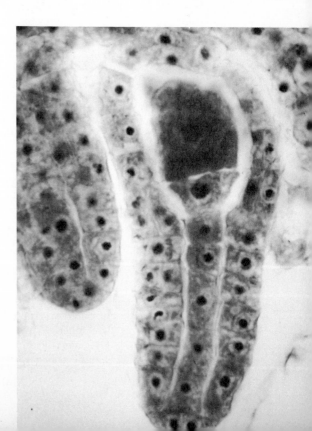

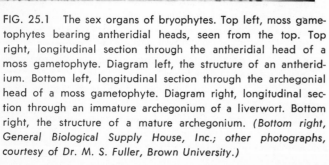

FIG. 25.1 The sex organs of bryophytes. Top left, moss game-tophytes bearing antheridial heads, seen from the top. Top right, longitudinal section through the antheridial head of a moss gametophyte. Diagram left, the structure of an antherid-ium. Bottom left, longitudinal section through the archegonial head of a moss gametophyte. Diagram right, longitudinal sec-tion through an immature archegonium of a liverwort. Bottom right, the structure of a mature archegonium. (Bottom right, General Biological Supply House, Inc.; other photographs, courtesy of Dr. M. S. Fuller, Brown University.)

portion consists of a large egg in the interior and of a single-layered **venter** on the outside. The venter continues into the narrow portion of the sex organ as the **neck,** a canal which provides a sperm path to the egg (Fig. 25.1).

In all bryophytes, fertilization depends on free water. Either water must form continuous films between nearby sex organs or fluid droplets must splash sperms to archegonia. After sperms enter an archegonium, one fertilizes the egg. The zygote then grows into a diploid embryo, and the embryo later matures

into an adult sporophyte. As shown in Chap. 10 in detail, such a sporophyte consists of basal **foot**, a **stalk** of different lengths in different bryophyte groups, and a terminal sporangial **capsule**. The structure of the capsule differs in the three bryophyte classes, as does the nutrition of the entire sporophyte. Moreover, as sporophyte development progresses in mosses and liverworts, the nutritional pattern changes from autotrophism to heterotrophism (see Chap. 10).

Spore maturation in the capsule includes the process of meiosis (Fig. 25.2). Each spore-producing cell is

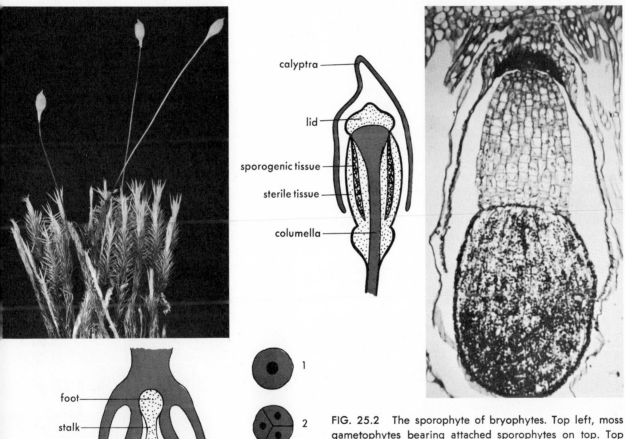

FIG. 25.2 The sporophyte of bryophytes. Top left, moss gametophytes bearing attached sporophytes on top. Top middle, the internal structure of the capsule of a moss sporophyte. Top right, the sporophyte of the liverwort *Marchantia*. Bottom left, diagrammatic representation of top right; bottom right, meiosis of a spore mother cell and mature spores. *(Top left, Carolina Biological Supply Co.; top right, courtesy of Dr. M. S. Fuller, Brown University.)*

a **spore mother cell.** After such a cell has undergone meiosis, the four resulting haploid meiospores remain joined together temporarily as a **spore tetrad.** Each spore cell soon secretes a heavy wall around itself, and this separates a tetrad into individual spores. In all bryophytes except the mosses, elaters develop in the spore-forming regions along with the spores (see Chap. 10). After discharge from the sporangia, the spores germinate into new haploid gametophytes. The pattern of the life cycle is outlined in Fig. 25.3.

One important feature in this life cycle is the multicellularity of the sex organs and the sporangia. As noted earlier, such multicellularity is not in evidence in the diplohaplontic green algae, the ancestors of which may also have been the ancestors of the bryophytes. However, although chlorophytic reproductive structures are unicellular, the ancestral chlorophytes undoubtedly did possess the potential of producing multicellular reproductive structures. Even today, practically the whole body of a chlorophyte such as *Ulva*, for example, is in effect a reproductive structure: *any* vegetative cell of a gametophyte may become gamete-producing and *any* vegetative cell of a sporophyte may become spore-producing. If, in such an organism, reproductive capacity were to be retained only in a localized group of cells but were lost everywhere else, a multicellular reproductive tissue would arise. Such localization may conceivably have occurred in ancestors of bryophytes (Fig. 25.4). Perhaps the evolutionary stimulus for this was the terrestrial way of life. In adapting

to terrestrial conditions, the body of bryophyte ancestors became internally specialized into absorptive, conductive, and photosynthetic regions. However, effective performance of these functions probably precluded a continuing reproductive role on the part of each cell. Moreover, once a specialized multicellular reproductive structure is in existence, the advantage of an external protective sheath is clear, especially in a terrestrial plant. We may therefore envisage that, in ancestral bryophytes, the outermost cells of a multicellular gamete- or spore-producing structure lost reproductive capacity too and came to function instead as a sterile sheath. The reproductive structure so became a true organ.

A second important feature in the diplohaplontic life cycle of bryophytes is the subordination of the sporophyte. Such subordination is not in evidence in the diplohaplontic green algae, where the sporophytes are independent individuals and structurally usually indistinguishable from the gametophytes. Bryophytic sporophytes, on the other hand, are dependent and attached, are most often nongreen in the adult condition, and are quite dissimilar from the gametophytes. In all probability, these bryophyte characteristics may also have developed as adaptations to or as consequences of the terrestrial way of life (Fig. 25.5). As noted in Chap. 24, the zygotes of many diplohaplontic chlorophytes are flagellate and swimming. Since a swimming zygote would be quite inadequate on land, a first prerequisite for a diplohaplontic terrestrial plant

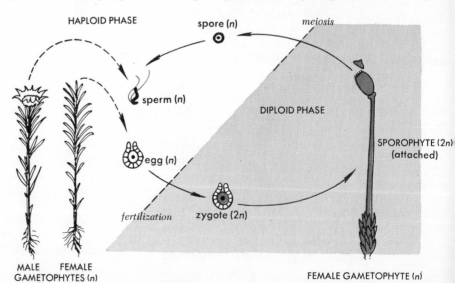

FIG. 25.3 The life cycle of a bryophyte (moss).

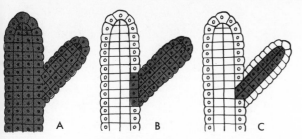

FIG. 25.4 The probable evolution of multicellular sex organs. *A*, all cells of a plant are potentially reproductive. *B*, reproductive potential restricted to specific groups of cells. *C*, reproductive cells surrounded by sterile sheath.

would be oögamy: a sessile egg would be formed and it would be retained in the archegonium. This would mean in turn that the sporophyte developing after fertilization on the gametophyte would have to remain attached, for it could not readily swim away on land. Bryophytes have actually evolved along such lines.

But once a sporophyte is attached, its whole structural and metabolic character is likely to change, in correlation with its *dependent* way of life. For example, it no longer absorbs from the physical environment, but from the gametophyte. It therefore does not require rhizoids for nutrient absorption from soil. Indeed, it may economize even further by becoming a heterotrophic parasite altogether. Bryophytes exhibit this clearly. In short, we may interpret the dissimilarities

of structure and nutrition between gametophyte and sporophyte as an evolutionary consequence of the attached condition of the sporophyte. (That attachment can lead to dissimilarity is shown also in the red algae. In these organisms, the attached carposporophyte is quite different from the gametophyte, but the free-living tetrasporophyte remains similar to the gametophyte; see Chap. 24.)

TRACHEOPHYTA

Dominance of the haploid gametophyte generation, as in bryophytes, puts emphasis on the generation which produces the motile sperms. Therefore, regardless how well adapted to land the gametophyte may be in other respects, it can never be really well adapted in its reproduction; gametic reproduction requires free external water for swimming sperms and this is not always available in a terrestrial environment. As we have seen, bryophytes "make do" by gearing their sperm release to wet periods.

Primitive tracheophytes actually cannot do much better. But they put the emphasis on the diploid sporophyte, not the gametophyte. The sporophyte produces encapsulated (meio)spores, which are excellently adapted to terrestrial conditions. And by reducing the gametophyte to microscopic dimensions and to a generally short-lived existence, they correspondingly reduce the water problem of the weak link in their life cycle.

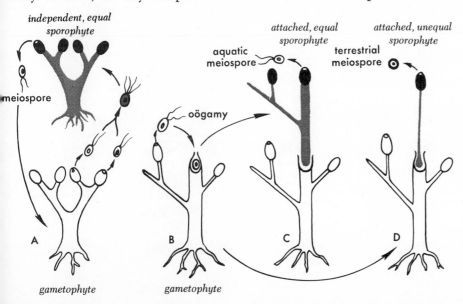

FIG. 25.5 Evolution of the dependent sporophyte. *A*, both gametophyte and sporophyte independent. *B, C*, oögamy and equal attached sporophyte. *B, D*, oögamy and reduced attached sporophyte.

FIG. 25.6 Top left, sporangia on *Psilotum*. Top right, cross section through a sporangium of *Psilotum*. Bottom left, strobilus of *Lycopodium*. Bottom middle, strobilus of *Equisetum*. Bottom right, spores of *Equisetum*, showing elaters aiding in dispersal. Diagram, sporangial sac showing spore mother cells and nutritive tissue. (*Photographs, courtesy of Dr. M. S. Fuller, Brown University.*)

tapetum

Moreover, deemphasis of the gametophyte also prepares the way for a complete circumvention of the water problem, realized in advanced tracheophytes. Here the gametophyte is so reduced that it never becomes an independent plant at all; it is retained within the spore wall. And instead of sperms *swimming* to eggs, evaporation-resistant spore walls carry *nonmotile* sperms to similarly protected eggs.

PSILOPSIDA, LYCOPSIDA
SPHENOPSIDA

As outlined in Chap. 10, the sporangia of the psilopsids are bulbous sacs formed as very short branches on aerial stems. In the lycopsids, the sporangia are sacs on **sporophylls**, special scalelike leaves formed on terminal branches. Groups of sporophylls make up a **cone** or **strobilus.** Sphenopsids similarly develop terminal strobili. Each consists of an axial stem and of lateral stalks bearing hexagonal plates. Sporangial sacs grow on the inside of such a plate. A sporangial sac in any of these plants consists of several layers of external protective and nutritive tissue and of an inner spore-producing tissue. The cells of the latter are spore mother cells. They undergo meiosis and form spore tetrads. Each haploid meiospore subsequently develops a thickened wall, and the tetrads separate. As the spores so mature, the sporangial sacs become dry and brittle, and they open along specialized weak regions. Also, the strobili of lycopsids and sphenopsids dry and open out and facilitate spore discharge in this manner (Fig. 25.6).

Spores germinate on suitable ground and grow into tiny independent gametophytes, as described in Chap. 10. Such gametophytes are either hermaphroditic or separately sexed. In most species all spores are alike and one cannot tell ahead of time whether a given spore will develop into a male or female gametophyte. This condition of equal spores is known as **homospory.** It is characteristic not only of most members of the tracheophyte groups here under discussion but also of all bryophytes and indeed of all Protista as well.

The pattern is different in a group of lycopsids which includes *Selaginella* (Fig. 25.7). In this group, the sex potential of a spore *is* apparent even before it actually matures into a gametophyte. The spores come in two sizes. Smaller ones, or **microspores,** always develop into *male* gametophytes. Larger ones, or **megaspores,** always develop into *female* gametophytes.

Microspores are said to develop within *microsporangia,* which form on *microsporophylls;* and megaspores are said to develop within *megasporangia,* which form on *megasporophylls.* This condition of unequal spores is called **heterospory.** In heterosporous lycopsids, both spore types may arise within the same plant, indeed often within the same strobilus. Note that in a heterosporous species the gametophytes are automatically of separate sexes.

Microspores form through meiosis of **microspore mother cells.** Analogously, megaspores are the meiotic product of **megaspore mother cells.** In a megasporangium, virtually all potential spore-forming cells disintegrate and only one, or at most a few, actually become megaspore mother cells. These few are large, and after meiosis the resulting megaspores are correspondingly large.

When the tiny gametophytes are mature, they develop sex organs which are structured as in bryophytes. Fertilization too takes place as in bryophytes, during wet periods. In many species of *Selaginella*, fertilization occurs as in other cases, after the gametophytes are fully developed as separate plantlets on the ground. But in certain species the gametophytes mature *precociously*, before spores are even discharged from the sporangia in the cones. It may then happen that male gametophytes, within their microspore walls, are dispersed to open megasporangia nearby, which contain mature female gametophytes within megaspore walls. Under such conditions, fertilization may occur right within the megasporangia. And the resulting zygotes, still retained in the body of the old sporophyte adult, may develop into new sporophyte embryos. The whole process is a very close—but not a complete—approach to pollination and seed formation as encountered in advanced tracheophytes.

In psilopsids, lycopsids, and sphenopsids generally, a zygote within an archegonium divides and produces two cells (Fig. 25.8). One of these in many cases does not contribute to the formation of an embryo. Instead, with or without further divisions, it may function as a microscopic holdfast or **suspensor.** This structure is equivalent to the foot of bryophyte embryos, i.e., it anchors the embryo to the archegonium and the female gametophyte. The second cell formed by the zygote gives rise to the actual embryo. Through repeated divisions it produces a cell mass which soon becomes organized into an embryonic stem and root (only stem in psilopsids). As these early organs elongate further, they penetrate through the tissues of the gametophyte and establish independent contact with the ground. Tiny erect branch shoots eventually break through the soil and on them then form the first microphylls. At this stage the embryo is a young adult, far larger than the gametophyte which gave rise to it. Indeed, the gametophyte may already have degenerated completely. But note that the sporophyte is initially dependent on the gametophyte.

FERNS

In this class of the Pteropsida, sporangia develop on or within the leaves. For example, in the common stone fern *Polypodium* a single cell on the lower surface

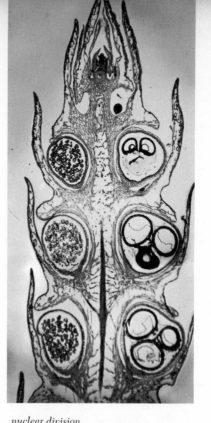

FIG. 25.7 Photo, longitudinal section through strobilus of *Selaginella*, showing microsporophylls with microsporangia on left and megasporophylls with megasporangia on right. Diagram, formation and development of (A) megaspore mother cells and (B) microspore mother cells in *Selaginella*. (Photograph courtesy of Dr. M. S. Fuller, Brown University.)

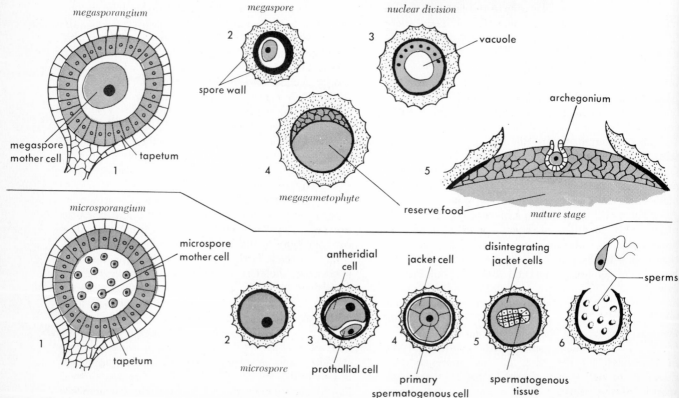

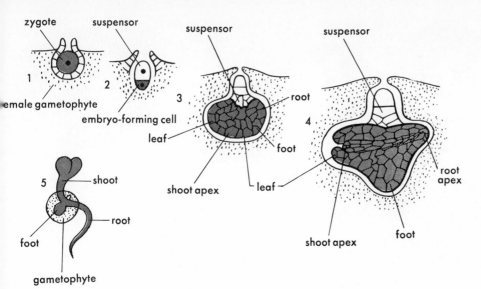

FIG. 25.8 The development of a zygote in primitive tracheophytes such as *Selaginella*.

of a leaf divides and produces a series of cells. These become arranged into a basal stalk and a terminal lens-shaped sporangium. Numerous sporangia usually arise from the same area of the leaf, and such a sporangial group is a **sorus.** It is covered over by a single-layered shield of tissue, the **indusium.** Sori appear in regular double rows, one row on each side of a main vein (see Fig. 10.45). Internally, a sporangium contains some 12 to 16 spore mother cells. These undergo meiosis and form spore tetrads, and the latter mature into 48 to 64 encapsulated meiospores.

The exterior wall of a mature sporangium is single-layered (Fig. 25.9). One row of cells around the edge of the lens-shaped sporangium is specialized as an **annulus.** The cells here are boxlike, and each has a greatly thickened wall on all sides except on the outer surface. Where one end of the annulus joins the sporangial stalk, a few **lip cells** remain thin-walled on all surfaces. When the sporangium is mature, it loses water by evaporation and dries. As water disappears from annulus cells, they tend to shrink, but only the thin outer walls are nonrigid. Each such wall is therefore sucked inward, into the "box" of the annulus cell. These suction forces, generated over the entire annulus, are sufficiently strong to rupture the lip cells and the sidewalls of the sporangium. Freed of its constraints

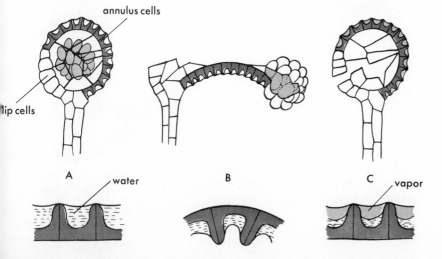

FIG. 25.9 Mechanism of spore dispersal in ferns.

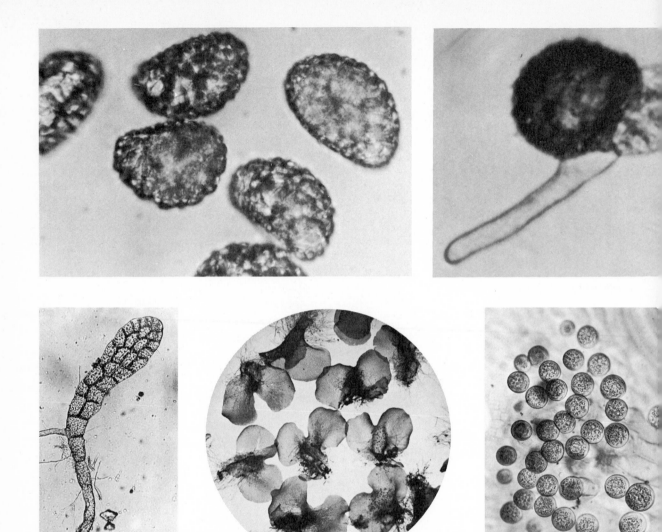

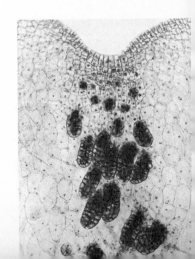

FIG. 25.10 Top right, development of a fern gametophyte. Top left, spores. Top right, germinating spore. Note rhizoid. Middle left, very young prothallium. Note spore wall near bottom of photo. Center, mature prothallia. Middle right, antheridia on prothallium. Bottom right, archegonia on prothallium. *(Top left and right, middle left, R. H. Noailles, Museum of Natural History, Paris; middle center and right, bottom right, General Biological Supply House, Inc.)*

by these ruptures, the annulus straightens out and then bends backward, acquiring an opposite curvature. Many mature spores cling to it as it curves back. But eventually the tensile strength of the water within each annulus cell is no longer sufficiently great to hold the thin outer wall in a sucked-in position. The water molecules can no longer "hang together," as it were, and as they are torn away from one another, liquid water becomes water vapor. As a result, the thin wall of an annulus cell is pushed outward explosively. This occurs similarly in all annulus cells. Thus the whole annulus suddenly snaps back into its original position. In the process the spores are forcibly catapulted into the air, just as a ball is propelled by an overhand throw.

With only a few heterosporous exceptions, ferns are homosporous. On suitable ground a spore germinates and grows into a small, heart-shaped gametophyte rather similar in structure to a thallose bryophyte (Fig. 25.10). Gametophytes are hermaphroditic in most cases, and the sex organs develop on the lower surfaces. After fertilization, the zygote within an archegonium undergoes repeated divisions and forms a sporophyte embryo. In it, four organ zones become recognizable: a **foot,** which anchors the whole embryo to the base of the archegonium; a **radicle,** the embryonic root; a **hypocotyl,** the embryonic stem; and a **cotyledon,** the embryonic leaf (Fig. 25.11). Root and stem elongate rapidly, penetrate through the arche-

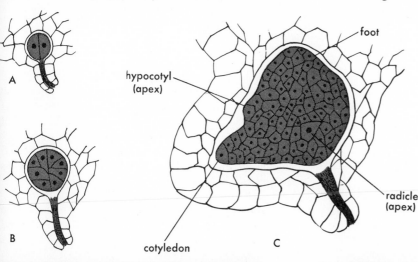

FIG. 25.11 Development of a fern sporophyte. Diagram, A, zygote; B, early embryo; C, later embryo showing organ zones. Photographs, left, young sporophyte; middle, gametophyte with attached sporophyte, the latter showing root and first two leaves; right, early adult leaves of sporophyte. (Photographs, left, courtesy of Dr. M. S. Fuller, Brown University; center and right, R. H. Noailles, Museum of Natural History, Paris.)

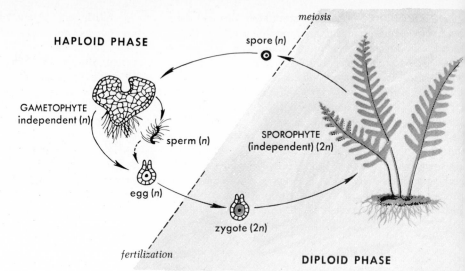

FIG. 25.12 Summary of the life cycle of ferns.

gonial tissues, and establish the young sporophyte in soil and air, respectively. Until the leaf greens, the gametophyte nourishes the sporophyte. But thereafter the gametophyte shrivels and degenerates. The life cycle of ferns is summarized in Fig. 25.12.

SEED PLANTS

All Metaphyta considered so far exhibit essentially the same system of reproduction. Regardless of whether the sporophyte is dependent or independent, the gametophyte is independent. Moreover, the gametophyte produces sex organs of the same basic type in all groups and requires external water for fertilization. As noted, certain species of *Selaginella* suggest some of the features of the second major system of reproduction among Metaphyta, namely, the system encountered among seed plants. Here the gametophyte is always *dependent;* it is parasitic on the sporophyte. Furthermore, external water is *not* needed for fertilization.

The reproductive pattern of seed plants may be characterized as follows (Fig. 25.13). First, all seed

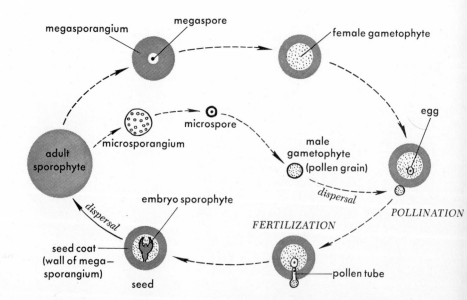

FIG. 25.13 The basic pattern of reproduction in seed plants.

plants are heterosporous (and thus they invariably possess gametophytes with separate sexes). As we shall see presently, heterospory is a necessary prerequisite for the seed habit. Many of the tracheophyte groups have evolved heterospory independently, but only gymnosperms and angiosperms appear to have been able to advance it all the way to the formation of seeds. Like *Selaginella*, some seed plants produce both microspores and megaspores in the same individual. This will be referred to here as a **monoecious** condition. But many seed plants produce only microspores in one individual, only megaspores in another. This is a **dioecious** condition (Fig. 25.14).

Second, a microspore gives rise to a male gametophyte consisting of a few cells only and this whole gametophyte is retained within the wall of the microspore. Such a wall with gametophyte is a **pollen grain.** Analogously, a megaspore gives rise to a few-celled female gametophyte, which is retained within the wall of the megaspore. The megaspore in turn does not leave the megasporangium in which it is produced. Megasporangia are often called **ovules.**

Third, pollen grains are dispersed from the microsporangia and are carried by wind or animals to the ovules. Such dispersion, leading eventually to contact between a pollen grain and an ovule or associated structures, is called **pollination.**

Fourth, the male gametophyte within a pollen grain develops a **pollen tube,** which carries sperms or sperm nuclei at the tip. This tube digests its way to the female gametophyte and makes contact with an egg. A sperm nucleus then enters the egg and fuses with its nucleus. This is *fertilization.* Note that pollination and fertilization are distinct and separate events; several months may in some cases intervene between them. Note also that it is the pollen tube which circumvents the requirement of free water in fertilization. The success of seed plants therefore rests in large measure on the evolutionary development of such tubes.

Fifth, the fertilized egg, the female gametophyte, the surrounding wall of the megaspore, and the surrounding tissues of the ovule, all together constitute a **seed.** The outer layers of the ovule usually harden into a tough **seed coat.** Within a seed, the zygote develops into a new sporophyte embryo. Through subsequent dispersion of the seed from the parent sporophyte and through seed germination, the young sporophyte becomes an independent plant. Thus the gametophyte generation remains hidden throughout and the grossly

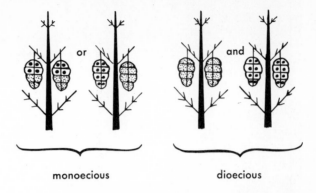

FIG. 25.14 The monoecious and dioecious conditions. In a monoecious organism, a given individual produces both micro- and megasporangia, either within the same strobilus or in different strobili. In a dioecious organism, a given individual produces only microsporangia or only megasporangia.

visible reproductive pattern of a seed plant becomes

sporophyte $\longrightarrow$ seed $\longrightarrow$ sporophyte.

GYMNOSPERMS

In virtually all of these seed plants the reproductive structures form in cones. In a pine, for example, microstrobili develop in clusters on the ends of branches. A microstrobilus bears microsporophylls each of which develops two microsporangia on the underside (Fig. 25.15). Microspore mother cells undergo meiosis, and spore tetrads give rise to microspores. Each possesses a wall composed of two layers. The outer one subsequently separates partially and forms two conspicuous "wings." Within its wall, the microspore cell divides and forms one small and one large cell. The small cell divides once more, producing two **prothallial cells.** These represent the whole vegetative portion of the male gametophyte. They eventually disintegrate and play no further role. The larger cell also divides, forming one smaller **generative cell** and one larger **tube cell.** At such a stage of development a pollen grain is mature and is shed from the microsporangium.

Megastrobili of pines are formed on short lateral branches. Such cones are small and green at first, and they harden only after pollination and considerable growth (Fig. 25.16). The axis of a megastrobilus bears lateral scales on each of which two ovules develop. An ovule is bounded on the outside by an **integument**

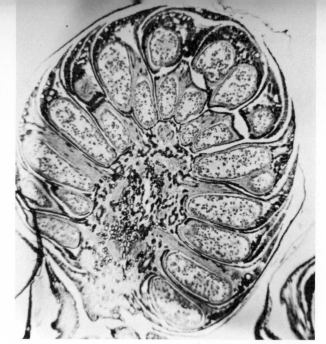

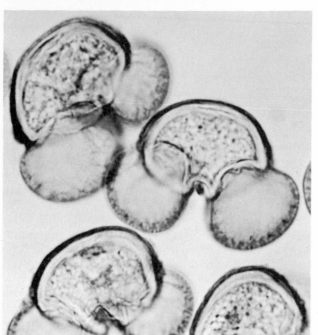
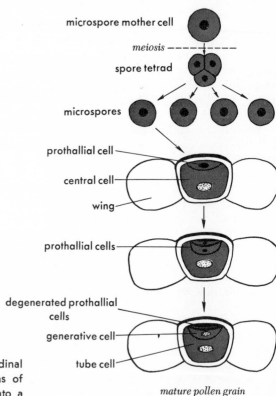

microspore mother cell

meiosis -----------------

spore tetrad

microspores

prothallial cell

central cell

wing

prothallial cells

degenerated prothallial cells

generative cell

tube cell

mature pollen grain

FIG. 25.15 Top left, microstrobili of pines. Top right, longitudinal section through such a cone. Bottom left, mature pollen grains of pines. Bottom right, development of a microspore of a pine into a pollen grain. *(Top left, R. H. Noailles, Museum of Natural History, and Flammarion Publishing Co., Ramures, Paris; top right, courtesy of Dr. M. S. Fuller, Brown University; bottom left, Ward's Natural Science Establishment, Inc.)*

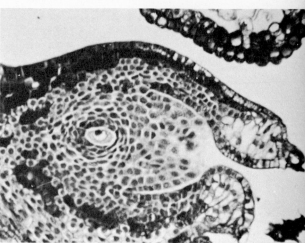

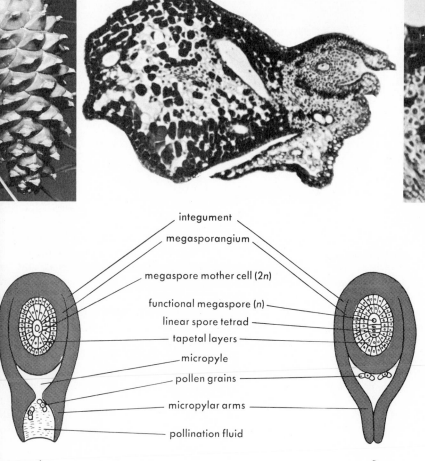

integument

megasporangium

megaspore mother cell (2n)

functional megaspore (n)

linear spore tetrad

tapetal layers

micropyle

pollen grains

micropylar arms

pollination fluid

A

B

FIG. 25.16 Photos: left, mega-strobilus of pines; middle, an ovulif-erous scale with a megasporangium (top right corner); right, enlarged view of a megasporangium, show-ing integument, micropylar arms, and, in center, megaspore mother cell. Diagram, the early development of a megasporangium. A, before meiosis; B, after meiosis. (Left, R. H. Noailles, Museum of Natural History, and Flammarion Publishing Co., Ra-mures, Paris; middle and right, cour-tesy of Dr. M. S. Fuller, Brown University.)

layer, and this layer is fused interiorly with a small megasporangium. At the base of the ovule, i.e., on the side facing the axis of the megastrobilus, the integument is extended into two flaps, the **micropylar arms.** Be-tween the arms the integument leaves a narrow canal, the **micropyle,** which leads to the megasporangium. In the latter, a single cell functions as a megaspore mother cell. A *linear spore tetrad* of four haploid cells is pro-duced by meiosis. Of these four cells, three degenerate and the remaining one is the *functional megaspore.*

When pollination occurs, the ovule is usually de-veloped to the point where a megaspore mother cell has differentiated. Pollen grains are carried into the megastrobilus, and some fall into the space between the micropylar arms. In this region the ovule secretes a

pollination fluid, which traps pollen grains and permits them to float into the micropyle. Pollen grains so come to make contact with the megasporangium. After polli-nation, the external tips of the scales of a megastrobilus grow and fuse to one another, and this seals off the whole cone.

Subsequent events within a pine ovule occur ex-ceedingly slowly; about a year elapses between polli-nation and fertilization. During this time, the whole cone and its contents increase in size. A functional megaspore is formed, and it enlarges and elongates. The megaspore nucleus divides repeatedly, until some 2,000 haploid nuclei are present. Cell walls are then laid down between the nuclei, and in this way the megaspore is transformed into a multicellular female

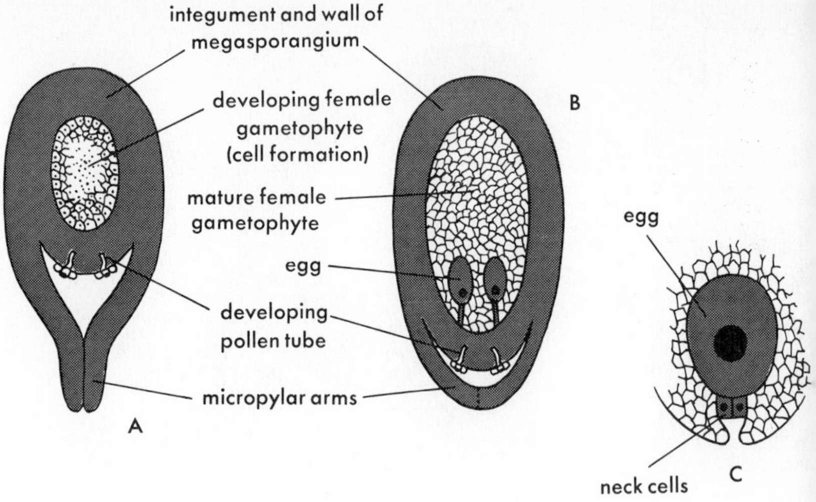

integument and wall of
megasporangium

developing female
gametophyte
(cell formation)

mature female
gametophyte

egg

developing
pollen tube

micropylar arms

egg

neck cells

B

C

A

FIG. 25.17 The female gametophyte of pines. Diagram: A, cell formation in the developing female gametophyte; B, the mature female gametophyte, with eggs; C, the archegonium. Diagram B corresponds to middle photo, diagram C corresponds to right photo, both on preceding page.

gametophyte. On the side of the micropyle a few highly reduced archegonia develop, each with an egg (Fig. 25.17).

In the meantime, the pollen grain resting against the megasporangium develops also. The tube cell of each pollen grain elongates slowly, producing a pollen tube. This tube secretes enzymes which digest a path through megasporangial tissue. The generative cell of the male gametophyte divides, forming one **stalk cell** and one **body cell**. These cells migrate toward the tip of the pollen tube, where a tube cell nucleus is already present. Later, the body cell nucleus divides once again, forming two **sperm nuclei** within the cytoplasm of the body cell. Fertilization occurs when a pollen tube penetrates into an egg. Usually, all four nuclei at the tip of the pollen tube are discharged into the egg. One sperm nucleus fuses with the egg nucleus and the remaining nuclei disintegrate within the egg cytoplasm (Fig. 25.18).

We may note that, in cycads and ginkgoes, division of the body cell results not in two nuclei only, but in two whole sperm *cells*. These become multiflagellate, and they *swim* through the pollen tube into the egg. Undoubtedly this is an evolutionary relic-condition reminiscent of the swimming sperms of the pteropsid ancestors.

Several or all of the eggs present in a female gametophyte of a pine may be fertilized independently

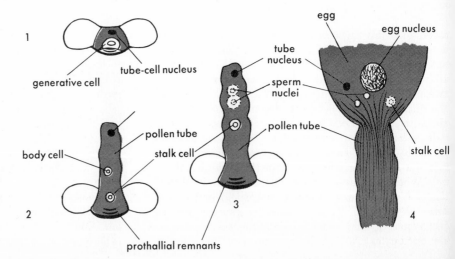

generative cell

tube-cell nucleus

1

body cell

pollen tube

stalk cell

2

prothallial remnants

tube
nucleus

sperm
nuclei

pollen tube

stalk cell

3

egg

egg nucleus

stalk cell

4

FIG. 25.18 The development of a pollen grain and fertilization in pines.

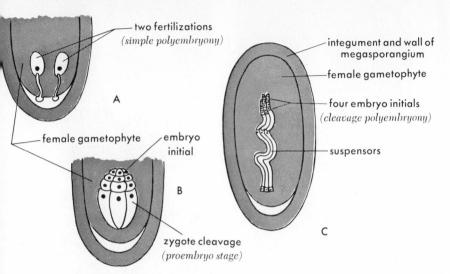

two fertilizations
(*simple polyembryony*)

A

female gametophyte — embryo initial

B

zygote cleavage
(*proembryo stage*)

integument and wall of megasporangium

female gametophyte

four embryo initials
(*cleavage polyembryony*)

suspensors

C

FIG. 25.19 Fertilization and early development of the zygote in pines. *A*, fertilization; *B*, cleavage; *C*, formation of embryo initials. Note the two possible kinds of polyembryony.

(Fig. 25.19). This is known as **simple polyembryony** and is equivalent to the formation of fraternal twins in animals (i.e., several embryos formed from several zygotes). In pines, however, only one zygote usually develops much further. Such a zygote soon forms 16 cells arranged as 4 groups of 4, one quartet below the other. This is the **proembryo** stage of sporophyte development. The uppermost quartet of cells consists of four **embryo initials.** Each of these begins to produce an embryo. Multiple development of this sort, called **cleavage polyembryony,** is equivalent to the formation of identical twins in animals (i.e., several embryos formed from a single zygote). The next lower quartet of cells elongates greatly and develops into a strand known as a **suspensor** (Fig. 25.20). As it lengthens, it pushes the embryo initials deep into the female gametophyte. Enzymes secreted by the embryo initials digest some of the gametophyte tissue and make room for further expansion. Of the four embryo initials, one usually develops faster than the others. Eventually only that one develops further and the other three degenerate.

Continuing divisions of the persisting embryo initial soon produce a sporophyte embryo with young root, stem, and two or more embryonic leaves called cotyledons. The whole embryo is embedded in the remains of the female gametophyte tissue, which in turn is surrounded by the remains of the megasporangium and the external integument. The latter has hardened by this time into a seed coat, and a flap of integument which extends away from the seed coat has matured into the "wing" of the seed (Fig. 25.21).

Pine seeds are ripe several months after fertilization. At that time the scales of the megastrobilus spread open and the naked, exposed seeds may be dispersed. In gymnosperms and angiosperms generally, mature seeds may remain *dormant,* often for very long periods (even centuries in some cases). This is a major adaptive device, for if seeds were to germinate immediately after they are mature, the emerging seedlings would frequently find themselves in totally unsuitable environments. Actually, further development of a dormant seed appears to be triggered specifically by a favorable environment. The dormant condition is in some respects similar to the state of hibernation encountered in vari-

FIG. 25.20 Two stages in the development of a pine embryo.

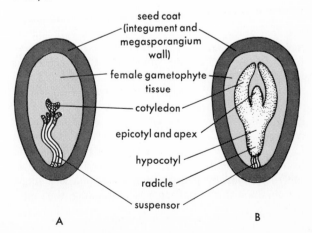

seed coat
(integument and megasporangium wall)

female gametophyte tissue

cotyledon

epicotyl and apex

hypocotyl

radicle

suspensor

A   B

FIG. 25.21   Seeds and seed germination in pines. Top left, the location of a seed in a strobilus. Top middle, the mature, winged seed at time of dispersal. Top right, dissected seed showing embryo and surrounding female gametophyte. Bottom left to right, stages in seed germination. *(Photographs by R. H. Noailles from the book "A Tree Is Born," published in America by Sterling Publishing Co., Inc., New York.)*

ous mammals. That is, the rate of respiration and of metabolism generally is exceptionally low and reserve foods are used up exceedingly slowly. The mechanisms by which such states are initiated, maintained, and terminated are as yet largely unknown.

Not all conifers require two or three years for seed formation like pines, in which pollination occurs one year and fertilization not until the next. In spruces, for example, the time interval between pollination and fertilization is only a few weeks. Many other conifers similarly complete their whole reproduction in a single season. Such time variations notwithstanding, the repro-

ductive processes themselves are basically the same in all conifers (Fig. 25.22).

ANGIOSPERMS

In this group of plants, the equivalents of gymnosperm cones are *flowers* (Fig. 25.23). Like a strobilus, a flower consists of an axis and of leaves attached to the axis. But here the internodes are extremely shortened and the conelike arrangement becomes obscured.

A flower is formed on a **receptacle**, which is the terminal expanded part of a stem. From the receptacle

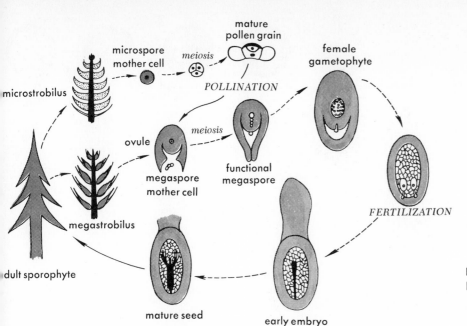

FIG. 25.22 Summary of the life cycle of a pine.

arise a **calyx**, consisting of a whorl of **sepals**; a **corolla**, consisting of a whorl of **petals**; a circularly arranged set of **stamens**, equivalent to microsporophylls; and a central **pistil**, or **carpel**, equivalent to a megasporophyll. A stamen consists of a stalk, the **filament**, and a terminal **anther**. The latter contains the microsporangia. A pistil consists of a terminal **stigma**, a middle **style**, and an expanded basal **ovary**. Within the ovary are the ovules.

Flowers may be with or without calyx or corolla. Where these leaves are present, they may or may not be pigmented (other than green) and they may or may not produce scents. Pigments and scents are familiar adaptations which attract various pollen-dispersing animals (bees, wasps, butterflies, moths, in some cases small birds, as well as men). Plants depending on animals for pollination generally also secrete abundant nectar (sugar water) in their flowers. Many ingenious structural devices have evolved whereby only particular animal types may have access to the nectar of a particular flower type. Potential "robbers" either cannot enter the flower or cannot reach the nectar stores. On the other hand, qualified animals such as bees may find landing platforms, colored guide marks on petals, and other conveniences. As such animals reach for nectar deep down in the flower, they brush against stamens and pistil. In the process they pick up new pollen on their body surfaces or deposit pollen from other flowers visited earlier.

Some species of angiosperms are regularly *self-pollinating;* pollen grains fall on the stigma of the same

FIG. 25.23 The parts of a flower. See also Fig. 25.25. (R. H. Noailles, Museum of Natural History, and Larousse Publishing Co., Paris.)

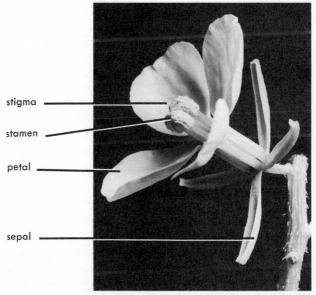

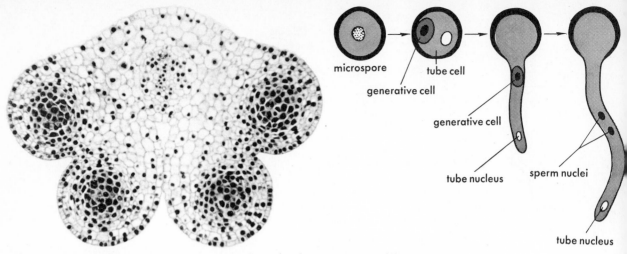

microspore   tube cell

generative cell

generative cell

tube nucleus   sperm nuclei

tube nucleus

FIG. 25.24 Photograph, cross section through a developing stamen. Microspore mother cells are in four darkly stained groups. Diagram, the development of a microspore. (*Photograph courtesy of Dr. M. S. Fuller, Brown University.*)

flower and develop normally thereafter. In the majority of angiosperms, however, *cross-pollination* must occur. In such cases, many pollen grains undoubtedly do chance on the stigma of the same flower. But such pollen grains may not begin to develop at all or may develop abnormally. Events proceed normally only when pollen grains from one flower are transferred to the stigmas of other flowers of the same species.

In the anthers, formation of microspores occurs as in gymnosperms but the subsequent development of a male gametophyte is abbreviated still more (Fig. 25.24). The microspore nucleus divides only once, producing a **generative nucleus** and a **tube nucleus**. Prothallial cells are not formed at all. The generative nucleus subsequently divides once more, forming two **sperm nuclei**. Thus the whole male gametophyte in a pollen grain consists of one trinucleate cell.

An analogously condensed development occurs in the ovary, which may contain one or more ovules (Fig. 25.25). In each ovule, as in gymnosperms, a micropyle leads through the integument to the megasporangium (Fig. 25.26). Within the latter, a single megaspore mother cell undergoes meiosis and produces a linear spore tetrad. In most cases, three of the four haploid cells degenerate (not in the lily, however; see below). In the remaining and enlarging functional megaspore, the nucleus undergoes three divisions. Four of the resulting eight haploid nuclei come to be situated at one end of the spore cell, four at the other. Three

of each group of four then become partitioned off as cells and the remaining two, the so-called **polar nuclei**, migrate to the center of what is now a seventh large middle cell. These seven cells constitute the entire female gametophyte. Archegonia are not formed at all.

FIG. 25.25 Cross section through the ovary of a lily. Note the ovary wall (which will eventually give rise to the "meat" of a fruit) and the three pairs of ovules containing female gametophytes. (*Ward's Natural Science Establishment, Inc.*)

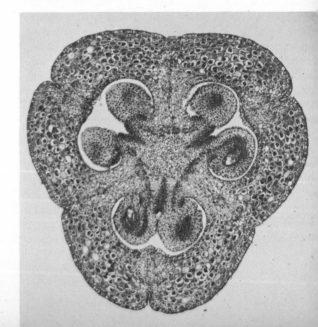

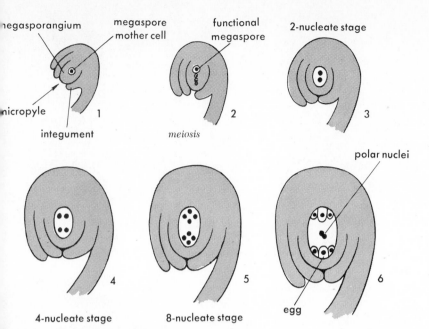

megasporangium

megaspore
mother cell

functional
megaspore

2-nucleate stage

micropyle

integument

meiosis

1

2

3

polar nuclei

4

5

6

egg

4-nucleate stage

8-nucleate stage

FIG. 25.26 The basic pattern of the development of a female gametophyte in angiosperms.

instead, of the three gametophyte cells near the micropyle, one becomes an egg directly.

The lily is representative of a small group of angiosperms in which the female gametophyte develops slightly differently (Fig. 25.27). In the megaspore mother cell the meiotic divisions are *nuclear* only, and all four resulting haploid nuclei contribute to gametophyte formation. One of the four nuclei migrates to the future egg end of the spore cell. There it divides twice, forming a group of four haploid nuclei. The three remaining megaspore nuclei migrate to the other end of the spore cell and *fuse.* This results in a *triploid* nucleus, i.e., one having three sets of chromosomes. Such a nucleus divides twice and produces a group of four triploid nuclei. One triploid nucleus and one nucleus from the haploid group again migrate to the center of the spore cell as polar nuclei. All remaining six nuclei become partitioned off as cells, as above. One of the haploid cells becomes the egg.

Pollen of angiosperms is dispersed partly by wind, partly by insects and other animals. Numerous pollen grains may land on a stigma of a pistil. The stigma is sticky and traps the pollen grains. Each then produces (usually) one pollen tube, which grows between the cells of the style toward the ovary. Such a tube usually enters an ovule through the micropyle and then digests a path through the megasporangial tissues. The tip of the tube contains the tube nucleus and the two sperm

nuclei. All three are eventually discharged into the female gametophyte (Fig. 25.28).

The next event is **double fertilization,** unique to the angiosperms (Fig. 25.29). One of the sperm nuclei enters the egg and effects fertilization. The other sperm nucleus migrates to the two polar nuclei, and all three of these nuclei now fuse together into a so-called **endosperm nucleus.** In most cases this nucleus is *triploid,* inasmuch as it is formed from two female and one male haploid nuclei. In the lily group of angiosperms the endosperm nucleus is *pentaploid,* since it is formed from one triploid and one haploid polar nucleus plus one sperm nucleus. In either case, the endosperm nucleus divides repeatedly, cell walls are then usually laid down between the nuclei, and the tissue so formed is the **endosperm.** It soon fills up the space formerly occupied by the female gametophyte and the megasporangial tissues. Endosperm cells accumulate food substances from the parent sporophyte.

While the endosperm develops, the zygote divides and gives rise to a sporophyte embryo (Fig. 25.30). The latter possesses one or two cotyledons, depending on the subclass of angiosperms (see Chap. 10). The whole embryo is embedded in endosperm, and this tissue gradually contributes more or less of its food to the developing sporophyte. In a germinating seed, therefore, endosperm may or may not be present. If the endosperm is still extensive, the cotyledons are

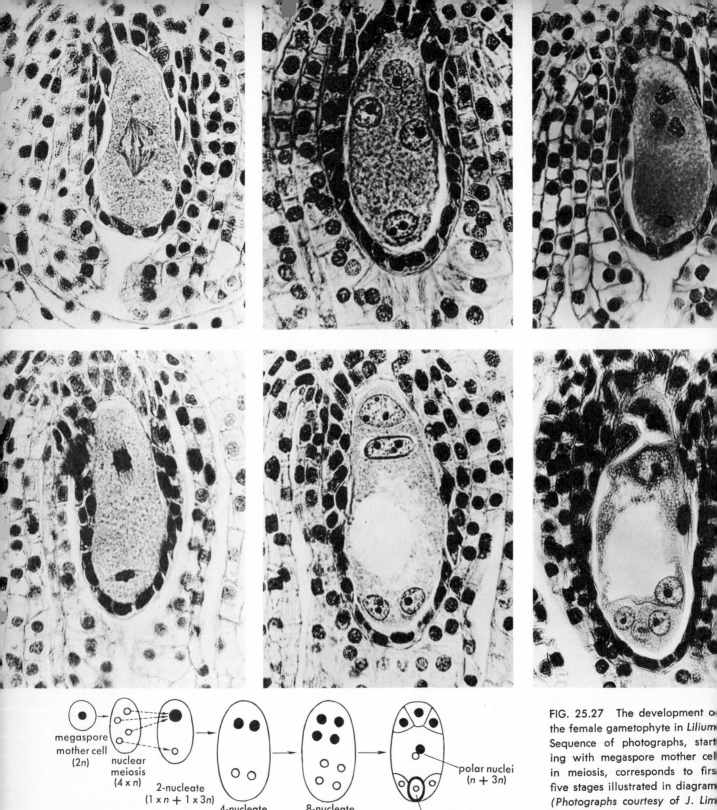

megaspore
mother cell
(2n)

nuclear
meiosis
(4 x n)

2-nucleate
(1 x n + 1 x 3n)

4-nucleate
(2 x n + 2 x 3n)

8-nucleate
(4 x n + 4 x 3n)

polar nuclei
(n + 3n)

egg (n)

FIG. 25.27 The development o
the female gametophyte in *Lilium*
Sequence of photographs, start
ing with megaspore mother cell
in meiosis, corresponds to firs
five stages illustrated in diagram
(*Photographs courtesy of J. Lim
bach, Ripon Microslides.*)

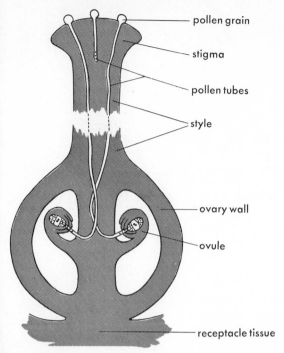

pollen grain

stigma

pollen tubes

style

ovary wall

ovule

receptacle tissue

FIG. 25.28 The growth of pollen tubes after pollination in angiosperms.

likely to be thin and leafy (e.g., squash, castor beans). But if the endosperm is absent, its substance is incorporated into the cotyledons and these are likely to be massive (e.g., peanuts, peas).

Soon after fertilization, the integuments around the developing embryos harden into seed coats and much of the flower withers. On the contrary, the ovary and in some cases also parts of the receptacle enlarge rapidly and mature into a **fruit**. This structure may become *dry* or *fleshy*, and it "hides" the seeds of "angiosperms" within it (Fig. 25.31).

Thus the reproduction of angiosperms is characterized by three major features not encountered in gymnosperms: the *flower* itself; double fertilization, resulting in the inclusion of *endosperm* tissue within seeds; and the *fruit*, which contains a number of seeds. Each of these evolutionary innovations is of pronounced adaptive value. The flower often promotes pollination by attracting insects. The endosperm nourishes the embryo. And the fruit promotes seed dispersal and seed germination; for fleshy fruits may be eaten by animals and seeds may be spit out or may be expelled undigested with the feces, in new locations. Dry fruits like nuts may be carried about by squirrels, for example, and may be left by them in some forgotten hiding

FIG. 25.29 Photograph, the female gametophyte of the lily after double fertilization. Note the three central nuclei, which, after fusion, will form the endosperm nucleus. Also note the zygote near bottom of photograph. Diagram: (1), (2), (3), double fertilization and early embryo in angiosperms generally; (4), (5) double fertilization in the lily. *(Photograph courtesy of J. Limbach, Ripon Microslides.)*

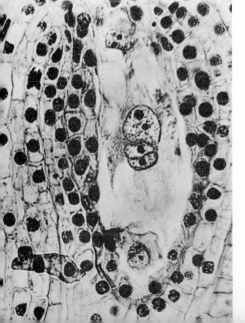

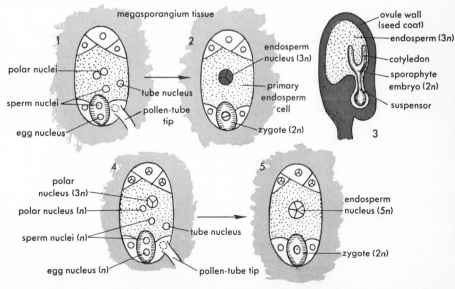

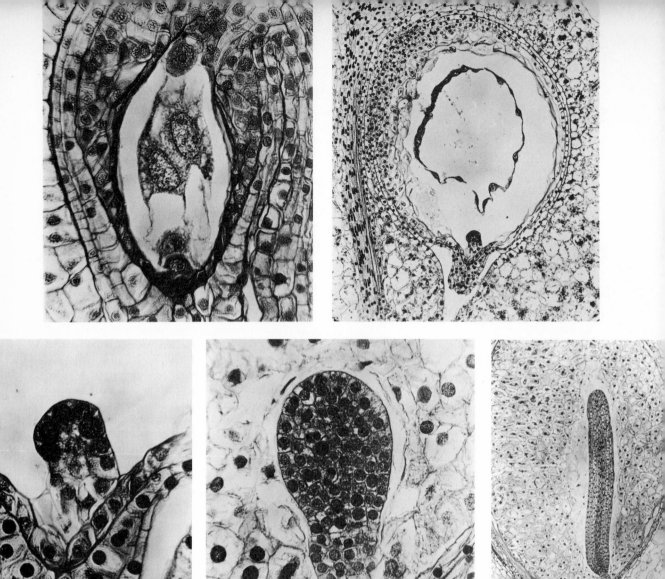

FIG. 25.30   The early development of endosperm and embryo in the lily. Top left, the two large central nuclei represent the products of the first division of the endosperm nucleus. Top right, the early embryo near bottom of photograph and, above it, the developing tissue of the endosperm. Bottom left, enlarged view of the embryo shown in top right. Bottom middle, later stage in embryo development. Bottom right, older embryo surrounded by endosperm. Note suspensor attaching embryo to wall of ovule. *(Courtesy of J. Limbach, Ripon Microslides.)*

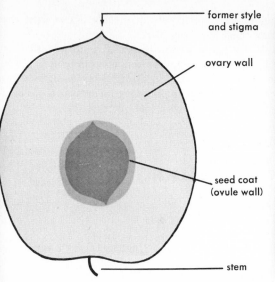

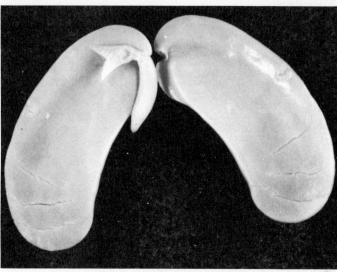

FIG. 25.31 Fruit and seed in angiosperms. In the photograph of a dissected bean seed, note the two large endosperm-filled cotyledons and the small embryo with rootlet and developing leaves. (*Photograph courtesy of Dr. M. S. Fuller, Brown University.*)

place. Fruits with burrs, hooks, or wing blades are distributed widely by animals and wind. Fruits which simply fall to the ground eventually decay, and this aids seed development by enriching a patch of soil.

We note that the solution to the problem of terrestrial reproduction is rather similar in seed plants and in terrestrial animals. As the next chapter will show, most terrestrial animals circumvent the need for external water by copulation and *internal* fertilization: a male animal deposits sperms directly into a female animal which contains mature eggs. In seed plants the depositing is done by wind or animals, but internal fertilization in a sense takes place also. As we have seen, a sporophyte produces microspores and, through them, sperms or sperm nuclei. Another sporophyte produces megaspores and, through them, eggs. The sperm nuclei then reach the eggs by means of pollen tubes, which are the plant equivalents of the copulating organs of animals.

REVIEW QUESTIONS

1. List features which characterize the reproduction of Metaphyta generally. Describe the structure of the sex organs of Metaphyta.

2. Describe the detailed life cycle of a bryophyte. In what respects is it (*a*) well, (*b*) poorly adapted to terrestrial life?

3. Define: homospory, heterospory, microsporangium, megasporophyll, megaspore mother cell, spore tetrad.

4. What reproductive characteristics distinguish the tracheophytes? In what ways are these character-

istics adaptive? Describe the reproduction of (*a*) *Psilopsida*, (*b*) *Lycopodium*, (*c*) *Selaginella*, (*d*) *Equisetum*.

5. Describe the life cycle of a fern, with particular attention to the mechanism of spore discharge. Describe the structure of a fern gametophyte.

6. Review the general reproductive processes among seed plants. What are monoecious and dioecious conditions? Distinguish between pollination and fertilization. In what ways are seeds particularly advantageous for terrestrial life?

7. Describe the life cycle of a pine. Distinguish

between simple and cleavage polyembryony. Review the structure and development of a sporophyte embryo of a pine.

8. Describe the structure and adaptive significance of a flower. Distinguish between self- and cross-pollination.

9. Review the life cycle of a flowering plant. Define double fertilization, endosperm. Show how mega-gametophyte development in the lily differs from that of most other flowering plants.

10. What is a fruit and what is its adaptive significance? Review the ways in which reproductive processes of gymnosperms differ from those in angiosperms. Review the general reproductive adaptations of Metaphyta as contrasted with those of Protista.

SUGGESTED COLLATERAL READINGS

Various aspects of the reproduction of flowering plants are discussed in the following articles:

Grant, V.: The Fertilization of Flowers, *Sci. American,* vol. 184, 1951.

Heslop-Harrison, J.: The Sexuality of Flowers, *New Biol.,* vol. 23, 1957.

Manning, A.: Bees and Flowers, *New Biol.,* vol. 21, 1956.

Additional information on the reproduction of Metaphyta may be obtained in the books cited below and at the end of Chap. 10.

Maheshwari, P.: "An Introduction to the Embryology of the Angiosperms," McGraw-Hill, New York, 1950.

Pool, R. J.: "Flowers and Flowering Plants," 2d ed., McGraw-Hill, New York, 1941.

Smith, G. M.: "Cryptogamic Botany," vol. II, "Bryophytes and the Pteridophytes," 2d ed., McGraw-Hill, New York, 1955.

REPRODUCTION: METAZOA

26

The principal and often the only form of multiplication in Metazoa is gametic reproduction. Gamete formation occurs in multicellular sex organs and is accompanied by meiosis. The life cycle is therefore diplontic, mature gametes representing the only haploid phase. All Metazoa are oögamous, and fertilized eggs develop into distinct embryos. These may grow into adults directly or, as is more typical, may first become *larvae* and then adults.

We shall first discuss the main patterns of reproduction encountered among Metazoa as a whole and shall then concentrate on the specific processes of reproduction in vertebrates, man in particular. The vertebrate example provides a good illustration of reproductive events in animals generally and, incidentally, also illustrates how hormones control living processes.

REPRODUCTIVE PATTERNS

Vegetative reproduction occurs regularly in some animal groups as a normal process of propagation. It may take the form of fragmentation (as in some flatworms and sea anemones) or of budding of the parent animal (as in sponges, coelenterates, endoprocts, tunicates, and other groups). Regenerative reproduction after injury is widespread (e.g., starfishes, earthworms, hydras), but in the majority of groups the capacity of regeneration is severely restricted. Pieces separated from the parent simply die, and in such cases the only remnant of vegetative reproduction is wound healing.

Species dispersal among animals is achieved by locomotion of the adults or the larvae. Sporulation is therefore largely superfluous and indeed does not occur among any motile animals. Even where the adults are sessile, moreover, only a few primitive groups such as sponges produce sporelike cells.

Whatever other forms of reproduction may or may not occur in given cases, gametic reproduction occurs in all cases. The sexes typically are separate, but hermaphroditism is common, particularly in sessile and sluggish animals.

Virtually all hermaphroditic types are cross-fertilizing. Animal sex organs, or gonads, usually are components of distinct reproductive systems which include ducts leading from the sex organs to the exterior of the body. Gametes are formed from special groups of diploid generative cells in the gonads. Such cells become sperms or eggs by processes of maturation involving both the cell nucleus and the cytoplasm.

Nuclear maturation consists of meiosis. In a male gonad, or testis, meiosis in a diploid generative cell results in four haploid cells all of which become functional sperms (Fig. 26.1). In a female gonad, or ovary, a diploid generative cell undergoes a first meiotic division and produces two cells. Of these, one is small and soon degenerates. Its remnants, now called the **first polar body,** remain attached to the other cell. This cell subsequently passes through the second meiotic division. Of the two cells produced here, one becomes the

FIG. 26.1   Meiosis in males and females. In males, all four haploid cells formed become functional sperms. In females, one cell formed by the first meiotic division is small and degenerates and becomes the first polar body. Similarly, one cell formed by the second meiotic division becomes the second polar body. Thus only one cell matures as a functional egg.

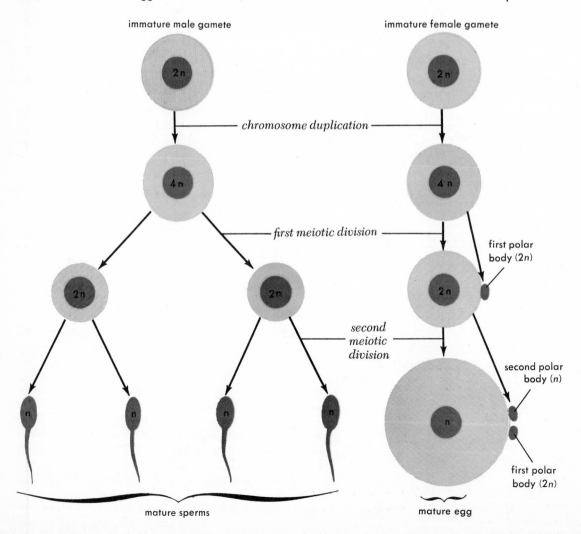

immature male gamete

immature female gamete

2n

2n

chromosome duplication

4n

4n

first meiotic division

first polar body (2n)

2n

2n

2n

second meiotic division

second polar body (n)

n

n

n

n

n

first polar body (2n)

mature sperms

mature egg

FIG. 26.2   Polar body formation. Left, section through the edge of an immature egg of the whitefish, and the extremely eccentric position of the spindle and the chromosomes during a meiotic division. The chromosomes are in anaphase, and cleavage, which will occur at right angles to the spindle axis, will therefore produce an extremely large and an extremely small cell. Right, cytoplasmic cleavage is under way. The small cell formed will degenerate, and the remnants will persist as a polar body. *(General Biological Supply House, Inc.)*

egg and the other again is small and degenerates. Its remnants form the **second polar body** which, like the first, remains attached to the egg. Each generative cell thus gives rise to only one functional egg (Fig. 26.2).

In parallel with the meiotic divisions, cytoplasmic maturation takes place. Its particular form varies for different animal groups. In the sperm-forming cells of vertebrates, for example, much of the cytoplasm degenerates altogether. The nucleus enlarges into an oval **sperm head,** and the mature sperm retains only three structures having a cytoplasmic origin: a long posterior **sperm tail,** which serves as locomotor flagellum; a **middle piece,** which contains mitochondria and which joins the sperm tail with the sperm head; and an **acrosome,** a structure at the forward end of the sperm head, by means of which the sperm will make contact with an egg. As a result of losing all other cytoplasm, a mature sperm is among the smallest cells within the body (Fig. 26.3).

Mature eggs, on the other hand, are among the largest cells; their cytoplasms have become specialized for the accumulation and storage of **yolk,** food reserves for the future embryos. The amount of yolk may be insignificant, as in mammals, where the embryo will be nourished by the female parent, or it may be comparatively enormous, as in birds, where yolk represents the very substance out of which an offspring bird will be constructed.

Like plants, most animals manufacture gametes only at specific times of the year, i.e., during *breeding seasons.* Some animals, however, notably mammals like apes and man, may produce gametes the year round. As in plants, sperms invariably require a water medium. Such a medium is always available for aquatic animals, sessile or motile. On land, the water problem in sperm distribution is reduced substantially by animal locomotion; terrestrial animals (all of which are motile) may migrate either toward one another or to natural bodies of water for sperm release. Indeed, only two basic patterns of mating and fertilization occur among animals. In **external fertilization,** mating partners come into more or less close proximity and simultaneously then

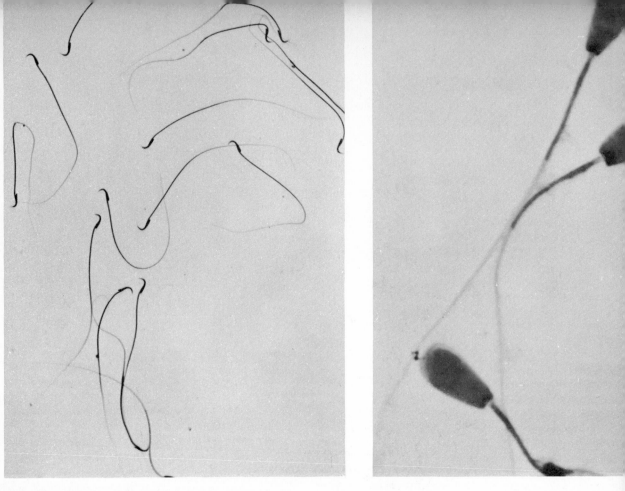

FIG. 26.3   Sperms of rats (left) and bulls (right). At right particularly, note sperm head (with acrosome faintly visible at forward end), sperm tail, and the middle piece, the darkly stained portion just behind the sperm head, which superficially appears to be part of the sperm tail. *(General Biological Supply House, Inc.)*

spawn, i.e., release sperms and eggs directly into water. Frequent chance collisions among the closely placed gametes then lead to many fertilizations. This pattern is characteristic of most aquatic animals and also of terrestrial animals such as frogs and toads, which migrate to permanent bodies of water for reproduction. The second pattern is **internal fertilization.** Mating partners here come into physical contact and a copulating organ of the male ejects swimming sperms directly into the reproductive system of the females. The female tissues then provide moisture for the sperms, and the need for external water is thereby circumvented altogether. Internal fertilization is characteristic of most terrestrial animals, e.g., mammals, birds, reptiles, insects, spiders, and many worms (Fig. 26.4).

Where fertilization is external, development of the zygotes into new adults takes place externally as well,

in natural bodies of water. In many cases where fertilization is internal, the zygotes are released from the female parent and zygote development then also occurs externally. All animals in which the eggs are shed to the outside, either in an unfertilized or a fertilized state, are said to be **oviparous.** Among vertebrates, for example, many fishes are oviparous and externally fertilizing, whereas all birds are oviparous and internally fertilizing. In all cases of oviparity, the eggs develop essentially on their own, food being supplied within each egg by the yolk. Eventually the embryos *hatch* as larvae or as miniature, immature adults. Such a pattern of events is characteristic for most animals (Fig. 26.5).

If the development of oviparous animals takes place in water, the zygotes often have coats of jelly around them (e.g., frog eggs) but are otherwise pro-

FIG. 26.4 External fertilization. In these copulating toads, the larger female will shed eggs to the outside and the male will similarly release sperms over the eggs. An instance of internal fertilization is illustrated in Fig. 23.22. (*Courtesy of Dr. Roberts Rugh, from "Experimental Embryology," Burgess Publishing Co., 1948.*)

tected very little. Coats of this sort are secreted by the tissues of the female reproductive system before the eggs are laid. Zygotes developing on land possess more elaborate protection, particularly against evaporation. For example, earthworms, spiders, and insects such as grasshoppers and cockroaches form a cocoon or a hard casing around batches of just-laid fertilized eggs. Other insects and also reptiles and birds secrete shells around individual eggs after fertilization and before laying. As will be shown in a later section, the "land eggs" of reptiles and birds are adapted particularly well to terrestrial conditions.

Some animals are **ovoviviparous.** Fertilization in such cases is always internal, and the zygotes are then retained within the female reproductive system. Development therefore occurs inside the female. However,

FIG. 26.5 In oviparous animals, fertilization is either external or internal, but the zygote is always external and development accordingly takes place externally. In ovoviviparous animals, fertilization and zygote development take place internally, but the maternal body does not otherwise contribute to offspring development; the young are born. In viviparous animals, fertilization and zygote development again occur internally, but the maternal body here does contribute importantly to offspring development, via a placenta; the young are born.

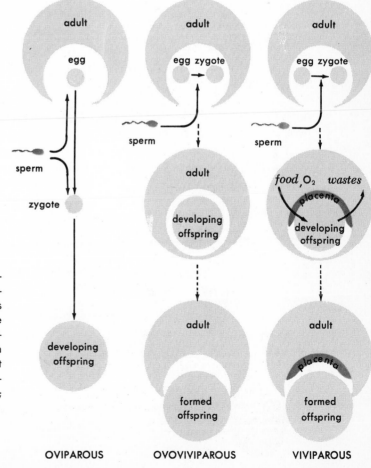

beyond providing a substantial measure of protection, the female body does not otherwise contribute to zygote development; as in oviparous types, food is supplied by the yolk included within each egg. Ultimately, the young are *born* rather than hatched, i.e., the females release fully formed animals, not eggs. Among vertebrates, some of the fishes, amphibia, and reptiles are ovoviviparous.

A third group of animals comprises **viviparous** types (see Fig. 26.5). In these, fertilization is again internal, zygotes are retained within the female, and the young are born as developed animals. However, the female body here influences the development of the young not merely by providing protection. It also supplies food and contributes to offspring metabolism generally in numerous and vital ways. Among vertebrates, the principal viviparous types are mammals. We shall examine some of the details of this particular reproductive pattern in the following sections.

REPRODUCTIVE SYSTEMS

As in animals generally, the basic structural plan of the reproductive system of a mammal such as man is

FIG. 26.6 The male reproductive system, diagrammatic. Testis on left shown in section.

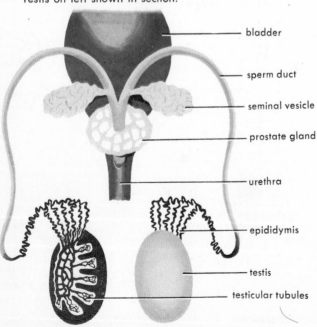

- bladder
- sperm duct
- seminal vesicle
- prostate gland
- urethra
- epididymis
- testis
- testicular tubules

comparatively simple. In both males and females, a pair of gonads is connected with a system of ducts which leads to the exterior of the body. In males, these ducts carry sperms to the outside. In females, the ducts carry sperms to the eggs, provide a place for zygote development, and eventually play the principal role in accomplishing the birth of the young.

THE MALE SYSTEM

In human males, the testes are located in a **scrotum,** a skin sac between the legs. Each testis is honeycombed extensively with **testicular tubules,** groups of which are separated from one another by partitions of connective tissue (Fig. 26.6). In the partitions are found specialized endocrine cells. These manufacture and secrete **androgens,** the male sex hormones.

We recall that these hormones, *testosterone* in particular, maintain primary and secondary sex characteristics and that their manufacture in the testes is in turn under the control of pituitary gonadotropic hormones (see Chap. 20). Two such hormones are secreted by the pituitary: **FSH** and **LH.** The function of FSH in males is still obscure, but pituitary LH is known to be the hormone which stimulates the testes to produce androgens. If the androgen concentration in blood becomes too high, the sex hormones inhibit the pituitary from producing more LH. Androgen secretion then declines. Conversely, if androgen concentrations are too low, the pituitary will not be inhibited, LH will therefore be produced in greater amount, and this increases the rate of androgen production. Through such feedback control, the androgen concentration in males is maintained automatically at a fairly steady level (Fig. 26.7).

The sperm-producing tissue of the testes is located in the testicular tubules (Fig. 26.8). The cells lining these tubules divide mitotically at a great rate. New cells so formed then accumulate in the interior of the tubules and there they mature into sperms. As pointed out earlier, such maturation includes meiosis and specific cytoplasmic changes. Newly formed sperms do not lash their tails. Much respiratory CO_2 tends to accumulate in the confined spaces of the testicular tubules, and sperm motility is probably depressed by this CO_2.

The tubules of each testis join into a common **sperm duct** which emerges from the testis (see Fig. 26.6). Just outside the testis the duct is greatly looped and coiled, and this portion is called the **epididymis.**

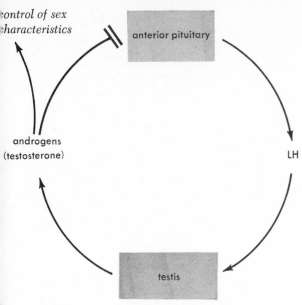

*control of sex
characteristics*

anterior pituitary

androgens
(testosterone)

LH

testis

FIG. 26.7 The control of androgen secretion. LH is one of the gonadotropic hormones of the pituitary. Compare with Figs. 20.4 and 20.5. Arrow tipped with transverse double bar denotes inhibition.

It stores sperms which are crowded out from the testicular tubules. During copulation, nerve impulses may bring about contraction of the muscular walls of the epididymis and then the collected sperms are propelled forward, into the straight part of the sperm duct.

This part of the duct leaves the scrotum and passes through the groin. It eventually opens into the **urethra,** close to the point where the urinary bladder also opens into the urethra. Near its termination, the sperm duct receives watery secretions from the **seminal vesicle** and the **prostate gland.** These secretions, together with sperms, constitute **semen.** It is here that sperms begin to lash their tails. Semen may contain specific sperm-activating substances. Moreover, CO_2 probably becomes diluted sufficiently in this terminal part of the sperm duct to permit sperm movement.

Note that urine and semen are expelled along the same exit path, the urethra, a channel which leads to the outside through the **penis.** However, simultaneous discharges are prevented by reflexes. The bladder-urethra juncture constricts when semen is expelled and the sperm-duct–urethra juncture constricts when urine is expelled.

Sperm-producing capacity develops at puberty and continues to old age, often until death. Unlike man

and some other mammals, most mammals manufacture sperms only during an annual breeding season. Possibly in correlation with this, the testes are found in different positions in different mammals. In one group, which includes the opossum, for example, the testes are located permanently where ovaries are located in females, i.e., within the body cavity, not far from the kidneys. In a second group of mammals, which includes elephants, the testes are again found within the body cavity for most of the year. But during the breeding season, when sperms are actually produced, the testes migrate into a scrotum. After the breeding season, the testes migrate back into the body cavity. Finally, in man and a few other mammals, the testes are internal only during embryonic stages. The organs migrate into the scrotum before birth and then remain in this sac permanently.

It is known that the temperature in a scrotum is slightly lower than within the body. It is also known that lower temperatures tend to promote sperm production and that higher temperatures tend to inhibit it.

FIG. 26.8 Section through a mammalian testis, showing the tubular chambers in which sperms are produced. Mature sperms accumulate in the central spaces of the tubules. The tissue between the tubules manufactures androgens, the male sex hormones, under the stimulus of LH from the pituitary. *(General Biological Supply House, Inc.)*

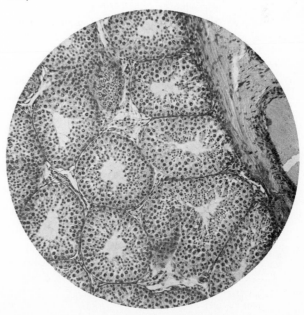

Temperature, testis location, and continuity or discontinuity of sperm manufacture therefore may well be correlated.

THE FEMALE SYSTEM

The ovaries of human females are a pair of walnut-sized organs situated at the back of the abdominal cavity, at hip level. They are partially enveloped by the funnel-shaped terminals of the **oviducts**, also called *egg ducts* or *Fallopian tubes*. These ciliated channels lead into the **uterus**. The young develop in this muscular organ, which may stretch and enlarge considerably. The mouth of the uterus opens into the **vagina**, and this channel leads to the outside (Fig. 26.9). Note that, in contrast to the arrangement in males, the reproductive tract in females is entirely separate from the urinary tract. Each of these duct systems in females leads to the outside through its own opening.

The outer layers of the ovaries are the egg-producing tissues. As in testes, new cells are manufactured mitotically and are crowded into the interior of the organ. But in contrast to events in the testis, not all the new cells in the ovary become eggs. In a given batch of newly produced cells, all of which are probably potential eggs, usually only one actually matures into a reproductive cell. Meiosis occurs in such a cell, and its cytoplasm enlarges and accumulates some yolk. The surrounding cells are inhibited in some unknown way from also maturing as eggs (Fig. 26.10).

However, these surrounding cells acquire other functions. More specifically, they specialize as endocrine

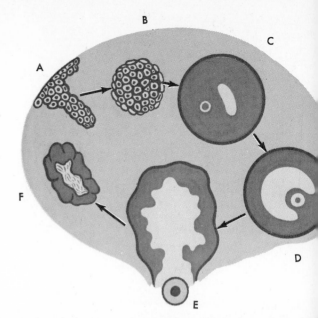

FIG. 26.10 The growth of an egg, diagrammatic. A and B, newly formed potential egg cells within the ovary. C and D, maturation of one of the cells into an egg and development of surrounding cells into a follicle. Note the enlarging follicular cavity. E, ovulation. F, the remnants of the follicle have transformed into a corpus luteum.

tissue and secrete **estrogens**, the female sex hormones. Like androgens in males, estrogens maintain the primary and secondary sex characteristics of females. The endocrine cells surrounding the egg become arranged into a **follicle**, a ball of tissue which soon develops a slowly enlarging central cavity. This follicular cavity is filled with fluid in which the estrogenic hormones accumulate before they are carried away by blood. In such a follicle, the egg is located eccentrically, in a thickened region of the follicular wall (Figs. 26.10 and 26.11).

As in males, gonadotropic hormones secreted by the pituitary gland, i.e., FSH and LH, control the formation and growth of follicles and thus egg production. As in males also, the endocrine control has built-in feedbacks and operates cyclically, with the result that eggs are manufactured in cyclic patterns. In most mammals and in vertebrates generally, the durations of such egg-producing cycles are relatively short and eggs form in fairly rapid succession. In chickens, for example, the egg-laying cycle lasts approximately one day. In man, apes, and old-world monkeys, the egg-

FIG. 26.9 Diagram of the female reproductive system.

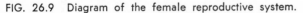

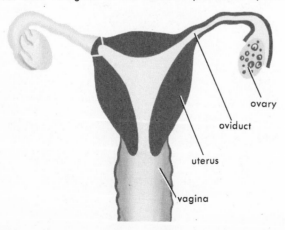

ovary

oviduct

uterus

vagina

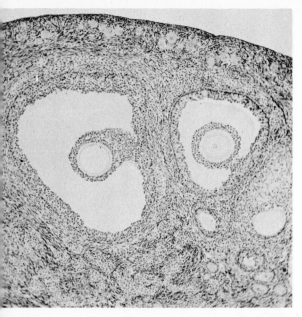

FIG. 26.11 Section through a mammalian ovary. Note the two large follicles, the follicular cavities, and the large egg cell in each follicle embedded within a mass of cells along the follicular wall. Near the top of the photo, along the edge of the ovary, note the relatively large cells. These are immature eggs which will become mature later, within follicles yet to be formed. *(Ward's Natural Science Establishment, Inc.)*

producing cycles are rather elaborate and of longer duration than in most other mammals. A rate of one egg per month is typical for human females, for example. In mammals generally, egg-producing cycles occur only during the annual breeding season and cease when the animal is fertilized and is pregnant. Year-round egg production characterizes mammals such as apes and man, puberty marking the onset of the reproductive period. In man this period continues for about 30 years. Because a month-long egg-forming cycle of man terminates in *menstruation*, it is called a *menstrual cycle*. We shall discuss its course in the following section.

THE MENSTRUAL CYCLE

Such a cycle may be considered to begin with FSH production by the pituitary. The name of this hormone, short for *"follicle-stimulating hormone,"* describes its function. Under its influence, a follicle grows,

an egg matures within it, and the endocrine follicle cells secrete increasing amounts of estrogen.

This last has two specific consequences. First, the increasing concentration of estrogen in the blood eventually reaches a level which *inhibits* the pituitary from secreting more FSH. Second, high concentrations of estrogen *stimulate* the pituitary to begin secreting LH, the other gonadotropic hormone. In other words, continued growth of the follicle and the correlated rising estrogen output ultimately bring about a sharp fall in FSH concentration and a sharp rise in LH concentration (Fig. 26.12).

This stage is usually attained some 10 to 14 days after a follicle has begun to grow. During this roughly two-week-long period, the follicle has migrated within the ovary and has come to be stationed just under the ovary surface, where it may form a pronounced outward bulge. Follicle and egg are fully matured at this time and now, as noted, FSH concentration falls rapidly and LH concentration rises. These hormonal changes form the specific stimulus for **ovulation,** or egg release. The ovary surface and the follicle wall both rupture and the mature egg falls out of the ovary (see Fig. 26.10).

An immediate consequence of ovulation is that the ruptured and eggless follicle remaining in the ovary loses its fluid and collapses. Another consequence is that, since FSH production by the pituitary has now ceased, the remnant of the follicle ceases to manufacture estrogen. Instead, under the specific influence of the LH produced in increasing quantities by the pitui-

FIG. 26.12 The hormonal changes during the follicular phase of a menstrual cycle, leading to ovulation. Arrow tipped with double bar denotes inhibition.

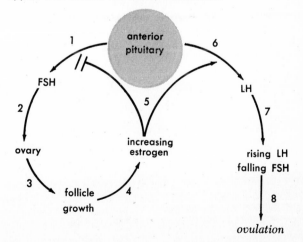

tary, the remnant of the follicle transforms into a yellowish body, the **corpus luteum.** The name "LH" stands for "*luteinizing hormone.*" Under the continuing influence of this hormone, the corpus luteum begins to secrete a new hormone of its own, namely, **progesterone.** Thus, ovulation marks the time when, owing to the change from FSH control to LH control, an egg is released and the follicle becomes a corpus luteum, and when estrogen production gives way to progesterone production.

Progesterone, chemically very much like estrogen and the male sex hormones, is a control agent peculiar to mammals. Being viviparous animals, mammals become pregnant, i.e., the offspring develop within the female body, specifically in the uterus. Progesterone is an evolutionary adaptation to viviparity; the hormone prepares the uterus to receive an egg and subsequently controls the retention of the developing offspring within the uterus. Progesterone may therefore be described as the "pregnancy hormone." When an egg leaves the ovary during ovulation, it normally falls into the funnel of the oviduct. From there the egg is slowly propelled toward the uterus by the cilia which line the oviduct. The uterus in the meantime is readied for the arrival of the egg. Under the influence of progesterone, the inner lining of the uterus thickens, becomes greatly

pitted with glandular pockets, and acquires a rich supply of blood capillaries. As a result, the inner surface of the uterus is transformed into a spongy carpet of particularly well-nourished tissue (Fig. 26.13).

What happens next depends on whether the egg is fertilized or not. If fertilization does occur, the event normally takes place as the egg travels through the upper part of the oviduct. The fertilized egg then continues to migrate toward the ready uterus and arrives there some two days after ovulation.

If fertilization does not occur, the egg disintegrates when it is about halfway down the oviduct. In such a case the uterus will have been made ready for nothing. But the pituitary and the corpus luteum have not yet received any information about the nonoccurrence of fertilization. Indeed, progesterone continues to be produced in increasing quantities. About a week after ovulation, the progesterone concentration in blood then becomes so high that the hormone begins to have an inhibitory feedback effect on the pituitary. As a result, less and less LH is secreted and the corpus luteum correspondingly produces gradually less progesterone (Fig. 26.14). The corpus luteum actually begins to degenerate, and it eventually secretes so little progesterone that the "ready" uterus can no longer remain ready. The glandular pockets of the uterus wall are

FIG. 26.13 The effect of sex hormones on the structure of the uterus. The left photo shows the inner glandular tissues of a human uterus during the follicular phase of a menstrual cycle, when progesterone is absent. Note the layer of uterine muscle underneath the glandular layer. The right photo, taken at the same magnification, shows the glandular tissues during the luteal phase, when the progesterone concentration is high. Note the tremendous increase in thickness of the glandular layer and the increased elaboration of the glandular pockets. *(Courtesy of Dr. B. J. Serber, College of Medicine, New York University.)*

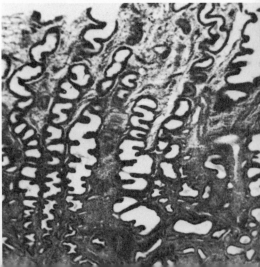

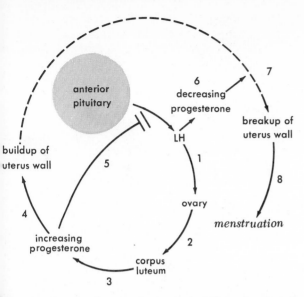

FIG. 26.14 The hormonal changes during the luteal phase of a menstrual cycle, leading to menstruation.

esorbed, the blood capillaries break up, and the whole pongy lining disintegrates. Tissue fragments separate rom the uterus wall and some blood escapes from the orn vessels. Over a period of a few days, all this debris s expelled through the vagina to the outside. This is nenstruation. It begins some two weeks after ovulation, und we note that it is brought about by the ultimate cessation of LH and progesterone production. At this ime, the pituitary resumes FSH production and a new nonth-long egg-producing cycle is initiated.

As we have seen, roughly the first two weeks of a nenstrual cycle are dominated by FSH, estrogen, and the follicle. This period is the *follicular phase*. The second two weeks are dominated by LH, progesterone, and the corpus luteum. This period is the *luteal phase*. FSH and estrogen are components of one control cycle, LH and progesterone of another; and these two occur alternately, the termination of one being the stimulus for the initiation of the other. Here is one of the best illustrations of the way in which hormones control body functions and how such control is self-adjusting. The sequence of events in an entire menstrual cycle is summarized in Fig. 26.15.

We may note now that estrogen is not absent altogether during a luteal phase. Some can be shown to be present in the blood even then, despite the absence of follicles at that time. Similarly, some progesterone is present during the follicular phase of the menstrual cycle (Fig. 26.16). Exactly where these hormones come from is still undetermined. Immature follicles which will reach maturity only during future cycles might secrete some estrogen during a given luteal phase. Analogously, corpora lutea from past cycles and in process of degeneration might secrete some progesterone during a given follicular phase. Or other ovarian tissues might secrete the hormones. Yet, although both female sex hormones are present at every stage of the menstrual cycle, their quantities do fluctuate sharply. Estrogen reaches a definite peak late during the follicular phase and at the time of ovulation, whereas progesterone reaches peak concentrations during the luteal phase.

This fluctuation has far-reaching consequences. In addition to its effect on the uterus, progesterone promotes the development of the duct system in the mammary glands. A slight swelling of these glands generally occurs during the luteal phase of the menstrual cycle. Body temperature increases somewhat during the follicular phase, then falls during the luteal phase. Sex drive is likely to be more pronounced during the follicular phase, since estrogen maintains it. And since estrogens, like androgens in males, affect mental processes, it is possible that the monthly fluctuation of these hormones contributes to the emotional fluctuations rather characteristic of females.

As pointed out earlier, menstrual cycles essentially are elaborate egg-producing mechanisms. They ensure that female gametes are formed in a controlled, rhyth-

FIG. 26.15 The hormonal interrelations during a menstrual cycle. After step 8, step 1 recurs and initiates a new cycle.

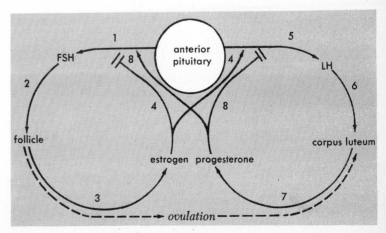

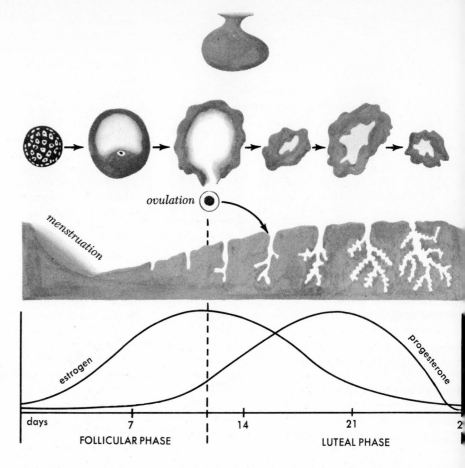

ovulation

menstruation

estrogen

progesterone

days   7   14   21   2

FOLLICULAR PHASE   LUTEAL PHASE

FIG. 26.16 Summary of some of the events during a menstrual cycle. Top, events in the ovary, indicating follicle growth, ovulation, and corpus luteum formation. Middle, events in the wall of the uterus. Bottom, variations in the sex hormone concentrations.

mically timed manner. In conjunction with sperm production, menstrual cycles set the stage for fertilization.

FERTILIZATION

Once it is discharged from the male reproductive system, a sperm can live only a few hours. Analogously, eggs erupted from the ovary do not persist for more than a few hours. The time of greatest fertility in man therefore coincides roughly with the time of ovulation. Sperms deposited into the female swim from the vagina through the uterine cavity into the oviducts. Defective sperms largely succumb along the arduous path. If a ripe living egg is encountered in the upper part of the oviduct, fertilization may occur.

Sperms which collide with the egg at an angle are likely to bounce off. Sperms hitting head on are likely to remain attached, for the acrosome at the sperm tip is specialized to adhere to the egg. One, and only

one, sperm is able to fertilize any one egg. As soon as the first sperm makes contact, a **fertilization membrane** rises from the egg surface. This membrane is formed earlier, during egg maturation. On contact with a sperm, the egg rapidly secretes some water between its surface and the membrane. As a result, the membrane lifts off, the sperm which has made contact is trapped inside, and any other sperms are prevented from entering (Fig. 26.17).

Now the successful sperm rests against the egg surface proper. Contrary to wide belief, the sperm does not penetrate into the egg by boring in; instead the egg engulfs the sperm. (Indeed, the eggs of sponges and some other animals are very obviously amoeboid.) During the entry of a sperm into the egg, the sperm tail drops off. At this point the egg is *activated* but not yet fertilized. This means that the development of the egg has been triggered off. A mature egg is ready and able to develop, but this ability remains latent until a spe-

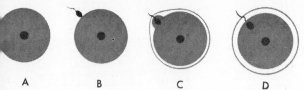

FIG. 26.17 Diagrammatic representation of fertilization. A sperm enters an egg by being engulfed by the egg, through an egg cone which comes to surround the sperm (C). A so-called fertilization membrane lifts off the egg surface after a sperm has made contact. This prevents additional sperms from being engulfed (C and D). The sperm tail is left at the egg surface, and the sperm head (nucleus) alone migrates into the egg cytoplasm, where it fuses with the egg nucleus. An egg is fully fertilized only after sperm and egg nuclei have fused.

cific stimulus makes development start. Sperm penetration into the egg normally serves as this stimulus. Such an arrangement ensures that sex occurs before development begins. As noted in Chap. 23, unfertilized eggs of frogs and other animals may be activated by experimental means to develop parthenogenetically, without sperms. Such eggs remain haploid and all the cells of the resulting embryos are correspondingly haploid.

Under normal conditions, a sperm nucleus which has activated an egg moves toward the egg nucleus and the meeting of the two haploid nuclei then completes fertilization. The membranes of the two nuclei dissolve and a mitotic spindle forms. The chromosomes, now diploid in number, line up in a metaphase plate and the zygote undergoes its first **cleavage division**. Very shortly after fertilization, therefore, two cells are formed from the zygote. These two cells then divide again, and many successive cleavage divisions follow thereafter. The development of an offspring is launched in this manner and *pregnancy* is initiated.

PREGNANCY

Zygote development after fertilization occurs in all animals and is not unique to viviparous types, i.e., animals which become pregnant. We shall defer a discussion of zygote development as such to the next chapter. Here we shall concentrate largely on those events after fertilization which *are* unique to viviparous types, namely, processes through which the body of the pregnant female contributes vitally to offspring develop-

ment. The most extensive maternal contribution is made while the offspring is retained within the environment of the uterus, i.e., during the period of **gestation**. A final contribution is made when the course of pregnancy terminates, during the process of **birth**.

GESTATION

The Luteal Phase

As noted above, fertilization in man occurs in the upper part of the oviduct and is followed immediately by division of the zygote. Therefore, when the zygote reaches the uterus a few days after fertilization, it is actually already an embryo composed of several hundred cells. This embryo is deposited on the inner surface of the uterus wall, which has been readied for reception of the egg by progesterone.

The embryo next becomes **implanted** in the wall of the uterus; i.e., it is gradually surrounded by uterus tissue (Fig. 26.18). Such implantation leads to a suppression of menstruation. Through still poorly identified nervous pathways, the presence of an embryo in the uterus wall is signaled via the brain to the pituitary, which continues to produce LH as a result. The corpus luteum consequently continues to secrete progesterone. The thickened wall of the uterus then can be maintained without tissue disintegration and menstruation does not take place. Thus, the luteal phase of the menstrual cycle in which fertilization occurs now does not terminate as usual but continues directly as a luteal phase of gestation. Moreover, further menstrual cycles are suppressed throughout pregnancy (Fig. 26.19).

In man, the corpus luteum persists for roughly the first 12 weeks of pregnancy. During this luteal phase, the progesterone output increases and the uterine lining becomes even more glandular and vascularized. The early embryo, embedded and held fast within the wall of the uterus, soon comes to consist of two groups of cells. One group, in the center of the mass, represents the embryo proper. These cells give rise to the future offspring. Surrounding this central group are cells which do not become part of the offspring body as such (Fig. 26.20). Instead, the cells form into four so-called **extraembryonic membranes.** To appreciate the crucial function of these membranes, it is necessary to consider that they are an evolutionary reminder of the reptilian ancestry of mammals. Reptiles were the first vertebrates to lay eggs on land, and extraembryonic membranes evolved as specific adaptations to egg development under terrestrial conditions.

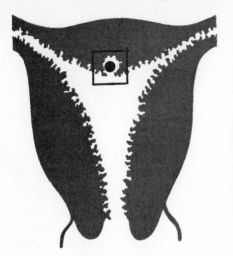
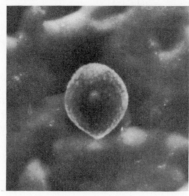
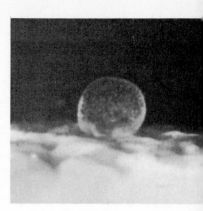

FIG. 26.18 Implantation of the egg in the uterus. Left, diagram showing position of egg relative to wall of uterus, at the time of implantation. Middle and right, top and side views of early monkey embryo just arrived in the uterus and beginning to implant. *(Photos courtesy of Dr. G. W. Corner and Department of Embryology, Carnegie Institution of Washington.)*

FIG. 26.19 Summary of hormonal changes when the luteal phase of menstrual cycle becomes the luteal phase of pregnancy. Under sterile conditions, step 4a would lead to menstruation. But if fertilization has occurred, step 4b leads to continued production of progesterone and pregnancy is initiated.

FIG. 26.20 A rabbit embryo about four days after fertilization. Only the dense cell mass aggregated in one area of the ball of cells constitutes the embryo proper and will develop into the adult. The other cells of the ball will form supporting membranes (see text). *(General Biological Supply House, Inc.)*

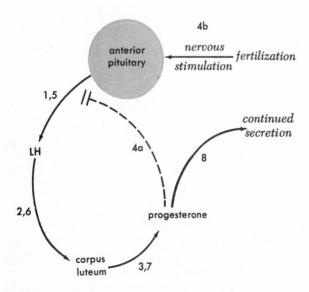
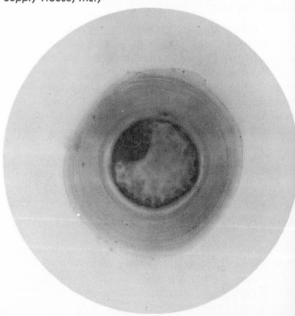

Early reptilian stocks then gave rise independently to birds and mammals. Birds inherited the adaptations of the egg virtually unchanged, but in most mammals the membranes came to function in new ways.

Reptiles and birds are oviparous, and they lay shelled eggs. The shells are porous enough to permit aerial gas exchange, yet not porous enough to permit leakage of water. Just inside the egg shell and enclosing all interior structures lies one of the extraembryonic membranes, the **chorion** (Fig. 26.21). It prevents undue evaporation of water through the shell. A second membrane, the **amnion**, surrounds the developing embryo everywhere except on its ventral side. This membrane holds lymphlike fluid, the *amniotic fluid,* which bathes the embryo as in a "private pond." The fluid may be regarded as the equivalent of the freshwater ponds in which the ancestors of reptiles and birds developed. The two remaining membranes pouch out from the ventral side of the embryo—more specifically, from the alimentary tract. One of these is the **allantois,** which comes to lie against the egg shell, just inside the chorion. Blood vessels ramify through the allantois, and this membrane is the breathing structure of the embryo; gas exchange occurs between it and the air outside the shell. Also, the allantois serves as an embryonic urinary bladder in which metabolic wastes are stored up to the time of hatching. The second membrane on the ventral

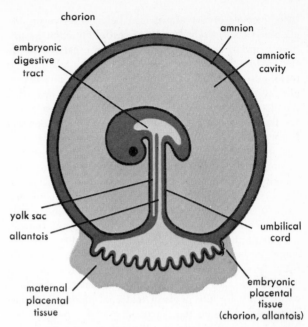

FIG. 26.22 The extraembryonic membranes in mammals and the placenta, diagrammatic. Note that yolk sac and allantois are rudimentary and collapsed.

side is the **yolk sac,** which contains the ample food stores for development and which gradually gets smaller as the yolk is used up during the growth of the embryo.

Mammals (with the exception of egg-laying mammals; see Chap. 11) are viviparous and do not produce egg shells. But the four extraembryonic membranes are still in evidence in all cases (Fig. 26.22). In man, for example, the chorion again forms as an outer enclosure around the other membranes and the embryo; it is in direct contact with the tissue of the uterus. In one region the chorion develops numerous fingerlike outgrowths which branch extensively and erode paths through the spongy uterine wall. In this manner the tissues of the chorion and the uterus become attached to each other firmly. These interfingering and interlacing tissues are known as the **placenta.** When fully developed, the placenta functions both as a mechanical and as a metabolic connection between the embryo and the female body.

The allantois in mammals still serves as in reptiles and birds as an embryonic lung, except that now gas exchange occurs in the placenta, between the embryonic blood vessels of the allantois and the maternal

FIG. 26.21 The extraembryonic membranes in reptile and bird eggs. Note that yolk sac and allantois are large and functional.

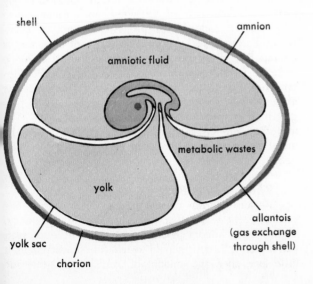

blood vessels of the uterus (see below). However, the allantois has entirely lost its ancestral function as urinary bladder; embryonic wastes now are carried off by the maternal blood in the placenta. The allantois in mammals is actually a collapsed, empty sac. This is true also of the yolk sac, food being supplied by maternal blood, again through the placenta. On the other hand, the fluid of the amnion still functions as in reptiles and birds as a "private pond" and shock absorber. As more and more amniotic fluid accumulates during the course of pregnancy, the amnion distends greatly and the surrounding chorion and uterus are stretched correspondingly. This enlargement, more than growth of the embryo itself, eventually leads to the characteristic bulging out of the abdomen of the pregnant female.

Beginning to form after the early embryo has become implanted in the uterus, the placenta is usually fully developed by the twelfth week of pregnancy. In the placenta, the microscopic terminals of the chorionic outgrowths dip into pools of maternal blood which has accumulated within the placental spaces. The maternal blood circulates extensively through the maternal side of the placenta. On the embryonic side, an artery leaves

FIG. 26.23 The embryonic blood circulation and the placenta. Note that embryonic and maternal bloods do not mix, being separated by the chorionic and allantoic membranes.

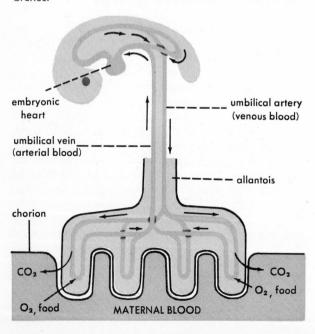

the embryo proper, travels through the allantoic membrane, and capillarizes abundantly in the placenta, just underneath the chorion (Fig. 26.23). The capillaries eventually join and form a large vein which leads back through the allantoic membrane to the embryo proper. The artery, the vein, the yolk sac, and the allantois become enveloped by connective tissue and skin, and the whole represents the **umbilical cord.** This is the lifeline between placenta and embryo; its point of origin in the embryo leaves a permanent mark in the later offspring in the form of the navel.

Note that maternal and embryonic bloods do not mix in the placenta. The two circulations approach each other closely, but the chorion always separates them. This membrane forms a selective boundary. Nutrients of all kinds and oxygen are passed across into the embryonic circulation, and metabolic wastes are passed in the opposite direction. If a raw material is in low supply in the maternal circulation, it is usually in still lower supply in the embryonic circulation. Diffusion therefore tends to occur *into* the embryo, even if this produces a pronounced deficiency in the prospective mother. In this sense, the embryo is parasitic on maternal metabolism. The placenta also ferries defensive antibodies from the maternal to the embryonic circulation. The newborn thereby acquires much of his mother's immunity for the first few months of life, usually sufficiently long to allow the newborn to manufacture his own antibodies in response to exposure to infectious agents.

The placenta also specializes as an endocrine organ. As it grows and develops, it manufactures slowly increasing amounts of estrogen and progesterone (Fig. 26.24). Indeed, the progesterone output eventually becomes far greater than that of the corpus luteum. The latter actually degenerates and its hormone secretion subsides as the twelfth week of gestation approaches. From that time on, the placenta provides the main hormonal control of pregnancy; through its progesterone output it maintains its own existence. We may therefore say that, at about the twelfth week, the luteal phase of gestation changes over to a placental phase.

The Placental Phase

Because of the change in hormonal control, the twelfth week is a rather critical period of pregnancy. If the corpus luteum should degenerate a little too soon and if the placenta should reach full development a little late, then the amount of available progesterone

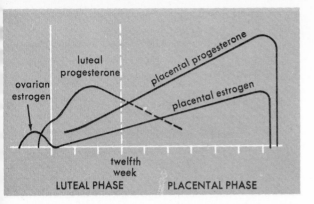

FIG. 26.24 Curves indicating the amounts and the sources of sex hormones present during pregnancy.

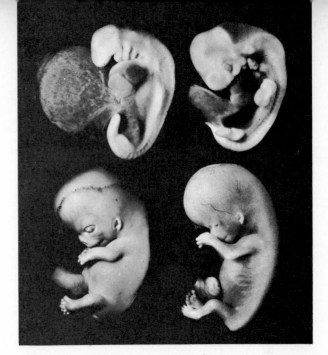

FIG. 26.25 Stages in embryonic development of man. Top left, approximately 25 days after fertilization. Top right, 33 days; bottom left, 6 weeks; bottom right, 8 weeks. (Courtesy of Dr. G. W. Corner and Department of Embryology, Carnegie Institution of Washington.)

during this gap is likely to be inadequate. And in the absence of the hormone, placental tissues could not be maintained. Just as at the end of a menstrual cycle, the uterine lining would disintegrate and the embryo, no longer anchored securely, would be aborted. Miscarriages occur frequently near the end of the third month of pregnancy. Such mishaps due to hormone deficiency can be prevented by injecting some progesterone into the pregnant female.

We may note in passing that sex hormones normally produced by the placenta pass not only into the maternal but also into the embryonic circulation. This has a curious effect; in newborn infants, the genitals and the breast region are often precociously enlarged and swollen, superficially resembling a mature condition. After a short time, however, the sex hormones in the infant are destroyed metabolically without being replaced till puberty and the external effects then disappear.

During the twelfth week of pregnancy in man, it is already amply clear that the developing offspring will be a human being. Basic forms and functions have become elaborated earlier, in surprisingly rapid sequence. For example, 3 weeks after fertilization, the human embryo is about the size of a coarse grain of sand, some three-quarters of it consisting of head structures. It is characteristic of the development of all animals that the head end forms earlier and faster than other regions. Four weeks after fertilization, the eyes are partly developed and the heart is already beating (Fig. 26.25, upper left). Limb buds appear in the fifth week; ears are elaborated at that time; and the embryo now responds to mechanical stimuli by muscular con-

tractions (Fig. 26.25, upper right). Human form is vaguely recognizable 8 weeks after fertilization, when the embryo is about 1 in. long (Fig. 26.25, lower right, and Fig. 26.26). From this stage on, one speaks of a **fetus** rather than an embryo.

By the twelfth week fingers have formed, the semicircular canals in the ears are functional, and the embryo moves of its own accord within its amniotic water pool. Eyelids are still fused, but the eyes may move underneath. Five months after fertilization, the fetus is about 8 in. long, weighs about 1 lb, and the facial features show signs of individual personality. In the ensuing weeks, the breathing machinery develops rapidly. The fetus is now in a perpetual drowsy state, neither sleeping nor waking. Overt body movements are sporadic and uneven, but important facial reflexes are being developed. For example, eyelids open and close and lips purse rhythmically, as if the fetus were learning to suck. But there is some doubt whether these prenatal movements are being "learned," in preparation for the future. In primitive vertebrates, at least, overt movement may be suppressed experimentally, yet upon hatching the animals are fully capable of performing necessary motions.

FIG. 26.26 Photograph of human embryo, about 8 weeks after fertilization, obtained after surgical removal of portions of the reproductive system of female patient. Chorion pushed to one side, revealing the amniotic sac. Note umbilical cord. *(From Fig. 10, "The Embryology of Behavior," by permission of Dr. A. Gesell and Harper & Brothers.)*

In the eighth and ninth months, periods of true wakefulness occur increasingly. Arms and legs are moved frequently and the hands open and close. Body fat is being laid down and the fetus acquires a sturdier stature generally. Growth in size has proceeded apace, and by the end of the ninth month the microscopic fertilized egg has become a whole human being.

With several exceptions, the gestation period of mammals generally is roughly proportional to adult size. For example, the period of pregnancy is 3 weeks in mice and 22 months in elephants. However, pregnancy lasts only a year, approximately, in whales.

BIRTH

In parallel with the growth and development of the fetus the amnion gradually enlarges and the uterus stretches (Fig. 26.27). Also, the mammary glands enlarge markedly during the last months of pregnancy, under the stimulus of the increasing quantities of sex hormones from the placenta. Numerous ducts form in the interior of the glands, and in later stages the milk-secreting cells mature. Flow of secretion starts soon thereafter. However, the first product is not milk but **colostrum,** a watery, lymphlike fluid.

The process of birth normally begins when the chorion and the amnion rupture and when the amniotic fluid escapes to the outside. Labor contractions of the uterine muscles then occur with increasing frequency and strength, pressing against the fetus and pushing it out through the vagina. In these labor contractions, the possible role of hormones produced in the posterior lobe of the pituitary has already been mentioned (Chap. 20). At the time of birth, the interlocked maternal and embryonic tissues which form the placenta loosen away from the wall of the uterus. The mechanical and metabolic connection between mother and offspring is thereby severed.

An important result of this is that CO_2 produced by the offspring must accumulate in his own circulation. Within seconds or minutes, the concentration of the gas then becomes high enough to stimulate the breathing center of the newborn. In correlation with this switchover from placental breathing to lung breathing, several structural changes occur in the heart and in the large blood vessels around the heart. In the fetus before birth, the dividing wall between the right and left auricles is incomplete (Fig. 26.28). A movable flap of tissue provides an opening between these two chambers and blood may pass freely from one chamber into the other. Once lung breathing is initiated at birth, the blood-pressure pattern within the heart changes and

FIG. 26.27 The fetus, within its membranes in the uterus: amnion on the inside, chorion on the outside.

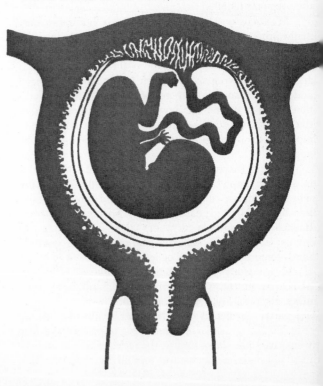

the tissue flap is pressed over the opening interconnecting the auricles. The flap eventually grows into place and the left and right sides of the heart so become separated permanently.

Another structural change involves a fetal blood vessel, the **ductus arteriosus,** which before birth conducts blood from the pulmonary artery to the aorta. In this manner, the ductus arteriosus shunts blood around the nonfunctional lung (see Fig. 26.28). At birth, a specially developed muscle in the ductus arteriosus constricts. This muscle never relaxes thereafter but degenerates into scar tissue. Blood is thus forced to pass through the lungs. The ductus arteriosus as a whole degenerates soon after birth.

The loosened placenta, still connected to the umbilical cord, is expelled to the outside as the *afterbirth* within an hour or so after the offspring is expelled. Mammalian mothers, modern human ones excepted, bite the umbilical cord off their young and carnivorous mothers then often eat the cord and the placenta. The escaped amniotic fluid may also be lapped up and may quench thirst at a time when need for water may be great but locomotion is difficult. Indeed, among carnivorous mammals it is not uncommon that in the course of drinking the fluid and eating the placenta the just-born offspring is swallowed as well.

In the majority of mammals, litter size corresponds roughly to the number of nipples present on the mother's body. For the first few feedings, mammary secretions remain lymphlike, as before birth. This fluid has some laxative action, clearing the infant's alimentary tract of debris and mucus accumulated during uterine development. Milk begins to be produced soon, however. Production continues as long as *lactogenic* hormones are manufactured by the pituitary and as long as milk is not allowed to accumulate in the glands. The females of certain primitive human tribes in northern Australia have been reported to produce milk for sometimes up to 6 years after a pregnancy. Cows milked after a pregnancy may "dry up" after a year or so. Incidentally, contrary to surprisingly wide belief among urban people, cows do not give milk at just any time; they must have been pregnant first.

Even though the source of progesterone is removed with the expulsion of the placenta, normal menstrual cycles in man are generally not resumed as long as nursing continues. The manufacture of lactogenic hormones by the pituitary apparently inhibits FSH production. But once the offspring is weaned, FSH is formed again in quantity and a new ovarian

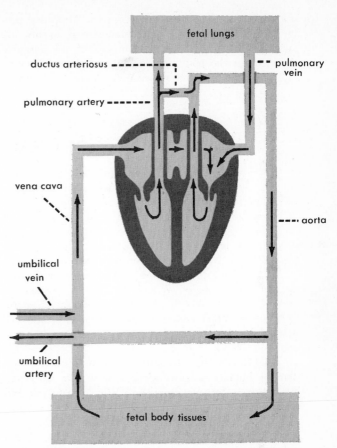

FIG. 26.28 The fetal circulation, diagrammatic. Note that the fetal lung is nonfunctional in breathing and that most of the blood flowing through the pulmonary artery is shunted through the ductus arteriosus directly into the aorta. Oxygenation of blood occurs in the placenta; hence the umbilical artery carries venous blood to the placenta, and the umbilical vein carries arterial blood to the vena cava. Note the opening between the right and left auricles, permitting blood to pass directly from the right to the left side of the heart. Compare with the adult circulation, Fig. 21.12.

follicle then begins to mature. After a few months of establishing new hormone balances, the reproductive machinery of the female reverts to rhythmic nonpregnancy operation.

The reproductive period of human females comes to a close in middle age, at the time of **menopause.** For ill-understood reasons, the sex-hormone control system ceases to operate, estrogen manufacture declines rapidly, and the reproductive system atrophies progressively during later life. Menopausal events are attended by profound readjustments of all hormone balances in the body, hence by more or less incisive upsets of mental and physical functions. Menopause may occur rather abruptly. In such cases, the effects may be eased by injection of estrogen in slowly decreasing doses. In males, processes equivalent to menopause may occur in old age or may not occur at all.

REVIEW QUESTIONS

1. What are the first and second polar bodies? Are they found in males as well as females? Explain. What is the general structure of a mature sperm and of a mature egg? In which animals is fertilization (a) external, (b) internal? Define oviparity, ovoviviparity, viviparity. In which vertebrates does each occur?

2. Review the structure of the reproductive system of human males. Where, specifically, are sperms produced? Describe the hormonal controls of sperm production. What is semen? Describe the relation of testis location and breeding season in different mammals.

3. Review the structure of the reproductive system of human females. Specifically where, and from what tissues, are eggs produced? What is a follicle and what is its structure?

4. Describe the hormonal controls and the process of follicle growth up to the time of ovulation. What events take place during ovulation? After ovulation, what happens to (a) the egg and (b) the follicle?

5. Describe the hormonal controls and the events in the uterus up to the time of menstruation. What happens during menstruation? Review the entire menstrual cycle from the standpoint of (a) hormonal control, (b) events in the ovary, and (c) events in the uterus.

6. If fertilization occurs, what hormonal events (a) prevent menstruation and new menstrual cycles and (b) promote the further development of the uterus? Describe the hormonal controls during (a) the luteal phase and (b) the placental phase of pregnancy.

7. Distinguish between fertilization and activation of an egg. Where and when does fertilization occur? What is parthenogenesis? What happens to an egg (a) after fertilization and (b) after it arrives in the uterus?

8. Describe the location and function of the extraembryonic membranes in (a) reptiles and birds and (b) mammals. In which vertebrates and how is a placenta formed? What are the functions of a placenta?

9. Review the structure of the human placenta, with attention to embryonic and maternal blood circulation through it. Describe the whole pathway of the embryonic circulation. What is a fetus?

10. Review the changes in the fetal circulation at birth. What events in the uterus result in birth of offspring? How is milk production initiated and maintained? What is colostrum?

SUGGESTED COLLATERAL READINGS

Additional background information on most of the topics dealt with in this chapter may be found in the following, largely popularly written accounts.

Bishop, D. W.: Sperm Maturescence, *Sci. Monthly,* vol. 80, 1955.
Bullough, W. S.: "Hormones and Reproduction," Methuen, London, 1952.

Corner, G. W.: "The Hormones in Human Reproduction," Princeton University Press, Princeton, N.J., 1942.
————: "Ourselves Unborn," Yale University Press, New Haven, Conn., 1944.
Csapo, A.: Progesterone, *Sci. American,* vol. 198, 1958.
Farris, E. J.: Male Fertility, *Sci. American,* vol. 182, 1950.

Gray, G. W.: Human Growth, *Sci. American,* vol. 189, 1953.

Loeb, J.: On the Nature of the Process of Fertilization, and the Artificial Production of Normal Larvae from the Unfertilized Eggs of the Sea Urchin, in M. L. Gabriel and S. Fogel, "Great Experiments in Biology," Prentice-Hall, Englewood Cliffs, N.J., 1955.

Milne, L. J., and M. J. Milne: Animal Courtship, *Sci. American,* vol. 183, 1950.

——— and ———: "The Mating Instinct," Little, Brown, Boston, 1954.

Monroy, A.: Fertilization of the Egg, *Sci. American,* vol. 183, 1950.

Patten, B. M.: The First Heart Beats and the Beginning of the Embryonic Circulation, *Am. Scientist,* vol. 39, 1951.

Pincus, G.: Fertilization in Mammals, *Sci. American,* vol. 184, 1951.

Reynolds, S. R. M.: The Umbilical Cord, *Sci. American,* vol. 187, 1952.

———: Circulatory Adaptations to Birth, *Sci. Monthly,* vol. 77, 1953.

Stone, A.: The Control of Fertility, *Sci. American,* vol. 190, 1954.

Tinbergen, N.: The Courtship of Animals, *Sci. American,* vol. 191, 1954.

Tyler, A.: Fertilization and Antibodies, *Sci. American,* vol. 190, 1954.

Van Beneden, E.: Researches on the Maturation of the Egg and Fertilization, in M. L. Gabriel and S. Fogel, "Great Experiments in Biology," Prentice-Hall, Englewood Cliffs, N.J., 1955.

DEVELOPMENT

27

"Living" implies turnover: continuous breakdown and destruction counter-balanced by continuous synthesis and construction. Through turnover, living matter acquires a *history*. And history, or change with time, is the essence of development.

Development is one of the three universal dimensions of living matter. The other two are structure and function. Living matter can be described completely by describing its structure, its function, and its development. In this chapter we shall first outline what has been learned about the general **nature** of development and shall then discuss actual **processes** of development in specific organisms, protist, plant, and animal.

THE NATURE OF DEVELOPMENT

The universal scope of development implies that any type of change, occurring on any level of living organization and at any time in living history, should have developmental significance. This is so.

Developmental changes can be structural or functional, quantitative or qualitative, progressive or regressive, normal or abnormal. Actually, as we shall see, development always involves all these simultaneously. But in given instances, one or the other form of change may predominate or may be more readily apparent to the observer. Development is universal too with respect to the living unit in which change takes place and with respect to time. A molecule develops no less than a cell or a tissue, a whole organism no less than a whole species. And whether we measure it in microseconds as on the molecular level or in millions of years as on the species level, development occurs at every moment in living history. The developmental domain, clearly, is as extended as that of biology as a whole. However, developmental studies traditionally have concentrated most on the particular events which relate to the formation of *organisms* and of their parts.

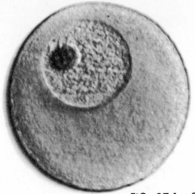

FIG. 27.1   Single egg cells, such as shown on the left, transform through development into plant and animal adults, such as shown next to the egg. Explaining and understanding transformations of this kind are the key objectives of developmental studies. *(Guinea pig, Carolina Biological Supply Co.; others, General Biological Supply House, Inc.)*

We are already familiar with the three ways in which new organisms can arise: by vegetative means, from spores or sporelike cells, and from zygotes. Therefore, the maximum problem of developmental studies is to explain how single cells are transformed into whole multicellular organisms (Fig. 27.1). A simple answer here would be "by cell division." This is not incorrect, to be sure, but the answer is not very informative either. The real issues are far more subtle and far more complicated. Now we shall dissect these issues into their basic components.

MORPHOGENESIS

If the problem is to transform single cells into whole organisms, then a first obvious developmental requirement is increase in size, or **growth.** Overall growth may occur by either or all of three types of changes. Structural parts may increase in *number*, they may increase in *size*, or the *spaces* between the parts may enlarge.

Singly and in combination, these alternatives actually occur at every level of the living organization. We already know, for example, that molecules increase in number either by being accumulated ready-made from the environment or by being newly synthesized within cells, that they increase in size by combining with other molecules, and that they increase in spatial distribution by dilution with water. Together, these ways of molecular growth constitute the means by which the size of cells increases. The number of cells increases by division, and the spacing increases by the accumulation between cells of water, cementing substance, or other secreted deposits. These ways of cellular growth in turn bring about increase in the size, the number, and the spacing of tissues and organs. The net result is overall growth of the organism. Note, however, that molecular growth is the fundamental prerequisite: the living system grows from its molecules up.

Growth introduces qualitative as well as quantitative changes. For example, certain types of molecules may be synthesized or accumulated at a greater rate or in greater amount than others. Indeed, some molecular types may disappear altogether, whereas others, not previously present, may appear for the first time. Similarly, the growth of cells, of tissues, or of organs may take place disproportionately in different parts of the developing organism. As a result of such **differential growth,** the structure and composition of the organism may be altered not only quantitatively but also qualitatively (Fig. 27.2).

Moreover, growth does not proceed randomly in all directions. How does it happen, for example, that developmental growth stops just when the nose, the brain, the rootlet, the leaflet, and all other body parts are of the "right" proportional size and the "right" proportional shape? How does it happen that the different parts of the fully grown adult *retain* correct proportions and shapes? And how does it happen that, when the limb of a salamander is cut off, regenerative growth stops just when the newly developing limb has the size and the shape of the original one? In short, what deter-

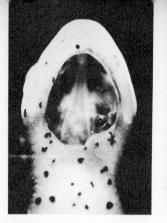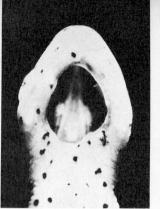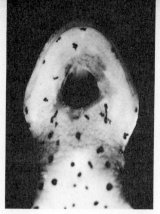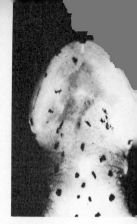

FIG. 27.2 Differential growth. The floor of the mouth of this salamander has been cut out (left). The photos show successive stages in the regeneration of a new floor. Evidently, the regenerating tissues grow faster than the rest of the animal. Unequal growth of this sort is termed "differential growth." *(Courtesy of Dr. R. J. Goss and M. W. Stagg, J. Exptl. Zool., vol. 137, 1958, p. 9.)*

mines the **form** of an organism, with respect to both size of parts and geometrical configuration of parts? Evidently, development of form, in addition to growth as such, is a second requirement if a reproductive unit is to be converted into a whole organism.

At any level of living organization, the basic aspects of form are **polarity** and **symmetry.** If *they* are given, a great deal about the general appearance of an object is already specified. The polarity of a structure indicates its orientation with reference to the three axes of space. A structure is polarized if one axis is in some way dominant. For example, the head-tail axis in most animals is longer than the other two. This axis is the principal guide line around which the whole animal is organized, and such organisms are said to be polarized longitudinally. Symmetry indicates the degree of mirror-image regularity. A structure may be symmetrical in three, two, one, or in no dimensions; i.e., it may be **spherical, radial, bilateral,** or **asymmetrical** (Fig. 27.3).

Each organism exhibits a certain polarity and a certain symmetry. Polarity and symmetry are the first and most permanent expressions of living form. Invariably, the earliest definitive features to appear during the development of any plant or animal are its polarity and its symmetry. Many features of an organism can be changed by experimental means, but its original polarity and symmetry can hardly ever be changed. Millions of years later, long after the organism has become a fossil, polarity and symmetry may still be recognizable even if all other signs of form have disappeared. It is a fairly general principle of development that the earlier a particular feature appears, the later it disappears.

Form is first blocked out in the rough, through establishment of polarity and symmetry, and then it becomes progressively more refined in regional detail. Whereas an organism *grows* from the molecule up, it *forms* from gross shape down. For example, the organ system is delineated ahead of its component organs. The tissue acquires definitive shape in advance of its component cells. And the molecules of the organism are last to assume final form. In the living system, evidently, form develops as in a sculpture, from the coarse to the fine, from the general to the specific. In both instances, this may be the only feasible way to ensure that the small remains appropriately subordinated to the large, structurally as well as functionally.

Specifically, establishment of form requires that cellular aggregates be molded into various configurations. Cells must become arranged and rearranged to produce regional enlargements and diminutions, to transform compact masses into sheets and vice versa, to produce channels, openings, cavities, and the like. Two general types of processes bring about such changes: **directed differential growth** and **form-regulating movements.** As a result of these two processes, an organism and its parts acquire not only particular polarities and symmetries but also particular detailed shapes.

For example, if differential growth proceeds differently in different parts of a developing system, so that the amount and rate of growth vary for different directions of space, then regional enlargements and diminutions will be produced. Local elongations, thickenings, overgrowths, altered contours, layers, and other new shapes can arise in this manner. Also, a solid mass can become hollow if the outer layers of the mass grow faster than the core. And a hollow structure can become solid if the inner layers of the rind grow faster than the outside. Directed differential growth of this sort can be effective at every level of developmental organization.

Form-regulating movements involve shifts and migrations of growing parts relative to one another. Directed migrations of parts can result in the piling up of material in one region and in attenuation in others. Sheets or compact masses can slide over one another, can fuse together, or can separate. Compact masses can spread out and become sheets or loose aggregations, or aggregations can condense and form larger masses. Sheets may fold and form ducts or cavities, and compact masses may undergo internal redistribution of parts and assume any number of shapes. Clearly, with material as plastic and malleable as living matter and with a built-in mechanism of moving parts, an infinite array of forms can be produced. Add directed growth to directed movements and a sufficient machinery is available to translate the form of the reproductive unit into the specific form of the adult.

Form, growth, and all their qualitative and quantitative expressions together determine the architectural design of living matter. This architectural aspect of development is called **morphogenesis**. It is the first major component of the developmental process.

DIFFERENTIATION

A living system develops not only architecturally but also operationally. Thus, growth of a zygote produces not simply an aggregate of many identical cells, but an aggregate of *mutually different cells*. In an animal, for example, some become nerve cells, some liver cells, some skin cells, etc. How does a reproductive unit

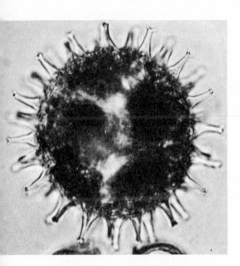

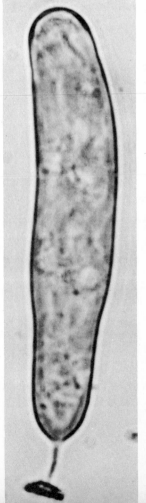

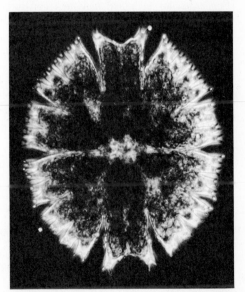

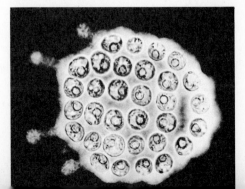

FIG. 27.3 The symmetries of organisms, illustrated through Protista. Top left, spherical. Middle, radial. Top right, bilateral. Bottom right, asymmetrical. *(Top left and bottom right, courtesy of Dr. R. C. Starr, Indiana University; middle and top right, courtesy of Dr. M. S. Fuller, Brown University.)*

give rise to a multitude of differently specialized cells? Cell division as such certainly does not alter the characteristics of a cell. As already noted, daughter cells inherit the same set of genes and the same kinds of cellular components generally as are present in a mother cell. Cell division does copy faithfully and a dividing reproductive cell therefore *should* give rise to many identical cells. Yet it does not; cell characteristics do change radically during development (Fig. 27.4).

Such inconstancy holds for every other organizational level as well. Molecules, tissues, organs, whole organisms, all change their operational characteristics in the course of time. The changes are often in the direction of progressively greater operational novelty, but they may also be in the direction of regressively less operational novelty. As a result, every living unit possesses structures and carries out functions which are not yet in existence at earlier developmental stages and which may no longer be in existence at later stages. For example, an apical meristem cell today may be a photosynthetic cortex cell tomorrow; a cortex cell today may be a suberized cork cell tomorrow. A mature organism reproduces, but the senile organism no longer can.

Such dramatic changes of operational potential are brought about by the second and perhaps the most important major component of the developmental process, namely, by **differentiation.** A developing system need not necessarily grow and it need not necessarily change form, but by the very meaning of development, it must differentiate. Through differentiation, living units become *specialized* in various ways. It is sometimes useful to distinguish between "chemodifferentiation," "cytodifferentiation," "histodifferentiation," "organ differentiation," etc., according to the level of organization at which operational change takes place.

The basis of differentiation, as of any living process, is *interaction*. In most interactions of living parts with one another or with their physical environment, the operational potentialities of the system are not altered lastingly. But in some cases they are, and then the result is differentiation. For example, if some of the many interactions among molecules lead to the continuing production of novel categories of molecules, then these interactions contribute to chemodifferentiation. Or if a cell produces a hormone which, on reaching a second cell, causes that second cell to ma-

FIG. 27.4   Differentiation. In the cross section through an onion root on the left, the tissues are not yet differentiated. In the section on the right, taken farther back from the root apex, tissue differentiation has already occurred. *(Courtesy of Dr. W. A. Jensen, University of California, Berkeley.)*

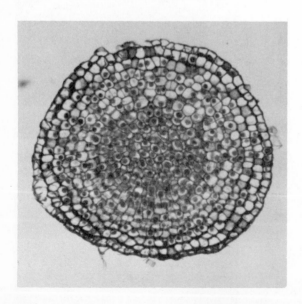
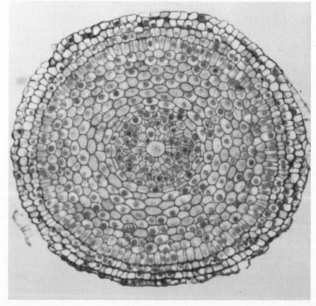

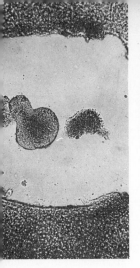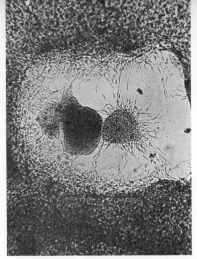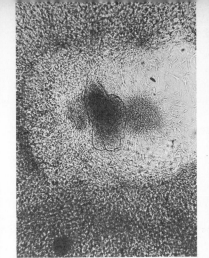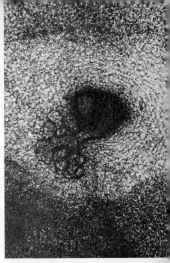

FIG. 27.5 Differentiation by interaction. Development of salivary gland of mouse in tissue culture. One piece of undifferentiated salivary ectoderm and two pieces of undifferentiated salivary mesoderm from a mouse embryo were put together into a culture (first photo). These pieces grew and interacted (second and third photos) and eventually differentiated into secretion pockets and ducts characteristic of normal salivary glands (fourth photo). *(Courtesy of Dr. C. Grobstein, Stanford University, and 13th Growth Symposium, Princeton University Press, 1954.)*

...ure, to become abnormal, or to change operationally in some other lasting way, then this is an instance of cytodifferentiation. Or again, if in response to a persisting climatic change, organisms transform into new types able to withstand the altered conditions, then this is a case of organismic differentiation, otherwise known as evolution (Fig. 27.5).

In short, to be differentiation, operational changes must have a certain degree of permanence. We may make an animal vitamin-deficient, for example, and many of its cells will then behave differently. But if we now add the missing vitamin to the diet, normal cellular operations will probably be resumed very promptly. Here cellular capacities have not been changed in any fundamental way. Only their expression has changed temporarily, in response to particular conditions. Such easily alterable, transient, reversible changes are spoken of as **modulations.** The concept of differentiation, on the contrary, implies a more or less fundamental, relatively lasting alteration of operational potentials. A vitamin-deficient cell which, after addition of the missing vitamin, *maintained* its altered characteristics would have differentiated (Fig. 27.6).

How does differentiation come about? On the organismic level, the process is understood comparatively well, and we shall discuss it in detail in the chapters on evolution. However, differentiation on the molecular and cellular levels is not fully understood as yet. Three general possibilities exist.

First, cell differentiation might be a result of progressive changes in gene action. Genes themselves probably do not change during development, for, as already noted, their stability is an essential requirement for the preservation of species characteristics. But the *activity* of different genes could vary with time. For example, in a given cell some genes might become active at certain developmental stages, whereas others might become inactive. Such differential activity pat-

FIG. 27.6 Differentiation versus modulation. In differentiation, the developmental change is permanent; in modulation, it is not.

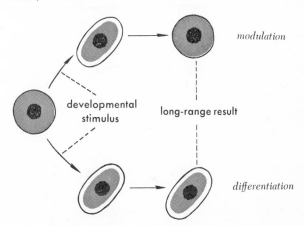

terns might occur differently in different cells and this might contribute to differentiation.

Or, second, gene actions might remain the same, but the operations of the cytoplasm could become altered progressively. For example, one round of cytoplasmic reactions might use up a certain set of starting materials, and in the subsequent absence of these, similar reactions could then no longer take place. A next round of reactions would proceed with different starting materials and would therefore produce different endproducts. The net result could be progressive differentiation.

Or, third, nuclear and cytoplasmic changes might both occur, in reciprocal fashion. This is probably the likeliest possibility, and much current research is devoted to a study of this very complex key problem.

Like growth, differentiation occurs from the molecule up. Just as a house cannot be any more serviceable than its component rooms will permit, so also the operational capacities of any living level are based on the capacities of subordinated levels. Chemodifferentiation therefore is the key to all differentiation. It is this which makes the problem of understanding so enormous. For if the process of differentiation is as complex as the totality of molecular interactions in cells, then it cannot be any less complex than the very process of life itself.

METABOLISM

Morphogenesis and differentiation are two of the forces which drive development processes. A third is *metabolism*. To be sure, metabolism is not a uniquely developmental requirement, but there could be no growth, no establishment of form, no differentiation, if energy were not available and if molecular syntheses did not occur. On the other hand, there could be no metabolism if morphogenesis and differentiation did not develop it.

Rates of metabolism are correlated with rates of development. At no point in the life cycle of any living unit is metabolism more intensive and development more rapid than during the earliest stages. Both then decline in rate, until the zero point is reached at death; the metabolic clock is wound only once, at the beginning.

This circumstance introduces a number of major problems. Early in development, just when metabolic fires burn most fiercely, well-developed means of nutrition are not yet in existence. Neither the zygote nor the spore nor in many cases the regenerating fragment possesses a functioning food-procuring machinery. Three general solutions of this dilemma are possible; all three occur. First, enough food may be packed into the reproductive unit to last till it differentiates a functioning nutritional apparatus of its own. The endosperm-filled seed of plants and the yolk-filled egg of animals are the best examples. Or, second, the developing unit may be fed more or less continuously by the parent, via a persisting functional connection between the two. This is well illustrated by the parasitic sporophytes of bryophytes, the parasitic gametophytes of seed plants, and the placental mechanism of most mammals.

A third solution is frequently necessary in vegetative regeneration, when injury has put the nutritional apparatus out of commission and reserve food sources are not available. Under such conditions, the regenerating unit may be able to draw foods from its own structural framework. One result of such partial self-destruction is decrease in size, or *degrowth*. Another is the mobilization of enough raw materials for effective redevelopment on a smaller scale. Mouthless fragments of many animals may degrow and regenerate with the foods so obtained (Fig. 27.7).

With fuel supplies assured, respiration and synthesis become possible. But initial dilemmas must be resolved here as well. Intensive respiration requires oxygen and reproductive cells must exchange gases through their cell surfaces. But this requirement limits the size of a reproductive cell, for diffusion alone could not be effective in too large a cellular mass. The requirement of smallness, however, limits the amount of food that can be stored in the reproductive cell, and this in turn places a time limit on the amount of development possible. Clearly, the developmental consequences of so "simple" a requirement as oxygen supply are quite far-reaching.

Once gas-supply problems are solved, respiration may proceed. The molecular equipment for energy production is inherited complete by all reproductive units and is more or less fully functional from the start. This is an absolute necessity for survival. But such is not the case for cellular syntheses; only relatively few kinds of synthetic reactions are possible initially. Most of the molecular equipment required for intricate development syntheses must itself first develop. Endproducts of a first round of synthesis must become the starting materials for a second, more complex round. In this manner, synthetic capacities must be increased and

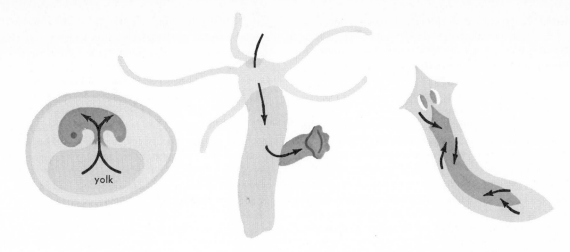

THE FOOD-RICH EGG   THE FEEDING PARENT   DEGROWTH

FIG. 27.7 The three principal forms of nutrition in developing systems. Diagram, inclusion of food in the embryo (as in yolky animal egg); attachment of embryo to parent, and embryo nourished by parent (as in hydra buds); degrowth, i.e., food obtained by partial breakdown of body (as in planarians). Photos, food-laden eggs and endosperm-filled seeds in plants. (Photos courtesy of Dr. M. S. Fuller, Brown University.)

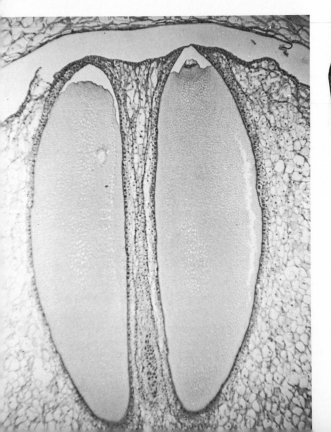

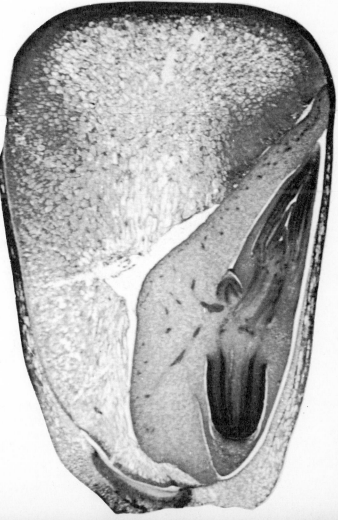

broadened progressively. Evidently synthesis metabolism is as much a *result* of development as it is a prerequisite; it is one aspect of chemodifferentiation.

Morphogenesis, differentiation, and metabolism are three of the universal components of every developmental process. It should be stressed that the boundaries between these three are not at all sharp. Any one of them grades into and overlaps with each of the other two. Architectural development cannot be achieved without operational development. The nature of the operations in turn determines the design of the architecture. But operations and architecture together depend on and at the same time make possible metabolic development. Any one part of the developmental process thus can be regarded as "merely" a phase of any other. The point is that development is a unified, four-dimensional space-time continuum of events. While the human observer may for purposes of analysis dissect from this continuum any number of parts, such parts are selected quite arbitrarily for human convenience. Development as it actually occurs in nature knows nothing of them.

CONTROL

How does a reproductive unit happen to give rise to just the right kinds and right numbers of parts? For example, how does the zygote of a seed plant produce just one stem apex and one root apex, not two stem apices at opposite ends or, alternatively, two root apices at opposite ends? Later, in the mature plant, if the stem apex is cut off, a node lower down develops a new apex: not a root-forming apex but a stem-forming one. Yet if that same node, together with the stem system above it, is cut off and put into soil, the node now will form a new root apex, not a stem apex. In another example, if the head of an earthworm is cut off, the worm develops a new head: not two or three heads or half a head, but one and only one; and not another tail, but another head. Even more strikingly, a single animal zygote does not yet possess any of the features of the adult. How then does it happen to produce just one head and one tail, not two or more of each, but in a man, for example, two arms and two legs, not one of each? And why arms and legs at all— why not wings or fins?

Considerations such as these bring us to the most puzzling of all aspects of development. What integrates development? How do morphogenesis, differentiation, and metabolism mesh together to produce an elegant,

sensibly functioning whole? By any standard, this smooth, seemingly unerring directedness and this persistent, concerted advancing toward *wholeness* is probably the most dramatic and most remarkable property of development. The headless earthworm, for example, never ceases its quiet internal revolution till it has a new head. The armless salamander never halts the violent shuffling of its molecules until the last finger is again in place. The transfigurations of the egg or the spore do not stop before the adult whole has come into being. Evidently, the healthy developing system behaves as if it "knew" its objectives precisely and it proceeds without apparent trial and error. For normally there is no underdevelopment, no overdevelopment, and there are no probing excursions along the way. Development is *directed* straight toward wholeness (Fig. 27.8).

Only one conclusion can be drawn: the course of development must somehow be rigorously *controlled*. Such control represents a fourth major component of every developmental process. However, recognition of the occurrence of control does not of itself provide an explanation of it. We know in general terms that the control systems must reside within a developing unit itself and that, like any other living process, development must be self-controlling. But the nature and operations of these built-in control systems have in most cases not yet been identified. Today it is fashionable to say that genes control development, as they control every other living process. This is unquestionably correct. But again such an answer is not very informative and is actually little more than a restatement of the problem. *How* do genes control development? More specifically, how does a particular gene, through control over a particular enzyme or other protein, regulate a particular developmental occurrence? Answers to such small problems are just beginning to be obtained. The collective larger issue, i.e., the controlled, directed emergence of wholeness in an entire organism, remains a matter of future research. In the following sections, we shall examine how some of the actual small-scale problems of development have been analyzed experimentally.

CELLULAR DEVELOPMENT

As noted, development takes place at all levels of the living organization. The broad issue to be answered is roughly the same for each level: how do the internal

FIG. 27.8 Both arms of this salamander larva were amputated, one above and one below the elbow. From left to right, this sequence of photos shows the degree of regeneration attained after 1, 14, 22, and 31 days, respectively. The problem of development, in this or any other living unit: how is wholeness established, how does a living unit "know" when it is or is not whole, and in the latter case, how does it "know" what its particular pattern of wholeness must be? (*Courtesy of Dr. Charles Thornton, Kenyon College.*)

structural and functional components interact with one another and with the external environment and how do such interactions produce given developmental changes? If we apply this general question to the level of the cell, we may readily formulate two specific problems. What are the relative contributions of the nucleus and the cytoplasm to the morphogenesis and differentiation of a whole cell? And if several whole cells develop together, how if at all do the cells interact and how does such interaction affect the developmental result? A few of the ways in which answers have been sought will be outlined now.

NUCLEUS AND CYTOPLASM

Acetabularia

One of the most elegant studies of the roles of the nucleus and the cytoplasm in cellular development has been carried out on the coccoid green alga *Acetabularia*. As shown in Chap. 9, this unicellular marine protist is large (1 to 3 in. in height) and consists of a rhizoidal base, a stalk with a single basal nucleus, and a terminal cap. In one species, *A. mediterranea* (*med*), the cap is umbrellalike; it is composed of closely joined fingerlike outgrowths which radiate away from the tip of the stalk. In another species, *A. crenulata* (*cren*), the cap contains fewer fingerlike outgrowths and these project outward freely (Fig. 27.9).

In either species, a new stalk and cap may regenerate if the original upper parts of the cell are cut

away. Suppose that a nucleated *med* base is prepared and onto it is grafted a piece of *cren* stalk without nucleus. Will the regenerating cap be of a *med* or a *cren* type? The experimental answer is clear: the newly developing cap is of the *med* type. The result of the reverse experiment is analogous. That is, if to a nucleated *cren* base is grafted an enucleated piece of *med* stalk, then the new cap formed will be of the *cren* type.

FIG. 27.9 The gross structure of two species of *Acetabularia*.

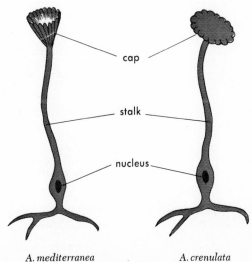

A. mediterranea   A. crenulata

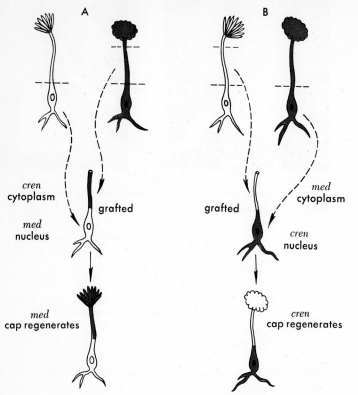

FIG. 27.10 Grafting experiments with two species of *Acetabularia* to show nuclear control of cytoplasmic development. *A* and *B* illustrate reciprocal graft series.

In other words, morphogenesis of the cap is always i line with the nature of the nucleus, regardless of th nature of the cytoplasm (Fig. 27.10).

Other kinds of experiments reinforce this conclu sion. For example, if a nucleated *med* base is grafte to a nucleated *cren* base, then a single stalk grows ov near the graft area of this binucleate combination. Th stalk eventually regenerates a new cap and the charac teristics of the cap are intermediate between a pure *med* and a purely *cren* type of cap. Evidently, bot nuclei control cap development here and the cap e hibits mixed features as a result. If three nucleate bases are grafted together, then the single new ca formed again follows the predominant nuclear typ For example, if two nuclei are *cren* and one is *med* then the cap will be of the *cren* type. But if one nucleu is *cren* and the other two are *med*, then the cap wi be of the *med* type. It is quite clear, therefore, that ca development is under nuclear—hence presumabl genic—control. Moreover, a given nucleus directs th cytoplasm not simply to develop a cap; it directs deve opment of a cap of a particular structural type. Thu nuclear control is species-specific (Fig. 27.11).

However, it can be shown that the nuclear effec on cytoplasmic development is not direct. If an enucle ated piece of stalk is isolated and maintained independ ently, then a new cap may still regenerate on this piec even though a nucleus is now not present. This prob ably indicates that, in an intact alga, the nucleu secretes certain "morphogenetic substances" into th cytoplasm and these substances, as they accumulate then control cap development. Even if the nucleus i

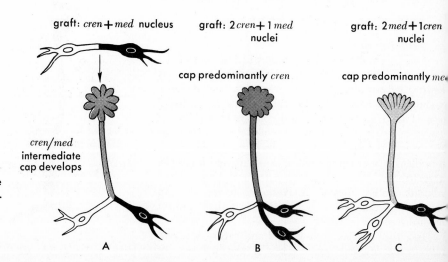

FIG. 27.11 Double and triple grafts with two species of *Acetabularia*.

emoved, therefore, cap formation may still occur so ong as the morphogenetic substances persist in the ytoplasm. Nuclear control evidently is indirect and ong-range. The nature of the postulated morphogenetic ubstances is so far unknown; they may conceivably nclude RNA (Fig. 27.12).

It can also be shown that just as the nucleus con-rols cap development, so the cap controls nuclear development. In a mature intact alga, the nucleus ooner or later divides repeatedly and the resulting uclei are then carried by cytoplasmic streaming into he cap. Gametes are subsequently formed in the cap. t can be demonstrated readily that if the cap of a nature plant is cut off, nuclear division is suppressed. Division will remain suppressed until a new cap has developed. Moreover, one may prepare a capless nucle-ated base of a young immature alga and one may graft o it an enucleated stalk and cap of an old mature alga. n the original young alga, nuclear division would nor-

mally not have occurred for two months or more. But with the mature cap now grafted on, nuclear division occurs within two weeks. It is clear that the mature cap induces premature nuclear division. It may be concluded, therefore, that the cap controls nuclear division. To state this case in a different manner, the cytoplasm has control over the development of the nucleus (see Fig. 27.12).

The results obtained from experiments on *Acetabularia* have provided a model applicable to developmental processes in cells generally. That is, numerous investigations on cells from a large variety of organisms, protist, plant, and animal, have shown fairly conclusively (1) that cellular morphogenesis and differentiation are under basic nuclear control, (2) that the nucleus acts via products released into the cytoplasm, and (3) that developmental processes in the cytoplasm act back on the nucleus and control its development in turn. Thus, cyclical interactions between nucleus and

FIG. 27.12   *A*, experiment suggesting the release of morphogenetic substances from the nucleus in the control of cytoplasmic development. *B, C, D*, experiments illustrating the role of the cytoplasm in controlling nuclear events.

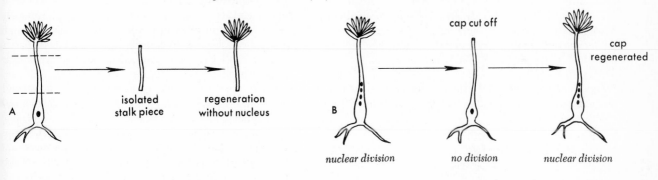

A   isolated stalk piece   regeneration without nucleus

B   *nuclear division*   cap cut off   *no division*   cap regenerated   *nuclear division*

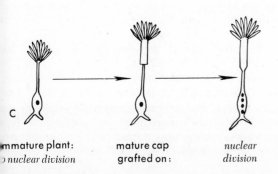

C   immature plant: no nuclear division   mature cap grafted on: *nuclear division*

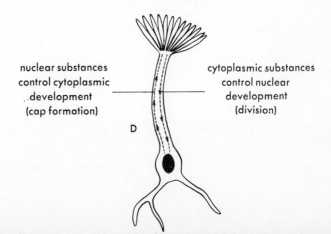

D   nuclear substances control cytoplasmic development (cap formation)   cytoplasmic substances control nuclear development (division)

cytoplasm must be envisaged to underlie any developmental event (as also any metabolic event) in a cell.

Does nuclear control here actually mean gene control? Probably yes, as the following experiments suggest.

Paramecium

If paramecia are injected into the bloodstream of a rabbit, the surface proteins of the paramecia, particularly the proteins of the cilia, will act as antigens; the rabbit will manufacture specific antibodies against the ciliary proteins. If then rabbit blood serum containing such antibodies is placed into a dish in which the same kinds of paramecia are growing, the specific antibodies will become attached to the cilia of the paramecia. As a result, the cilia will stick to one another and the paramecia will become immobilized (Fig. 27.13).

By such means, it has been shown that organisms of the species *Paramecium aurelia* may manufacture different ciliary proteins at different times. If we symbolize a series of ciliary proteins as *a, b, c,* etc., then a given paramecium and its immediate descendants may produce protein *a,* for example. But later descendants may manufacture protein *b,* still later ones may form

FIG. 27.13 Antigen-antibody reaction with *Paramecium.* If paramecia are injected into a rabbit, the protozoa will act as antigens against which specific antibodies will be produced in the rabbit. If the rabbit blood serum containing such antibodies is then placed into the original *Paramecium* population, the cilia of the protozoa will be immobilized by the antibodies and the organisms will be unable to move.

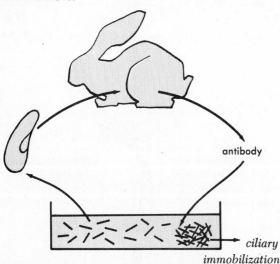

antibody

ciliary immobilization

protein *c,* and so on. In other words, although the cilia are visibly and functionally the same at all times, rabbit tests may show that the proteins composing the cilia do not always remain the same in their molecular structure. We may say that the proteins are of a particular **antigenic type** at a given time but that this antigenic type may change at some later time. Such change clearly represent developmental processes, more specifically, processes of molecular development or chemodifferentiation. What controls the development of a given antigenic type and what controls the change from one type to another?

A first set of experiments has shown that antigenic types are controlled by both the nucleus and the cytoplasm of paramecium. A paramecium known to be able to manufacture only protein *a,* for example, may be mated to another paramecium which is known to be able to produce only the protein *b.* As shown in Chap. 23, mating in these organisms involves nuclear exchange, such that after a mating both partners possess genetically identical nuclei. Thus, when antigenic type *a* mates with antigenic type *b,* the mating results in two paramecia with identical nuclei. It is then found that, despite such genetic identity, the paramecium of type *a* and its descendants *remain* of type *a.* Similarly, the paramecium of type *b* and its descendants remain of type *b.* This result indicates that, inasmuch as the nuclei are alike in both cases, the antigenic types must be controlled by the cytoplasm (Fig. 27.14).

However, it can also be shown that later descendants of the *a* parent may on occasion change to the *b* type. Analogously, descendants of the *b* parent may occasionally change to the *a* type. Evidently, the original mating has endowed *both* mating partners and their respective descendants with the capacity to produce *both* antigenic types. To be sure, this capacity may not become apparent immediately. Nevertheless, since the capacity exists and is a result of mating and since mating means nuclear exchange, nuclear control of antigenic type may be inferred. It may be concluded, therefore, that both the nucleus and the cytoplasm contribute to type control (see Fig. 27.14).

A second set of experiments has shown that changes of antigenic type can be induced at will by alterations of the temperature at which paramecia are grown. For example, organisms raised at 18°C may exhibit type *a,* but if the organisms subsequently are raised at 25°C, their descendants will soon exhibit type *b.* Numerous mating tests carried out between different strains of paramecia raised at various temperatures

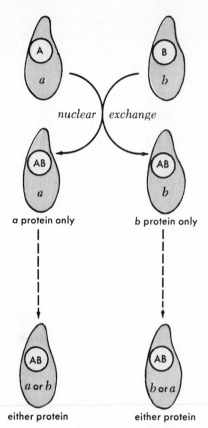

FIG. 27.14 The control of antigenic type in *Paramecium*. One organism containing A genes and a ciliary proteins is mated to another organism containing B genes and b ciliary proteins. After nuclear exchange, both organisms contain identical genes (A, B), yet the ciliary proteins are manufactured as before. This indicates cytoplasmic control of antigenic type. In later generations, however, the offspring of both original mating partners may manufacture either a or b proteins, indicating ultimate nuclear, genetic control of antigenic type.

have yielded the following significant conclusions. First, each antigenic type is under the ultimate control of a specific gene. Any given paramecium possesses an experimentally identifiable series of such genes. Thus if an organism contains the genes A, B, C, and D, it will have the capacity to manufacture antigenic types a, b, c, and d. Second, at any given time only one gene is active and only one antigenic type may actually be exhibited. If gene A is active, the antigenic type a will be manufactured. Later gene A may become inactive

and gene B may become active, in which case the antigenic type will change to b. Third, it can be shown that it is the cytoplasm which determines what specific gene type will be active at any given time. Thus if a paramecium is raised at a given temperature, this environmental condition will affect a (so far unidentified) cytoplasmic control system. The system in turn will then affect the genes in such a way that a particular gene will become activated and all others in the series will become inactivated. A particular antigenic type will then be the result (Fig. 27.15).

The implications of these investigations for developmental processes generally are at least as important as those obtained in the studies on *Acetabularia*. First, the *Paramecium* data show again that cellular development—in this case development of a structural protein—is controlled by both nucleus and cytoplasm. Second, nuclear control is clearly suggested to mean direct gene control. Third, cells appear to be capable of developing several *alternative* states of differentiation. However, only one of the possible states is actually exhibited, and the selection of this state appears to be under the specific control of the cytoplasm. The nucleo-cytoplasmic interaction is therefore cyclical: nuclear genes provide the control apparatus for the development of cytoplasmic traits such as ciliary proteins, but the cytoplasm provides the control apparatus

FIG. 27.15 The temperature selection of gene activity in the control of antigenic types in *Paramecium*. If an organism possesses genes A, B, C, D, then a temperature α will activate gene A selectively, a temperature β will activate gene B selectively, etc. According to which gene is active at any given time, only the corresponding ciliary protein will then be manufactured.

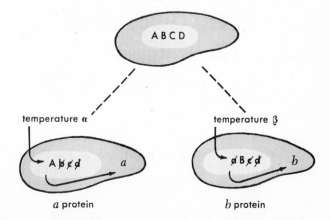

for the effective activation of one of the genes. Fourth, environmental factors are shown to have a decisive influence on the particular course of development a cell will follow.

Entirely analogous conclusions have been obtained from many other kinds of studies on many other kinds of organisms. Like *Acetabularia,* therefore, *Paramecium* provides a broadly applicable model of developmental processes in cells generally.

CELL-CELL INTERACTIONS

Slime Molds

The effect of one cell on the development of another is illustrated most strikingly in the life cycle of the Acrasieae, the cellular slime molds. Much of the pertinent experimental work has been done on the species *Dictyostelium discoideum,* which exhibits a life cycle typical of the Acrasieae generally (see Chap. 9). Spores germinate and form vegetative amoebae. These increase in size by feeding on bacteria and increase in number by cell divisions. When food becomes unavailable, the amoebae cease their independent existence and aggregate together into a pseudoplasmodium, i.e., a united multicellular mass (see Fig. 9.30).

What directs these cells to stream and to stick together and to behave subsequently as a cooperative unit? Experiments show that certain of the amoebae secrete a diffusible substance, **acrasin,** which has a powerful orienting and attracting effect: other amoebae are stimulated to migrate into regions of increasing acrasin concentrations. Since the highest concentrations are in the immediate vicinity of an acrasin-producing cell, all the cells in a population eventually aggregate into a clump around the secreting cells. Acrasin also changes the surface properties of amoebae, making them adhere to one another quite readily. Accordingly, cells which collide during their migration to a common center tend to remain sticking together. A pseudoplasmodium is formed in this manner. It is

still not fully known what factors determine which cell in an amoebal population will become acrasin-producing. However, it is quite clear that such a cell influences the subsequent activity and development of all others.

Once a pseudoplasmodium, or "slug," has formed, it secretes a thin slime sheath over the surface on which it glides. The slug is therefore never in direct contact with the surface itself and the moving organism may somehow gain traction on its own slime track. After a period of moving and feeding, the slug comes to rest and develops into a fruiting body (Fig. 27.16). In this morphogenetic process, the forward tip of the slug turns upward and curves back, into the main mass of its body. The cells of the tip then secrete a cellulose envelope around themselves and become arranged as the base of a hollow stalk. Other amoebae migrate upward on the outside of this stalk and add to its height. The last group of cells flowing up the stalk forms the terminal sporangium (see Chap. 9).

It can be shown that the developmental fates of different amoebae are determined long before construction of a fruiting body actually begins. If, in preliminary experiments, independent vegetative amoebae are fed on red-colored bacteria, a pseudoplasmodium which will be red may be obtained. Similarly, by supplying colorless bacteria to another group of amoebae, the slug they form will be unpigmented. Pieces of two such slugs may now be grafted together. It is found that, in graft combinations of this sort, red-colored cells tend to remain together in one portion of the moving slug and unpigmented cells tend to remain together similarly. The amoebae in a normal pseudoplasmodium therefore appear to intermix relatively little; each maintains largely the same position relative to the other cells in the united population.

The position of a given cell in a slug apparently determines the role of this cell in the development of the fruiting body. If the forward portion of a slug is red-colored, the stalk will be formed by red cells and the terminal sporangium by unpigmented cells. Con

FIG. 27.16 Stages in the formation of a fruiting body in the slime mold *Dictyostelium.*

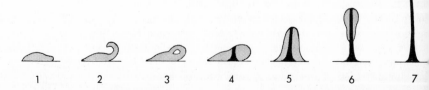

1   2   3   4   5   6   7

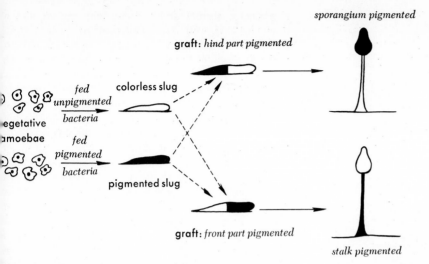

sporangium pigmented

graft: *hind part pigmented*

*fed
unpigmented
bacteria*   colorless slug

)egetative
amoebae

*fed
pigmented
bacteria*

pigmented slug

graft: *front part pigmented*

stalk pigmented

FIG. 27.17 Grafting experiments with *Dictyostelium*.

ersely, if the leading part of a slug is unpigmented, hat part will form stalk and the red trailing part will orm sporangium (Fig. 27.17). Such results suggest that, vhen amoebae aggregate into a pseudoplasmodium, he cells soon differentiate either into stalk-forming or nto spore-forming types, depending on their position vithin the cellular mass. Indeed, several chemical differences between these two cell groups have been discovered. Slime molds therefore demonstrate that cells vhich are originally equal in developmental potential nay differentiate unequally, as a result of their mutual nteraction and their fate-directing effect on one another. This too is a model for a generally applicable principle of cellular development.

Tissue Culture

The technique of tissue culture represents one of he most fruitful means of studying developmental processes within and among cells. In such cultures, pieces of living material—populations of loose cells, compact tissues, and even organs—are isolated from an organism and are grown aseptically in various artificial media to which nutrients and growth factors have been added. One may then observe the developmental behavior of the isolated cells or cell groups, investigate heir changing chemical characteristics, and determine now their development is affected by changes in the composition of the medium. The technique has been applied successfully to both plant and animal material.

Tissue culture studies have shown, for example, hat undeveloped embryonic cells differentiate chemically well before their microscopically visible structure

becomes differentiated. At an early stage, all cells of an embryo are microscopically quite alike. But during this time their future specializations become marked out on the molecular level. For example, at a time when the future heart region of a chicken embryo is still unrecognizable on the basis of cell structure, i.e., when distinct heart muscle is not yet present, the region already contains a unique kind of myosin, a muscle protein characteristic of the heart. Analogous findings have been obtained in experiments on plants. For example, well before embryonic root tissues of onions are distinguishable microscopically as epidermis, cortex, xylem, and phloem, the later fates of these undeveloped tissues are already foreshadowed by characteristic chemodifferentiations. The general conclusion appears warranted that cells develop first on the molecular level and only later on the microscopic level.

Moreover, tissue culture work has demonstrated convincingly that soon after cells have developed on the chemical level they behave as if they already "knew" what tissues they are to form. For example, undeveloped tissue taken from a future cartilage region of an embryo may be treated in such a way that the tissue becomes disaggregated into a population of loose cells. These cells may then be grown in tissue culture. Before long, the cells are found to migrate toward one another and to form a compact tissue again. This tissue soon differentiates as cartilage. Analogously, one may treat undeveloped tissue from a future kidney region so that the cells no longer adhere to one another. Placed into culture, the loose cells of such a population similarly migrate into a compact mass and the latter

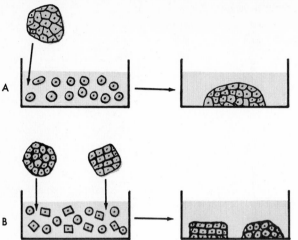

FIG. 27.18 If a compact tissue such as embryonic cartilage is disaggregated and the loose cells are grown in a
culture medium, then the cells tend to migrate together
and reaggregate into compact cartilage tissue (A). If two
tissues such as embryonic cartilage and kidney are disaggregated and the loose cells are mixed and grown in
the same culture medium, then the cells will correspondingly tend to reaggregate into two separate tissue
masses (B).

eventually differentiates as kidney tissue. Populations
of both types of loose cells may now be mixed and may
be grown together in the same culture dish. If this is
done, it is found that the mixed cells appear to become
"unscrambled" and that they migrate to form *two* compact masses. One of these later differentiates as cartilage, the other as kidney tissue. It may be concluded
that cells in which chemodifferentiation is already under way are able to "recognize" if other cells are of
like or of unlike type. Perhaps the molecular properties
of the cell surfaces are already developed sufficiently
that they permit only cells of like type to adhere to
one another and thus to aggregate into compact groups
comparable to those existing normally in an intact embryo. Furthermore, well before such cell groups are
fully differentiated as microscopically distinct tissues,
the cells already predetermine the characteristics of
the future tissues (Fig. 27.18).

Indeed, it can be shown that cellular properties
predetermine not only the differentiation but also the
morphogenesis of tissues. For example, cells from the
future lung region of a mouse embryo will, when grown
in tissue culture, form into a portion of lung exhibiting

a perfectly normal architecture; lung alveoli and ai
ducts become well developed and are clearly recog
nizable as such. By similar experiments, isolated por
tions of normally formed kidneys, salivary glands, and
other organs may be produced in culture. Experiment
of this sort indicate generally that embryonic cell
which are already launched on a particular path o
development continue to develop in culture more o
less as they would in an intact organism (Fig. 27.19)

A different result is obtained when a culture con
sists of cells which have not yet started to develop i
given directions and thus are still more or less com
pletely undeveloped. For example, if single cells from
very early embryos of certain animals (e.g., sea urchins
frogs) are isolated, each such cell may develop into a
whole animal. Analogously, isolated embryonic cells o
plants (obtainable even from adult plants, e.g., variou
meristem cells) may develop into whole new plant
under appropriate culture conditions. Evidently, cell
which are still virtually undifferentiated exhibit a fa
greater developmental potential in isolation than in th

FIG. 27.19 Future lung tissue of an 11-day old mous
embryo was placed into tissue culture. After 6 days o
growth in the culture, the well-formed lung shown i
this photo had developed. Note ducts, branches, an
alveoli. *(Courtesy of Dr. C. Grobstein, Stanford Univer
sity, and 13th Growth Symposium, Princeton Universit
Press, 1954.)*

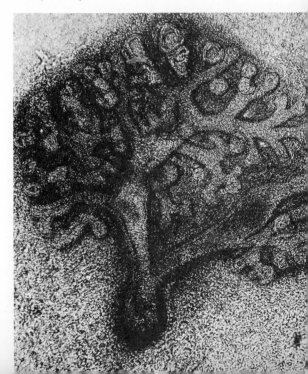

ntact organism; the capacity of forming entire plants
r animals actually resembles the similar capacity of
egetative reproductive units. Later, after such cells
ave begun to differentiate and have become special-
zed to a certain extent, their developmental potential
ecomes restricted progressively. They then form only
arts of organism under isolated conditions, the same
arts they would have formed had they not been
solated.

The restriction of developmental potentials be-
omes greatest when cells reach the fully differentiated
dult state. At best, such cells may be able to produce
nore of themselves if they are capable of division, but
hey may no longer form any other kind of cell type.
Tissue culture data at first glance seem to suggest a
different answer; for when a single adult tissue is
grown in culture, the cells usually do not remain dif-
erentiated. Instead, the tissue appears to *dedifferenti-*
te, i.e., it loses its adult specializations and comes to
xhibit a less developed, more or less embryonic state.
t can be shown, however, that such dedifferentiation
loes not change the fundamental characteristics of the
issue. For example, if a dedifferentiated tissue from a
ulture is grafted back into an intact organism, the
issue soon redifferentiates and then exhibits the same
dult properties it did originally; it cannot redifferenti-
te into another kind of tissue. Clearly, the developed
haracteristics of a greatly specialized adult tissue
appear to be fixed and irreversible, even though these
haracteristics may become obscured temporarily when
he tissue exists in isolation (Fig. 27.20).

The results suggest that dedifferentiation in cul-
ure might occur because an isolated tissue may be
unable to interact with other tissues as it would nor-
nally do in an intact organism. Returning a cultured
issue to an intact organism would make tissue-tissue
nteraction again possible and the observed rediffer-
entiation could be a consequence. Such an interpre-
ation is supported by experiments in which whole
solated organs are grown in culture. The several closely
associated tissues of the organ then do not dedifferenti-
te but tend to retain their adult characteristics; pre-
umably, normal tissue-tissue interaction may still occur.
t appears, therefore, that the cells and tissues of multicellular organisms are interdependent developmentally.
n isolation they do not develop in quite the same
nanner as in integrated groups, a finding which war-
ants the conclusion that group integration is a neces-
ary condition for the formation and maintenance of a
oroperly organized living whole.

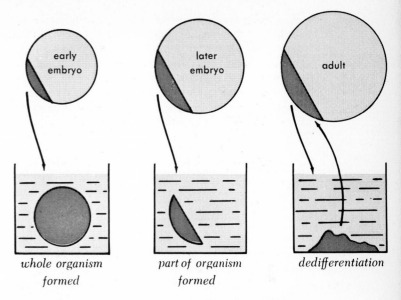

FIG. 27.20   If isolated cells from a very early embryo
are cultured, the cells may form a whole organism (left).
If isolated cells from a later embryo are cultured, the cells
tend to form only that part of the organism they would
have formed if they had been left intact in the embryo
(middle). If isolated cells from an adult are cultured, the
cells tend to dedifferentiate (right); but if such dedifferentiated cells are replanted into the adult donor, then the
cells will redifferentiate the structural and functional characteristics they had before they were isolated.

For often poorly understood reasons, group integration sometimes breaks down in intact organisms.
Various developmental abnormalities then result, tumors and cancers among them. The investigation of
such abnormal expressions of development are again
aided greatly by the technique of tissue culture. For
example, tumor tissues may be grown in culture and
their chemical characteristics may be compared with
those of normal tissues. Drugs and other agents may
be introduced into the culture medium and their effects
may be observed. Moreover, by growing normal tissues
in culture and by changing the environmental conditions in various ways, one may discover some of the
factors which may lead to abnormal development.
Clearly, the tool of tissue culture is applicable to a wide
variety of developmental problems. Much of our present total knowledge about both normal and abnormal
development has actually been obtained entirely
through tissue culture work.

To be sure, cells and tissues generally do not develop in man-made cultures but in naturally forming organisms. Ultimately, therefore, every developmental problem refers back and is suggested by events in whole organisms. In the following we shall examine the development of whole organisms, with particular attention to some of the readily discernible problems and their often quite undiscernible answers.

ORGANISMIC DEVELOPMENT

THE PATTERN

The course of development varies considerably according to whether the starting unit is a zygote produced by a sexual process or an asexually developing spore or vegetative body.

Zygotic development starts with **fertilization** and continues with the formation of an **embryo.** During the embryonic period, all basic structures and functions of the future adult body are elaborated in at least rough detail. In Metaphyta, the embryonic phase merges imperceptibly into the young adult phase, the general time of transition being the establishment of a self-supporting sporophyte in soil and air. In the majority of Metazoa, the embryonic phase typically terminates more distinctly with a process of **hatching,** in which the embryo emerges from its original egg envelopes and becomes a free-living **larva.**

A larval phase is characteristic of virtually all animal phyla, but it is often absent in some of the more advanced subgroups within a phylum or a large taxonomic group (e.g., reptiles, birds, and mammals among vertebrates). Larvae are temporary organisms having a variety of functions (Fig. 27.21). For example, they may serve in geographic dispersal, especially if the adult is sessile or sluggish (e.g., clams, many worms, tunicates). Or they may serve as temporary feeding machines, which accumulate enough raw materials in the form of larval tissues to make lengthy further development possible (e.g., insect caterpillars). Or they may simply represent a developmental stage resembling a similar stage of ancestral organisms (e.g., frog tadpoles, which resemble the larvae of fishes).

Larvae eventually undergo **metamorphosis,** a more or less gradual but in many cases quite sudden transformation into the **adult** condition (Fig. 27.22). Note that this last phase in the developmental history of an individual is not any more static than preceding phases.

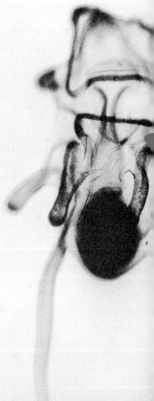

FIG. 27.21 A variety of larvae. Left, caterpillar. Bottom left, a *pluteus* larva, characteristic of sea urchins. Bottom middle, a *pilidium* larva, characteristic of proboscis worms. Bottom right, a *Mueller's* larva, characteristic of flatworms. Right, a *brachiolaria* larva, characteristic of starfish. (*Left, Carolina Biological Supply Co.; bottom middle, courtesy of Dr. P. Grant, Johns Hopkins University; bottom left and right, right, General Biological Supply House, Inc.*)

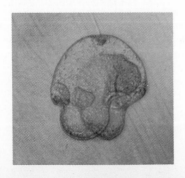

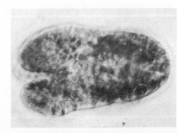

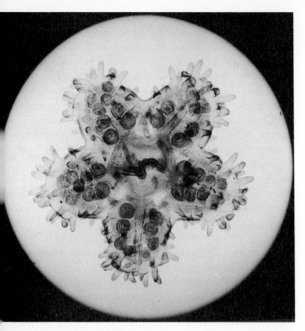

FIG. 27.22 Metamorphosis. This immature starfish, just metamorphosed, has formed from a brachiolaria larva such as shown in Fig. 27.21. Note the immature tube feet and the incompletely developed water-vascular system. Another illustration of metamorphosis may be found in Fig. 11.45. *(General Biological Supply House, Inc.)*

On the contrary, as shown in the chapters on metabolism, the components of the adult are steadily being demolished and redesigned or replaced. In this continuing turnover, internal as well as external features become altered. Adolescence so passes into maturity, maturity into senescence, and only death brings development to a halt.

Thus, the typical developmental pattern following gametic reproduction is either fertilization ⟶ embryo ⟶ adult, as in Metaphyta and certain Metazoa, or fertilization ⟶ embryo ⟶ larva ⟶ adult, as in most Metazoa (Fig. 27.23). In sharp contrast to this lengthy multistage course of sexual development, all forms of asexual development are exceedingly direct. In the development of spores, sporelike cells, or vegetative units of any type there is no sex, hence no fertilization; there is no larva, hence also no metamorphosis. Instead, the reproductive unit becomes an adult in a smoothly continuous, single developmental step (Fig. 27.24).

Without doubt, this marked difference between sexual and asexual patterns of development must be due to the presence or absence of the sexual process itself. Unlike spores or vegetative units, an egg is *more* than simply a reproductive unit. As we have seen, it is also the agent for sex; i.e., it is an *adaptive* device. Through fertilization the egg acquires new genes,

FIG. 27.23 These stages of the life cycle of the frog symbolize the main stages in the sexual development of animals: egg (top left), embryo (bottom left), larva (top right), adult (bottom right). The photographs are not reproduced to the same scale. *(Eggs, Carolina Biological Supply Co.; tadpole, American Museum of Natural History; others, General Biological Supply House, Inc.)*

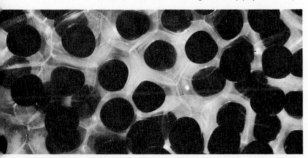

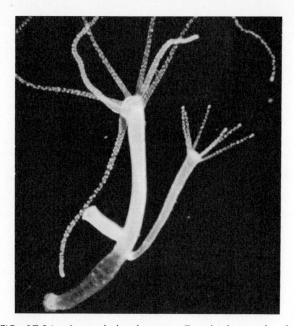

FIG. 27.24 Asexual development. Two buds are developing on this parental hydra, and when the buds are mature they will separate from the parent and take up independent existence. Formation and maturation of such a bud do not involve any sexual processes, and development occurs in a smooth, single sequence of events. *(Courtesy of Dr. Roman Vishniac, New York.)*

which may endow the future offspring with new, better adapted traits. However, before any new traits can actually be displayed, they must be *developed* during the transition from egg to adult. Embryonic and larval periods are the result. These phases provide the opportunity for translating the genetic instructions acquired sexually by the zygote into the adaptively improved structures and functions of the adult. Spores and vegetative units do not acquire new genetic instructions through sex; hence equivalent time for executing such instructions is not needed. Correspondingly, embryos and larvae are absent here (Fig. 27.25).

Of all forms and phases of development in various plants and animals, the embryonic phase of animals has been studied most. Particular attention has been given to externally fertilizing types such as frogs and sea urchins. The sperms and eggs of animals of this kind may be put into a dish of water, where fertilization and development may be observed under the microscope and where experiments may be performed readily. Much has also been learned by cutting windows into developing chicken eggs and by observing and experimenting on the exposed embryos. Comparative studies have shown that, although the details often vary considerably, certain basic processes are common in the development of all animal embryos. The main sequence of these processes will be outlined in the next section.

FIG. 27.25 Sexual vs. asexual development. In sexual development (top), new genetic instructions are introduced into the zygote via the gametes, and during subsequent embryonic and larval stages these instructions are elaborated explicitly. Hence the mature offspring may differ to a greater or less extent from the parent. In asexual development (bottom), on the other hand, new genetic instructions are not introduced, and the offspring therefore resembles the parent exactly.

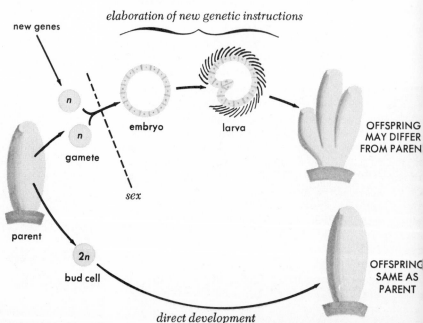

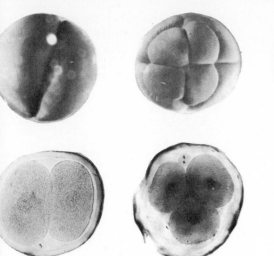

FIG. 27.26 Top row, cleavage in frog eggs: left to right, two-cell stage, eight-cell stage, later stage. Bottom row, left and middle, two- and four-cell stages in cleavage of rabbit egg. Bottom right, two-cell stage in cleavage of starfish egg. Note, especially in top series, how cell size decreases with successive cleavage divisions. *(Top row, Carolina Biological Supply Co.; bottom row, General Biological Supply House, Inc.)*

THE EMBRYO

Early Development

The first clearly visible event after fertilization is cleavage, the repeated division of the zygote into many cells. Growth does not occur during this phase. Therefore, as cleavage proceeds, the cells become progressively smaller. The original egg is a comparatively huge cell, and cleavage usually continues until the cells have a species-characteristic mature size (Fig. 27.26).

Even before cleavage begins, the egg is subjected to invisible and poorly understood molecular changes which establish the fundamental polarity and symmetry of the future embryo. On the basis of the demonstrable results of the molecular changes, two categories of eggs may be distinguished: **mosaic** or *determined* eggs and **regulative** or *undetermined* eggs.

The first type is encountered among mollusks, annelids, insects, and many other invertebrates. In these animals, the future developmental fate of every portion of the egg becomes fixed unalterably before or at the time of fertilization. The zygote therefore is already fully polarized and the head-tail, dorsal-ventral, and left-right axes are firmly established. Moreover, experiments show that each portion of the egg behaves as if it already "knew" what it is going to develop into. For example, after cleavage in such an egg has produce two or more cells, it is possible to separate these cells from one another. Each isolated cell, here called a **blastomere**, then continues to develop and forms a *partial* embryo. More specifically, it produces the same portion of the embryo it would have produced if the cleaving egg had been left intact. In other words, the determined egg is like a quiltwork, a mosaic, in which each portion of the cytoplasm develops into a fixed, unalterable part of the whole embryo; and the nature of the mosaic is established before or, at the latest, during the time of fertilization (Fig. 27.27).

FIG. 27.27 Development in mosaic eggs. If the cells of early cleavage stages of such eggs are isolated experimentally, each cell develops as it would have in any case, even if it had not been isolated. The inference is that the fate of the cytoplasm of mosaic eggs is determined very early.

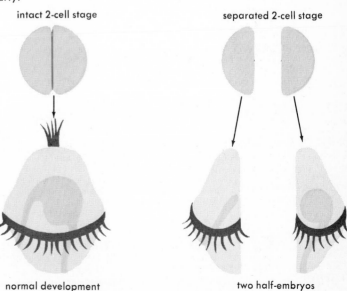

intact 2-cell stage

separated 2-cell stage

normal development

two half-embryos

By contrast, vertebrate and echinoderm eggs are examples of the regulative variety. In these, the future fate of various egg portions similarly becomes unalterably fixed, but such fixing occurs comparatively much later, during the embryonic phase. Moreover, different features becomes determined at different times. For example, at fertilization only the main egg axis is determined. That is, the direction of "top" and "bottom" is already given, but other aspects of polarity and symmetry or of any other feature are not as yet fixed.

That this is so can be demonstrated very strikingly by experiment. If the two cells formed by the first cleavage division are left as they are, then these two blastomeres will eventually form the left and right halves of the future animal. Further, cytoplasm in the center of the egg will develop into central internal structures of the adult. But if the two blastomeres are separated from one another, then they do *not* develop

FIG. 27.28 Development in regulative eggs. If the cells of early cleavage stages of such eggs are isolated experimentally, each cell develops into a smaller, but whole, organism. The inference is that the fate of the cytoplasm of early cleavage stages is still undetermined. For example, the central cytoplasm of the two-cell stage normally forms central body parts (left figures, shaded portions). But if the cells are separated, the central cytoplasm forms left structures in one case, right structures in the other (right figures, shaded portions).

into two half animals as would be the case in a mosaic egg. Instead, the two blastomeres develop into two *whole* animals. Moreover, the central cytoplasm of the original egg now gives rise to the right side of one whole animal and to the left side of another. Evidently central material at the two-cell stage does not yet "know" whether to form left, right, or internal mid body structures. In short, it is not yet determined (Fig. 27.28).

Analogously, if the cells of later cleavage stages are isolated and grown separately, then each may again give rise to a whole instead of a partial animal. But a limit is reached fairly soon. After the first four cleavages, for example, 16 blastomeres are present. If these are separated from one another, 16 whole animals cannot be obtained. Instead, each blastomere forms only one-sixteenth of an embryo, as it would have done if the 16-cell stage had been left intact. In other words, the developmental fate of the cells has become determined by now and the embryo henceforth is like a mosaic.

We may conclude that mosaic and regulative eggs differ mainly in the timing of developmental determination. The early timing in mosaic eggs contrasts with the comparatively late timing in regulative eggs. During the undetermined phase in regulative eggs, any cell may substitute for any other cell and may develop into any structure, including a whole animal. Note here that developmental determination is a form of differentiation and that the underlying mechanism is still completely unknown.

Note also that the formation of two or more whole animals from separated blastomeres is equivalent to the experimental production of identical **twins**, triplets, quadruplets, etc. Natural twinning undoubtedly occurs through similar separations. However, the forces or accidents which actually isolate such blastomeres in nature are not understood. If the blastomeres are separated incompletely, Siamese twins result. This can also be demonstrated by laboratory experiments (Fig. 27.29). Twins are *identical* when they develop from a single fertilized egg, as above. They are *fraternal* when two or more whole eggs are fertilized separately at the same time. Fraternal twins are formed normally by cats, pigs, and other litter-producing animals. The offspring here may be of different sexes and they need not resemble one another. By contrast, identical twins are of the same sex and they do resemble one another. Indeed, they tend to be structural mirror images.

The ultimate result of normal cleavage is a ball

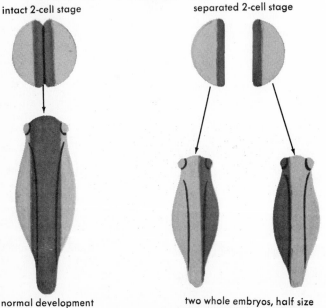

intact 2-cell stage   separated 2-cell stage

normal development   two whole embryos, half size

FIG. 27.29   X-ray photo of Siamese twinning in fish. Abnormalities like these result from incomplete divisions of cells during early cleavage. (American Museum of Natural History.)

f a few hundred cells, called a **blastula.** This ball may be hollow or solid, and it represents a developmental stage characteristic of virtually all Metazoa (Fig. 27.30). Cell divisions continue in a blastula, but growth now occurs as well and successive cell generations thus no longer become smaller. The main subsequent developmental event is the transformation of the blastula into an embryo consisting of three distinct layers of tissue. This process of transformation is called *gastrulation,* and the three-layered result is the **gastrula.** It too is a developmental stage common to virtually all Metazoa.

Patterns of gastrulation vary widely. For purposes of illustration, we may examine events in the embryos of sea urchins and other echinoderms. In these, the blastula is a hollow, one-layered sphere. When gastrulation occurs, one side of this sphere *invaginates,* i.e., becomes indented. A two-layered cup-shaped structure is formed in this manner. The resulting outer layer is called the **ectoderm** and the inner layer is called the **endoderm** (see Fig. 27.30).

Later a third tissue layer, the **mesoderm,** arises between the ectoderm and the endoderm. As described in Chap. 11, several major categories of animals may be distinguished on the basis of how mesoderm forms. For example, in the enterocoelomates, a category which includes echinoderms and vertebrates, the mesoderm arises as a lateral pocket growing out on each side of the endoderm. Regardless of how the mesoderm originates, however, the fully formed gastrula is a hollow, triple-walled ball with an opening at one point (Fig. 27.31).

This opening is the **blastopore,** which marks the region of the future anus in enterocoelomates and the region of the future mouth in all other animals (see Chap. 11). A mouth or an anus will later break through at the opposite end of the gastrula. The interior cavity, the **archenteron,** is the future alimentary cavity. The endoderm which encloses this space will develop into the alimentary system, the breathing system, and all glands and ducts associated with these: liver, pancreas, salivary glands, trachea, etc. The ectoderm will give rise to the whole nervous system and to the skin, including hair, nails, and skin glands. The mesoderm will form the remaining parts of the body, namely,

FIG. 27.30   The early development of starfish embryos. Left to right, late cleavage; blastula; invagination, early gastrula; late gastrula, beginning of mesoderm formation; mesoderm formation under way. (General Biological Supply House, Inc.)

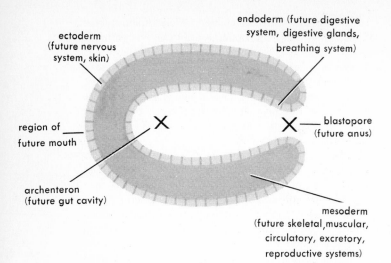

FIG. 27.31 The general structure of a vertebrate gastrula, and the adult organ systems formed by each of the primary germ layers, diagrammatic.

bones, muscles, and the circulatory, excretory, and reproductive systems. The endocrine system arises partly from ectoderm, partly from mesoderm, and partly from endoderm.

Clearly, with the formation of the gastrula, the basic architectural design of the body is already established. In man, the gastrula forms a few days after fertilization, roughly when the embryo reaches the uterus.

Later Development

How are the *primary germ layers* of ectoderm, mesoderm, and endoderm transformed into well-defined body parts? The principle involved is fundamentally the same in all cases and we may illustrate it by considering the development of the vertebrate nervous system (Fig. 27.32).

On the upper surface of the gastrula develop two ectodermal ridges, one along each side of the midline. These ridges grow upward and toward each other and soon meet along the midline. As their edges fuse, they

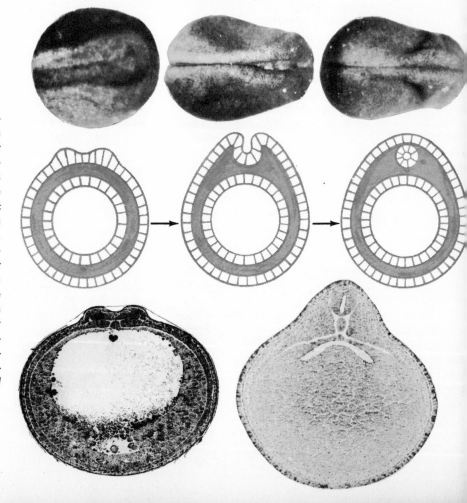

FIG. 27.32 The initial development of the nervous system in vertebrates (frogs). Top: left to right, dorsal views, progressive stages. The anterior ends of the embryos are toward the right. Middle: diagrammatic cross sections corresponding to the stages shown above. Bottom: photos of cross sections corresponding to the first and last stages illustrated in middle series. Note large amounts of yolk in bottom photos. *(Top photos, courtesy of Dr. Roberts Rugh, from "Experimental Embryology," Burgess Publishing Company; bottom photos, General Biological Supply House, Inc.)*

orm a tube of ectoderm which runs from front to back nd is covered over by an outer ectoderm layer. This ube is the basis of the nervous system; it develops into rain in the front part of the embryo and into spinal ord in the hind part.

The essential event here is the outfolding of a tissue layer, followed by fusion of the fold edges. Virtually all other formative processes of later embryonic development similarly consist of outfolding or infolding, utpouching or inpouching, of portions of the three erm layers of the gastrula. For example, limb buds rise by combined outpouchings from ectoderm and mesoderm. Lungs and digestive glands develop as outpouchings from various levels of the endoderm. The eye develops in part as an outpouching from the brain. All other body parts develop analogously. The ultimate esult of these processes of morphogenesis and differentiation is a fully formed embryo, clearly recognizable as a young stage of a particular species.

Experiments have shown how these orderly sequences of development may come about (Fig. 27.33). In amphibian embryos it is possible to cut out the dorsal ectoderm which, under normal circumstances, would fold up and form a neural tube. If this excised issue is then transplanted to another region of the embryo, it will not form a neural tube and its cells will not differentiate into neurons. This suggests that the dorsal mesoderm, which in an intact embryo lies just under the dorsal ectoderm, normally affects this ectoderm in such a way that it will fold out and differentiate into neural tissue. That this is actually so can be shown by another experiment. The dorsal *mesoderm* can be cut out and can be transplanted, for example, into the belly region of an embryo just under the belly ectoderm. Normally, belly ectoderm forms only skin. But if dorsal mesoderm lies under it, it will form a neural tube and its cells will differentiate into neural tissue.

The implications are clear. Somehow, the dorsal mesoderm of a normal embryo *induces* the outfolding of the overlying ectoderm, the formation of ridges, and the later differentiation of neural tissue. Such induction can actually be shown to occur whenever outfoldings or infoldings and outgrowths or ingrowths develop in the embryo. The formation of the eye provides a particularly striking example.

Eye development (Fig. 27.34) begins with the growing out of a pocket from the side of the future brain. This pocket is narrow at the base and bulbous at the tip. Soon the bulbous portion invaginates (indents) from the forward end and a double-layered cup

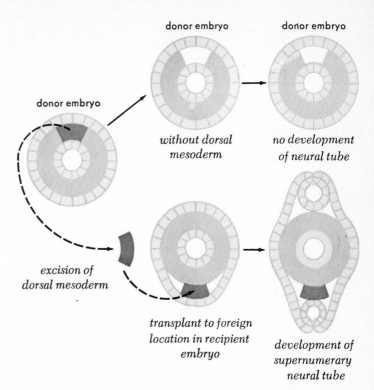

donor embryo *donor embryo*

donor embryo

without dorsal mesoderm *no development of neural tube*

excision of dorsal mesoderm

transplant to foreign location in recipient embryo

development of supernumerary neural tube

FIG. 27.33 Neural induction. If the dorsal mesoderm of a donor embryo is transplanted under the belly ectoderm of a host embryo, then the transplant will induce the formation of an abnormally located neural tube in the host.

is formed. The cup represents the future eyeball. As it grows outward from the brain, its rim comes into contact with the outer ectoderm layer which overlies the whole nervous system and which represents the future skin. Just where the eyecup rests against it, the ectoderm layer now begins to thicken. This thickening eventually grows into a ball of cells, which is nipped off toward the inside. It fits neatly into the mouth of the eyecup and represents the future lens. The cells of this ball and the ectoderm overlying them later become transparent. The basic structure of the eye is then established.

The following type of experiment has shown dramatically how these developmental processes are controlled. It is possible to cut off the eyecup and its stalk before they have grown very far. Eyecup and stalk may then be transplanted. For example, they may be inserted into a region just under the belly ectoderm of an embryo. Under such conditions, the patch of

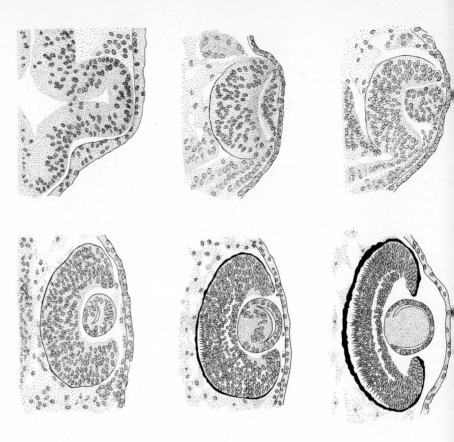

FIG. 27.34 Development of the vertebrate eye (amphibian; semidiagrammatic). This series of successive stages shows the outgrowth of a pocket from the brain, contact of this pocket with the outer body ectoderm, formation of an eyecup, gradual formation of a lens from the outer ectoderm, and development of the pigmented and other tissue layers of the eyeball. (Courtesy of Dr. D. Bodenstein, from originals of figs. 2 and 3, J. Exptl. Zool., vol. 108, pp. 96 and 97, by permission.)

FIG. 27.35 Experiments in eye transplantation. Diagram, if an embryonic eyecup is excised from a donor embryo A and is transplanted into an abnormal location in a host embryo B, then a structurally perfect eye will develop at that abnormal location. Photo, a larva of the amphibian *Amblystoma*, with two supernumerary eyes grafted into abnormal locations. The procedure followed that outlined in the diagram, and the photo was taken 43 days after the transplant operation. (Photo from original fig. 16, S. R. Detwiler and R. H. Van Dyke, J. Exptl. Zool., vol. 69, p. 157.)

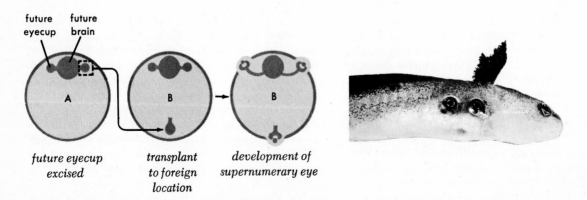

future eyecup   future brain

A   B   B

*future eyecup
excised*

*transplant
to foreign
location*

*development of
supernumerary eye*

belly ectoderm overlying the eyecup soon thickens, a ball of cells is nipped off toward the inside, and a lens differentiates. Moreover, lens and overlying skin become transparent. In effect, the transplanted structures have caused the formation of a structurally normal eye in a highly abnormal location (Fig. 27.35).

A common conclusion emerges from this and many similar types of experiments. One embryonic tissue layer interacts with an adjacent one and the latter is thereby induced to differentiate, to grow, to develop in a particular way. This developed tissue then interacts with another one in turn and induces it to develop. In short, sequential induction must occur if progressive development is to take place. As in the induction sequence: dorsal mesoderm ⟶ neural tube ⟶ eyecup ⟶ lens, so also generally; one tissue provides the stimulus for the development of the next. The phenomenon of **embryonic induction** consequently may account well for the orderly, properly timed, and properly spaced elaboration of body parts.

Although inductive processes among embryonic tissues may be identified and described, the nature of such interactions in terms of reactions within and among cells is still obscure. Even so, the ultimate result of these various occurrences is a fully formed embryo which may later hatch and become a larva or may develop into an adult directly. A new individual emerges in either event, and when this individual becomes mature, the entire cycle of reproduction and development will be repeated.

This concludes the series of chapters on reproduction. We have found that the extension of living matter in space-time undoubtedly includes some of the most fascinating of all living processes, but also some of the least understood. We firmly recognize the self-perpetuative role of reproductive events and we may describe these events in considerable detail. But whether we deal with cell division or with life cycles, with morphogenesis or with differentiation, we have so far been able only to peel off the outermost of the veils which hide the actual developmental mechanisms. Throughout, the ultimate controlling activity of genes either has been demonstrated already or is strongly suspected. In this regard, reproductive processes do not differ from those of steady-state control.

This brings us directly to the last ingredient of self-perpetuation, namely, adaptation. In adaptation even more obviously than in reproduction or in steady-state control, genes are similarly at the root of all happenings. As they reproduce, these time capsules of living tradition become the basis of heredity. And out of heredity is woven the fabric of evolution.

REVIEW QUESTIONS

1. Define morphogenesis, differential growth, form-regulating movements, polarity. Through what types of growth processes does an organism enlarge in size? Explain the meaning of the phrase "Organisms grow from their molecules up."

2. What different types of symmetries are exhibited by living units? In what ways do polarity and symmetry circumscribe the form of an organism? Specify the polarity and symmetry of (a) man and (b) a tree. What is the role of differential growth in the development of form?

3. Define and distinguish between differentiation and modulation. What is the relation between differentiation and specialization? Cite examples of differentiative changes on the level of (a) molecules, (b) cells, (c) organisms, and (d) societies. What kinds of changes within cells might bring about cytodifferentiation?

4. What role does metabolism play in development? How does metabolic rate vary during the developmental history of an organism? In what different ways may an incompletely developed reproductive unit acquire (a) nutrients and (b) respiratory gases? What cellular metabolic capacities (a) are and (b) are not in existence in a zygote?

5. Describe experiments performed on the development of *Acetabularia* and indicate what general principles of cellular development these experiments illustrate. Similarly review experiments on (a) control of antigenic type in *Paramecium,* and (b) cellular aggregation in *Dictyostelium*. What is the general significance of the results obtained?

6. What is a tissue culture? What kinds of developmental studies can be undertaken with the aid of tissue cultures? What has been learned about the developmental behavior of cells, tissues, and organs grown in tissue culture?

7. Describe and define the principal developmental phases in the life history of an animal if this history (a) includes and (b) does not include a sexual process. What is the significance of the greater number of phases under condition a? What events usually terminate (a) the embryonic period and (b) the larval period?

8. What events occur during the cleavage of an egg? What is meant by developmental determination? Distinguish between mosaic and regulative eggs. How can it be established by experiment whether a given egg is mosaic or regulative? In which animals do each of these egg types occur? How are twins formed? Distinguish between identical and fraternal twinning. Can identical twinning take place in mosaic eggs?

9. Describe the processes leading to the formation of (a) a blastula and (b) a gastrula. Define ectoderm, endoderm, mesoderm, blastopore, archenteron. How does mesoderm form in vertebrates? Which structural components of an adult vertebrate develop from each of the primary germ layers?

10. By what general processes of morphogenesis do the primary germ layers develop into adult structures? Illustrate this in the development of the nervous system and the eye. What differentiative role does induction play in such transformations? Again illustrate in the development of the nervous system and the eye and describe supporting experiments.

SUGGESTED COLLATERAL READINGS

The following sources may be consulted for additional information on most topics discussed in this chapter:

Barth, L.: "Embryology," rev. ed., Dryden, New York, 1953.

Berrill, N. J.: "Growth, Development, and Pattern," Freeman, San Francisco, 1961.

Gabriel, M. L., and S. Fogel: "Great Experiments in Biology," section on Embryonic Differentiation, Prentice-Hall, Englewood Cliffs, N.J., 1955.

McElroy, W. D., and B. Glass: "The Chemical Basis of Development," The Johns Hopkins Press, Baltimore, 1958.

Waddington, C. H.: "Principles of Embryology," G. Allen, London, 1956.

Willier, B. H., P. A. Weiss, and V. Hamburger: "Analysis of Development," Saunders, Philadelphia, 1955.

The books and articles listed below give popular accounts of development and related topics.

Ashby, E.: Leaf Shape and Physiological Age, *Endeavour*, vol. 8, 1949.

Biesele, J. J.: Tissue Culture and Cancer, *Sci. American*, vol. 195, 1956.

Bonner, J. T.: "Morphogenesis," Princeton University Press, Princeton, N.J., 1952.

————: Differentiation in Social Amoebae, *Sci. American*, vol. 201, 1959.

Braun, A. C.: Plant Cancer, *Sci. American*, vol. 186, 1952.

Conklin, G.: Cancer and Environment, *Sci. American*, vol. 180, 1949.

Dahlberg, G.: An Explanation of Twins, *Sci. American*, vol. 184, 1951.

Danielli, J. F.: On Transplanting Nuclei, *Sci. American*, vol. 186, 1952.

Gautheret, R. J.: Plant Tissue Culture, *Endeavour*, vol. 7, 1948.

Greene, H. S. N.: On the Development of Cancer, *Sci. American*, vol. 179, 1948.

Lansing, A. I.: Experiments in Aging, *Sci. American*, vol. 188, 1953.

Moog, F.: The Biology of Old Age, *Sci. American*, vol. 179, 1948.

————: Up from the Embryo, *Sci. American*, vol. 182, 1950.

Smith, C. S.: The Shape of Things, *Sci. American*, vol. 190, 1954.

Snow, R.: Problems of Phyllotaxis and Leaf Determination, *Endeavour*, vol. 14, 1956.

Waddington, C. H.: How Do Cells Differentiate? *Sci. American*, vol. 189, 1953.

Wardlaw, C. W.: The Study of Growth and Form in Plants, *Endeavour*, vol. 11, 1952.

White, P. R.: Plant Tissue Cultures, *Sci. American*, vol. 182, 1950.

PART 7
SELF-PERPETUATION: ADAPTATION

On the molecular as on the organismic level, in structure as in function, every organism is *adapted* to its environment. For example, among thousands of shapes that a fish *might* possess, it actually possesses one which is well suited for rapid locomotion in water. A bird is cast in a form eminently suited for aerial life, yet its ancestry traces to fish. Over long periods of time, clearly, organisms may change their particular adaptations in response to new environments.

Being adapted is a universal attribute of all organisms, and adaptation is the long-range process of development which creates and maintains this attribute. Through adaptation, organisms change *with* their environments, and this makes them potentially immortal as a group.

Based on steady-state control and reproduction, adaptation consists of three components: *sex, heredity,* and *evolution.* Of these, the adaptive role of sex has already been discussed. In this last series of chapters, therefore, we begin with an analysis of the adaptive roles of **heredity** and continue with a similar analysis of **evolution.**

HEREDITY

28

The key problem in studies of heredity is to explain the inheritance of *likeness* and of *variation:* how an offspring usually comes to resemble its parents in certain major respects but differs from the parents in many minor respects. Are such hereditary patterns in any way regular and predictable, and if so, what are the underlying principles?

It should be clear that organisms do not inherit blue eyes, clever minds, red blood, or any other trait. Organisms inherit *genes,* not traits. Moreover, they do not inherit genes only, but *all* the components of reproductive units, i.e., *whole cells.* Visible traits then *develop* in an offspring, under the control of inherited genes and within the limitations imposed by given intracellular and extracellular environments.

Genes cannot be seen, but traits can be. Studies of heredity therefore consist in examining the traits of successive generations of organisms and inferring from the visible likenesses and variations what the heredity of the genes has been. The first important studies of this sort were made in the last half of the nineteenth century by the Austrian monk Gregor Mendel. He discovered two basic rules of inheritance which laid the foundation for all later advances in understanding of processes of heredity.

Accordingly, this discussion of heredity will include an examination of the general relationship between **genes and traits,** an account of the rules of **Mendelian inheritance,** and a survey of the main aspects of **non-Mendelian inheritance** brought to light since the time of Mendel.

GENES AND TRAITS

HEREDITY AND ENVIRONMENT

The pattern of inheritance varies according to whether reproduction is **uniparental** or **biparental.** Where an organism is produced by a single parent,

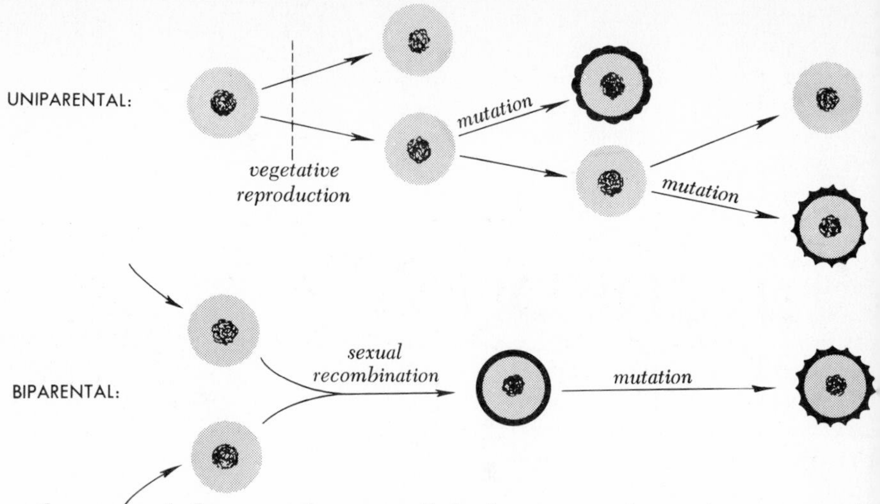

UNIPARENTAL:

vegetative reproduction

mutation

mutation

FIG. 28.1   The sources of genetic variations. In uniparental inheritance, the only source is mutation. In biparental inheritance, genetic variations may arise both by mutation and by sexual recombination of genes.

BIPARENTAL:

sexual recombination

mutation

e.g., as in vegetative reproduction, the genes of the parent are passed on unchanged to the offspring. In uniparental reproduction, therefore, offspring and parent are genetically identical and usually display the same visible traits. The only source of genetic variation in such cases is **mutation.** For example, if some gene of a bud cell undergoes a mutational change, then, and only then, may the offspring become genetically different from the parent. Trait variations may then also be displayed.

By contrast, *two* sources of genetic variation exist in cases of biparental, e.g., gametic, reproduction. One is again mutation, in this instance mutation in one or both gametes. The other is a direct result of sex; *two* sets of genes are pooled in the zygote. The genetic endowment of the offspring consequently may differ from that of either parent. Through such **sexual recombination** of genes, the offspring may become unlike the parents.

We conclude, for both uniparental and biparental reproduction, that *likeness* to parents will be inherited to the extent that the genes of the offspring are the same as those of the parents and that *variation* will be inherited to the extent that mutation, recombination, or both, have changed the genes of the offspring (Fig. 28.1).

But inheriting a certain ·gene is not automatically equivalent to developing a certain trait; the development of traits is affected by the environment. Genes supply a reasonable promise, as it were, and the total environment of the genes subsequently permits or does not permit the translation of promise into reality.

The environment of genes includes, first of all,

other genes. Indeed, gene-gene interactions are exceedingly common, as we shall see. The functional integration of genes in a cell is actually so intimate and so complex that it becomes relatively meaningless to speak of "a" gene as if it were an independent, clearly distinct particle (see also Chap. 18). Only the interacting totality of genes in a cell, called the **genome,** has functional reality.

The environment of genes also includes the cell cytoplasm, and it too influences the development of traits in major ways. For example, *all* cells of a flower-

FIG. 28.2   Even though all cells of an organism possess the same kinds of genes, gene action is influenced differently by different cells, resulting in differential expression of traits. Thus all cells of a plant may have pigment-producing genes, but actual pigmentation may develop only in the cells of leaves such as petals.

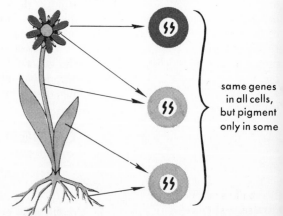

same genes in all cells, but pigment only in some

ing plant possess flower-color genes, but only cells in the petals express that color. *All* cells of man possess eye-color genes, but only iris cells actually develop the color. Evidently, the cytoplasms of different cells are differentially sensitive to the genes they contain. Traits will be expressed differentially as a result, through different developmental and environmental influences (Fig. 28.2).

We may therefore distinguish between **inherited variations** of traits, produced by basic genetic differences, and noninherited, **acquired variations** of traits, produced by environmental or developmental effects. And we are led to the fundamental principle that visible traits are always a product of inherited genes *and* of environment. To the extent that variations of traits may be advantageous to the organism in its way of life, heredity, like sex, has adaptive value.

TRAITS

It is almost as difficult to define "a" trait as it is to define "a" gene. For example, consider the trait of disease resistance, clearly hereditary in nature. Disease resistance is not really "a" trait. Inasmuch as it is a functional property of a whole organism, it is a composite property of millions of cooperating cells. Each of these contributes some particular function to the total trait, and specific genes in each of these cells control each of these functions. Therefore, disease resistance must be a combination of perhaps millions of different cellular traits controlled by a large, equally unknown number of genes.

In very many instances, actually, what is normally regarded as a trait is of such composite nature. Body size, the fine structure and the functional capacities of organs, general vigor, intelligence, fertility, and many others—all are interaction products of several dozens or hundreds or thousands of different genes. Indeed, there is reason to believe that most of such highly composite traits are controlled by the collective action of possibly all genes of an organism, each contributing a tiny effect to the total trait. Such traits may then be expressed in a correspondingly great variety of ways. As is well known, for example, the expression of traits like body size or intelligence in different individuals may range from one extreme to another, through enormously varied series of intergradations.

But if *all* genes contribute to the control of a trait like body size, for example, and if *all* genes also control disease resistance and other highly composite traits,

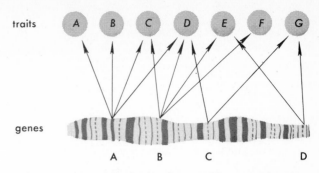

FIG. 28.3   The principle that one trait (for example, *D*) is controlled by many genes and that one gene (for example, *B*) controls many traits.

then any *one* gene clearly must contribute to the control of *more* than one trait. We are led to the generalization that *one trait may be controlled by many genes and one gene may control many traits*. Note, however, that the meaning of such a generalization depends on the meaning of the terms "one" gene and "one" trait (Fig. 28.3).

In some instances, the functional relation between genes and traits is comparatively less complex. We know from Chap. 18 that the general pattern of gene action within a cell may be symbolized by the sequence gene ⟶ enzyme ⟶ reaction ⟶ reaction product. Sometimes such a reaction product does not participate in the elaboration of a more complex trait but constitutes a final trait itself. For example, a *pigment* produced within a cell is a gene-controlled reaction product, and it is often a visible *end*product, a final trait. In cases of this sort, a readily specifiable trait is correlated directly with one particular gene (Fig. 28.4). From the pattern in which such a trait is expressed visibly in successive generations, one may readily infer the pattern of gene inheritance. It was from studies of just such color traits in plants that Mendel deduced his two rules of heredity. If he had happened to investigate, instead, any of the numerous composite traits of plants, then regularities in hereditary patterns would not have been clearly apparent and his name might not be immortal today.

MENDELIAN INHERITANCE

THE CHROMOSOME THEORY

If two red-flowered snapdragon plants are mated, all offspring produced are exclusively red-flowered.

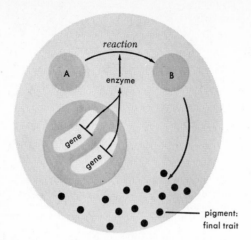

FIG. 28.4 In certain special cases, one gene is known to control just one trait. A cytoplasmic pigment may be a final trait, and a single gene may govern the manufacture of the enzyme which in turn controls the metabolic reaction which produces such a pigment.

Moreover, all later generations also develop only red flowers. Similarly, a mating of two white-flowered snapdragons yields exclusively white-flowered progeny in all subsequent generations. Red and white flower colors in this case are said to be **true-breeding** traits (Fig. 28.5).

When a red-flowered snapdragon is mated with a white-flowered plant, all offspring develop *pink* flowers. In Mendel's time, it was generally supposed that results of this kind were due to a *blending* of traits. Thus if red and white plant pigments were mixed together, like paints, a pink color would be produced. But if blending really occurs, pinkness should be equally true-breeding; a mating of two pink-flowered plants should yield pink offspring exclusively.

However, the actual results of such a mating are strikingly different. Two pink-flowered parents consistently produce pink *and* red *and* white offspring. Numerically, an average of 50 per cent of the offspring are pink, roughly 25 per cent are red, and the remainder are white (Fig. 28.6). Evidently, pinkness does *not* breed true, for from pink can be re-created pure red and white as well as pink. Hence pink color cannot be a permanent blend of red and white.

It may be concluded that blending inheritance does not occur and that, instead, traits remain distinct and intact. They may become joined temporarily in one generation and may again become separated, or *segregated*, from one another in a following generation.

Mendel was the first to reach such a conclusion, and this denial of blending was Mendel's most significant contribution. It ultimately reoriented the thinking about heredity completely and paved the way for all modern insights. Mendel himself supplied the first of such insights, for he not only negated the old interpretation but also postulated a new one.

He realized that traits trace back to the sperm and the egg which produce a plant, and he suspected that some specific components within the gametes controlled the later development of traits. Mendel called these hypothetical components "factors." For any given trait, he argued, a plant must inherit at least one factor from the sperm and one from the egg. Therefore, the offspring must possess at least two factors for each trait. When that offspring in turn becomes an adult and produces gametes, each gamete must similarly contribute *one* factor to the next generation. Hence, at some point before gamete production, two factors must be reduced to one. Mendel consequently postulated the existence of a factor-reducing process.

FIG. 28.5 True-breeding in snapdragons. If two red-flowered plants are mated, all offspring will be red-flowered (top); and if two white-flowered plants are mated, all offspring will be white-flowered (bottom).

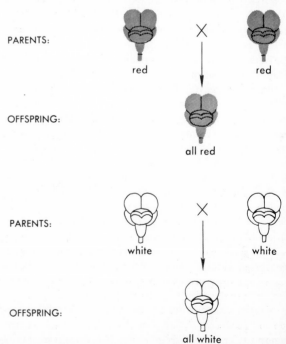

PARENTS:

red   ×   red

OFFSPRING:

all red

PARENTS:

white   ×   white

OFFSPRING:

all white

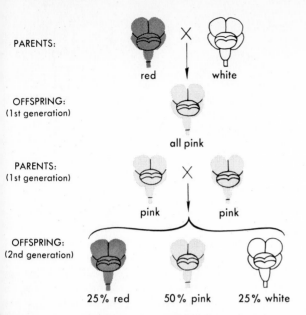

PARENTS:

red × white

OFFSPRING:
(1st generation)

all pink

PARENTS:
(1st generation)

pink × pink

OFFSPRING:
(2nd generation)

25% red   50% pink   25% white

FIG. 28.6   If a red-flowered snapdragon is mated with a white-flowered plant, all offspring will be pink-flowered. And if two of these pink-flowered plants are then mated in turn, the offspring will be red, pink, and white, in the ratios shown.

With this he in effect predicted the occurrence of meiosis. When near the end of the nineteenth century meiosis was actually discovered, it was recognized that the reduction of chromosomes at some point before fertilization matched precisely the postulated reduction of Mendel's factors. Chromosomes then came to be regarded as the carriers of the factors, and the *chromosome theory of heredity* so emerged. This theory has since received complete confirmation, and Mendel's factors became the genes of today.

THE LAW OF SEGREGATION

Transmission of Genes

On the basis of the chromosome theory, we may interpret the snapdragon data above as follows. A true-breeding red-flowered plant possesses a pair of red-pigment–producing genes in each cell. These genes which we may symbolize by the letters *AA*, are located on a given pair of chromosomes, one of which is maternal and one paternal in origin. We say that the **genotype,** or gene content, of the plant is *AA* and that the **phenotype,** or visible appearance, is *red*. Before such a

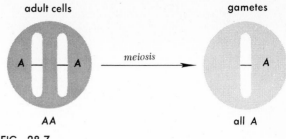

adult cells   gametes

A — A   *meiosis*   →   A

AA   all A

FIG. 28.7

plant produces gametes, meiosis occurs. Mature gametes therefore contain only one of the two chromosomes, hence only one of the two genes (Fig. 28.7).

Note that it is entirely a matter of chance which of the two adult chromosomes will become incorporated into a given gamete. Since both adult chromosomes here carry the same color gene, all gametes will be genetically alike in this respect. We may understand now why *AA* plants are true-breeding, i.e., why a mating of *AA* × *AA* will produce only red-flowered, *AA* offspring (Fig. 28.8).

In precisely analogous manner, we may symbolize the genotype of a true-breeding white-flowered snapdragon as *aa*. The letters here represent genes which do not produce any pigment at all. The white coloration in such flowers is a result of this lack of pigment. A mating of two such plants will yield only white-flowered offspring (Fig. 28.9).

If we now mate a red-flowered and a white-flowered plant, *all* offspring will be *pink* (Fig. 28.10).

FIG. 28.8

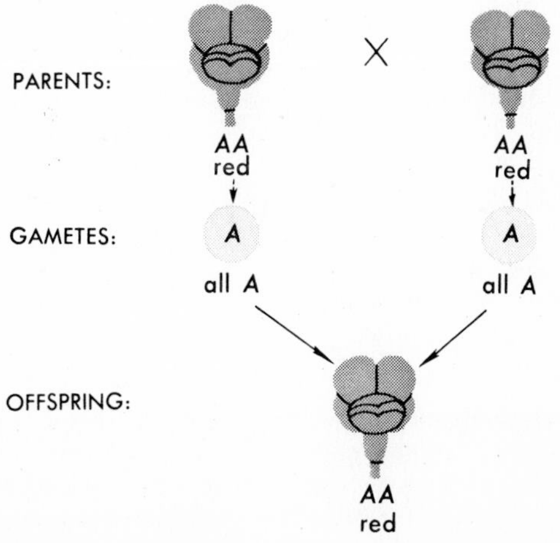

PARENTS:

AA
red   ×   AA
red

GAMETES:

A   A

all A   all A

OFFSPRING:

AA
red

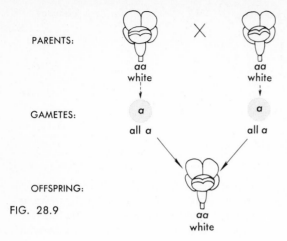

FIG. 28.9

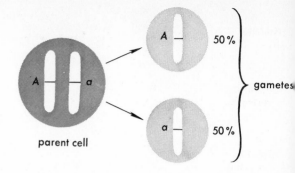

FIG. 28.11

We may note here that an *Aa* offspring plant possesses only *one* pigment-producing gene per cell, namely, *A*. Such a cell consequently develops only *half* as much pigment as an *AA* cell, which possesses two pigment-producing genes. This lesser amount of pigment in the *Aa* offspring appears as a dilute red, i.e., pink.

If now two pink-flowered *Aa* plants are mated, after meiosis each plant will give rise to two types of gametes. Given the genes *Aa*, either the *A* gene or the *a* gene could become incorporated into any given gamete. What actually happens in each specific case is determined by chance. Hence if, as is usually the case in plants, large numbers of gametes are produced, each possibility will be realized with roughly equal frequency. Consequently, approximately 50 per cent of the gametes will carry the *A* gene, the other 50 per

cent the *a* gene. We may write: *Aa* parent ⟶ 50 per cent *A* gametes, 50 per cent *a* gametes (Fig. 28.11).

Now fertilization occurs. There are two genetically different sperm types and two genetically different egg types, and it is wholly a matter of chance which of the two sperm types fertilizes which of the two egg types. If many fertilizations occur simultaneously, as is usually the case, then all possibilities will be realized with appropriate frequency (Fig. 28.12).

We note that half the offspring are pink-flowered and resemble their parents in this respect. One-quarter are red-flowered, one-quarter white-flowered, and these offspring resemble their grandparents. We may conclude that the visible results can be explained adequately on the basis of nonblending, freely segregating genes and the operations of chance.

Genetic Dominance

Genes like *A* and *a*, which control the same trait but produce different expressions of that trait, are called allelic genes, or **alleles.** In the snapdragon example above, trait expression evidently depends on the number of *A* alleles. Presence of *A* in single dose, as in *Aa* plants, gives only half as much pigment as presence of *A* in double dose, as in *AA* plants. Most traits are affected in this way by gene dosage.

In some cases, however, a maximum trait may be produced even if an allele is present only in single dose. In garden peas, for example, as in snapdragons, true-breeding red-flowered plants may be symbolized as *AA*, true-breeding white-flowered plants as *aa*. But when two such plants are mated, *all* offspring are *red*, not pink (Fig. 28.13).

Evidently, the single *A* gene in *Aa* plants suffices to bring out the full red color. Two *A* genes, as in *AA*, do not produce substantially more redness. Therefore,

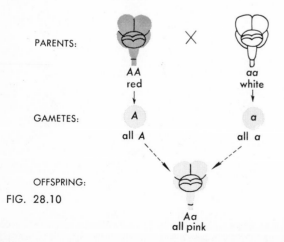

FIG. 28.10

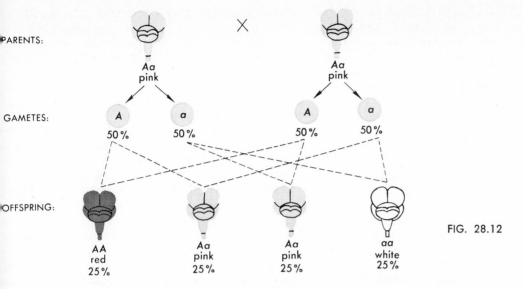

FIG. 28.12

if two red-flowered *Aa* plants are mated, three out of every four offspring will be red-flowered (Fig. 28.14).

Genes which produce a maximum trait even when present only in single dose, like the *A*'s of garden peas, are called **dominant** genes. They mask more or less completely the effect of other alleles, like the *a*'s of garden peas. These latter are called **recessive** alleles. Offspring in ratios of ¾ : ¼ are characteristic for matings involving dominant and recessive alleles, as above.

But complete dominance of this sort is far rarer than the allelic relationship illustrated above for snapdragons. There the *A* gene is said to be *partially* dominant, the *a* gene, *partially* recessive. Offspring ratios of ¼ : ½ : ¼ are then characteristic. We may note in this connection that allelic pairs like *AA* or *aa*, in which both genes are the same, are called **homozygous** combinations. By contrast, *Aa* pairs are called **heterozygous** combinations. For example, an *AA* genotype in garden peas is said to be "homozygous dominant."

In modern terminology, Mendel's first law, the **law of segregation,** may now be stated as follows: *Genes do not blend, but behave as independent units. They*

FIG. 28.13

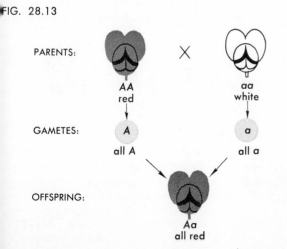

FIG. 28.14

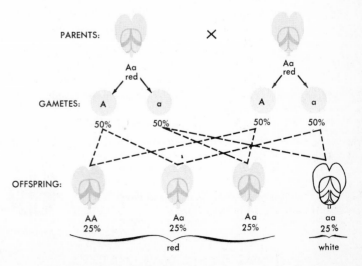

pass intact from one generation to the next, where they may or may not produce visible traits, depending on their dominance characteristics. And genes segregate at random, thereby producing predictable ratios of traits in the offspring. Implied in this law are chromosome reduction by meiosis and the operation of chance in the transmission of genes.

THE LAW OF INDEPENDENT ASSORTMENT

Organisms do not express traits one at a time, but exhibit all their traits simultaneously. Analogously, genes are not inherited one at a time, but all of them are inherited together. Therefore, given certain parents, what will the offspring be like with respect to two or more simultaneous traits?

Mendel discovered a fundamental rule here. Phrased in modern terms, this **law of independent assortment** states: *The inheritance of a gene pair located on a given chromosome pair is unaffected by the simultaneous inheritance of other gene pairs located on other chromosome pairs.* In other words, two or more traits produced by genes located on two or more chromosome pairs "assort independently"; i.e., each trait will be expressed independently, as if no other traits were present.

The Evidence

Suppose we analyze, as Mendel did, the simultaneous inheritance of two traits of garden peas, *seed shape* and *seed color*. Seed shape can be either **round** or **wrinkled**. Round can be shown to be dominant over wrinkled, and the possible alleles can be symbolized as *R* for round and *r* for wrinkled. Therefore, on a given

chromosome pair of peas is located either an *RR*, an *rr*, or an *Rr* pair of alleles. Similarly, **yellow** seed color (*Y*) is dominant over **green** seed color (*y*). Hence on another chromosome pair is located a *YY* or a *yy* or a *Yy* pair of alleles (Fig. 28.15).

Mendel mated two *RrYy* plants, i.e., individuals developed from round, yellow seeds but heterozygous for both traits. He obtained four categories of offspring, in the proportions given in Fig. 28.16. Mendel here noted that a total of 76.1 (56.7 plus 19.4) per cent of the offspring were round-seeded and that a total of 74.9 (56.7 plus 18.2) per cent were yellow-seeded. In other words, each of the two dominant traits, considered *separately*, amounted to very nearly 75 per cent, or three-fourths, of the total. The two recessive traits, considered separately, each amounted to about 25 per cent, or one-fourth, of the total. Evidently, as expected on the basis of the law of segregation, each dominant and its correlated recessive appeared in ratio of ¾ : ¼; i.e., dominants were three times as abundant as recessives.

Moreover, the two dominants were also three times as abundant *even if they were considered together.* That is, among the 76.1 per cent total of round-seeded offspring, 56.7 per cent, or very nearly three-fourths, were at the same time also yellow-seeded. And among the 74.9 per cent total of yellow-seeded offspring, 56.7 per cent, or again nearly three-fourths, were at the same time also round-seeded. In other words, the 56.7 per cent round- *and* yellow-seeded offspring amounted to *three-fourths of three-fourths*, or *nine-sixteenths*, of the total. The over-all ratio thus was very nearly %₁₆ : ³⁄₁₆ : ³⁄₁₆ : ¹⁄₁₆. Mendel concluded that such a ratio could be obtained only if *each* trait obeyed the law of segregation and if it were therefore expressed independently of other traits; hence his law of independent assortment.

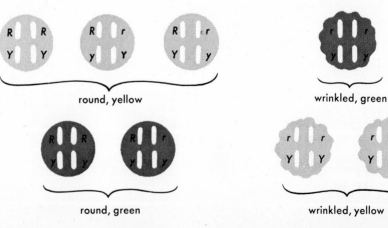

FIG. 28.15 Seed color and seed shape in garden peas. Four kinds of seed types may occur, namely, round-yellow, round-green, wrinkled-green, and wrinkled-yellow. Some of the possible gene combinations which could produce such seed types are shown in the diagram.

round, yellow

wrinkled, green

round, green

wrinkled, yellow

parents matured from
seeds of this type:

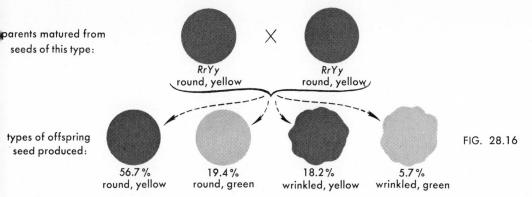

types of offspring
seed produced:

FIG. 28.16

56.7%
round, yellow

19.4%
round, green

18.2%
wrinkled, yellow

5.7%
wrinkled, green

The validity of this second law may be appreciated readily if we consider chromosomes, meiosis, and gametes. In the mating above, the cells of the parents are as shown in Fig. 28.17.

After meiosis, each gamete will contain only *one* seed-shape gene and only *one* color gene. But which of each pair? The dominant or the recessive gene? This is a matter of chance. There are four possibilities. A gamete might contain the genes R and Y, or R and y, or r and Y, or r and y. Many gametes are produced and all four combinations will therefore occur with roughly equal frequency (Fig. 28.18).

Fertilization is also governed by chance. Consequently, *any* one of the four sperm types might fertilize *any* one of the four egg types. Hence there are 16 different ways in which fertilization can occur. If large numbers of fertilizations take place simultaneously, all 16 ways will be realized with roughly equal frequency. We may determine these 16 ways by using a grid where the gametes of one parent are put along a horizontal edge and the gametes of the other parent along a vertical edge (Fig. 28.19).

Among the 16 offspring types now formed, we find some individuals which contain *both* dominant genes at least once, some which contain one *or* the other of the dominant genes at least once, and some

which contain none of the dominant genes. A count reveals round-yellow, round-green, wrinkled-yellow, and wrinkled-green to be present in a ratio of 9:3:3:1. This is the ratio Mendel actually obtained, as we have seen.

The Consequences

Mendel's second law applies specifically to gene pairs located on *different* chromosome pairs. The law will therefore hold for as many different gene pairs as there are chromosome pairs in each cell of a given organism. Suppose we considered the inheritance of *three* different gene pairs, each located on a different chromosome pair. For example, what would be the offspring of a mating of two triple heterozygotes, such as $AaBbCc \times AaBbCc$?

FIG. 28.18

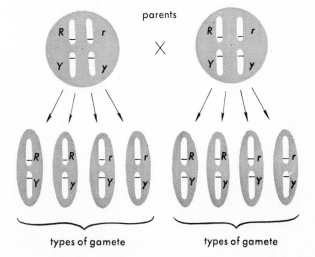

parents

types of gamete

types of gamete

FIG. 28.17

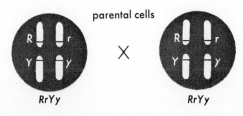

parental cells

RrYy

RrYy

parents:

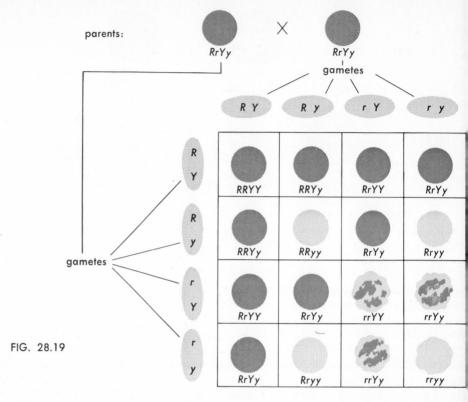

FIG. 28.19

We have found above that a double heterozygote *AaBb* produces *four* different gamete types. It should not be too difficult to verify that a triple heterozygote produces *eight* different gamete types, namely, *ABC, ABc, AbC, Abc, aBC, aBc, abC,* and *abc*. To determine all possible genotypes of the offspring, we may make a grid 8 squares by 8 squares and place the 8 gamete types of each parent along the sides of the grid, as above; and 64 offspring types will then result. Of these, 27 will express all three traits in dominant form. The complete phenotype ratio may easily be verified as 27:9:9:9:3:3:3:1.

Two quadruple heterozygotes, *AaBbCcDd*, would manufacture 16 gamete types each, and we would need a grid 16 by 16 to represent the 256 different genotype combinations. Evidently, the possibilities rapidly become astronomical once we consider more than a few traits simultaneously.

Organisms which are heterozygous for a large number of traits are known as **hybrids**. *Aa* types are sometimes referred to as *monohybrids, AaBb* types as *dihybrids, AaBbCc* types as *trihybrids*. In man there are 23 pairs of chromosomes per cell. Consequently,

Mendel's second law will apply to any 23 different traits controlled by genes located on different chromosome pairs. We might then study a mating of, for example, two 23-fold hybrids: *AaBb . . . Ww × AaBb . . . Ww*. How many gamete types would each such hybrid produce? We know that:

a monohybrid yields $2^1 = 2$ gamete types

a dihybrid yields $2^2 = 4$ gamete types

a trihybrid yields $2^3 = 8$ gamete types

a quadruple hybrid yields $2^4 = 16$ gamete types

Carrying this progression further, we find that a 23-fold hybrid will produce 2^{23} or over 8 million genetically different gamete types. Therefore, in considering just 23 traits, we would require a grid 8 million by 8 million to represent the over 64 trillion possible genotypes.

A particular individual then inherits just one of these genotypes. Of all the possible genotypes, a few millions or billions will produce resemblance to parents and another few millions or billions to grandparents or earlier ancestors. But there are bound to be a good many million or billion genotypes which have never yet become expressed during the entire history of man. Accordingly, there is a very excellent chance that every newly born human being differs from every other one, past or present, in at least some genes controlling just 23 traits. And the genetic differences for *all* traits must be enormous indeed. Here is one major reason for individual variations and a genetic basis for the universal generalization that no two organisms are precisely identical.

Any given chromosome contains not just one gene but anywhere from a few hundred to a few thousand genes. What is the inheritance pattern of two or more gene pairs located on the *same* chromosome pair? This question leads us beyond Mendel's two laws.

THE LAW OF LINEAR ORDER

Genes located within the same chromosome are said to be **linked**: as the chromosome is inherited, so are all its genes inherited. Such genes clearly do *not* assort independently, but are transmitted together in a block. The traits controlled by linked genes are similarly expressed in a block. For example, assume that in the heterozygote *AaBb* the two gene pairs are linked. When such an organism produces gametes, only *two* different gamete types are expected, 50 per cent of each (Fig. 28.20). We recall that if the gene pairs *Aa* and *Bb* were not linked, we should expect *four* gamete types through independent assortment, namely, *AB*, *ab*, *Ab*, and *aB*, 25 per cent of each.

Linkage studies were first undertaken by T. H.

FIG. 28.20

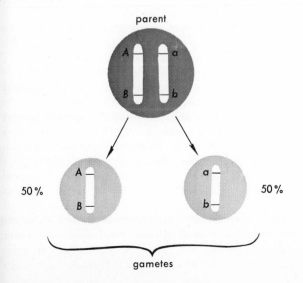

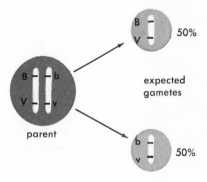

FIG. 28.21 Top, the phenotypes of two traits of *Drosophila*, controlled by linked genes. Bottom, the expected gametes of a heterozygous fly *BbVv*.

Morgan, a renowned American biologist of the early twentieth century. Experimenting with fruit flies, *Drosophila*, Morgan discovered a curious phenomenon. When genes were linked, the expected result of two gamete types in a 50:50 ratio was obtained relatively rarely. Instead, there were usually somewhat fewer than 50 per cent of each gamete type, and there were correspondingly small percentages of two additional, completely unexpected gamete types.

For example, fruit flies possess a gene for *gray* body color (*B*), dominant over a gene for *black* body color (*b*). These alleles are located on the same chromosomes which also carry genes controlling wing shape: an allele for *normal* wings (*V*), dominant over an allele for highly reduced, *vestigial* wings (*v*). If now a gray-bodied, normal-winged heterozygous female fly, *BbVv*, produces gametes, only two types should be expected, namely, *BV* and *bv* (Fig. 28.21). However, Morgan consistently obtained *four* gamete types, in the proportions given in Fig. 28.22.

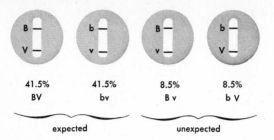

41.5% BV	41.5% bv	8.5% B v	8.5% b V

expected — unexpected

FIG. 28.22

If these four types had formed to an extent of about 25 per cent each, the experiment could have been regarded simply as a case without linkage, governed by Mendel's second law. But the actual results included significantly *more* than 25 per cent each of the expected gamete types and significantly *fewer* than 25 per cent each of the unexpected types.

To explain these odd results, Morgan proposed a new hypothesis. He postulated that, during meiosis, paired chromosomes in some cases might *twist around each other* and might break where they are twisted. The broken pieces might then fuse again in the "wrong" order (Fig. 28.23).

This would account for the large percentage of expected and the small percentage of unexpected gamete types. To test the validity of this hypothesis, cells undergoing meiosis were examined carefully under the microscope: could chromosome twists and breaks actually be seen? They could indeed, and the phenomenon of **crossing over** was so proved.

The implications of this discovery were far-reaching. It was reasoned that the frequency of crossovers should be an index of the *distance* between two genes. If two genes on a chromosome are located near

FIG. 28.23

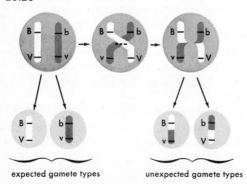

expected gamete types — unexpected gamete types

each other, the chances should be relatively small that a twist will occur between these close points. But if two genes are relatively far apart, then twists between these points should be rather frequent. In general, the frequency of crossovers should be proportional to the distance between two genes (Fig. 28.24).

Inasmuch as the crossover percentage of two genes could be determined by breeding experiments, it became possible to construct **gene maps** showing the actual location of given genes on a chromosome. Since Morgan's time, the exact position of few hundred genes has been mapped in the fruit fly. Smaller numbers of genes have similarly been located in corn plants, in mice, and in various other organisms. Many of these determinations have been corroborated by X-ray work. When irradiated, a chromosome may break into pieces, and a small piece of this sort may be lost from a gamete. Offspring resulting from such deficient gametes will be abnormal in certain traits. In many cases microscopic examination can show where a chromosome piece is missing and a trait so can be correlated with a particular spot on a chromosome.

A second implication of crossing over is that genes on a chromosome must be lined up single-file. Only if this is the case can linkage and crossing over occur as it actually does occur. This generalization has become known as the **law of the linear order of genes.** It constitutes the third major rule which governs Mendelian inheritance.

Thirdly, crossing over has provided a functional definition of "gene": *A gene is the smallest section of a chromosome within which crossovers do not take place.* The assumption here is that the minimum chromosome unit able to cross over is one *whole* gene, not a fractional part of one gene. Recall the two other acceptable definitions of "gene" discussed in Chap. 18.

Lastly, a further implication of crossing over during meiosis is that meiosis is a *source of genetic variations.* For example, when a diploid cell in a testis undergoes meiosis and produces four haploid sperms, these four do not contain merely the same whole chromosomes as the original cell, even though redistributed. For if the original diploid cell possesses a chromosome pair M' and M", then a given sperm will not simply receive either the M' or the M" chromosome. Instead, as a result of crossing over, it will receive a quiltwork chromosome composed of various joined *pieces* of *both* M' and M". In each set of four sperms, actually, two will contain like chromosomes composed of one set of M' and M" pieces and two will contain like chromosomes composed of the remaining, complementary M′ and M″ pieces. Moreover, the original diploid cell possesses not only a single chromosome pair but several pairs, and each such pair is likely to be subjected to crossing over in an unpredictable fashion. Chances are therefore excellent that the four sperms will be genetically different from one another as well as from the original diploid cell. Further, even two genetically identical diploid cells are not likely to give rise to genetically identical sets of sperms. In general, the gene-shuffling effect of crossing over is in evidence wherever or whenever meiosis occurs. Genetic variations consequently are produced by both phases of sex, i.e., by chromosome doubling through fertilization as well as by chromosome reduction through meiosis.

The three rules of heredity here outlined describe and predict the processes of Mendelian inheritance, i.e., the parent-to-offspring transmission of one or more independent gene pairs which control *an equal number* of independent traits. However, a great many hereditary phenomena have been found to be beyond the scope of the three basic rules. Some of these non-Mendelian processes will be the subject of the following section.

NON-MENDELIAN INHERITANCE

MUTATION

We have found above that hereditary patterns are Mendelian and obey the laws of Mendel and Morgan to the extent that genetic variations are brought about by sexual pooling of different gene sets in the zygote. But inheritable variations may arise also in non-Mendelian fashion. Two instances of this kind are bacterial **transformation** and **transduction,** already discussed in Chap. 18. In these cases, it will be recalled, the gene content of bacteria is altered by the introduction of additional genetic material through the agency of either human experimenters or viruses. However, transformation and transduction have strictly limited significance. A far more important type of non-Mendelian variation, of universal significance in all organisms, is **mutation.**

Any stable, inheritable change in the genetic material present in a cell constitutes a mutation. For example, the accidental doubling, tripling, etc., of the normal chromosome number represents a stable, transmissible change. This is a *chromosome mutation.* Acci-

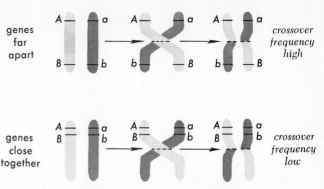

FIG. 28.24 Crossover frequency in relation to gene distance. If two genes are far apart, crossing over between them is likely to occur rather frequently (top). But if genes are close together, crossing over between them is less likely. In general, the farther apart given genes are on a chromosome, the more frequent crossing over will be.

dental loss or addition of a whole chromosome, loss of a chromosome piece, fusion of such a piece with another chromosome or fusion with the original chromosome in inverted position—these also are chromosome mutations. But by far the most common type of mutation is a *point mutation,* a stable change of one gene. Recall that a possible definition of "gene" is that it is a unit of mutation (Fig. 28.25).

It has been known for many years that mutational changes can be induced by high-energy radiation such as X rays. The frequency of mutation has been found to be directly proportional to the amount of radiation a cell receives. Are naturally occurring mutations similarly produced by radiation, e.g., by cosmic rays and other space radiation, or by radioactive elements in the earth? Probably not entirely; it can be shown that the unavoidable natural radiation which affects all organisms is not sufficiently intense to account for the mutation frequency characteristic of genes generally. This frequency has been estimated as about 1 mutation per million cells, on the average. However, natural "background" radiation does produce some mutations. Most others probably represent errors in gene reproduction (see Chap. 18). And still others are undoubtedly caused by man-made radiation, which adds to and so increases the natural background radiation. Mutations can also be produced experimentally by physical agents other than radiations and by various chemical agents.

As far as can be ascertained, mutations appear to be completely random events. Any gene may mutate

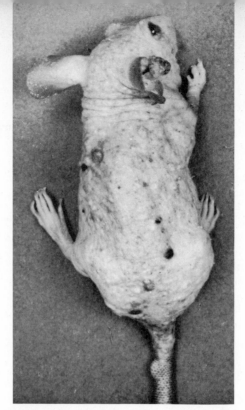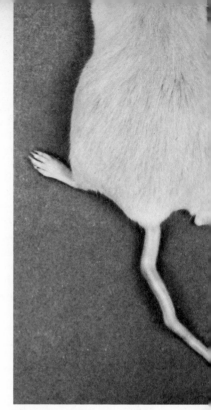

FIG. 28.25 Mutant types in mice. Left, the effects of the mutation "eyelessness." Middle, the effects of the mutation "hairlessness." Right, the effects of the "kinky-tail" mutation. Each of these alterations in structure is correlated with a single mutant gene; and the alterations are stable and inheritable. (*Courtesy of Dr. H. B. Chase and R. Hughes, Brown University.*)

at any time, in unpredictable ways. A given gene may mutate several times in rapid succession, then not at all for considerable periods. It may mutate in one direction, then mutate back to its original state or in new directions. There is little question that *every* gene existing today is a **mutant** which has undergone many mutations during its past history.

The effect of a mutation on a trait is equally unpredictable. Some are "large" mutations, i.e., they affect a major trait in a radical, drastic manner. Others are "small," with but little effect on a trait. Some mutations are dominant, producing immediate positive alterations of traits. Other mutations are recessive, and in diploid cells they remain masked by normal dominant alleles.

Most mutations are disadvantageous. Indeed, inasmuch as a living cell is an exceedingly complex, very finely adjusted whole, it is to be expected that *any* permanent change in cellular properties would be more or less disruptive and harmful. In many cases, therefore, dominant mutations tend to be eliminated as soon

as they arise, through death of the affected cell. In other cases, the effect of a dominant mutation, particularly a "small" dominant mutation, may become integrated successfully into cellular functions. Such a cell may then survive even though it exhibits an altered trait. By and large, however, recessive mutations are likely to persist more readily in diploid cells, since their effects may be masked by normal dominant alleles. Accumulated evidence actually shows that surviving mutations are very largely recessive ones.

A small percentage of mutants produces advantageous traits and new traits which are neither advantageous nor disadvantageous. Consider mutations in man for example. Many trillions of cells compose the human body and mutations occur at an average rate of 1 in every million cells. Therefore, several million mutations are likely to occur in each individual. Many of these may be lethal to the cells in which they occur and many others will remain masked by normal dominants. But some mutations may produce traits which do not kill a cell. Such new traits, arising in individual cells

re then transmitted to all cells formed from the origi-
al ones by division. For example, "beauty spots" prob-
bly develop in this manner.

Gene changes of this type, occurring in body cells
enerally, are known as **somatic mutations.** They affect
he heredity of the cell progeny, i.e., a patch of tissue
t most. But in multicellular organisms such mutations
ave little direct bearing on the heredity of the indi-
idual. Entire multicellular offspring are affected only
y so-called **germ mutations,** stable genetic changes in
mmature and mature gametes or spores or zygotes.
uch mutations will be transmitted to all cells compos-
g the offspring (Fig. 28.26). To the extent that germ
utations may be recessive and masked by normal
ominants, the traits of the offspring will not be altered.
ut if the offspring is haploid or is diploid but homo-

IG. 28.26 The effects of germ mutations and somatic
utations. If a mutation occurs late during development,
n a somatic cell, then only the progeny of that cell will
nherit the mutation and the total effect on the adult
rganism will be small. But if a mutation occurs early
uring development, e.g., in a gamete, then all cells of
he resulting adult will inherit such a germ mutation, and
ll cells may feature altered traits.

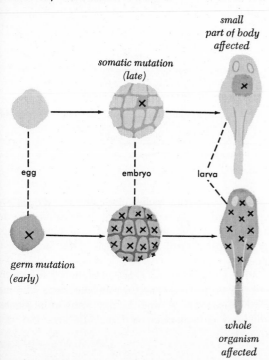

*small
part of body
affected*

*somatic mutation
(late)*

egg   embryo   larva

*germ mutation
(early)*

*whole
organism
affected*

zygous recessive for a mutation, or if a mutation is
dominant, then a particular trait may be expressed in
altered form. Provided such a new trait is not lethal,
it will persist as an individual (and non-Mendelian)
variation. Mutations may therefore affect the adaptation
of an individual as much as sexual recombination of
genes.

MUTONS, RECONS, CISTRONS

When a gene mutates, how much of the structure
of the gene actually becomes altered? And when a gene
controls the production of a trait, how much of the
structure of the gene is active? Until quite recently, it
was believed that a gene represented the indivisible
minimum unit of heredity, just as atoms were once
thought to be the smallest units of matter. However,
smaller functional subunits are now known to exist not
only in atoms but also in genes.

After it became clear that a gene could be regarded as a section of a DNA chain consisting of joined
nucleotides (see Chap. 18), the existence of genic subunits became theoretically quite likely. For example,
the presence of subdivisions can be inferred from the
phenomenon of alleles. As noted earlier, alleles are
alternative functional forms of a gene, e.g., dominants
and recessives. In some cases a gene is known to occur
in not just two but in several dozens of alternative
forms, each allele having a specifically different effect
on the expression of the same trait. Thus all allelic
forms of a gene might affect eye color, but the actual
color produced by one of the alleles might differ
slightly from that produced by any of the other alleles.
Inasmuch as allelic forms do affect the same trait, it is
quite unlikely that their DNAs are totally different. It
is far more likely that all alleles of a gene have essentially the same basic sequence of joined nucleotides
and that the functional differences between alleles are
due to relatively slight chemical differences. For example, one or perhaps a few of the nucleotides present
at a given point along the DNA chain of one allele
might differ from the nucleotides present at the corresponding point of another allele. In terms of molecular
structure, therefore, any given allelic state of a gene
might differ from any other by not more than one or at
most a few nucleotides along otherwise identical DNA
chains.

New allelic states are produced by gene mutation.
In line with the above, a mutation would not have to
involve the whole DNA chain of a gene but would pro-

duce a detectable new allele even if it affected only a small segment within a gene. The term **muton** has been proposed to designate the smallest segment within a gene which by mutation can produce an altered trait. Based in part on data from bacteriophage viruses, a muton has been estimated to consist of some three or four joined nucleotides, possibly only of just one or two. A whole gene may be envisaged to consist of a linear array of very many mutons.

If consecutive segments within a single gene may mutate independently, a gene should include a linear series of functionally different regions. That this is actually the case has been shown in recent studies on gene-controlled enzyme synthesis in bacteria and other organisms. These studies indicate that small, functionally distinguishable segments of genes can become transferred to other chromosomes. Such transfers are not crossovers. As outlined earlier, crossing over takes place between whole genes, and we recall that a possible definition of a whole gene is that it is the smallest chromosome unit capable of crossing over. Crossing over is also a reciprocal process. For example, suppose that genes A and B are linked on one chromosome and that the corresponding alleles a and b are linked on the other chromosome of a pair. If crossing over occurs between A and B, the result will be the combination Ab as well as the reciprocal combination aB.

By contrast, transfers of small segments within a gene are occasionally nonreciprocal. Suppose that a gene R contains the subunits R_1 and R_2 and that an allele r on the other chromosome of a pair contains the corresponding subunits r_1 and r_2:

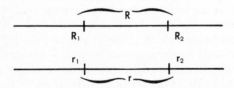

When the genes R and r reproduce and form duplicates, it happens in some cases that one of the genes appears to make a reproduction error. For example, R_1R_2 may form a normal duplicate but r_1r_2 may not. The r_1 region may be duplicated correctly, but instead of also forming a copy of the r_2 region, the gene copies the R_2 region of the nearby allele on the other chromosome. The result is a new gene which contains the subunits r_1R_2:

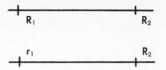

The combination r_1R_2 is clearly nonreciprocal, for R_1r_2 is not formed.

Evidently, the r_2 region behaves as if it could make a **copy choice** during reproduction; it may produce either another r_2 or an R_2 region. Recombinations of subunits within genes generally appear to result from "wrong" copy choices. The smallest segment within a gene capable of forming new recombinations as just described has been called a **recon**. Such a unit may consist of perhaps not more than a single nucleotide. It is therefore conceivable that, in some cases at least, a recon may be identical with a muton.

Can a genetic function continue to be performed if the mutons and recons of a gene are not united together on the same chromosome? For example, suppose that a given gene A controls the synthesis of a particular enzyme protein and that this gene consists of a series of consecutive mutons. Suppose also that the mutons form two adjacent groups A_1 and A_2, and that an allelic recessive gene a contains the corresponding muton groups a_1 and a_2:

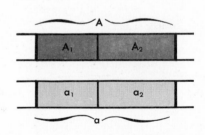

So arranged on the same chromosome, the muton groups A_1 and A_2 are said to be in a *cis* position. Under such conditions the whole gene A will function normally and will control the synthesis of the enzyme, as assumed.

What is the effect on genetic function if the muton groups A_1 and A_2 are not within the same chromosome? For example, A_1 and A_2 may come to be located on different chromosomes and may be arranged in a *trans* position:

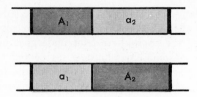

In such a *trans* arrangement, control of enzyme synthesis may or may not continue normally, depending on the specific nature of the gene and its muton groups A_1 and A_2. If the genetic function of A does continue normally, the muton groups A_1 and A_2 are said to **complement** each other. In this case, evidently, the functional effectiveness of the gene is not interfered with even though the gene is subdivided structurally and each muton group is located on a different chromosome. In other cases, however, a *trans* arrangement of muton groups does lead to cessation of enzyme synthesis; complementation does not occur and genetic function then stops.

Such results can be explained if it is assumed that given numbers of consecutive mutons (or recons) within a gene form larger functional sets. For example, if a gene consisted of 50 mutons, 30 of these might form an integrated block which might have to stay intact structurally if function is to be maintained. Thus if this block of 30 were on one chromosome and the remaining 20 were in *trans* position on another chromosome, then complementation could occur and genetic function could continue. But if only 29 mutons were on one chromosome and the remaining 21 were on the other, then complementation could not occur since an intact block of 30 mutons would no longer be present. The actual existence of such integrated blocks of mutons within genes has been verified. The term **cistron** has been coined for the smallest set of mutons or recons of a gene which must remain together on one chromosome if genetic activity is to be preserved. The mutons within a cistron undoubtedly interact with one another in some intimate way, and if the interaction is prevented by a subdivision of the cistron, then the whole cistron will become nonfunctional. Tests show that a single gene consists of relatively few cistrons, one adjacent to the next and each composed of specific numbers of mutons (or recons).

We may conclude, therefore, that for each operational definition of a whole gene we now also have a corresponding operational definition of a genic subunit. A whole gene is a unit of mutation, or a unit of recombination by crossing over, or a unit of biochemical action. Within a gene, analogously, the mutational unit is the muton, the recombinational unit is the recon, and the functional unit is the cistron. Both sets of definitions are operational ones reflecting the nature and refinement of the experimental methods we use. If we regard a whole protein molecule as the smallest genetically controlled trait, then our experimental methods will lead us correspondingly to a smallest unit of heredity; we have called such a unit a gene. Until recently, the best conclusion actually permitted by available methods was that a whole gene controlled the synthesis of a whole protein molecule, more specifically, an enzyme. However, we know that a protein molecule has subtraits, namely, amino acids and polypeptide chains. And it is now possible to study the inheritance of such subtraits by means of refined experimental methods. The results have shown that a whole Mendelian gene is a relatively crude hereditary unit within which finer subunits may be identified—mutons, recons, and cistrons. Conceivably, mutons and recons may control the synthesis of individual amino acids, and cistrons may control the synthesis of polypeptide chains. In any event, a gene must be regarded as a complex chromosome region composed of many interacting functional parts. The latter appear to have a definite though not yet fully specified relation to the structural units of the DNA chain.

Interaction is known to occur not only among the parts within a gene but also among whole genes. As pointed out earlier, the activity of a gene is influenced by its environment and this environment includes other genes. Like the interactions within genes, those among genes also tend to produce non-Mendelian results, i.e., results which cannot be predicted by the three rules of Mendelian inheritance.

GENE-GENE INTERACTIONS

Groups of genes within a cell often cooperate in controlling a highly composite trait. One of the best illustrations of this is the trait of sexuality, which in numerous organisms is controlled not by individual genes acting separately but by whole chromosomes acting as functionally integrated units.

Sex Determination

It has been known for a long time that the primary determiners of sex in various plants and animals are chromosomes. Special **sex chromosomes** are present, as in the cells of the liverwort *Sphaerocarpos*, for example. These chromosomes are of two kinds, called *X* and *Y*. They differ in shape from each other and also from all other chromosomes, which are called **autosomes** for contrast. In *Sphaerocarpos,* the gametophytes are of separate sexes. Examination reveals that each cell of a female gametophyte contains one *X* chromosome. Analogously, each cell of a male gametophyte contains one *Y* chromosome (Fig. 28.27). Eggs and sperms are then similarly *X* and *Y*, respectively. Fertilization therefore produces a diploid zygote which is

FIG. 28.27   Sex determination in the bryophyte *Sphaerocarpos.* The sex chromosomes are named *X* and *Y*, the former determining femaleness, the latter maleness. Note that gametophytes are haploid and thus carry only a single sex chromosome per cell; sporophytes are diploid and carry two, namely *X* and *Y*. This endows sporophytes with *potential* genetic bisexuality, even though structurally the plants represent the asexual generation.

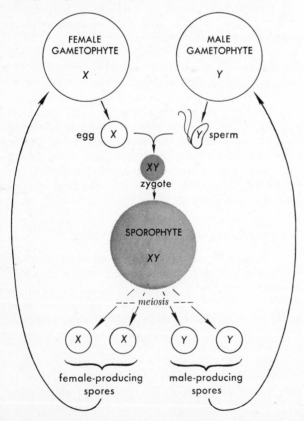

XY in constitution. Each cell of the sporophyte subsequently inherits the *XY* chromosomes. When a spore-producing cell of the sporophyte later undergoes meiosis, the two sex chromosomes become segregated into different spore cells. The final result is that of the four mature spores formed, two contain an *X* chromosome each and two a *Y* chromosome each. Thus even though all spores look alike, they are genetically of two different sex types. Spores with *X* chromosomes subsequently mature into female gametophytes; spores with *Y* chromosomes mature into male gametophytes. Evidently, the whole *X* chromosome appears to determine femaleness, the whole *Y* chromosome, maleness. We may conclude that, probably in addition to serving in other trait-controlling roles, each gene of a sex chromosome also contributes toward the control of the sexual characteristics of the plant.

An entirely similar sex-determining mechanism exists in a number of other bryophytes. However, the pattern of inheritance is somewhat different in all other organisms in which genetic sex determination is known to occur, e.g., in tracheophytes such as *Elodea* and in animals such as insects and vertebrates. Man may serve as a representative example. In each human cell, a *pair* of sex chromosomes is present. A cell of a female contains 22 pairs of autosomes plus two *X* chromosomes: 44A + *XX*. In males, each cell again contains 22 pairs of autosomes but the sex chromosomes are *X* and *Y:* 44A + *XY*.

All autosomes and *X* chromosomes carry genes. On the other hand, functioning genes are almost completely absent from *Y* chromosomes, which appear to be quite inert genetically. *Y* chromosomes may be lost from cells without appreciable interference with the normal expression of traits. Evidently, the *Y* chromosomes of man (and of animals generally) are quite different from those of *Sphaerocarpos*, which do contain sex-determining genes. In view of the inert *Y* chromosomes of man, the cells of human males contain only 45 functional chromosomes but female cells contain 46. This difference of one whole *X* chromosome, with its hundreds of genes, lies at the root of the sexual differences between males and females.

It can be shown that it is the ratio of autosomes to *X* chromosomes which is significant in the expression of sex. *Autosomes* promote the development of *maleness; X chromosomes* promote the development of *femaleness.* In a human 44A + *XX* cell, the total feminizing influence of the two *X* chromosomes outweighs the total masculinizing influence of the 44 autosomes individuals composed of such cells are females. But if the cells contain $44A + XY$, then the masculinizing effect of the 44 autosomes is sufficiently strong to override the feminizing effect of the single X chromosome. Such individuals are male.

The sexual nature of man, as of other animals, thus appears to depend on a particular *balance* between two genetic influences. If this is correct, should it not be possible to alter the expression of sex by experimentally altering the numerical balance between autosomes and X chromosomes? This is indeed possible. Experiments of this kind actually have given the first clues that chromosome balances play a role in sex determination.

In the fruit fly *Drosophila*, for example, the numbers of autosomes and X chromosomes in sperms and eggs can be varied by certain laboratory procedures. One may then obtain offspring characterized by normal paired sets of autosomes, but by *three* X chromosomes instead of two. These individuals grow into so-called **superfemales**: all sexual traits are greatly accentuated in the direction of femaleness. **Supermales** and **intersexes** may be produced analogously. In intersexes, sexual traits are intermediate between those of males and females. The chromosome balances are shown in Fig. 28.28. Paradoxically, supersexes and also intersexes are generally sterile; as a result of the abnormal chromosome numbers, meiosis occurs abnormally and the sperms and eggs then produced are defective.

In the light of such balances, we may appreciate readily how the sex of an offspring is inherited normally. For example, human females, $44A + XX$, give rise to eggs of which each contains $22A + X$ after meiosis. Males, $44A + XY$, produce two kinds of sperms, namely, $22A + X$ and $22A + Y$, in roughly equal numbers. Fertilization now occurs at random, i.e., a sperm of either type may unite with an egg. Therefore, in about 50 per cent of the cases the result will be $(22A + X) + (22A + X)$, or $44A + XX$, or female-producing zygotes. In the remaining 50 per cent of the cases, the zygotes will be $(22A + X) + (22A + Y)$, or $44A + XY$, or male-producing (Fig. 28.29).

Note that it is the prospective father who, at the moment of fertilization, determines the probable sex of the offspring. When only a single offspring is produced, there exists a 50:50 chance of its being a son or a daughter. When many offspring are produced, the number of males will generally equal the number of females.

Note also that the absence of a functional mate to the X chromosome in males has other genetic conse-

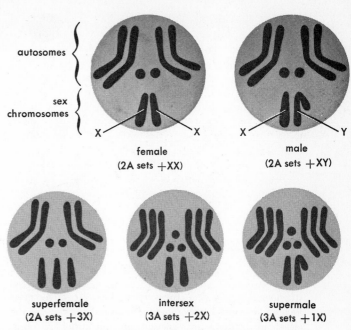

FIG. 28.28 Top, the chromosomes of the fruit fly *Drosophila*. In each cell, $2n = 8$. Note the differences in the sex chromosomes of males and females. In man, $2n = 46$, sex-chromosome differences being as in fruit flies. Bottom, sex and chromosome balance in the fruit fly. The sexual character of an individual is determined by the specific balance of autosomes and X chromosomes.

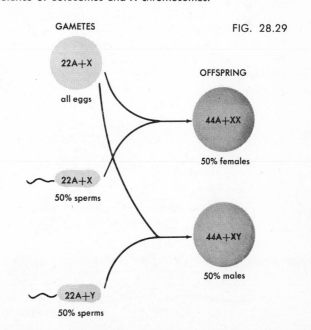

FIG. 28.29

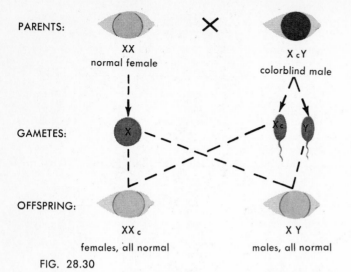

PARENTS:

XX
normal female

X cY
colorblind male

GAMETES:

X

Xc   Y

OFFSPRING:

XX c
females, all normal

X Y
males, all normal

FIG. 28.30

quences. In females, the effect of a recessive gene located on one X chromosome may be masked by the effect of a dominant located on the other X chromosome. But in males, recessive genes on the X chromosome may exert their effect, since another X chromosome with masking dominants is never present. Genes located on X chromosomes are called **sex-linked** genes.

Because males possess only a single X chromosome, such genes are inherited according to a characteristic pattern. For example, red-green color blindness in man is traceable to a sex-linked recessive gene c. Suppose that a color-blind male, X_cY, marries a normal female, XX. In this symbolization, an X chromosome without the subscript c is tacitly assumed to contain the dominant gene C, which prevents the expression of color

FIG. 28.31

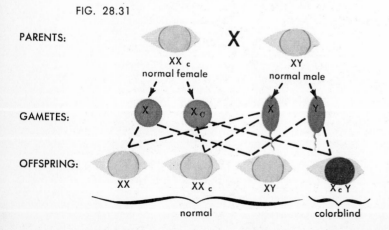

PARENTS:

XX c
normal female

XY
normal male

GAMETES:

X   Xc

X   Y

OFFSPRING:

XX

XX c

XY

XcY

normal

colorblind

blindness. The offspring of such a mating, shown in Fig. 28.30, include sons and daughters in equal numbers. The daughters carry the recessive gene c, but all offspring have normal vision.

Suppose now that one of these daughters marries a normal male, as shown in Fig. 28.31. All daughters resulting from such a mating are normal, but half the sons are color-blind. Thus the trait has been transmitted from color-blind grandfather via normal mother to color-blind son. Such a zigzag pattern of inheritance is characteristic of all recessive sex-linked traits. Males typically exhibit the trait; females merely transmit it. Evidently, the presence of a second X chromosome may protect females from expressing recessive sex-linked traits. Color blindness is one of several characteristically male, sex-linked abnormalities. Another is *haemophilia*, a bleeder's disease resulting from absence of blood platelets.

Genetic Systems

The examples of genetic sex determination given above show clearly that genes of one or more chromosomes may act in concert and control one highly composite trait. The implication is that genes are not merely independent "beads on a string," lined up haphazardly on given numbers of chromosomes. On the contrary, the genes in every chromosome appear to interact in very specific ways, and the expression of traits is influenced by such interactions.

Many other illustrations of this principle are known. For example, if genes were simply independently functioning units, then it should not matter if the position of genes relative to one another were rearranged. But experiment shows that such rearrangement actually does matter. It is possible to change the position of given sections of a chromosome. A piece lost by one chromosome may become attached to another, or it may become reattached to the same chromosome but in inverted position or at the other end. Genes here are neither removed from nor added to a cell; only their position relative to one another is rearranged. Under such conditions the cell may nevertheless develop altered traits, a clear indication that genes normally interact with their neighbors.

The phenomenon of dominance provides another good illustration of the interdependence of genes. A dominant gene acts as it does not only because of its inherent characteristics, but also because other genes *permit* it to act in dominant fashion. If the functional characteristics of the recessive allele of a given domiant were to change, then the status of dominance of that gene would change correspondingly. And if the functional characteristics of any other genes in the cell were to change, then the status of dominance of that gene would again change. It is now well established that given genes boost, suppress, partially inhibit, or otherwise change the effects of other genes. For example, **modifier** genes are known which intensify or minimize the traits produced by other genes. Analogously, **suppressor** genes completely prevent traits produced by other genes from becoming expressed explicitly. Some genes affect not the traits produced by other genes but the other genes themselves. Among them are **operator** genes, which must be present if certain other genes are to function, and **regulator** genes, which apparently turn the action of other genes on and off. We may conclude, therefore, that the effects of genes are of two general types, viz., effects leading to the expression of traits and effects influencing other genes and the products of gene action. It is possible that every gene in a cell, in addition to a specific trait-producing function, also may have a more or less decisive influence on the action of one or more other genes present.

Thus, whereas the pre-Mendelians thought that *traits* were inherited and whereas the Mendelian era advanced to the concept that individual factors, or *genes,* were inherited, the present post-Mendelian era recognizes that actually neither traits nor genes nor even subunits of genes are inherited. Instead, what are inherited are whole chromosome *sets,* coordinated *complexes* of genes, subtly integrated and interacting **genetic systems.** Moreover, even genetic systems are not inherited by themselves but are transmitted within *whole* cells. The functional integration between genetic system and cell system is never lost, and it is biologically almost meaningless to consider one without the other. Actually, the cell cytoplasm also is a carrier of heredity. For example, cell membranes, mitochondria, kinetosomes, nuclear membranes, and many other intracellular structures are inherited not through genes but through "self-duplication" of preexisting parental structures. The genetic system of a cell undoubtedly controls such cytoplasmic self-duplication, but the cytoplasmic system certainly also controls the self-duplication of the genetic system. Ultimately, therefore, the smallest real unit of inheritance is one whole cell.

In this chapter we have found that the inheritance of genetic systems and of the traits they control is governed by the biological nature of sex, by various probabilistic Mendelian rules, by random mutational changes, by interactions within genes and between genes, and by the effects of the environment on gene-trait relationships. In the individual organism, this interplay between sex, heredity, and environment produces relative adaptedness. In the long reproductive succession as a whole, this interplay becomes *evolution.*

REVIEW QUESTIONS

1. What are the sources of genetic variations in (a) uniparental, (b) biparental inheritance? Distinguish between inherited and acquired variations. What contributions are made to the expression of traits by (a) genes, (b) the environment? What is an "inherited disease"?

2. What was meant by "blending inheritance"? Describe the experiments through which Mendel came to deny blending. What hypothesis did Mendel substitute for the blending concept? State the chromosome theory of heredity. What is the evidence that genes are actually contained within chromosomes?

3. Define: genome, true breeding, phenotype, genotype, allele, dominant gene, recessive gene, homozygous, heterozygous, hybrid.

4. Review the experiments on inheritance of flower color in snapdragons in terms of genes and chromosomes. What are the quantitative results of the mating $Aa \times Aa$ if (a) A is dominant over a, (b) neither gene is dominant over the other?

5. In your own words, state the law of segregation. If A is dominant over a, what phenotype ratios of offspring are obtained from the following matings: (a) $Aa \times aa$, (b) $AA \times aa$, (c) $Aa \times Aa$, (d) $Aa \times AA$?

6. In your own words, state the law of independent assortment. By what kinds of breeding experiments, and by what reasoning, did Mendel come to discover this law? Interpret the law in terms of genes, meiosis, and gametes. How many genetically different gamete types will be produced by an organism heterozygous in 10 gene pairs? If two such organisms were mated, how many genetically different offspring types could result?

7. Define linkage. Why does inheritance of linked genes not obey Mendel's second law? What are the quantitative and qualitative differences here? What were Morgan's observations which led him to the hypothesis of crossing over? Describe this hypothesis. How do crossover data permit the construction of gene maps? State the law of the linear order of genes. What definition of gene is based on the phenomenon of crossing over? Review other definitions.

8. Distinguish between chromosome mutations and point mutations and between somatic mutations and germ mutations. What is the relation between mutation frequency and radiation intensity? What are the characteristics of mutations from the standpoint of (a) predictability, (b) functional relation to normal alleles (c) effects on traits, and (d) relative advantage to the organism?

9. What are mutons, recons, and cistrons? Review the genetic basis of sex determination in (a Sphaerocarpos and (b) man. What is the significance of a given numerical balance between autosomes and sex chromosomes? What are supersexes and intersexes

10. What are sex-linked genes? Describe the inheritance pattern of the sex-linked recessive haemophilia gene h, assuming that a haemophilic male mate with a normal female. What are modifier genes? Describe specific instances of gene-gene interactions.

SUGGESTED COLLATERAL READINGS

The original work of the founder of modern genetics will always be of special interest:

Mendel, G.: "Experiments in Plant Hybridization." A translation of the original (1865) was published by Harvard University Press, Cambridge, Mass., 1941.

Two standard texts on genetics, recommended as supplements to topics covered in this chapter:

Snyder, L. H.: "The Principles of Heredity," Heath, Boston, 1951.
Srb, A., and R. D. Owen: "General Genetics," Freeman, San Francisco, 1955.

Of the readings below, the second is a collection of reprints of classic original articles on which much of modern genetics is based. The first is a "progress report" after the first fifty years of genetics and consists of essays written by eminent biologists.

Dunn, L. C. (ed.): "Genetics in the 20th Century," Macmillan, New York, 1951.
Gabriel, M. L., and S. Fogel: "Great Experiments in Biology," section on Genetics, Prentice-Hall, Englewood Cliffs, N.J., 1955.

The following are general books and articles on genetics:

Dobzhansky, T.: "Evolution, Genetics, and Man," Wiley, New York, 1955.
Dunn, L. C., and T. Dobzhansky: "Heredity, Race, and Society," Penguin, Baltimore, 1946.
Goldschmidt, R. B.: "Understanding Heredity," Wiley New York, 1952.
Hollander, W. F.: Lethal Heredity, Sci. American, vol 187, 1952.
Knight, C. A., and D. Fraser: The Mutation of Viruses Sci. American, vol. 193, 1955.
Muller, H. J.: Radiation Damage to the Genetic Material, Am. Scientist, vol. 38, 1950.
———: Radiation and Human Mutation, Sci. American, vol. 193, 1955.
———, C. C. Little, and L. H. Snyder: "Genetics Medicine, and Man," Cornell University Press Ithaca, N.Y., 1947.
Scheinfeld, A.: "The New You and Heredity," Lippincott, Philadelphia, 1950.
Snyder, L. H.: Human Heredity and Its Modern Applications, Am. Scientist, vol. 43, 1955.
Spoerl, E.: The Lethal Effects of Radiation, Sci. American, vol. 185, 1951.
Stern, C.: Man's Genetic Future, Sci. American, vol 186, 1952.
———: Two or Three Bristles, Am. Scientist, vol. 42 1954.
Strong, L. C.: Genetics and Cancer, Sci. American, vol 183, 1950.

EVOLUTION: THE MECHANISM

29

No biologist today seriously questions the principle that species arise from preexisting species. Evolution on a small scale can actually be brought about in the laboratory, and the forces which drive and guide evolutionary processes are understood quite thoroughly.

That evolution really occurs did not become definitely established till the nineteenth century. For long ages man was unaware of the process, but he did wonder about the origin of his kind and of other living creatures. Indeed, he developed a succession of simple and rather crude theories about evolution. Unsupported by real evidence, these were ultimately proved untenable one by one. Yet the early ideas occasionally still color the views of those who are unacquainted with the modern knowledge.

It is advisable, therefore, that we begin this chapter with a brief survey of the historical **background** of evolutionary thought. Based on such a perspective, we may then discuss the **forces of evolution,** as these are understood today, and follow with an analysis of the **nature of evolution,** as determined by the underlying forces.

BACKGROUND

EARLY NOTIONS

The earliest theory of organic creation is contained in the Old Testament: God made the world and its living inhabitants in six days, man coming last. On this were based the theological ideas of *special creation* and of *immutability of species,* which largely held sway until the eighteenth and nineteenth centuries. Each species was considered to have been created separately, completely developed, from dust, dirt, and other nonliving sources. And once created, a species was held to be fixed and immutable, unable to change its characteristics.

In the sixth to fourth centuries B.C., Anaximander, Empedocles, and Aristotle independently considered the possibility that living forms might represent a *succession* rather than unrelated, randomly created types. However, the succession was thought of in an essentially philosophical way, as a progression from "less nearly perfect" to "more nearly perfect" forms. The *historical* nature of succession and the continuity of life were not yet recognized. Nor was the notion of continuous succession exploited further in later centuries, for clerical dogma by and large discouraged thinking along such lines.

Francesco Redi, an Italian physician of the seventeenth century, was the first to obtain evidence against the idea of special creation, by showing experimentally that organisms could not arise from nonliving sources. Contrary to notions held at the time and earlier, Redi demonstrated that maggots would never form "spontaneously" in meat if flies were prevented from laying their eggs on the meat. But old beliefs die slowly, and it was not until the nineteenth century, chiefly through the work of Louis Pasteur, that the notion of special creation finally ceased to be influential.

By this time, the alternative to special creation, namely, the idea of continuity and historical succession, or **evolution,** had occurred to a number of thinkers. Some of them recognized that any concept of evolution demanded an earth of sufficiently great age, and they set out to estimate that age. Newton's law of gravitation provided the tool with which to calculate the weight of the earth. One could then bring a small weighed ball of earth to white heat and measure its rate of cooling. From such measurements, one could calculate how long it must have taken the whole earth to cool to its present state. Determinations of this sort provided the many millions of years required to fit evolution into, and this time span gradually lengthened as techniques of clocking improved. As a result of these efforts, the notion of evolution was clearly in the air when the nineteenth century began. In 1809, the first major theory of evolution was actually published. This was the theory of the French biologist Lamarck.

LAMARCK

Lamarck considered the reality of evolution as established. He believed, correctly, that to explain *how* evolution occurred was equivalent to explaining *adaptation*—how individual variations arise among organisms and how such variations lead to the emergence of

different species suited to different environments and ways of life. To account for such evolution, Lamarck proposed the two ideas of **use and disuse of parts** and of **inheritance of acquired characteristics.** He had observed that if a part of an organism was used extensively, such a part would enlarge and become more efficient, and that if a structure was not fully employed it would degenerate and atrophy. Therefore, by differential use and disuse of various parts during its lifetime, an organism would change to some extent and would acquire individual variations. Lamarck then thought that such acquired variations were inheritable and could be transmitted to offspring.

Evolution, according to the Lamarckian scheme, would come about somewhat as follows. Suppose a given short-necked ancestral animal feeds on tree leaves. As it clears off the lower levels of a tree, it stretches its neck to reach farther up. During a lifetime of stretching, the neck becomes a little longer, and a slightly longer neck is then inherited by the offspring. These in turn feed on tree leaves and keep on stretching their necks; and so on, for many generations. Each generation acquires the gains of previous generations and itself adds a little to neck length. In time, a very long-necked animal is formed, something like a modern giraffe.

This theory was exceedingly successful and did much to spread the idea of evolution. But Lamarck's views ultimately proved to be untenable. That use and disuse *do* lead to acquired variations is quite correct. For example, it is common knowledge that much exercise builds powerful muscles. However, Lamarck was mistaken in assuming that such (nongenetic) acquired variations were inheritable. We may say categorically that *acquired characteristics are not inheritable.* They are effects produced by environment and development, not by genes (see Chap. 28). Only *genetic* characteristics are inheritable, and then only if such characteristics are controlled by the genes of the reproductive cells. What happens to cells other than reproductive cells through use and disuse, or in any other way for that matter, does not affect the genes of the gametes. Accordingly, although Lamarck observed some of the effects of use and disuse correctly in some cases, such effects cannot play a role in evolution.

One famous attempt at experimental refutation of Lamarckism was carried out by Weismann, an eminent biologist of the nineteenth century. The tails of mice were cut off for very many successive generations. According to Lamarck, such enforced disuse of tails should eventually have led to tailless mice. Yet mice in the last generation of the experiment still grew tails as long as their ancestors.

DARWIN AND WALLACE

The year in which Lamarck published his theory was also the year in which Charles Darwin was born. During his early life, Darwin undertook a 5-year-long circumglobal voyage as the biologist on the naval expeditionary ship *H.M.S. Beagle.* He made innumerable observations and collected a large number of different plants and animals in many parts of the world. Returning home, he spent nearly twenty years sifting and studying the collected data. In the course of this work, he found evidence for certain generalizations. Another biologist, Alfred Wallace, had been led independently to substantially the same generalizations, at the same time as Darwin. Darwin and Wallace together then announced a new theory of evolution, which was to supplant that of Lamarck. Darwin subsequently elaborated the new theory into book form. This famous work, entitled "On the Origin of Species by Means of Natural Selection, or the Preservation of Favored Races in the Struggle for Life," was published in 1859.

In essence, the Darwin-Wallace **theory of natural selection** is based on three observations and on two conclusions drawn from these observations.

Observation. Without environmental pressures, every species tends to multiply in geometric progression.

In other words, a population doubling its number in a first year possesses a sufficient reproductive potential to quadruple its number in a second year, to increase eightfold in a third year, etc.

Observation. But under field conditions, although fluctuations occur frequently, the size of a population remains remarkably constant over long periods of time.

We have already spoken of this in the discussion of food pyramids (Chap. 7).

Conclusion. Evidently, not all eggs and sperms will become zygotes; not all zygotes will become adults; and not all adults will survive and reproduce. Consequently, there must be a "struggle for existence."

Observation. Not all members of a species are alike; i.e., there exists considerable individual variation.

Conclusion. In the struggle for existence, therefore, individuals featuring favorable variations will enjoy a competitive advantage over others. They will survive in proportionately greater numbers and will produce offspring in proportionately greater numbers.

Darwin and Wallace thus identified the environment as the principal cause of natural selection. Through the processes above, the environment would gradually weed out organisms with unfavorable variations but preserve those with favorable variations. Over a long succession of generations and under the continued selective influence of the environment, a group of organisms would eventually have accumulated so many new, favorable variations that a new species would in effect have arisen from the ancestral stock.

Nonbiologists today often are under the impression that Darwin's and Wallace's theory is *the* modern theory of evolution. This is not the case. Indeed, Darwinism was challenged even during Darwin's lifetime. What, it was asked, is the *source* of the all-important individual variations? How do individual variations arise? Here Darwin actually could do no better than fall back on the Lamarckian idea of inheritance of acquired characteristics. Ironically, the correct answer regarding variations began to be formulated just six years after Darwin published his theory, when a monk named Mendel announced certain rules of inheritance. But Mendel's work went unheeded for more than thirty years and progress in understanding evolutionary mechanisms was retarded correspondingly.

Another objection to Darwinism concerned natural selection itself. If this process simply preserves or weeds out what already exists, it was asked, how can it ever create anything new? As we shall see, natural selection actually does create novelty. The earlier criticism arose in part because the meaning of Darwin's theory was—and still is—widely misinterpreted. Social philosophers of the time and other "press agents" and disseminators of "news," not biologists, thought that the essence of natural selection was described by the phrase "struggle for existence." They then coined alternative slogans like "survival of the fittest" and "elimination of the unfit." Natural selection so came to be conceived almost exclusively as a negative, destructive force. This had two unfortunate results. First, a major implication of Darwin's theory, namely, the creative role of natural selection, was missed, and, second, the wrong emphasis was often accepted in popular thinking as the last and final word concerning evolution.

Such thinking proceeded in high gear even in Darwin's day. Many still did not accept the reality of evolution and were prompted variously to debate, to scorn, and to ridicule the merits of the evidence. It was felt also (quite without basis) that evolution implied "man descended from the apes," and man's sense of superiority was duly outraged. Moreover, because evolutionary views denied the special creation of man, they were widely held to be antireligious. In actuality, the idea of evolution is not any more or less antireligious than the idea of special creation. Neither really strengthens, weakens, or otherwise affects belief in God. To the religious person, only the way God operates, not God as such, is in question.

But many were properly convinced by the evidence for evolution. However, under the banner of phrases like "survival of the fittest," evolution was interpreted to prove an essential cruelty of nature; and human behavior, personal and national, often came to be guided by the ethic of "jungle law," "might is right," "every man for himself." Only in that way, it was thought, could the "fittest" prevail. Even today, unfortunately, the mechanism of evolution is still commonly—and erroneously—thought to be a matter of "survival of the fittest."

By now, a full century after Darwin and Wallace, the emotion-charged atmosphere has cleared, and the impact of their theory may be assessed calmly. That Darwin made the greater contribution cannot be questioned. In voluminous writings, he, far more than Wallace, marshaled the evidence for the occurrence of evolution so extensively, and so well, that the reality of the process has never been in doubt since. Moreover, the theory of natural selection was the most convincing explanation of the evolutionary mechanism offered up to that time. Indeed, carrying new meaning today, it still forms a *part* of the modern theory of evolution. As now understood, however, natural selection is preeminently a peaceful process and has very little to do with "struggle," "weeding out," or "the fittest." Also, we know that Darwin and Wallace, like Lamarck, were unsuccessful in identifying the actual sources of individual variations. In short, the explanation supplied by Darwin and Wallace was incomplete, but as far as it went, their theory was the first to point in the right direction.

The modern theory of evolution is not the work of any one man and it did not arise by "special creation," fully developed. Rather, it evolved slowly during the first half of the current century, many biologists of various specializations contributing to it. The theory is the spiritual offspring of Mendel and of Darwin, but the family resemblance, though present, may not be immediately evident. We shall be concerned with this modern theory in what follows.

THE FORCES OF EVOLUTION

THE EVOLUTIONARY PROCESS

The medium of evolution is the Mendelian *population*. The raw materials of the evolutionary process are the *inheritable variations* which appear among the individuals of such a population. And the mechanism of evolution may be described as **natural selection acting on the inheritable variations of a population.**

We already know from Chap. 6 that a Mendelian population is a geographically localized group of organisms of the same species, in which the members interbreed preferentially with one another and also interbreed occasionally with members of neighboring populations. We may note now that the result of the close sexual communication within a population is a *free flow of genes*. Hereditary material present in a part of a population may in time spread to the whole population, through the gene-pooling and gene-combining effect of sex. Therefore, in the course of successive sexual generations, the total genetic content of a population may become shuffled and reshuffled thoroughly. We may say that a population possesses a given **gene pool** and that the interbreeding members of the population have free access to all components of that pool. Moreover, inasmuch as sister populations are in occasional reproductive contact, the gene pool of one population is connected also to the gene pools of sister populations. In this way, the total genetic content of an entire species continues to be shuffled about among the member organisms (Fig. 29.1).

Evolution operates via the gene pools of populations. We already know from Chap. 28 how changes in genetic systems, hence inheritable variations, may arise: by **sexual recombination** and by **mutation**. In each generation, some individuals may appear featuring new trait variations, as a result of either recombinational or mutational processes. If these variant organisms survive and have offspring of their own, then their particular genetic innovations will persist in the gene pool of the population. In the course of successive generations, the genetic novelty may spread to many or all members of the population.

Whether or not such spreading actually takes place depends on natural selection. This term is synonymous with **differential reproduction.** Either "natural selection"

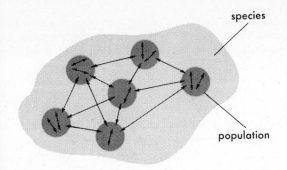

FIG. 29.1 The concept of a gene pool. In a species, gene flow occurs within and between populations. The total gene content of the species thus represents a gene pool to which all members of the species have access. Gene flow cannot occur between the gene pools of two different species.

or "differential reproduction" means simply that *some individuals of a population have more offspring than others*. Clearly, those which leave more offspring will contribute a proportionately greater percentage of individuals to the numerical total of the next generation than those which leave fewer offspring. If, therefore, differential reproduction continues in the same manner over many generations, the abundant reproducers will contribute a progressively larger number of individuals to the whole population. As a result, *their* genes will become preponderant in the gene pool of the population (Fig. 29.2).

Which individuals leave more offspring than others? Usually, but by no means necessarily, those that are *best adapted* to the environment. Being well adapted, such individuals on the whole are healthier and better fed, may find mates more readily, and may care for their offspring appropriately. However, circumstances may on occasion be such that comparatively poorly adapted individuals have the most offspring. Instances of this are sometimes encountered in human populations, for example. In any event, what counts most in evolution is not how well or how poorly an organism copes with its environment, but how many offspring it manages to leave. The more there are, the greater a role will the parental genes play in the total genetic content of the population. By and large, the well-adapted organism contributes most to the gene pool.

Therefore, if an inheritable variation appears in an organism and if, through differential reproduction in successive generations, the progeny of that organism becomes numerically more and more abundant, then a given genetic novelty will spread rapidly throughout the population. As a result, a trait variation originating in one organism will have become a standard feature of the population as a whole.

This is the unit of evolutionary change. Many such unit changes must accumulate in a population before the organisms are sufficiently altered in structure or function to be established as a new species. All evolution operates through the basic process just described. In brief, it consists of:

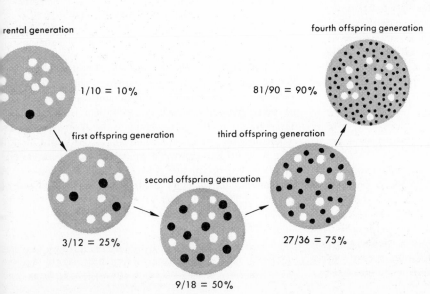

FIG. 29.2 The effect of differential reproduction, or natural selection. Assume that a variation arises in one individual of a parental generation (black dot) and that the variant organism is able to leave three offspring. Each nonvariant organism (white dot) on the other hand only manages to leave one offspring. The complexion of the population will then change as shown during subsequent generations; i.e., the variant type will represent a progressively larger fraction of the numerical total. Such spreading of variations, brought about by differential reproduction, constitutes natural selection.

1. appearance of inheritable variations by sexual recombination and mutation

2. spreading of these variations through a population, by differential reproduction in successive generations

Inasmuch as inheritable variations originate at random, evolutionary innovations similarly appear at random. And inasmuch as the best reproducers are generally the best adapted, evolution as a whole is directed by adaptation and is oriented toward continued or improved adaptation.

Note that, in this modern view of evolution, *natural selection is fundamentally a creative force; for its important effect is to spread genetic novelty,* hence new traits, through a population. It is also a peaceful force, involving *reproduction,* not "struggle for existence" or "survival of the fittest." Organisms actually struggle rather rarely. Indeed, animals try to avoid struggle and attempt to pursue life as inconspicuously as possible, eating when they can, reproducing when they can; and plants have never been seen to engage in struggles at all. Moreover, natural selection does not "eliminate the unfit." The "fit" may be the mightiest and grandest organism in the population, but it might happen to be sterile. And the "unfit" could be a sickly weakling, yet have numerous offspring. The point is that neither "survival" nor "elimination" is actually at issue. The only issue of consequence here is comparative reproductive success. Indirectly, to be sure, health, fitness, and even actual physical struggles may affect the reproductive success of organisms. To that extent, such factors can have evolutionary consequences. But what in Darwin's day was regarded as the whole of natural selection is now clearly recognized to have only a limited, indirect effect on evolution. The whole of natural selection, directly and indirectly, undoubtedly is differential reproduction.

THE GENETIC BASIS

The Hardy-Weinberg Law

From the preceding, we may describe evolution as a *progressive change of gene frequencies.* This means that, in the course of successive generations, the proportion of some genes in the population increases and the proportion of others decreases. For example, a mutation may at first be represented by a single gene, but if by natural selection this mutation spreads to more and more individuals, then its frequency increases

whereas the frequency of the original unmutated gene decreases. Clearly, the *rates* with which gene frequencies change will be a measure of the *speed* of evolution. What determines such rates?

Suppose we consider a large population in which two alleles, *A* and *a*, occur in certain frequencies. In such a population, three kinds of individuals will be found, namely, *AA, Aa,* and *aa.* Let us assume that the numerical proportions happen to be

AA	Aa	aa
36%	48%	16%

Assuming further that the choice of sexual mates is entirely random, that all individuals produce roughly equal numbers of gametes, and that the genes *A* and *a* do not mutate, we may then ask how the frequency of the genes *A* and *a* will change from one generation to the next.

Since *AA* individuals make up 36 per cent of the total population, they will contribute approximately 36 per cent of all the gametes formed in the population. These gametes will all contain one *A* gene. Similarly, *aa* individuals will produce 16 per cent of all gametes in the population and each will contain one *a* gene. The gametes of *Aa* individuals will be of two types, *A* and *a*, in equal numbers. Since their total amounts to 48 per cent, 24 per cent will be *A* and 24 per cent will be *a*. The overall gamete output of the population will therefore be

parents	gametes	parents	gametes
36% AA ⟶	36% A	16% aa ⟶	16% a
48% Aa ⟶	24% A	48% Aa ⟶	24% a
	60% A		40% a

Fertilization now occurs in four possible ways: two *A* gametes join; two *a* gametes join; an *A* sperm joins an *a* egg; and an *a* sperm joins an *A* egg. Each of these possibilities will occur with a frequency dictated by the relative abundance of the *A* and *a* gametes. There are 60 per cent *A* gametes. Accordingly, *A* will join *A* in 60 per cent *of 60 per cent* of the cases, i.e., in 60×60, or 36 per cent of the time. Similarly, *A* sperms will join *a* eggs in 60×40, or 24 per cent of the cases. The total result:

sperms	eggs		offspring
A	+	A ⟶ 60×60 ⟶	36% AA
A	+	a ⟶ 60×40 ⟶	24% Aa
a	+	A ⟶ 40×60 ⟶	24% Aa
a	+	a ⟶ 40×40 ⟶	16% aa

We note that the new generation in our example population will consist of 36 per cent *AA*, 48 per cent *Aa*, and 16 per cent *aa* individuals. These are precisely the same proportions we started with originally. Evidently, *gene frequencies have not changed*.

It can be shown that such a result is obtained regardless of the number and the types of gene pairs considered simultaneously. The important conclusion is that, *if mating is random, if mutations do not occur, and if the population is large, then gene frequencies in a population remain constant from generation to generation*. This generalization is known as the **Hardy-Weinberg law**. It is to the theory of evolution what Mendel's laws are to the theory of heredity (Fig. 29.3).

The Hardy-Weinberg law indicates that, when a population is in genetic equilibrium, i.e., when gene frequencies do not change, the rate of evolution is zero. That is, genes continue to be reshuffled by sexual recombination and, as a result, individual variations continue to originate from this source. But the overall gene frequencies do not change. Of themselves, therefore, the variations are *not* being propagated differentially. Evolution consequently does not occur.

What does make evolution occur are deviations from the "ifs" specified in the Hardy-Weinberg law. Thus, mating is decidedly not random whenever natural selection takes place; genes actually do mutate; and populations are not always large. Singly and in combination, these three factors may disturb the genetic equilibrium of a population and may produce evolutionary change.

The Effect of Nonrandom Mating

This effect may be appreciated readily if we assume that, in our example above, *AA*, *Aa*, and *aa* individuals are not adapted equally well. Suppose that the *A* gene in double dose, as in the *AA* combination, has a particular metabolic effect, such that death in embryonic stages will occur in one-third of the individuals possessing these genes. Under these conditions, 36 per

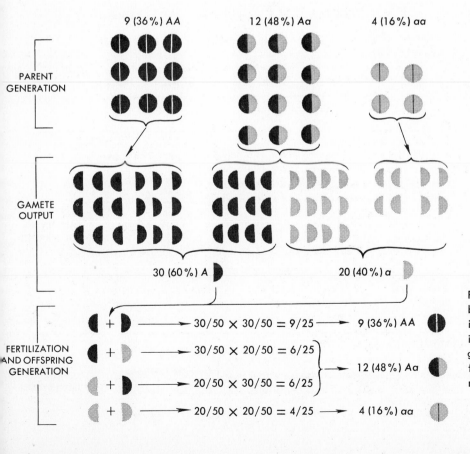

FIG. 29.3 The Hardy-Weinberg law. If mating is random, if mutations do not occur, and if the population is large, then gene frequencies do not change from one generation to the next.

cent *AA* individuals will be produced as zygotes, but only two-thirds of their number will reach reproductive age. Consequently, the *Aa* and *aa* individuals will constitute a proportionately larger fraction of the reproducing population and will contribute proportionately more to the total gamete output. The ultimate result over successive generations will be a progressive decrease in the frequency of the *A* gene and a progressive increase of the *a* gene. A certain *intensity* of natural selection, or **selection pressure,** here operates *against* the *A* gene and *for* the *a* gene (Fig. 29.4). Whenever such selection pressures exert an effect, Hardy-Weinberg equilibria are not maintained. Instead, as gene frequencies become altered more or less rapidly, given traits spread or disappear, and this represents evolutionary change. In nature, most traits are steadily being selected for or selected against. In the course of many generations, even a very slight selection pressure affects the genetic makeup of a population substantially.

The Effect of Mutations

Inasmuch as mutations do occur in populations, Hardy-Weinberg equilibria change for this reason also. Depending on whether a mutation has a beneficial or harmful effect on a trait, selection will be made either for or against the mutated gene. In either case gene frequencies will change, for the mutated gene will either increase or decrease in abundance.

Mutations in haploid organisms affect traits immediately. But the evolutionary effect of mutations in diploid organisms varies according to whether the gene changes are dominant or recessive. A newly originated dominant mutation will affect traits immediately, and selection for or against the mutation will take place at once. But if a mutation is recessive, it does not affect traits immediately. Natural selection therefore does not influence the mutation immediately either. This is the case with most mutations, since, as noted in Chap. 28, most actual mutations are recessive.

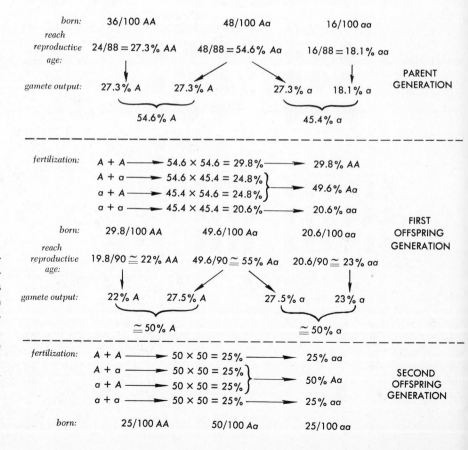

FIG. 29.4 The effect of non-random mating. If only two-thirds of all *AA* individuals reach reproductive age, then in the course of two generations the frequency of the *A* gene will decrease and the frequency of the *a* gene will increase, as shown in the calculation.

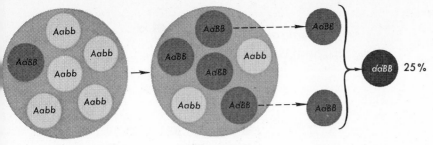

recessive mutation
(a') appears

spreading of B gene,
hence also a'

selection for B may lead to
appearance of mutant (a'a') types

FIG. 29.5 If a recessive mutation a' appears in an organism and if that organism also carries a gene B which is strongly selected for, then both B and a' may spread through a population. The appearance of mutant phenotypes a'a' then becomes rather likely.

Nevertheless, recessive mutations may spread through a population. For example, an organism may carry a recessive mutant gene a', and it may also carry a linked dominant gene B which produces an adaptively very desirable trait. Natural selection could then operate *for* the gene B; i.e., the organism possessing B might reproduce abundantly and its genes would spread through the population. This means that the mutant gene a' would be spread at the same time. Many recessive mutations actually do propagate in this way, by being inherited along with other, adaptively useful dominant genes.

Recessive mutants simply accumulate in the gene pool without visible effect. However, if two individuals carrying the same recessive mutation happen to mate, then one-fourth of their offspring will be homozygous recessive: $Aa' \times Aa' \longrightarrow$ 25 per cent a'a'. These offspring will exhibit altered visible traits and natural selection will then affect the mutation directly (Fig. 29.5).

Mutational effects in evolution also vary according to how greatly a given mutation influences a given trait. A "large" mutation which affects a vital trait in major ways is likely to be exceedingly harmful and will usually be lethal. For example, *any* change in the principal structure and function of the human heart is likely to cause immediate death. Indeed, large variations are usually eliminated as soon as they arise. By contrast, an organism may survive far more readily if a mutation is "small." Evolutionary alterations of organisms actually occur almost exclusively through the accumulation of *many*, *small* changes in traits, not through single, large changes.

The Effect of Population Size

The third condition affecting Hardy-Weinberg equilibria is population size. If a population is large, any regional imbalances of gene frequencies which may

arise by chance are quickly smoothed out by the many random matings among the many individuals. The principle underlying this holds in statistical systems generally. In a coin-flipping experiment, for example, heads and tails will each come up 50 per cent of the time, but only if the number of throws is large. If only three or four throws are made, it is quite possible that *all* will come up heads, by chance alone. Analogously, gene combinations attain Hardy-Weinberg equilibria only if a population is large. In small groups, chance alone may produce major deviations.

Assume, for example, that AA, Aa, and aa individuals are expected in a certain ratio, in accordance with existing gene frequencies. If the population contains many hundreds of individuals, this ratio will actually materialize. But if the population consists of a few individuals only, *all* these might by chance turn out to be of the *same* genotype, rather than of the three expected genotypes. We say that, in small populations, chance leads to **genetic drift**, i.e., to the random establishment of genetic types which numerically are not in accordance with Hardy-Weinberg equilibria (Fig. 29.6).

This effect resembles that of natural selection; if several genotypes are possible, a particular one would likewise come to predominate if there were a selection pressure for it. But whereas natural selection normally propagates the *adaptive* trait, genetic drift is governed solely by chance and is therefore not oriented by adaptation. The result is that, in small populations, nonadaptive and often bizarre traits become established. These may actually be harmful to the population and may promote its getting even smaller. Genetic drift is often observed among plants and animals on islands and in other small, reproductively isolated groups of organisms.

By way of summary, the forces of evolution may now be described as follows. First, recombinational or mutational genetic novelty originates at random among

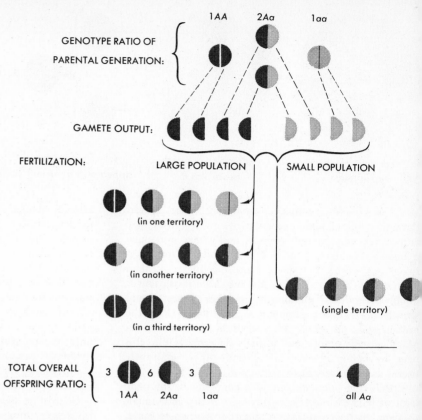

GENOTYPE RATIO OF PARENTAL GENERATION:

GAMETE OUTPUT:

FERTILIZATION:

LARGE POPULATION

SMALL POPULATION

(in one territory)

(in another territory)

(single territory)

(in a third territory)

TOTAL OVERALL OFFSPRING RATIO:

3 · 1AA · 6 · 2Aa · 3 · 1aa

4 · all Aa

FIG. 29.6 Genetic drift. Given a population as at top of the figure, the genetic constitution of offspring populations is influenced by population size. In large populations (left), gene combinations produced in different territories will average out to form a total offspring population in which gene frequencies are as in the parent population. But in small populations (right), chance alone may produce significant deviations from Hardy-Weinberg expectations.

certain individuals of a population. If this novelty happens to be adaptively advantageous in a given environment and if the population is large, then greater or lesser selection pressure for the novelty will disturb the equilibria of existing gene frequencies. Consequently, this pressure of natural selection, operating through differential reproduction, will bring about a correspondingly rapid or slow propagation of the genetic innovation throughout the population. The final result will be the establishment of new adaptive traits.

Evolution as it actually occurs must be interpreted in terms of this mechanism. That it in fact can be interpreted on this basis will become clear in the following section.

THE NATURE OF EVOLUTION

SPECIATION

The key process to be explained is how unit evolutionary changes in a population eventually culminate in the origin of new species and higher taxonomic categories. The main principles of speciation have already been referred to briefly in Chap. 6. A species, we recall, is a collection of populations within which reproductive communication is maintained by interbreeding. We may now define a species alternatively as a group of populations sharing the same gene pool (see Fig. 29.1). Within the pool a free flow of genes is maintained, but genetic flow between two such pools does not occur; a reproductive barrier isolates one species from another. The problem of speciation, therefore, is to show how reproductive barriers arise.

Geographical barriers between sister populations usually develop before biological, reproductive barriers come into existence. Among geographical isolating mechanisms, *distance* is probably the most effective. Suppose that, in the course of many generations, the populations of a given species grow in size and number and that, as a result of the increasing population pressure, the organisms radiate into a progressively larger territory. In time, two populations A and Z at opposite ends of the territory may be too far apart to permit

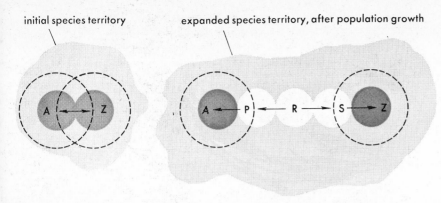

initial species territory

expanded species territory, after population growth

FIG. 29.7 Species populations may in time become separated by distance, with the result of comparative reproductive isolation, hence a reduction of gene flow.

reproductive ranges of A and Z overlap: *gene flow direct*

reproductive ranges of A and Z no longer overlap: *gene flow indirect*, via populations P, R, S

direct interbreeding of their members. Although gene flow still takes place via the interconnecting populations between A and Z, individuals of A and Z no longer come into reproductive contact directly (Fig. 29.7).

It is then almost certain that, by chance, different genetic innovations arise in A and Z and that different ones will be propagated within A and Z by natural selection. Such an effect will be particularly pronounced if the environments of A and Z are or become more or less different. If now the evolutionary changes *within* A and *within* Z occur faster than the speed of genetic flow *between* A and Z, then A and Z will actually become progressively different in structure or function. These two populations thus may come to represent two distinct **subspecies** (Fig. 29.8).

Geographical isolation here has set the stage for the development of initial differences between members of A and Z. If the differences accumulate, they may eventually become so great that gene flow between A and Z will stop altogether. For example, population A (or Z) may undergo a change in the reproductive organs such that mating with neighboring populations becomes mechanically impossible. Or the protein specificities of A may so change that the gametes become incompatible with those of neighboring populations. Or the time of the annual breeding season in A may become advanced or delayed relative to that of neighboring populations. Or the individuals of A may become changed psychologically, so that they no longer accept mates from neighboring populations. *Biological barriers of this sort will interrupt all gene flow between A and Z. These subspecies, isolated reproductively,*

then in effect will have become two different **species** (Fig. 29.9).

Although an initial distance isolation is probably the most common kind, other forms of geographical isolation are also encountered. The development of terrestrial islands surrounded by water or of aquatic islands surrounded by land, the interposition of a forest belt across a prairie or of a prairie belt across a forest,

FIG. 29.8 Different populations of a species may, by selective spreading of variant types, develop into different subspecies.

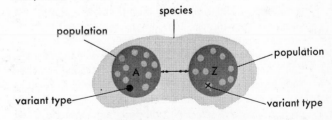

species

population

population

variant type

variant type

different variant types appear in A and Z

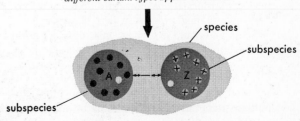

species

subspecies

subspecies

variant types dominant, but gene flow still possible

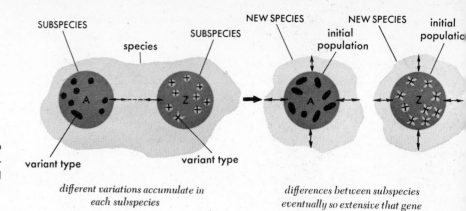

FIG. 29.9 The origin of two new species from two subspecies of a single ancestral species.

different variations accumulate in each subspecies

differences between subspecies eventually so extensive that gene flow no longer possible; new species formed

the appearance of mountain barriers, river barriers, temperature barriers, or of many another physical barrier, each may result in geographical isolation. This may be followed in time by biological reproductive isolation and speciation. The evolution of a new species takes, on the average, roughly one million years.

Consciously or unconsciously making use of this principle of reproductive isolation, man has been and is now contributing to the evolution of many other organisms. Here may be found direct proof that evolution actually occurs and, indeed, that it operates according to the mechanism described above.

The most ancient evolution-directing effort of man is his successful *domestication* of various plants and animals. Darwin was the first to recognize the theoretical significance of domestication, and it was this, actually, which led him to his concept of natural selection. He reasoned that if man, by *artificial selection* and isolation, can transform wild varieties of given plants and animals into domesticated varieties, then perhaps *natural selection* and isolation, acting for far longer periods, can bring about even greater evolutionary transformations in nature. We know now that the domesticating process in fact does involve all the elements of natural evolution: first, deliberate physical, hence reproductive and genetic, isolation of a wild population by man; and second, long-continued, carefully controlled, differential reproduction of individuals "adapted" to human desires, i.e., of individuals exhibiting traits considered desirable by man. The result is the creation of new strains, races, subspecies, and even species (Fig. 29.10).

Furthermore, during the last few decades, rather

rapid, man-directed evolution has taken place among certain viruses, bacteria, insects, various parasites, and other pest organisms. These live now in an environment in which antibiotics and numerous pest-killing drugs have become distinct hazards. And the organisms have evolved and are still evolving increasing resistance to such drugs. Indeed, the very rapid evolution of viruses and bacteria becomes a problem in research; laboratory populations of microorganisms may evolve resistance to a drug even while the drug is being tested. Because microorganisms have exceedingly short generation times, because their populations are physically small, compact, and easily reared, and because high mutation

FIG. 29.10 Red jungle fowl, an example of a wild animal from which man has bred domesticated varieties by artificial selection. (*New York Zoological Society.*)

rates may be induced readily by X rays, they have become favorite test objects in evolution experiments.

Clearly, then, small-scale evolution unquestionably occurs and is observable directly. Moreover, it may be made to occur under conditions based on the postulated modern mechanism of evolution. That this mechanism actually operates as implied by theory is therefore no longer in doubt.

Does the same mechanism operate in large-scale evolution, i.e., in the formation of higher taxonomic categories? In the recent past, a few biologists have expressed the belief that small-scale and large-scale evolution are not governed by the same forces. Differences between orders, classes, and phyla are far too great, it has been argued, to be accounted for by a gradual accumulation of many small, minor variations among organisms. Whereas the origin of species and even of genera can be explained on this basis, it has been maintained that for higher taxonomic categories a different machinery may be required.

A mechanism involving "large" mutations has therefore been postulated. According to this hypothesis, a major mutation affecting many vital traits simultaneously transforms an organism suddenly, in one jump, into a completely new type which represents a new, high-ranking taxonomic category. In most cases such an organism could not survive, for it would undoubtedly be entirely unsuited to the local environment. But it is assumed that, in extremely rare cases, such *hopeful monsters* might have arisen by freak chance in environments in which they could survive. Only a few successes of this sort would be needed to account for the existing major taxonomic variants among organisms. Evolution by jumps would also explain why transitional fossil forms between various phyla are rare, whereas transitional fossils between different species and different genera, created by gradual evolution, are extremely common.

Few biologists today accept the hypothesis of jump evolution. In studies of natural and experimental mutations over many years, it has always been found that sudden genetic changes with major effects are immediately lethal. This is the case not only because the external environment is unsuitable, but also, and perhaps mainly, because the internal metabolic upheaval caused by a major mutation is far too drastic to permit continued survival. Indeed, large mutations lead to death well before hatching or birth. But even supposing that a hopeful monster could develop beyond birth, it would by definition be so different from the other individuals of the population that it certainly could not find a mate. Also, although transitional fossils between major taxonomic categories are rare, they are by no means nonexistent. On the whole, therefore, it is far more consistent with available evidence to explain the evolution of high taxonomic categories on a basis other than that of fortuitous hopeful monsters.

The almost universally accepted view is that large-scale evolution is governed by the very same mechanism as small-scale evolution. Thus the origin of high-ranking taxonomic categories is envisaged to involve isolation and accumulation of small trait variations, only more of them than in the case of a species and accumulating for a longer period of time. Although the differences between phyla and other major categories are great, they are not so great that one such category could not have evolved gradually from another category. Indeed, the evidence from fossils and embryos shows quite well how such derivations have probably been achieved. Moreover, as the next section will show, important aspects of the evolutionary process cannot be explained in terms of jump evolution but can be explained rather well in terms of gradual evolution.

CHARACTERISTICS OF EVOLUTION

Rates of Change

Even on the species level, evolution is an exceedingly slow process. As noted, a very large number of very small variations of traits must accumulate, bit by bit over many generations, before a significant structural or functional alteration of organisms is in evidence. Moreover, genetic innovations occur at random, whereas natural selection is directed by adaptation. Therefore, if a substantial environmental change necessitates a correspondingly substantial adaptive change in a group of organisms, then the organisms must *await* the random appearance of appropriate genetic innovations. If useful innovations do not happen to arise by chance, then the organisms will not be able to readapt and will die out. Yet even if useful genetic novelty does arise in a given generation, there is no guarantee that more novelty of similar usefulness will originate in the next generation. In short, even though evolution may occur, it could occur too slowly to permit successful adaptation to changed environments.

The actual speeds of past evolution, though slow in all instances, have varied considerably for different types of organisms, differently at different times. As a rule, the more stable a given environment has been, the slower has been the evolution of the organisms living in it. Thus terrestrial organisms by and large have evolved faster than marine organisms. Also, during periods of major geologic upheavals, e.g., in times of glaciation or of mountain building (see Chap. 30), evolution has been fairly rapid generally. On the other hand, in a few existing types of organisms, the rate of evolution has been practically zero for hundreds of millions of years. Horseshoe crabs, certain lampshells, and some of the radiolarian protozoa are among the oldest of such "living fossils" (see Fig. 11.49). In these and similar cases, the specific environment of the organisms has been stable enough to make the ancient way of life still possible. Given the general evolutionary mechanism of small random variations acted on by adaptively oriented natural selection, it is not surprising that speeds of evolution should have varied in step with environmental changes.

Adaptive Radiation

A general feature of evolution is the phenomenon of **adaptive radiation.** We have seen how, in speciation, one original parent species gives rise simultaneously to two or more descendant species. A similar pattern of *branching* descent characterizes evolution on all levels. A new type evolves, and it then becomes a potential ancestor for many different, *simultaneous* descendant lines. For example, the ancestral mammalian type has given rise simultaneously to several lines of grazing plains animals (e.g., horses, cattle, goats), to burrowing animals (e.g., moles), to flying animals (e.g., bats), to several lines of aquatic animals (e.g., whales, seals, sea cows), to animals living in trees (e.g., monkeys), to carnivorous predators (e.g., dogs, cats), and to many others. Evidently, the original mammalian type branched out and exploited many different available environments and ways of life. Each descendant line thereby became adaptively specialized in a particular way. The sum of the various lines, all leading away from the common ancestral type, formed an "adaptive radiation."

Within each such line, furthermore, adaptive radiations of smaller scope can take place. For example, the line of tree-living mammals in time evolved several simultaneous sublines and each of these in turn gave rise to subsublines, etc. The specific results today are animals as varied as monkeys, lemurs, tarsiers, apes, and men. Evidently, man did not "descend from the apes." Rather, apes and man have had a common ancestor, and they are *contemporary* members of the same adaptive radiation.

FIG. 29.11   The bush pattern of evolution. The uppermost tips of the branches represent currently living forms, and branches terminating below the top represent extinct forms. Fork points such as *B* and *C* are ancestral types. *B* is more ancient and of higher taxonomic rank than *C*. *A* represents the archancestor of all living types.

The important implication here is that evolution is *not* a "ladder" or a "scale." The pattern is more nearly that of a greatly branching bush, where the tips of all uppermost branches represent currently living species (Fig. 29.11). Of these, none is "higher" or "lower" than any other. Instead, they are simply contemporary groups of different structure, function, and history. And as already pointed out in Chap. 8, the all-too-frequent picture of evolution as a "progression from amoeba to man" is and always has been utterly without foundation. Leading down from the branch tips to progressively thicker branches, the evolutionary bush goes backward in time. Junctions of branches represent common ancestors, and these are the higher in taxonomic rank the more closely the main stem is approached.

Extinction

Not all the branches on a bush ramify right to the top, but some terminate abruptly at various intermediate points. In evolution, similarly, **extinction** has been a general feature. In many actual cases of extinction, the specific causes may never be known. But the general cause of all extinctions emerges from the nature of the evolutionary mechanism. That cause is change in environment without rapid enough readaptation of organisms to the change. Evidently, unlike death, which is inherent in the life history of every individual, extinction is *not* a foregone conclusion inherent in the evolutionary history of every group. Rather, extinction occurs only if and when the group cannot make adaptive adjustments to environmental change (Fig. 29.12).

Such change need not necessarily be physical. For example, biological *competition* between two different types occupying the same territory often has led to the extinction of one. However, note that competition most often does not involve direct combat or "struggle." Characteristically, the competition is usually quite indirect, as when two different types of herbivores draw on the same limited supply of grass. The more narrowly specialized type here usually prevails over the more generalized type. For example, a herbivore like a rabbit is *specialized* to feed on vegetables. It is therefor likely to have the competitive advantage over an omnivore like a man or a bear if that omnivore happens by circumstance to be forced to eat only vegetables. The rabbit will be able to find vegetables more easily and to make more efficient use of them. On the other hand, if vegetables should disappear locally, the specialized herbivore would quickly become extinct, whereas the generalized omnivore might find other food and survive. Clearly, specialization and adaptive flexibility each has certain evolutionary advantages and certain disadvantages. The issue of survival or extinction depends on a fine balance between the two.

This probably accounts for the observation that extinction is the more common the lower the taxonomic category. Extinction of species and even of genera has been a nearly universal occurrence, but relatively few orders and still fewer classes have become extinct. And virtually all phyla that ever originated continue to be in existence today. The phylum evidently includes so broad and so far-flung an assemblage of different adaptive types that at least some of them have always persisted, regardless of how environments have changed. Species, on the other hand, are usually adapted rather narrowly to limited, circumscribed environments. Given these rigid conditions, the chances for extinction are therefore greater.

Replacement

In conjunction with extinction, **replacement** has been another common occurrence in evolution. As noted, competition may be a direct cause for the replacement of one group in a given environment by another. For example, pouched marsupial mammals were very abundant in the Americas a few million years ago, but with the exception of forms like the opossum, they were replaced in the Western Hemisphere by the competing placental mammals. Competition is not a necessary prerequisite for replacement, however. A group may become extinct for some other reason and another group may then evolve into the vacated environment and way of life. A good example of this is provided by the *ammonites,* fossil mollusks related to the living chambered nautilus (see Chap. 30). Some 200 million years ago, ammonites were represented by about a dozen families. All but one of these later became extinct, and the surviving group rapidly evolved into some two dozen new families of ammonites. The latter then exploited the adaptive niche vacated by the earlier ammonites.

Replacement in this case was more or less immediate. On occasion, however, many millions of years may elapse before a new group evolves into a previously occupied environmental niche. *Delayed replacement* of this sort took place, for example, in the case of the ichthyosaurs. These large, marine, fishlike reptiles became extinct some 100 million years ago, and their particular niche subsequently remained unoccupied for about 40 million years. Dolphins and porpoises evolved then, and these mammals replaced the ichthyosaurs. Similarly delayed replacement occurred between the

FIG. 29.12 An animal which has become extinct relatively recently. The dodo survived till just a few hundred years ago. *(American Museum of Natural History.)*

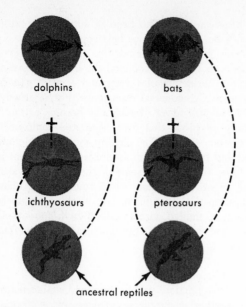

dolphins   bats

ichthyosaurs   pterosaurs

ancestral reptiles

FIG. 29.13   Diagrams of evolutionary replacement.

flying reptilian pterosaurs and the later mammalian bats (Fig. 29.13).

Convergence and Divergence

The phenomenon of replacement is often accompanied by that of convergence, a frequent feature in evolution generally. We have seen how, in an adaptive radiation, a common ancestral type gives rise to two or more descendant lines, all adapted in different ways to different environments. Such development of dissimilar characteristics in closely related groups is often called evolutionary **divergence**. By contrast, when two or more *unrelated* groups adapt to the *same* type of environment, then their evolution is oriented in the same direction. Such organisms may come to resemble one another in one or more ways. Evolution of a common set of characteristics in groups of different ancestry is called **convergence** (Fig. 29.14).

For example, the development of wings in both pterosaurs and bats or of finlike appendages in both ichthyosaurs and dolphins illustrates evolutionary convergence in replacing forms. Inasmuch as the replacing type occupies the same adaptive niche as the type which is being replaced, the appearance of convergent features is not surprising. But convergence is also encountered in nonreplacing forms. For example, the eyes of squids and of fish are remarkably alike. Squids and fish are not related directly and neither replaces the

other. However, both groups comprise large, fast swimmers, and good eyes of a particular construction are a distinct advantage in the ways of life of both. Selection actually has promoted variations which have led to eyes of similar structure, and the observed convergence is the result.

Opportunism

We may note that although the eyes of squids and fish are strikingly alike, they are by no means identical. Similarly, although the wings of pterosaurs and bats or of insects and birds are convergent, in the sense that all carry out the same functions of flying, the various wing types are quite different structurally and operate in different ways. Convergence leads to *similarity*, never to identity. Moreover, neither squids nor fish possess a theoretically "best" eye structure for fast swimmers, and none of the flying groups possesses a theoretically "best" wing design. Actually, the design of an organ or of an organism need not be theoretically "best" or "most efficient." The design only needs to be practically workable and just efficient enough for a necessary function. In a way of life based on flying, wings of *some* sort are clearly essential. But virtually all requirements for living can have *multiple* solutions, and so long as a given solution works at all it does not matter how the solution is arrived at. The various animal wings do represent multiple solutions of the same problem, each evolved from a different starting point and each functioning in a different way. All other instances of evolutionary convergence are similar in these respects.

We are led to one of the most important and most universal characteristics of evolution, that of **random opportunism**. Evolution has produced not what is theoretically desirable or best, but what is practically *possible*. There has been no predetermined plan, no striving for set "goals," but only the exploitation of actually available opportunities offered by selection among random hereditary changes. For example, it might have been adaptively exceedingly useful for terrestrial plants to grow legs or for terrestrial animals to grow wheels. But neither occurred, because it could not occur. The ancestors simply did not possess the necessary structural and functional potential. However, they did possess the potential to evolve adequate, workable, alternative solutions. In the case of plants, already existing spores could be encapsulated and distributed by wind, and in the case of animals, already existing fins could be reshaped into walking legs.

DIVERGENCE

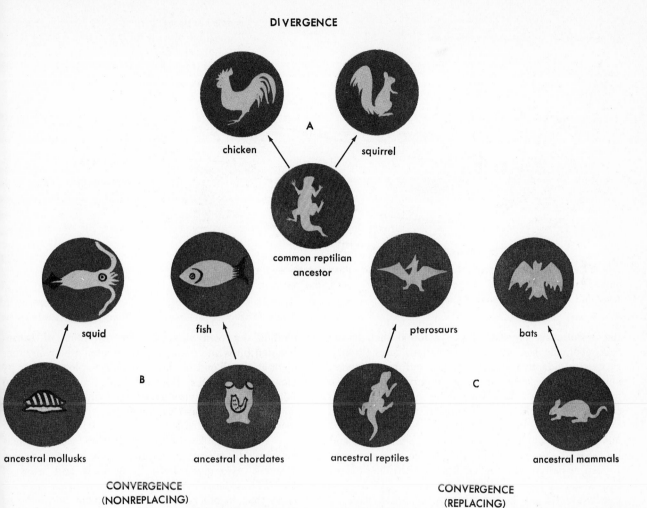

chicken

A

squirrel

common reptilian
ancestor

squid

fish

pterosaurs

bats

B

C

ancestral mollusks

ancestral chordates

ancestral reptiles

ancestral mammals

CONVERGENCE
(NONREPLACING)

CONVERGENCE
(REPLACING)

FIG. 29.14   In evolutionary divergence (A), a common ancestor gives rise to different descendant lines. In evolutionary convergence (B) and (C), relatively unrelated
ancestors give rise to rather similar lines.

Clearly, evolution can only remodel and build on what already exists, in small, successive steps. Since, given a long enough time span, *every* feature of *every* organism undergoes random variations in many different directions, opportunities for diverse evolutionary changes have been and still are very numerous. Some of these opportunities have been and are actually exploited.

Therefore, every organism, man not excepted, is a patchwork of good opportunities seized by selection at the right time. In man, for example, the bones of the middle ear have arisen opportunistically from pieces of earlier vertebrate jawbones. The musculature of the lower face has evolved from the gill muscles of ancestral fish. The voice box has developed from the gill bones of ancient fish (Fig. 29.15). Such instances of evolutionary opportunism are legion. We consequently conclude that specific organisms are *not* the result of any planned, goal-directed, or predetermined course of creation. Instead, they are the result of a cumulative, opportunistic process of piece-by-piece building based on preexisting organisms and governed entirely by natural selection acting on random variations.

The above outlines the general characteristics of

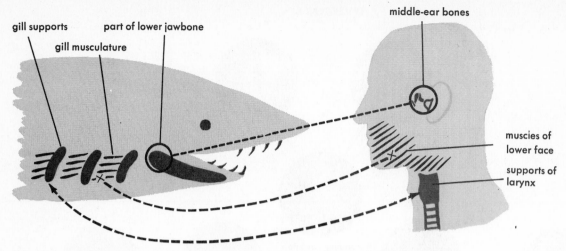

gill supports
gill musculature
part of lower jawbone
middle-ear bones
muscles of lower face
supports of larynx

FIG. 29.15   Evolutionary opportunism. The diagram illustrates the evolutionary origin among ancestral fishes of one of the middle-ear bones, the muscles of the lower face, and laryngeal cartilages of men.

the evolutionary process. We have found that, in the past, evolution has proceeded at various rates through successive adaptive radiations, has led to extinction here and to replacement there, to further divergence in some instances, to convergence in others, and to opportunistic exploitation of possibilities in all. As an overall result, the living mass on earth has been increasing fairly steadily in individual numbers and types and has seeped into practically all possible environments. Indeed, it has created new environments in the process. For example, the evolution of trees has created new possibilities of life in the treetops, exploited later by some new plants and by very many new animals, in-

cluding our own ancestors. The evolution of warm-blooded birds and mammals has created a new environment in the blood of these animals, exploited later by many new parasites. The evolution of man has created numerous new environments in human installations, and these have been exploited by a large variety of new plants and animals.

We recognize here yet another general characteristic of evolution: a progressive, creative **expansiveness,** as regards both living mass and ways of life. The expansion is still under way, faster in some cases than in others, and the end cannot be predicted as yet.

REVIEW QUESTIONS

1. Describe the essential points of the evolutionary theories of (a) Lamarck, (b) Darwin and Wallace. How could the evolution of giraffes from short-necked ancestors be explained in terms of each of these two theories? What were the weaknesses of each theory?

2. What different kinds of inheritable variations may arise in organisms? Do such variations appear randomly or are they oriented toward usefulness? How do noninheritable variations arise and what role do they play in evolution?

3. Define the modern meaning of natural selec-

tion. Show how natural selection has little to do with "survival of the fittest" or "struggle" or "weeding out" and how it is both a peaceful and a creative force. How does it happen that natural selection is oriented toward improved adaptation?

4. State the Hardy-Weinberg law. If a population consists of 49 per cent *AA*, 42 per cent *Aa*, and 9 per cent *aa* individuals, show by calculation how the law applies. If a Hardy-Weinberg equilibrium exists in a population, what are the rate and amount of evolution?

5. What three conditions disturb Hardy-Weinberg

equilibria? For each condition, show in what way such equilibria are disturbed and how evolution is therefore affected. How do recessive genes spread through a population? What is genetic drift and where is it encountered?

6. Define "species" in genetic terms. Describe the process of speciation. What are some common geographical isolating conditions and what is their effect on gene pools? What is a subspecies? How do reproductive barriers arise between populations?

7. Review some actual evidence for past and present evolution. Describe the hypothesis of jump evolution. What are its weaknesses and what is the commonly accepted alternative hypothesis?

8. How have rates of evolution varied in the past? What is an adaptive radiation? Illustrate in the case of mammals. How many and which implications are wholly erroneous in the following statement: "If we examine the evolutionary scale, we find that the lowly amoeba has given rise to higher forms such as man." Rephrase this statement into an appropriate number of correct ones.

9. What are the general causes of extinction? What has been the pattern of extinction on different taxonomic levels? How do narrow specialization and broad adaptability contribute to either extinction or survival? What is evolutionary replacement? Distinguish between immediate and delayed replacement and give examples. Distinguish between evolutionary divergence and convergence and give examples.

10. In what important way is evolution randomly opportunistic? List 10 structural and functional features of man and show for each (a) how it has evolved opportunistically, and (b) that it cannot be labeled as being "theoretically best." What has been the general evolutionary trend regarding the total quantity of life on earth? Show how evolution has created new environments, hence new opportunities for evolution.

SUGGESTED COLLATERAL READINGS

This first group of references is of outstanding historical importance:

Darwin, C.: "The Origin of Species & the Descent of Man," Modern Library, New York, 1948.

———— and A. R. Wallace: On the Tendency of Species to Form Varieties; and of the Perpetuation of Varieties and Species by Natural Means of Selection, original 1858 statement of theory of natural selection, reprinted in M. L. Gabriel and S. Fogel, "Great Experiments in Biology," Prentice-Hall, Englewood Cliffs, N.J., 1955.

Lamarck, de, J. P. P. A.: Evolution through Environmentally Produced Modifications, translation of 1809 original in T. S. Hall, "A Source Book in Animal Biology," McGraw-Hill, New York, 1951.

Pasteur, L.: Examination of the Doctrine of Spontaneous Generation, translation of 1862 original in Gabriel and Fogel.

Redi, F.: Experiments of the Generation of Insects, translation of 1688 original in Gabriel and Fogel.

Any of the following books, especially the first of the two by Simpson, is recommended for background reading on evolutionary theory as a whole:

Blum, H.: "Time's Arrow and Evolution," Princeton University Press, Princeton, N.J., 1951.

Dobzhanski, T.: "Genetics and the Origin of Species," 2d ed., Columbia University Press, New York, 1951.

Dodson, E. O.: "Evolution: Process and Product," Reinhold, New York, 1960.

Dunn, L. C., and T. Dobzhanski: "Heredity, Race, and Society," Mentor Books, M74, New York, 1952.

Huxley, J. S.: "Evolution: the Modern Synthesis," Harper, New York, 1943.

Mayr, E.: "Systematics and the Origin of Species," Columbia University Press, New York, 1942.

Simpson, G. G.: "The Meaning of Evolution," Yale University Press, New Haven, Conn., 1949, or Mentor Books, M66, New York, 1951.

————: "The Major Features of Evolution," Columbia University Press, New York, 1953.

Stebbins, G. L.: "Variation and Evolution in Plants," Columbia University Press, New York, 1950.

The articles and books below discuss various specific topics in the field of evolution.

Blum, H.: Perspectives in Evolution, *Am. Scientist*, vol. 43, 1955.

Deevey, E. S.: The End of the Moas, *Sci. American,* vol. 190, 1954.

Dobzhanski, T.: Evolution in the Tropics, *Am. Scientist,* vol. 38, 1950.

————: The Genetic Basis of Evolution, *Sci. American,* vol. 182, 1953.

Dunn, L. C.: Genetic Monsters, *Sci. American,* vol. 182, 1950.

Florkin, M.: "Biochemical Evolution," Academic Press, New York, 1949.

Hardy, G. H.: Mendelian Proportions in a Mixed Population, in Gabriel and Fogel.

Horowitz, N. H.: On the Evolution of Biochemical Syntheses, in Gabriel and Fogel.

Lack, D.: Darwin's Finches, *Sci. American,* vol. 188, 1953.

Metcalf, R. L.: Insects vs. Insecticides, *Sci. American,* vol. 187, 1952.

Ryan, F. J.: Evolution Observed, *Sci. American,* vol. 189, 1953.

Stebbins, G. L.: Cataclysmic Evolution, *Sci. American,* vol. 184, 1951.

EVOLUTION: THE PAST

30

One of the main lines of investigation which reveals the time course of past evolution is **paleontology,** the study of *fossils.* Representing the remains of formerly living plants and animals, fossils provide the most direct evidence of the kinds of organisms in existence at various earlier times. A second main line of investigation is **comparative morphology,** the study of the structure of presently living organisms. Being the products of past plants and animals, modern organisms reflect in their architecture the evolutionary history of their antecedents. All levels of structure embody the record of past evolution. Molecular and cellular evolution is revealed by studies in *comparative biochemistry* and *comparative cytology,* and tissue and organ evolution is revealed through *comparative embryology* and *comparative anatomy.*

Unfortunately, the fossil record does not go back more than 500 million years, a span of time representing only the last quarter or so of living history. Events during the crucial first three-quarters must therefore be inferred indirectly through a study of organisms now living.

THE GEOLOGIC RECORD

FOSSILS

Fossils are any long-preserved remains of organisms. They may be skeletons or shells, perhaps recrystallized under heat and pressure and infiltrated with mineral deposits from surrounding rock. They may be footprints later petrified or the remnants of organisms trapped in arctic ice, amber, quicksand, gravel pits, tar pits, and swamps. Or they may be imprints of carbon black on rock, left when the soft parts of plants or animals vaporized under heat and pressure. Whenever a buried organism or any part of it becomes preserved in some way before it decays, it will be a fossil.

Fossils formed in the past are embedded in earth layers of different ages. In a geologically undisturbed section of the earth's crust, the deeper layers are the older layers. Material eroded from high-lying land gradually piles up on low land and on the sea bottom. A deep layer today therefore was on the surface in past ages and the earth's surface today will be a deep layer in the future. Fossils embedded in successive layers so provide a time picture of evolution. To be sure, deep-lying fossils are normally not accessible. But on occasion, a canyon-cutting river, an earthquake fracture, or an upbuckling and consequent breaking of the earth's crust may expose a cross section through the rock strata. Moreover, erosion gradually wears away top layers, exposing deeper rock. Geological changes of this sort have been sufficiently abundant to expose layers of all different ages in various parts of the world (Fig. 30.1).

How is the actual age of a rock layer determined? Very excellent clocks are built right into the earth's crust: radioactive substances. The disintegration rate of these substances is known accurately, as are the end-products of disintegration. For example, a given quantity of radium is known to "decay" into lead in a certain span of time. When radium and lead are found together in one mass within a rock, the whole mass presumably had been radium originally, when the rock was formed. From the relative quantities of radium and lead present today, one can then calculate the time required for that much lead to form. This dates the rock, exactly to about 10 per cent of its total age.

An analogous principle underlies age determinations by potassium-argon dating and by radiocarbon dating. In the potassium-argon process, one measures how much of the unstable isotope potassium 40 has decayed into the isotope argon 40. Radiocarbon dating involves measurements of carbon 14, an isotope of "natural" carbon 12. Whereas the potassium-argon method can be used for dating fossils many millions of years old, the carbon 14 method is accurate only for fossils formed within the last 50,000 years. Fossils themselves often help in fixing the age of a rock layer. If such a layer contains a fossil which on the basis of other evidence is known to be of a definite age, then the whole layer, including all other fossils in it, is likely to be of the same general age.

Based on data obtained from radioactive and fossil clocks, geologists have constructed a *geologic time table* which indicates the age of successive earth layers and so provides a calendar of the earth's past history. This calendar consists of five successive main divisions,

FIG. 30.1 Rock layers of different ages are often exposed to view. The deeper a layer in the earth's crust, the older it is. *(American Museum of Natural History.)*

so-called **eras.** The last three of these are subdivided in turn into a number of successive **periods.** The names of the eras and periods and their approximate durations are indicated in Table 15.

TABLE 15
*The geologic time table**

era	period	duration		beginning date
Cenozoic ("new life")	Quaternary	75	1	1
	Tertiary		74	75
Mesozoic ("middle life")	Cretaceous	130	60	135
	Jurassic		30	165
	Triassic		40	205
Paleozoic ("ancient life")	Permian	300	25	230
	Carboniferous		50	280
	Devonian		45	325
	Silurian		35	360
	Ordovician		65	425
	Cambrian		80	505
Precambrian		1,500		2,000
Azoic ("without life")		3,000		5,000

* All numbers refer to millions of years; older ages are toward bottom of table, younger ages toward top.

The beginning and terminal dates of the eras and periods have not been chosen arbitrarily but have been made to coincide with major geological events known to have occurred at those times. The transitions between eras in particular were times of great upheaval, characterized by mountain building and by severely fluctuating climates. For example, the transition from the Paleozoic to the Mesozoic dates the **Appalachian revolution,** during which the mountain range of that name was built up. By now, these mountains are already greatly reduced by erosion. Similarly, the transition between the Mesozoic and the Cenozoic was marked by the **Laramide revolution,** which produced the high mountain ranges of today: the Himalayas, the Rockies, the Andes, and the Alps. As we shall see, these major geological events led to major biological ones, marked by evolutionary crises and large-scale replacement of types.

THE PRECAMBRIAN ERA

The first geologic era, the immensely long Azoic, spans the period from the origin of the earth to the origin of life. Living history begins with the next era, the Precambrian.

Fossils are not lacking altogether from these distant Precambrian ages. But the record is exceedingly fragmentary and it shows mainly that life, simple cellular life at least, already existed about 1 billion years ago. This must mean that the actual origin of life must have occurred earlier; we place it at about 2 billion years ago, at the start of the Precambrian. We also know how far evolution must have proceeded by the end of the Precambrian, for from that time on we have a continuous and abundant fossil record.

It is a very curious circumstance that rocks older than about 500 million years are so barren of fossils, whereas rocks younger than that are comparatively rich in them. Many hypotheses have been proposed to account for this, but to date a satisfactory explanation has not been found. Did the Precambrian environment somehow preclude the formation of fossils? Were fossils destroyed in some way before the Paleozoic? Or is the Precambrian fossil record so scanty because the organisms then were still too unsubstantial to leave fossilizable remains? We simply cannot be sure.

But we *are* reasonably sure that Precambrian evolution must have brought about not only the origin of life and the origin of cells but also the origin of three of the four present main groups of organisms, namely, the Monera, the Protista, and the Metazoa. Moreover, practically all phyla within these three groups were in existence by the end of the Precambrian. To be sure, the organisms then representing these phyla were not the organisms of today; extinction and replacement by new types was still to occur many times. But the ancient types nevertheless did belong to the same phyla we recognize now.

In what sequence these various ancient organisms evolved from the first cells must, in the absence of fossils, be inferred from the nature of presently living forms. In different contexts, we actually have already made such inferences in various earlier chapters. Thus, primitive ancestral cell types are believed to have given rise to two major descendant lines, the Monera and the Protista. Ancestral forms of these in turn each evolved several subgroups; and among the early Protista so appeared the algal types, the fungal types, and the protozoan types. Each of these subsequently produced adaptive radiations of their own, leading to the various protistan phyla we know today. Out of one or more of these adaptive radiations also came a new group, namely, the Metazoa. These ancestral animals sooner or later gave rise to five superphyla, viz., the Radiata, the Acoelomata, the Pseudocoelomata, the Schizocoelomata, and the Enterocoelomata. Primitive representatives of them eventually produced ancient organisms which typified the various animal phyla of today and which we now find as fossils dating back some 500 million years (Fig. 30.2).

Note that this presumed sequence of Precambrian events is based on an analysis of actual structures and functions among current organisms, and so it probably incorporates a measure of validity as well as a measure of error. The degree of validity is certain to be improved and to be made more detailed through research; but a given degree of error may never be resolved, for direct evidence is simply unobtainable. Note also that the sequence has the form of a bush and consists of a succession of adaptive radiations. This is as it should be, on the basis of known evolutionary mechanisms.

Evidently, the long Precambrian spanned not only three-quarters of evolutionary time but also three-quarters of evolutionary substance. The organisms in existence at the end of the Precambrian probably were all aquatic. With the possible exception of some of the bacteria and some of the Protista, the land apparently had not been invaded as yet. The ensuing last quarter of evolution brought about principally a rich and extensive further diversification within the existing phyla.

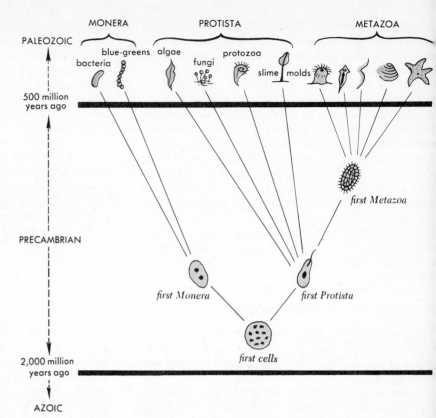

FIG. 30.2 Summary of the probable course of Precambrian evolution.

PLANT EVOLUTION

This produced replacement of ancient forms by new ones, including in each of the three main groups the evolution of types which could live on land. And among the land-adapted descendants of the Protista, more specifically the green algae, there were organisms which established a new main group, namely, the Metaphyta. These appear to have been the last to evolve among the four main categories now living.

Starting with the Cambrian period of the Paleozoic era, the course of evolution is documented fairly amply by fossils. These show that, on the phylum level, every group in existence in the Cambrian has persisted to the present. But on the species level, no group has persisted. In the following sections, we shall examine the evolutionary history of the Metaphyta and the Metazoa in greater detail.

PLANT EVOLUTION

The Cambrian and Ordovician periods lasted for almost half of the entire 300-million-year-long Paleozoic era.

During this time, the land surface remained free of living organisms (some microscopic forms probably excepted, as noted). But the seas and later also the fresh waters abounded with many diverse moneran, protistan, and metazoan types. The first Metaphyta appear in the fossil record of the Silurian. Terrestrial Metazoa had not yet evolved at this time.

It is interesting to note that these earliest land plants were tracheophytes, specifically, psilopsids and lycopsids. Bryophytes seem to have evolved much later; their first fossils do not appear till the Carboniferous.

THE PALEOZOIC

In 1903, the French botanist Lignier proposed the hypothesis that the ancestors of the terrestrial tracheophytes were green algae with a dichotomously branching, rather *Fucus*-like structure. Such an ancestral stock was postulated to have become terrestrial by development of an epidermis with cuticles and stomata; gradual straightening of some of the dichotomous branches, leading to the formation of a main stem with

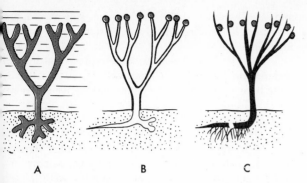

A   B   C

FIG. 30.3   The Lignier hypothesis. Dichotomously branch-ing algae as in A may have evolved via stages as in B into primitive, rhizome-possessing tracheophytes as in C.

lateral branches; growth of some of the lowest branches into the ground as roots; development of vascular tissue in the interior of stem and root; and restriction of reproductive capacity to the terminals of stems. Lignier considered that the evolution of alga into tracheophyte might have occurred along sea or freshwater shores, where intermittent terrestrial conditions would have promoted the development of adaptations to land life (Fig. 30.3).

Later evidence has supported this hypothesis, which is now accepted quite widely. Numerous psi-lopsid fossils have been discovered in the Rhynie de-posits of Scotland, regions which probably were swamps during the Paleozoic. Ancient psilopsids living there must have become flooded and their bodies impreg-nated with silica. As a result, the plants are very well preserved today and even the internal organization of cells is still recognizable in amazing detail. These ear-liest land plants were structured more or less exactly as postulated by the Lignier hypothesis.

Silurian and Devonian

One of the Silurian fossil psilopsids is *Rhynia*, named after the Rhynie region. This plant (Fig. 30.4) possessed a rhizome with rhizoids, dichotomous upright branches about 1 ft in height, and terminal sporangia. Leaves were absent. Quite similar to this plant were two others, *Horneophyton* and *Psilophyton*. The latter carried short spines which were probably microphyllous leaves. Only the sporophytes of these fossil psilopsids have been found. Various other extinct psilopsids show clearly that these early plants could indeed have been ancestral to all other evolutionary lines of vascular plants. For example, *Asteroxylon* exhibited rootlike

FIG. 30.4   Fossil psilopsids. Note rhizomes, dichotomous branching, terminal spo-rangia, and microphylls in C and D and absence of leaves in A, B, and E. (A, B, D, after Kidston and Lang; C, after Dawson; E, after Krausel and Weyland.)

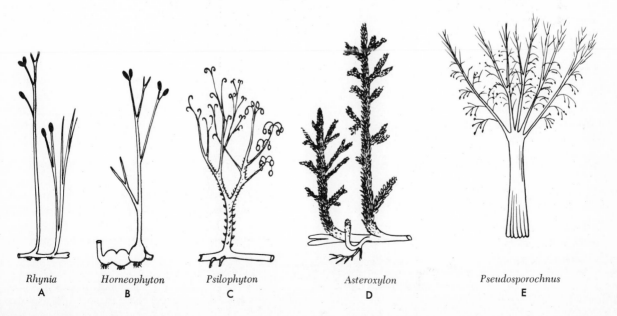

Rhynia   *Horneophyton*   *Psilophyton*   *Asteroxylon*   *Pseudosporochnus*

A   B   C   D   E

branches, numerous microphylls, and other characteristics which indicate a lycopsid direction of psilopsid
evolution. The sphenopsid direction is suggested by
fossil plants such as *Hyenia,* which possessed microphylls arranged in nodal whorls and which is believed
to have been closely related to the psilopsids. Several
fossil psilopsids, among them *Pseudosporochnus,* point
to the pteropsid direction of evolution. In these 9-ft-
high treelike plants the leaves were terminal and flattened, with a webbing which may have foreshadowed
the macrophyllous condition characteristic of ferns.

Thus the fossil record of the Silurian and early
Devonian appears to warrant the same conclusion suggested independently by a study of vascular plants now
living, namely, that psilopsids are the most primitive
tracheophytes and that they must have been ancestral
to all other lines of tracheophyte evolution. By middle

and late Devonian times, the lycopsid, sphenopsid, and
pteropsid lines were already in existence and flourishing (Fig. 30.5).

The Devonian lycopsids were represented by **lepi
dodendrids,** the giant club mosses (Fig. 30.6). All were
huge trees up to 120 ft in height, with active secondary
growth, leaves some 20 in. long and cones up to 1 ft
long. The "scale tree" *Lepidodendron* became particularly abundant, as did *Sigillaria,* the "seal tree." The
60-ft-high stem of this tree bore leaves in a terminal
tuft which gave the plant the general appearance of a
giant paint brush. The lepidodendrids were largely
heterosporous. In some of them the female gameto
phytes developed precociously in the megasporangia
(as in *Selaginella* today). Other lepidodendrids came
exceedingly close to forming true seeds.

The sphenopsids of the Devonian are represented

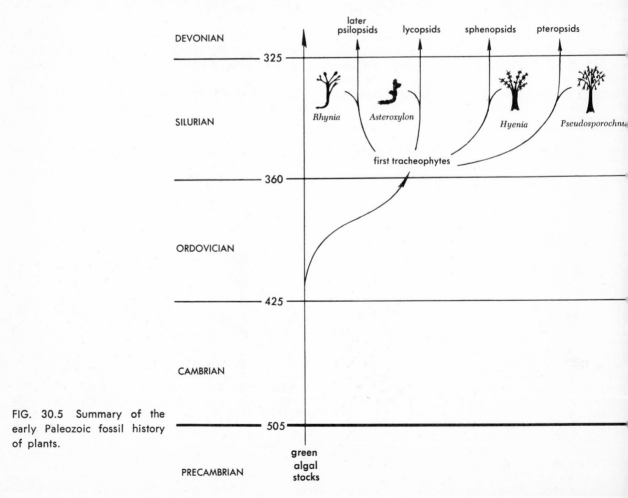

FIG. 30.5 Summary of the
early Paleozoic fossil history
of plants.

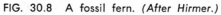

FIG. 30.6 Fossil lycopsids. Left, reconstruction of *Lepidodendron*; right, reconstruction of *Sigillaria*. (*Chicago Natural History Museum.*)

by fossils such as *Calamophyton, Sphenophyllum,* and *Calamites* (Fig. 30.7). The first-named possessed a jointed stem, with narrow leaves arranged in nodal whorls. Secondary growth occurred in *Sphenophyllum,* characterized by whorls of triangular leaves, and in *Calamites,* the giants of the Devonian sphenopsids, which formed trees up to 100 ft high. Both homospory and heterospory were common in all the ancient sphenopsids.

In comparison with the large lycopsids and sphenopsids, the pteropsids of the Devonian were still rela-

tively small and had not yet attained the stature they were to achieve later. All known fossil ferns, or Coenopteridales, were homosporous (Fig. 30.8). This stock must have produced an adaptive radiation which included a line leading to the seed plants; fossil seed plants appear for the first time in late Devonian rocks. These plants were gymnosperms belonging to two groups, the **seed ferns** and the **fossil conifers.** The former (which were not really "ferns" despite their name) probably arose first and in turn gave rise to the latter. But neither achieved prominence until the next period of the Paleozoic (Fig. 30.9).

FIG. 30.7 Fossil sphenopsids. (*After Krausel and Weyland, Zeiller, and Hirmer.*)

FIG. 30.8 A fossil fern. (*After Hirmer.*)

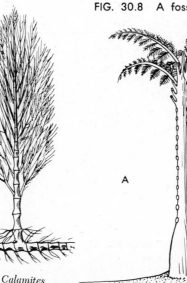

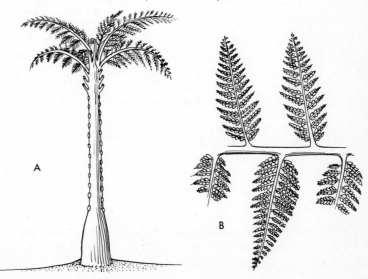

Calamophyton   *Sphenophyllum*   *Calamites*   A   B

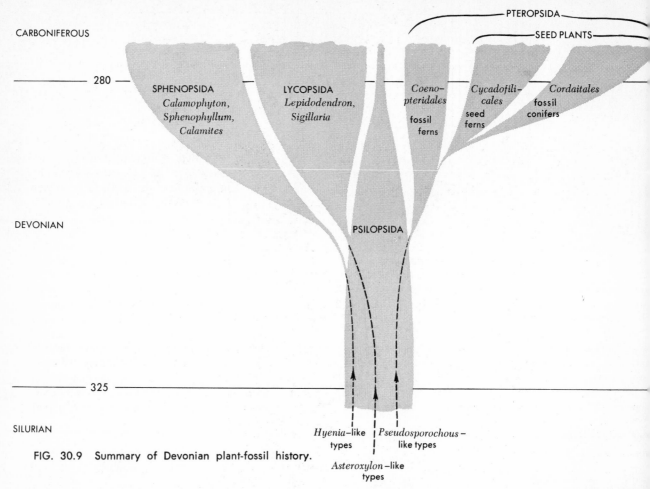

FIG. 30.9   Summary of Devonian plant-fossil history.

Carboniferous and Permian

During the Carboniferous (Fig. 30.10), most of the tracheophytes which had evolved during the Devonian reached their peak abundance. Lycopsids and sphenopsids produced huge forests, and ferns too attained the stature of trees. Bryophytes appear for the first time in the fossil record of this period. It is possible that their evolution was promoted by the generally wet, tropical and subtropical conditions then prevailing over much of the earth. In addition, gymnosperms came to be important members of the world's flora. The two already existing groups, seed ferns and fossil conifers, became dominant during the Carboniferous. A third gymnospermous group, the **fossil cycads**, evolved in this period from the seed ferns but did not achieve prominence until much later.

The Carboniferous is sometimes called the "age of seed ferns." These plants, known technically as *Cycadofilicales*, were at first thought to be ferns, which they resembled greatly; and after their seeds were discovered, the misleading name persisted (Fig. 30.11). The seed ferns gave rise to an extensive and important adaptive radiation. It probably included lines which sooner or later led to all other gymnosperms, extinct as well as living, and it is possible that one of the seed fern stocks later also evolved into the flowering plants. One of the derived gymnospermous groups, the fossil conifers, attained its peak during the Carboniferous. As noted, this group had already been in existence since the Devonian. A giant representative was the fossil conifer *Cordaites*, a tree up to 100 ft high with parallel-veined leaves which sometimes reached lengths of 3 ft. During the later part of the Carboniferous, many

FIG. 30.10 Reconstruction of Carboniferous swamp forest. Trees on left, *Sigillaria*. Upper left corner, strobili of lepidodendrids. Small plants in center foreground, *Sphenophyllum*. Tree on right, *Calamites*. (Chicago Natural History Museum.)

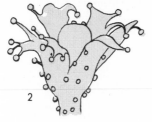

FIG. 30.11 Fossil gymnosperms. Diagrams, (1) seed fern, (2) external view of seed fern megasporangium, (3) section through seed fern megasporangium. Photograph, reconstruction of *Cordaites*. (Diagrams, after Oliver; photograph, Chicago Natural History Museum.)

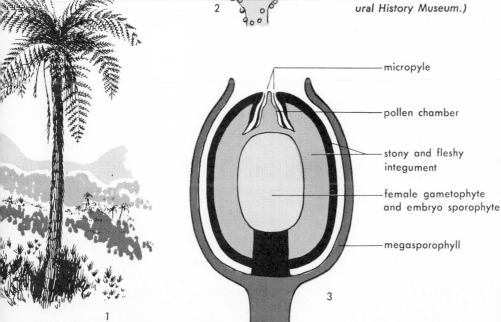

micropyle

pollen chamber

stony and fleshy integument

female gametophyte and embryo sporophyte

megasporophyll

regions became so wet that they were transformed into vast tracts of swamps and marshes. In these, much of the woody flora of the time died. Later geological changes converted the bodies of the plants into coal. Hence the name of the whole period, "coal-bearing." The rich coal beds of Pennsylvania and West Virginia came into being at that time, and the coal itself represents the remains of forests of lepidodendrid lycopsids, calamite sphenopsids, tree ferns, seed ferns, and fossil conifers.

However, many of these plants survived and persisted into the Permian. They were joined then by the newly evolved ginkgoes. Yet for many of the ancient forms the time of dominance was about over. The long Paleozoic terminated with the geological upheavals of the Appalachian revolution, which in turn precipitated a so-called *Permo-Triassic crisis* among living organisms. This unstable time of transition was marked by widespread extinction of archaic forms and later replacement with rapidly evolving new types. Also, the total amount of life decreased temporarily. Evolutionary turnover in the sea was extensive, particularly among animals (see below). On land, many plant groups became extinct: virtually all of the psilopsids, lepidodendrids, and early sphenopsids, as well as many of the ancient ferns, gymnospermous seed ferns, and fossil conifers. Some of the archaic lycopsids and sphenopsids lingered on into the Triassic, but eventually they died out altogether. Other remnant groups of psilopsids, lycopsids, and sphenopsids managed to survive, and from these later arose the relic genera living today. After the Permo-Triassic crisis, however, none of the psilopsids, lycopsids, and sphenopsids achieved major stature again (Fig. 30.12).

On the other hand, the surviving groups of ferns and gymnosperms began to flourish anew, and they became the ancestors of the expanding flora of the new Mesozoic era.

FIG. 30.12   Summary of late Paleozoic and early Mesozoic plant-fossil history.

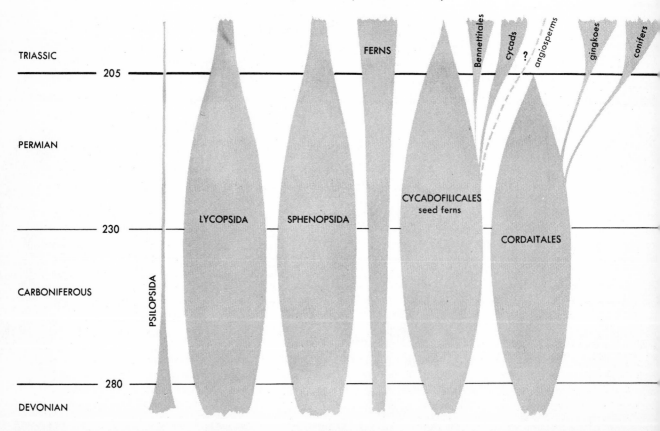

FIG. 30.13 Diagrammatic reconstruction of a Jurassic landscape. Note *Sphenophyllum* in foreground and abundance of fossil cycads throughout. *(American Museum of Natural History.)*

THE MESOZOIC

The Mesozoic as a whole is often called the "age of gymnosperms" in plant evolution. Within the era, the Triassic and Jurassic periods qualify as the "age of cycads," and the Cretaceous as the "age of conifers" (Fig. 30.13).

As noted, fossil cycads had evolved from the seed ferns and had already been in existence since the Carboniferous. This group reached its peak during the Jurassic, when it formed extensive forests. The representative type *Bennettites* (Fig. 30.14) was a tree some 10 ft high with terminal leaves almost as long as the tree trunk. The reproductive structures were arranged in a somewhat flowerlike manner. This circumstance has on occasion given rise to the suggestion that fossil cycads may have been the ancestors of the flowering plants. It is now clear, however, that the resemblance is superficial and that it probably represents little more than an instance of convergent evolution. The fossil cycads died out during the Cretaceous (and their ample remains may still be found, for example, in the Fossil Cycad National Monument in the Black Hills of South Dakota). The group was replaced on a reduced scale by the true cycads, probably evolved independently from seed ferns. Descendants of these plants are still living in various warm-climate areas today.

During the early part of the Mesozoic, the ginkgoes steadily increased in abundance. They reached their peak during the Jurassic and early Cretaceous. Concurrently, new groups of coniferous gymnosperms, related to the earlier cordaites, came into ascendancy. These groups dominated the whole later part of the Mesozoic and included many of the present living conifers, e.g., cypresses, yews, redwoods, and pines.

However, the forests formed by these large trees did not dominate the late Mesozoic landscape alone. They had to share space with the *angiosperms,* which produced a first extensive radiation at that time. Fragmentary fossils of angiosperms date back to the Jurassic, but the first ample finds occur in Cretaceous layers. The origin of angiosperms is quite obscure; the best guess at present is that they evolved from some seed fern stock which had survived into the Mesozoic. As will become apparent below, the late Mesozoic expansion of angiosperms coincided with a similarly extensive radiation of insects. Most of the Mesozoic angiosperms

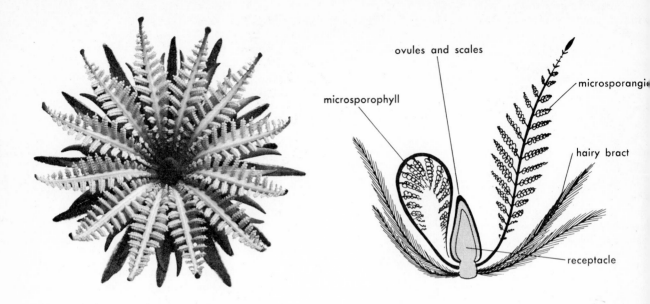

FIG. 30.14   Left, model of the "flower" of *Bennettites*. Right, a section through a "flower" of *Bennettites*. (Left, Chicago Natural History Museum; right, after Wieland.)

were woody. They included many of the tree-forming types still living today, e.g., elms, oaks, maples, magnolias, and palms. Forests of these were already flourishing, and in the closing phases of the Mesozoic they began to rival those of the conifers (Fig. 30.15).

THE CENOZOIC

If the Mesozoic was the age of gymnosperms, the Cenozoic was unquestionably the "age of angiosperms" in plant evolution. The increasing dominance of the angiosperms and the corresponding decline of the gymnosperms was in large measure a consequence of the Laramide revolution which terminated the Mesozoic.

This revolution brought on a crisis similar to the one at the end of the Paleozoic. As noted earlier, the main effect of the Laramide revolution was the formation of the high mountain ranges of today. Their emergence substantially changed the pre-Cenozoic patterns of air circulation between ocean and land, and the new patterns led to new climatic conditions. For example, the east-west barrier of the Himalayas in Asia and of the Alps in Europe prevented warm south winds from reaching the northern portions of Eurasia. These regions became colder as a result. Such cooling in turn

undoubtedly facilitated the development of ice ages during the last million years.

Ice ages had occurred before during the earth's history, and during the last million years there were four. In each, ice sheets spread from the North Pole southward, covered much of the land of the Northern Hemisphere, then receded. Warm interglacial periods intervened between successive glaciations. The last recession began some 20,000 years ago, the beginning of the recent epoch, and it is still in progress; polar regions are still covered with ice.

The Laramide revolution had immediate effects on animals. As we shall see, for example, it brought about the extinction of the dinosaurs, which had reigned throughout the Mesozoic. The effect on plants was more gradual, and it was a direct result of the slowly cooling climates. High, even temperatures had predominated during previous ages, when much of the earth was tropical and subtropical and when the poles were ice-free. This was an advantageous climate which offered a continuous, uninterrupted growing season. The early gymnosperms and angiosperms of the time adapted well to such conditions; they evolved secondary growth and the woody perennial habit, adding more and more wood with each passing year. Indeed ossil trees from the Mesozoic and early Cenozoic are without annual rings, indicating the existence of even, warm conditions. The trees were typically warm-climate forms; e.g., angiosperms included types such as figs, laurels, sycamores, eucalyptus, and palms.

But as climates became cooler during the later Cenozoic, distinct tropical, temperate, and cold polar zones became established. This meant that seed plants already living in the tropics could remain tropical but that species in other regions could not. Three choices were open to them. They could migrate to the tropics, or they could die and become extinct, or they could readapt right where they lived to the succession of winter and summer. All three possibilities were actually realized in different groups. Of the groups which did not migrate, many became extinct. The decline of gymnosperms traces to this time. Today only some 700

species are left, and these survive because they now manage to protect themselves against the cold through processes of winter-hardening. Many woody angiosperms similarly survive today in temperate and northern regions, but they have adapted to winter conditions by becoming deciduous, i.e., by shedding their leaves. Even so, the luxuriant forests of gymnosperms and angiosperms once characteristic of northern regions thinned out and became less extensive. Fossil trees from the later Cenozoic do show annual rings like trees today, indicating clearly that uninterrupted year-round growth was no longer possible.

Furthermore, in response to late Cenozoic climates the surviving angiosperms of temperate and northern regions produced a whole new adaptive radiation. The plants of this radiation coped with the cool seasons in new ways: they either reduced their cambial activity

FIG. 30.15 Summary of Mesozoic and Cenozoic plant-fossil history.

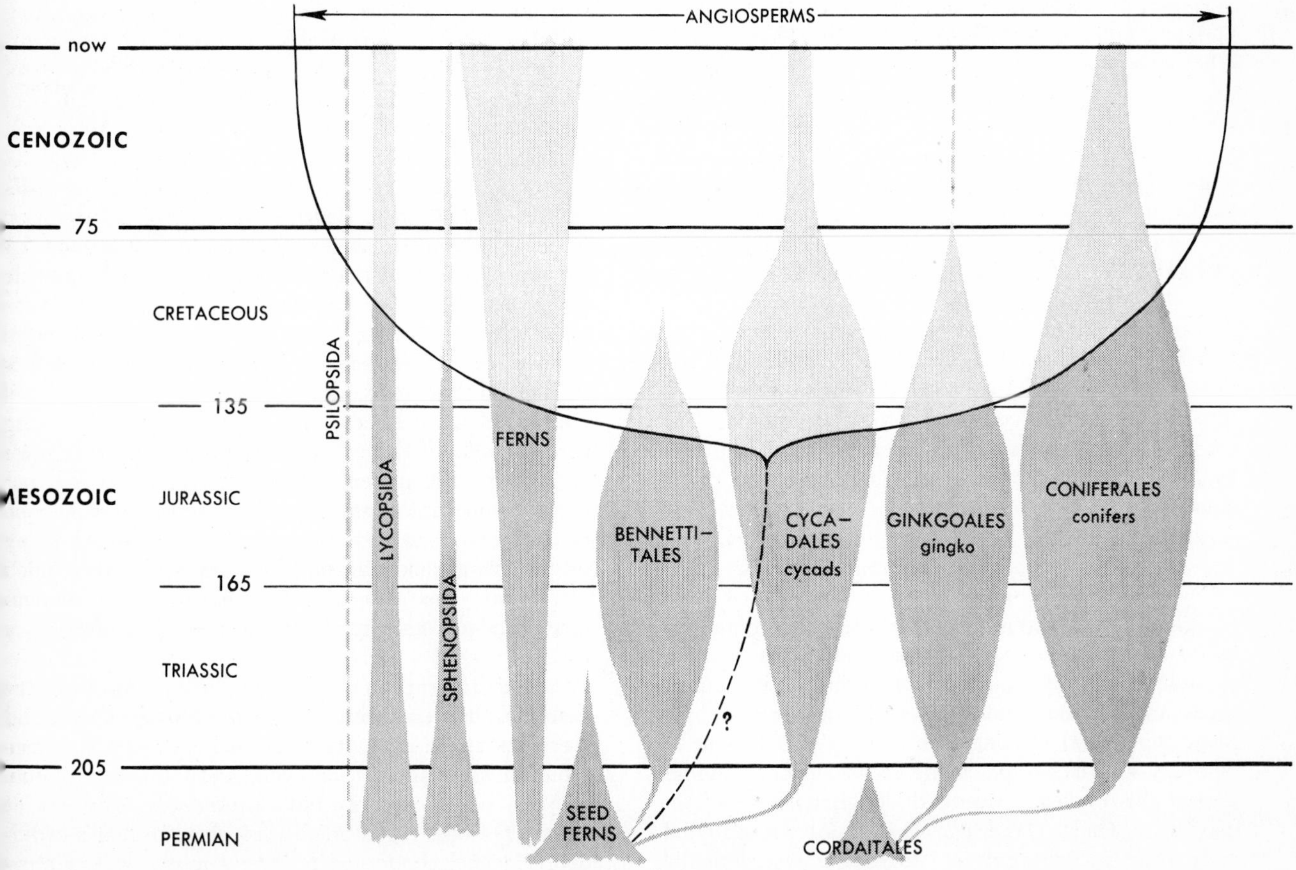

or lost cambia altogether, which left them as non-woody herbaceous biennials and annuals. Winter then could not harm them, for during the winter they simply died and became nonexistent as mature plants. For the rest of the year their primary growth gave them only a minimum body, just barely sufficiently large to permit them to reproduce. Thus the small herbaceous angiosperms now do not waste energy and materials in accumulating wood which soon becomes nonfunctional in any case; yet they are winter-protected nevertheless. We note that the long-range consequences of the Laramide revolution were the reduction of the woody seed plants in all regions except the tropics and the gradual emergence of the modern small-bodied flowering herbs. These became dominant in the northern and arctic zones. Such areas today are inhabited by about 80 per cent of all the herbaceous angiosperms, whereas the tropics are inhabited by a similar percentage of all the woody angiosperms.

As we shall see shortly, the reduction of forests during the middle and late Cenozoic was to prove highly significant for animal evolution. For example, arboreal temperate-zone mammals were forced out of the tree tops, which no longer provided continuous overhead canopies. Some of these mammals then evolved walking feet on the ground, and during the last million years they transformed into men.

ANIMAL EVOLUTION

As pointed out earlier, all metazoan phyla recognized today appear to have been already established 500 million years ago. The various basic animal types therefore must have evolved during the Precambrian. This early evolution consequently cannot be documented by fossils but must be inferred from the nature of the animal groups now in existence.

EARLY HISTORY

The first and most important steps of animal evolution remain even more obscure than those of plant evolution. Part of the problem is that basic animal types are far more numerous and diverse than basic plant types, and existing forms often give few or no clues as to which type is the more ancient. Another part of the problem concerns the original source of animals as a whole. Did Metazoa originate **monophyletically,** from a single protistan stock, or **polyphyletically,**

from several protistan stocks? Biologists have largely tended to favor the monophyletic view, but the reasons are exceedingly tenuous and far from sufficient. Besides, it is not known which protistan stock or stocks actually might have been ancestral to animals. Most hypotheses derive the first Metazoa from protozoa. However, other origins are equally possible. For example, Metazoa might trace back directly to some of the very first flagellate protistan ancestors, which might have lost chlorophyll and evolved in the animal direction thereafter. Conclusive answers simply are not available.

One of the notable attempts at inferring the course of animal evolution from existing forms was made by Haeckel, a German biologist of the late nineteenth century. His views are now largely discredited, but they were once so influential that many of them still persist today under various guises. Haeckel recognized, as did others before him, that the early embryonic development of all animals passed through certain common stages. Thus, development starts with the unicellular zygote, proceeds by cleavage to a blastula stage, then to a gastrula stage, and continues later with mesoderm formation. Haeckel thought that such common stages had evolutionary meaning. More specifically, he believed that each stage represented an adult form of an ancestral type. Accordingly, the succession of embryonic stages would mirror a succession of past evolutionary stages. The zygote would represent the unicellular protistan stage of evolution. The blastula would correspond to an evolutionary stage when animals were, according to Haeckel, hollow one-layered spheres. Haeckel coined the term *blastea* for such hypothetical adult animals, and he thought that his ancestral blasteas may have been quite similar to currently living green algae like *Volvox*. Analogously, the gastrula stage in animal development would correspond to a hypothetical ancestral adult type which he called a *gastrea*. He believed that gastreas were still represented today by the living coelenterates, which are indeed very much like certain gastrulae; e.g., they have a single alimentary opening, corresponding to the blastopore of a gastrula.

The Haeckelian hypothesis further implied, for example, that a caterpillar larva represented an annelid stage in insect evolution, that a frog tadpole represented a fish stage in frog evolution, and that a human embryo, which exhibits rudimentary gill structures at certain periods, represented a fish stage in man's evolution. Haeckel condensed his views into a *law of reca-*

pitulation, the essence of which is described by the phrase "ontogeny recapitulates phylogeny." This statement means that the embryonic development of an egg (ontogeny) repeats the evolutionary development of the phyla (phylogeny).

Therefore, if one wishes to determine the course of animal evolution, he need only study the course of embryonic development. For, according to the law, evolution occurs by the addition of extra embryonic stages to the end of a given sequence of development. If to a protozoon is added cleavage, the protozoon becomes a zygote and the new adult is a blastea. If to a blastea is added the process of gastrulation, then the blastea becomes a blastula and the new adult is a gastrea. Similarly, if to a fish are added lungs and four legs, then the fish represents a tadpole and the new adult is a frog. And if to such an amphibian are added a four-chambered heart, a diaphragm, a larger brain, an upright posture, and a few other features, then the frog is a fetus and the new adult is a man.

We can attribute to Haeckel, not to Darwin, this erroneous idea of an evolutionary "ladder" or "scale," more and more rungs being added on top as time proceeds. Corollary ideas, equally erroneous but nevertheless still widely current, picture evolution as a progression from the "simple" to the "complex" or from "amoeba to man." All such notions are invalid because Haeckel's basic thesis is invalid. Indeed, Haeckel's arguments were shown to be unsound even in his own day, but his generalizations were so neat and they seemed to explain so much so simply that the fundamental difficulties were ignored by many.

A central objection is that evolution of a new type does not occur by addition of extra stages to the end of the embryonic development of an existing type. No matter how often a protozoon divides, the resulting cells still are protozoa, not a blastea or even a blastula. Regardless of how much more a fish develops, it will still be a fish, larger perhaps than before, but not a frog or a man. The developing embryo of a man does not really represent a successive transformation of a protozoon into a coelenterate, a flatworm, a fish, etc. Moreover, it is hardly conceivable that the billion or more years of animal evolution could be crowded into the few weeks or months of embryonic development. The conclusion is certainly warranted that recapitulation in the Haeckelian sense simply does not occur; the embryonic stages of given animals do *not* repeat the evolutionary development of the phyla as represented by the adult stages of other animals. Besides, we know

from available fossil data and our understanding of evolutionary mechanisms that evolution must have occurred not in ladderlike but in bushlike fashion.

Another objection is that the common embryonic stages in animal development are not nearly as alike as Haeckel's law postulates. For example, the blastula is a hollow sphere only in certain cases. It is solid in most coelenterates, in mammals and in numerous other types, and it has altogether different forms in various other animal groups. The gastrula does arise by invagination in some echinoderms and some other animal embryos, but in most animals it arises by various non-invaginative and often unique processes. Similarly, the embryos of fish and of man actually resemble each other only in very general, superficial ways. Even the eggs exhibit specific differences unique to the species, and these differences become progressively more pronounced as development proceeds.

In short, if the development of an egg repeats anything, it merely repeats the development of previous generations of its own species, not the evolutionary development of other animals. Each animal is a unique construction which must be developed in a unique way. This uniqueness starts directly with the egg and is not simply tacked on at the end of development. The *whole* life cycle is species-specific, including all embryonic stages. Such stages do indicate a great deal about the construction processes necessary to form an animal of a given type, but it does not follow that they also indicate past evolutionary histories. Fish and men both develop via a gastrula stage because a gastrula happens to be a constructional requirement in both cases. However, the detailed constructional requirements differ in the two cases and the gastrulae differ correspondingly. We may conclude that whereas the common stages in animal development may give evidence of general similarities, they do not give evidence of specific identities. Haeckel ignored these embryological realities. Instead, he formulated a pure abstraction far removed from the actual evidence.

It is undeniable nevertheless that some of the embryonic stages of animals do resemble one another, even if only in a general way. Indeed, the closer two animals are related in evolutionary history, the more similar are their embryos. For example, the embryos of man and of monkeys resemble each other till relatively late in development, and the developmental paths diverge only then. The embryos of man and of fish are similar for considerably shorter periods; here the developmental paths diverge much sooner. Such correla-

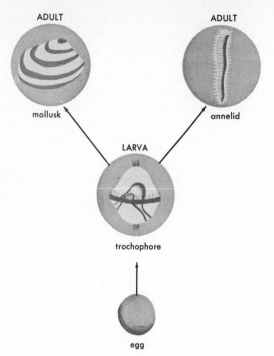

FIG. 30.16   Although the adults of mollusks and annelid worms resemble one another very little, the embryos and larvae of the two groups are hardly distinguishable. Trochophore larvae are characteristic of both.

tions were clearly recognized before Haeckel and even before Darwin. We know today that they have evolutionary meaning, but not in the Haeckelian sense. It is quite natural that related animals descended from a common ancestor should resemble one another in some of their adult as well as some of their embryonic features. Such resemblances may or may not be pronounced, depending entirely on how widely the evolutionary paths have diverged. Accordingly, human embryos resemble those of fish and frogs in certain respects not because an egg of man becomes a fish embryo first, changes to a frog embryo next, and transforms into a human embryo last. The similarities arise, rather, from the common ancestry of all three animal types. Each of the three types has inherited certain common characteristics from an early vertebrate ancestor. These characteristics include general embryonic processes such as gastrulation, which permit the formation of the basic vertebrate body. Beyond this, each type has modified the general processes in its own specific way. Any lingering resemblances are little more

than the incidental remains of the common heritage left over after the adaptive radiation of the ancestral vertebrate stock had taken its course. The resemblances are not an indication of a ladderlike cause-and-effect recapitulation.

Within limits, similarities among embryos (as among adults) may actually be quite useful in determining degrees of evolutionary relatedness. For example, it is partly on the basis of developmental resemblances that animals are grouped into five superphyla, viz., radiates, acoelomates, pseudocoelomates, schizocoelomates, and enterocoelomates. Analogously, developmental similarities have helped to reveal the close evolutionary relation between mollusks and annelids and between echinoderms and chordates, phyla which do not appear to be particularly closely related if only their adults are considered (Figs. 30.16 and 30.17). In many cases, however, neither the adults nor the embryos give clues to evolutionary interrelation. For example, despite numerous attempts at analysis, we still cannot be sure just how the five animal superphyla are related to one another or how certain phyla within a superphylum may be related to one another. What we do know reasonably well is how the evolutionary bush has grown during the last 500 million years. Haeckel and other theorists notwithstanding, the lower, Precambrian por-

FIG. 30.17   Although the adults of echinoderms and hemichordates are very dissimilar, their larvae in many cases are quite alike. On the left is a diagram of an echinoderm larva; on the right, a diagram of a larva of hemichordates.

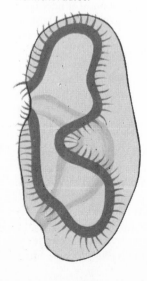
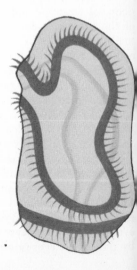

FIG. 30.18 Seascapes of the early Paleozoic, restorations. Left, Cambrian seas. Various algae, trilobites (in center foreground), eurypterids (in center background), sponges, jellyfish, brachiopods, and different types of worms are the most prominent organisms shown. Right, Ordovician seas. The large animal in foreground is a straight-shelled nautiloid. *(Left, American Museum of Natural History; right, Chicago Natural History Museum.)*

tions of the bush, where the important junctions of the main branches occur, are as yet hidden from view.

THE PALEOZOIC

Every animal phylum in existence in the Cambrian has persisted to the present, but not a single species has persisted. So far as is known, only a single *genus* has survived from the Ordovician, the period after the Cambrian. This genus is *Lingula*, of the phylum Brachiopoda (see Chap. 11). Apart from this 400-million-year-old relic, all ancient genera have become extinct as well. Indeed, the dominant theme of the animal fossil record as a whole is extensive and repeated replacement within major groups, with relatively few additions of new major groups.

Cambrian and Ordovician

The land during these two periods remained free of animals, but animal life in the sea was already abundant. Sponges, coelenterates, brachiopods, bryozoa, echinoderms, mollusks, arthropods, and a large variety of worms were particularly common (Fig. 30.18). The most prominent arthropods belonged to two groups, both now extinct. One included the **eurypterids**, large animals which resembled crustacea to some extent but which were more closely related to the horseshoe crabs and scorpions of today. The other group comprised the **trilobites**, whose bodies were marked into three lobes by two longitudinal furrows (Fig. 30.19). Among mollusks, archaic clams and snails were present, as were the **nautiloids.** Related to modern squids, octo-

FIG. 30.19 Left, fossils of trilobites. Middle, eurypterid. Right, crinoid or sea lily, a sessile echinoderm. *(American Museum of Natural History.)*

puses, and particularly to the living chambered nautilus, the nautiloids probably included the largest animals of the time; some had uncoiled shells 5 to 6 yd long. During the later Devonian period, the nautiloids gave rise to and were in turn replaced by the **ammonites,** which came to be the dominant mollusks for long ages.

From the human standpoint, the most important event of the early Paleozoic was the rise of the subphylum Vertebrata. The chordate ancestors of vertebrates probably were marine tunicates, already present at the start of the Paleozoic. Some of the descendants

of these ancestral tunicates later evolved into vertebrates, presumably in freshwater rivers (see Chap. 7) The first fossil vertebrates date to the late Ordovician These were members of the class Agnatha, the **jaw-less fishes.** Lampreys and hagfishes are the only surviving descendants (see Chap. 11). The Cambrian Ordovician record is summarized in Fig. 30.20.

Silurian and Devonian

We recall that the Silurian was the period during which the first land plants evolved. Animals soon fol-

FIG. 30.20 Summary of Cambrian-Ordovician events. The level at which jawless fishes are drawn corresponds roughly with the time of their first appearance in the fossil record. All other forms were present throughout the time period shown, and all groups represented in the chart continued on into later periods.

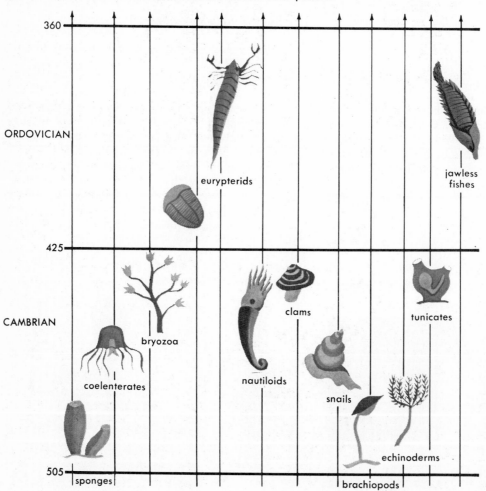

lowed the plants to land; fossil scorpions from the late Silurian are the earliest known terrestrial animals. Other land arthropods appeared in the Devonian: spiderlike creatures, archaic mites, and probably the ancestors of insects. Moreover, at the very end of the Devonian the first terrestrial vertebrates made their appearance.

The Devonian as a whole is often called the "age of fishes" in animal evolution. During the early Silurian, ancestral jawless fishes had given rise to a new line, the *jawed fishes,* or **placoderms.** The name of this separate class of vertebrates refers to the armor plates with which the skins of these fishes were equipped (see Fig. 5.24). Probably evolved in fresh water, the placoderms became abundant when the Devonian began and some placoderm stocks then spread into the ocean. Thus the placoderms replaced the jawless fishes more or less completely in all aquatic environments. Some of the placoderms were small, but others reached lengths of 12 yd or more. Most exploited the possession of jaws by adopting a fiercely carnivorous way of life.

The dominance of the placoderms was relatively short-lived. Early during the Devonian, ancestral placoderms had given rise to two new lines of fishes which came to replace the later placoderms. By the end of the Devonian, placoderms had disappeared completely. We may note that this is the only vertebrate class (and one of the few classes of animals generally) which has become extinct.

The two new types of fishes evolved from early placoderms during the Devonian were the **cartilage fishes** and the **bony fishes,** each representing a separate class. The former includes sharks, skates, and rays,

adapted now as in Devonian times largely to the marine environment. The bony fishes at first remained in fresh water, where they had probably evolved. They soon radiated into three main subgroups: the so-called **paleoniscoid fishes,** the **lungfishes,** and the **lobe-finned fishes.** The paleoniscoids later spread into the ocean and became the ancestors of virtually all bony fishes in existence today, both freshwater and marine. The lungfishes were common in Devonian and later Paleozoic times, but thereafter they declined and today they are represented by only three surviving genera. The lobe-fins similarly are virtually extinct today (Fig. 30.21).

But the Devonian representatives of the lobe-fins included the ancestors of the first land vertebrates, the **amphibia.** As indicated by their name, the lobe-fins had fleshy appendages, usable to some extent as walking legs. These fishes probably lived in fresh waters which dried out periodically, and their fins may have enabled them to crawl overland to other bodies of water. We may conclude therefore that terrestrial vertebrates arose not because certain fish preferred the land, but because they had to use the land if they were to survive as fish.

Thus, when the Devonian came to a close, sharks dominated in the ocean and bony fishes in fresh waters. On land, terrestrial arthropods had become abundant and the first amphibia had made their appearance (Fig. 30.22). Many of the land animals could shelter in the stands of lycopsid and sphenopsid trees already established at that time.

Carboniferous and Permian

In these later Paleozoic times, the character of aquatic animal life did not change in major ways, but

FIG. 30.21   Below, a modern lungfish from West Africa. Right, restoration of fossil lobe-finned fishes. (*American Museum of Natural History.*)

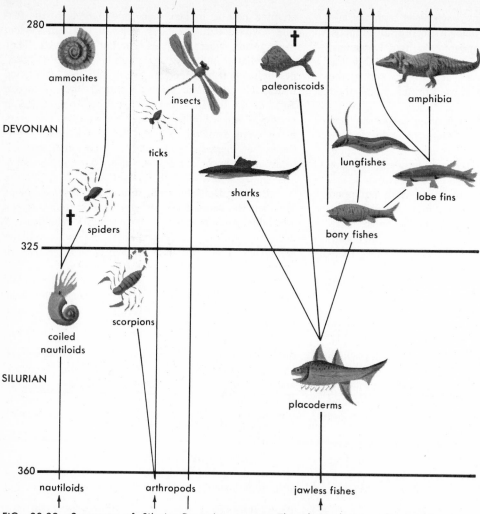

FIG. 30.22 Summary of Silurian-Devonian events. The chart shows only newly evolved groups and those which became extinct during the time period under consideration. Groups already established during earlier periods are not otherwise indicated. The level at which a given group is placed here corresponds roughly to the time of its first appearance in the fossil record. Daggers signify extinction, at the appropriate time level.

that of terrestrial life did. Additional terrestrial groups evolved from aquatic ancestors, and some other groups, already terrestrial, began to diversify. More specifically, land snails appeared for the first time during the Carboniferous, centipedes arose, and spiders and scorpions became still more abundant than before. Above all, insects produced extensive adaptive radiations at that time. Some of these ancient insect types reached sizes well above the modern maximum. A Permian dragonfly, for example, is known to have had a wingspread of close to a yard (Fig. 30.23).

Among vertebrates, the early amphibia gave rise to a large variety of more or less clumsy, often bizarre forms, the **labyrinthodonts** (Fig. 30.24). During the Permian, however, most of these began to be replaced by members of a new vertebrate class, the **reptiles.** The

FIG. 30.23 The wing of a Permian insect, shown in actual natural size. Insects larger than this existed in the Permian era, but even the owner of the wing shown was far larger than any insect today. (*Courtesy of Dr. C. O. Dunbar and Peabody Museum, Yale University.*)

latter had evolved from ancestral labyrinthodonts late during the Carboniferous and were represented at first by one main group, the **cotylosaurs,** or **stem reptiles** (see Fig. 30.26). Inasmuch as they laid hard-shelled land eggs, they were the first completely terrestrial vertebrates. The cotylosaurs produced a major reptilian radiation during the Permian, which set the stage for a subsequent "age of reptiles" during the Mesozoic era.

As noted earlier, the Paleozoic era terminated with

the Permo-Triassic crisis precipitated by the Appalachian revolution. This crisis was characterized as among plants by widespread extinction of archaic animal forms, by replacement and rapid evolution of new groups, and by a general, temporary decrease in the total amount of animal life. In the sea, the trilobites disappeared altogether. The previously very abundant brachiopods declined. Archaic echinoderms, mollusks, and crustacea were replaced by newly evolved repre-

FIG. 30.24 Labyrinthodonts. Reconstruction of *Diplovertebron*, a Permian amphibian. (*American Museum of Natural History.*)

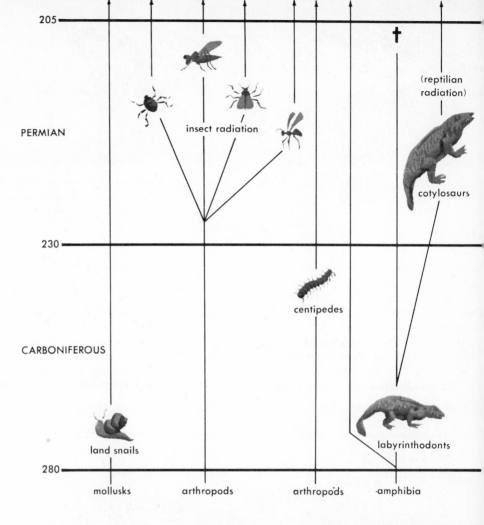

FIG. 30.25 Summary of Carboniferous-Permian events. Placement of groups corresponds roughly with time of first appearance in the fossil record. Only newly evolved groups are indicated.

sentatives. Similar intragroup replacement occurred among the cartilage and bony fishes. On land, the labyrinthodonts became extinct and the amphibian tradition thus became limited to a small group of inconspicuous types, the direct ancestors of the modern salamanders, frogs, and toads. When the new Mesozoic era opened, reptiles were already dominant. The Carboniferous-Permian record is summarized in Fig. 30.25.

THE MESOZOIC

Several major evolutionary events occurred during this era. As pointed out earlier, the flowering plants arose during the Jurassic and underwent an explosive expansion during the Cretaceous which established them as the dominant land plants from then on. In parallel with this, insects reradiated enormously, and their present importance traces to this Mesozoic expansion. An equally extensive radiation occurred among the bony fishes. During the Cretaceous, the paleoniscoid fishes gave rise to a multitude of new freshwater and marine types, the modern bony fishes. These became the dominant animals of the aquatic environment, a status they still retain today. Thus the sea and the land began to acquire relatively modern characteristics.

However, the most spectacular Mesozoic event was the expansion of the reptiles. These animals not only evolved many different terrestrial ways of life but also invaded the water and the air. As a group they reigned supreme on earth for 130 million years, longer than any other animals to date. When their dominance was eventually broken, they were replaced by two new groups they themselves had given rise to, the birds and the mammals.

At the beginning of the Mesozoic, five major reptilian stocks were in existence, all evolved during the Permian from the cotylosaurian stem reptiles (Fig. 30.26.) One group, the so-called **thecodonts**, reradiated extensively during the Triassic and in turn gave rise to the following types: the ancestral *birds;* the ancestors

FIG. 30.26 The great reptilian radiation of the Mesozoic. Placement of groups corresponds roughly with the time of their greatest abundance.

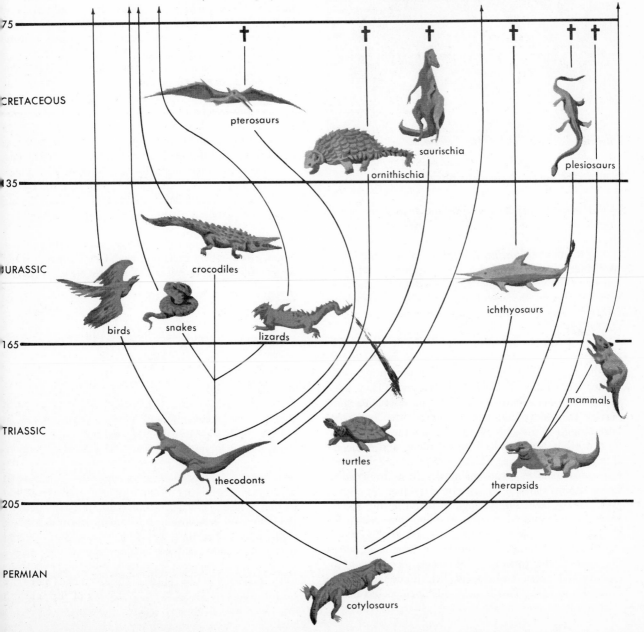

FIG. 30.27 Therapsids, mammallike reptiles of the Triassic. *(American Museum of Natural History.)*

of the modern *crocodiles, lizards,* and *snakes;* the flying *pterosaurs;* and two other groups, referred to collectively as *dinosaurs.* A second reptilian stock was ancestral to the modern *turtles.* A third and fourth produced two kinds of marine reptiles, the porpoiselike **ichthyosaurs** and the unique, long-necked **plesiosaurs.** The fifth stock comprised the so-called **therapsids,** mammallike reptiles, which included the ancestors of the true *mammals* (Fig. 30.27).

These various reptilian types did not all flourish at the same time. The Triassic was dominated largely by the ancestral thecodonts and the therapsids. The former were rather birdlike in appearance. They possessed large hind limbs for walking, an enormous supporting tail, and diminutive forelimbs, often not even long enough to shovel food into the mouth. Therapsids, on the other hand, walked on all fours, and some of them gave rise to types which were less reptilelike and more mammallike. True mammals arose from such stocks during the late Triassic or early Jurassic. However, these new fur-bearing vertebrates still were greatly overshadowed by the reptiles; they remained small and inconspicuous during the rest of the Mesozoic, i.e., for a period of about 80 or 90 million years.

During the Jurassic, ichthyosaurs became abundant in the ocean and one of the thecodont groups evolved into birds. This transition is documented beau-

tifully by a famous fossil animal called *Archeopteryx* (Fig. 30.28). The organism possessed teeth and a lizardlike tail, two features which are distinctly reptilian. But it also possessed feathers and wings, and presumably it flew like a bird. Like the early mammals, the ancestral birds similarly remained inconspicuous during the whole remaining Mesozoic. They were overshadowed particularly by their thecodont kin, the pterosaurs. These flying reptiles had their heyday during the Cretaceous, the period when reptiles as a whole attained their greatest abundance and variety. Plesiosaurs then were common in the ocean, and the dinosaurs came into undisputed dominance on land (Fig. 30.29).

The two dinosaurian groups are called the *Ornithischia* and the *Saurischia.* Both evolved from the thecodonts. Not all dinosaurs were large, but some of the group were enormous. The saurischian *Brontosaurus* was the largest land animal of all time, exceeded in size only by the modern blue whale. This dinosaur was herbivorous and it probably lived in swamps or lagoons, where it could support its 20- to 30-ton bulk in water. Another saurischian, the giant *Tyrannosaurus,* probably was the fiercest land carnivore of all time. Among

FIG. 30.28 Cast of *Archeopteryx.* Note feathered tail, wings. Head is bent back, and teeth-bearing mouth is not easily visible here. *(American Museum of Natural History.)*

FIG. 30.29 Reconstruction of plesiosaurs (left) and ichthyosaurs (right). (*Chicago Natural History Museum.*)

its victims undoubtedly were animals like *Ankylosaurus* and *Triceratops,* herbivorous and heavily armored ornithischian giants (Fig. 30.30).

As the Cretaceous came to a close, virtually all the reptilian multitude became extinct. Today the class is represented only by turtles, crocodiles, lizards, snakes, and *Sphenodon,* a lizardlike "living fossil" in New Zealand (Fig. 30.31). The specific reasons for this large-scale dying out have been sought for a long time, but fully satisfactory explanations have not yet been found. Climatic changes at the end of the Mesozoic, coincident with the Laramide revolution, are believed to have played a decisive role. Mesozoic reptiles were adapted to rather warm environments, as their modern descendants still are. However, climates appear to have become cooler toward the close of the Cretaceous, as a result of the Laramide revolution. Much tropical and sub-tropical vegetation may then have died out, which must have meant that herbivorous reptiles lost their food supplies. And as the herbivorous stocks so declined, the carnivorous reptiles would have had to die out as well.

Whatever the precise causes, the extinction of the Mesozoic reptiles cleared the way for a great expansion of mammals and birds.

THE CENOZOIC

Just as each geological era may be subdivided into periods, so each period in turn may be subdivided into **epochs**. The periods and epochs of the Cenozoic era are shown in Table 16. As noted earlier, the era as a whole began with the great upheavals of the Laramide revolution, which produced the present high mountain ranges and led to progressively cooler climates during the Tertiary period. These climatic changes culminated in the four ice ages spread throughout most of the last million years, the Pleistocene epoch. The biological importance of Cenozoic climates in general and of Pleistocene ice in particular is great, for these environmental conditions materially influenced the evolution of all organisms, plant or animal, man not excepted. Man in a sense is one of the products of the ice ages.

TABLE 16
*The epochs and periods of the Cenozoic era**

period	epoch	duration	beginning date
Quaternary	Recent	20,000 years	20,000 B.C.
	Pleistocene	1	1
Tertiary	Pliocene	11	12
	Miocene	16	28
	Oligocene	11	39
	Eocene	19	58
	Paleocene	17	75

* Unless otherwise stated, all figures refer to millions of years.

FIG. 30.30 Dinosaurs. Top, *Triceratops* on left, *Tyrannosaurus* on right. Bottom left, *Ankylosaurus*. Bottom right, *Brontosaurus*. (Top, *Chicago Natural History Museum; bottom left and right, American Museum of Natural History.*)

The radiation of mammals and birds came to be the main feature of animal evolution during the Cenozoic era. Terrestrial mammals replaced the dinosaurs; aquatic mammals eventually took the place of the former ichthyosaurs and plesiosaurs; and bats, but more especially birds, gained the air left free by the pterosaurs. The Cenozoic is often designated as the "age of mammals"; it might equally well be called the "age of birds."

The Mammalian Radiation

When the Cenozoic began, the great mammalian radiation was just getting under way. Three subclasses came into existence, including a total of some two dozen independent lines (each ranked as an order). As already noted in Chap. 11, the subclasses are the **Prototheria**, or *egg-laying* mammals, of which the duck-billed platypus is the most familiar living representative; the **Metatheria**, or *pouched* mammals, to which belong the opossum, the kangaroo, and a large variety of other *marsupials* now confined largely to the Australian continent; and the **Eutheria**, or *placental* mammals, the most abundant group which includes the most familiar mammals: cats, dogs, seals, and walruses; rodents; whales and dolphins; bats; moles and shrews; cattle, sheep, pigs, and camels; horses and zebras; elephants and tapirs; monkeys and men; and many others.

The fossil record of this mammalian radiation is fairly extensive for most groups and extremely good

FIG. 30.31   *Sphenodon*, the tuatera from New Zealand. *(American Museum of Natural History.)*

members took to the trees, which then still formed vast forests, and adapted to an *arboreal* life.

Soon after such a stock of arboreal mammals had evolved during the early Paleocene, it must have reradiated and produced two major sublines, the order **Insectivora** and the order **Primates** (Fig. 30.33). Most modern insect-eating mammals, particularly the moles and the hedgehogs, are clearly distinct from modern primates, of which man is a late member. But some of the shrews now living are exceedingly like insectivores on the one hand and like primitive living primates on the other. Indeed, one group of shrews is actually classified with the Insectivora and another with the Primates. Fossil data similarly support the view that insectivorous mammals and primates are very closely related, through a common, shrewlike, arboreal, insect-eating ancestor (Fig. 30.34).

The Primate Radiation

The first distinct primates evolved from this insect-eating ancestor during the Paleocene may be referred to as the **early prosimians**. They were small, still shrewlike in appearance, with a fairly long snout and a long bushy tail. They were also agile and nimble, an important adaptation in a life among the treetops. Undoubtedly they possessed good eyes and good neuromuscular coordination, but in these respects they were probably not equipped very much better than early mammals in general. Of the many lines which radiated from the early prosimians during the Paleocene, four major ones survive today (Fig. 30.35).

for a few, such as horses and elephants (Fig. 30.32). Each mammalian line descended from the common ancestral stock exploited a particular way of life available at the time. The animals came to occupy either a new environmental niche or one left free after the extinction of the Mesozoic reptiles. One mammalian line is of particular interest, for it eventually led to man. This line exploited a relatively new environmental possibility. Its

FIG. 30.32   Reconstruction of horse evolution, based on abundant fossil evidence. The evolutionary sequence begins at the right of photo, with the fossil horse *Eohippus*, and ends at the left, with the modern horse *Equus*. The drawings are to scale and show how the average size and the outline shape of horses have changed during their evolution in the Cenozoic. Progressive reduction in the number of toes occurred, as well as changes in dentition and size. Note, however, that the animals shown represent a *selected* series, and it should not be inferred that horse evolution followed a straight-line pattern. Here, as elsewhere, a bush pattern is actually in evidence. *(American Museum of Natural History.)*

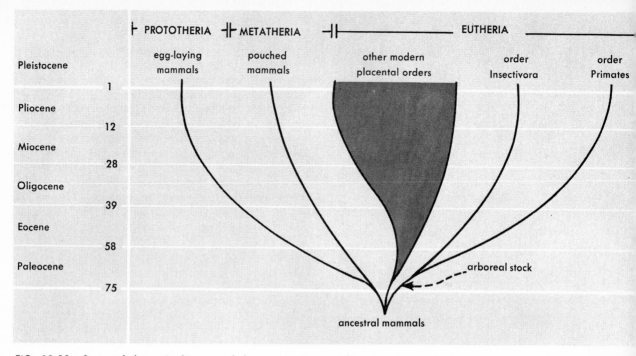

	PROTOTHERIA	METATHERIA	EUTHERIA

FIG. 30.33 Some of the main features of the mammalian radiation during the Cenozoic.

One of these four largely retained the prosimian characteristics and gave rise to a number of sublines during subsequent epochs. The **modern prosimians** are the collective result. This group includes the *lemurs* and the *aye-ayes,* found today largely on the island of Madagascar (Fig. 30.36). These animals still possess long snouts and long tails, but instead of claws they possess flat nails, a general primate characteristic. It is likely that nails are a specific adaptation to arboreal life, for nails probably interfere less with locomotion along tree branches than long claws. The modern prosimians also include the *tarsiers* of Southern Asia and Indonesia. In these animals, the snout has receded considerably and a fairly well-defined face has appeared. Moreover, the eyes, which in lemurs are still more or less on the side, have moved well into the face. As a result, tarsiers may focus on one point with both eyes; i.e., they are endowed with stereoscopic vision and efficient depth perception.

FIG. 30.34 Arboreal squirrel shrew. This animal belongs to the order Insectivora. *(American Museum of Natural History.)*

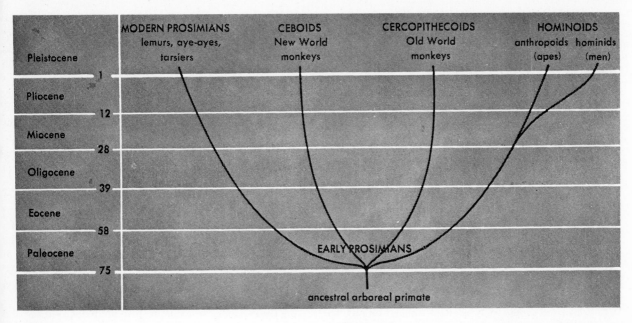

FIG. 30.35 Diagram of the radiation of primates.

These features are additional adaptations to a tree-dwelling existence. In a plains animal such as a horse, for example, the eyes are located advantageously on the side, where they enable the animal to scout the open environment even while grazing. But among the branches of a tree, lateral vision is less important. Quite the contrary, it becomes important to look ahead along a branch, almost a necessary requirement if balance is to be retained during precarious limb-over-limb locomotion. Note also that tarsiers possess fairly well-defined fingers, with a gripping pad at the end of each.

The second of the main groups descended from the early prosimians comprises the **ceboids**, or *New World monkeys*. These attained their present diversity during the Oligocene and Miocene. Ceboid monkeys today are confined to South and Central America. The

FIG. 30.36 Left, a modern lemur from Madagascar. Right, modern tarsier from Indonesia. (*American Museum of Natural History.*)

animals are characterized by long, strong tails, which are used as fifth limbs. The third main group evolved independently from Paleocene prosimians consists of **cercopithecoids**, or *Old World monkeys*. They too radiated during the Oligocene and Miocene, and they are found today in Africa and Asia. These monkeys possess tails, but they are not used as limbs.

In both groups of monkeys, adaptations to arboreal life have evolved a good deal farther than in modern prosimians. A monkey possesses a very well developed face, stereoscopic vision, and, in addition, independently movable fingers on all four limbs. Moreover, it possesses opposable thumbs, which allow it to grip tree branches very firmly. Also, limbs may be rotated freely within their sockets. In a plains animal like a horse, limbs move predominantly back and forth. The limb sockets here permit very little lateral play, an energy-saving feature in running. In jumping among tree branches, on the other hand, freely movable limbs are clearly advantageous.

Correlated with such skeletal specializations to arboreal life, monkeys have also evolved important muscular, sensory, and neural adaptations. Through a general enlargement of the cerebral cortex and a particular enlargement of the optic lobes, monkeys have become capable of precision timing, of judging distances to the inch, and of coordinating limb and finger muscles in new, complex ways. In turn, increase in brain size has led to a quickness of mind and a level of intelligence well above the prosimian average. We may note here that the evolution of intelligence has been correlated particularly with the improvement of coordination between the eyes and the limbs. Evidently, primate intelligence too is basically an adaptation to the arboreal way of life.

Trends of the same kind, but developed very much farther than in monkeys, are apparent also in the fourth group of living primates. Descended independently from Paleocene prosimians, this group comprises the so-called **hominoids**. During the early Miocene, some 30 million years ago, the hominoid line branched into two main sublines. One of these led to the **anthropoids**, or apes, the other to the **hominids**, the family of man and manlike types (see Fig. 30.35). Both groups are characterized by the absence of an external tail and by an increase in body size over the average of other primates. Moreover, the brain of anthropoids and hominids is still further enlarged and elaborated functionally.

Apes are represented today by four genera: gibbons, orangutans, chimpanzees, and gorillas. The group is fundamentally arboreal, like the ancestral hominoid stock as a whole. But modern apes include types which have abandoned the arboreal way of life more or less completely. For example, orangutans and especially chimpanzees can be quite at home out of trees. Gorillas are ground animals altogether, using trees as little as men do. Correlated with this abandonment of tree life is a tendency toward more or less two-legged walking and toward a more or less upright posture. In such a way of life on the ground, arboreal adaptations can be used to advantage. For example, the long arms of a gorilla enable it to assume a half-erect, crouching stance, and the animal may also support itself on its hind legs and walk bipedally for short distances. The agile forelegs and fingers then need not participate in locomotion and become free to perform other tasks.

These trends became very much more elaborated in the hominids, the line leading to man. After branching away from the common hominoid stock during the Miocene, the hominids left the trees completely. Forelimbs remained adapted for gripping, but the feet evolved into flat walking platforms. A half-erect, bent-kneed, four-limbed shuffle must have been characteristic for a long time, but as the feet became perfected, forelimbs were completely relieved of a locomotor function. Undoubtedly, it was this total freeing of arms and fingers for many new functions which made possible the evolution of the most basic human characteristics. For, correlated with new opportunities for exceedingly complex hand-eye coordination, brain size enlarged still further and intelligence increased spectacularly.

These and other features which now distinguish men and apes came to be superimposed on the characteristics of pre-Miocene arboreal primates. We recognize, therefore, that the modern human type could not have evolved if the ancestral type had not first been specialized for life in trees.

MAN

Leaving the trees was clearly essential to the emergence of man. What prompted our Miocene ancestors, along with some of the early apes, to abandon arboreal life? As pointed out earlier, the progressively cooler climates during the Tertiary led to a thinning out of forests. In many regions, therefore, continuous overhead canopies of branches and foliage disappeared.

As a result, our prehuman ancestors would have had to travel on the ground if they wished to move from one stand of trees to another. Such forced excursions may well have been fraught with considerable danger, for saber-toothed carnivores and other large mammals dominated the ground at those times. Consequently, ability to dash quickly across open spaces may have had great selective value, and this may have oriented the evolution of running feet in the human direction. Moreover, strong muscles would be required to move the hind limbs in new ways. Indeed, a unique trait of the human line is the possession of such muscles, partly in the form of enlarged buttocks.

It is conceivable, therefore, that the hominids came out of the trees because they had to. Life on the ground then promoted the gradual evolution of running feet, bipedal locomotion, newly functioning fore-limbs, complex hand-eye coordination, and powerful brains.

The Hominid Radiation

After the hominid stock had separated from the anthropoid stock at about the beginning of the Miocene, the hominid group must have given rise to an adaptive radiation of its own. Moreover, each line of this radiation must have produced various sublines and sub-sublines in turn. The detailed pattern of this hominid radiation is unknown, but that it occurred can be inferred from available fossil evidence. To be sure, this evidence is tantalizingly scanty; we can trace the recent evolution of almost any mammal far better than our own. Nevertheless, such fossils of hominid types as have been found show clearly that a substantial number of separate lines of descent must have evolved. In other words, the members of the hominid radiation known to date, including ourselves, do not appear to be related directly. They probably trace back independently and through an unknown pattern of branching to various earlier and equally unknown common ancestors, and ultimately to the original hominid stock of the early Miocene. Thus the path of descent of our own species remains undiscovered as yet; other known hominids are related to us somewhat as uncles or cousins (Fig. 30.37).

With the exception of the line leading to ourselves, all other lines of the hominid radiation have become extinct at various periods during the last 30 million years. Exact times of extinction are as uncertain as times of origin, for whereas a fossil find indicates when a given hominid was alive, it does not indicate

when it originated or died out. It is not necessary to find whole fossilized skeletons to reconstruct the probable appearance of their once-living owners. The proportions of body parts to one another may be deduced with reasonable accuracy from living man, from apes, and from such whole skeletons of hominid types as have been found. For example, a tooth, a jawbone, a skullcap, or a leg bone may not only be identified from its shape as belonging to a particular hominid, but may also give important clues about the missing remainder. By and large, the skull gives the greatest amount of information. Thick or thin bones, prominent or reduced eyebrow ridges, receding or vertical forehead, small or large brain case, poorly or well-defined chin, all indicate fairly well whether or not a given fossil is a primitive or an advanced hominid.

Much may also be learned from various signs of cultural activity often associated with a fossil find. For example, the type of tool, the type of camp site, the type of weapon found with a fossil, each may reveal a great deal about the evolutionary status of the hominid in question. Note, incidentally, that apart from their biological distinctions, hominids are regarded as being prehuman or truly human on the basis of cultural achievements. Any hominid which *made* tools in addition to using them can be called a "man." If a hominid used only stones or sticks found ready-made in his environment, he is considered prehuman; if he deliberately fashioned natural objects into patterned tools, no matter how crude, he is considered human. By this criterion, quite a few hominid types were men.

The early parts of hominid history are almost completely unknown. Some clues about the common ancestor from which both the anthropoids and the hominids have arisen are provided by 25-million-year-old fossil apes of the genus *Proconsul*, found in East Africa. *Proconsul* clearly belongs to the anthropoid radiation, but certain features of the skull, particularly the teeth, suggest that the base of the hominid radiation could well have been represented by an animal similar to this ape. More definitely allied to or perhaps actually part of the hominid radiation is *Oreopithecus*, the "mountain ape," whose remains were found in northern Italy. This primate dates back some 10 million years, to the early Pliocene. The teeth and the organization of the jaw of *Oreopithecus* were distinctly hominid, but in other respects the animal was still apelike.

After *Oreopithecus* the hominid record of the Tertiary is blank, with the notable exception of *Zinjanthro-*

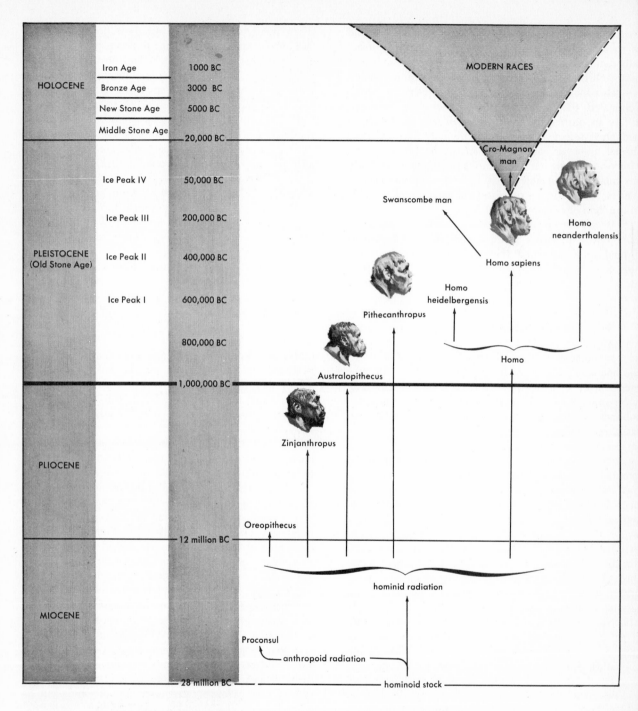

FIG. 30.37 The hominid radiation and some of its principal known members. Each hominid type is shown roughly at a time level at which that type is known to have existed. The detailed interrelations of the various hominid lines are unknown.

FIG. 30.38 Reconstruction of *Zinjanthropus*, the East Africa man. Note the exceptionally low forehead and small brain case. *(Adapted from Peter Bianchi, National Geographic Society.)*

pus, the "East Africa man," discovered in Tanganyika in 1959 (Fig. 30.38). Potassium-argon dating has shown that *Zinjanthropus* lived 1¾ million years ago, in the late Pliocene. This hominid made tools and thus was a true man, the most ancient man now known. The tools included wooden clubs and stone hammers with which *Zinjanthropus* killed small animals and broke open their bones. The diet was mainly coarse vegetation, however, as the large molars clearly indicate. Bone structure in the skull reveals that the head was held very erect and that jaw muscles were attached as in modern man, suggesting that *Zinjanthropus* probably knew speech. On the other hand, a forehead was virtually absent; the volume of the brain could not have been larger than 600 cm³, comparable to the brain volume of a modern gorilla. Also, a low bony ridge was present on top of the skull, another apelike characteristic. We may note that the status of *Zinjanthropus* as first man may be short-lived, for the location where he was found gives evidence of another, even more ancient tool-making hominid.

All other known hominid fossils are of Pleistocene origin, i.e., not older than 1 million years. The oldest of these form a group of several genera of which *Australopithecus,* the "southern ape," is representative (Fig. 30.39). The remains of this australopithecine group have been discovered in South Africa and have been shown to date back roughly 1 million years or somewhat less. Although the australopithecines thus lived much later than *Zinjanthropus,* they probably were not as far advanced. For example, they apparently did not make tools. Their brain volume averaged 600 cm³, and they probably walked erect or almost erect. Skulls and skeletons reveal a mixture of apelike and manlike traits, but the latter predominate and it is clear that the australopithecines are within the hominid family. Indeed, some investigators regard these near-men to be fairly closely related to the line which gave rise to modern man.

A more recent and comparatively much better known hominid is *Pithecanthropus,* a true man who made tools of stone and bone and used fire for cooking (Fig. 30.40). Remains of several species of *Pithecanthropus* were found in Java and China and were shown to be about 500,000 years old. The brain volume of this "erect apeman" averaged 900 to 1,000 cm³. The skull had a flat, sloping forehead and thick eyebrow ridges, and the massive protruding jaw was virtually

FIG. 30.39 Skull of *Australopithecus.* *(After Dart, American Museum of Natural History.)*

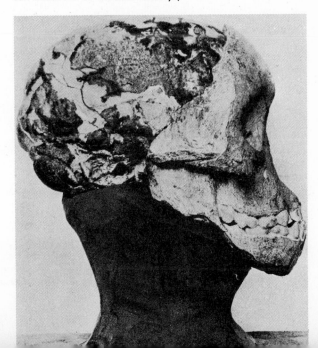

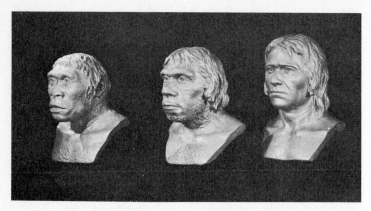

FIG. 30.40 The presumed appearance of various hominids. Reconstructions based on skull structure. From left to right: *Pithecanthropus*, Neanderthaler, Cro-Magnon. *(American Museum of Natural History.)*

chinless. Like several other hominids, *Pithecanthropus* probably practiced cannibalism. His fossil remains include separate skullcaps detached cleanly from the rest of the skeleton; sheer accident does not appear to have caused such neat separations.

The first representative of the genus *Homo*, to which we belong, may have been *Homo heidelbergensis*, the Heidelberg man. Like *Pithecanthropus*, he lived about 500,000 years ago. Unfortunately, Heidel-

berg man is known only from one fossil jaw, and his status therefore cannot be fully assessed. Far more complete information is available about another representative of the genus *Homo*, namely, *Homo neanderthalensis*, the best known of all prehistoric men (Figs. 30.40 and 30.41). Neanderthal man probably arose some 150,000 years ago, flourished during the period of the last ice age, and became extinct only about 25,000 years ago, when the ice sheets began to retreat. The brain of the Neanderthalers had a volume of 1,450 cm³, which compares with a volume of only 1,350 cm³ for modern man. The Neanderthal brain was also proportioned differently; the skull jutted out in back where we are relatively rounded, and the forehead was low and receding. Heavy brow ridges were still present and the jaw was massive and again virtually without chin.

Culturally, the Neanderthalers were Stone Age cavemen. All Pleistocene hominids are generally regarded as belonging to the **Old Stone Age**. But whereas earlier hominids made only crude stone implements, Neanderthal man fashioned a variety of weapons, tools, hunting axes and clubs, and household equipment. Yet he was still a nomad living from hand to mouth and he had neither agriculture nor domesticated animals. He did not make pottery and did not leave any art. His territory covered most of Europe, with fringe populations along the African and Asian coasts of the Mediterranean. He was a contemporary of modern man, and

FIG. 30.41 Restoration of a Neanderthal group. *(Chicago Natural History Museum.)*

it appears that modern man was at least partly responsible for his extinction.

Homo Sapiens

The time of origin of our own species cannot be pinpointed very precisely. The oldest representative of *Homo sapiens* appears to be **Swanscombe man,** known only through a few skull bones. These are from 500,000 to 250,000 years old. Early groups of modern man thus may have been contemporaries of *Pithecanthropus.*

Later groups include **Cro-Magnon man** (see Fig. 30.40), who lived from about 50,000 to 20,000 years ago and who may have caused the extinction of Neanderthal man in Europe. Cro-Magnon was 6 ft tall on the average, with a brain volume of about 1,700 cm³. His culture still belongs to the Old Stone Age. In addition to stone implements, Cro-Magnon used bone needles with which he may have sewn animal skins into crude garments. The dog became his companion, but he still did not domesticate food animals and he did not practice agriculture; Cro-Magnon was a cave-dwelling hunter. He developed a remarkable art, however, as his murals on cave walls indicate.

Cro-Magnon man was a contemporary of other groups of *Homo sapiens* living in different parts of the world. The racial division of modern man into **caucasoids, negroids,** and **mongoloids** may have taken place then. However, any original racial traits became diluted or obliterated fairly rapidly, through interbreeding among the extensively migrating human populations. None of the present human types represents a "pure" race.

By the time the Pleistocene came to a close, some 20,000 or 25,000 years ago, all human species other than *Homo sapiens* had become extinct. The ice started to retreat, milder climates gradually supervened, and eventually man no longer needed to shelter in caves. For the next 15,000 years he produced what is known as the **Middle Stone Age** culture. It was characterized chiefly by great improvements in stone tools. Man was still a nomadic hunter.

The **New Stone Age** began about 5,000 B.C., about the time Abraham settled in Canaan (see Fig. 30.37). A great cultural revolution took place then. Man learned to fashion pottery; he developed agriculture; and he was able to domesticate animals. From that period on, modern civilization moved on with rapid strides. By 3,000 B.C. man had entered the **Bronze Age.** Some 2,000 years later the **Iron Age** began. And not very long afterward man discovered steam, electricity, and now the atom and outer space. Measured by geological standards, the hairy beast which lumbered down from the trees 30 million years ago turned into college professor in a flash.

That modern man has evolved through the operation of the same forces which produced all other organisms is clear. And it should also be clear that this organism is by far the most remarkable product of evolution. Man is sometimes described rather offhandedly as being "just" another animal. Often, on the contrary, he is considered to be so radically distinct that the appellation "animal" assumes the character of an insult. Neither view is justified.

Man certainly *is* an animal, but an animal with very unique attributes. Structurally, man is fully erect and possesses a double-curved spine, a prominent chin, and walking feet with arches. He is a fairly generalized type in most respects, being not particularly specialized for either speed, strength, agility, or rigidly fixed environments.

At some stage during this evolution, his rate of embryonic development slowed down and his whole life cycle became stretched out in duration. Thus man became perhaps the longest-lived of all animals. This stretching of the life cycle also lengthened substantially the period of postnatal growth and adolescence. In this manner, another uniquely human characteristic emerged, namely, a proportionately very long *youth.* A chimpanzee, mature at the age of two, is senile at the age of twenty, when man is only beginning to attain adulthood. Man therefore has *time* to learn and to gather experiences, and in his learning capacity man is also unique. To be sure, other animals may also learn, but the quantitative difference is so great that it is in effect a qualitative difference.

Learning presupposes a powerful brain, and in this department man clearly has no equal. Note here again that the human nervous system develops as it does because it has *time* to do so, because the embryonic period is greatly stretched out. The most characteristically human traits depend directly or indirectly on man's brain. Man is far more aware of himself and far more individualized in personality and behavior than any other creature. He displays a greater range of emotions than any other animal, and he is the only animal able to laugh and to weep. Moreover, only man knows beauty. And the human capacities of planning ahead, of having reasoned purposes, and of making considered choices far outclass anything similar among other animals.

Above all, only man has *traditions* and only he *accumulates* knowledge over successive generations. This transmission of knowledge occurs by nonbiological means, and we actually deal here with a new kind of evolution. The old is biological evolution, its vehicle being the gene. The new is social evolution, its vehicle being spoken and written *speech*. Man is quite unique in having evolved and in continuing to evolve through inherited traditions passed on not only by genes, but also by words.

Conceivably, this changeover from the merely biological to the human may have as much future signifi- cance as the earlier changeover, 2 billion years ago, from the inorganic to the biological. The first transition gave rise to totally new opportunities through which matter became organized into a wealth of previously nonexistent arrangements. The recent transition may create new possibilities of like scope. But the realiza- tion of this potential is now in the hands of man, for with the coming of man, the chance operations of nature have begun to be modified and manipulated by human purpose. The activities of man block chance increasingly. Man's fate will therefore be decided by man's purpose.

REVIEW QUESTIONS

1. What is a fossil? How can the age of a fossil be determined? Review the names and dates of the geologic eras and periods. What were the Appalachian and Laramide revolutions? List the major groups of plants not yet in existence 500 million years ago.

2. Describe the key events of plant evolution dur- ing the Cambrian and Ordovician periods. Review Lignier's hypothesis regarding the origin of tracheo- phytes.

3. Describe the characteristics of various fossil psilopsids. Cite fossil evidence in support of the view that psilopsids were ancestral to all other vascular plants.

4. Describe the key events of plant evolution dur- ing the Silurian and the Devonian periods. What were the characteristics of lepidodendrids? Name and de- scribe fossil sphenopsids. Which pteropsid groups were in existence by the end of the Devonian?

5. Describe the key events of plant evolution dur- ing the Carboniferous and the Permian periods. What were the seed ferns? Which other plant groups are they believed to have given rise to?

6. Describe the causes and events of the Permo- Triassic crisis. At what date did it take place? Review the key events of plant evolution during (a) the Meso- zoic era, and (b) the Cenozoic era. Name the time and the events of the Laramide revolution. What were the consequences of the Laramide revolution on plants? Review the evolutionary events of the whole Cenozoic era. When did the last ice ages occur?

7. State and describe the significance of the law of recapitulation. Why is the Haeckelian interpretation of this law no longer considered to be valid? Does comparative animal embryology give any clues about the probable course of early animal evolution? Discuss.

8. Describe the key events of animal evolution during the (a) Cambrian-Ordovician, (b) Silurian- Devonian, (c) Carboniferous-Permian. Review the course of vertebrate evolution during the entire Paleo- zoic.

9. Describe the main events of animal evolution during the Mesozoic and Cenozoic. Review the princi- pal features and the time pattern of the Mesozoic reptilian radiation. Name reptilian stocks now extinct and stocks now in existence. How many and which vertebrate classes have evolved since the Cambrian and which ones survive today?

10. Describe the principal features of the Ceno- zoic mammalian radiation, with special attention to the origin of primates. Describe the major features and the time pattern of the primate radiation and name living animals representing each of the main lines. When and from where did the line leading to man branch off?

11. Describe the various adaptations of each of the primate stocks to arboreal life. Which structural, functional, and behavioristic features of man trace back specifically to the arboreal way of life of his ancestors? How does the hominoid line differ from other descend- ants of early prosimians? How does the hominid line differ from the anthropoid line?

12. Describe the known members of the hominid

radiation. When was each of them probably in existence? What culture was associated with each? Roughly when did *Homo sapiens* arise? Review the biological characteristics which *Homo sapiens* shares with (*a*) all other hominids, (*b*) all other hominoids, (*c*) all other primates, (*d*) all other mammals. Review in detail the biological characteristics which distinguish man uniquely from all other animals.

SUGGESTED COLLATERAL READINGS

The following, some of which are textbooks and some of which are popular articles, supplement the topics dealt with in this chapter:

Abelson, P. H.: Paleobiochemistry, *Sci. American*, vol. 195, 1956.

Andrews, H. N.: "Ancient Plants and the World They Lived in," Comstock, Ithaca, N.Y., 1947.

Arnold, C. A.: "An Introduction to Paleobotany," McGraw-Hill, New York, 1947.

Berrill, N. J.: "Man's Emerging Mind," Dodd, Mead, New York, 1955.

————: "The Origin of Vertebrates," Oxford University Press, New York, 1955.

Bogert, C. M.: The Tuatara: Why Is It a Lone Survivor? *Sci. Monthly*, vol. 76, 1953.

Colbert, E. H.: The Ancestry of Mammals, *Sci. American*, vol. 180, 1949.

————: "The Dinosaur Book," American Museum of Natural History, 1954.

————: "Evolution of the Vertebrates," Wiley, New York, 1955.

Deevey, E. S.: Radiocarbon Dating, *Sci. American*, vol. 185, 1951.

Eiseley, L. C.: Antiquity of Modern Man, *Sci. American*, vol. 179, 1948.

————: Fossil Man, *Sci. American*, vol. 189, 1953.

————: Man, the Firemaker, *Sci. American*, vol. 191, 1954.

Janssen, R. E.: The Beginnings of Coal, *Sci. American*, vol. 179, 1948.

Jarvik, E.: The Oldest Tetrapods and Their Forerunners, *Sci. Monthly*, vol. 80, 1955.

Matthew, W. D.: "Climate and Evolution," 2d ed., New York Academy of Science, New York, 1939.

Millot, J.: Coelacanth, *Sci. American*, vol. 193, 1955.

Moore, R.: "Man, Time, and Fossils," Knopf, New York, 1953.

Moore, R. C., C. G. Lalicker, and A. G. Fisher: "Invertebrate Fossils," McGraw-Hill, New York, 1952.

Romer, A. S.: "Vertebrate Paleontology," University of Chicago Press, Chicago, 1945.

Shrock, R. R., and W. H. Twenhofel: "Principles of Invertebrate Paleontology," McGraw-Hill, New York, 1953.

Simpson, C. G.: "Life of the Past," Yale University Press, New Haven, Conn., 1953.

Stebbins, G. L.: "Variation and Evolution in Plants," Columbia University Press, New York, 1950.

Thomas, G.: Processes of Fossilization, *New Biol.*, vol. 8, 1950.

GLOSSARY

abscission (ăb·sĭzh′ŭn) [L. *abscindere,* to cut off]: separation of a body part from a plant, particularly after a special layer of cells weakens and dies.

Acanthocephala (à·kăn′thŏ-sĕf′à·là) [Gr. *akantho,* a thorn, + *kephalē,* head]: spiny-headed worms, a small phylum of parasitic acoelomate animals.

acentric (à·sĕn′trĭk): without center; applied specifically to type of mitosis in which a centriole is absent.

acoel, acoelomate (à·sēl′) [Gr. *a,* not, + *koilos,* cavity]: (1) without coelom; also a group of free-living flatworms without digestive cavity; (2) an animal without coelom, i.e., flatworms, proboscis worms, and spiny-headed worms.

acid (ăs′ĭd) [L. *acidus,* sour]: a substance which releases hydrogen ions in water; having a pH of less than 7.

Acrania (à·krā′nĭ·à) [Gr. *a,* not, + *kranion,* skull]: headless chordates, including urochordates and cephalochordates.

acromegaly (ăk′rŏ·mĕg′à·lĭ) [Gr. *akros,* outermost, + *megas,* large]: a condition characterized by skeletal overgrowths, particularly in the extremities, produced by excessive growth-hormone secretion from the pituitary.

acrosome (ăk′rŏ·sōm) [Gr. *akros,* outermost, + *soma,* body]: structure at the tip of the sperm head (nucleus) which makes contact with the egg during fertilization.

actinostele (ăk·tĭn′ŏ·stēl) [Gr. *aktinos,* ray, + *stēlē,* upright post]: a type of protostele in which the cross-sectional arrangement of vascular tissues has the form of a star with various numbers of points.

adenine (ăd′ĕ·nēn): a pyrimidine component of nucleotides and nucleic acids.

adenosine (di-, tri-) phosphate (ADP, ATP) (à·dĕn′-ŏ·sēn): phosphorylated organic compounds functioning in energy transfers within cells.

adipose (ăd′ĭ·pōs) [L. *adipis,* fat]: fat, fatty, fat-storing tissue.

adrenal, adrenalin (ăd·rē′năl, ăd·rĕn′ăl·ĭn) [L. *ad,* to, + *renalis,* kidney]: (1) endocrine gland; (2) the hormone produced by the adrenal medulla.

adrenergic (ăd′rĕn·ûr′jĭk): applied to nerve fibers which release an adrenalinlike substance from their axon terminals when impulses are transmitted across synapses.

adventitious (ăd′vĕn·tĭsh′ŭs): appearing not in usual place; as in adventitious root, which may sprout from anywhere on a stem.

aerobe, aerobic (ā′ĕr·ōb, —ō′bĭk) [Gr. *aeros,* air, + *bios,* life]: (1) oxygen-requiring organism; (2) pertaining to oxygen-dependent form of respiration.

Agnatha (ăg′nà·thà) [Gr. *a,* not, + *gnathos,* jaw]: jawless fishes, a class of vertebrates including lampreys and hagfishes.

alga (ăl′gà), pl. *algae* (—jē): any member of a superphylum of protists; blue-green, green, golden-brown, brown, red algae.

alkaline (ăl′kà·lĭn): produced by substances which release hydroxyl ions in water; having a pH greater than 7.

allantois (ă·lăn′tŏ·ĭs) [Gr. *allantoeidēs,* sausage-shaped]: one of the extraembryonic membranes in reptiles, birds, and mammals; functions as embryonic urinary bladder or as carrier of blood vessels to and from placenta.

allele (ă·lēl′) [Gr. *allēlōn,* of one another]: one of a group of alternative genes which may occupy a given locus on a chromosome; a dominant and its correlated recessive are allelic genes.

alveolus (ăl·vē′ŏ·lŭs), pl. *alveoli* (—lī) [L. dim. of *alveus,* a hollow]: a small cavity or pit, e.g., a microscopic air sac of the lungs.

amino, amino acid, amination (ă·mē′nō, ă·mĭnā′shŭn): (1) —NH₂ group; (2) acid containing amino group, constituent of protein; (3) addition of amino group to other compound.

amnion, amniote, amniotic (ăm′nĭ·ŏn) [Gr. dim. of *amnos,* lamb]: (1) one of the extraembryonic membranes in reptiles, birds, and mammals, forming a sac around the embryo; (2) any reptile, bird, or mammal, i.e., any animal possessing an amnion during the embryonic state; (3) pertaining to the amnion, as in amniotic fluid.

Amphineura (ăm′fī·nū′rà) [Gr. *amphi,* both, + *neuron,* nerve]: a class of mollusks, including the chitons, characterized by a primitive ladder-type nervous system.

amylase (ăm′ĭ·lās) [L. *amylum,* starch]: an enzyme promoting the decomposition of polysaccharides into smaller carbohydrate units.

amyloplast (ăm′ĭ·lŏ·plăst′): a starch-storing, nonpigmented plastid; a type of leucoplast.

anaerobe, anaerobic (ăn·ā′ĕr·ōb, —ō′bĭk) [Gr. *an,* not, + *aeros* + *bios*]: (1) an oxygen-independent organism; (2) pertaining to an oxygen-independent form of respiration.

anamniote (ăn·ăm′nĭ·ōt): any vertebrate other than a reptile, bird, or mammal, i.e., one in which an amnion does not form during the embryonic phase.

anaphase (ăn′à·fāz) [Gr. *ana*, up, + *phasis*, appearance]: a stage in mitotic cell division, characterized by the migration of chromosome sets toward the spindle poles.

anastral (ăn·ăs′trăl): without stars; applied specifically to type of mitosis in which asters around the centrioles are absent.

anatomy (à·năt′ȯ·mĭ) [Gr. *ana*, up, + *temnein*, to cut]: the gross structure of an organism, or the science which deals with gross structure; a branch of the science of morphology.

androgen (ăn′drȯ·jĕn) [Gr. *andros*, man, + *genēs*, born]: one of a group of male sex hormones.

angiosperm (ăn′jĭ·ȯ·spûrm′) [Gr. *angeion*, a vessel, + *sperma*, seed]: a member of a class of tracheophytic plants, characterized by the possession of flowers and fruits; a flowering plant.

anisogamy (ăn·ī′sŏg′ăm·ī) [Gr. *anisos*, unequal, + *gamos*, marriage]: sexual fusion in which the gametes of opposite sex type are unequal in size.

annelid, Annelida (ăn′ĕ·lĭd) [L. *anellus*, a ring]: (1) a segmented worm; (2) the phylum of segmented worms.

annulus (ăn′ů·lŭs) [L., ring] a ringlike structure, e.g., the thick-walled cells around the edge of a sporangium.

anther (ăn′thĕr) [Gr. *anthos*, flower]: the microsporangia in a stamen of flowering plants.

antheridium (ăn′thĕr·ĭd′ĭ·ŭm) [Gr. *anthēros*, flowery]: the sperm-producing organ of plants.

anthocyanin (ăn′thȯ·sī′à·nĭn) [Gr. *anthos*, flower, + *kyanos*, blue]: a water-soluble pigment in plants, producing red, purple, and blue colors.

antibody (ăn′tĭ·bŏd′ĭ): a substance, produced within an organism, which opposes the action of another substance; in specific usage, an antibody is a globulin type of protein which combines and renders harmless an antigen, i.e., a foreign protein introduced into an organism by infectious processes.

antigen (ăn′tĭ·jĕn): a foreign substance, usually protein in nature, which elicits the formation of specific antibodies within an organism.

apical (ăp′ĭ·kăl) [L. *apex*, tip]: belonging to an apex, being at or near the tip; as in apical meristem, the embryonic plant tissue at the tip of root or stem.

aplanospore (à·plăn′ȯ·spōr) [Gr. *a*, without, + *planos*, roaming]: a nonmotile spore.

apothecium (ăp′ȯ·thē′shĭ·ŭm) [Gr. *apothēkē*, storehouse]: disk- or cup-shaped fruiting body in ascomycetous fungi.

archegonium (är′kė·gō′nĭ·ŭm) [Gr. *archegonos*, first of a race]: the egg-producing organ of plants.

archenteron (är·kĕn′tĕr·ŏn) [Gr. *archein*, to be first, + *enteron*, gut]: the central cavity of a gastrula, lined by endoderm, representing the future digestive cavity of the adult.

arthropod, Arthropoda (är′thrȯ·pŏd, är·thrŏp′ȯ·dà) [Gr. *arthron*, joint, + *podos*, foot]: (1) a jointed-legged invertebrate, such as an insect or a crustacean; (2) the phylum of jointed-legged invertebrates.

ascogonium (ăs′kȯ·gō′nĭ·ŭm) [Gr. *askos*, bladder, + *gonos*, offspring] a female sexual hypha of Ascomycetes which receives antheridial nuclei and produces asci or ascus-forming hyphae.

ascus (ăs′kŭs) [Gr. *askos*, a bladder]: the tubular spore sac of a class of fungi; eight spores typically form within an ascus.

astral (ăs′trăl) [L. *astrum*, star]: applied specifically to type of mitosis in which asters around centrioles are present.

atactostele (ă·tăkt′ȯ·stēl) [Gr. *a*, without, + *tassein*, to arrange]: type of stele in which vascular bundles are scattered throughout stem, as in monocots.

atom (ăt′ŭm) [Gr. *atomos*, indivisible]: the smallest whole unit of a chemical element; composed of given numbers of protons, neutrons, and other particles which form an atomic nucleus, and of given numbers of electrons, which orbit around the nucleus.

auricle (ô′rĭ·k′l) [L. dim. of *auris*, ear]: a chamber of the heart receiving blood from the circulation and pumping it into a ventricle.

autolysis (ȯ·tŏl′ĭ·sĭs) [Gr. *autos*, self, + *lysis*, dissolution]: enzymatic self-digestion or dissolution of tissue or other part of an organism.

autosome (ô′tȯ·sōm) [Gr. *autos*, self, + *soma*, body]: any chromosome which is not a sex chromosome.

autotroph, autotrophism (ô′tȯ·trŏf′, —ĭz′m) [Gr. *autos*, self, + *trophos*, feeder]: (1) an organism which manufactures organic nutrients from inorganic raw materials; (2) a form of nutrition in which only inorganic substances are required as raw materials.

auxin (ôk′sĭn) [Gr. *auxein*, to increase]: a plant hormone promoting cell elongation, hence growth.

auxospore (ôk′sȯ·spōr): a zygote of diatoms.

avicularium (ā·vĭk′ů·lā′rĭ·ŭm) [L. dim. of *avis*, bird]: a specially differentiated individual in a colony of ectoprocts, shaped like a bird's head, serving a protective function.

axil, axillary (ăk′sĭl) [L. *axilla*, armpit]: (1) the angle between a branch or leaf and the stem from which it arises; (2) adjective.

axon (ăk′sŏn): an outgrowth of a nerve cell, conducting

impulses away from the cell body; a type of nerve fiber.

bacillus (ba·sĭl′ŭs) [L. dim. of *baculum,* rod]: any rod-shaped bacterium.

bacteriophage (băk·tẽr′ĭ·ȯ·fāj) [*bacterium* + Gr. *phagein,* to eat]: one of a group of viruses which infect, parasitize, and eventually kill bacteria.

bacterium (băk·tẽr′ĭ·ŭm) [Gr. dim. of *baktron,* a staff]: a small, typically unicellular organism characterized by the absence of a formed nucleus; genetic material is dispersed in clumps through the cytoplasm.

basidium (ba·sĭd′ĭ·ŭm) [Gr. dim. of *basis,* base]: a spore-bearing organ of a class of fungi; typically, four spores are formed on each basidium.

benthos, benthonic (bĕn′thŏs) [Gr., depth of the sea]: (1) collective term for organisms living along the bottoms of oceans and lakes; (2) adjective.

beriberi (bĕr′ĭ·bĕr′ĭ) [Singhalese *beri,* weakness]: disease produced by deficiency of vitamin B_1 (thiamine).

bicuspid (bī·kŭs′pĭd) [L. *bi,* two, + *cuspis,* point]: ending in two points, as in bicuspid heart valve, two flaps of tissue guarding opening between left auricle and left ventricle; see also *mitral.*

biennial (bī·ĕn′ĭ·ăl) [L. *bi,* two, + *annus,* year]: occurring once every two years; as in biennial plant, which flowers and forms seeds every second year.

bioluminescence (bī′ȯ·lū′mĭ·nĕs′ĕns) [Gr. *bios,* life, + L. *lumen,* light]: emission of light by living organisms.

blastopore (blăs′tȯ·pōr): opening connecting archenteron of gastrula with outside; represents future mouth in some animals, future anus in others.

blastula (blăs′tŭ·la): stage in early animal development, when embryo is a hollow and in some cases a solid sphere of cells; the sphere typically is constructed from a single layer of cells.

blepharoplast (blĕf′a·rȯ·plăst′) [Gr. *blepharon,* eyelid]: the basal granule of a flagellum or cilium; equivalent to *kinetosome.*

brachiopod, Brachiopoda (brā′kĭ·ȯ·pŏd, brā·kĭ·ŏp′ȯ·da) [L. *brachium,* arm, + Gr. *podos,* foot]: (1) a sessile, enterocoelomate, marine organism possessing a pair of shells (valves) and, internally, a pair of coiled arms which bear ciliated tentacles; (2) phylum name.

bronchus, bronchiole (brŏng′kŭs, brŏng′kĭ·ōl) [Gr. *bronchos,* windpipe]: (1) a main branch of the trachea; (2) a smaller branch of a bronchus.

bryophyte, Bryophyta (brī′ȯ·fīt) [Gr. *bryon,* moss, + *phyton,* a plant]: (1) a moss, liverwort, or hornwort, i.e., any metaphyte which is not tracheophytic; (2) phylum name.

buffer (bŭf′ẽr): a substance which prevents appreciable changes of pH in solutions to which small amounts of acids or bases are added.

bulb (bŭlb): an underground stem with thickened leaves adapted for food storage.

caecum (sē′kŭm) [L. *caecus,* blind]: cavity open at one end, e.g., the blind pouch at the beginning of the large intestine, connecting at one side with the small intestine.

callus (kăl′ŭs) [L., hardened skin]: a tissue consisting of parenchymalike cells, formed as a tumorous overgrowth, or over a wound, or in tissue culture.

Calorie (kăl′ȯ·rĭ) [L. *calor,* heat]: unit of heat, defined as that amount of heat required to raise the temperature of 1 kg of water by 1°C; a *small calorie* is a thousandth part of the unit above, which is often designated as a "large" Calorie.

calyx (kā′lĭks) [fr. Gr. *kalyx*]: the outermost whorl of leaves (sepals) in a flower.

cambium (kăm′bĭ·ŭm) [L., exchange]: embryonic tissue in roots and stems of tracheophytes, giving rise to secondary xylem and phloem.

carapace (kăr′a·pās) [fr. Sp. *carapacho*]: a hard case or shield covering the back of certain animals, e.g., the calcareous carapace of lobsters, the horny carapace of turtles.

carbohydrate, carbohydrase (kär′bȯ·hī′drāt): (1) an organic compound consisting of a chain of carbon atoms to which hydrogen and oxygen, present in a 2:1 ratio, are attached; (2) an enzyme promoting the synthesis or decomposition of a carbohydrate.

carnivore, Carnivora (kär′nĭ·vōr, kär·nĭv′ȯ·ra) [L. *carnivorus,* flesh-eating]: (1) any bulk-feeding organism subsisting on animals or parts of animals; (2) an order of mammals; includes cats, dogs, seals, walruses.

carotene, carotenoids (kăr′ȯ·tēn, ka·rŏt′ĕ·noid) [L. *carota,* carrot]: (1) a pigment producing cream-yellow to carrot-orange colors; precursor of vitamin A; (2) a class of pigments of which carotene is one.

carpogonium (kär′pȯ·gōn′ĭ·ŭm) [Gr. *karpos,* fruit, + *gonos,* offspring]: the female sex cell in red algae.

catalysis, catalyst, catalytic (ka·tăl′ĭ·sĭs) [Gr. *katalysis,* dissolution]: (1) acceleration of a chemical reaction by a substance which does not become part of the endproduct; (2) a substance which accelerates a reaction as above; (3) adjective.

cathepsin (kă·thĕp′sĭn): one of a group of enzymes within cells promoting the synthesis or decomposition of proteins.

ceboid (sē′boid): a New World monkey; uses its tail as a fifth limb.

Cenozoic (sē'nō·zō'ĭk) [Gr. *kainos*, recent, + *zōē*, life]: geological era after the Mesozoic, dating approximately from 75 million years ago to present.

centric (sĕn'trĭk): adjective applied specifically to type of mitosis in which centrioles are present.

centriole (sĕn'trĭ·ōl): cytoplasmic body forming spindle pole during mitosis and meiosis; present in cells of many Protista and most Metazoa.

centromere (sĕn'trō·mēr): region on chromosome at which spindle fibril is attached during mitosis and meiosis.

Cephalochordata, Cephalopoda, cephalothorax (sĕf'-a·lō—) [Gr. *kephalē*, head]: (1) a subphylum of chordates; the lancelets or amphioxus; (2) a class of mollusks; squids, octopuses, nautiluses; (3) the fused head and thorax in certain arthropods, e.g., crustacea.

cercaria (sûr·kā'rĭ·a) [Gr. *kerkos*, tail]: a larval stage in the life cycle of flukes; produced by a redia and infects fish, where it encysts.

cercopithecoid (sûr'kō·pĭ·thē'koĭd): an Old World monkey; possesses tail, which is not used as limb.

cerebellum (sĕr'ē·bĕl'ŭm) [L. dim. of *cerebrum*]: a part of the vertebrate brain, controlling muscular coordination.

cerebrum (sĕr'ē·brŭm) [L., brain]: a part of the vertebrate brain, especially large in mammals; controls many voluntary functions and is seat of higher mental capacities.

chaetognath, Chaetognatha (kē'tŏg·năth, —a) [Gr. *chaitē*, hair, + *gnathos*, jaw]: (1) small marine wormlike enterocoelomate, with curved bristles on each side of mouth; (2) phylum name.

charophyte, Charophyta (kā'rō·fīt, ka·rŏf'ĭ·ta): (1) a stonewort; (2) phylum name.

chelicera (kē·lĭs'ĕr·a) [Gr. *chēlē*, claw]: a pair of pincerlike head appendages in spiders, scorpions, and arachnids generally.

chemolithotroph (kĕm'ō·lĭth'ō·trŏf) [Gr. *chemo* + *lithos*, stone, + *trophos*, feeder]: an organism which manufactures food with the aid of energy obtained from chemicals and with inorganic raw materials.

chemoorganotroph (kĕm'ō·ôr·găn'ō·trŏf): an organism which manufactures food with the aid of energy obtained from chemicals and with organic raw materials.

chemosynthesis (kĕm'ō·sĭn'thē·sĭs): a form of autotrophic nutrition in certain bacteria, in which energy for the manufacture of carbohydrates is obtained from inorganic raw materials.

chemotropism (kē·mŏt'rō·pĭz'm): the growth or movement response of organisms to chemical stimuli.

chitin (kī'tĭn): a horny organic substance forming the exoskeleton of arthropods, the epidermal cuticle of many other invertebrates, and the cell wall of certain Protista.

chloroplast, chlorophyll, chlorophyte (klō'rō—) [Gr. *chloros*, green]: (1) chlorophyll-containing plastid; (2) green light-trapping pigment essential as electron donor in photosynthesis; (3) a green alga, member of the phylum Chlorophyta.

cholinergic (kō'lĭn·ûrjĭk): refers to a type of nerve fiber which releases acetylcholine from the axon terminal when impulses are transmitted across synapses.

Chondrichthyes (kŏn·drĭk'thĭ·ēz) [Gr. *chondros*, cartilage, + *ichthyos*, fish]: fishes with cartilage skeleton, a class of vertebrates comprising sharks, skates, rays, and related types.

Chordata (kôr·dā'ta) [L. *chorda*, cord]: animal phylum in which all members possess notochord, dorsal nerve cord, and pharyngeal gill slits at least at some stage of the life cycle; three subphyla, the Urochordata, the Cephalochordata, and the Vertebrata.

chorion (kō'rĭ·ŏn) [Gr.]: one of the extraembryonic membranes in reptiles, birds, and mammals; forms outer cover around embryo and all other membranes and in mammals contributes to structure of placenta.

choroid (kō'roĭd): mid-layer in wall of eyeball, between retina and sclera; carries blood supply to eye and contains light-absorbing black pigment.

chromatophore (krō'ma·tō·fōr') [Gr. *chrōmatos*, color, + *phoros*, bearing]: pigment-containing body; specifically applied to chlorophyll-bearing granules in bacteria.

chromoplast (krō'mō·plast): a pigmented plastid which does not contain chlorophyll; carotenoids are among pigments usually present.

chromosome (krō'mō·sōm) [Gr. *chroma*, color, + *soma*, body]: gene-containing filamentous body in cell nucleus, becoming conspicuous during mitosis and meiosis; the number of chromosomes per cell nucleus is constant for each species.

chrysophyte, Chrysophyta (krĭs'ō·fīt) [Gr. *chrysos*, gold, + *phyton*, a plant]: (1) a golden-brown alga, e.g., a diatom; (2) phylum name.

Ciliophora (sĭl'ĭ·ŏf'ôra) [L. *cilium*, eyelid, + Gr. *phoros*, bearing]: a protozoan phylum, in which member organisms possess cilia on body surface; includes ciliates, e.g., *Paramecium*.

cilium (sĭl'ĭ·ŭm): microscopic bristlelike variant of a flagellum, present on surfaces of many cell types and capable of vibratory motion; functions in cellular locomotion and in creation of currents in water.

circinate (sûr'sĭ·nāt) [Gr. *kirkinos*, circle]: rolled up along an axis, with the apex as center, as in young fern leaves.

circumnutation (sûr'kŭm·nū·tā'shŭn): curve or ellipse

described by growing portion of a plant; akin to twining.

cleistothecium (klīs'tṓ·thē'shĭ·ŭm) [Gr. *kleistos*, closed]: fruiting body without opening in ascomycetous fungi.

coccoid (kŏk'oid): grainlike, spherical; applied specifically to protistan types in which vegetative cell divisions do not occur.

coccus (kŏk'ŭs), pl. *cocci* (kŏk'sī) [Gr. *kokkos*, a grain]: a spherical bacterium.

cochlea (kŏk'lē·ȧ) [Gr. *kochlias*, snail]: part of the inner ear, coiled like a snail shell; houses the organ of Corti.

coelenterate (sė·lĕn'tēr·āt) [Gr. *koilos*, hollow, + *enteron*, gut]: an invertebrate animal possessing a single alimentary opening and tentacles with sting cells, e.g., jellyfish, corals, sea anemones, hydroids.

coelom (sē'lŏm) [Gr. *koilōma*, a hollow]: body cavity of animals, lined entirely by mesoderm.

coenobium (sė·nō'bĭ·ŭm) [Gr. *koinos*, common]: colonial aggregate of independent protistan cells held together by a common sheath, with cells arranged in an orderly pattern.

coenocyte (sē'nṓ·sīt) [Gr. *koinos* + *kytos*, vessel]: a multinucleate cell found particularly among Protista.

coenzyme (kō·ĕn'zīm): a substance required if a given enzyme is to be active.

coleoptile (kō'lē·ŏp'tĭl) [Gr. *koleos*, sheath]: the tissue mantle surrounding a shoot of plants such as oats.

collenchyma (kȯ·lĕng'kĭ·mȧ) [Gr. *kolla*, glue]: a slightly specialized type of plant cell, elongated, with walls somewhat thickened, especially at the angles; frequently present as support in maturing plant tissues.

colloid (kŏl'oid) [Gr. *kolla*, glue]: a substance divided into fine particles, where each particle is larger than a particle of a true solution but smaller than one in a coarse suspension; a colloid system contains particles of appropriate size and a medium in which the particles are dispersed.

colon (kō'lŏn): the large intestine, portion of alimentary tract between caecum and rectum.

colostrum (kȯ·lŏs'trŭm): the first, lymphlike secretion of the mammary glands of pregnant mammals.

columella (kŏl'ŭ·mĕl'ȧ) [L., little column]: a sterile axial shaft within a sporangium or a capsule.

commensal, commensalism (kȯ·mĕn'săl, —ĭz'm) [L. *cum*, with, + *mensa*, table]: (1) an organism living symbiotically with a host, where the host neither benefits nor suffers from the association; (2) noun.

compound (kŏm'pound) [L. *componere*, to put together]: a combination of atoms or ions in definite ratios, held together by chemical bonds.

conceptacle (kŏn·sĕp'tȧ·k'l) [L. *conceptaculum*, container]: a cavity containing gametangia, as in *Fucus*.

conidium, conidiophore (kȯ·nĭd'ĭ·ŭm, kȯ·nĭd'ĭ·ṓ·fōr')

[Gr. *konis*, dust]: (1) one of a linear series of spores formed on a conidiophore; (2) a spore-producing branch hypha in fungi.

conjugation (kŏn·jṓo·gā'shŭn) [L. *conjugare*, to unite]: a mating process characterized by the temporary fusion of the mating partners; occurs particularly in unicellular organisms.

convergence (kŏn·vûr'jĕns) [L. *convergere*, to turn together]: the evolution of similar characteristics in organisms of widely different ancestry.

corm (kôrm) [Gr. *kormos*, tree trunk]: an axially shortened and enlarged underground stem.

corolla (kȯ·rōl'ȧ) [L., little crown]: the whorl of petals in a flower.

corpus luteum (kôr'pŭs lū'tė·ŭm), pl. *corpora lutea* [L.]: progesterone-secreting bodies in vertebrate ovaries formed from remnants of follicles after ovulation.

cortex (kôr'tĕks), pl. *cortices* [L., bark]: the outer tissue layers of an organ or body part, e.g., adrenal cortex, cerebral cortex; also, in plants, the tissue underneath the epidermis.

cotyledon (kŏt'ĭ·lē'dŭn) [Gr. *kotylēdōn*, a cup shape]: the first leaf of a seed plant, developed by the embryo within the seed.

cotylosaur (kŏt'ĭ·lṓ·sôr') [Gr. *kotylē*, anything hollow, + *sauros*, lizard]: a member of a group of Permian fossil reptiles, evolved from labyrinthodont amphibian stock and ancestral to all other reptiles.

Craniata (krā'nĭ·ā'tȧ) [Gr. *kranion*, skull]: head-possessing chordates, i.e., vertebrates.

cretinism (krē'tĭn·ĭz'm) [fr. L. *christianus*, a Christian]: an abnormal condition resulting from underactivity of the thyroid in the young.

Cryptophyceae (krĭp'tṓ·fī'sė·ē) [Gr. *kryptos*, hidden]: a class of algae, vaguely related to dinoflagellates.

crystalloid (krĭs'tăl·oid) [Gr. *krystallos*, ice]: a system of particles within a medium, able to form crystals under appropriate conditions; a true solution.

ctenophore, Ctenophora (tĕn'ṓ·fōr, tė·nŏf'ṓ·rȧ) [Gr. *ktenos*, comb, + *phoros*, bearing]: (1) a marine radiate animal possessing tentacles without sting cells and a locomotor apparatus consisting of eight comb plates; a comb jelly; (2) phylum name.

cutaneous (kṳ·tā'nė·ŭs) [L. *cutis*, skin]: pertaining to the skin; e.g., cutaneous sense organ.

cyanophyte, Cyanophyta (sī·ăn'ṓ·fīt) [Gr. *kyanos*, dark blue, + *phyton*, plant]: (1) a blue-green alga; (2) phylum name.

cyclosis (sī·klō'sĭs) [Gr. *kyklos*, circle]: circular streaming and eddying of cytoplasm.

cytochrome, cytolysis, cytoplasm, cytosine (sī'tṓ—, sī·tŏl'—) [Gr. *krytos*, vessel]: (1) one of a group of hydrogen carriers in aerobic respiration; transfers hydrogen from FAD to oxygen; (2) dissolution or disintegration of a cell; (3) the living matter of a cell between cell membrane and nucleus; (4) a purine, present in nucleotides and nucleic acids.

deamination (dē·ămǐ·nā′shŭn): removal of an amino group, especially from an amino acid.

decarboxylation (dē·kär·bŏk′sǐ·lā′shŭn): removal of a carboxyl group (—COOH).

deciduous (dě·sǐd′ů·ŭs) [L. *decidere,* to fall off]: to fall off at maturity, as in plants which shed foliage during the autumn.

dedifferentiation (dē·dǐf′ĕr·ĕn′shǐ·ā′shŭn): a regressive change toward a more primitive, embryonic, or earlier state; e.g., a process changing a highly specialized cell to a less specialized cell.

degrowth (dē′grōth): negative growth; becoming smaller.

dehydrogenation, dehydrogenase (dě·hī′drŏ·jĕn·ā′shŭn): (1) removal of hydrogen, as from a molecule; (2) an enzyme promoting dehydrogenation.

denaturation (dē·nǎ′tŭr·ā′shŭn): disruption of the tertiary or secondary structure of a protein molecule.

dendrite (děn′drīt) [Gr. *dendron,* tree]: filamentous outgrowth of a nerve cell, conducting nerve impulses from its free end toward the cell body.

denitrify, denitrification (dē·nǐ′trǐ·fī): (1) to convert nitrates to ammonia and molecular nitrogen, as by denitrifying bacteria; (2) noun.

denticle (děn′tǐ·k′l) [L. *denticulus,* small tooth]: small toothlike scale on shark skin.

deoxyribose (dē·ŏk′sǐ·rī′bōs): a 5-carbon sugar having one oxygen atom less than parent-sugar ribose; component of deoxyribose nucleic acid (DNA).

diabetes (dī′á·bē′tĕz) [Gr. *diabainein,* to pass through]: abnormal condition marked by insufficiency of insulin, sugar excretion in urine, high blood-glucose levels.

diastole (dī·ăs′tŏ·lē) [Gr. *diastolē,* moved apart]: phase of relaxation of auricles or ventricles, during which they fill with blood; preceded and succeeded by systole, i.e., contraction.

diastrophism (dī·ăs′trŏ·fĭz′m) [Gr. *diastrophē,* distortion]: geological deformation of the earth's crust, leading to rise of land masses.

dichotomy (dī·kŏt′ŏ·mĭ) [Gr. *dicha,* in two, + *temnein,* to cut]: a repeatedly bifurcating pattern of branching.

dicotyledon (dī·kŏt′ǐ·lē′dŭn) [Gr. *dis,* twice, + *kotylēdōn,* a cup shape]: a plant having two seed leaves or cotyledons; often abbreviated as dicot.

dictyostele (dĭk′tǐ·ŏ·stē′lě): a type of stele in which the vascular tissue is arranged in cylindrically placed bundles.

differentiation (dǐf′ĕr·ĕn′shǐ·ā′shŭn): a progressive change toward a permanently more mature or advanced state; e.g., a process changing a relatively unspecialized cell to a more specialized cell.

diffusion (dǐ·fū′zhŭn) [L. *diffundere,* to pour out]: migration of particles from a more concentrated to a less concentrated region; the process tends to equalize concentrations throughout a system.

dimorphism (dī·môr′fĭz′m) [Gr. *dis,* twice, + *morphē,* form]: difference of form between two members of a species, e.g., as between males and females; a special instance of polymorphism.

Dinophyceae (dǐ′nŏ·fī′sě·ē) [Gr. *dinos,* a whirling]: a class of Pyrrophyta.

dioecious (dī·ē′shŭs) [Gr. *di,* two, + *oikos,* house]: with megaspores and microspores produced in different individuals, in heterosporous plants.

diplococcus (dǐp′lŏ·kŏk′ŭs): member of a bacterial colony composed of two joined cocci.

diplohaplontic (dǐp′lŏ·hăp·lŏn′tǐk) [Gr. *diploos,* double, + *haploos,* single]: designating a life cycle with sporogenic meiosis, i.e., with alternation of diploid and haploid generations.

diploid (dǐp′loid): a chromosome number twice that characteristic of a gamete of a given species.

diplontic (dǐp·lŏn′tǐk): designating a life cycle with gametogenic meiosis, i.e., with diploid adults.

diplophase (dǐp′lŏ·fāz): a phase in the life cycle of ascomycetous and basidiomycetous fungi characterized by binucleate conditions, the nuclei of a pair being of opposite sex type; the phase between plasmogamy and karyogamy.

disaccharide (dī·săk′á·rĭd) [Gr. *dis,* twice, + *sakcharon,* sugar]: a sugar composed of two monosaccharides; usually refers to 12-carbon sugars.

dissociation (dǐ·sō′sǐ·ā′shŭn) [L. *dissociare,* to disassociate]: the breakup of an electrolyte in water, resulting in the formation of free ions.

divergence (dī·vûr′jĕns) [L. *divergere,* to incline apart]: evolutionary development of dissimilar characteristics in two or more lines descended from the same ancestral stock.

DNA: abbreviation of deoxyribose nucleic acid.

dominance: a functional attribute of genes; a dominant gene exerts its full effect regardless of the effect of its allelic partner.

DPN: abbreviation of diphosphopyridine nucleotide; a hydrogen carrier in respiration, transferring hydrogen from fuel either to FAD (aerobic) or to pyruvic acid (anaerobic).

ductus arteriosus (dŭk′tŭs är·tē′rǐ·ō′sŭs): an artery, present only in the embryo and fetus, which conducts blood from the pulmonary artery to the aorta; shrivels at birth, when the lungs become functional.

duodenum (dū′ŏ·dē′nŭm) [L. *duodeni,* twelve each]:

most anterior portion of the small intestine, continuation of the stomach; bile duct and pancreatic duct open into it.

echinoderm, Echinodermata (ė·kī′nȯ·dûrm) [Gr. *echinos,* urchin, + *derma,* skin]: (1) one of the spiny-skinned animals, i.e., starfishes, sea urchins, brittle stars, sea cucumbers, sea lilies; (2) phylum name.

Echiuroidea (ĕk′ī·ûr·oi′dė·ȧ): a phylum of wormlike, schizocoelomate animals.

ectoderm, ectoparasite, Ectoprocta (ĕk′tȯ—) [Gr. *ektos,* outside]: (1) outer tissue layer of an embryo; (2) a parasite attached to the outside of a host, i.e., to skin, hair, etc.; (3) a phylum of sessile schizocoelomate animals, in which the intestine is U-shaped, the mouth is surrounded by a ring of ciliated tentacles, and the anus opens outside this ring.

egestion (ė·jĕs′chŭn) [L. *egerere,* to discharge]: the elimination from the alimentary system of unusable and undigested material.

elater (ĕl′ȧ·tẽr) [Gr. *elatēr,* driver]: a hygroscopic filament in the capsule of spore-bearing plants; functioning in spore dispersal.

electrolyte (ė·lĕk′trȯ·līt) [Gr. *ēlektron,* amber, + *lytos,* soluble]: a substance which dissociates into ions in aqueous solution and so makes possible the conduction of electric current through the solution.

element (ĕl′ė·mĕnt): one of about 100 distinct natural or man-made types of matter, which, singly or in combination, compose all materials of the universe; an atom is the smallest representative unit of an element.

embryo (ĕm′brĭ·ō) [Gr. *en,* in, + *bryein,* to swell, teem]: an early developmental stage of an organism, produced from a fertilized egg.

emulsion (ė·mŭl′shŭn) [L. *emulgere,* to milk out]: a colloidal system in which both the dispersed and the continuous phase are liquid.

endergonic (ĕn′dẽr·gŏ·nĭk): energy-requiring, as in a chemical reaction.

endocrine (ĕn′dȯ·krīn) [Gr. *endon,* within, + *krinein,* to separate]: applied to type of gland which releases secretion not through a duct but directly into blood or lymph; functionally equivalent to hormone-producing.

endoderm, endodermis (ĕn′dȯ·dûrm): (1) inner tissue layer of an embryo; (2) single layer of tissue in a root or stem which separates the cortex from the stele; the layer is waterproofed with suberin, but contains nonwaterproofed passage cells.

endoparasite (ĕn′dȯ·păr′ȧ·sīt): a parasite living in the interior tissues of a host, i.e., not on surface tissues.

endoplasm, endoplasmic (ĕn′dȯ·plăz′m): the inner portion of the cytoplasm of a cell, i.e., the portion immediately surrounding the nucleus; contrasts with ectoplasm or cortex, i.e., the portion of cytoplasm immediately under the cell surface.

endoskeleton (ĕn′dȯ·skĕl′ė·tŭn): a skeleton in the interior of an animal, providing support from within.

endosperm (ĕn′dȯ·spûrm): triploid, often nutritive tissue within seed, formed by union of one sperm nucleus with two nuclei of female gametophyte.

endospore (ĕn′dȯ·spȯr): a resting cell commonly formed in Monera by the walling off of a central portion of a vegetative cell.

energy (ĕn′ẽr·jĭ) [Gr. *energos,* active]: capacity to do work; the time rate of doing work is called power.

enterocoel, enterocoelomate (ĕn′tẽr·ȯ·sēl′) [Gr. *enteron,* gut, + *koilos,* hollow]: (1) a coelom formed by the outpouching of a mesodermal sac from the endoderm; (2) an animal possessing an enterocoel, e.g., echinoderms, vertebrates.

enterokinase (ĕn′tẽr·ȯ·kī′nās) [Gr. *enteron* + *kinētos,* moving]: an enzyme which is present in intestinal juice and which converts trypsinogen into trypsin.

Entoprocta (ĕn′tȯ·prŏk′tȧ) [Gr. *entos,* within, + *prōktos,* anus]: a phylum of sessile, pseudocoelomate animals, possessing a U-shaped alimentary tract, a mouth surrounded by a ring of ciliated tentacles, and an anus opening within this ring.

enzyme (ĕn′zīm) [Gr. *en,* in, + *zymē,* leaven]: a protein produced within an organism, capable of accelerating a particular chemical reaction; a type of catalyst.

epidermis (ĕp′ĭ·dûr′mĭs) [Gr. *epi,* over, + *derma,* skin]: the outermost surface tissue of an organism.

epididymis (ĕp′ĭ·dĭd′ĭ·mĭs) [Gr. *epi* + *didymos,* testicle]: the greatly coiled portion of the sperm duct adjacent to the testis.

epiglottis (ĕp′ĭ·glŏt′ĭs) [Gr. *epi* + *glōssa,* tongue]: a flap of tissue above the glottis; contains elastic cartilage, and in swallowing folds back over the glottis, so closing the air passage to the lungs.

epinasty (ĕp′ĭ·năs′tĭ) [Gr. *epi* + *nastos,* pressed together]: faster growth on the upper or inner surface of a leaf or other flattened plant part, leading to outfolding.

epiphyte (ĕ′pĭ·fīt) [Gr. *epi* + *phyton,* a plant]: a plant living commensalistically on another plant.

epitheca (ĕp′ĭ·thē′kȧ): the larger half or valve of the shell of a diatom.

epithelium (ĕp′ĭ·thē′lĭ·ŭm) [Gr. *epi* + *thēlē,* nipple]: an animal tissue type in which the cells are packed tightly together, leaving little intercellular space.

esophagus (ė·sŏf′ȧ·gŭs) [Gr. *oisō,* I shall carry, + *phagein,* to eat]: part of alimentary tract connecting pharynx and stomach.

estrogen (ĕs′trȯ·jĕn) [Gr. *oistros,* frenzy, + *genēs,* born]:

one of a group of female sex hormones, produced by a follicle.

etiolation (ē'tĭ·ȯ·lā'shŭn) [F. *étioler,* to blanch]: pathological condition in plants produced by prolonged absence of light; characterized by whitened leaves, excessively long, weak stems.

eurypterid (ū·rĭp'tĕr·ĭd) [Gr. *eurys,* wide, + *pteron,* wing]: extinct Paleozoic arthropod, related to spiders and horseshoe crabs.

eustachian (ů·stā'kĭ·ȧn): applied to canal connecting middle-ear cavity with the nasopharynx.

eustele (ū'stēl): a type of dictyostele derived from a siphonostele; in a vascular bundle, phloem is on the outside, xylem on the inside.

exergonic (ĕk'sĕr·gŏ·nĭk): energy-yielding, as in a chemical reaction.

exocrine (ĕk'sȯ·krĭn) [Gr. *exō,* outside, + *krinein,* to separate]: applied to type of gland which releases secretion through a duct.

exoskeleton (ĕk'sȯ·skĕl'ė·tŭn): an external skeleton of an animal, providing support from the outside.

exteroceptor (ĕk'stĕr·ȯ·sĕp'tĕr): a sense organ receptive to stimuli from external environment of an organism.

fermentation (fûr'mĕn·tā'shŭn): synonym for anaerobic respiration, i.e., fuel combustion in the absence of oxygen.

fetus (fē'tŭs) [L., offspring]: prenatal stage of development in man and other mammals, following the embryonic stage; roughly from third month of pregnancy to birth.

fiber (fī'bĕr) [L. *fibra,* thread]: a strand or filament produced by cells but located outside cells; a type of sclerenchyma cell.

fibril (fī'brĭl) [L. dim. of *fibra*]: a strand or filament produced by cells and located within cells.

fibrin, fibrinogen (fī'brĭn, fī·brĭn'ȯ·jĕn): (1) coagulated blood protein forming the bulk of a blood clot; (2) a protein present in blood which upon coagulation forms a clot.

flagellate, flagellum (flăj'ě·lāt, flȧ·jĕl'·ŭm) [L., whip]: (1) equipped with one or more flagella; an organism possessing flagella; (2) a microscopic, whiplike filament serving as locomotor structure in flagellate cells.

floridean (flȯ·rĭd'ė·ăn): pertaining to Florideae, or red algae generally.

florigen (flō'rĭ·jĕn) [L. *flos,* flower, + Gr. *genēs,* born]: flowering hormone, believed to be produced as a result of appropriate photoperiodic treatment of plants.

fluorescence (flōō'ȯ·rĕs'ĕns) [L. *fluere,* to flow]: emission of radiation (light) by a substance which has absorbed radiation from another source.

follicle (fŏl'ĭ·k'l) [L. *folliculus,* small ball]: hollow ball of cells in the mammalian ovary containing a maturing egg.

Foraminifera (fȯ·răm'·ĭ·nĭf'ĕr·ȧ) [L. *foramen,* hole, + *ferre,* to bear]: a group of sarcodine protozoa, characterized by delicate calcareous shells with holes, through which pseudopods are extruded.

fovea centralis (fō'vĕ·ȧ·sĕn·trā'lĭs) [L., central pit]: small area in the optic center of the retina; only cone cells are present here and stimulation leads to the most acute vision.

fucoxanthin (fū'kȯ·zăn'thĭn): a brownish pigment found in diatoms, brown algae, and dinoflagellates.

fundus (fŭn'dŭs) [L., bottom]: the bottom or base of a hollow structure, i.e., the fundus of the stomach, the part to the left of the esophagus, farthest away from the intestinal opening.

fusiform (fū'zĭ·fôrm) [L. *fusus,* spindle]: spindle-shaped, tapered at the ends.

gamete (găm'ēt) [Gr. *gamein,* to marry]: reproductive cell which must fuse with another before it can develop; sex cell.

gametophyte (găm·ē'tȯ·fīt): a gamete-producing plant; phase of life cycle in diplohaplontic organisms which alternates with a sporophyte phase.

ganglion (găng'glĭ·ŭn) [Gr., a swelling]: a collection of cell bodies of neurons located outside the brain or the spinal cord.

gastrin (găs'trĭn): a hormone produced by the stomach wall when food makes contact with the wall; stimulates other parts of the wall to secrete gastric juice.

Gastropoda (găs·trŏp'ȯ·dȧ) [Gr. *gastros,* stomach, + *podos,* foot]: a class of mollusks; comprises snails and slugs.

Gastrotricha (găs'trŏt'rĭ'kȧ) [Gr. *gastros* + *trichos,* hair]: a phylum of minute, multicellular, aquatic, pseudocoelomate animals, possessing cilialike bristles on the body surface.

gastrula, gastrulation (găs'trōō·lȧ, —lā'shŭn): (1) a two-layered and later three-layered stage in the embryonic development of animals; (2) the process of gastrula formation.

gel (jĕl) [L. *gelare,* to freeze]: quasi-solid state of a colloidal system, where the solid particles form the continuous phase and the liquid forms the discontinuous phase.

gemma (jĕm'ȧ) [L., a bud]: cup-shaped vegetative bud in bryophytes, capable of developing into whole plant.

gene (jēn) [Gr. *genēs,* born]: a segment of a chromosome, definable in operational terms: repository of a unit of genetic information.

genome (jēn'ōm): the totality of genes in a haploid set

of chromosomes, hence the sum of all different genes in a cell.

genotype (jĕn′ȯ·tīp): the particular set of genes present in an organism and its cells; the genetic constitution.

genus (jē′nŭs) [L., race]: a rank category in taxonomic classification, between species and family; a group of very closely related species.

geotropism (jȇ·ŏt′rȯ·pĭz′m) [Gr. *gē*, earth, + *tropē*, a turning]: behavior governed and oriented by gravity, i.e., growth of roots toward center of earth.

gestation (jĕs·tā′shŭn) [L. *gestare*, to bear]: process or period of carrying young in uterus.

globulin (glŏb′ū·lĭn): one of a class of proteins present in blood plasma; may function as antibody.

glomerulus (glȯ·mĕr′ū·lŭs) [L. dim. of *glomus*, ball]: a small meshwork of blood capillaries found in the cup-shaped capsule of a nephron.

glottis (glŏt′ĭs) [Gr. *glōssa*, tongue]: slitlike opening in the larynx, formed by the vocal cords.

glucose (gloō′kōs) [Gr. *gleukos*, sweet wine]: a 6-carbon sugar; principal form in which carbohydrates are transported from cell to cell in plants and animals.

glycerin (glĭs′ĕr·ĭn) [Gr. *glykeros*, sweet]: an organic compound possessing a 3-carbon skeleton; may unite with fatty acids and form a fat.

glycogen (glī′kȯ·jĕn): a polysaccharide consisting of some 12 to 18 glucose units; a principal storage form of carbohydrates.

glycolysis (glī·kŏl′ĭ·sĭs): respiratory breakdown of glucose (or starch or glycogen) to pyruvic acid; anaerobic respiration of carbohydrates.

goiter (goi′tēr) [L. *guttur*, throat]: an enlargement of the thyroid gland; may be an overgrowth resulting in excessive secretion of thyroid hormone or may be a compensatory overgrowth occasioned by undersecretion of thyroid hormone.

Golgi body (gôl′jȇ): a particulate component of cell cytoplasm; probably plays a role in the manufacture of certain cell secretions.

gonad (gōn′ăd) [Gr. *gonē*, generator]: collective term for the testes and ovaries of animals.

gradation (gra·dā′shŭn) [L. *gradus*, step]: leveling of land by the geological effects of erosion.

granum (grăn′ŭm) [L., grain]: a functional unit of a chloroplast; smallest particle capable of carrying out photosynthesis.

guttation (gŭ·tā′shŭn) [L. *gutta*, drop]: extrusion of water droplets from leaf pores by root pressure.

gymnosperm (jĭm′nȯ·spûrm) [Gr. *gymnos*, naked, + *sperma*, seed]: a plant belonging to a class of seed plants in which the seeds are not enclosed in an ovary; includes the conifers.

haematochrome (hĕm·ȧ′tȯ·krōm) [Gr. *haima* + *chrōma*, color]: red pigment related to carotene and present in protistan eyespots.

haeme (hēm) [Gr. *haima*, blood]: a red-colored tetrapyrrol pigment.

haemoglobin (hē′mȯ·glō′bĭn) [Gr. *haima*, blood, + L. *globus*, globe]: oxygen-carrying constituent of red blood corpuscles; consists of red pigment haeme and protein globin.

haemophilia (hē′mȯ·fĭl′ĭ·ȧ) [Gr. *haima* + *philos*, loving]: a hereditary disease characterized by excessive bleeding from even minor wounds; clotting mechanism is impaired by failure of blood platelets to rupture after contact with torn edges of blood vessels.

haploid (hăp′loid) [Gr. *haploos*, single, simple]: a chromosome number characteristic of a mature gamete of a given species.

haplontic (hăp·lŏn′tĭk): designating a life cycle with zygotic meiosis and haploid adults.

haplophase (hăp′lȯ·fāz): a uninucleate phase in the life cycle of ascomycetous and basidiomycetous fungi; the phase between the meiospore and the succeeding plasmogamy.

haplostele (hăp′lȯ·stēl): the simplest type of protostele, with central xylem and surrounding phloem.

hemichordate (hĕm′ĭ·kôr′dāt) [Gr. *hēmi*, half, + L. *chorda*, cord]: a member of a phylum of enterocoelomate animals; wormlike, body composed of proboscis, collar, and trunk; head absent.

hepatic (hȇ·păt′ĭk) [Gr. *hēpar*, liver]: pertaining to the liver; as in hepatic vein, hepatic portal vein.

herbaceous (hûr·bā′shŭs) [L. *herbaceus*, grassy]: having the characteristics of an herb; contrasts with woody.

herbivore (hûr′bĭ·vōr) [L. *herba*, herb, + *vorare*, to devour]: a plant-eating animal.

hermaphrodite (hûr·măf′rȯ·dīt) [fr. Gr. *Hermes* + *Aphrodite*]: an organism possessing both male and female reproductive structures.

heterocyst (hĕt′ĕr·ȯ·sĭst′): colorless cell in filamentous blue-green algae, permitting easy fragmentation of a filament.

heterosporous (hĕt′ĕr·ŏs′pȯ·rŭs): producing two different types of spores, viz., microspores and megaspores; microspores give rise to male gametophytes, megaspores to female gametophytes.

heterothallic (hĕt′ĕr·ȯ·thăl′ĭk) [Gr. *heteros* + *thallos*, young shoot]: hermaphroditic and cross-fertilizing.

heterotroph, heterotrophism (hĕt′ĕr·ȯ·trŏf) [Gr. *heteros* + *trophos*, feeder]: (1) an organism which must obtain both inorganic and organic raw materials from the environment; (2) form of nutrition characteristic of heterotrophs.

heterozygote, heterozygous (hĕt′ĕr·ȯ·zī′gōt) [Gr. *het-*

eros + *zygōtos*, yoked]: (1) an organism in which a pair of alleles for a given trait consists of different (e.g., dominant and recessive) kinds of genes; (2) adjective.

hexose (hĕk′sōs) [Gr. *hex*, six]: any 6-carbon sugar.

holotroph, holotrophism (hō′lȯ·trŏf) [Gr. *holos*, whole, + *trophos*, feeder]: (1) a bulk-feeding organism for which nutrition includes the process of alimentation; an animal; (2) form of nutrition characteristic of animals.

hominid (hŏm′ĭ·nĭd) [L. *homo*, man]: a living or extinct man or manlike type; the family of man or pertaining to this family.

hominoid (hŏm′ĭ·noid) [L. *homo*, man]: a superfamily including hominids, the family of man, and anthropoids, the family of apes, living or extinct.

homology (hȯ·mŏl′ȯ·jĭ) [Gr. *homologia*, agreement]: similarity in embryonic development and adult structure, indicative of common evolutionary ancestry.

homosporous (hȯ·mŏs′pȯ·rŭs): producing spores of the same size or form; each gives rise either to a male or to a female gametophyte.

homothallic (hō′mȯ·thăl′ĭk): hermaphroditic and self-fertilizing.

homozygote, homozygous (hō′mȯ·zī′gōt) [Gr. *homos*, same, + *zygōtos*]: (1) an organism in which a pair of alleles for a given trait consists of the same (e.g., either dominant or recessive, but not both) kinds of genes; (2) adjective.

hormogone (hôr′mȯ·gōn): a section of a filament of blue-green algae, located between two consecutive heterocysts.

hormone (hôr′mōn) [Gr. *hormaein*, to excite]: a growth factor produced within an organism and affecting another part of that organism.

humus (hū′mŭs) [L., soil]: the organic portion of soil.

hybrid (hī′brĭd) [L. *hibrida*, offspring of tame sow and wild boar]: an organism which is heterozygous for one or more (usually many) gene pairs.

hydathode (hī′dȧ·thōd) [Gr. *hydatis*, water vesicle]: channel or gland in leaf for water excretion.

hydrolysis (hī·drŏl′ĭ·sĭs) [Gr. *hydōr*, water, + *lysis*, a loosening]: dissolution through the agency of water; especially decomposition of a chemical by the addition of water.

hydrophyte (hī′drȯ·fīt): a water plant, or one living in water-rich areas.

hydroponics (hī′drȯ·pŏn′ĭks) [Gr. *hydōr* + *ponos*, labor]: growing plants without soil by immersing the roots in a nutrient-rich water medium.

hyperparasitism (hī′pĕr—) [Gr. *hyper*, above]: infection of a parasite by one or more other parasites.

hypertonic, hypertonicity (hī′pĕr·tŏn′ĭk): (1) exerting greater osmotic pull than the medium on the other side of a semipermeable membrane, hence possessing a greater concentration of particles and acquiring water during osmosis; (2) noun.

hypha (hī′fȧ) [Gr. *hyphē*, a web]: a filamentous structural unit of a fungus; a meshwork of hyphae forms a mycelium.

hyponasty (hī′pȯ·năs′tĭ) [Gr. *hypo*, under, + *nastos*, pressed together]: faster growth on the lower or outer surface of a leaf or other flattened plant part, leading to infolding.

hypothalamus: a region of the forebrain, containing various centers of the autonomic nervous system.

hypotheca (hī′pȯ·thē′kȧ): the smaller half or valve of the shell of a diatom.

hypothesis (hī·pŏth′ė·sĭs) [Gr. *hypo*, under, + *tithenai*, to put]: a guessed solution of a scientific problem; must be tested by experimentation and, if not validated, must then be discarded.

hypotonic, hypotonicity (hī′pȯ·tŏn′ĭk): (1) exerting lesser osmotic pull than the medium on the other side of a semipermeable membrane; hence possessing a lesser concentration of particles and losing water during osmosis; (2) noun.

ichthyosaur (ĭk′thĭ·ȯ·sôr) [Gr. *ichthyos*, fish, + *sauros*, lizard]: extinct marine Mesozoic reptile, with fish-shaped body and porpoiselike snout.

induction, inductor (ĭn·dŭk′shŭn) [L. *inducere*, to introduce]: (1) process in embryo in which one tissue or body part causes the differentiation of another tissue or body part; (2) an embryonic tissue which causes the differentiation of another.

indusium (ĭn·dū′zĭ·ŭm) [L., undergarment]: in ferns, tissue covering sori.

ingestion (ĭn·jĕs′chŭn) [L. *ingerere*, to put in]: intake of food from the environment into the alimentary system.

insulin (ĭn′sȧ·lĭn) [L. *insula*, island]: a hormone produced by the islets of Langerhans in the pancreas; promotes the conversion of blood glucose into tissue glycogen.

integument (ĭn·tĕg′ȧ·mĕnt) [L. *integere*, to cover]: covering; external coat; skin.

intermedin (ĭn·tĕr·mē′dĭn): hormone produced by the mid-portion of the pituitary gland; adjusts degree of extension of pigment cells in skin of certain vertebrates, e.g., frogs.

internode (ĭn′tĕr·nōd′): section of a plant stem located between two successive nodes.

interoceptor (ĭn′tĕr·ȯ·sĕp′tĕr): a sense organ receptive to stimuli generated in the interior of an organism.

invagination (ĭn·văj′ĭ·nā′shŭn) [L. *in*—, in, + *vagina*, sheath]: local infolding of a layer of tissue, leading to the formation of a pouch or sac; as in invagination during gastrulation.

invertase (ĭn·vûr′tās) [L. *invertere,* to invert]: enzyme promoting the splitting of sucrose into glucose and fructose, or the reverse.

ion, ionization (ī′ŏn, —ī·zā′shŭn) [Gr. *ienai,* to go]: (1) an electrically charged atom or group of atoms; (2) addition or removal of electrons from atoms.

isogamy (ī·sŏg′à·mĭ) [Gr. *isos,* equal, + *gamein,* to marry]: sexual fusion in which the gametes of opposite sex types are structurally alike.

isotonic (ī′sô·tŏn′ĭk): exerting same osmotic pull as medium on other side of a semipermeable membrane, hence possessing the same concentration of particles; net gain or loss of water during osmosis is zero.

isotope (ī′sô·tōp) [Gr. *isos* + *topos,* place]: one of several possible forms of a chemical element, differing from other forms in atomic weight but not in chemical properties.

karyogamy (kăr′ĭ·ŏg′à·mĭ) [Gr. *karyon,* nut]: fusion of nuclei in process of fertilization.

keratin (kĕr′à·tĭn) [Gr. *keratos,* horn]: a protein formed by certain epidermal tissues, e.g., those of mammalian skin.

kinetosome (kĭ·nĕt′ô·sōm) [Gr. *kinētos,* moving, + *soma,* body]: granule at base of flagellum, presumably motion-controlling.

Kinorhyncha (kĭn′ô·rĭng′kà): a small phylum of pseudocoelomate animals.

labyrinthodont (lăb′ĭ·rĭn′thô·dŏnt) [Gr. *labyrinthos,* labyrinth]: extinct, late Paleozoic fossil amphibian.

lacteal (lăk′tê·ăl) [L. *lactis,* milk]: lymph vessel in a villus of the intestinal wall.

lactogenic (lăk′tô·jĕn′ĭk): milk-producing; as in lactogenic hormone, secreted by the pituitary.

lamella (là·mĕl′à) [L., small plate]: pectin-containing layer cementing adjacent plant cells in a tissue; usually called **middle lamella.**

lamina (lăm′ĭ·nà) [L., thin plate]: the blade of a leaf.

larva (lär′và), pl. *larvae* (—vē) [L., mask]: period in developmental history of animals, between embryo and adult; the larval period begins at hatching and terminates at metamorphosis.

larynx (lăr′ĭngks) [Gr.]: voice box; sound-producing organ in mammals.

leaflet: one of the divisions of a compound (pinnate or palmate) leaf.

lenticel (lĕn′tĭ·sĕl) [F. *lenticelle,* little lentil]: porous region in periderm of woody stem, aiding gas exchange.

leucocyte (lū′kô·sīt) [Gr. *leukos,* white, + *kytos,* vessel]: a type of white blood cell, characterized by a beaded, elongated nucleus.

leucoplast (lū′kô·plăst) [Gr. *leukos,* white]: an unpigmented plastid; see also *amyloplast.*

leukemia (lŭ·kē′mĭ·à): a cancerous condition of blood, characterized by overproduction of leucocytes.

lichen (lī′kĕn) [Gr. *leichēn*]: a symbiotic, mutualistic association of an algal type and a fungal type.

lignin (lĭg′nĭn) [L. *lignum,* wood]: a complex substance present in substantial quantities in wood.

lipase (lī′pās) [Gr. *lipos,* fat]: an enzyme promoting the conversion of fat into fatty acids and glycerin, or the reverse.

lipid, lipoid (lĭp′ĭd): (1) fat, fatty, pertaining to fat; (2) fatlike.

littoral (lĭt′ô·răl) [L. *litus,* seashore]: the sea floor from the shore to the edge of the continental shelf.

luciferase, luciferin (lŭ·sĭf′ĕr·ās, —ĭn) [L. *lux,* light, + *ferre,* to bring]: (1) enzyme contributing to the production of light by living organisms; (2) a group of various substances essential in the production of bioluminescence.

lutein (lū′tê·ĭn) [L. *luteus,* yellow]: a yellow xanthophyll pigment.

lycopsid (lī·kŏp′sĭd) [Gr. *lykos,* wolf]: a member of a subphylum of tracheophytes; the club mosses.

lymph (lĭmf) [L. *lympha,* goddess of moisture]: the body fluid outside the blood circulation; leaks out of and eventually returns to the blood circulation.

lymphocyte (lĭm′fô·sīt): a type of white blood cell, characterized by a rounded or kidney-shaped nucleus.

macronucleus (măk′rô·nū′klê·ŭs) [Gr. *makros,* long, + *nucleus,* kernel]: a large type of nucleus found in ciliate protozoa; controls all but reproductive functions in these organisms.

madreporite (măd′rê·pô·rīt) [It. *madre,* mother, + *poro,* passage]: a sievelike opening on the upper surface of echinoderms, connecting the water-vascular system with the outside.

maltose (môl′tōs): a 12-carbon sugar formed by the union of two glucose units.

marsupial (mär·sū′pĭ·ăl) [Gr. *marsypion,* little bag]: a pouched mammal, member of the mammalian subclass Metatheria.

Mastigophora (măs′tĭ·gŏf′ô·rà) [Gr. *mastix,* scourge, whip, + *phoros,* bearing]: a phylum of primarily unicellular, flagellate protozoa.

maxilla (măk·sĭl′à) [L.]: in arthropods, one of the head appendages; in vertebrates, one of the upper jawbones.

maxilliped (măk·sĭl′ĭ·pĕd) [L. *pedis*, foot]: one of three pairs of segmental appendages in lobsters and other crustacea, located posterior to the maxillae.

medulla (mĕ·dŭl′ȧ) [L.]: the inner tissue layers of an organ or body part, e.g., adrenal medulla; the medulla oblongata is a region of the hindbrain which connects with the spinal cord.

medusa (mĕ·dū′sȧ): the free-swimming stage in the life cycle of coelenterates; a jellyfish.

megagametophyte (mĕg′ȧ·gȧ·mē′tŏ·fīt) [Gr. *megas*, great]: in heterosporous plants, the gametophyte produced by a megaspore; the female gametophyte.

megaphyll (mĕg′ȧ·fĭl) [Gr. *megas* + *phyllon*, leaf]: a leaf with numerous vascular bundles in a vein; it leaves a leaf gap in the stele of the stem.

megasporangium (mĕg′ȧ·spŏ·răn′jĭ·ŭm): a sporangium which produces megaspores.

megaspore (mĕg′ȧ·spōr′): a meiospore formed in a megasporangium and developing into a megagametophyte.

megasporophyll (mĕg′ȧ·spō′rŏ·fĭl): a leaf or modified leaf on which a megasporangium is formed.

megastrobilus (mĕg′ȧ·strŏ′bĭ·lŭs) [Gr. *megas* + *strobilos*, a pine cone]: a cone formed by a series of megasporophylls.

meiosis (mī·ō′sĭs) [Gr. *meioun*, to make smaller]: process occurring at different points in the life cycles of different organisms in which the chromosome number is reduced by half; compensates for the chromosome-doubling effect of fertilization.

meiospore (mī′ŏ·spōr): a spore produced by meiosis within a sporangium; it is always haploid.

menopause (mĕn′ŏ·pôz) [Gr. *menos*, month, + *pauein*, to cause to cease]: the time at the end of the reproductive period of (human) females when menstrual cycles cease to occur.

menstruation (mĕn′strŏŏ·ā′shŭn) [L. *mensis*, month]: the discharge of uterine tissue and blood from the vagina, at the end of a menstrual cycle in which fertilization has not occurred.

meristem (mĕr′ĭ·stĕm) [Gr. *meristos*, divided]: embryonic tissue in plants, capable of giving rise to additional tissues.

mesoderm (mĕs′ŏ·dûrm) [Gr. *mesos*, middle, + *derma*, skin]: the middle tissue layers of an animal embryo, between ectoderm and endoderm.

mesogloea (mĕs′ŏ·glē′ȧ) [Gr. *mesos* + *gloios*, glutinous substance]: the jellylike layer between the ectoderm and endoderm of coelenterates and comb jellies.

mesophyll (mĕs′ŏ·fĭl) [Gr. *mesos* + *phyllon*, leaf]: tissue in the interior of leaves, composed of chlorophyll-containing cells arranged either into compact layers (palisade mesophyll) or into loose aggregations (spongy mesophyll).

mesophyte (mĕs′ŏ·fīt): a plant adapted to live in regions with intermediate amounts of water supply.

metabolism (mĕ·tăb′ŏ·lĭz′m) [Gr. *metabolē*, change]: a group of life-sustaining processes including principally nutrition, production of energy (respiration), and synthesis of more living substance.

metabolite (mĕ·tăb′ŏ·līt): any chemical participating in metabolism; a nutrient.

metamorphosis (mĕt′ȧ·môr′fŏ·sĭs) [Gr. *metamorphoun*, to transform]: transformation of a larva into an adult.

metaphase (mĕt′ȧ·fāz) [Gr. *meta*, between]: a stage during mitotic cell division in which the chromosomes line up in a plane at right angles to the spindle axis.

Metaphyta (mĕ·tăf′ĭ·tȧ): a major category of living organisms, consisting of the phyla Bryophyta and Tracheophyta; the category is distinguished in part by possession of reproductive structures which are organs and by the presence of embryo stages during sporophyte development.

Metazoa (mĕt′ȧ·zō′ȧ): a major category of living organisms, consisting of all multicellular animals.

micrococcus (mī′krŏ·kŏk′ŭs) [Gr. *mikros*, small]: member of a type of colony of spherical bacteria in which the cells are arranged as irregular plates or clumps.

microgametophyte (mī′krŏ-): in heterosporous plants, the gametophyte produced by a microspore; the male gametophyte.

micron (mī′krŏn), pl. *microns*, *micra* [Gr. *mikros*, small]: one-thousandth part of a millimeter, a unit of microscopic length.

micronucleus (mī′krŏ·nū′klĕ·ŭs): a small type of nucleus found in ciliate protozoa; controls principally the reproductive functions of these organisms.

microphyll (mī′krŏ·fĭl) [Gr. *mikros* + *phyllon*, leaf]: a leaf with a vein consisting of a single vascular bundle; it does not leave a leaf gap in the stele of the stem.

micropyle (mī′krŏ·pīl) [Gr. *mikros* + *pilē*, gate]: an opening in the integument of an ovule, permitting entry of a pollen grain or pollen tube.

microsome (mī′krŏ·sōm) [Gr. *mikros* + *soma*, body]: an early term for a particulate constituent of cytoplasm; contains RNA and is the site of protein synthesis; see also *ribosome*.

microsporangium (mī′krŏ·spŏ·răn′jĭ·ŭm): a sporangium which produces microspores.

microspore (mī′krŏ·spōr): a meiospore formed in a microsporangium and developing into a microgametophyte; in seed plants, equivalent to pollen grain.

microsporophyll (mī′krŏ·spō′rŏ·fĭl): a leaf or modified leaf on which a microsporangium is formed.

microstrobilus: a cone formed by a series of microsporophylls.

mimicry (mĭm′ĭk·rĭ) [Gr. *mimos*, mime]: the superficial resemblance of certain animals, particularly insects, to other more powerful or more protected ones, resulting in a measure of protection for the mimics.

mineral (mĭn′ēr·ăl) [L. *minera*, ore]: a compound or substance of the inorganic world; an inorganic material.

miracidium (mī′ră·sĭd′ĭ·ŭm): a larval stage in the life cycle of flukes; develops from an egg and gives rise in turn to a sporocyst larva.

mitochondrion (mī′tŏ·kŏn′drĭ·ŏn) [Gr. *mitos*, thread, + *chondros*, grain]: a particulate constituent of cytoplasm; the site of respiration.

mitosis (mī·tō′sĭs) [Gr. *mitos*, thread]: a form of nuclear division characterized by complex chromosome movements and exact chromosome duplication.

mitospore (mī′tŏ·spōr): a spore produced by mitosis within a sporangium; may be haploid or diploid, depending on the ploidy of the parent organism.

mitral (mī′trăl) [fr. *miter*]: applied to valve between left auricle and ventricle of heart; syn. *bicuspid*.

molecule (mŏl′ē·kūl) [L. *moles*, mass]: a compound in which the atoms are held together by covalent bonds.

Mollusca, mollusk (mŏ·lŭs′kà, mŏl′ŭsk) [L. *molluscus*, soft]: (1) a phylum of schizocoelomate animals; unsegmented body composed of visceral mass, foot, and shell; comprises chitons, snails, clams, squids, and others; (2) a member of the phylum Mollusca.

Monera (mŏn·ē′rà) [Gr. *monos*, alone]: a major category of living organisms, comprising the bacteria and the blue-green algae; characterized in part by absence of true nuclei or chromosomes.

monocotyledon (mŏn′ŏ·kŏt′ĭ·lē′dŭn) [Gr. *monos*, single]: a plant having a single seed leaf or cotyledon; often abbreviated as monocot.

monoecious (mŏ·nē′shŭs) [Gr. *monos* + *oikos*, house]: in heterosporous plants, a given individual producing both megaspores and microspores.

monophyletic (mŏn′ŏ·fī·lĕt′ĭk) [Gr. *monos* + *phylon*, tribe]: developed from a single ancestral type; contrasts with polyphyletic.

monopodial (mŏn′ŏ·pō′dĭ·ăl) [Gr. *monos* + *podos*, foot]: a growth pattern in which a main axis continues to elongate in one direction but produces lateral branch axes at intervals.

monosaccharide (mŏn′ŏ·săk′à·rīd) [Gr. *monos* + *saccharon*, sugar]: a simple sugar such as 5- and 6-carbon sugars.

morphogenesis (môr′fŏ·jĕn′ē·sĭs) [Gr. *morphē*, form, + *genēs*, born]: development of size, form, and other architectural features of organisms.

morphology (môr·fŏl′ŏ·jĭ) [Gr. *morphē* + *logos*, study]: the study or science of structure, at any level of organization, e.g., cytology, study of cell structure; histology, study of tissue structure; anatomy, study of gross structure of organisms.

mucosa (mŭ·kō′sà) [L. *mucosus*, mucus]: a mucus-secreting membrane, e.g., the inner lining of the intestine.

mutation (mŭ·tā′shŭn) [L. *mutare*, to change]: a stable change of a gene, such that the changed condition is inherited by offspring cells.

mycelium (mī·sē′lĭ·ŭm) [Gr. *mykēs*, mushroom]: the vegetative portion of a fungus, consisting of a meshwork of hyphae.

Mycophyta (mī′kŏ·fī′tà) [Gr. *mykēs* + *phyton*, plant]: the phylum comprising the fungi.

myelin (mī′ē·lĭn) [Gr. *myelos*, marrow]: a fatty material which surrounds the axons of nerve cells in the central nervous system.

myofibril (mī′ŏ·fī′brĭl) [Gr. *myos*, muscle]: a contractile filament within a cell, especially a muscle cell or muscle fiber.

myosin (mī′ŏ·sĭn): a protein which can be isolated from muscle; forms an integral component of the contraction machinery of muscle.

myxedema (mĭk′sĕ·dē′mà) [Gr. *myxa*, slime, + *oidēma*, a swelling]: a disease resulting from thyroid deficiency in the adult, characterized by local swellings in and under the skin.

myxomycete (mĭk′sŏ·mī·sēt′) [Gr. *myxa* + *mykēs*, mushroom]: a slime mold, member of one of the classes of the Myxophyta.

myxophyte, Myxophyta (mĭk′sŏ·fīt, mĭks·ŏf′ĭ·tà): (1) a member of the phylum of slime molds; (2) phylum name.

nastic (năs′tĭk): pertaining to a change in position, as in nastic growth movement; see *epinasty, hyponasty.*

nekton (nĕk′tŏn) [Gr. *nēktos*, swimming]: collective term for the actively swimming organisms in the ocean.

nematode (nĕm′à·tōd) [Gr. *nēmatos*, thread]: a roundworm, member of the pseudocoelomate phylum Nematoda.

Nematomorpha (nĕm′à·tŏ·môr′fà) [Gr. *nēmatos* + *morphē*, form]: hairworms, a pseudocoelomate phylum.

Nemertinea (nĕm·ēr·tĭn′ē·à) [Gr. *Nemertēs*, a Nereid]: proboscis worms, an acoelomate phylum.

nephric, nephron (nĕf′rĭk, —rŏn) [Gr. *nephros*, kidney]: (1) pertaining to a nephron; (2) a functional unit of the vertebrate kidney, consisting of glomerulus, capsule, convoluted tubules, Henle's loop, and collecting tubule.

neritic (nē·rĭt′ĭk) [fr. *Nereus*, a seagod]: oceanic habitat zone, subdivision of the pelagic zone, comprising the open water above the continental shelf, i.e., above the littoral.

neuron (nū'rŏn) [Gr., nerve]: nerve cell, including cell body, dendrites, and axons.

nitrify, nitrification (nī'trĭ·fī, —fī·kā'shŭn): (1) to convert ammonia and nitrites to nitrates, as by nitrifying bacteria; (2) noun.

node (nōd) [L. *nodus*, knot]: in plants, a joint of a stem; place where branches and leaves are joined to stem.

notochord (nō'tŏ·kôrd) [Gr. *noton*, the back, + L. *chorda*, cord]: longitudinal elastic rod of cells serving as internal skeleton in the embryos of all chordates and in the adults of some; in most adult chordates the notochord is replaced by a vertebral column.

nucleic acid (nŭ·klē'ĭk): one of a class of molecules composed of joined nucleotide complexes; the principal types are deoxyribose nucleic acid (DNA) and ribose nucleic acid (RNA).

nucleolus (nŭ·klē'ŏ·lŭs): an RNA-containing body within the nucleus of a cell; a derivative of chromosomes.

nucleoprotein (nū'klē·ŏ—): a molecular complex composed of nucleic acid and protein.

nucleotide (nū'klē·ŏ·tīd): a molecule consisting of joined phosphate, 5-carbon sugar (either ribose or deoxyribose), and a purine or a pyrimidine (adenine, guanine, uracil, thymine, or cytosine).

nucleus (nū'klē·ŭs) [L., a kernel]: a body present in all cell types except the bacteria and the blue-green algae and consisting of external nuclear membrane, interior nuclear sap, and chromosomes and nucleoli suspended in the sap.

nutation (nŭ·tā'shŭn) [L. *nutare*, to nod]: a slow, nodding growth movement in plants, more or less rhythmical, produced by antonomic stimuli.

nutrient (nū'trĭ·ĕnt) [L. *nutrire*, to nourish]: a substance usable in metabolism; a metabolite; includes inorganic materials and organic materials (foods).

oidiospore (oi'dĭ·ŏ·spōr) [Gr. *eidos*, form]: a spore formed by partitioning of a hyphal filament.

olfaction, olfactory (ŏl·făk'shŭn, —tŏ·rĭ) [L. *olfacere*, to smell]: (1) the process of smelling; (2) pertaining to smell.

omnivore (ŏm'nĭ·vōr) [L. *omnis*, all, + *vorare*, to devour]: an animal which may subsist on plant foods, animal foods, or both.

oögamy (ŏ·ŏg'á·mĭ) [Gr. *ōion*, egg, + *gamein*, to marry]: sexual fusion in which the gametes of opposite sex type are unequal, the female gamete being an egg, i.e., nonmotile, the male gamete being a sperm, i.e., motile.

oögonium (ŏ·ŏ·gō'nĭ·ŭm) [Gr. *ōion* + *gonos*, offspring]: the female gametangium of oögamous fungi and other Protista; contains one or more eggs.

operculum (ŏ·pûr'kŭ·lŭm) [L., a lid]: a lidlike structure, e.g., the plate on each side of the head of bony fishes which covers and protects the gills.

organ (ôr'găn) [fr. Gr. *organon*]: a group of different tissues joined structurally and cooperating functionally to perform a composite task.

organism (ôr'găn·iz'm): an individual living creature, either unicellular or multicellular.

ornithine (ôr'nĭ·thēn) [Gr. *ornithos*, bird]: an amino acid which, in the liver of vertebrates, contributes to the conversion of ammonia and carbon dioxide into urea.

osmosis (ŏs·mō'sĭs) [Gr. *ōsmos*, impulse]: the process in which water migrates through a semipermeable membrane, from a side containing a lesser concentration of particles to the side containing a greater concentration; migration continues until particle concentrations are equal on both sides.

Osteichthyes (ŏs·tĕ·ĭk'thĭ·ēz) [Gr. *osteon*, bone]: a class of vertebrates, comprising the bony fishes.

ovary (ō'vá·rĭ) [L. *ovum*, egg]: the egg-producing organ of female animals; the ovule- (megasporangium-) containing organ of flowering plants.

oviparity, oviparous (ō'vĭ·păr'ĭ·tĭ, ŏ·vĭp'á·rŭs) [L. *ovum* + *parere*, to bring forth]: (1) animal reproductive pattern in which eggs are released by the female; offspring development therefore occurs outside the maternal body; (2) adjective.

ovoviviparity, ovoviviparous (ō'vŏ·vĭv'ĭ·păr'ĭ·tĭ, ō'vŏ·vī·vĭp'á·rŭs): (1) animal reproductive pattern in which eggs develop within the maternal body, but without nutritive or other metabolic aid by the female parent; offspring are born as miniature adults; (2) adjective.

ovulation (ō'vŭ·lā'shŭn): expulsion of an egg from the ovary and deposition of egg into the oviduct.

ovule (ō'vūl): the integument-covered megasporangium of a seed plant.

oxidation (ŏk'sĭ·dā'shŭn): internal rearrangement of a molecule so as to create a high-energy bond; often achieved by dehydrogenation.

paleoniscoid (pā'lĕ·ŏ·nĭs'koid): extinct Devonian bony fish, ancestral to modern bony fishes, lungfishes, and lobe-finned fishes.

paleontology (pā'lĕ·ŏn·tŏl'ŏ·gĭ) [Gr. *palaios*, old, + *onta*, existing things]: study of past geological times, principally by means of fossils.

Paleozoic (pā'lĕ·ŏ·zō'ĭk) [Gr. *palaios* + *zōē*, life]: the geological era between the Precambrian and the Mesozoic, dating approximately from 500 to 200 million years ago.

palmelloid (păl·mĕl'oid): a transient or permanent state in algal life histories, characterized by nonmotility and the secretion of jellylike envelopes around cells.

paramylum (på·răm′ĭ·lŭm) [L. *par*, equal, + Gr. *amylon*, fine meal]: characteristic carbohydrate food-storage compound in Euglenophyta; starchlike.

paraphysis (på·răf′ĭ·sĭs) [Gr. *para*, beside, + *physis*, nature]: one of the sterile filaments in the reproductive organs of many organisms (e.g., *Fucus*).

parapodia (păr′å·pō′dĭ·å) [Gr. *para*, beside, + *podos*, foot]: fleshy segmental appendages in polychaete worms; serve in breathing, locomotion, and creation of water currents.

parasite (păr′å·sīt) [Gr. *para* + *sitos*, food]: an organism which lives symbiotically on or within a host organism, more or less detrimental to the host.

parasympathetic (păr′å·sĭm′på·thĕt′ĭk): applied to a subdivision of the autonomic nervous system; centers are located in brain, most anterior part of spinal cord, and most posterior part of spinal cord.

parathyroid (păr′å·thī′roid): an endocrine gland, usually paired, located near or within the thyroid; secretes parathormone, which controls calcium metabolism.

parenchyma (på·rĕng′kĭ·må) [Gr. *para* + *en*, in, + *chein*, to pour]: designating a type of adult cell in plants, relatively little specialized, thin-walled, often 14-sided, and containing chlorophyll; may function in food storage; parenchyma cells are a component of many tissue types.

parthenogenesis (păr′thē·nō·jĕn′ė·sĭs) [Gr. *parthenos*, virgin, + *genēs*, born]: development of an egg without fertilization; occurs naturally in some organisms (e.g., rotifers) and may be induced artificially in others (e.g., frogs).

pathogenic (păth′ō·jĕn′ĭk) [Gr. *pathos*, suffering, + *genēs*]: disease-producing, e.g., many bacteria, fungi, and other parasites.

pectin (pĕk′tĭn) [Gr. *pektos*, curdled]: one of a group of compounds frequently present in cell walls of plants.

pedicellaria (pĕd′ĭ·sĕl′å′rĭ·å) [L. *pedicellus*, little stalk]: a tiny pincerlike structure on the surface of starfish and other echinoderms; protects skin gills.

pedipalp (pĕd′ĭ·pălp): one of the paired head appendages in spiders and other arachnids.

pelagic (pė·lăj′ĭk) [Gr. *pelagos*, ocean]: oceanic habitat zone, comprising the open water of an ocean basin; subdivided into the neritic zone and the oceanic zone.

Pelecypoda (pė·lė′sĭp′ō·då): a class of the phylum Mollusca, comprising clams, mussels, oysters.

pentose (pĕnt′ōs): any 5-carbon sugar.

pepsin (pĕp′sĭn) [Gr. *peptein*, to digest]: a protein-digesting enzyme present in gastric juice.

peptidase (pĕp′tĭ·dās) [Gr. *peptein*]: an enzyme promoting the liberation of individual amino acids from a peptide, i.e., an amino acid complex smaller than a whole protein.

perennial (pĕr·ĕn′ĭ·ål) [L. *perennis*, throughout a year]: a plant which lives continuously throughout the year and persists in whole or in part from year to year.

perianth (pĕr′ĭ·ănth) [Gr. *peri*, around, + *anthos*, flower]: collective term for calyx and corolla, i.e., all sepals and petals.

pericycle (pĕr′ĭ·sī′k′l) [Gr. *perikyklos*, spherical]: a tissue layer composed of parenchymatous or sclerenchymatous cells surrounding the vascular tissues of the stele; may be reduced or absent in stems.

periderm (per′ĭ·dûrm) [Gr. *peri* + *derma*, skin]: collective term for cork cambium and its products, viz., cork and phelloderm.

peristalsis (pĕr′ĭ·stăl′sĭs) [Gr. *peristaltikos*, compressing]: successive contraction and relaxation of tubular organs such as the alimentary tract, resulting in a wavelike propagation of a transverse constriction.

perithecium (pĕr′ĭ·thē′shĭ·ŭm) [Gr. *peri* + *thēkē*, box]: spherical or flask-shaped fruiting body in ascomycetous fungi, usually opening by a terminal pore.

permeability (pûr′mė·å·bĭl′ĭ·tĭ) [L. *permeare*, to pass through]: penetrability, as in membranes which let given substances pass through.

petal (pĕt′l) [Gr. *petalos*, outspread]: one of the leaves of a corolla in a flower.

petiole (pĕt′ĭ·ōl) [L. *petiolus*, little foot]: leafstalk; the slender stem by which a leaf blade is attached to a branch or a stem.

pH: a symbol denoting the relative concentration of hydrogen ions in a solution; pH values run from 0 to 14, and the lower the value, the more acid is a solution, i.e., the more hydrogen ions it contains.

Phaeophyta (fē′ō·fī′t·å): the phylum of brown algae.

pharynx (făr′ĭngks) [Gr.]: the part of the alimentary tract between mouth cavity and esophagus; it is also part of the air channel from nose to larynx.

phellem (fĕl′ĕm) [Gr. *phellos*, cork]: cork, the exterior product of the cork cambium.

phelloderm (fĕl′ō·dûrm): the parenchymatous tissue formed by the cork cambium toward the inside; becomes part of cortex.

phellogen (fĕl′ō·jĕn): cork cambium.

phenotype (fē′nō·tīp) [Gr. *phainein*, to show]: the physical appearance of an organism resulting from its genetic constitution (genotype).

phloem (flō′ĕm) [Gr. *phloos*, bark]: one of the vascular tissues in tracheophytic plants; consists of sieve tubes and companion cells and transports organic nutrients both up and down.

Phoronidea (fōr′ō·nĭd′ė·å): a phylum of wormlike, marine, tube-dwelling, schizocoelomate animals.

phosphagen (fŏs′fă·jĕn): collective term for creatine-phosphate and arginine-phosphate, i.e., compounds which store and may be sources of high-energy phosphates.

phosphorylation (fŏs′fô·rĭ·lā′shŭn): the addition of a phosphate group (for example, —H₂PO₃) to a compound.

photolithotroph (fō′tô·lĭth′ô·trōf) [Gr. *photos*, light, + *lithos*, stone, + *trophos*, feeder]: an organism which manufactures food with the aid of light energy and with inorganic raw materials.

photolysis (fô·tŏl′ĭ·sĭs) [Gr. *phōtos*, light, + *lysis*, a loosening]: a component process of photosynthesis in which water is dissociated and the hydrogen is joined to TPN under the indirect influence of solar energy.

photoorganotroph (fō′tô·ôr·gắn′ô·trōf): an organism which manufactures food with the aid of light energy and with organic raw materials.

photoperiod, photoperiodism (fō′tô·pĕr′ĭ·ŭd, -ĭz′m): (1) day length; (2) the responses of plants to different day lengths.

photosynthesis (fō′tô·sĭn′thĕ·sĭs) [Gr. *phōtos*, light, + *syn*, together, + *tithenai*, to place]: process in which energy of light and chlorophyll are used to manufacture carbohydrates out of carbon dioxide and water.

phototropism (fô·tŏt′rô·pĭz′m) [Gr. *phōtos* + *tropē*, a turning]: behavior oriented by light, e.g., growth of plant stems toward light source.

phrenic (frĕn′ĭk) [Gr. *phrenos*, diaphragm]: pertaining to the diaphragm, e.g., phrenic nerve, innervating the diaphragm.

phycobilin (fī′kô·bĭ′lĭn) [Gr. *phykos*, seaweed, + L. *bilis*, bile]: straight-chain tetrapyrrol compounds, some being pigments in blue-green and red algae.

phycocyanin, phycoerythrin (fī′kô·sī′ă·nĭn, fī′kô·ê·rĭth′-rĭn) [Gr. *phykos*, seaweed, + *kyanos*, a dark-blue substance, and *phykos* + *erythos*, red]: blue and red phycobilin pigments found in blue-green and red algae; those of blue-green algae differ from those of red algae, and they are distinguished accordingly by the prefixes "*c-*" for cyanophytes and "*r-*" for rhodophytes.

Phycomycetes (fī′kô·mī·sē′tēz): the class of nonseptate fungi.

phyllotaxy (fĭl′ô·tăk′sĭ) [Gr. *phyllon*, leaf, + *taxis*, arrangement]: the arrangement of leaves on a stem.

phylum (fī′lŭm), pl. *phyla* [Gr. *phylon*, race, tribe]: a category of taxonomic classification, ranked above class.

physiology (fĭz′ĭ·ŏl′ô·jĭ) [Gr. *physis*, nature, + *logos*, study]: study of living processes, activities, and functions generally; contrasts with morphology, the study of structure.

phytoplankton (fī′tô·plăngk′tŏn) [Gr. *phyton*, plant, + *planktos*, wandering]: collective term for the plants and plantlike organisms present in plankton; contrasts with zooplankton.

pineal (pĭn′ê·ăl) [L. *pinea*, pine cone]: a structure in the brain of vertebrates; functions as a median dorsal eye in a few (e.g., lampreys), but does not have a demonstrable function in most.

pistil (pĭs′tĭl) [L. *pistulus*, a pestle]: the megaspore-producing organ of a flower; consists of stigma, style, and ovary.

pituitary (pĭ·tū′ĭ·tĕrĭ) [L. *pituita*, phlegm]: a composite endocrine gland in vertebrates, attached ventrally to the brain; composed of anterior, intermediate, and posterior lobes, each representing a functionally separate gland.

placenta (plȧ·sĕn′tȧ) [L., cake]: a tissue complex formed in part from the inner lining of the uterus and in part from the chorion of the embryo; develops in most mammals and serves as mechanical, metabolic, and endocrine connection between the adult female and the embryo during pregnancy.

placoderm (plăk′ô·dûrm) [Gr. *plakos*, flat plate, + *derma*, skin]: a member of a class of Devonian vertebrates (fishes), all now extinct; ancestral to cartilage and bony fishes.

planarian (plȧ·nâr′ĭ·ăn) [L. *planarius*, level]: any member of the class of free-living flatworms.

plankton (plăngk′tŏn) [Gr. *planktos*, wandering]: collective term for the passively floating or drifting flora and fauna of a body of water; consists largely of microscopic organisms.

plasmodesma.. (plăz′mô·dĕz′mȧ), pl. *plasmodesmata* [Gr. *plasma*, form, + *desmos*, chain]: fine cytoplasmic strand interconnecting adjacent cells in many plant tissues.

plasmodium (plăz·mō′dĭ·ŭm): multinucleate coenocytic amoeboid mass, representing aggregated diploid phase in slime molds of the class Myxomycetes.

plasmogamy (plăz·mô′gă·mĭ) [Gr. *plasma* + *gamein*, to marry]: mating union of cytoplasms, a component of fertilization; plasmogamy is followed by karyogamy (v.s.), the time interval being appreciable in many Basidiomycetes.

plastid (plăs′tĭd) [Gr. *plastēs*, a molder]: a cytoplasmic, often pigmented body in cells; three types are leucoplasts, chromoplasts, and chloroplasts.

Platyhelminthes (plăt′ĭ·hĕl·mĭn′thēz) [Gr. *platys*, flat, + *helminthos*, worm]: flatworms, a phylum of acoelomate animals; comprises planarians, flukes, and tapeworms.

plectostele (plĕk'tô·stēl) [Gr. *plektos,* twisted]: a type of protostele in which the vascular tissues have a cross-sectional arrangement of parallel bars or bands.

plesiosaur (plē'sĭ·ô·sôr) [Gr. *plesios,* near, + *sauros,* lizard]: a long-necked, marine, extinct Mesozoic reptile.

plexus (plĕk'sŭs) [L., braid]: a network, especially of nerves or of blood vessels.

-ploid (-ploid) [Gr. *-ploos,* -fold]: the number of chromosome sets per cell, e.g., haploid, diploid.

pollen (pŏl'ĕn) [L., fine dust]: microspore of seed plants.

pollination (pŏl'ĭ·nā'shŭn): transfer of pollen to the micropyle or to a receptive surface associated with an ovule (e.g., a stigma).

polyclad (pŏl'ĭ·klăd): a member of a group of free-living flatworms, characterized by a digestive cavity with many branch-pouches.

polymorphism (pŏl'ĭ·môr'fĭz'm) [Gr. *polys,* many, + *morphē,* form]: differences of form among the members of a species; individual variations affecting form and structure.

polyp (pŏl'ĭp) [L. *polypus,* many-footed]: the sessile stage in the life cycle of coelenterates; a sea anemone.

polypeptide (pŏl'ĭ·pĕp'tīd): a molecule consisting of many joined amino acids.

polyphyletic (pŏl'ĭ·fī·lĕt'ĭk) [Gr. *polys,* many, + *phylon,* tribe]: derived from more than one ancestral type; contrasts with monophyletic.

polyploid (pŏl'ĭ·ploid): possessing many complete chromosome sets per cell.

polysaccharide (pŏl'ĭ·săk'á·rīd): a carbohydrate composed of many joined monosaccharide units, e.g., glycogen, starch, cellulose, all formed out of glucose units.

population: a localized grouping of members of the same species, interbreeding preferentially with one another but also occasionally with members of sister populations.

Porifera (pô·rĭf'ẽr·á) [L. *porus,* pore, + *ferre,* to bear]: the phylum of sponges.

Priapulida (prĭ'ā·pū'lĭ·dá): a small phylum of pseudocoelomate animals.

primordium (prī·môr'dĭ·ŭm) [L., beginning]: the earliest developmental stage in the formation of an organ or body part.

proboscis (prô·bŏs'ĭs) [L.]: any tubular process or prolongation of the head or snout.

procambium (prô·kăm'bĭ·ŭm) [L. *pro,* before, + *cambium,* exchange]: one of the three primary meristems; gives rise to vascular tissues and pericycle.

proembryo (prō·ĕm'brĭ·ō) [L. *pro* + Gr. *bryein,* to swell]: a few-celled stage in the development of seed plants.

progesterone (prô·jĕs'tẽr·ōn): hormone secreted by the corpus luteum and the placenta; prepares the uterus for the reception of a fertilized egg and later maintains the capacity of the uterus to hold the embryo and fetus.

prophase (prō'fāz'): a stage during mitotic division in which the chromosomes become distinct and a spindle forms.

prosimian (prô·sĭm'ĭ·ăn) [L. *pro,* before, + *simia,* ape]: an ancestral primate and certain of primitive living primates, e.g., a lemur, a trasier.

protein (prō'tê·ĭn) [Gr. *prōteios,* primary]: one of a class of organic compounds composed of many joined amino acids.

proteinase (prō'tê·ĭn·ās): an enzyme which promotes the conversion of a protein into smaller units, e.g., amino acids, or the reverse; also called **protease.**

prothallium (prô·thăl'ĭ·ŭm): the gametophyte of a fern.

prothrombin (prô·thrŏm'bĭn) [L. *pro* + Gr. *thrombos,* clot]: a constituent of blood plasma; converted to thrombin by thrombokinase in the presence of calcium ions, and so contributes to blood clotting.

Protista (prô·tĭs'tá) [Gr. *prōtistos,* first]: a major category of living organisms, including all groups of algae, slime molds, protozoa, and fungi; characterized by usually unicellular reproductive structures, true nuclei, and chromosomes.

protoderm (prō'tô·dŭrm) [Gr. *prōtos,* first, + *derma,* skin]: one of the three primary meristems; gives rise to epidermis.

protonema (prō'tô·nē'má) [Gr. *prōtos* + *nēmatos,* thread]: the prostrate first-formed portion of a moss gametophyte, filamentous or thallose.

protoplasm (prō'tô·plăz'm) [Gr. *prōtos* + *plasma,* form, mold]: synonym for living matter, living material, or living substance.

protostele (prō'tô·stēl') [Gr. *prōtos* + *stēlē,* upright post]: a general type of stele in which the vascular tissues form a solid central aggregation within the stem or root, phloem being outside the xylem; the principal protostelic variants are haplosteles, actinosteles, and plectosteles.

protozoon (prō'tô·zō'ăn) [Gr. *protos* + *zōion,* animal]: a member of either of four protistan phyla (Mastigophora, Sarcodina, Ciliophora, Sporozoa).

pseudocoel, pseudocoelomate (sū'dô·sēl, —ô·māt) [Gr. *pseudēs,* false]: (1) an internal body cavity lined not by mesoderm but by ectoderm and endoderm; (2) an animal possessing a pseudocoel, e.g., rotifers, roundworms.

pseudoplasmodium (sū'dô·plăz·mō'dĭ·ŭm): multicellular amoeboid mass, representing aggregate diploid phase in slime molds of the class Acrasieae.

pseudopodium (sū′dȯ·pō′dĭ·ŭm): a temporary cytoplasmic protrusion from an amoeboid cell; functions in locomotion and feeding.

Psilopsida (sī·lŏp′sĭ·dȧ) [Gr. *psilos,* bare]: a subphylum of tracheophytes; includes the earliest representatives of the vascular plants; evolved probably from green algae and in turn ancestral to all living tracheophytes.

Pteropsida (tĕ·rŏp′sĭ·dȧ) [Gr. *pteridos,* fern]: a subphylum of tracheophytes; includes ferns and all seed plants, i.e., large-leafed vascular plants; probably evolved from psilopsids.

pterosaur (tĕr′ȯ·sôr) [Gr. *pteron,* feather, + *sauros,* lizard]: a flying, extinct Mesozoic reptile.

pulmonary (pŭl′mȯ·nĕr′ĭ) [L. *pulmonis,* lung]: pertaining to the lungs, e.g., pulmonary artery, vein.

pulvinus (pŭl·vī′nŭs) [L., cushion, elevation]: an enlargement of a petiole at its base; in the sensitive plant *Mimosa* it is the effector of the response to touch.

pylorus (pī·lō′rŭs) [Gr. *pylōros,* gatekeeper]: the opening from stomach to intestine.

pyrenoid (pī·rē′noid) [Gr. *pyrēn,* fruit stone]: starch-containing granular bodies on or near a chloroplast in many Protista.

Pyrrophyta (pĭ·rŏf′ĭ·tȧ) [Gr. *pyrros,* fiery]: a phylum of algae; includes dinoflagellates and possibly also Cryptophyceae.

Radiolaria (rā′dĭ·ȯ·lā′rĭ·ȧ) [L. dim. of *radius*]: a group of sarcodine protozoa, characterized by silicon-containing shells.

radula (răd′ū·lȧ) [L. *radere,* to scrape]: the horny rasping organ in the alimentary tract of chitons, snails, squids, and other mollusks.

receptacle (rĕ·sĕp′tȧ·k′l) [L. *receptaculum,* receiver]: (1) conceptacle-containing thallus tip in *Fucus;* (2) modified branch of thallus bearing sex organs in *Marchantia;* (3) expanded terminal of stalk bearing the components of a flower.

recessive (rĕ·sĕs′ĭv) [L. *recedere,* to recede]; a functional attribute of genes; the effect of a recessive gene is masked if the allelic gene is dominant.

redia (rē′dĭ·ȧ): a larval stage in the life cycle of flukes; produced by a sporocyst larva and in turn gives rise to many cercariae.

reduction (rē·dŭk′shŭn): the chemical opposite of oxidation; addition of hydrogen to a molecule.

reflex (rē′flĕks) [L. *reflectere,* to bend back]: the unit action of the nervous system; consists of stimulation of a sense receptor, interpretation and emission of nerve impulses by a neural center, and execution of a response by an effector organ.

renal (rē′nȧl) [L. *renes,* kidneys]: pertaining to the kidney.

rennin (rĕn′ĭn) [Middle Engl. *rennen,* to run]: an enzyme present in gastric juice; promotes the coagulation of milk.

respiration (rĕs′pĭ·rā′shŭn) [L. *respirare,* to breathe]: the liberation of metabolically useful energy from fuel molecules within cells; may occur anaerobically or aerobically.

reticulum, reticulate (rĕ·tĭk′ū·lŭm, -lȧt) [L. *reticulum,* little net]: (1) a network or mesh of fibrils, fibers, or filaments, as in **endoplasmic reticulum** within cytoplasm; (2) netlike, as in veins of some leaves.

retina (rĕt′ĭ·nȧ) [L. *rete,* a net]: the innermost tissue layer of the eyeball; contains the receptor cells sensitive to light.

rhabdocoel (răb′dȯ·sēl) [Gr. *rhabdos,* rod, + *koilōma,* a hollow]: member of a group of free-living flatworms having a straight, unbranched digestive cavity.

rhizoid (rī′zoid) [Gr. *rhiza,* root]: rootlike absorptive filament.

rhizome (rī′zōm) [Gr. *rhizōma,* mass of roots]: underground stem.

Rhodophyta (rȯ′dŏf′ĭ·tȧ) [Gr. *rhodon,* rose, + *phyton,* plant]: the phylum of red algae.

ribosome (rī′bȯ·sōm): a submicroscopic cytoplasmic particle; contains RNA and is the site of protein synthesis; see also *microsome.*

rickettsia (rĭk·ĕt′sĭ·ȧ) [after H. T. Ricketts, American pathologist]: a type of microorganism intermediate in nature between a virus and a bacterium, parasitic within cells of insects and ticks.

Rotifera (rȯ·tĭf′ĕr·ȧ) [L. *rota,* wheel, + *ferre,* to bear]: a phylum of microscopic pseudocoelomate animals, characterized by whorls of motile bristles around the mouth.

saccule (săk′ūl) [L. *sacculus,* little sack]: portion of the inner ear containing the receptors for the sense of static balance.

saprotroph (săp′rȯ·trŏf) [Gr. *sapros,* rotten]: an organism subsisting on dead or decaying matter.

sarcina (sär′sĭ·nȧ) [L. *sarcina,* bundle]: a type of colony of spherical bacteria in which the cells divide in three planes of space, resulting in cuboidal arrangements.

Sarcodina (sär′kȯ·dīnȧ) [Gr. *sarkos,* flesh]: a phylum of protozoa; includes amoebae, foraminifera, radiolaria, and others.

Scaphopoda (skȧ·fŏp′ȯ·dȧ) [Gr. *skaphē,* boat]: tooth shells, a class of the phylum Mollusca.

schizocoel, schizocoelomate (skĭz′ŏ·sēl) [Gr. *schizein,* to split]: (1) a coelom formed by a splitting of embryonic mesoderm; (2) an animal possessing a schizocoel, e.g., mollusks, annelids, arthropods.

Schizophyta (skĭz′ŏf′ĭ·tȧ) [Gr. *schizein* + *phyton,* plant]: the phylum of bacteria.

sclera (sklē′rȧ) [Gr. *skleros,* hard]: the outermost coat of the eyeball, continuous with the cornea.

sclereid (sklē′ĕr·ĭd): a type of sclerenchyma cell, characterized by irregular and different shapes in different cases.

sclerenchyma (sklē·rĕng′kĭ·mȧ) [Gr. *skleros,* hard, + *en,* in, + *chein,* to pour]: plant cells with greatly thickened and lignified walls and without living substance when mature; two variants of sclerenchyma are fibers and sclereids.

scrotum (skrō′tŭm) [L.]: external skin pouch containing the testes of most mammals.

semiherbaceous (sĕm′ĭ·hûr·bā′shŭs) [L. *semi,* half, + *herbaceus,* grassy]: applied to stem type intermediate in character between woody and herbaceous types; young parts of stem possess strips of cambium, as in herbaceous types; old parts possess tube of cambium, as in woody types.

semipermeable (sĕm′ĭ·pûr′mē·ȧ·b′l): permeable to small particles (e.g., water, certain inorganic ions), but not to larger particles (e.g., proteins, fat molecules).

sepal (sē′pȧl): one of the leaves in the outermost whorl of a flower.

septum, septate (sĕp′tŭm, -tāt) [L., enclosure]: (1) a complete or incomplete transverse partition; (2) adjective.

serum (sēr′ŭm) [L.]: the fluid remaining after removal of fibrinogen from blood plasma.

simian (sĭm′ĭ·ăn) [L. *simia,* an ape]: pertaining to monkeys; also used as noun.

sinus (sī′nŭs) [L., a curve]: a cavity, recess, or depression, especially in bone.

siphon (sī′fŏn) [Gr. *siphōn,* a pipe]: tubular structure for drawing in or ejecting fluids, as in mollusks, tunicates.

siphonaceous (sī′fŏn·ā′shŭs) [Gr. *siphōn,* pipe]: tubular; applied specifically to coccoid, elongate Protista.

siphonostele (sī′fŏ·nŏ·stēl): a general type of stele in which the vascular tissues are arranged around a central pith or a central hollow cavity.

Sipunculoidea (sī·pŭng′kŭ·loi′dĕ·ȧ): a phylum of wormlike schizocoelomate animals.

sol (sŏl): quasi-liquid state of a colloidal system, where water forms the continuous phase and solid particles the dispersed phase.

somatic (sŏ·măt′ĭk) [Gr. *sōma,* body]: pertaining to the body, e.g., somatic mutation, stable gene change occurring in a cell of the body generally, rather than in a reproductive, or germ, cell.

somite (sō′mīt): one of the longitudinal series of segments in segmented animals; especially an incompletely developed embryonic segment or a part thereof.

sorus (sō′rŭs) [Gr. *soros,* heap]: a cluster of sporangia on a fern leaf.

species (spē′shĭz), pl. *species* (spē′shēz) [L., kind, sort]: a category of taxonomic classification, below genus rank, defined by breeding potential or gene flow; interbreeding and gene flow occur among the members of a species but not between members of different species.

specificity (spĕs′ĭ·fĭs′ĭ·tĭ): uniqueness, especially of proteins in a given organism and of enzymes in given reactions.

spectrum (spĕk′trŭm) [L., image]: a series of radiations arranged in the order of wavelengths, e.g., solar spectrum, visible spectrum.

spermatangium (spûr′mȧ·tăn′jĭ·ŭm) [Gr. *sperma,* seed]: sperm-producing structure; male gametangium.

spermatium (spĕr·mā′shĭ·ŭm): name for the male gamete in red algae and some fungi.

spermatogenous (spûr′mȧ·tŏj′ĕ·nŭs): sperm-producing.

Sphenopsida (sfē·nŏp′sĭ·dȧ) [Gr. *sphēn,* a wedge]: a subphylum of tracheophytes; includes the horsetails.

sphincter (sfĭngk′tēr) [Gr. *sphingein,* to bind tight]: a ring-shaped muscle capable of closing a tubular opening by constriction, e.g., pyloric sphincter, which closes the opening between stomach and intestine.

spicule (spĭk′ūl) [L. *spiculum,* little dart]: a slender, pointed, often needle-shaped secretion of sponge cells; serves as skeletal support.

spirillum (spī·rĭl′ŭm) [L. *spirilla,* little coil]: any bacterium possessing a wavy, coiled, or spiral body.

sporangiospore (spŏ·răn′jĭ·ŏ·spōr′): a spore produced in a sporangium (as distinct from conidia and oidiospore).

sporangium (spŏ·răn′jĭ·ŭm): a spore-producing structure, unicellular or multicellular.

spore (spōr) [Gr. *spora,* a seed]: a reproductive cell capable of developing into an adult directly.

sporocyst (spō′rŏ·sĭst): a larval stage in the life cycle of flukes; produced by a miracidium larva and in turn gives rise to many rediae.

sporogenous (spŏ·rŏj′ĕ·nŭs): spore-producing.

sporophyll (spō′rŏ·fĭl): a sporangium-bearing leaf.

sporophyte (spōr′ŏ·fīt): a spore-producing organism; phase of diplohaplontic life cycle which alternates with a gametophyte phase.

Sporozoa (spō′rŏ·zō′ȧ): a phylum of parasitic protozoa;

most familiar member is the organism which produces malaria.

stamen (stā'mĕn) [L., a thread]: the microspore-producing organ of a flower; consists of stalk and anther.

stele (stēl) [Gr. *stēlē*, upright post]: collective term for those portions of stem and root which contain vascular tissues and, where present, pericycle and pith.

sterol, steroid (stĕr'ōl, stĕr'oid): one of a class of organic compounds containing a molecular skeleton of four fused carbon rings; includes cholesterol, sex hormones, adrenocortical hormones, and vitamin D.

stigma (stĭg'mȧ) [Gr., the mark of a pointed instrument]: the uppermost part of a pistil, serving as receptive surface for pollen grains.

stimulus (stĭm'ù·lŭs) [L.]: any environmental change which activates a receptor.

stipule (stĭp'ūl) [L. *stipula*, stalk]: one of a pair of appendages at the base of the petiole in many plants.

stoma (stō'mȧ), pl. *stomata* [Gr., a mouth]: a microscopic opening in the epidermis of a leaf, formed by a pair of guard cells; interconnects the interior air spaces of a leaf with the external atmosphere.

streptococcus (strĕp'tȯ·kŏk'ŭs) [Gr. *streptos,* curved]: member of a type of colony of bacterial cocci in which the cells divide in one plane only, forming chains.

strobilus (strŏb'ĭ·lŭs) [L., pine cone]: a cone or cone-like aggregation of sporophylls.

style (stīl) [Gr. *stylos,* a pillar]: stalklike part of a pistil which connects the stigma with the ovary.

suberin (sū'bĕr·ĭn) [L. *suber,* cork tree]: a waterproofing material secreted by cork and endodermis cells.

substrate (sŭb'strāt) [L. *substratus,* strewn under]: a substance which is acted upon by an enzyme.

suspensor (sŭs·pĕn'sĕr) [L. *suspensus,* suspended]: an elongated strand connecting a plant embryo to the surrounding tissue layers.

symbiont, symbiosis (sĭm'bĭ·ŏnt, sĭm'bĭ·ō'sĭs) [Gr. *syn,* with, + *bios,* life]: (1) an organism which lives in symbiotic association with another; (2) the intimate living together of two organisms of different species, for mutual or one-sided benefit; the principal variants are mutualism, commensalism, and parasitism.

sympathetic (sĭm'pȧ·thĕt'ĭk): applied to a subdivision of the autonomic nervous system; centers are located in the mid-portion of the spinal cord.

synapse (sĭ·nǎps') [Gr. *synapsis,* conjunction]: the microscopic space between the axon terminal of one neuron and the dendrite terminal of another adjacent neuron.

syncytium (sĭn·sĭ'shĭ·ŭm) [Gr. *syn* + *kytos,* vessel]: a multinucleate animal tissue without internal cell boundaries.

synergistic (sĭn'ĕr·jĭs'tĭk) [Gr. *syn* + *ergon,* work]: cooperative in action, e.g., hormones or other growth factors which reinforce each other's activities.

synthesis (sĭn'thĕ·sĭs) [Gr. *syn* + *tithenai,* to place]: the joining of two or more molecules resulting in a single larger molecule.

syrinx (sĭr'ĭngks) [Gr., a pipe]: the vocal organ of birds, located where the trachea branches into the bronchi.

systole (sĭs'tȯ·lē) [Gr. *syn* + *stellein,* to place]: the phase of contraction of auricles or ventricles, during which blood is pumped forward along the circulation path.

taiga (tī'gȧ) [Russ.]: terrestrial habitat zone characterized by large tracts of coniferous forests, long, cold winters, and short summers; bounded in the north by tundra; found particularly in Canada, northern Europe, and Siberia.

taxonomy (tăks·ŏn'ȯ·mĭ) [Gr. *taxis,* arrangement, + *nomos,* law]: classification of organisms, based as far as possible on natural relationships.

tectorial membrane (tĕk·tō'rĭ·ȧl): component of the organ of Corti in cochlea of ear.

telophase (tĕl'ȯ·fāz) [Gr. *telos,* end]: a stage in mitotic division during which two nuclei form; usually accompanied by partitioning of cytoplasm.

template (tĕm'plĕt): a pattern or mold guiding the formation of a duplicate; term applied especially to gene duplication, which is explained in terms of a template hypothesis.

temporal lobe (tĕm'pȯ·rȧl) [L. *tempora,* the temples]: a part of the vertebrate cerebrum; contains neural centers for speech and hearing.

testis (tĕs'tĭs) [L.]: male reproductive organ of animals; produces sperms.

tetracoccus (tĕt'rȧ·kŏk'ŭs) [Gr. *tetra-,* four]: member of a type of colony of bacterial cocci in which the cells divide into two planes, forming quartets.

tetrad (tĕt'răd): (1) the four meiospores produced by a spore mother cell, arranged as a tetrahedron or linearly; (2) one of two chromosome pairs present during the first metaphase of meiosis.

Tetrapoda (tĕ·trăp'ȯ·dȧ) [Gr. *tetrapodia,* four feet]: four-legged vertebrates; a superclass including amphibia, reptiles, birds, and mammals.

tetrapyrrol (tĕt'rȧ·pī'rŏl): a molecule consisting of four united pyrrol units, each of the latter being a five-membered ring of carbon and nitrogen; the four pyrrols may be joined linearly or as a larger ring; tetrapyrrols include pigments such as chlorophyll.

tetrasporine (tĕt'rȧ·spō·rēn): pertaining specifically to unicelled, colonial, and filamentous types of Protista with sessile vegetative cells which retain the power of multiplication.

thallus, thallose (thăl′ŭs, -ōs) [Gr., young shoot]: (1) a body without differentiation into root, stem, and leaf, usually flat and prostrate, sometimes filamentous; name applied mainly to some fungi, algae, and bryophytes; (2) adjective.

theory (thē′ṓ·rĭ) [Gr. *theōrein*, to look at]: a scientific statement based on experiments which verify a hypothesis; the last step of the scientific method.

therapsid (thĕ·răp′sĭd): extinct Mesozoic mammallike reptile; true mammals evolved from same group.

thigmotropism (thĭg·mŏt′rṓ·pĭz′m) [Gr. *thigma*, touch]: growth of organisms toward or away from contact stimuli.

thorax (thō′răks) [L.]: part of animal body between neck or head and abdomen.

thrombin (thrŏm′bĭn) [Gr. *thrombos*, clot]: substance participating in blood clotting; formed from prothrombin and in turn converts fibrinogen into fibrin.

thrombokinase (thrŏm′bṓ·kĭn′ās): enzyme released from blood platelets during clotting; transforms prothrombin into thrombin in presence of calcium ions; also called **thromboplastin.**

thrombus (thrŏm′bŭs): a blood clot within the circulatory system.

thymus (thī′mŭs) [fr. Gr.]: a lymphoid gland in most young and many adult vertebrates; disappears in man at puberty; located in lower throat and upper part of thorax.

thyroxin (thī·rŏk′sĭn): the hormone secreted by the thyroid gland.

tissue (tĭsh′ū) [L. *texere*, to weave]: an aggregate of cells of similar structure performing similar functions.

trachea, tracheal (trā′kĕ·ȧ) [Gr. *trachys*, rough]: (1) air-conducting tube, as in windpipe of mammals and breathing system of insects; (2) adjective.

tracheid (trā′kĕ·ĭd): plant cell type formed from procambium and maturing into a conducting component of xylem.

tracheophyte, Tracheophyta (trā′kĕ·ṓ·fīt): (1) a vascular plant, i.e., one possessing xylem and phloem; (2) phylum name.

transduction (trăns·dŭk′shŭn): transfer of genetic material from one bacterium to another through the agency of a virus.

translocation (trăns·lṓ·kā′shŭn): transport of organic substances in phloem.

transpiration (trăn′spĭ·rā′shŭn) [L. *trans*, across, + *spirare*, to breathe]: evaporation of water from leaves or other exposed surfaces.

trichogyne (trĭk′ṓ·jĭn) [Gr. *trichos*, hair, + *gynē*, female]: in red algae and some fungi, an elongated projection from the female gamete receptive to the male gamete or gamete nucleus.

triclad (trī′klăd): a member of a group of free-living flatworms, characterized by a digestive cavity with three branch-pouches; a planarian.

tricuspid valve (trī·kŭs′pĭd) [L. *tri*, three, + *cuspis*, a point]: valve consisting of three flaps, guarding opening between right auricle and right ventricle of heart.

trilobite (trī′lṓ·bīt): an extinct, marine Paleozoic arthropod, marked by two dorsal longitudinal furrows into three parts or lobes.

triploid (trĭp′loid) [Gr. *triploos*, triple]: possessing three complete chromosome sets per cell.

trochophore (trŏk′ṓ·fōr) [Gr. *trochos*, wheel, + *phoros*, bearing]: a free-swimming ciliated marine larva, characteristic of schizocoelomate animals.

trophic (trŏf′ĭk) [Gr. *trophos*, feeder]: pertaining to nutrition, i.e., autotrophic, heterotrophic.

tropic, tropism (trŏp′ĭk) [Gr. *tropē*, a turning]: (1) pertaining to behavior or action brought about by specific stimuli, i.e., phototropic (light-oriented growing), gonadotropic (stimulating the gonads); (2) noun.

trypsin (trĭp′sĭn) [Gr. *tryein*, to wear down]: enzyme promoting protein digestion; acts in small intestine, but pancreas produces it as inactive trypsinogen.

tuber (tū′bĕr) [L., knob]: a short, fleshy, underground stem with axillary buds, e.g., potato.

tundra (tōōn′drȧ) [Russ.]: terrestrial habitat zone, between taiga in south and polar region in north, characterized by absence of trees, short growing season, and frozen ground during much of the year.

turgor (tûr′gŏr) [L. *turgere*, to swell]: the distention of a cell by its fluid content.

umbilicus (ŭm·bĭl′ĭ·kŭs) [L.]: the navel; during pregnancy, an umbilical cord connects the placenta with the offspring, and the point of connection with the offspring later becomes the navel.

urea (ů·rē′ȧ) [Gr. *ouron*, urine]: an organic compound formed in the liver out of ammonia and carbon dioxide and excreted by the kidneys; represents principal means of ammonia disposal in mammals and some other animal groups.

ureter (ů·rē′tĕr) [fr. Gr.]: duct carrying urine from a kidney to the urinary bladder.

urethra (ů·rē′thrȧ) [fr. Gr.]: duct carrying urine from the urinary bladder to the outside of the body; in the males of most mammals, the urethra also leads sperms to the outside during copulation.

Urochordata (ů′rṓ·kôr·dā′tȧ) [Gr. *oura*, tail, + L. *chorda*, cord]: a subphylum of chordates; comprises the tunicates.

uropod (ū′rṓ·pŏd) [Gr. *oura* + *podos*, foot]: an abdominal appendage in lobsters and other crustaceans; contributes to the formation of a "tail."

uterus (ū′tẽr·ŭs) [L., womb]: enlarged region of the female reproductive duct in which offspring develops during pregnancy and receives maternal nourishment.

utricle (ū′trĭ·k′l) [L. *utriculus*, little bag]: portion of the inner ear containing the receptors for dynamic body balance; the semicircular canals lead from and to the utricle.

vacuole (văk′ů·ōl) [L. *vacuus*, empty]: a small, usually spherical space within a cell, bounded by a membrane and containing fluid, solid matter, or both.

vagus (vā′gŭs) [L., wandering]: the tenth cranial nerve; it is a mixed nerve, innervating many organs in the chest and the abdomen.

vasomotion (văs′ô·mō′shŭn) [L. *vasum*, vessel]: collective term for the constriction (vasoconstriction) and dilation (vasodilation) of blood vessels.

venous (vē′nŭs) [L. *vena*, vein]: pertaining to veins; also applied to oxygen-poor, carbon dioxide–rich blood.

ventricle (vĕn′trĭ·k′l) [L. *ventriculus*, the stomach]: a chamber of the heart which receives blood from an auricle and pumps out blood from the heart.

vernalization (vûr′năl·ĭ·zā′shŭn) [L. *vernalis*, spring]: induction of flowering by cold (or heat) treatment of seeds or later developmental stages.

vernation (vŭr·nā′shŭn) [L. *vernare*, to be verdant]: the arrangement of leaves within a bud, e.g., circinate vernation, a rolled-up arrangement of a young leaf, as in ferns.

vestigial (vĕs·tĭj′ĭ·ăl) [L. *vestigium*, footprint]: degenerate or incompletely developed, but more fully developed at an earlier stage or during the evolutionary past.

villus (vĭl′ŭs), pl. *villi* [L., a tuft of hair]: a tiny fingerlike process projecting from the intestinal lining into the cavity of the gut; contains blood and lymph capillaries and is bounded by the intestinal mucosa.

virus (vī′rŭs) [L., slimy liquid, poison]: a submicroscopic noncellular particle, composed of a nucleic acid core and a protein shell; parasitic, and within a host cell it may reproduce and mutate.

vitamin (vī′tȧ·mĭn) [L. *vita*, life]: one of a class of organic growth factors contributing to the formation or action of cellular enzymes.

vitreous (vĭt′rê·ŭs) [L. *vitrum*, glass]: glassy; as in vitreous humor, the clear transparent jelly which fills the posterior part of the eyeball.

viviparity, viviparous (vĭv′ĭ·păr′ĭ·tĭ, vī·vĭp′ȧ·rŭs) [L. *vivus*, alive, + *parere*, to bring forth]: (1) reproductive pattern in which eggs develop within female body with nutritional and other metabolic aid of maternal parent; offspring are born as miniature adults; (2) adjective.

xanthophyll (zăn′thô·fĭl) [Gr. *xanthos*, yellow, + *phyllon*, leaf]: one of a group of yellow pigments; members of the carotenoid group.

xerophyte (zē′rô·fīt) [Gr. *xēros*, dry]: a plant adapted to live under dry or desert conditions.

xylem (zī′lĕm) [Gr. *xylon*, wood]: tissue which conducts water from roots upward; consists of tracheids, vessels, and other cell types; in bulk represents wood.

zooplankton (zō′ô·plăngk′tŏn) [Gr. *zōion*, animal]: collective term for the nonphotosynthetic organisms present in plankton; contrasts with phytoplankton.

zoospore (zō′ô·spōr) [Gr. *zōion*, animal]: a motile, flagellate spore.

zygospore (zī′gô·spōr) [Gr. *zygon*, yoke, pair]: an encysted zygote, as in *Spirogyra*.

zygote (zī′gōt) [Gr. *zygōtos*, yoked]: the cell resulting from the sexual fusion of two gametes; a fertilized egg.

INDEX

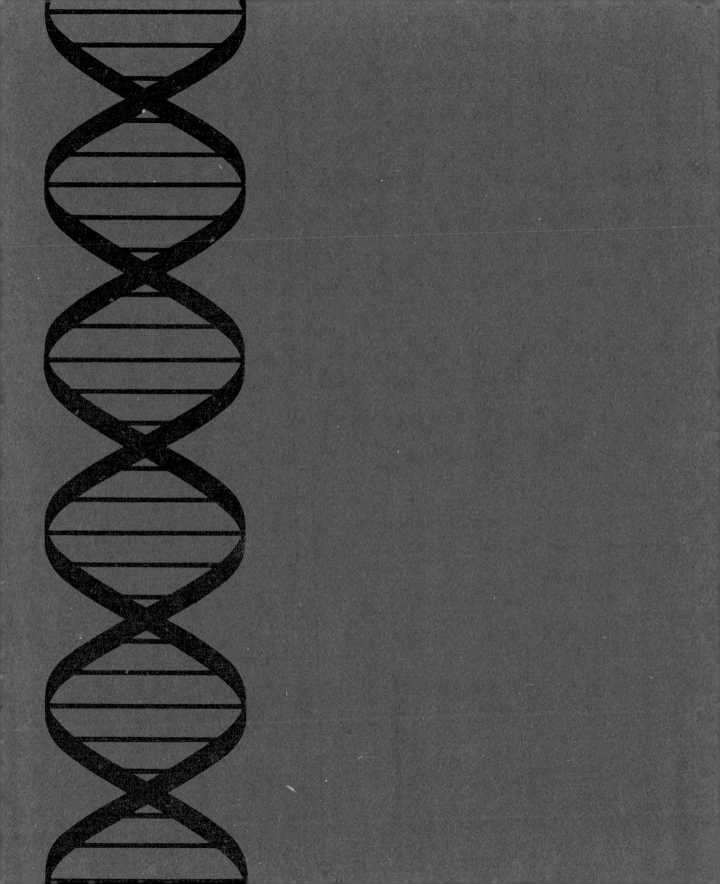